IN THE UNITED STATES

te Agricultural
ons
es
oratories
rs

Orono

Burlington

Durham

Amherst

St. Paul

Madison

East Lansing

Ithaca

Kingston

New Haven

State
College

New Brunswick

Ames

Newark

Wooster

La-Fayette

Beltsville

Morgantown

College Park

Urbana

Columbia

Lexington

Blacksburg

Raleigh

Fayetteville

Knoxville

Clemson

State
College

Experiment

Auburn

Baton
Rouge

Gainesville

N

W

S

House Document No. 708
79th Congress, 2d Session

The Yearbook
of
Agriculture

1943–1947

FOR SALE BY THE
SUPERINTENDENT OF DOCUMENTS
WASHINGTON 25, D. C.
Price $2.00

THE YEARBOOK COMMITTEE, 1943–1947

W. V. Lambert, Agricultural Research Administration, *Chairman*

Hugh C. McPhee, Bureau of Animal Industry

O. E. Reed, Bureau of Dairy Industry

Carl F. Speh, Bureau of Agricultural and Industrial Chemistry

F. C. Bishopp, Bureau of Entomology and Plant Quarantine

M. A. McCall, Bureau of Plant Industry, Soils, and Agricultural Engineering

C. M. Coons, Bureau of Human Nutrition and Home Economics

Sherman E. Johnson, Bureau of Agricultural Economics

Ernest G. Moore, Agricultural Research Administration

W. H. Larrimer, Forest Service

Mark L. Nichols, Soil Conservation Service

Alfred Stefferud, Office of Information
Editor

The Yearbook of Agriculture

1943–1947

Science in Farming

UNITED STATES DEPARTMENT OF AGRICULTURE

U. S. GOVERNMENT PRINTING OFFICE : WASHINGTON 1947

Life More Abundant

A Foreword by Clinton P. Anderson, Secretary of Agriculture

On my farm in New Mexico and on farms the country over I have watched, marveling, the onward surge of science in farming. We now have tractors and attachments that pull our heavy equipment and can dig holes, grade roads, clean barnyards, lift loads, and grind feed. We have hens that lay twice as many eggs as chickens did a few years ago. We have alfalfa, wheat, flax, and oats that are wonderfully resistant to plant diseases. We can buy a kind of chemical that kills weeds and, used in another way, stimulates the growth of fruits and vegetables. We have new kinds of sheep and cattle and hogs that give us more wool or meat or bacon; and we have surer ways to keep them healthy and free of pests. Insecticides make our houses and barns more sanitary and comfortable. We have hybrid trees, hybrid corn, and hybrid onions of almost unbelievably higher yields. Many of the mysteries of the good earth have been disclosed to us, and we use the knowledge to till the soil for its welfare and ours. Airplanes take some of our produce to market; new kinds of packages and processes keep it fresh and wholesome. The corncobs that we used to burn or throw away have been given a good use in industry. These are results of a few years of agricultural research. More are coming. They, and many more, are told in this Yearbook, in a continuing story that holds a deep meaning for city people no less than for farmers.

I have great joy of them, as a fruit of man's brain and hand, of his patient research, ingenuity, will. These developments the American farmer combined with his sweat and skill to perform the miracle of food production during the war. They have had a part in increasing by 70 percent in 25 years the average efficiency of the farm worker in the United States. They reveal the possibility of a self-sustaining American agriculture, and are a manifestation of the resources within us and about us. They can give us a better life, a life more abundant for every family.

But in truth the very bounty of the research and invention here set forth might cause uneasiness. The thoughtful reader is bound to ask one question or many, unlike in wording but alike in intent: Does not the same DDT that kills the Japanese beetle also kill the honeybee? By breeding a new wheat that withstands rust are we not making it more susceptible to a different enemy? Can we never be satisfied—must we go on with research forever? Does not this technology lead sooner or later to overproduction?

On such points I have no fear: We did not stop making automobiles, for fear we would wreck them; or leave off erecting dams, lest they burst; or refuse to construct houses because they might cave in. And need we be concerned that life be too abundant, that we and others in the world will have too much good food, too many clothes, too many medicines for our ills, too much leisure to look upward? Rather, let us give thought to getting food to people who need it, feeding ourselves and our neighbors better, putting farm goods to further uses in industry, taking better care of our land, trading willingly and freely, and cooperating effectively to maintain full employment.

That—a life more abundant—will come to farmer and city worker from knowing more about each other. To that end this book makes a contribution.

A Note to the Reader

You have here a report on some new developments in farm science. It contains practical information about research of the past few years pertaining to animals, plants, insects, trees, soils, water, machines, conservation, processes, marketing, industrial uses of farm products, agricultural chemistry, food, clothing, and economics. It offers a background for understanding the further results of research as they are announced from day to day. Its purpose is to help everybody to make the most of the products of the laboratory, the test plot, and the pilot plant. It is not a general or complete treatise on agriculture—a large library is needed these days to embrace all the details of the profession of farming.

This book was prepared primarily for farmers, but we have always had in mind other persons whose interests and work have to do with gardening, chemistry, beekeeping, stock raising, conservation, horticulture, housekeeping, and such. The Yearbook should be particularly useful to returning servicemen who want to farm and to persons who will find in these pages details of a product that may help them build or enlarge businesses of their own.

To that end, we are as specific as we can be—in giving names of persons, places, and organizations where you can get further information if you need it. Questions can be addressed to them or to the Office of Information, Department of Agriculture, Washington 25, D. C.

In some instances, for clarity, we use trade names of products. But that should not be taken as an endorsement by the Department of the product, or preference over another product.

To avoid undue preoccupation with details of organization, we usually refer to the United States Department of Agriculture merely as the Department or the Department of Agriculture; the Agricultural Research Center at Beltsville, Md., as Beltsville; and a specific bureau or laboratory or State agricultural experiment station (where the designation is clear from the context or is given in the author's note at the end of each article) as the bureau, the laboratory, the station.

The Department has 16 bureaus or major units. Among those that conduct a great deal of research in the physical sciences are the Bureau of Plant Industry, Soils, and Agricultural Engineering; the Bureau of Entomology and Plant Quarantine; the Bureau of Animal Industry; the Bureau of Dairy Industry; the Bureau of Agricultural and Industrial Chemistry, and the Bureau of Human Nutrition and Home Economics. These units, with the Office of Experiment Stations and the Agricultural Research Center at Beltsville, comprise the Agricultural

Research Administration. They have offices in Washington and Beltsville and laboratories and projects at Beltsville and in various parts of the country. Among the other units of the Department that conduct research work and contributed to this book are the Bureau of Agricultural Economics, the Forest Service, and the Soil Conservation Service.

This Yearbook is the first issued since 1942, when war interrupted a sequence that began in 1894—or earlier, if the first annual reports on agricultural matters are considered Yearbooks. The book was given its present form in 1936, under the editorship of Gove Hambidge; to him the Yearbook, as an institution, will always be beholden.

An expression of thanks also is due the Congress of the United States, whose document this is, and to a number of individual Congressmen for their encouraging interest.

Science in Farming was produced in a time of rising costs and growing shortages of some materials. These we could not foresee. Several excellent articles had to be omitted at the last minute, therefore. Among them are: Improving the Cattle Range, by D. A. Savage; Growing Better Tobacco, by J. E. McMurtrey, Jr.; The Marketing of Milk, by C. J. Babcock and R. W. Bell; Making Better Cheese, by George P. Sanders; The Making of Fertilizers, by K. D. Jacob and A. L. Mehring; Rubber for War and Peace, by E. W. Brandes; Sedimentation, by Carl B. Brown; Drainage of Farm Lands, by R. D. Marsden; Starch From Sweetpotatoes, by Paul R. Dawson; Science and Ice Cream, by Alan Leighton; Beef Cattle Husbandry, by Ralph W. Phillips; Plants for Special Uses, by D. M. Crooks; Pastures and Forage, by J. B. Shepherd, M. A. Hein, and R. E. Hodgson; Abaca Comes to the West, by H. T. Edwards; Seedlings From the South, by W. D. Moore, S. P. Doolittle, E. K. Vaughan, and H. Rex Thomas; Soybeans as Vegetables, by W. J. Morse; Equipment for Fumigation, by Randall Latta and H. H. Walkden; and Farm Science in Industry, by D. S. Burch. We hope the articles can be made available in some other way to persons who have particular need for them.

Many persons whose names do not appear elsewhere helped in the preparation of this Yearbook: Roy E. Miller, Charlotte L. White, Mary A. Bradley, Mabel H. Doyle, Herbert E. Goodrich, Charles M. Arthur, and Katherine A. Smith. Many of the photographs are by Charles A. Knell, William J. Forsythe, Wilfred J. Mead, and Walter A. Stenhouse. Joseph H. Stevenson and Wynne Johnson and his staff prepared the charts and drawings.

On the staff of the Yearbook are Stanley H. Gaines, managing editor, and Helen E. Balaguer, assistant to the editor.

—ALFRED STEFFERUD.

Contents

Plants

Insects

New Products

Conclusions

List of Pictures

Science in Farming

The Yearbook of Agriculture

1943–1947

Nothing is impossible to labour, aided by ingenuity. The true objects of the agriculturist are likewise those of the patriot. Men value most what they have gained with effort; a just confidence in their own powers results from success; they love their country better, because they have seen it improved by their own talents and industry; and they identify with their interests, the existence of those institutions which have afforded them security, independence, and the multiplied enjoyments of civilized life.

—SIR HUMPHRY DAVY
Elements of Agricultural Chemistry
[1813]

Men Who Went Before

by ERNEST G. MOORE

THOSE who work in farm science have a noble tradition to live up to. It is the tradition of Marion Dorset, Theobald Smith, Henry Ayers, L. O. Howard, Erwin Smith, Harvey Wiley, W. O. Atwater. It is a tradition of vision and hard sense, of service and the eternal quest.

It is a tradition of inquiry. Marion Dorset was an inquiring man and a hard-headed one. He came to work for the Department of Agriculture in 1894, a time when hog cholera was causing large losses. In some of the bad years losses amounted to more than 65 million dollars. Associates in the Bureau of Animal Industry assured the 23-year-old lad from Tennessee that they had already found the cause of the disease to be a bacterium. Dorset's job, they explained, was to find a preventive or cure. His superiors had even made a start on this—they had prepared a serum from the bacteria that seemed to be causing the trouble.

In the summer of 1897 hog cholera flared up in Iowa, so Dorset was sent posthaste, armed with the new serum. He spent a good part of the summer injecting this serum into sick hogs and well hogs, but they still died of cholera. He returned to Washington and began all over. After his experience in Iowa both Dorset and his immediate chief, E. A. de Schweinitz, questioned the widespread belief that bacteria were responsible for the cholera. This took courage, because it amounted to defying their own superiors and nearly all scientific thought at the time. Dr. de Schweinitz died before Dorset discovered the true cause of cholera.

It was 6 years before there was another disastrous outbreak of the disease. The interval gave Dorset time to work on other things, to get his degree in medicine by attending night classes, and to challenge, with growing success, the bacteria theory about hog cholera. He demonstrated that the causative agent was not a bacterium at all, but an ultramicro-

1

scopic virus. He also proved that hogs that recovered from the disease were immune for life.

Back to Iowa he went in the summer of 1903, but this time he was armed with more potent weapons. With the help of C. N. McBryde and W. B. Niles, he went to work again. They found that blood from immune hogs gave temporary immunity to other hogs, but it lasted only a few weeks. Then Dorset hit upon the idea of using two injections. The first was a serum from the blood of a hog that had lived through an attack of cholera and further demonstrated its immunity by surviving a large shot of virus, the blood from an infected hog. The other injection was virus. With slight modification, this treatment is still in use.

Marion Dorset died in 1935. Citizens of his native Tennessee have placed a plaque in his honor in the Agricultural Hall of Fame in Nashville.

Like many other Department scientists, Dr. Dorset patented his discovery and dedicated it to the public, making it possible for anyone to use his method for making serum without paying royalty.

Another part of the tradition of those who work in farm science is that costs must be counted closely, but not the credit or the value, because one can measure only a part of the value of agricultural research. You can often make a pretty fair estimate of the money it has saved or added to our national income; you can even make a fair guess as to the value of agricultural research to the health of the people, but there is no yardstick for measuring its ultimate value. Those evaluations come only with the passage of years. When Theobald Smith found that the way to control tick fever of cattle was to control the ticks, no one knew that his brilliant research would pave the way for control of malaria, yellow fever, and many other scourges of the Tropics. These developments came several years later and were the work of other men.

Around 1890 tick fever of cattle was causing widespread losses, especially in the South. Southern cattle were often driven to northern markets, and they usually left a trail of fever along the way. Northern cattle, taken to the South for breeding, usually contracted the disease and died. Many southern cattlemen believed that ticks were somehow responsible for the disease, because cattle that died from it always had ticks on them. At first, there was no scientific evidence to support the belief, but the scientists eventually proved that the cattlemen were right.

Theobald Smith began work on tick fever in 1888. Later he was joined by Dr. F. L. Kilborne and Dr. Cooper Curtice. Smith and Kilborne discovered the cause of the disease to be a protozoan parasite, found in the blood of infected animals. In the summer of 1890 they definitely established the fact that the disease was spread from animal to animal by the cattle tick. That was the first demonstration that a disease-producing micro-organism can be transmitted by an insect carrier from one animal to another. (Working independently, as far as I can learn, Dr. M. B. Waite made the same fundamental discovery in relation to insect transmission of plant diseases.) The obvious cure for the disease was to get rid of cattle ticks, and this was done through a long-time eradication program conducted jointly by the Department and the States.

Getting rid of cattle ticks and tick fever has meant untold millions of dollars to cattle growers of the South; this research cost $65,000, for salaries and expenses, and the Department sets the value of the discovery at about 40 million dollars a year. But you cannot fully measure its value: The implications of the research that paved the way for the discovery go far beyond the borders of our country and the monetary value of livestock. Other research men were quick to see the possibilities for conquest of human diseases. In a few years the mosquito was recognized as the carrier of yellow fever, and the work of another Department scientist, Dr. L. O. Howard, furnished basic information for campaigns to eradicate mosquitoes. With this malady under control, it was possible for the United States to build the Panama Canal. French engineers had failed because they were unable to control yellow fever.

The Courage of Dr. Hall

Courage, mental and physical, also counts in farm science. Millions of people in tropical and subtropical parts of the world have been freed of the dread hookworm disease because courageous research men found new ways to protect livestock from injurious parasites. In searching for effective treatments for hookworms of livestock, Maurice C. Hall saw references to chloroform described as giving fair results. This led him in 1921 to try carbon tetrachloride, a related chemical that was cheaper. But was it safer than chloroform? Was it better for the purpose? Dr. Hall had to know. He tried his new treatment on various animals, but there was still a question of its safety for human use. So he took doses of it himself on three occasions to test its reaction. He suffered no harmful effects, and in a short time carbon tetrachloride was being used widely in both human and veterinary medicine.

A few years later Hall and his coworker, J. E. Shillinger, discovered that tetrachlorethylene was even better than carbon tetrachloride for treating dogs infested with hookworms. Again Dr. Hall took his own medicine with no ill effects. It soon replaced the earlier treatment.

There is no way to evaluate a discovery of this kind. No one knows how many animals, including man's good friend the dog, have been freed of hookworms. It is estimated that at least 15 million persons have benefited from the treatments that Dr. Hall first developed for livestock.

Like Hall, Henry Ayers was a great benefactor of mankind. Probably no work ever done in the Department, or anywhere else for that matter, has had a more profound effect upon the health of United States citizens than that of S. Henry Ayers, a bacteriologist. His work, and that of his associates, laid the ground work for present-day sanitary regulations governing the handling and pasteurization of milk.

It may be surprising to many to learn that there was much opposition—even among scientists and doctors—to the pasteurization of milk even as late as 1910. The practice was first recommended as a health measure in 1875, but many people in positions of responsibility believed that it would do more harm than good. They argued that pasteurization destroyed the lactic acid bacteria in milk, causing it to putrefy instead of souring. It was also thought that destruction of the lactic acid bacteria allowed the growth of undesirable organisms that produced toxins that made pasteurized milk unfit for human consumption.

Ayers made a painstaking study of milk, recording the presence of bacteria in raw and pasteurized milk obtained from retail outlets of several cities. He made thousands of counts of bacteria. His work, first published in 1910, showed that pasteurization did not destroy all of the lactic-acid-forming bacteria, that organisms did not multiply faster in milk that had been pasteurized, and that pasteurization merely prolonged the condition of clean raw milk. His publications convinced many physicians and public officials that pasteurized milk was safer than raw milk. These publications take their place beside the most illustrious ever issued by the Department. His work shows another facet of our tradition—the value of persistent, careful, maybe slow, progress toward the goal.

So does the work of L. A. Rogers and C. E. Gray, to whose painstaking research we owe, in large degree, the quality of our butter. Rogers and Gray devoted a good share of their time for 10 years, beginning in 1902, to improving the storage quality of butter.

When their work began, almost all butter was made from raw, sour cream. This had been the practice for centuries, and it was common belief that high acidity of the cream was necessary to insure desirable flavor in the butter. Butter held in cold storage usually developed off-flavors, but these were thought to be a result of bacterial action.

Rogers and Gray spent many months making bacteriological studies but were unable to find any bacteria that would cause the undesirable flavors. What they did find was that butter that developed the bad flavors almost always had been made from sour cream, and that such flavors never occurred in butter made from pasteurized sweet cream.

By 1907 Rogers and Gray had ample proof that most of the deterioration in storage butter was a result of chemical changes, promoted by the presence of acids, that bacteria were only indirectly concerned, and that butter of good flavor and superior keeping quality could be made from pasteurized sweet cream.

Their discovery revolutionized the practice of making creamery butter and opened up a new field of investigations that have resulted in improving the keeping quality of all fat-containing dairy products.

We in agricultural research inherit also a tradition of simplicity—the mechanisms and bases of our studies often are technical and involved, but the result, to be useful, must be simple, clear, workable. The best example I know of is the Babcock test for butterfat.

Many scientific discoveries, inventions, and ideas have contributed to the advancement of the dairy industry in the past half century, but no other single discovery has done so much to advance dairy science or remained so universally in continuous use as the Babcock test.

In Every Milk Bottle

Professor S. M. Babcock was employed in the dairy department at the University of Wisconsin when he introduced his test in 1890. It is so well known among students of agriculture that it will need no detailed description here. With inexpensive equipment, it is possible to tell within a few minutes the butterfat content of a sample of milk. By adding a specified amount of sulfuric acid to a measured sample of milk and whirling it for a few minutes in a properly graduated container one may get the percentage of butterfat at a glance; and this percentage multiplied by the total weight of the milk will give the total amount of butterfat—in a can of milk, a cheese vat, or in the day's milk from a single cow.

Before the development of the test, a cow or a herd of cows was considered good or poor according to the amount of butter or cheese that was made from the year's milk. Few farmers, or others for that matter, understood that the amount of butter or cheese varied with the butterfat content of the milk. Neither the butter nor the cheese was an accurate measure of the value of the milk, because so much butterfat was lost in skimming the cream from crocks and pans and careless methods of making cheese left large quantities of fat in the whey.

The Babcock test gave creamerymen, cheese makers, and other dairy processors a more equitable basis for buying milk and cream and gave farmers a better way to measure the real value of their cows. This led to official testing of cows by the various breed associations and later to the Dairy Herd Improvement Association program, in which more than a thousand groups of dairy farmers all over the United States keep production records on more than a half million cows. Because of the check afforded by the Babcock test, housewives also can be assured of the legal amount of butterfat in every bottle of milk or cream.

Part of our tradition also is to evaluate science as science, to understand that a basic discovery has an importance as a foundation, if not as a superstructure. Among the early workers in plant sciences who made such fundamental discoveries was Merton B. Waite.

As a student at the University of Illinois, he came under the influence of T. J. Burrill, one of the great plant pathologists of his day and the first to demonstrate that bacteria caused many plant diseases. Only a few years earlier Pasteur had announced his discovery of bacterial diseases of man and animals. Young Waite was greatly impressed and decided to make his career the study of plant diseases.

He joined the Department in 1888. One of his first assignments was to make a study of pear blight, a disease that kills young branches of pear trees. In a few years the tree usually dies. At that time almost nothing was known about the disease except that it was caused by a bacterium. Waite observed insects feeding on pear blossoms and wondered if they might be responsible for spreading the disease from tree to tree. By carefully controlled experiments, he demonstrated his theory to be correct. He reported this work before the Association for the Advancement of Science in 1891, the year that the work of Theobald Smith and associates on tick fever was published. It would be interesting to know if either of these great men influenced the thinking of the other. At any rate, Waite's discovery helped to explain many of the plant diseases that are spread by insects and provided a foundation for other workers to build upon.

Like many another scientist who advances a new idea, Dr. Waite had many critics at first. One of these was a well-known doctor who owned an orchard on the Eastern Shore of Maryland. This doctor, according to a story that has been told in the Department for years, publicly challenged Waite to bring the pear blight bacteria to his orchard and infect his trees. Waite reluctantly accepted the challenge, and soon the doctor's pear trees began showing signs of blight, which eventually killed them.

Another far-reaching discovery by Waite was that most varieties of pears must be cross-pollinated with other varieties if they are to set a full crop. This finding was later found to apply to many other fruits, including apples, and has been a prominent factor in the choice of varieties for planting orchards.

Despite the brilliant work of Waite and many other plant pathologists, no fully satisfactory control has yet been found for pear blight. Some success has been achieved in breeding by crossing certain high-quality varieties with the Kieffer, which has much resistance to blight but is of poor quality. So far, only one new blight-resistant variety has been introduced by the Department. Its name, quite properly, is Waite.

Plant Science and Cancer

The work of Erwin F. Smith illustrates our conviction that agricultural research is a relative and component of all science. Of all the giants among Department research men, it would be hard to find one who has influenced more fellow scientists or contributed more to his chosen branch of science than he. Professor Burrill, of Illinois, had demonstrated that bacteria could cause diseases in plants, but it remained for Smith to prove this truth to the world.

He came to work for the Department in 1886, just 8 years after Burrill's famous work. Smith's first years were spent working on peach yellows. He proved that the current ideas as to its cause were wrong; that it could be held in check by systematically destroying all affected trees. His evidence was accepted by the growers, who united their efforts for compulsory eradication programs, and the peach industry was saved. He concluded that the techniques available at the time were inadequate to show the cause of this disease and turned his attention to bacterial and fungus diseases. He investigated, and described for the first time, many kinds of bacteria that caused destructive plant diseases and determined how they cause such diseases as well as what plants were susceptible. Besides numerous bulletins and other scientific papers, he published three quarto volumes in which he gave the methods he had found most useful and a monographic treatment of the diseases on which he had worked most.

Despite the high caliber of the work done by Burrill, Waite, and Smith, leading bacteriologists of Europe, particularly of Germany and England, were not convinced that bacteria could cause diseases in plants. In fact, one of these men, Dr. Alfred Fischer, of Germany, a prominent writer of textbooks, became the spokesman for the doubters, and Erwin Smith took up the fight for the Americans. The debate went on for years in one of the leading German scientific publications. It was bitter at times, but Smith finally won the decision and, with it, fame. He carried on countless experiments to provide evidence for his international debate. It was in this connection that he and two of his assistants, C. O. Townsend and Nellie Brown, discovered that certain plant tumors are caused by bacteria. This discovery led to another great contribution by Smith, which was destined to bring him more lasting and widespread recognition perhaps than all his other scientific work combined—his studies on the bacterial crown gall of plants.

The first two papers—published with Townsend in both English and German—described and named the bacterial cause. Then followed in rapid succession the long series of papers dealing with many phases of the development of plant tumors, bringing the grand total on this subject to some 40 or more. His intensive comparative researches on these malignant growths in plant and animal tissues won him wide attention among cancer specialists. In 1913 the American Medical Association awarded him its certificate of honor for his work on cancer in plants and in 1925, only a little over a year before his death, he was elected president of the American Association for Cancer Research—signal honors for a man engaged in plant research, and evidence of the kinship of the sciences.

About the time that Erwin F. Smith was devoting his attention to the wilt diseases, a young man named William A. Orton came to work for the Department. He was from Vermont and was trained in plant pathology. His first assignment was to investigate the wilt disease of cotton, a disease that lives over from year to year in the soil. Young Orton had never seen a field of cotton. The disease was spreading at an alarming rate when he made his first visit to the islands off the coast of South Carolina in 1899. He found a grower there named Rivers who had been selecting seed from occasional plants that showed resistance to the wilt. Orton encouraged Rivers to continue the work and helped him make selections. By this time the disease was also threatening the main Cotton Belt of the South, so Orton laid out experimental breeding plots and went to work to breed a new kind of cotton. This was the beginning of the breeding of plants for resistance to disease. The trial plots were in Dillon County, S. C., and the first new cotton variety to come from these plots was named Dillon.

Orton's work was a landmark in farm research. To me, it shows another aspect of our tradition, that of seeing a need and bending every effort to fill it. A similar landmark is the work of Dr. E. C. Stakman, of the University of Minnesota. In 1913 he reported work which established the existence of strains or races of disease-causing organisms. He confirmed earlier work done in Sweden indicating that stem rust on wheat differed from stem rust on oats or rye.

He went further and showed that stem rust on wheat or oats is not produced by a single organism, as previously believed. Instead, he found that several closely related organisms could produce stem rust. These he called pathogenic races. This opened up a new approach in the understanding and control of many plant diseases. It explained why a new variety of wheat, for instance, bred for resistance to one form of stem rust may look promising for a few years, only to succumb to another form of stem rust. Apparently the form that caused the trouble originally was the one best adapted to the environment. When a new variety of wheat resistant to this form is introduced, the dominant race becomes subordinate and is no longer a serious factor in crop production. However—and this is why plant breeders cannot quit when they develop a new disease-resistant variety—still another race of the disease organism may, and usually does, quickly increase its numbers because the new variety is not resistant to all races.

Basing their work on the foundation provided by Stakman, plant pathologists and plant breeders of the Department and State agricultural experiment stations have successfully combined their knowledge to produce many new varieties of crop plants that resist several races of disease organisms. These include many promising new kinds of oats, wheat, and other cereal crops.

Cooperation and collaboration bulk large in the traditions of science in farming. There are hundreds of examples of what I mean, but I give one, that of breeding plants for resistance to insects, which has been a tougher job than breeding for control of diseases. The idea dates from 1782, when a variety of wheat sown by Isaac Underhill of New York and his neighbors was reported to yield well, while all other kinds sown nearby were ruined by the hessian fly.

C. W. Woodworth, of California, probably did the first actual research on breeding plants that are resistant to insects when he made a systematic study of the variations in fly resistance of wheat in 1890. J. W. McColloch and S. C. Salmon, of Kansas, reported similar observations in 1918, and many wheat breeders tried to develop varieties that had fly resistance.

Through the work of many State and Federal plant breeders, we now have several varieties of crop plants that are resistant to insects. Besides several varieties of wheat that resist the hessian fly, the Sequoia potato resists leafhoppers, several lines of hybrid corn resist attacks of chinch bugs, others resist the corn earworm; and some varieties of sorghum resist attacks of chinch bugs. Work in progress gives promise of developing resistance to aphids in alfalfa and cotton.

Patience and persistence are part of the research tradition, too. These qualities are exemplified by W. W. Garner and H. A. Allard, two of the most modest men it has been my good fortune to know.

The desire of farmers in southern Maryland to grow seed of a giant tobacco that appeared as a sport led Garner and Allard to make one of the most profound botanical discoveries of all time. They were investigating other problems of tobacco in Maryland at the time, so they set out to make the giant tobacco flower and produce seed. This was in 1906.

They worked on this problem off and on for several years, and this work led them to discover the fundamental law of nature that many plants can flower and produce seed only when the duration of light, that is, the length of day, is right for that particular plant. The discovery explained many things not previously understood about the flowering and fruiting of plants, and it has many practical applications in present-day agriculture.

Garner and Allard got their first hunch that they were on the trail of something big when the giant tobacco that would not flower outdoors in Maryland readily flowered and set seed when grown in tubs in a house that could be darkened in midafternoon. (It also flowered in Florida, but nematodes often killed the plants before they could mature seed.) These investigators were also keenly interested in a report from Tennessee saying that successive plantings of soybeans throughout the summer months tended to blossom at the same time, for they themselves had made the same observation.

Over a period of several years—for this was a side line to their regular work—the scientists painstakingly eliminated every other factor they could think of that might explain the behavior of the tobacco and soybeans. They added several other plants to their list. They tricked chrysanthemums into blooming in midsummer by moving potted plants into a dark house in midafternoon. Then, finally, in 1920 they announced their discovery. In the meantime, they had found that some plants seemed to get along all right with either a short or a long day. Others required a short day, and a third group required a long day.

Many practical gains to agriculture have resulted from this work. These are recounted in another article in this volume. Potatoes that would not produce seed for plant breeders now do so. Varieties of plants that bloom at different times can now be made to bloom to suit the convenience of the plant breeder. Failures with crops like onions may often be prevented by knowing their day-length requirements. Chrysanthemums can be brought into flower before or after their normal season—for football games, for instance.

The Ingenious Professor Riley

Ingenuity is another quality prized by one generation of researchers after another. The idea of using one insect to control another insect that is interfering with man's crops was talked about for many years, but the first person to do something about it was Prof. C. V. Riley, chief entomologist for the Department for many years.

His first successful introduction was a parasitic insect, an enemy of the imported cabbage worm, from Europe. His success in this venture led to the most famous of all insect introductions, the Australian ladybird, and started a new chapter in man's fight against insects. The experiment so successfully controlled the cottony cushion scale of citrus trees in California that it has become a lighthouse in entomological history.

The cottony cushion scale was known to exist in Australia, but was not a bad pest there. No one knew just why, but Riley reasoned that there must be an insect in Australia that was holding the scale in check. Acting on this theory, he sent Albert Koebele to Australia in the fall of 1888 to find this unknown insect benefactor.

Koebele himself was a remarkable observer—or the whole experiment might have failed. Entomologists in Australia had seen the ladybird beetle and had associated it with control of the scale, but they had no actual proof. After finding several of these beetles feeding upon eggs of the scale, Koebele became convinced that the ladybird beetle must be the one he had been sent to get.

Another of Riley's assistants, D. W. Coquillett, remained in California to take care of the insects sent back by Koebele. The first three shipments totaled 129 beetles alive on arrival. Within 6 months these had increased to about 11,000 and had been sent out to more than 200 citrus growers. Within a year after the first shipment arrived, "the scale insect was practically no longer a factor to be considered in the cultivation of oranges and lemons in California," according to Dr. L. O. Howard, Riley's chief assistant and his successor as chief entomologist in the Department.

Riley had the knack of overcoming obstacles. In planning to send a man to Australia he was confronted with two difficulties—lack of funds to pay for the trip and lack of authority for travel outside the United States. These circumstances would have discouraged most men—but not Riley. The State Department had just received an appropriation to send a representative to the Melbourne Exposition to be held in 1889. Riley arranged with the Honorable Frank McCoppin, head of the commission to the exposition, to send Koebele to Australia on funds appropriated for the exposition. McCoppin, a native of California, agreed to pay the travel expense of Koebele but insisted that Riley send along another of his assistants to prepare a comprehensive report on the fair. The salaries of both men were paid by the Department and their expenses by the exposition commission. In the words of Dr. Howard, "the story of Koebele's work has become a classic in applied entomology and horticulture."

Attention to detail is also traditional, even if the detail is the smallest spore on the smallest insect. Witness G. F. White's work. It has been known for many years that diseases hold certain species of insects in check when weather and other conditions are favorable. Because of this knowledge, entomologists have spent much time studying these diseases, in the hope of using them to man's advantage. Probably the most intensive work was on a disease of chinch bugs. But the work was given up with the conclusion that the disease was already present in most fields and needed only the right kind of weather to multiply. When weather conditions were unfavorable, spreading the disease did little good. This conclusion seemed to apply to insect diseases in general.

After many years of work on insect diseases, Dr. White began a study of diseases of Japanese beetle grubs in 1933. Within 2 years he was convinced that a bacterial disease known as "milky disease" was responsible for reducing the population of beetles in older infested areas and could be used in control work. He died in 1937, but others carried his work on to completion. Dr. White spent almost a lifetime studying diseases of insects and, although he had made a name for himself in connection with diseases of honeybees and certain destructive caterpillars, his last job—development of the milky disease—proved a fitting climax to his career.

The milky disease is caused by bacteria that attack the grubs, causing them to become milky white in appearance. Although the organism is fatal to the beetle, it is harmless to plants, domestic animals, and people. When an area becomes fairly heavily infested, the disease is "planted" on top of the ground in the form of a dust. Spores are used for this purpose and are obtained from the bodies of infected grubs. The grubs are ground up and mixed with talc and lime. The disease multiplies very rapidly if enough grubs are present in the soil. It has been used widely in public parks in Washington, D. C., and is one of the most effective control measures so far found for Japanese beetle grubs.

Dr. Howard's Versatility

Versatility, of the kind possessed by L. O. Howard, is another inheritance. In his 50 years of public service, over half of it as head of research in entomology, he directed many noteworthy investigations. None had more far-reaching importance than a simple little experiment he conducted in the Catskill Mountains in 1892.

Dr. Howard was spending a short vacation at his cottage in July and noticed a few mosquitoes on the porch. The pests were rare at that elevation, but the early summer had been wet, and he feared a whole host of them later in the summer, when he planned to return to the cottage. As a boy Dr. Howard had used kerosene to control breeding of mosquitoes in a water trough, but apparently no one had tried this treatment on a pond or pool. He decided to try it. In a few days no mosquito larvae could be found.

The result of that little test was soon known around the world, and when Army and Public Health doctors proved that the way to clean up yellow fever was to clean up mosquitoes (thanks to the work of Theobald Smith on cattle ticks), Dr. Howard's kerosene treatment plus drainage played a big part in getting rid of the mosquitoes and with them some of the worst scourges of man.

Perhaps the greatest fighter in the group of scientists mentioned in this article was Dr. Harvey W. Wiley. From his battles many a present-day scientist has learned how to stand up for the truth. He was a great scientist, a good administrator, writer, and educator. Day in and day out for 21 years he hammered everywhere on a vital point—shocking adulteration of foods and drugs. Finally he aroused the American public to demand action. Then Congress passed the Food and Drugs Act in 1906 and the Bureau of Chemistry, headed by Wiley, was placed in charge of enforcement. He had won the first round of his battle.

Wiley's work dates from about 1885, when his publications on methods of analysis for foods and other agricultural products were accepted as the last word on the subject. They were used in colleges and universities, in public and private laboratories, and later in the enforcement of the new food law. His researches covered many subjects for which no satisfactory methods of analysis had been published.

These early publications were paving the way for passage of the Food

and Drugs Act. Another series on adulterants published at intervals between 1887 and 1902 disclosed that cottonseed oil was commonly used
as an adulterant in butter; that all kinds of foreign matter were mixed
with spices; and that many poisonous dyes were commonly used in candy
and other foods.

Besides his brilliant fight to protect the health of the American public,
which earned for him the designation of "father of the pure food law,"
Wiley is also known as the father of the sugar-beet industry in the United
States. Efforts to establish sugar beets as a crop in this country had been
based on haphazard knowledge, and the industry had not flourished.
Wiley made studies of soils, climatic conditions, and yields and sugar
content of the beets in several parts of the country. With this information
he mapped the areas adapted to the crop. His recommendations were
followed and are still good.

Hybrid corn illustrates still another segment of the scientific tradition,
namely, that research that appears to be purely theoretical may turn out
to be extremely practical. For example, one of the foremost authorities on
hybrid corn now living has said that hybrid corn is perhaps the outstanding example of the influence of theoretical scientific research in
revolutionizing the production practices of an agricultural crop.

The early work on hybrid corn was done by men not connected with
the Department. Prof. W. J. Beal, of the Michigan Agricultural College,
began breeding corn about 1870. In 1881 he crossed two varieties by
detasseling one of them, and this was probably the first attempt to utilize
hybrid vigor in corn breeding.

G. H. Shull, of the Carnegie Institution, began inbreeding corn in
1905, but at the time he was interested solely in theoretical genetics. He
wanted to find out whether the number of rows of kernels on an ear was
influenced by inbreeding and crossbreeding. By 1908, however, he realized the practical possibilities of the method for increasing yields and
recommended inbreeding and crossing of inbred lines for commercial
corn production.

E. M. East, of the Illinois Agricultural College, also began inbreeding
corn in 1905. In the fall of that year he moved to the Connecticut Experiment Station and continued his corn breeding there. He, too, was
interested at first in theoretical aspects, but, like Shull, he soon saw the
possibilities of increasing yields for farmers by using the new method
of corn breeding.

In the next few years other State experiment stations began breeding
hybrid corn, and Department breeders joined the ranks. Because of the
need to inbreed lines, a practice that takes several years, results were
modest at first. By 1925, however, several States were getting results. In
that year 12 States and the Department set up a cooperative hybrid-corn-
breeding program. Promising parent material was freely interchanged

and valuable time was saved. The program has made possible the fullest use of all information on the subject, and the phenomenal spread of hybrid corn across the Corn Belt has been largely a result of this cooperation.

The spread of hybrid corn is probably the greatest food-production story of the century. Like a prairie fire it swept across the central part of the country. In 1933 only 1 acre of corn out of a thousand in the United States was planted to hybrids. Ten years later the percentage of land planted to hybrids was a little more than 51. Since that time it has jumped to 67.5 percent.

Farmers like to grow hybrid corn because it gives greater yields. Larger yields are due in part to hybrid vigor, but because hybrids are "hand-tailored" to meet the needs of a given area, they have more resistance to drought and other unfavorable weather, more resistance to diseases and insects, and stronger stalks, so they are easier to harvest with machines.

Hybrid-corn yields for the country as a whole average about 25 percent above those of open-pollinated corn. In the 4 years 1942–45, United States farmers grew an extra 2 billion bushels of corn because of hybrids. In 1945 alone this increase was 600 million bushels, worth three-quarters of a billion dollars.

Human Welfare

The essence of research, as it has come down to us, is that it must be tied inseparably to human welfare. I cite Dr. W. O. Atwater, one of the pioneers of modern human nutrition. He was director of the first State agricultural experiment station, the one in Connecticut. He and two associates designed the first calorimeter for the study of human metabolism in relation to food consumed and energy expended. He published in 1869 the first analysis of an American food, corn, and later (1896) published as a Department bulletin tables showing the composition of familiar foods. It was the first such publication in the United States.

Dr. Atwater organized and became the first director of the Office of Experiment Stations in the Department in 1889. This position gave him an excellent opportunity to arrange for nutrition studies in cooperation with State experiment stations and other agencies interested in developing this young science. In his first annual report he said: "In studying the food of animals we have no right to neglect the food of man." One of the first cooperative studies of the Office of Experiment Stations was a survey to find out what people in different areas actually ate.

To him the problems of human nutrition included what the body needs in its food, what nutrients the different foods supply, how the nutrients are utilized by the body, what diets are actually used in different regions, and what foods and methods of food preparation furnish the most economical and healthful diet. All this, he said, leads to the fundamental question: How can national food production be made to yield best returns in economic progress and social welfare? Although many advances have been made in the study of human nutrition since Dr. Atwater's death in 1907, research in this field still follows the pattern he laid down.

The respiration calorimeter for the study of the energy relations of nutrition to the human body was developed by Dr. Atwater, E. B. Rosa, and F. G. Benedict in the basement of the chemical laboratory of Wesleyan University, Middletown, Conn. At the same time, Atwater, with other coworkers, devised an improved type of bomb calorimeter for the determination of the fuel values of foods by burning them in compressed oxygen.

Atwater's work on human nutrition later grew into an Office of Home Economics, which in 1923 became the Bureau of Home Economics, and in 1943 the Bureau of Human Nutrition and Home Economics.

The Soil

Hand in hand with dedication to human welfare is the inherited love and concern for the soil, its use, conservation, and nature. Curtis F. Marbut is one of the great names in the development of soil science in the United States. Dr. Marbut came to the Department in 1909 from the University of Missouri at the request of Milton Whitney, chief of the Bureau of Soils. At that time the views of the famous German soil chemist, Justus Liebig, dominated the thinking of most students of soils and plant nutrition. Liebig's theory was that the soil was a sort of reservoir from which man could take out no more than he put in. The lack of wide variations in soils of western Europe, and the necessity for intensive cultivation (with constant application of manures and fertilizers) made the Liebig theory seem reasonable to scientists of England, France, and Germany. But it did not fit soil conditions in the United States.

Meanwhile, a school of eminent soil scientists had developed in Russia, where the large expanse of the country included wide differences in geographic features and soil types, some of which were extremely fertile, in contrast to the generally impoverished soils of western Europe. The Russians departed from the Liebig theory, which stressed the analysis of plants and soils, and went outdoors to study soils in field and garden.

Marbut recognized that useful understanding of soils must begin with the soils themselves. He recognized the contributions of the Russian scientists and was stimulated to develop a program of field study in the United States that incorporated many of their ideas. But he went considerably farther into the detailed study and classification of the local soil types that must be used as a basis for giving recommendations to individual farmers.

Whitney had already departed from the Liebig theory when Marbut joined him in 1909. In fact, he went almost to another extreme in advancing his belief that all soils had sufficient nutrients to support plant growth and that yields of crops were determined by rainfall and other factors of climate, by mechanical condition, by management, and by the presence of toxic compounds in the soil.

Marbut had the ability to see much truth in all of these schools of thought, and he used all of them to build a body of soil science that fitted conditions in the United States. He laid the foundation for the present system of soil classification and mapping. Although improvements and refinements have been made since his death in 1935, he left us the tools with which to fashion a modern soil science.

We are using Marbut's tools—and Marion Dorset's, Theobald Smith's, L. O. Howard's, Harvey Wiley's, W. O. Atwater's.

THE AUTHOR

Ernest G. Moore, coordinator of information for the Agricultural Research Administration, joined the Department of Agriculture as a writer in 1929. He has been in charge of information for the Bureau of Plant Industry, chief of the Department's Press Service, and Assistant Director of Information in Charge of Press and Radio. Mr. Moore is a graduate of North Carolina State College and for 2 years was assistant editor at the Florida Agricultural Experiment Station.

What Is Farm Research?

by CHARLES E. KELLOGG

R IGHT NOW, in peace again, is a good time to look at the methods of agricultural science and assess its deeds and prospects.

We know that science has changed nearly all the common farm practices over the past 50 years or so. By no means equally nor everywhere: Millions of farmers in the world carry on about as their grandfathers did; even in the United States today many farmers do not follow the best practices. But where really put to work on the ordinary successful farm, the total effects of science have been tremendous. Although average acre yields of most of our crops have not risen greatly, farmers have been able to reduce labor and effort; their aim has been increased efficiency, not simply high yields; and the choice of crops has been greatly widened. The old farming arts have been improved, especially in their refinement to fit specific conditions. We cannot say that the old knowledge was all poor, simply because it developed over thousands of years of trial and error and was passed on from conservative father to conservative son. In fact, some of the old practices were sound, and only recently has science given us reasons why they were. The trouble is that trial and error is a costly system in a fast-changing world.

We know that science is bound to remake the world even faster, either in an orderly and not too slow a way, or in a series of catastrophes. This very fact of change gives us another chance to solve the problems that lead to war. Any solution will recognize that because farm science touches all our lives, a good world will be one where farm science is strong and alert.

What some of us do not realize, perhaps, is that science can make abundance physically possible. That is important, because we should know by now that no group can be secure while others are without confidence and hope. Maybe I cannot prove it to everyone's satisfaction, but I

am convinced that the world has enough soil for farmers to produce
enough food for all our needs, and do so efficiently on a secure basis.
Problems, of course, stand in the way; to them laymen and scientists
should address themselves with courage.

Although few would wish to return to the old days and ways, all must
admit that advances in technology have created new problems as well as
solved old ones. Again and again new machines and processes have made
old skills obsolete. If some farmers get to be more efficient, others must
fall in line or suffer the consequences. Efficiency among farmers has come
to mean much more than being able to grow big yields of corn or fat
cattle. Farming—at least successful farming—has become an exceedingly
complicated business. All branches of science are involved and a myriad
of industrial developments growing out of science, as well as the eternal,
unchanging forces of nature. A farmer never knows enough. Thus, from
whichever direction we approach the problem or whatever name we give
to it, we must be concerned with the disparities of opportunity that result from the unevenness of scientific advances and from failures to
view science as a whole.

We do not separate agricultural science from all science. Agricultural
research workers use the principles worked out in the fundamental or
basic sciences—like chemistry, geology, and botany—and also contribute
to them. The term is useful but misleading. By it we mean, generally, all
scientific principles as they apply to farming and rural living. But the
principles could not exist apart from other sciences. We could not have
an agricultural chemistry apart from chemistry, nor agricultural economics apart from economics; the fundamental principles of production
economics are the same, whether applied to farm organization or to the
manufacture of automobiles. In striving for solutions to agricultural
problems, then, it is often necessary to carry on research deeply in the
basic natural and social sciences to develop principles for application.

This fact is important. A constant hazard to effective agricultural research is that its supporters may insist that too large a proportion of the
effort be devoted to immediately practical objectives. But remember:
Practical attempts to control some insect pest, for example, may be nearly
futile until its detailed life history has been learned; much basic research
preceded the development of hybrid corn.

The Scientific Method

Agricultural science also must be reasonably balanced among the different fields. Think of the technical problems involved in developing more
livestock in the South: High-yielding, disease-resistant pasture and feed
crops, their adaptability to soil types and management requirements,
suitable breeds of livestock, animal nutrition, control of pests, marketing

and storage facilities, farm organization, efficient machinery, and so on. Failure to develop any one of them may keep us from reaping benefits from the other lines of research.

The scientific method of working and thinking that distinguishes a scientist includes observation, often supplemented with planned experiments, classification and correlation of the facts, and the development of ideas. Scientific inquiry is carried out with thousands of special devices and kinds of apparatus. These are constantly being improved so that more facts and more kinds of facts may be gathered. But it is the method, not apparatus, that makes a scientist.

A scientist observes carefully. He records what he sees. For this, he needs training. He must know what to look for and not let significant things escape him. His likes and dislikes do not influence his measurements. His records are complete—not just made up of the facts that are "important," according to some unproved notion, or that are "typical examples," according to some preconceived theory. His observations are as nearly quantitative as possible. A thing is not just long or heavy, but is so long and weighs so much. He exercises judgment on how far to go into detail, based upon experience and the nature of the subject under inquiry. He follows an orderly procedure. Where samples are taken, he uses some definite plan to avoid accidental sorting, even through some unconscious bias of his own. The purpose of observation is to learn—to test old ideas or develop new ones; but the scientist doesn't go about observing at random; some general notion of the end result is necessary.

Ideas and principles do not emerge from a miscellaneous collection of facts. These must be organized into a system of classification. Each unit has to be defined and named. The system must be precise to fulfill its purpose, so we can remember the facts, see relationships, and develop principles.

The accuracy of any classification and its usefulness depend upon how much is known about the subject, and the better the classification, the easier it is to discover new knowledge. Thus the classification is always being changed and improved. Classification itself is a tool. Just because one knows the name of a thing, it doesn't follow that he possesses knowledge about it or can discover new knowledge. In fact, mere knowing of names is useless unless we remember the characteristics, or can learn them by reading or from someone else. But we do need to know names in order to find out what is already known. Much of what a farmer wants to know about his crops, animals, and soils is classified under the names of the things, like Ranger alfalfa, Jersey cows, and Miami silt loam.

Simple observation often does not tell us much about causes or results, so the scientist must set up experiments. Suppose we want to know how to increase yields. Think of all the factors that influence yield: The kind of soil, and how it is managed, weather, insects, diseases, kind of seed, rotations, and many another. All operate at once and, unless we can control the varying influences, or at least account for their separate effects, we cannot tell how any one operates. Thus the problem is broken down and special conditions set up so that all possible factors can be controlled or accounted for. In doing so, the scientist is cautious, careful; his experiments are part of a general plan. On a uniform area of known soil, small plots are laid of the several varieties of soybeans, for example. These all get the same treatment. Careful records are taken of the weather conditions, and the trials are repeated enough to see how the varieties behave with extremes of weather and with normal conditions.

Such would be a simple experiment but not an easy one. Diseases or insects could spoil it. Yields must be measured accurately. Even more refined experiments will be needed to test other variations. On other soil types the same varieties may react quite differently. The various varieties may not each yield the best with the same time of seeding, depth of planting, and fertilizer treatment. They may vary in quality for hay, for food, or for industrial uses. After classifying the results of his experiments, the scientist can draw conclusions about the yield and quality of soybeans that may be expected according to variety, soil type, and the several cultural practices.

The scientist's experiments must be distinguished from ordinary experience. We all make "experiments," in the sense of trying this and that. Some people even publish such experiences as scientific experiments. One can find almost anything "proved" by them—all sorts of new practices hailed as panaceas for solving the farmer's problems or for avoiding ruinous hazards. But before accepting such conclusions, one must insist upon seeing the facts that support the idea and also a clear description of the experiments. Were they so controlled that the results could only have been due to the factors claimed? Or could they have been caused by something else or perhaps come about by pure chance?

Many matters that must come under scientific study cannot be subjected to ordinary experiment. One cannot hold all the stars still and move just one, for example; mountains and volcanoes cannot be moved or controlled; even true soils cannot be gathered into a laboratory or in one place. We can get samples of rocks or soils and subject these small parts to experiment, but that is far from the real mountains or soils as they exist in nature. Indeed, the experimental method is often confused with the scientific method, when, in fact, it is only one part or one method in science. With his instruments for measuring, the scientist often puts himself in a particular position to take advantage of natural phenomena. Astronomers go to places where they can expect a particular view of an eclipse, let us say. Or a soil scientist will take measurements of the temperature, moisture content, and other characteristics of a natural soil as it freezes and thaws. These are sometimes called "natural" experiments, in contrast to the more usual kind that may be set up in the laboratory or greenhouse.

A scientist may study plants in a wild, untouched landscape to see what conditions of soil, climate, light, and so on favor one plant, or one group of plants, over another. Then he will find other places, like the first one, except that the natural vegetation has been burned, or severely grazed, or cleared away and abandoned again. Through a combination of such natural experiments he can develop principles for predicting the kinds of plants and their growth that may be expected under various conditions—principles of immense practical importance in forestry and range management.

As a general method of scientific study, correlation is partly a matter of both controlled and natural experiment, and partly one of classification. Soil science furnishes a good example. It is utterly unthinkable to set up experiments on all fields and farms to see what practices are best. But millions of farmers are already following different methods. By studying the growth of plants in unused areas and the results of experiments and farmer experience with various methods of soil use, in relation to defined sets of soil conditions, the scientist can gradually build up a set of principles with which he can make predictions about what will happen when a soil with any given set of characteristics is used in a particular way. Each soil with an individual set of characteristics is given a name for convenience. It is one unit in the system of classification. By comparing the set of characteristics of a new or unknown soil with those of soils already in the system, its name and place in the scheme of classification is determined.

The essential coordination for planning, conducting, and interpreting agricultural research in the United States is achieved largely through voluntary cooperation. During years of working together, arrangements have been evolved for cooperation among different kinds of scientists and between State and Federal research groups. The advantages of such cooperation are so obvious and so generally accepted among all thoughtful agricultural scientists, that a noncooperator soon loses the respect of his colleagues.

Both facts and ideas are essential to scientific inquiry. Often ideas come to the trained mind as flashes, as new combinations of principles in the mind. As facts are obtained to test the idea, it may be found to be wrong; for every success, the scientist has many failures. Or it may take form and become more precise. The scientist then draws a tentative conclusion, which, if true, means that other things are true. These he sets out to test. The results of the new research may lead to the results he expected and confirm the idea, or perhaps to something quite different. Then he must revise his original notion. In this way facts lead to ideas, ideas to more facts, these to revised or new ideas, and so on. The process never ends.

Among modern scientists, the place of the lone worker is becoming smaller. The larger part of our problems requires many people with different skills, working together. Nevertheless, efficiency of organization to get facts must not be allowed to stifle ideas or to lull the individual scientist into the complacency of a cogwheel. A perfect scientific research organization, with all responsibility clear, with each man in his proper niche, and with no overlapping or duplication, might be a bureaucrat's dream—but it would be an empty one. Scientific research requires the flashes of the human mind. They are like lightning; we cannot know where they will strike or how. Scientists need to organize themselves in ways to get the advantages of group research without losing the essential freedom of the individual researcher.

Free criticism is essential to science. People get ideas, test them, and improve them with experience. The same may be said of a functioning democracy. Thus are the scientific method and the democratic process similar. Of course, scientific questions cannot be settled by voting in committees. We can only say that the scientific truth currently accepted is what informed scientists say it is—their present opinion. No man has been granted the gift of absolute knowledge, and scientists are men. But free publication by the scientist and free criticism by his peers—his informed colleagues—are essential to the scientific method. No man can be trusted to speak with authority without such criticism. He is too close to his own ideas to see them whole, no matter how hard he tries.

Our society is becoming more and more dependent upon science. Scientists must be supported in their work and their opinions must be respected. But they are human, subject to all the vanities and fears of other men. Some are good workmen and honest ones; others are not. There can be no absolute guide to tell us whom to believe. Even the scientist himself is a layman in most fields. If he simply uses the special techniques of his own field without undertaking the deeper meaning of the scientific method as applied generally, he may be as blindly dogmatic or as bad a dupe as anyone in other fields. We can ask these questions about a scientist: Has he sincerely and competently followed the scientific method? Is he free to tell the truth as he sees it—free of personal prejudices and of political or social pressure? Has his work been tested by free and open criticism? Has he the respect (not necessarily personal friendship) of competent colleagues in the same field? If the answer to any of these questions is "No," we should be slow to believe him.

Agricultural scientists work mostly in public institutions; only a few are supported by private industries or groups of farmers. This is because farming is mostly carried on in small units that would find it hard, even in combinations, to undertake research, and because most problems of agriculture involve so many skills that even a group of minimum size for effective work requires considerable land, buildings, and equipment. Besides, effective educational and demonstration programs must be closely allied with the research activity if farmers are to benefit from the results.

For more than 75 years most agricultural research in this country has been carried on by the United States Department of Agriculture and the State land-grant colleges. Nevertheless, the great importance of other institutions carrying on research in the basic sciences should not be overlooked.

State Experiment Stations

The State agricultural experiment station is usually an integral part of the land-grant college. It is financed by State appropriations and Federal grants-in-aid. Usually it is located with the other units of the college or university on the same campus. A few States have two more-or-less independent stations. Most States have substations, working on the special problems of other parts of the State, but under the control of the main station.

The directors of these stations report to a State governing board, which appoints them, directly, or indirectly through the president of the college or through the dean of agriculture and the president. The directors are State officials. Even though they handle Federal funds, made available by the Congress as grants-in-aid for research, the States may appoint whom they please as long as the funds are handled competently within the broad area of purpose and intent provided by law. Annually the Secretary of Agriculture must certify to the Secretary of the Treasury that the funds are being so handled for the States to receive their grants. It is a function of the Office of Experiment Stations of the Department of Agriculture to consider and approve projects of the State experiment stations in order to assist in coordination of the work among States and to insure compliance with the law.

Formerly the Department of Agriculture was looked upon primarily as an agricultural research agency; yet it had other functions, which have grown enormously in recent years. The State experiment stations have grown steadily, along with college teaching and extension, or farm advisory services, in the land-grant colleges.

Besides financial support to the Department, the Congress has made various provisions from time to time for financial grants to the State experiment stations to supplement their State funds. This has been both necessary and logical. Through national taxation the cost is equitably distributed; by grants-in-aid to the State institutions, the control of the work has been vested in people close to the problems.

The detailed history of the growth of these institutions, and their record of solid accomplishment, is an interesting and revealing tribute to our democracy, although quite beyond the scope of this discussion. A complex set of relationships among the Federal and State research groups has gradually evolved.

Dependence on cooperation among scientists for achieving coordination, rather than on central administrative control, is the distinguishing feature of our system of agricultural research. Strictly administrative direction is decentralized among the States. In actual practice, each research unit within the Department of Agriculture, and within most State experiment stations, has a wide latitude of freedom in the conduct of its research program.

Two circumstances make this necessary. First, our country reaches across a whole continent and has within it such a variety of lands—so many combinations of climate, soil, and topography—that no one group, however diligent, could possibly grasp the detail of our local farm problems. Nor can scientific research be closely supervised, like most other activities. In the search for new knowledge, no one can predict just what will happen or when. In most lines of work a few failures, or even one, would disqualify a man, while the very best scientist trying to develop a superior strain of wheat or a method for controlling some insect, fails to reach his objective most times he tries. Occasionally he has a success. That one may return several thousandfold for all his work.

Control of Research

The people, through their representatives in State legislatures and the Congress, strongly influence the relative emphasis given the individual lines of research through the distribution of appropriations. Sometimes, items of popular interest receive undue emphasis at the expense of more important fundamental research, but, on the whole, the agricultural research program has benefited from this procedure; it has been forced to keep close to the real problems of the people. At least once a year in formal budget hearings, and much oftener in letters, in interviews, and other contacts, men responsible for various lines of work give congressional committees an accounting of their stewardship, explain the degree of progress, propose new projects. They have a sympathetic, thorough, and strict audience; each respects the responsible role of the other, and out of the exchange comes a wholesome contribution to the national well-being. Thus Congress has a sentient, important role in our research program, more vital and productive, perhaps, than many Americans realize. Excellent teamwork between scientists and legislators is becoming increasingly important. Thought must be given to ways for broadening the scope of individual appropriation items to allow greater discretion to the scientists themselves; holding scientists accountable for their use of public funds; and avoiding unreasonable dictation as to what scientists shall investigate. Yet the public must always guard itself against any "aristocracy of scientists," if not directly in control, perhaps as a servant for some determined minority. So far no serious problem of this sort has appeared, but it might, as the importance of science grows.

Research at the experiment stations is concerned with local agricultural problems primarily, but not exclusively. The problems are brought to their attention by farm groups or by workers in the State extension or advisory services; for instance, county agricultural agents. Scientists assist the county agents and other educators in supplying information for farmers and developing demonstrations. In fact, often certain researches are conducted on operating farms as well as on special experimental farms. Perhaps one of the most useful devices of all is the demonstration farm in which all practices are brought together, in combination, to achieve the optimum in efficiency. This technique has developed remarkably in the past 10 years, as in the Tennessee Valley, and promises to increase the effectiveness of research enormously.

Many farm problems extend far beyond the boundaries of individual States, which cut across soil boundaries and type-of-farming areas. Some are national in scope. These must be dealt with by research groups operating on a broader basis than a State. Such groups are commonly made up of scientists from the State experiment stations and the Department of Agriculture.

Research in the Department of Agriculture

Research in the Department of Agriculture is directed mainly toward problems of regional or national significance. Many of the same problems are dealt with by the State experiment stations as they relate to local conditions. The Department takes major responsibility for regional coordination among States, for certain basic research that no one State can undertake, and for international cooperation. National plant and animal breeding programs with wheat, potatoes, oats, corn, alfalfa, pasture crops, and clover, with dairy cattle, beef cattle, swine, poultry, and sheep, and with other crops and animals, are examples. The national soil survey program, in cooperation with all the States, is another. Farm-management research requires both local and regional study.

In some programs national research groups must take the principal responsibility. The extensive research in agricultural and industrial chemistry, carried on mainly in four large regional laboratories at Philadelphia, Peoria, New Orleans, and Albany, Calif., requires large staffs of specialists. A few State stations do some of this work also, and their representatives assist the Department in developing the program, but most of the work is carried on by federally employed scientists. Similarly, most of the research in forestry is conducted at Federal experiment stations. Responsibility for management of the national forests has led the Department to undertake extensive research in this field. Those State stations that have a research program in forestry cooperate with the Department on problems of mutual interest, especially farm forestry.

Economic research of national scope must be organized by the Department. Many problems of supply, price, consumption, and trade relations, requiring the interpretation of national as well as local statistics, can only be dealt with nationally. As another sort of example, research on food preservation during shipment may be cited. It may be difficult for a local station to carry on effective research to discover the best ways to ship vegetables from California or Florida to New York City.

These are only examples. The kinds of work are illustrated in detail through the separate articles in this book. Mere listing of the research projects of the Department would fill many pages.

Location of Research

Some research can be done as well in one place as another. The initial laboratory research for improved methods of fertilizer manufacture can be done anywhere that adequate laboratory and library facilities are available. The same is true of fundamental work in genetics, nutrition, soil chemistry, and many other fields. Economic studies based upon national statistics are made mainly in Washington; farm management research must be carried on in the field.

Other problems must be studied in certain places or regions. Many soil researches can only be conducted on the soil types themselves in the field, wherever they are. Most of the work with specific plants and animals can only be done in regions where they grow to best advantage. On the other hand, it is often best to grow seedlings in greenhouses outside the region of their use, to avoid disease, and to experiment with plant diseases and insects in special laboratories and greenhouses far from the commercial areas of production.

Decentralization of research throughout the country has both advantages and handicaps. The scientist likes to be as close to his problem as possible. But he also needs equipment and libraries. He needs to consult other scientists, both in his own field and in other fields. These needs must be balanced against each other. Too much decentralization can be as bad as too much centralization.

The Agricultural Research Center

The Department has developed at Beltsville, Md., a great research institution. At this Agricultural Research Center those basic phases of physical and biological research that can be done in one place as well as another, together with those that are appropriate within the climatic and other limitations of that place as a biological environment, are carried on. It is one of the finest research establishments in the world.

Fundamental breeding work is carried on in the Center, and the young plants and animals sent out to field stations for trial. During the war, for example, disease-free cinchona seedlings were grown there for planting throughout the tropical parts of the hemisphere. Facilities exist for studying both plant and animal nutrition, as well as diseases and insect pests, under well-controlled conditions.

Since most of the research groups of the Department have their headquarters at the Center, or nearby, the planning of large-scale undertakings is participated in by experienced scientists of all fields. Some of the most distinguished scientists in the world have conducted their investigations as members of the research staff. Including administrative and other necessary personnel, approximately 2,000 persons work there. The Center keeps about 3,000 experimental farm animals and 10,000 mature laying and breeding fowls. Some 5,500 rabbits, guinea pigs, rats, and mice are available for laboratory tests.

Thirty-six buildings, each constructed and equipped to meet special research needs, provide office and laboratory space. There are 31 greenhouses for plant experiments, an apiary for bees, and numerous barns and storage buildings. The land around the buildings, about 13,000 acres of it, is divided into experimental pastures, ranges, orchards, gardens, fields for cultivated crops, timber stands, and soil-treatment plots.

Impressive as this lay-out may appear, its real significance lies in its relation to the other research stations throughout the country. The visitor sees only a part—even though a vital part—of the picture at Beltsville. The investigations in the State experiment stations and the many regional laboratories and field stations are also vitally important to the whole.

Field Stations

Many Federal research scientists are located at the State experiment stations and carry on work there in cooperation with State scientists as part of a regional or national research program. Some are even joint employees of the Department and the State, especially when one man or a small group can conduct the researches most effectively to satisfy both the local need and the regional or national need. Federal scientists stationed in one State often have responsibility for work in a wide region that overlaps parts of several States.

Federal field stations have also been organized to deal with problems of broad interest, often at different locations from the State stations in places most suitable to the research work to be done. For example, there are several in the Western States to deal with the special problems of irrigation, dry-land farming, and grazing. Others deal with plant or animal breeding, insect or disease control, soil improvement and conservation, and other special problems of a significant natural area, which may include parts of several States. Such field stations are relatively specialized and deal only with a few closely related problems. Most of them are not equipped for intensive basic research but address themselves to applied research and practical testing of methods or breeding materials. Most of them are tied closely to the work at Beltsville. The programs are worked out cooperatively with the State experiment stations and are a functional part of the regional or national programs in the fields covered.

Federal Regional Research Laboratories

Some 15 years ago it was realized that more basic research than ordinarily can be undertaken at a Federal field station was needed to solve certain important agricultural problems. Although these problems are very important to several States, or even to most of them, no one State could be expected to devote the necessary funds and staff to them. Since they could not be handled conveniently at Beltsville, special laboratories were established in other places, usually at one of the land-grant colleges, where libraries and other facilities were available and where it seemed the problem could be attacked most effectively.

Nine of these United States regional laboratories, sometimes called the Bankhead-Jones laboratories, in addition to the four large ones dealing with agricultural and industrial chemistry, have been established as follows: Vegetable breeding, at Charleston, S. C.; pasture research, at State College, Pa.; swine breeding, at Ames, Iowa; animal disease research, at Auburn, Ala.; soybean, at Urbana, Ill.; sheep breeding, at Dubois, Idaho; poultry, at East Lansing, Mich.; salinity, at Riverside, Calif.; plant, soil, and nutrition, at Ithaca, N. Y.

A Federal scientist directs the work at each laboratory under the general administrative supervision of the bureau or division of the Department in which the subject matter falls. The original plans and programs are arrived at by agreement among the several State experiment stations concerned most vitally with the problems.

A separate board of collaborators is appointed for each laboratory. It is made up of established scientists in the fields of science covered, who also represent the several interested State experiment stations and other research groups. They meet from time to time to appraise the work critically and to suggest technical changes for its improvement.

The programs of the laboratories are not only consistent with those of the other research groups of the Department and the State experiment stations—they are a part of their programs too. Many important contributions have already come of the intensive specialized research at these laboratories. A few of the more outstanding ones will be found in subsequent articles in this book under the specific subjects listed in the Table of Contents.

The reasons that have led to such close cooperation among the scientists of our several States and of the Federal research organization apply in the broader international field. A crop or practice that is good on a soil in our Great Plains will likely be so on the same type of soil in the Russian steppe. Insects and diseases can ruin crops or livestock on either side of the Rio Grande. And so it goes. By exchanging results and helping one another, scientists of the different countries all make greater progress. Ultimately each farmer can have the benefit of agricultural science throughout the world, as applied to a farm like his own.

Through exchanges of agricultural attachés and other experts and students, and especially through the activities of international scientific societies, much has been done. But not nearly enough. These activities were suspended during the war as far as most of Europe was concerned. Within the Western Hemisphere, however, cooperation increased.

After nearly 3 years of preliminary work, the Food and Agriculture Organization of the United Nations—called the FAO—was organized in the autumn of 1945. Although it does not have a considerable research staff of its own, it serves as a stimulating and coordinating agency for all countries in somewhat the same way that the Department research group serves the States in our country.

Education, trade, and free exchange of ideas are necessary, as well as research. Science will lead the way because the language of science is international. Really there are no such things as American genetics, Russian soil science, or English mathematics; there are genetics, soil science, and mathematics. People from many nations and races have contributed. Common effort in research leads to mutual respect and understanding among scientists. With that step others may follow more easily.

A Continuing Process

It is natural that we take the present agricultural efficiency on good American farms for granted. But suppose all the people of the United States should leave the country suddenly, as the cliff-dwelling Indians left Mesa Verde many years ago, to return a hundred years later. How many of our modern cultivated plants and animals do you suppose would be found? Very few indeed. Perhaps a few straggly specimens might be found here and there from which to begin a breeding program all over again. But competition with wild plants and animals, diseases, and insects would have destroyed most of the best stocks.

Through careful selection and breeding, scientists and farmers have developed plants and animals to suit our taste, that may be grown with special cultural practices and protection. The whole level of production is high above that of the natural environment. It is exposed to all sorts of threats with which scientists must be prepared to deal.

In agriculture, research never ends. As the Queen told Alice in Wonderland: "Now *here,* you see, it takes all the running *you* can do, to keep in the same place. If you want to get somewhere else, you must run at least twice as fast as that!"

Some have even said, however, that we have too much science, too much efficiency. Scientists were even blamed for the great depression in farm prices a decade ago! If food had been scarcer, prices would have been higher; there would have been no surplus! All this is absurd to a scientist. As long as people want desperately for food and fiber, surpluses are market phenomena, due to failures in man-made economic and political arrangements. Of course, farmers will need to make adjustments among the products they produce to meet changing needs. But the more efficient our agriculture becomes, the more people can be released from the job of food gathering to produce the other things needed for health and comfort. And the better will be life in the country.

For the first time in human history the possibility exists for agricultural production, and industrial production, too, to become efficient enough to produce the goods needed for everyone to have health, education, and the amenities of civilization. The way to the good life is not to hold science back, but to push it forward and adopt the social and economic devices that will increase its use and spread its benefits.

Present Trends in Science

Today there are two strong trends in scientific research, increasing specialization among scientists and increasing breadth of the problems attacked by research. In a way these pull in opposite directions. While the problems are being conceived in ever-broader terms, covering wide ranges in subject matter, individual scientists work more intensively in a narrower range of subject matter. Both trends are inevitable. As knowledge advances in chemistry, let us say, one individual cannot hope to become intimately acquainted with the whole field. There is too much detail to learn. He must concentrate in a narrow part of the field to be able to learn what has gone before and push into the unknown.

Teams of workers are being organized. Each scientist must understand enough of the other specialties so that all may know one another's language. They will need to agree on the outline of the problem. The more these two trends continue, the greater will be the emphasis on cooperation in research. And it must be cooperation without the domination that stifles individual thought and responsibility. This kind of cooperation, with the benefits of group research and freedom for individual ideas, is already the outstanding feature of agricultural research in America.

Agricultural research has always been chiefly supported by the public. The trend is toward increasing public responsibility for all scientific research, including that in the basic sciences. Two important trends follow this one. First, scientists must accept a greater share of social responsibility for the consequences of new scientific knowledge. The implications of their own discoveries during the war have dramatically shown them that. Second, the fruits of science must be more quickly and generally available to all the people and must not become the basis for exploitation through monopoly controls.

Education and research go together. Even more important than mere teaching of technology is the teaching of the scientific method. Its cultural values perhaps exceed its purely practical ones, great as these are. The methods of science are those of democracy. Each citizen needs to learn how to use science himself and not rely wholly on the expert.

Nowhere is this more important than on farms. It would be a sorry day for democracy if farmers generally turned to experts to make decisions for them. They need to learn from scientists, of course. It is the job of scientists to give them the information in ways they can understand and use, and to work with them. It is definitely not one of doing the job of farming for the farmer.

The lag in time between the development of new knowledge and techniques through research and their use by farmers is too great. This is especially true of those things that require a considerable change in the farming system for realization of the benefits. The use of hybrid seed corn spread quickly because no change in practice was necessary other than the source of seed. But the substitution of new pasture and feed crops for cotton on soils better adapted to them may require a complete change in the farming system. Such changes come too slowly.

Partly this is because the research did not go far enough. Many promising techniques have left the experiment station to sit on the shelf for years until some enterprising farmer took the risk of trying them in a revised farming system—in other words, until some farmer undertook the necessary experimentation at the level of the farm unit. We need to use pilot research farms, representing the different kinds of farms to be dealt with, on which the new techniques are tested within a complete farming system and modified as the need is shown. Such tests can be conducted best on normal going farms operated by farmers under special agreements.

A few such pilot research farms have been started on a trial basis. Many more are needed. But even these will not carry the results to all farmers. The well-read farmer who is also a good organizer can read about the results of research and apply them to his own farm. Many others cannot; they need to see the new practices in farming systems on farms about like their own, operated by farmers like themselves. For years, individual techniques have been demonstrated for farmers. Although useful, again to the more fortunate farmers, it is not enough. What are needed are unit-demonstration farms where all the practices are fitted, or rather are being fitted, into a system. Experience with such demonstrations during the past 10 years has been very rewarding indeed.

The general course of scientific research as applied to the problems of farms is through five steps: Research in the basic sciences; research in the applied sciences, including experimental field tests; pilot research farms; unit-demonstration farms; and all farms.

Each step is vital to the others. Because of the popular appeal of the second, the first is always in danger of being slighted. Until recently the third and fourth have been left largely to chance, as something for the more enterprising farmers to do themselves. But the lag in time is often very great, especially as applied to the small farm. If science is really going to work and to distribute its benefits to all farmers, each step must be definitely provided for in the scheme of things. None should be allowed to lag. Nor should the time of peace be wasted.

THE AUTHOR

Charles E. Kellogg is chief of the Division of Soil Survey in the Bureau of Plant Industry, Soils, and Agricultural Engineering. Before joining the Department in 1934, he taught soil science and did research in that subject at Michigan State College, the University of Wisconsin, and the North Dakota Agricultural College. He is a graduate of Michigan State College.

Dr. Kellogg has written and lectured widely on soil science and general agriculture. His published work includes a recent book, The Soils That Support Us.

Breeding Better Livestock

by RALPH W. PHILLIPS

THE BREEDER uses three basic tools to bring about the genetic improvement of animals. They are selection, inbreeding, and crossing. The tools have been used to develop existing breeds; they will be used to effect further improvement in breeds, establish new types and breeds, and raise the productivity of commercial livestock. Besides them, the breeder uses a knowledge of the physiology of reproduction to insure maximum fertility and maximum opportunity for selection.

The breeder's ability to select superior animals as parents of the next generation is one of the most important of the factors that determine progress in animal breeding. If the breeder is to select genetically superior animals, he must have yardsticks that measure that superiority. And if he is to utilize effectively in selection the knowledge he obtains through application of those yardsticks, he must know which selection procedures will result in greatest progress. Several recent studies have yielded important information on those points.

A breeder may use one of the three basic methods of selection. These are: First, the "tandem" method, in which he selects for one character at a time until it is improved, then selects for another one, and so on, until all desired traits are improved; second, the "total score" method, in which selection for all desired traits is practiced simultaneously, the total score or index being constructed by adding into one figure the credits and penalties given each animal according to its superiority or inferiority for each trait considered; third, the "independent culling levels" method, in which he sets a certain level of merit for each trait, and discards all individuals below that level, regardless of their rating in other traits.

A careful investigation of the efficiency of the three methods of selection was made by L. N. Hazel and Jay L. Lush, of Iowa State College. From their study of the theories involved, they conclude that selection for a total score or index of net desirability is more efficient than selection on the basis of independent culling levels, and that the tandem method is the least efficient of the three methods.

Although selection on the basis of independent culling levels is generally less efficient than selection for total score, it does permit earlier selection for some traits, without waiting for other traits for which selection can best be made at later ages. The superiority of the independent culling level over the tandem method increases with the number of traits involved and the intensity of culling.

Dr. Hazel also studied the principles of constructing and using selection indexes, or the "total score" method of selection. He points out that the genetic gain that can be made within a group of animals by selecting for several traits at once is the product of the selection differential, or intensity of selection—the superiority of selected animals over the average of the entire group—the multiple correlation (a measure of relationship) between aggregate breeding value and the selection index, and genetic variability. The first of these, the selection differential, is limited by the rate of reproduction of each species, and it may be small because of the breeder's carelessness in making selections or in emphasizing unimportant points. The third, genetic variability, is relatively beyond man's control. Hence, the greatest opportunity for increasing progress from selection is by insuring that the second, the multiple correlation, is as large as possible.

Hazel gives a multiple correlation method of constructing indexes having maximum accuracy. To use it, one must know the constants:

1. Relative economic values for the different traits.
2. Standard deviations (measures of variation) for each trait.
3. Correlations (measures of relationship) between each pair of traits.
4. Heritability of each trait (a measure of the extent to which expression of trait is governed by heredity).
5. Genetic correlations between each pair of traits.

The genetic correlations show the extent to which traits are similar because of genes that affect both traits, and are determined by correlating one trait in one animal with the other in a relative. Using these principles, Hazel developed three indexes for swine. The first involved two characters for which data were available before breeding age. The index (I) was:

$$I = (0.137 \times W) - (0.268 \times S)$$

in which W is the pig's weight at 180 days and S is the pig's market score.

The second index was:

$$I = (0.136 \times W) - (0.232 \times S) + (0.164 \times P)$$

in which W and S are the same as in the first formula and P is the productivity of the dam, used as a measure of the pig's productivity, the lapse of one generation being compensated for by a suitable adjustment for the heritability of this trait.

The third index was designed to include information about the average weight (W) and score (S) of the litter in which each pig was born, in addition to the three traits in the second index. These were considered as fourth and fifth variables, using the correlations between the various traits and making allowances for the number of pigs per litter when arriving at the values to insert in the index.

The three indexes were compared to determine their relative efficiency in making genetic progress. This rate of progress is proportionate to the size of the correlation between genotypes of the selected animals and their indexes. The second and third indexes were 8.8 and 11.3 percent, respectively, more efficient than the first. Since the time and effort expended in keeping records is but a small fraction of the total labor connected with a breeding program, the second index would probably be preferable to the first in most cases. The third might also be chosen over the second, since genetic progress could be increased a little more through its use, and the extra labor would be only that of computing and using the litter averages from data already available.

The progress that could be made by using the three indexes studied by Hazel was 36.3, 39.5, and 40.4 percent, respectively, of that which could have been made by a perfect index, or one in which the phenotype, or appearance of the animal, was a perfect measure of the genotype, or genetic make-up, of the animal. The loss is due to the confusing effects of environment, dominance of one gene over its pair-mate, so that the recessive member of the pair is not evident in the phenotype, and epistasis, or interaction of genes, all of which can make phenotypes unlike genotypes.

A selection index for Rambouillet sheep has been developed at the Western Sheep Breeding Laboratory at Dubois, Idaho, based on the same principles as those outlined for swine indexes. These traits have been included: Face covering (F), length of staple (L), weaning weight (W), type score (T), condition score (C), and neck-fold score (N). The completed index (I) is as follows:

$$I = 75 - (15 \times F) + (7 \times L) + W + (0.4 \times T) + (7 \times C) - (11 \times N)$$

The constant of 75 is added to insure that the index will be positive and average around 100. Corrections for various factors, like twinning, age of dam, and inbreeding, may be made directly on the index, using suitable correction constants. The completed index varies from about 70 to 150 for individual lambs in the Rambouillet flock at Dubois, with an average of about 110. The value of the index may be estimated by comparing the progress when the index was used with that before it was available. Progress was roughly determined by combining the selection differentials for the various traits after each was weighted by its heritability and its economic importance. Over-all progress from selection at weaning age was increased in the range of 20 to 50 percent by the use of the index.

The breeding merit of an animal may be estimated in various ways, including the merits of its ancestors, the animal's own characteristics and performance, the merit of collateral relatives, such as sibs (brothers and/ or sisters) and half sibs, and the merit of its offspring.

The last is usually called the progeny test. Much has been written concerning its accuracy, compared to that of other methods that might give indirect measures of breeding merit. From the standpoint of rate of genetic progress, factors other than relative accuracy must be considered. The most important of these factors are the age at which progeny tests may be obtained and the rate of reproduction. The longer interval between generations that results from use of the progeny test tends to offset the advantage gained by more accurate selection, and may actually reduce the annual rate of improvement.

The relative merits of progeny testing and other methods of selection have been studied by G. E. Dickerson and Dr. Hazel. This is an intricate problem requiring detailed mathematical studies in order to obtain a solution. They considered a number of traits in various species, and concluded that the possibilities of increasing progress by a regular plan for use of progeny-tested sires are limited to certain kinds of livestock and to certain traits. The reasons therefor are outlined here:

1. The less the interval between generations is increased by progeny testing, the more likely it is that progeny testing will increase progress. This is illustrated by an example contrasting the results of selecting for weanling and yearling traits in sheep. Use of the best ram tested the year before on an optimum portion (60 to 70 percent) of the ewes increased progress by about 4 percent for weaning traits, but reduced it for yearling traits, as compared with progress to be expected from use of only the two best yearling rams each year. The only difference between these two examples is that 1 year is required to obtain progeny-test information on weanling traits, while 2 years are required for yearling traits.

2. When the rate of reproduction is low, progeny testing of sires is more likely to increase progress. The resulting increase in genetic superiority of parents tends to be larger, relative to the increase in age of parents, when there is less opportunity for early culling, particularly among females. For example, progeny testing affects progress more favorably for yearling traits in sheep than for growth rate in swine. Obviously, a much higher proportion of the female offspring must be retained in order to maintain the population in sheep than in swine.

3. If the basis for making early selections is relatively inaccurate, the progeny test is more likely to be effective. Therefore, the progeny test would be more apt to improve the annual progress in traits where

heritability is low, than in traits where it is high. Thus, the relative value of the progeny test is determined by a combination of circumstances that are largely beyond the breeder's control, and a regular plan of progeny testing is unlikely to increase (and may reduce) genetic progress unless the progeny-test information becomes available early in the animal's lifetime, the reproductive rate is low, and the basis for making early selections is relatively inaccurate. Dickerson and Hazel point out that improvement from selection is nearly maximum for most traits when culling is based on individual performance, family average, and pedigree, and when the interval between generations is kept short.

Dickerson and Hazel also studied the effectiveness of different methods of selecting for two specific characters in swine, growth rate of pigs and productivity of sows, and they have made some recommendations concerning the procedures that should be most effective. In selecting for growth rate, they recommend that 8 to 10 times as many boars and about 3 times as many gilts as are needed for breeding should be retained long enough after weaning (such as 180 days of age) to obtain a more reliable measure of growth rate than weaning weight. The rest may be culled without reducing appreciably the effectiveness of selection.

Several plans for culling were compared. Yearly progress from selection is greatest when sows are culled after the first litter, the best one-third to one-half being kept for a second litter 6 months later. Another plan, which is almost as effective, is to delay culling until after the second litter, and keep the best one-fifth to one-fourth of the sows for a third litter at 2 years of age. Progress is retarded by retaining more than the optimum proportion of older sows, because the less intense culling of sows and the longer interval between generations is only partly offset by the more severe culling of gilts and the greater accuracy of sow culling.

Having sows farrow two litters a year results in more rapid genetic improvement in productivity, since it permits the accuracy of selection of boars and gilts to be improved by basing the dam's productivity on two litters instead of one. It also permits the more productive sows to be kept for additional litters, with a minimum increase in the average interval between generations.

It is important that the breeder have effective yardsticks of merit, regardless of the selection procedures and breeding system he uses.

Evaluation of the fitted animal in the show ring has long been considered an important part of livestock improvement in the United States. In recent years it has become increasingly apparent that this procedure has many shortcomings as a tool in selection of improved breeding stock. For obvious reasons, only a small portion of the animals raised each generation can be prepared for evaluation. The condition of the animals at the time of the show is usually highly artificial, and quite often is very different from the condition that is desired in practice. Undue attention is often given to so-called fine points of little or no economic importance. Some traits, such as milk yield and efficiency of feed utilization, cannot be accurately evaluated by visual inspection. The practice of excessive fitting has been carried over to the conditioning of breeding stock for sale, and is found to a marked degree even in bulls and rams that are to be sold for use on western ranges. Thus the breeder spends an undue amount for feed to put excessive fat on the animals, for which the buyer must pay, but for which he has no use. Also, the excessive fat may obscure defects in conformation, a point that is aptly stated in the common phrase, "Fat is a pretty color."

Recognizing the need for improved yardsticks, many workers have turned their attention to the development of measures of the economically important characters. Some characters, like litter size in swine, may be observed directly. Others, like body size, rate of growth, milk yield, yield of grease wool, and length of staple, can be weighed or measured directly. Others, for example face covering, skin folds, and body conformation in sheep, require indirect methods of evaluation and the assignment of a score to represent the degree of development in each animal. Devices have been developed for measuring such characters as length of wool fibers, tenderness of meat (muscle), and diameter of wool fibers, density of wool fibers, and hardness of fat.

Much attention also has been given to the measuring of functional traits, such as efficiency of feed utilization in beef cattle and swine, physiological response of horses and mules to exercise, and performance of work by draft horses and mules and by light horses in carriage and under saddle. Many of the developments are still in the experimental stage, but active research is continuing at many institutions to test existing procedures, to develop new ones, and to simplify experimental procedures so they may be applied by breeders in evaluating and selecting their stock.

Heritability

The development of an animal depends upon its inherited make-up and the environment in which it lives. Improvements in heredity are permanent, except those that result from particular combinations of genes, the determiners of heredity, and that disappear when the genes recombine. Improvements in environment must be provided again for each succeeding generation.

The heritability of a trait is actually a measure of the observed variation in a group of animals that is caused by differences in heredity. Estimates of heritability are based on the degree that related animals resemble each other more than less closely related or unrelated animals.

These estimates are applicable primarily to characters or traits in which development depends upon many genes.

Considerable information has accumulated in recent years on the heritability of various characters in livestock. The information helps the breeder because it indicates the progress that can be made by selection and the plan of breeding that is likely to be most effective. Practically all the information on heritability of economically important traits in livestock has been obtained during the last decade. A summary of it is given in the accompanying tables.

There are, of course, variations in the estimates of heritability, and many apparent discrepancies. There are several reasons. Errors may occur in sampling, particularly in studies based on small numbers of animals, so the results are not representative. Variations in environment

1. Estimates of heritability for weights of swine at various ages

Age (days)	Heritability (percent)	Method used to determine heritability	Reference
Birth ..	6	Paternal half sib...................	Lush et al. (1934).
	0	....do.........................	Baker et al. (1943).
	0	....do.........................	Nordskog et al. (1944).
	4. 6	....do.........................	Krider et al. (1946).
	14	Intrasire regression................	Nordskog et al. (1944).
21	4	Paternal half sib...................	Baker et al. (1943).
	0	....do.........................	Nordskog et al. (1944).
	24	....do.........................	Krider et al. (1946).
	0	Intrasire regression................	Nordskog et al. (1944).
56	0	....do.........................	Comstock et al. (1942).
	15	Paternal half sib...................	Baker et al. (1943).
	0	....do.........................	Nordskog et al. (1944).
	13. 6	....do.........................	Krider et al. (1946).
60	7	....do.........................	Bywaters (1937).
	15	Intersire regression................	Do.
	18	Combination of different methods	Do.
84	26	Paternal half sib...................	Baker et al. (1943).
	0	....do.........................	Nordskog et al. (1944).
112 ...	28	....do.........................	Baker et al. (1943).
	0	....do.........................	Nordskog et al. (1944).
140 ...	19	....do.........................	Baker et al. (1943).
	21	....do.........................	Nordskog et al. (1944).
150 ...	16	Line difference due to selection.......	Krider et al. (1946).
	13. 7	Paternal half sib...................	Do.
168 ...	25	....do.........................	Baker et al. (1943).
	27	....do.........................	Nordskog et al. (1944).
180 ...	14	Intrasire regression................	Comstock et al. (1942).
	20	Paternal half sib...................	Whatley (1942).
	62	Intrasire regression................	Do.
	30	Intrasire offspring-dam correlation. ...	Do.
	40	Full sibs, not litter mates...........	Do.
	30	Regression of variance to genetic relationship.	Do.
	23	Paternal half-sib and intrasire regression.	Whatley and Nelson (1942).
	19	Line differences due to selection......	Krider et al. (1946).
	23. 9	Paternal half sib...................	Do.

2. Estimates of heritability for gain and rate of gain in swine

Period (days)	Heritability (percent)	Method used to determine heritability	Reference
Birth–21	7	Paternal half sib	Baker et al. (1943).
Birth–56	15	....do	Hazel et al. (1943).
21–56	0	....do	Nordskog et al. (1944).
	15	....do	Baker et al. (1943).
	0	Intrasire regression	Nordskog et al. (1943).
56–84	17. 7	Paternal half sib	Nordskog et al. (1944).
	20	....do	Baker et al. (1943).
	6	Intrasire regression	Nordskog et al. (1944).
84–112	25. 8	Paternal half sib	Do.
	31	....do	Baker et al. (1943).
	10	Intrasire regression	Nordskog et al. (1944).
112–140	27. 8	Paternal half sib	Do.
	4	....do	Baker et al. (1943).
	10	Intrasire regression	Nordskog et al. (1944).
140–168	24. 5	Paternal half sib	Do.
	13	....do	Baker et al. (1943).
	10	Intrasire regression	Nordskog et al. (1944).
56–112	28. 1	Paternal half sib	Do.
	28	....do	Hazel et al. (1943).
56–168	45. 3	....do	Nordskog et al. (1944).
112–168	17	....do	Hazel et al. (1943).
50–200	26	Intrasire regression	Comstock et al. (1942).
56–200	40	Paternal half sib	Nordskog et al. (1944).
	31	Intrasire regression	Comstock et al. (1942).
Birth–200	21	Paternal half sib	Nordskog et al. (1944).
	3	Intrasire regression	Do.
Weaning–200	21	....do	Do.
	24	Average of three methods	Lush (1936).

may be correlated for certain kinds of relatives. For example, data may have been collected over a period of years in which gradual changes in feed or management occurred. Thus, both dams and their progeny, raised at various times during this period, may have been exposed to an environment better or poorer than the average. Such environmental contributions to likenesses between relatives are difficult to measure. Another factor that may affect estimates of heritability is the mating system. A different approach is required to obtain a reasonably accurate estimate of heritability in an inbred population than in one where random mating has been practiced, a factor that has not been taken into account in some of the studies. In others, the mating system or the amount of inbreeding may have deviated more (or less) from random than the investigator supposed.

Data on the heritability of weights of swine at various ages, and on the heritability of rate of gain (tables 1 and 2) indicate that the estimates of heritability increase as pigs grow older. Therefore, selection for maximum weight should be most effective if practiced at 180 days, rather than at earlier ages. Heritability of weight at 180 days approximates 30 percent. This means the breeder should expect to make about 30 percent of the progress he "reaches for" in selection. For example, if he selects for parents of the next generation animals that weigh 20 pounds above the average of his stock at 180 days, their offspring should be expected to weigh about 6 pounds more than the average of offspring from parents picked at random from the same stock.

3. Estimates of heritability for fertility in swine

Measure of fertility	Herita-bility (percent)	Method used to determine heritability	Reference
Litter size at birth.	17	Maternal half-sib litters.......	Lush and Molln (1942).
	10	Estimated from published reports of various workers.	Do.
	17		
	18		
	34		
	44		
	13	Maternal half-sib litters.......	Hetzer et al. (1940).
	15. 6	Paternal half sib............	Stewart (1945).
	14. 8	Full sib....................	Do.
	13. 6	Intrasire regression...........	Do.
	14. 5	Average of three methods......	Do.
Live pigs farrowed.	17. 6	Paternal half sib............	Do.
	8. 8	Full sib....................	Do.
	15. 8	Intrasire regression...........	Do.
	13. 6	Average of 3 methods........	Do.
Litter size at 28 days.	16	Maternal half-sib litters........	Hetzer et al. (1940).
Litter size at 70 days.	20	.....do....................	Do.
Litter size at weaning.	17	.....do....................	Lush and Molln (1942).

4. Estimates of heritability for other characters in swine

Character	Herita-bility (percent)	Method used to determine heritability	Reference
Weaning weight of litter.	18	Maternal half-sib litters.	Lush and Molln (1942).
Productivity index of sow	16	Intrasire regression...	Hazel, quoted by Lush and Molln (1942).
Economy of gain.......	[1] 8	Average of 3 methods.	Lush (1936).
Body length...........	54	.....do............	Do.
Yield of export bacon...	20	.....do............	Do.
Thickness of belly......	46	.....do............	Do.
Thickness of back fat....	47	.....do............	Do.
Market score at slaughter	33	Average of 2 methods.	Whatley and Nelson (1942).
Conformation score.....	20	Intrasire regression...	Stonaker and Lush (1942).
Type score (within strains).	38	Paternal half sib.....	Hetzer et al. (1944).
Type score (between strains).	92	.....do............	Do.

[1] Minimum estimate.

5. Estimates of heritability for various characters in beef cattle

Character	Herita- bility (percent)	Method used to determine heritability	Reference
Birth weight..........	23	Paternal half sib........	Knapp and Nordskog (1946).
	42	Sire-offspring regression...	Do.
	34	Sire-offspring regression within year.	Do.
	29	Paternal half sib........	Dawson, Phillips and Black (1947).
	11	Paternal half sib; corrected birth weights.	Do.
Weaning weight........	12	Paternal half sib.........	Knapp and Nordskog (1946)
	0	Sire-offspring regression...	Do.
	30	Sire-offspring regression within year.	Do.
Final feed-lot weight....	81	Paternal half sib.........	Do.
	69	Sire-offspring regression...	Do.
	94	Sire-offspring regression within year.	Do.
Gain while on feed.....	99	Paternal half sib........	Do.
	46	Sire-offspring regression...	Do.
	97	Sire-offspring regression within year.	Do.
Economy of gain.......	75	Paternal half sib........	Do.
	54	Sire-offspring regression...	Do.
	48	Sire-offspring regression within year.	Do.
Score at weaning.......	53	Paternal half sib.........	Knapp and Nordskog (1946a).
	0	Sire-offspring regression...	Do.
Slaughter grade........	63	Paternal half sib.........	Do.
Carcass grade:.........	84	.....do.................	Do.
Dressing percent........	1	.....do.................	Do.
Area of eye muscle......	69	.....do.................	Do.

Litter size at birth is not so highly inherited as weight at 180 days. The unweighted average of the eleven estimates given (in table 3) is 19.2 percent. This means that the breeder can expect to realize about one-fifth of the progress in litter size that he reaches for in selecting the parents of the next generation. If selection for litter size is based only on sows, no attention being given to boars in this respect, then the progress will be only about one-half of one-fifth. The estimates of progress through selection are based on the assumption that all the heritability for each trait is due to additive effects of genes. If a portion of it is due to epistatic effects (interactions between different pairs of genes), the effectiveness of selection would be somewhat less.

Estimates of heritability for a number of other characters in swine have also been obtained (table 4), but only one study has been made of each of these characters, except type scores, for which there are two figures. The estimate for type score (between strains) is exceptionally high, 92 percent. This was obtained on a combination of three populations representing large, medium, and small-type Poland China swine, and indicates that the differences between these three strains were largely due to heredity. The estimate of 38 percent for type score (within strains) is the one that indicates the approximate amount of progress that might be made in selecting for type within one of the strains or in a relatively uniform breed. Most of the estimates of heritability for other traits are sufficiently high to indicate that fairly rapid progress can be made by selection. The estimate for economy of gain is quite low, and, if representative, indicates that little improvement could be made per generation as a result of selection for this trait. Further studies are necessary to establish, within reasonably accurate limits, the extent to which these and other important traits of swine are inherited.

We have estimates of heritability for a number of characters in beef cattle (table 5). Some of these are higher than seems reasonable in comparison with the figures obtained from swine and sheep and in view of the probable effects of environmental factors on such characters as final feedlot weight, rate of gain, and economy of gain in the feed lot. More information is needed before these figures can be accepted as generally representative, but at least they indicate that selection should be effective in improving most of the characteristics studied.

Data on heritability of various characters in sheep (table 6) also indicate that most of the various desirable traits studied can be improved by selection, although selection for such traits as yearling body score, type score at weaning, and condition score at weaning would not lead to rapid progress. The several figures for heritability of skin folds and those for face covering indicate that it should be possible to make rather rapid progress in the elimination of excessive skin folds and covered faces by selection for animals that are smooth and have open faces. One of the figures for heritability of neck folds (8 percent) is low, but it was obtained on breeds that are characterized by relatively few skin folds compared with the Rambouillet, on which the other estimates for this character are based.

The heritability of a trait is one of the most important factors to consider in deciding upon the breeding plan that is most apt to be successful in bringing about improvement in that trait. If the heritability of the desired trait is high, the best method of breeding to bring about improvemen will be the mating of animals possessing greatest development of the desired trait, little use being made of information on pedigrees and relatives. If heritability is low, the breeder is more apt to make progress if he uses information on pedigrees and collateral relatives and information he gets from progeny tests in deciding which animals to use for breeding. Also, if heritability is low, it is generally advisable to make relatively little use of inbreeding other than the inbreeding that is needed to make

6. Estimates of heritability for various characters in sheep

Character	Heritability (percent)	Method used to determine heritability	Reference
Birth weight..........	30	Paternal half sib........	Chapman and Lush (1932).
Yearling staple length...	36	Intrasire regression......	Terrill and Hazel (1943).
Yearling weight of clean wool.	38	.....do...............	Do.
	28	.....do...............	Do.
Yearling body weight...	40	.....do...............	Do.
Yearling body score.....	12	.....do...............	Do.
Face covering.........	32	.....do...............	Do.
Neck folds............	26	.....do...............	Do.
Body folds............	37	.....do...............	Do.
Weaning weight.......	26.9	Paternal half sib........	Hazel and Terrill (1945).
	17.0	Average 3 breeds, 2 methods..............	Hazel and Terrill (1946a).
	33.9	Intrasire regression......	Hazel and Terrill (1945).
Staple length at weaning.	30	Weighted average of 2 methods.	Do.
	41	Paternal half sib........	Do.
	38.7	Intrasire regression......	Do.
	40	Weighted average of 2 methods.	Do.
	43.0	Average 3 breeds, 2 methods..............	Hazel and Terrill (1946a).
	15.2	Paternal half sib........	Hazel and Terrill (1946).
	6.8	Intrasire regression......	Do.
Type score at weaning...	13.0	Weighted average of 2 methods.	Do.
	7.0	Average 3 breeds, 2 methods..............	Hazel and Terrill (1946a).
	2.4	Paternal half sib........	Hazel and Terrill (1946).
	13.8	Intrasire regression......	Do.
Condition score at weaning.	4	Weighted average of 2 methods.	Do.
	21.0	Average 3 breeds, 2 methods..............	Hazel and Terrill (1946a).
Skin folds.............	45.6	Average of 4 methods....	Jones et al. (1946).
	51.2	Average of 4 methods, within year.	Do.
	36.2	Paternal half sib........	Terrill and Hazel (1946).
	45.1	Intrasire regression......	Do.
Neck folds............	39	Weighted average of 2 methods.	Do.
	8	Average 3 breeds, 2 methods..............	Hazel and Terrill (1946a).
	51.0	Paternal half sib........	Terrill and Hazel (1946).
	60.3	Intrasire regression......	Do.
Face covering.........	56	Weighted average of 2 methods.	Do.
	46.0	Average 3 breeds, 2 methods..............	Hazel and Terrill (1946a).
Number of nipples......	14.4	Intrasire correlation.....	Phillips, et al. (1945).
Number of functional nipples.	26	.....do...............	Do.
	22	Intrasire regression......	Do.

families distinct from each other or to make full use of the progeny test.

Heritability of a trait may be due to additive effects of genes, or there may be variations in hereditary effects owing to epistatic effects of genes, or both types of effects may be present. The difference between these two types of effects may be illustrated by supposing that two dominant genes, A and B, located at different points on a chromosome or on different chromosomes, have values of 6 and 4, respectively, when one occurs without the other, insofar as they affect a certain trait. If their effects are strictly additive, the combined value of the two is 10, if both are present in an animal. If, however, the value is 12 when they occur together, the effects are not strictly additive, and the extra value resulting from the interaction of the two is called an epistatic effect. If additive effects of genes are low, but heritability of a trait appears to be fairly high because of epistatic effects, inbreeding to develop lines that are distinct from each other, selection of the outstanding lines, crossing these lines, and developing new ones from the more favorable crosses is the procedure that appears most likely to be effective.

There is need for much additional information on heritability of various economically important traits in livestock, and on the nature of the effects of genes that control the development of these traits, before it will be possible to prescribe methods of breeding that will be most effective in all situations with which breeders are confronted. However, sufficient information is available to indicate some of the advantages and limitations of inbreeding and crossing, and the possibilities of developing new types from crossbred foundations. These problems are discussed later.

Inbreeding

Inbreeding is the mating of animals that are more closely related to each other than the average relationship within the population concerned. Such matings tend to make the offspring more homozygous, on the average, than if their parents were of average relationship to each other. Genes occur in pairs. If both members of a pair are alike they are said to be homozygous; if they are different they are said to be heterozygous. Thus, inbreeding increases the proportion of pairs of homozygous genes, or determiners of heredity.

The results achieved by corn breeders with inbreeding and crossing of inbred lines seemed to justify investigations into the possibilities of speeding up livestock improvement by establishing inbred lines and testing the usefulness of these lines in various types of crosses. Hence, much work has been initiated in recent years. The major projects in this field are being conducted cooperatively by the Bureau of Animal Industry of the Department of Agriculture and various State experiment stations through the Regional Swine Breeding Laboratory, whose headquarters is in Ames, Iowa; the Western Sheep Breeding Laboratory at Dubois, Idaho, and the United States Range Livestock Experiment Station at Miles City, Mont. Work at Miles City is primarily with range beef cattle, but a limited amount of work is also under way with swine. Extensive work with swine, sheep, and cattle is also in progress at Beltsville.

Since inbreeding is the most powerful tool the breeder has for establishing uniform strains or families that are distinct from each other, and since much experimental work is now being conducted to determine how best to use it in livestock improvement, many readers may wish to know how the amount of inbreeding is measured.

The method that is now used almost exclusively was developed by Sewall Wright, formerly of the Department. His formula is:

$$F_x = \Sigma (\tfrac{1}{2})^{n+n'+1}(1+F_a)$$

The formula appears more technical than it actually is. F_x stands for the coefficient of inbreeding of an animal, which is to be calculated. The Greek letter Σ (sigma) represents all the hereditary contributions to the inbreeding, but has no numeral value of its own. For example, if two or more ancestors contribute to the inbreeding, the contribution of each is calculated and then all are added together to obtain the coefficient of inbreeding. The fraction $\tfrac{1}{2}$ is the animal's relationship to each of its two parents; n stands for the number of generations between the sire and a common ancestor; n' stands for the number of generations between the dam and a common ancestor. The factor $(1+F_a)$ represents the influence of a common ancestor, if that ancestor is itself inbred. If the common ancestor is not inbred, this part of the formula is omitted.

To illustrate, suppose an animal, A, has the following ancestors:

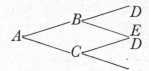

The animal has the same grandsire, (D), on both the sire's (B) and dam's (C) sides of the pedigree. Thus D is a common ancestor of both parents of A. Since there is only one generation between B and D, and also one between C and D, the value for n and n' in the formula are 1 and 1, thus:

$$Fx = (\tfrac{1}{2})^{1+1+1} \text{ or } (\tfrac{1}{2})^3$$

The third power or the cube of $\tfrac{1}{2}$ is $\tfrac{1}{8}$, which is expressed as 12.5 percent, and is the coefficient of inbreeding.

This coefficient indicates the increase in the proportion of homozygous pairs of genes that can be expected, on the average, in matings where there is one common grandparent, as compared with matings where there is no common ancestor. If we suppose that random breeding had been practiced in a herd, and that 50 percent of the pairs of genes were homozygous and 50 percent heterozygous, then 12.5 percent inbreeding would imply that 12.5 percent of the heterozygous pairs were homozygous in the new individual (12.5 percent of 50 is 6.25)—so, 56.25 percent of the pairs would be homozygous, while 43.75 would be heterozygous.

If the common ancestor, D, in the above example had already been inbred, for example 25 percent, then the factor $(1 + F_a)$ would have been $(1 + 0.25)$ or 1.25, and the inbreeding of animal A would have been 12.5×1.25 or 15.625, usually shortened to 15.6 percent.

Inbreeding does not create nor destroy any genes—it merely permits more of them to occur in homozygous pairs. Genes that favor development of both desirable and undesirable characters may become homozygous. Inbreeding thus uncovers many recessive genes that would otherwise remain concealed by their dominant-pair mates, or alleles (a recessive gene is one that is not able to express itself when it occurs as the pair-mate of a dominant gene, hence only the effect of the dominant gene is seen). Recessive genes generally have less desirable effects than dominant genes, so there is usually some degeneration in the average merit of individual animals when inbreeding is practiced. The chief danger of intense inbreeding, therefore, is that it may make undesirable genes homozygous so rapidly that it will be impossible to discard all the individuals that are homozygous for them.

The chief advantages of inbreeding are: It helps to uncover undesirable recessive genes so that animals possessing them may be culled; it may be used to develop uniform and distinct families so that interfamily selection may be more effectively practiced; new and often superior groups of animals may be produced by combining two or more inbred lines; it increases prepotency by increasing the chances that animals will pass on their traits to their offspring; and it is useful in maintaining a high relationship of stock to an especially desirable ancestor.

The extent of the experimental work that is being undertaken to test the possibilities of using inbreeding in livestock improvement can best be shown by details from some places where the work is being done.

The Regional Swine Breeding Laboratory and the cooperating State agricultural experiment stations in Illinois, Indiana, Iowa, Minnesota, Missouri, Nebraska, Oklahoma, and Wisconsin have a total of 46 lines of swine. These include 19 Poland China, 11 Duroc-Jersey, 4 Hampshire, 8 Chester White, and 1 Landrace line, and 3 lines that are being developed from crossbred foundations.

Eight new lines are being developed by the Bureau of Animal Industry at Beltsville. Another line is being developed in cooperation with the Maryland Agricultural Experiment Station, and two additional lines are being developed at Miles City, in cooperation with the Montana Agricultural Experiment Station.

Thirty-two lines of Rambouillet sheep are being developed at the Western Sheep Breeding Laboratory, Dubois, Idaho. In addition, the Bureau of Animal Industry is developing 10 lines of Columbia and 10 of Targhee sheep at the United States Sheep Experiment Station, which also is located at Dubois.

A few lines of beef cattle are being developed by the Bureau of Animal Industry and the Montana Agricultural Experiment Station at the United States Range Livestock Experiment Station at Miles City. Plans have been developed to establish up to 30 or 35 lines in cooperation with several State experiment stations in the range-cattle area, and lines of beef and dual purpose cattle are being established at Beltsville.

Breeding work with livestock progresses slowly, for obvious reasons. The reproductive level is low, compared with plants, and the time required for a generation is long. The long time per generation is illustrated by the following estimates made by Jay L. Lush: Horses, 10 to 13 years; beef cattle, 4.5 to 5 years; dairy cattle, 4 to 4.5 years; sheep, 4 to 4.5 years; swine, about 2.5 years. Also, with the exception of swine, a large proportion of the female progeny reared must be retained as replacements in order to maintain numbers. Lush gives the following estimates of the percentages of females that must be retained for this purpose: Horses, 35 to 45; beef cattle, 40 to 55; dairy cattle, 50 to 65; sheep, 45 to 55; swine, 10 to 15. While these factors, over which the breeder has no control, place limits on the rate of progress, they also make it imperative that the most effective methods of selection and breeding be used if the breeder is to have much real genetic progress to show for each generation of breeding effort. And despite the handicaps that limit the rate of progress in animal-breeding experimentation, much has been learned in recent years from the work with inbreeding of livestock.

That work has not progressed to a point where broad generalizations can be made, and many details of application of results must yet be worked out, but the results to date indicate that the breeder can make effective use of this tool in speeding up improvement. The work with swine naturally has gone ahead more rapidly than the work with sheep and beef cattle. To illustrate what is being accomplished, I outline some of the results in the Regional Swine Breeding Laboratory, which was established in 1937, with W. A. Craft as director, and the eight State experiment stations that are conducting projects in this regional effort, under the leadership of J. L. Krider (Illinois), J. R. Wiley (Indiana), Jay L. Lush (Iowa), L. M. Winters (Minnesota), L. A. Weaver (Missouri), M. L. Baker (Nebraska), O. S. Willham (Oklahoma), and A. B. Chapman (Wisconsin).

Increased inbreeding has generally been accompanied by some deterioration in the productivity of swine. This was expected, in view of the results obtained earlier with laboratory animals and corn. It has generally been more difficult to maintain vitality and litter size than growth rate in lines of swine that were being inbred.

Crossing of inbred lines has usually corrected the decline in performance that accompanied inbreeding, and in some cases appears to result in a considerable increase over the performance of noninbred stock.

Inbred lines developed from widely unrelated stock have produced more favorable results when crossed than lines developed from related stock. Inbred lines from different breeds have given more favorable results in crosses than those from the same breed.

The mating of inbred boars of selected inbred lines to noninbred sows appears to give a little increase in the performance of the pigs, in comparison with pigs from similar sows and sired by noninbred boars.

Inbreeding of 30 to 40 percent appears to be enough to make it possible to determine the value of a line of swine, and to make lines differ genetically, particularly if the lines are from unrelated stock. This is equivalent roughly to about 2 generations of brother-sister mating, 4 generations of half-brother-sister matings, or 12 generations of breeding in which single first cousins are mated.

Lines that were inbred 30 to 40 percent have been found to differ in physiological characters that were not evident in the appearance of the animals. For example, boars in different lines at the Minnesota station have been found to differ in the amount of male hormone excreted in the urine and in the rate of development of the testes.

Selection for one character may in some cases give rise to a change not desired by the breeder in another character. There is some evidence, for example, that maximum rate of fattening seems to be opposed to litter size and milking ability in sows. Some of the breeder's effort is canceled by the compromise necessary in selection between various characters. Studies now in progress have revealed that hereditary factors of the individual pig that cause rapid and economical gains when the pig is full-fed to 225 pounds, and that also lead finally to high ratings for conformation in the live pig, are largely the same features that cause rapid deposition of fat, resulting in fat carcasses at the time of slaughtering. These results tend to emphasize that selection based on conformation at market weight according to present standards constitute selection for fatter hogs because the differences in width, depth, and plumpness of body, which loom large in making choices, are largely differences in amount of fat.

Thus, it is evident that some compromise must be made in selections, and that care must be exercised to avoid selecting in an undesired direction. Sows possessing and transmitting the ability to fatten rapidly tend to be poor in suckling ability, and thereby reduce the gains and increase the feed requirements of their pigs during the period of fattening. It appears now, therefore, that in selection for rapid and economical gains, the indirect selection for fat carcasses associated with the most rapid gains may be offset if selections are based on individual gains of pigs during the early part of the growth period, perhaps at 85 to about 112 days of age, when more of the weight is muscle than later, and by giving much attention to suckling ability of sows, which is indicated by litter size and weight of pigs at 3 to 8 weeks of age.

Not all lines developed in any program with swine, or with other classes of livestock, will be valuable for use in livestock improvement. For example, it is becoming apparent that only a part of the 46 inbred lines of swine on hand in the Regional Swine Breeding Laboratory program will merit maintenance and use for improving purebred herds and for extensive use in pork production. Some wastage of lines is inevitable. Many inferior lines of corn have been discarded, and the same will apply to inbred lines of livestock. E. W. Lindstrom of Iowa made a survey of the results of inbreeding of corn (maize) in 1939, and estimated that only 2.4 percent of a total of about 30,000 inbred lines developed in the United States during several previous years had proved useful.

The expense of developing an inbred line of livestock is of course much greater than for a line of corn. For this reason, it is generally desirable to guide the development of lines as much as possible by selection, and to test them thoroughly before deciding to retain or discard them. But for the same reason, it is necessary to be ruthless in discarding lines, once it is clearly demonstrated that they can make no worthwhile contribution to improvement, rather than to follow a natural desire to retain expensive (but not valuable) stock with the hope that it may prove useful.

The outstanding inbred lines of swine may be used for crossing with noninbred stock or for crossing with other inbred lines to produce market hogs, or they may be used for crossing with other lines to develop still better lines from which stock will be available for use in commercial production or for improving purebred herds. The situation will be somewhat different for cattle and sheep than for swine. Since such a large proportion of the female offspring in inbred lines of cattle and sheep must be retained for replacements, the numbers that can be used for crossing with males from other lines for commercial production will be small. Experimental work has started to test the various ways of utilizing inbred lines, and further results should be had before recommendations are made.

One of the most urgent problems in connection with the use of inbred lines is the development of methods of preserving them and guarding their purity. The experiment stations cannot continue to maintain established lines indefinitely. Just as they developed many inbred lines of corn and placed them in the hands of organizations that were producing hybrid seed commercially, the inbred lines of livestock which they develop must be placed in the hands of private breeders who will expand numbers and make stock available to commercial livestock producers. Limited attempts are already being made to place some inbred swine in the hands of private breeders. Ways to guard the purity of the lines are yet to be found.

It is possible that the existing breed associations and their purebred-breeder members will take over this work as an additional function of the purebred association for each breed involved. This would be a logical development, and in the initial stages might be carried out with the help and guidance of the experiment stations that are developing the lines. If the associations do not expand their services to meet this need as it arises, other methods must be found. It is difficult to predict how rapidly the need will expand, but it should be remembered that the extensive hybrid-seed corn industry of today had its beginning only in 1926, when the first seed company was organized for the commercial production of hybrid corn, and that the first appreciable expansion began about 1932, when hybrid-seed production was taken up by several new companies.

Cross-breeding

Cross-breeding for the production of market animals has been practiced for many years, particularly with swine, sheep, and beef cattle. By this method of breeding, producers have taken advantage of the increased productivity (called hybrid vigor or heterosis) that frequently results from the crossing of distinct types and breeds.

The most extensive experimental work in this field has been with swine. J. L. Lush, P. S. Shearer, and C. C. Culbertson of Iowa State College have summarized the results of the important experiments in this field. They point out that any one piece of work, especially one in which small numbers of pigs were used, scarcely appears enough by itself to prove beyond question that there is a real advantage in favor of cross-breeding. Yet, almost every piece of work indicates that such an advantage is probable.

The Iowa workers conclude that the combined weight of all the scattered evidence is overwhelming in indicating that cross-breeding results in increased production. Crossbred pigs tend to be somewhat more vigorous and thrifty than would be expected from the average of the two parent breeds. Because of this added vigor, crossbreds generally show a lower death rate up to weaning, and consequently larger and heavier litters are weaned. Also, they generally gain a little more rapidly on a little less feed than the purebreds. For the same reasons, the crossbred gilts or sows, when used for breeding, can be expected to wean slightly larger and heavier litters than purebreds. Lush ˙and his co-workers emphasize that these are results that can be expected on the average, but they should not be expected to happen every time a cross is made, any more than slightly loaded dice should be expected to turn up a winning combination every time they are thrown.

Three general systems of cross-breeding may be practiced by the producer of market hogs. Purebred or high-grade females of one breed and purebred boars of another breed may be used for the production of each crop of pigs. This plan is simple, but it means that replacements of sows must be purchased or produced in a subsidiary breeding program.

Another plan is called crisscrossing, in which boars of two breeds are alternated in producing each new generation of pigs from dams saved from the previous generation. This plan takes advantage of any hybrid vigor expressed in the ability of the crossbred dam to raise large, vigorous litters, and eliminates the necessity of purchasing sow replacements.

Still another plan utilizes three breeds of boars. It is similar in all other respects to the crisscrossing system.

Our knowledge of the results that may be expected from crossbreeding beef cattle has been increased in recent years through work conducted cooperatively at Miles City, Mont., by the Department and the Montana Agricultural Experiment Station. The experiment was planned to test the possibility of maintaining heterosis through three-breed crossing. The first cross was Shorthorn bulls on Hereford cows. The first generation, or F_1, females (offspring of Shorthorn bulls and Hereford cows) were mated to Aberdeen-Angus bulls, and their triple-cross female offspring were mated to Hereford bulls. The latter phases of this work have not yet been completed, but results thus far indicate that three-breed crossing may be an effective method of increasing productivity in beef cattle. Some results:

Fifty-seven F_1 steers (Shorthorn × Hereford) were compared with 67 Hereford steers. The crossbred calves gained more rapidly in the feed lot and were heavier at the time of marketing. Crossbreds had fewer digestive disturbances, and they also had higher dressing percentages. Differences in efficiency of feed utilization, slaughter grade and carcass grade were not significant.

Fifty-three F_1 and 55 Hereford heifers were also compared. The crossbred heifers were heavier at birth and weighed 7.2 pounds more at weaning time. At 18 and 30 months the differences in favor of the crossbreds were 50.9 and 88.0 pounds, respectively.

Results with offspring produced by mating Aberdeen-Angus bulls to F_1 females show that the triple-cross steers weighed more at weaning and at the end of the feeding period, gained more rapidly during the feeding period, sold for more per pound and per head, had a higher dressing percentage, and returned more per head above feed and marketing costs than the Hereford steers with which they were compared. The triple-cross heifers also weighed more at weaning and at 18 months, and were given higher scores at 18 months than Hereford heifers raised under identical conditions. There were indications that the triple-cross calves had a faster rate of gain before weaning, but a slower rate after weaning than F_1 calves.

Further work is needed to determine the part that continued three-breed crossing can play in commercial beef production. Management of animals in several groups at breeding time may make it difficult for some producers to follow. Crisscrossing, in which only two breeds are used, should be more practical, and its use should be tested further experimentally.

Developing New Breeds

Many breeds of livestock have been developed. They vary widely in traits and adaptability. But circumstances sometimes arise in which no one of the existing breeds meets all the requirements of the breeder. Under such circumstances, it may be desirable to develop a new breed, combining characteristics of two or more breeds. An example of this is the Columbia sheep, which has become sufficiently well established to be recognized as a breed.

It has been rather common range practice for several decades, in some western areas, to cross-breed sheep by mating range ewes that predominate in Rambouillet or other fine-wool breeding with rams of long-wool breeds, such as Lincolns and Cotswolds, in order to get larger ewes that produce more lambs and pounds of marketable wool than can be produced with fine-wool ewes of the parent stock. Although the practice has advantages, it has given rise to considerable periodic variation in flocks because crossbred ewes that were produced in this way were, as a rule, alternately mated to fine-wool rams and then to long-wool rams.

In an effort to contribute stability to the production of large range ewes, the Columbia sheep has been developed by the Department. This breed is, in general, the result of cross-breeding select Lincoln rams with Rambouillet ewes and proceeding from this original crossbreed foundation by mating the most select first-cross rams with carefully selected first-cross ewes and interbreeding the rams and ewes descending from them. This undertaking was pursued at Laramie, Wyo., from 1912 to 1917, and since that time this development of the Columbia sheep by the Department has been conducted at the United States Sheep Experiment Station at Dubois, Idaho.

The Columbia is a white-faced sheep that is large, vigorous, moderately low-set, polled, and free from wool blindness and body wrinkles. The good body length balances well with the width and depth. It is especially well-fleshed in the loin, and has a square rump and a good leg of mutton. Mature rams range in body weight from 190 to 250 pounds, whereas mature ewes range from 135 to 155 pounds under range conditions in the fall. On the average, mature Columbia ewes produce about 12 pounds of unscoured wool per year, which, on a commercial basis, yields approximately 50 percent scoured clean wool. The average length of staple of the fleeces of 1 year's growth is approximately 3½ inches. Mature rams produce fleeces weighing 18 pounds or more for a growth of 12 months under range conditions. The annual length of staple for fleeces of rams averages about 3¾ inches. The fleece tends to stay well together in storms. Desirable market grades of the wool from Columbia sheep, on the basis of fineness, as determined commercially, are Three-eighths Blood and Quarter Blood.

Work of this type is also under way at other places, and with other types of livestock. The Department, working in cooperation with the Office of Indian Affairs, is developing a type of sheep that is adapted to the semiarid ranges of the Southwest and produces a good-quality carpet wool suitable for hand weaving. This work is conducted at the Southwestern Range and Sheep Breeding Laboratory, Fort Wingate, N. Mex. At its Iberia Livestock Experiment Farm, near Jeanerette, La., the Department is establishing and testing new lines of cattle containing varying amounts of zebu and Aberdeen-Angus blood.

The object of this work is to develop a type or types of beef cattle that can perform satisfactorily in the subtropical conditions along the Gulf of Mexico. Work is also under way with swine, in efforts to develop improved types having more lean and less fat, by combining the Danish Landrace (a bacon type) with various domestic and imported breeds of the fatter, or lard, type. The Bureau of Animal Industry has a number of these experimental lines at Beltsville and one at its Range Livestock Experiment Station in Miles City, Mont. The Minnesota Agricultural Experiment Station is also developing some new lines of swine. There are other experimental efforts of this type, but these should serve to illustrate the nature of the work being done.

The development of a new breed is not a task to be undertaken lightly. A definite need for a new type should be clearly evident before such a project is undertaken. Facilities should be available to handle a large number of animals and to continue the project for many years, so that the new type may be well established. The person or persons planning and supervising the work should have a clear understanding of the genetic principles involved. Work like this is obviously limited to Federal and State experiment stations and to the establishments of a limited number of private breeders who have unusual facilities and are willing to venture from the established breeding practices.

Maintenance of a satisfactory level of reproduction is essential to the success of any breeding program. Much work has been done in recent years on various phases of physiology of reproduction that have a bearing on fertility.

The importance of time of breeding in relation to the beginning and end of the heat period, or estrus, has received considerable attention. Data on length of estrus, time of ovulation, or release of the egg or eggs from the ovaries, speed of travel of spermatozoa in the reproductive tract, duration of life of spermatozoa in the female tract, and studies on the proportions of successful matings when breeding takes place at various stages of estrus all bear on the problem.

Some Factors Affecting Reproduction

The combined evidence from many sources indicates that a mating has the greatest chance of being successful if it takes place near the time of ovulation. In the various types of farm animals, recommended times of mating where hand mating is practiced are:

Horses—If mated only once, the third day of estrus appears best, on the average. If service can be had more than once, the best practice appears to be to mate on the third day, and on every second day thereafter until the end of estrus.

Cattle—If bred once, mate 12 to 20 hours after onset of estrus. If bred twice, mate immediately after onset of estrus and again 12 to 20 hours later.

Sheep—During the second half of estrus. If feasible, mate about 12 hours after estrus begins and at 12-hour intervals until estrus ends. Estrus lasts about 30 hours, on the average.

Goats—During the second half of estrus. Exact data are not available, but the duration of estrus is similar to that in the ewe.

Swine—Late on first day, or preferably on second day of estrus.

We conducted studies at the Utah Agricultural Experiment Station to determine if giving special feed to range lambs would influence sexual development and reproduction. The first winter is perhaps the most critical time in the development of the range ewe. Up to weaning, the lamb is provided with a reasonably adequate diet in most cases, while with its dam on spring and summer range. When the lamb is weaned and moved to winter range, there is often a decided drop in level and quality of nutrition, and this is accompanied by more severe environmental conditions in other respects.

Results of the study in Utah indicate that when ewe lambs are given special feed during the first winter the reproductive tract develops more fully, as compared with development in ewe lambs maintained on open range. These results, coupled with results of earlier work by A. C. Esplin, M. A. Madsen, and the writer in which larger lamb crops were produced at 2 years of age as a result of lot feeding during the first winter, indicate the desirability of giving special attention to the feeding of ewe lambs in range flocks. How far the rancher can afford to go in giving special attention to his ewe lambs is a problem needing further investigation.

The environment in which animals live may affect the fertility of livestock. An experiment has been conducted cooperatively by the Bureau of Animal Industry and the Florida Agricultural Experiment Station which gives some clear experimental evidence on this point. Thirty pairs of Columbia ewes and two pairs of rams were selected from the Department's flocks at the Dubois station. One member of each pair was retained at Dubois, and the other sent to the North Florida Experiment Station at Quincy. Wool production of the ewes at Quincy was comparable in grease weight and staple length to that of the ewes at Dubois, but the level of fertility as measured by percent of ewes lambing was not as high. This deficiency was especially marked during the first two years the ewes were at Quincy. Columbia ewes descended from those brought from Dubois and raised at Quincy also reproduced at a lower level and had smaller lambs at weaning than Columbia ewes at Dubois, but there was no noticeable reduction in wool production.

Most sheep and goats breed naturally during the fall and early winter months. In some instances, there would be an economic advantage in having part or all of the ewes and does in a flock bred during the spring or summer months. The possibility of stimulating estrus and ovulation in ewes and does during the spring and summer has received much attention in recent years. It has been possible to induce ovulation in a high proportion of the animals by the use of gonadotropic hormones, but induction of estrus in conjunction with ovulation has been quite erratic. No satisfactory explanation of these variable results has been found.

Fertility, as measured by percentage of conceptions, is generally lower in animals in which estrus has been induced or in those force-mated after induction of ovulation, than in animals bred during natural estrus. However, satisfactory fertility has been reported in some cases. Further work is needed to determine the endocrine physiology of normal and experimentally induced estrus in sheep and goats and the specific doses and time sequences that will induce estrus and ovulation, before procedures can be recommended for general use in practice.

THE AUTHOR

Ralph W. Phillips was formerly in charge of genetics investigations in the Bureau of Animal Industry. He took leave during 1943 and early 1944 to help the Governments of China and India with their livestock problems. Dr. Phillips is editor of the Journal of Animal Science and is the author or coauthor of about 100 publications on various phases of animal breeding. He is a graduate of Berea College and took graduate work at the University of Missouri.

FURTHER READING ABOUT HERITABILITY IN LIVESTOCK

Baker, Marvel L., Hazel, L. N., and Reinmiller, C. F.: *The Relative Importance of Heredity and Environment in the Growth of Pigs at Different Ages,* Journal of Animal Science, volume 2, pages 3–13, 1943.

Bywaters, James H.: *The Hereditary and Environmental Portions of the Variance in Weaning Weights of Poland China Pigs,* Genetics, volume 22, pages 457–468, 1937.

Chapman, A. B., and Lush, J. L.: *Twinning, Sex Ratios, and Genetic Variability in Birth Weight in Sheep,* Journal of Heredity, volume 23, pages 473–478, 1932.

Comstock, R. E., Winters, L. M., Jordon, P. S., and Kiser, O. M.: *Measures of Growth Rate for Use in Swine Selection,* Journal of Agricultural Research volume 65, pages 379–389, 1942.

Hazel, L. N., Baker, Marvel L., and Reinmiller, C. F..: *Genetic and Environmental Correlations Between the Growth Rates of Pigs at Different Ages,* Journal of Animal Science, volume 2, pages 118–128, 1943.

Hazel, L. N., and Terrill, Clair E.: *Heritability of Weaning Weight and Staple Length in Range Rambouillet Lambs,* Journal of Animal Science, volume 4, pages 347–358, 1945.

Hazel, L. N., and Terrill, Clair E.: *Heritability of Type and Condition in Range Rambouillet Lambs as Evaluated by Scoring,* Journal of Animal Science, volume 5; pages 55–61, 1946.

Hazel, L. N., and Terrill, Clair E.: *Heritability of Weanling Traits in Columbia, Corriedale, and Targhee Lambs,* Journal of Animal Science, volume 5, pages 371–377, 1946a.

Hetzer, H. O., Dickerson, G. E., and Zeller, J. H.: *Heritability of Type in Poland China Swine as Evaluated by Scoring,* Journal of Animal Science, volume 3, pages 390–398, 1944.

Hetzer, H. O., Lambert, W. V., and Zeller, J. H.: *Influence of Inbreeding and Other Factors on Litter Size in Chester White Swine,* U. S. D. A. Circular 570, 1940.

Jones, J. M., Warwick, B. L., Phillips, R. W., Spencer, D. A., Godbey, C. B., Patterson, R. E., and Dameron, W. H.: *Inheritance of Skin Folds of Sheep,* Journal of Animal Science, volume 5, pages 154–169, 1946.

Knapp, Bradford, Jr., and Nordskog, Arne W.: *Heritability of Growth and Efficiency in Beef Cattle,* Journal of Animal Science, volume 5, pages 62–70, 1946.

Knapp, Bradford, Jr., and Nordskog, Arne W.: *Heritability of Live Animal Scores, Grades and Certain Carcass Characteristics in Beef Cattle,* Journal of Animal Science, volume 5, pages 194–199, 1946a.

Krider, J. L., Fairbanks, B. W., Carroll, W. E., and Roberts, E.: *Effectiveness of Selecting for Rapid and for Slow Growth Rate in Hampshire Swine,* Journal of Animal Science, volume 5, pages 3–15, 1946.

Lush, Jay L.: *Genetic Aspects of the Danish System of Progeny-Testing Swine,* Iowa Agricultural Experiment Station Research Bulletin 204, 1936.

Lush, Jay L.: *Intra-Sire Correlations or Regressions of Offspring on Dam as a Method of Estimating Heritability of Characteristics,* American Society of Animal Production, Proceedings, pages 293–301, 1940.

Lush, Jay L., Hetzer, H. O., and Culbertson, C. C.: *Factors Affecting Birth Weights of Swine,* Genetics, volume 19, pages 329–343, 1934.

Lush, Jay L., and Molln, A. E.: *Litter Size and Weight as Permanent Characteristics of Sows,* U. S. D. A. Technical Bulletin 836, 1942.

Nordskog, Arne W., Comstock, R. E., and Winters, L. M.: *Hereditary and Environmental Factors Affecting Growth Rate in Swine,* Journal of Animal Science, volume 3, pages 257–272, 1944.

Phillips, Ralph W., Schott, Ralph G., and Spencer, Damon A.: *The Genetics, Physiology and Economic Importance of the Multinipple Trait in Sheep,* U. S. D. A. Technical Bulletin 909, 1945.

Stewart, H. A.: *The Inheritance of Prolificacy in Swine,* Journal of Animal Science, volume 4, pages 359–366, 1945.

Stonaker, H. H., and Lush, J. L.: *Heritability of Conformation in Poland China Swine as Evaluated by Scoring,* Journal of Animal Science, volume 1, pages 99–105, 1942.

Terrill, Clair E., and Hazel, L. N.: *Heritability of Yearling Fleece and Body Traits of Range Rambouillet Ewes,* Journal of Animal Science, volume 2, pages 358–359, 1943.

Terrill, Clair E., and Hazel, L. N.: *Heritability of Face Covering and Neck Folds in Range Rambouillet Lambs as Evaluated by Scoring,* Journal of Animal Science, volume 5, pages 170–179, 1946.

Whatley, J. A.: *Influence of Heredity and Other Factors on 180-Day Weight in Poland China Swine,* Journal of Agricultural Research, volume 65, pages 249–264, 1942.

Whatley, J. A., and Nelson, R. H.: *Heritability of Difference in 180-Day Weight and Market Score of Duroc Swine,* Journal of Animal Science, volume 1, page 70, 1942.

FOR FURTHER READING

Baker, A. L., and Quesenberry, J. R.: *Comparison of Growth of Hereford and F_1 Hereford $\times$ Shorthorn Heifers,* Journal of Animal Science, volume 4, pages 322–325, 1944.

Craft, W. A.: *Swine Breeding Research at the Regional Swine Breeding Laboratory,* U. S. D. A. Miscellaneous Publication 523, 1943.

Dickerson, G. E., and Hazel, L. N.: *Effectiveness of Selection on Progeny Performance as a Supplement to Earlier Culling in Livestock,* Journal of Agricultural Research, volume 69, pages 459–476, 1944.

Dickerson, G. E., and Hazel, L. N.: *Selection for Growth Rate of Pigs and Productivity of Sows,* Journal of Animal Science, volume 3, pages 201–212, 1944.

Hankins, O. G., Knapp, Bradford, Jr., and Phillips, Ralph W.: *The Muscle-Bone Ratio as an Index of Merit in Beef and Dual-Purpose Cattle,* Journal of Animal Science, volume 2, pages 42–49, 1943.

Hardy, John I.: *Cross-Section-Area Method for Determining Density of Wool Fibers,* U. S. D. A. Circular 654, 1942.

Hardy, John I.: *A Clipper for Obtaining Wool Density Samples,* Journal of Animal Science, volume 1, pages 34–37, 1942.

Hazel, L. N.: *The Genetic Basis for Constructing Selection Indexes,* Genetics, volume 28, pages 476–490, 1943.

Hazel, L. N., and Lush, J. L.: *The Efficiency of Three Methods of Selection,* Journal of Heredity, volume 33, pages 393–399, 1942.

Kibler, H. H., and Brody, Samuel: *Growth and Development with Special Reference to Domestic Animals,* Missouri Agricultural Experiment Station Research Bulletin 394, 1945.

Knapp, Bradford, Jr.: *Determination of Slaughter-Steer Grades from Weights and Measurements,* U. S. D. A. Circular 524, 1939.

Knapp, Bradford, Jr., Baker, A. L., Quesenberry, J. R., and Clark, R. T.: *Record of Performance in Hereford Cattle,* Montana Agricultural Experiment Station Bulletin 397, 1941.

Knapp, Bradford, Jr., Phillips, Ralph W., Black, W. H., and Clark, R. T.: *Length of Feeding Period and Number of Animals Required to Measure Economy of Gain in Progeny Tests of Beef Bulls,* Journal of Animal Science, volume 1, pages 285–292, 1942.

Lambert, W. V., and McKenzie, Fred F.: *Artificial Insemination in Livestock Breeding,* U. S. D. A. Circular 567, 1940.

Lindstrom, E. W.: *Analysis of Modern Maize Breeding Principles and Methods,* Proceedings of Seventh International Genetical Congress, Edinburgh, pages 191–196, 1941.

Lush, Jay L.: *Animal Breeding Plans,* Edition 3, Collegiate Press, Inc., Ames, Iowa, 1945.

Lush, Jay L., Shearer, P. S., and Culbertson, C. C.: *Cross-breeding Hogs for Pork Production,* Iowa Agricultural Experiment Station Bulletin 380, 1939.

Nalbandov, Andrew, and Casida, L. E.: *Ovulation and Its Relation to Estrus in Cows,* Journal of Animal Science, volume 1, pages 189–198, 1942.

Nichols, J. E.: *Livestock Improvement,* Edition 2, Oliver and Boyd, Edinburgh and London, 1945.

Nordby, Julius E.: *Improving Rambouillet Sheep for Western Ranges,* The National Wool Grower, volume 31, pages 12–17, March 1943.

Nordby, Julius E.: *Stabilizing Wool and Body Type in Whitefaced Crossbred Sheep,* The National Wool Grower, volume 31, pages 15–17, July 1943, and pages 16–18, August 1943.

Phillips, Ralph W., Black, W. H., Knapp, Bradford, Jr., and Clark, R. T.: *Cross-breeding for Beef Production,* Journal of Animal Science, volume 1, pages 213–220, 1942.

Phillips, Ralph W., and Dawson, W. M.: *Some Factors Affecting Survival, Growth, and Selection of Lambs,* U. S. D. A. Circular 538, 1940.

Phillips, Ralph W., Fraps, Richard M., and Frank, Archie H.: *Hormonal Stimulation of Estrus and Ovulation in Sheep and Goats,* American Journal of Veterinary Research, volume 6, pages 165–179, 1945.

Phillips, Ralph W., McKenzie, Fred F., Christensen, John V., Richards, Grant S., and Petterson, Wendell K.: *Sexual Development of Range Ewe Lambs as Affected by Winter Feeding,* Journal of Animal Science, volume 4, pages 342–346, 1945.

Phillips, Ralph W., Speelman, S. R., and Williams, J. O.: *Horse Breeding Research at the U. S. Morgan Horse Farm,* Vermont Horse and Bridle Trail Bulletin, volume 6, pages 7–14, 1942.

Pohle, Elroy M.: *Sampling and Measuring Methods for Determining Fineness and Uniformity in Wool,* U. S. D. A. Circular 704, 1944.

Rhoad, Albert O.: *The Iberia Heat Tolerance Test for Cattle,* Tropical Agriculture, volume 21, pages 162–164, 1944.

Rhoad, A. O., and Black, W. H.: *Hybrid Beef Cattle for Subtropical Climates,* U. S. D. A. Circular 673, 1943.

Rhoad, Albert O., Phillips, Ralph W., and Dawson, Walker M.: *Evaluation of Species Crosses of Cattle by Polyallel Crossing,* Journal of Heredity, volume 36, pages 367–374, 1945.

Rice, Victor Arthur: *Breeding and Improvement of Farm Animals,* Edition 3, McGraw-Hill Book Company, Inc., New York and London, 1942.

Schott, Ralph George, and Phillips, Ralph Wesley: *Rate of Sperm Travel and Time of Ovulation in Sheep,* Anatomical Record, volume 79, pages 531–540, 1941.

Spencer, D. A., Schott, R. G., Phillips, R. W., and Aune, B.: *Performance of Ewes Bred First as Lambs Compared with Ewes Bred First as Yearlings,* Journal of Animal Science, volume 1, pages 27–33, 1942.

Winters, Laurence M.: *Animal Breeding,* Edition 3, John Wiley & Sons, Inc., New York and London, 1939.

Wright, Sewall: *Coefficients of Inbreeding and Relationship,* American Naturalist, volume 56, pages 330–338, 1922.

ALSO, IN THIS BOOK

Producing Better Beefsteaks

by RALPH W. PHILLIPS

N<small>O</small> FORMULA can assure an adequate supply of beef at all times, although something like 15 million head of cattle are slaughtered every year in the United States to provide for a per capita consumption of 70 pounds. We have no formula for making all cuts tender. But new research points to many ways in which beef breeding and production can be improved. These include improvement in reproduction, efficiency of selection procedures, breeding methods, utilization of feeds, and management practices.

Cattle breeders use selection as a chief tool to improve their stock. They choose what look to be their best animals and mate them, hoping for offspring better than the parents. Of course, the point hinges on "best" and "better," for many factors of heredity are not apparent to even the trained eye of the cattleman or, indeed, the trained geneticist. The extent to which selection can improve cattle is determined largely by the degree to which the characters selected for are inherited. Many pairs of genes, the units of inheritance, are responsible for the inheritance of each of the characteristics that cattle breeders would like to see in all their young stock, like heavy weight when born, ability to grow fast, and tenderness of the steaks when the steer is slaughtered.

Bradford Knapp, Jr., of the Department, and Arne W. Nordskog, of the Montana Agricultural Experiment Station, studied the records of 177 steer calves sired by 23 bulls, and determined that several traits vary in the degree to which they are passed on from one generation to another. These figures for heritability—the degree of persistence of characters in successive generations—actually indicate the progress that a cattle grower should be able to make by selection in his herd. If the weight of calves at weaning time is 12 percent inherited, for example, and a cattle-

61

man chooses for breeding a group of animals that are 10 pounds above the average of the herd in weaning weight, the offspring of those selected animals should average about 1.2 pounds more in weight than offspring of the breeding stock if no selection for this character had been made.

Estimates of heritability obtained by Knapp and Nordskog were as follows:

Characteristic	Heritability (percent)	Characteristic	Heritability (percent)
Birth weight	23	Score at weaning	53
Weaning weight	12	Slaughter grade	63
Final feed-lot weight	81	Carcass grade	84
Gain in feed lot	99	Dressing percent	1
Efficiency of gain	75	Area of eye muscle	69

Some of the estimates of heritability seem too high in view of the results with other classes of livestock and the probable effects of environment on final weight, rate of gain, and efficiency of gain in the feed lot, and so on. Pending further investigation, the figures cannot be taken as generally representative, but they do indicate that selection should be effective in improving many characteristics. Conversely, they indicate that selection for higher dressing percent would not be effective.

If selection is to be based on characters other than those that a stockman can see, he needs measures of performance—yardsticks that he can apply to his animals. Measuring performance in beef and dual-purpose cattle is complicated. Measuring milk production is relatively simple, because milk can be weighed and the percentage of butterfat found. Weighing meat animals tells us their rate of gain, but efficiency of feed utilization, value of the live animal when ready for slaughter, merit of the carcass, and milk production in beef cows that are nursing calves are more difficult to determine.

Several men have tried to determine the relationship between the rate at which a beef animal gains weight and its ability, or efficiency, to turn feed into flesh. Knapp, J. R. Quesenberry, and R. T. Clark drew the conclusions from their study in 1941 that rate of gain and efficiency of feed utilization may not be highly correlated when all steers are fed for the same period; and that neither efficiency of gain nor rate of gain in the feed lot can be accurately predicted from rate of gain during the suckling period or from score on conformation at weaning time.

Knapp and A. L. Baker of the Department later studied 66 steers that were fed individually for 273 days, and obtained a correlation of 0.49 between rate and efficiency of gain. The steers weighed 298 to 492 pounds at the beginning of the feeding period and 759 to 1,134 at the end. After suitable corrections for differences in weight, the correlation was 0.83. The men concluded that comparisons of gross efficiency should be made only between animals of the same size and that selections based on gross efficiency are misleading when all animals are fed for the same length of time.

They recommend, under these conditions, that cattlemen select stock for breeding on the basis of rate of gain rather than efficiency of feed utilization.

H. R. Guilbert and P. W. Gregory, working at the California Agricultural Experiment Station, also concluded that rate of gain did not satisfactorily indicate efficiency of feed utilization in groups differing in potential mature size and in earliness of maturity. If efficiency of feed utilization was to be determined independently of variations in type, size, and rate of maturity, some means of approximate control of the composition of gains was necessary, they believed. Hence, the steers used in their study were fed as much of a standard ration as they would eat and were marketed when they were judged to have attained a definite degree of finish. Relative rate of gain and relative feed capacity were determined, expressed in relation to the 0.75 power of weight. These indexes appeared to be closely correlated with each other and with efficient feed utilization.

Level of feeding is important when one tries to find a yardstick to be applied in the feed lot. Observations by Knapp and Baker indicate there is greater opportunity for genetic variation to be expressed when animals get all the feed they want. They recommend that a cattle raiser full-feed or self-feed steers if he wants to measure their differences in ability to grow. The recommendation, made also by others, is intended for use under usual conditions of fattening cattle for market as rapidly as possible after they are placed in the feed lot, and would not necessarily apply under other conditions of environment or management.

The length of the feeding period is likewise important. To find out more about this problem, data were used from steers fed for 293 to 356 days. Feeding for 168 days was found sufficient to indicate differences in efficiency of feed utilization between groups of progeny from different bulls, provided the data were adjusted for differences in initial weight. This feeding period is too short to allow steers to fatten sufficiently for market. Where individual feeding is practiced, however, some expense might be saved by feeding in groups after the efficiency of individuals has been determined.

Still another factor is the number of progeny that must be tested in order to determine the merit of a bull. We decided, after investigation, that we can get just about all the information we need about the sire's value by studying 8 or 10 of his offspring.

Ranchers, feeders, packers, and others find that one of their hardest problems is to appraise properly the worth of the carcass of a meat animal. Market grades are widely used, but they are largely measures of degree of finish or fatness. Knapp demonstrated that grades can be estimated rather accurately from measurements of height at withers and heart girth. Consumers, packers, and retailers want beef that contains just enough bone to give it form, enough fat for palatability and ripening quality, and a large proportion of lean meat. O. G. Hankins, Knapp, and I studied the 9–10–11 rib cut in 55 beef and 80 dual-purpose steers to determine its value as an indicator of carcass merit. This rib cut was separated into the lean meat, fat, and bone. Constituents were weighed, and the ratio of lean meat to bone determined. The average muscle-bone ratios were 2.55 and 2.28, respectively, for the beef and dual-purpose types. Approximately 15.6 percent of the variation in the 135 carcasses was accounted for by the differences between the two types. Highly significant differences were observed between sires within the two types, and accounted for about 22 percent of the total.

Sex also affects weight. Marvin Koger and J. H. Knox investigated the weights at weaning of steer and heifer calves on New Mexico ranges. They report that steers averaged 443 pounds and heifers 411 pounds, a difference of 32 pounds. The variable must be considered when comparing groups of progeny, or other groups, particularly when the proportions of the sexes vary.

Considerable emphasis is placed on selection of low-set, compact animals for breeding. The possibility of carrying this practice too far is indicated in a recent study by Knox and Koger. They fed 350 yearling steers, during a 9-year period, which were classified as rangy, medium, or compact. Rangy steers gained most rapidly, but when corrected for initial weight, differences in their favor were not statistically significant. There were no important differences in economy of gain among the three types, when this factor was considered in relation to initial weight. Likewise, carcass grade was about the same in all types. The rangy steers yielded a higher average dressing percentage than either of the other types. These workers conclude that it may be more difficult to develop rapidly gaining strains of beef cattle if size is reduced by too greatly restricting height and length to obtain compactness.

Breeding for Hot Climates

We have done considerable work to determine the type of breeding best adapted to beef production in the plain around the Gulf of Mexico, which is hot and humid much of the year. This work has been carried out at the Iberia Livestock Experiment Farm, at Jeanerette, La. I summarize some results reported by A. O. Rhoad and W. H. Black.

Zebu, Aberdeen-Angus, Africander, Hereford, and Shorthorn bulls were used at Jeanerette. The females were native Louisiana stock, grade Herefords, purebred Aberdeen-Angus, and several generations of offspring of those cows and bulls. Comparisons were made on the basis of weights at birth, 6 months, and 2 years.

The procedure that gave best results in the early phases of the work, when Hereford bulls were used on native or grade Hereford foundation cows, was to mate the females to the Hereford bulls, then mate their female offspring to zebu bulls. The hybrid females were then mated to Hereford bulls, thus producing offspring that were five-eighths Hereford, one-fourth zebu, and one-eighth foundation breeding.

When Aberdeen-Angus cows were used as foundation female stock, best results were had by first mating them to zebu bulls, then backcrossing the hybrid heifers to Angus bulls, to produce offspring that were one-fourth zebu, and three-fourths Angus. Good results also were had with animals having three-eighths zebu, and five-eighths Angus blood. These were produced by mating first-generation heifers (one-half zebu, one-half Angus) to bulls having one-fourth zebu, three-fourths Angus blood, or by mating second-generation heifers (one-fourth zebu, three-fourths Angus) to hybrid bulls (one-half zebu, one-half Angus).

Other animals having varying amounts of zebu blood also gave reasonably satisfactory results. This work indicates that the amount of zebu blood needed in beef cattle in the coastal area lies somewhere between one-fourth and one-half, but sufficient data have not yet been accumulated to determine the proportion that can be expected to give best results in continued breeding operations.

In another phase of the work at Jeanerette we sought to determine the relative merits of the offspring of Aberdeen-Angus cows mated to Angus, zebu, Africander, and zebu × Angus bulls, and to demonstrate the possibilities of polyallel crossing in this and similar livestock breeding experiments. The zebu bulls were mostly of Kankrej breeding, commonly referred to in the United States as Guzerat, but there was also a trace of Gir blood.

The breed of sire was found to be significantly associated with birth weight of calves when four types of bulls were mated to the same 9 Angus cows. The calves ranked as follows in birth weight, by type of sire: Zebu, Africander, zebu × Angus, and Angus. In a group of 19 cows mated to 3 types of bulls, birth weight was also significantly associated with breed of sire and the calves ranked, by type of sire, in the following order: Zebu, Africander, and zebu × Angus. The breed of sire also influenced weight at 6 months in an analysis in which Angus, Africander, and zebu bulls were involved. This variation was largely due to the relatively small size of the Angus calves, compared with those from the other types of bulls. Calves sired by zebu bulls were only slightly heavier than those sired by Africander bulls. In another study in which offspring of zebu, Africander, and zebu × Angus bulls were involved, the calves ranked in that order, but the variation among the averages of the three groups was too small to be statistically significant.

The findings indicate that hybrid calves carrying zebu or Africander blood are superior to Angus calves under conditions prevailing in the area, measured by weight at 6 months. The difference between calves sired by zebu and Africander bulls was not so clear, but the averages favored those sired by zebu bulls. The same was true of differences in performance of the two types of hybrids as dams.

The warm-blooded animal can tolerate only relatively small variations in its body temperature, and physiological reactions in the body are tuned to the task of keeping heat production in the body and heat loss from the body in balance, or nearly so. Under tropical and sub-tropical conditions, the ability of an animal to keep heat production balanced by heat loss is often taxed to the utmost. Animals that have an efficient heat-regulating mechanism are therefore more apt to survive and perform satisfactorily than those not so efficient in this respect.

Zebu cattle (*Bos indicus*) seem superior to European cattle (*Bos taurus*) in ability to maintain a normal or nearly normal body temperature under tropical conditions. Body temperature and respiration rates of cattle rise and fall as atmospheric temperatures rise and fall during a summer day. One of the avenues by which heat is lost from the body is evaporation through the lungs, so an increase in respiration speeds up the loss of heat from the body. The temperature and respiration rate of zebu cattle rose less than that of European cattle (Aberdeen-Angus) when exposed to high temperatures. European cattle became feverish when exposed to direct sunlight in summer, under subtropical conditions in Louisiana, while zebu cattle were not so affected. Zebu × Aberdeen-Angus crossbreds were intermediate to the parent strains in ability to maintain a normal body temperature in the heat.

Another indication of the superior heat-regulating ability of zebu cattle is found in their grazing habits on hot, sunny days. Under these conditions zebu cattle have been observed to continue grazing during much of the day while Angus cattle spent most of the time in the shade. Crossbreds were intermediate in this respect.

Other data collected at the Department's Iberia Livestock Experiment Farm at Jeanerette, when the average afternoon temperature was 93.2° F. and relative humidity 71.7 percent, showed an average heat tolerance of 89 for zebu, 84 for zebu-Angus crossbreds, and 59 for Angus. The figures are indexes indicating the relative abilities of the three types to maintain a normal body temperature of 101° F.

The reasons for the zebu's superior heat-regulating ability are not well understood. Perhaps several factors are involved: The extra skin of the dewlap and sheath that provides more surface per unit of body weight, light color, basic physiological differences, or ability to sweat.

Commercial cross-breeding of beef cattle has not been practiced so extensively in recent years as in other classes of livestock, particularly swine and sheep. It was common before ranges were fenced, or before cooperative associations controlled the breed and type of bull used in herds where cattle belonging to the members were grazed as a unit.

In the years since the type of bull used for breeding has been controlled, emphasis has usually been placed on the use of bulls of one breed so that the cows in any one range herd are now, for the most part, high-grade Hereford, Shorthorn, or Aberdeen-Angus stock. This shift from casual to well-regulated breeding methods has resulted in the production of more uniform feeder stock, and by careful selection of bulls, most range operators have improved the quality of their cattle. It is possible, however, that the productivity of range cattle may be improved by taking advantage of the hybrid vigor that usually results from cross-breeding. Some cooperative work has been done in recent years by the Bureau of Animal Industry and the Montana Agricultural Experiment Station to obtain more information on this point.

The experiment was planned to test the possibilities of maintaining heterosis—that is, hybrid or crossbred vigor—through continual crossing. The first cross was made by mating Shorthorn bulls to Hereford cows. The F_1 females were mated to Aberdeen-Angus bulls, and their triple-cross female offspring were mated to Hereford bulls. This work is being conducted at the United States Range Livestock Experiment Station, at Miles City, Mont. The breeding program with Hereford cattle at this station is designed to develop superior strains of purebred Herefords, and selection of bulls is based on the results of progeny tests. Data from these experiments also serve as the basis for comparison of crossbred and purebred offspring. This breeding trial has not been completed, but we have results on parts of it.

A study of 57 steers sired by Shorthorn bulls and out of Hereford cows brought out several pertinent points. The crossbred calves gained more rapidly in the feed lot than the purebreds, and were heavier at time of marketing. The differences between the purebreds and crossbreds in efficiency of gain, slaughter grade, and carcass grade were not statistically significant. The dressing percentage was higher in the crossbred than in the purebred steers. The crossbreds had fewer digestive disorders in the feed lot than the purebreds. In general, the crossbred steers were less variable than the purebred steers.

The performance of 53 heifers produced by mating Shorthorn bulls to Hereford cows was compared with that of 55 Hereford heifers. The crossbreds were heavier at birth, and at weaning time weighed 7.2 pounds more than the Herefords. At 18 and 30 months, the differences in weight in favor of the crossbreds had increased to 50.9 and 88 pounds, respectively. The heifers ran together on native range, as yearlings and 2-year-olds, and had access to the same kinds and quality of feed.

Preliminary analyses of studies with steers and heifers produced by mating Aberdeen-Angus bulls to Shorthorn × Hereford females show that the triple-cross steers weighed more at weaning and at the end of the feeding period, gained more rapidly during the feeding period, sold for more per pound, had a higher dressing percentage, and returned more per head above feed and marketing costs than did the Hereford steers with which they were compared. The triple-cross heifers also weighed more at weaning and at 18 months, and were given higher scores at 18 months than Hereford heifers raised under identical conditions. There were indications that the triple-cross calves had a faster rate of gain before weaning, but a slower rate after weaning, than the first-cross calves. The triple-cross steers had somewhat higher slaughter and carcass grades and the heifers had higher scores for type than the first-cross animals.

Further work is needed to determine the part that continued crisscrossing can play in improvement of beef production. The results obtained to date in this experiment indicate that the procedure has good possibilities. However, the management of animals at breeding time and the careful record keeping necessary in connection with a crisscrossing scheme involving three breeds will make it difficult to use on many farms and ranches. The use of crisscrossing in which only two breeds are involved should be tested further, using the several possible combinations of established beef breeds.

Physiology of Reproduction

Maintenance of a high level of fertility is important if the beef enterprise is to be profitable. A study of the breeding and calving records at the United States Range Livestock Experiment Station at Miles City, Mont., was made by Baker and Quesenberry on 4,753 cow-years over an 18-year period.

The average calf crop was 83.1 percent. The effect of yearly variations due chiefly to environmental causes was statistically significant. The age of the cow had no significant effect on fertility. More than half of the shy-breeding cows could be identified by the time they reached 4 years, and approximately 80 percent by 6 years of age. There was a highly significant difference between bulls in percentage of calf crop; a variation of 45.5 to 94 percent was observed. The age of the bull did not have a significant effect on the percentage of calf crop, but the older bulls lost increasingly more weight during the breeding season. In a study comparing single and multiple bull-breeding units, herds with one bull had 6 percent more calves than herds with more than one.

On the basis of this study, the following recommendations should aid the rancher in raising the production level from the standpoint of calf-crop percentage:

Cows should be identified by proper brands, or marks, so that shy breeders can be eliminated at an early age. Good producing cows may be kept until at least 10 years of age without loss of fertility.

Cows that fail to produce calves in two successive years should be culled from the herd. This is especially true in the 4- and 5-year-old groups.

Where practical, it is advisable to test bulls for quality of semen before the breeding season, so that poor breeders can be eliminated from the herd.

There is an advantage in using bulls 4 years old or over of proved breeding ability. This is not only true for proved fertility, but by the time one calf crop has grown out the rancher has a chance to judge the value of the bull's calves as meat producers.

The establishment of small breeding pastures capable of maintaining herds of about 30 cows each is recommended as a means of increasing the calf crop.

Several researchers learned also that both beef and dairy cows ovulate about 14 hours after the end of estrus—a fact of importance in breeding practice, when considered together with information on the speed with which sperm travel. J. E. Brewster, Ralph May, and C. L. Cole found that spermatozoa require 6 to 9 hours in mature cows, and 4 to 7 hours in heifers, to reach the upper ends of the fallopian tubes. Results obtained by a number of workers have shown that a mating is more apt to be successful if it occurs during the latter part of estrus. The physiological basis for these results is indicated above, since spermatozoa deposited in the female tract near the end of heat reach the upper end of the tract, where fertilization takes place, a few hours before ovulation. Thus, fertilization can take place before the spermatozoa begin to degenerate.

THE AUTHOR

Ralph W. Phillips was formerly in charge of genetics investigations in the Bureau of Animal Industry. He joined the Food and Agriculture Organization of the United Nations in 1946.

FOR FURTHER READING

Baker, A. L., and Quesenberry, J. R.: Fertility of Range Beef Cattle, Journal of Animal Science, volume 3, pages 78–87, 1944.

Black, W. H., and Knapp, B., Jr.: A Method of Measuring Performance in Beef Cattle, American Society of Animal Production Proceedings, pages 72–77, 1936.

Guilbert, H. R., and Gregory, P. W.: Feed Utilization Tests With Cattle, Journal of Animal Science, volume 3, pages 143–153, 1944.

Hankins, O. G., Knapp, B., Jr., and Phillips, R. W.: The Muscle-Bone Ratio as a Measure of Merit in Beef and Dual-Purpose Cattle, Journal of Animal Science, volume 2, pages 42–49, 1943.

Knapp, Bradford, Jr.: Determination of Slaughter-Steer Grades From Weights and Measurements, U. S. D. A. Circular 524, 1939.

Knapp, Bradford, Jr., and Baker, A. L.: *Limited vs. Full-Feeding in Record of Performance Tests for Beef Cattle,* Journal of Animal Science, volume 2, pages 321–327, 1943.

Knapp, Bradford, Jr., and Baker, A. L.: *Correlation Between Rate and Efficiency of Gain in Steers,* Journal of Animal Science, volume 3, pages 219–223, 1944.

Knapp, Bradford, Jr., Baker, A. L., Quesenberry, J. R., and Clark, R. T.: *Record of Performance in Hereford Cattle,* Montana Agricultural Experiment Station Bulletin 397, 1941.

Knapp, Bradford, Jr., and Nordskog, Arne W.: *Heritability of Growth and Selection in Beef Cattle,* Journal of Animal Science, volume 5, pages 62–70, 1946.

Knapp, Bradford, Jr., and Nordskog, Arne W.: *Heritability of Live Animal Scores, Grades, and Certain Carcass Characteristics in Beef Cattle,* Journal of Animal Science, volume 5, pages 194–199, 1946.

Knapp, Bradford, Jr., Phillips, Ralph W., Black, W. H., and Clark, R. T.: *Length of Feeding Period and Number of Animals Required To Measure Economy of Gain in Progeny Tests of Beef Bulls,* Journal of Animal Science, volume 1, pages 285–292, 1942.

Knox, J. H., and Koger, Marvin: *A Comparison of Gains and Carcasses Produced by Three Types of Feeder Steers:* Journal of Animal Science, volume 5, pages 331–337, 1946.

Koger, Marvin, and Knox, J. H.: *The Effect of Sex on Weaning Weight of Range Calves,* Journal of Animal Science, volume 4, pages 15–19, 1945.

Nalbandov, Andrew, and Casida, L. E.: *Ovulation and Its Relation to Estrus in Cows,* Journal of Animal Science, volume 1, pages 189–198, 1942.

Phillips, Ralph W., Black, W. H., Knapp, Bradford, Jr., and Clark, R. T.: *Cross-Breeding for Beef Production,* Journal of Animal Science, volume 1, pages 213–220, 1942.

Rhoad, A. O., and Black, W. H.: *Hybrid Beef Cattle for Subtropical Climates,* U. S. D. A. Circular 673, 1943.

Rhoad, A. O., Phillips, R. W., and Dawson, W. M.: *Evaluation of Species Crosses of Cattle by Polyallel Crossing,* Journal of Heredity, volume 36, pages 367–374, 1945.

ALSO, IN THIS BOOK

New Ideas in Feeding, by N. R. Ellis, page 95.
Animal Diseases, by L. T. Giltner, page 81.
Hormones in Reproduction, by S. R. Hall and J. F. Sykes, page 123.
Drugs to Control Parasites, by Benjamin Schwartz, page 71.
Breeding Better Livestock, by Ralph W. Phillips, page 33.

Drugs To Control Parasites

by BENJAMIN SCHWARTZ

PARASITES are relatively low forms of animal life that live on or in the bodies of larger animals. There are about 100,000 kinds, and they do untold harm. One group includes insects, ticks, and mange or scab mites and are known collectively as arthropods. Another group, called helminths, or worms, include cestodes, or tapeworms; trematodes, or flukes; nematodes, or roundworms; and thornyheads, or acanthocephalids. A third class comprises single-celled microscopic organisms known as protozoa. Most of the arthropod parasites of livestock occur on the skin or in its layers. The worms and protozoa that affect domestic animals and poultry occur inside the body.

The relation between a parasite and its host is one-sided. The parasite gets food from the being that shelters it, but may cause its host's death (particularly if the host is a young animal or bird), or stunt its growth and reproductive capacity, or lower its vigor. The parasite can ruin hides used for leather; spoil meat and render it unfit for food; damage intestines needed for surgical sutures and other purposes; and hurt livers needed for food and medicinal preparations. It lowers production of fiber, causes uneconomical use of feed, and brings about other injuries. All this it does in its normal life processes of growing, feeding, and reproducing, or through specific destructive action.

Because so many kinds of parasites infest so many animals the world over and because they have tremendous reproductive capacity and have adapted themselves to our most useful animals, producers of livestock and poultry would be helpless without the weapons that have been developed to control parasites.

Parasiticides—drugs designed to destroy external and internal parasites—are among the most effective weapons. During the war years espe-

71

cially, when farmers had to meet unusual demands for animal food and fiber, drugs were used widely. New treatments were made possible by a backlog of scientific work conducted in peacetime by Federal, State, and other agencies, and by accelerated wartime research. As a result, producers had the advantage of a big and growing storehouse of practical knowledge.

Controlling Cattle Grubs

Soon after war came, we discovered that the domestic supply of leather would not meet the military and civilian demands for shoes and other leather articles. We went after cattle grubs, the worst enemy of cattle hides. The grubs, the larvae of heel flies, develop rather slowly in the bodies of cattle before they migrate to the back and puncture the skin. After a period of development in cysts under the skin, when the grubs increase greatly in size, they drop out, pupate on the ground, and emerge from their pupal cases as adult flies. The latter soon mate, and the females deposit eggs on the hair of cattle. The young grubs enter the skin through the hair follicles, and start the vicious annual cycle all over again.

The research that had been going on in the Department's laboratories, State agricultural experiment stations, and elsewhere showed that rotenone-containing materials, like derris powder and cube powder, are more destructive to grubs in their cysts than any other preparation tested for the purpose. The knowledge was quickly and widely disseminated, and research to improve control procedures were stepped up in order to conserve rotenone and to improve ways of applying it most economically and effectively. Normal imports of rotenone from Japanese-invaded countries of the Far East were cut off and only a limited supply could be had from South America.

Adding more urgency to the work were these facts: 35 percent of all cattle hides in this country are classed as grubby by the tanneries, meaning they have more than five grub holes each; grubs cause an annual loss of approximately 12,000,000 pounds of beef, because parts affected by the grubs are trimmed off; adult flies sometimes annoy cattle so severely as to interfere with grazing and proper growth.

We knew that the rotenone-containing material could be applied dry to the backs of cattle or in water suspensions as a wash, as a spray under high pressure, or as dips. We could do little to lower the amount of material needed by the water suspension, but we found out that the dry cube or derris powder could be used more economically by mixing it with inert matter in the ratio of one part of the medicament and two parts of inert powder, the mixture being applied to the backs of cattle with a shaker can and thoroughly rubbed into the grub sacs. The dusts used during the war, instead of being mixed with sulfur and talc, as had been the common practice in prewar years, were mixed with either double-ground cream Tripoli earth, or a micronized volcanic ash known commercially as Frianite M3x, or pyrophyllite, a clay-like substance, ground so fine that 90 percent of it will pass through a 325-mesh screen. The mixtures so prepared were more effective than those used before.

The rotenone-containing wash, developed before the war, was more critically tested to determine its usefulness in reducing the number of cattle grubs and to gage its practical value in grub eradication. In tests conducted by parasitologists of the Bureau of Animal Industry in Colorado in 1944 and 1945 on about 2,500 head of cattle over 120 square miles, the grub kill was approximately 95 percent in a single application. The wash was prepared by dissolving 12 ounces of derris powder or cube powder, having a 5-percent rotenone content, and 4 ounces of granular laundry soap in 1 gallon of water. The benefits of the treatment lasted; a year later the grub population in the cattle was about 70 percent lower than in previous years.

On the basis of experience gained during the war, we learned that the cheapest and easiest preparation to use in pressure sprayers should contain at least 7½ pounds of cube powder or derris powder having a 5-percent rotenone content to 100 gallons of water. No other ingredients are needed. Best results were had by applying the preparation to the backs of cattle as a fine spray with a power-operated orchard sprayer capable of obtaining a pressure of at least 400 pounds at the nozzle.

Dipping in rotenone-containing solutions, a procedure that likewise was critically tested during the war, proved to be practical and the preferred method of treating large herds in areas where the winters are not too severe. Not less than 10 pounds of derris or cube powder, having a 5-percent rotenone content, and 2 ounces of a suitable wetting agent, such as sodium lauryl sulfate, are needed for 100 gallons of water.

Rotenone for Lice and Ticks

Dip containing rotenone that is used to kill cattle grubs also destroys lice—pests that have become of increasing concern to cattlemen all over the country. Rotenone-containing materials, however, destroy only the motile lice; the eggs, or nits, escape and hatch at various intervals after dipping. The 30-day interval between two successive dippings for grubs will not eradicate lice. To destroy them, as well as grubs, one extra dipping, about 16 days after the first dipping for grubs, has to be given. The quantity of rotenone-containing powder for the extra dipping may be reduced to 1 pound to 100 gallons of water, because lice are more easily killed by rotenone than grubs.

Another important and economical use of derris and cube powder came to light in conection with the control of so-called sheep ticks, or keds. We made tests with weak solutions of the rotenone materials, prepared by adding small quantities of the medication to water, with a maximum of 6 ounces (5-percent rotenone content) to 100 gallons of cold water. A single dipping of tick-infested sheep, after all the shear cuts had healed, killed the pests. Because it is easy and cheap to make this dilute dip—it costs less than a cent a head—it will be possible for sheepmen everywhere to take common action and eradicate sheep ticks altogether.

Versatile Phenothiazine

Phenothiazine is a synthetic organic chemical, prepared commercially by combining diphenylamine—a synthetic coal tar product—with sulfur, under the influence of heat and a catalyst. Up to 1938, phenothiazine was known to organic chemists only as a chemical curiosity that had been synthesized in Europe in 1885, and to entomologists as an experimental insecticide for destroying mosquito larvae and controlling the codling moth. In December 1938 the Department, after considerable experimentation, first announced the discovery of the value of phenothiazine as an anthelmintic, or worm medicine, for swine. In the next 3 years the drug was found to possess exceptional merit in ridding farm animals, especially horses, cattle, sheep, and goats, of gastrointestinal roundworms.

A significant development in connection with the use of the drug as a worm killer was our wartime discovery that phenothiazine could be mixed with ordinary granular salt, and the salt mixture used safely to control sheep roundworms, the most injurious of the disease-producing agents that plague sheep.

Besides destroying most of the common stomach worms and nodular worms, phenothiazine has a significant anthelmintic action against other kinds of roundworms that live in the intestines of sheep and also kills the eggs of roundworms. About half of the drug passes unchanged through the sheep's digestive tract, and is, therefore, present in the droppings that contain the parasite eggs. So, it appeared logical and desirable to try to develop a scheme of self-medication that would insure that the sheep could take in the drug more or less continuously and at the same time eliminate small quantities of it with the droppings. Accordingly, our first experiments to test the possibility were designed shortly after the discovery of the anthelmintic values of the drug. Mixtures of phenothiazine in feed were tested. Later we used phenothiazine in salt in various ratios, on the assumption that a sheep's natural craving for salt might insure a sufficient intake of the drug to reduce the animal's worm population and, at the same time, kill the eggs in the droppings.

Considering the large numbers of eggs produced by parasitic roundworms and the relatively short period required for their development, it is quite evident that even a small number of worms not removed by treatment could pyramid to significant levels in a relatively short time in the late spring, summer, and early fall. In the past, stockmen had to resort, therefore, to the tedious task of costly and possibly dangerous treatment at 2- to 3-week intervals all summer. But a routine involving the more or less continuous intake of even small doses of a potent drug, however effective it might be to control parasites, could not be considered as being altogether free of chance, without extensive experimentation. Therefore, various possible risks had to be considered.

It was necessary to determine through long and painstaking tests the effects on the health of adult sheep and lambs of a continuous intake of small doses of phenothia- zine, to ascertain whether such treatments would ar- rest growth, injure the wool, impair reproductive functions, interfere with gestation, or prove injuri- ous in other ways. Not un- til after 2 years of continu- ous experimentation with a flock of Government- owned sheep at Beltsville did we anounce the value and safety of a phenothia- zine-salt mixture, in the ratio of 1 to 9 to control sheep roundworms.

This type of covered trough will protect the phenothiazine and salt mixture from the weather.

This self-medication, at once curative and preventive, is not to be re- garded as a substitute for the full therapeutic treatment with the drug, but rather as an adjunct to it. Heavily infested sheep should be treated early in the spring with a full therapeutic dose—about 1 ounce for adult sheep and one-half ounce for lambs weighing less than 60 pounds. Follow- ing this treatment, the phenothiazine-salt mixture should be placed in an open container or trough that is protected from the weather. The entire flock should have access to it during the pasture season, when the weather is sufficiently mild to permit the normal development of roundworm eggs and the transformation of the larvae to the infective stage.

In most cases this procedure will keep lambs from getting an injurious load of parasites, but as an additional precaution the flock should be treated with a full therapeutic dose whenever it appears that the medi- cated salt is not holding the parasite in check. Also, the breeder flock should be treated again with the full dose early in the winter to condition ewes for the cold months. To show how extensively sheepmen have adopted the practice: In 1939—just after phenothiazine was shown to have value as an anthelmintic—only 900 pounds was used; in 1944, total consumption was nearly 3,000,000 pounds.

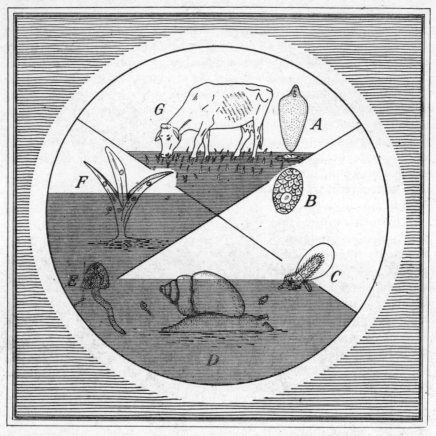

The life cycle of the common liver fluke: *A*. An adult fluke about natural size. While in the liver of an animal it produces many eggs that are expelled in the droppings; *B*. An egg, enlarged about 100 times. It develops in wet places of pastures; *C*. A free-swimming larva (enlarged about 100 times) that comes from each egg; this larva is attracted to and penetrates certain aquatic snails, *D*. After development in the snail, a new type of larva with a tail, *E,* (enlarged about 30 times) emerges and settles on the grass, *F,* and becomes encysted there. Cattle eat the contaminated grass and the life cycle starts all over again.

Liver Flukes

Liver flukes are the most deadly of the trematodes that affect livestock. Cattle, sheep, goats, and wild ruminants are particularly susceptible, and acquire the parasites while grazing on low, wet pastures that harbor certain species of fresh-water snails that serve as intermediate hosts. The flukes, by their presence or the lesions they produce, make the livers unfit for food, bring about unthriftiness and loss of flesh in all domestic ruminants, and cause death, especially of sheep. European investigators say also the flukes impair reproductive capacity in cattle, reduce milk flow, and cause other damage.

Of these losses, only those resulting from the condemnation of livers for food and for medicinal use are well known. The figures obtained from meat packers operating under Government inspection show that the annual average infection of cattle with liver flukes in the Gulf Coast area is 37.5 percent in adult cattle and 6 percent in calves. The loss of beef and calf livers must be enormous, because flukes in cattle are prevalent in parts of the South, the Southwest, the Rocky Mountain States, and the Pacific Coast States. It is estimated that nearly 90,000 pounds of beef and calf livers are lost annually in the Gulf Coast area. The loss of beef livers in 1945 amounted to more than a million dollars.

During the war we prepared a medication based on hexachlorethane, a solid that is related chemically to carbon tetrachloride and tetrachlorethylene, drugs developed in the Department about 25 years ago for removing internal parasites from various classes of farm animals. Because hexachlorethane is insoluble in water and can be dissolved only in solvents that are more or less injurious to cattle, sheep, and goats, we combined it with bentonite, a finely powdered clay, to form an aqueous anthelmintic drench. It was determined that, in proper combination, hexachlorethane and bentonite form a stable suspension in water, suitable for administration with a dose syringe.

The ingredients are mixed thus: 1 pound of finely ground hexachlorethane, 1½ ounces of bentonite, and 25 ounces of water. The addition of a quarter-teaspoon of white flour facilitates the mixing, which is done either with a power-driven apparatus of sufficient speed to insure even distribution or by passing the freshly prepared mixture twice through a 20-mesh screen. A dose of 6½ ounces for cattle and half that amount for calves more than 3 months old is administered. Younger calves need not be treated. The treatment is especially effective in removing about 70 percent of the adult flukes and about half of the immature flukes.

The treatment was tested successfully in sheep and goats, but in a few instances cattle and sheep tolerated the drug rather poorly, and some died. Much work remains to be done, therefore, to perfect the treatment.

Roundworms in Hogs

We also found a simple, inexpensive, and practical method of ridding pigs of large intestinal roundworms or ascarids, the most widespread and most injurious parasites affecting swine. Nearly all swine producers are familiar with the worms, and parasitologists have studied them for decades without finding a really good treatment. American wormseed oil— oil of chenopodium—was about 70 percent effective, but it is rather toxic and involves the usual difficulties of treating swine individually. Early

enthusiasm for phenothiazine as a substitute for oil of chenopodium—
especially because phenothiazine could be administered with the feed—
unfortunately was not sustained. Later investigations disclosed that
phenothiazine was about as toxic to swine as oil of chenopodium, it sometimes produced rather alarming symptoms, and was less effective.

In 1944 and 1945 we tested a number of fluorine compounds. Sodium
fluoride, a cheap and readily available chemical used to eliminate cockroaches and remove lice from livestock and poultry, pretty well filled the
rigid requirements of the ideal remedy for large roundworms. When
mixed with the feed in the proportion of 1 part by weight of the chemical
to 99 parts of the feed, sodium fluoride was generally eaten by swine.
One day's normal feeding with this medicated feed ration was enough,
in most cases, to remove nearly all the ascarids.

In practice, a successful method of treating pigs with sodium fluoride
is: On the day before the medicated feed is given, the pigs are slightly
underfed; on the day of treatment, the medicated feed is given in the
morning in amounts the animals normally consume in 1 day; the next
morning, regular feed is mixed with any left-over medicated feed and the
usual feeding continued thereafter.

Whether fed to suckling pigs, to pigs shortly after weaning, or to pigs
ready for market, the medicated feed caused expulsion of from 90 to 100
percent of all the roundworms. The treatment was effective whether
given to pigs individually or to groups up to 30, and was nontoxic, except
to pigs suffering from intestinal inflammation or other serious disorders.

Skim Milk and Whey for Internal Parasites

When fed liberally, skim milk and whey were found to be effective in
protecting swine from internal parasites. Either was fed to pigs for 3 days
in succession at intervals of 2 weeks, in place of all other feed, or was fed
once daily instead of the regular afternoon feeding of grain. Otherwise,
the pigs got a balanced ration of grain, tankage, and minerals. Although
the treated pigs were kept under conditions that favored the acquisition
of heavy loads of internal parasites, they escaped, for the most part, from
acquiring any large number of stomach worms, ascarids, nodular worms,
and whipworms—parasites that localize in the alimentary canal.

This special feeding did not keep them from getting lungworms and
other parasites that live outside the alimentary canal. Comparable pigs,
fed only the balanced ration, became rather heavily parasitized with
stomach and intestinal worms. Although our evidence is that pigs fed
whey or skim milk acquired ascarids, which migrated in the usual way
to the liver and lungs, the worms that reached the alimentary canal following the early migrations were evidently swept out by the purgative action
of the whey and skim milk.

It is known, however, that cathartics of various kinds do not exert any significant anthelmintic action, and it cannot be concluded that only the purgative action of the dairy products used was largely responsible for the removal of the parasites from the alimentary canal. Whatever the nature of the vermifuge action of skim milk and whey, the fact is that, when used as indicated, these dairy products prevented the accumulation in the stomach and intestines of pigs of the various species of the nematode parasites. Pigs thus kept free of worms grew better than their litter mates that were not fed skim milk or whey. The difference in gains is evidence of how parasites cut pork production.

We do not recommend the indiscriminate feeding of dairy products to pigs as a substitute for sound management to control parasites, but this method should be useful where skim milk or whey is available and where other practices designed to control parasites are not instituted, or for special reasons cannot be.

Sulfa Drugs and Coccidiosis

Coccidiosis, a disease of livestock and poultry, is caused by protozoan parasites known as coccidia. The organisms are highly injurious to poultry, the average mortality in affected flocks sometimes reaching 50 percent.

A few years after the sulfa drugs began to be used in human medicine, parasitologists began to experiment with some of them. Three of them, sulfaguanidine, sulfamethazine, and sulfamerazine, were tested extensively with considerable success, to see if they could cure or prevent coccidiosis in poultry.

In the control of cecal coccidiosis, the most severe form of the disease, satisfactory results were obtained by feeding mash containing 1 percent by weight of sulfaguanidine, as soon as bloody droppings—the characteristic symptom of poultry coccidiosis—were detected. The medicated mash is fed for 2 days and is then replaced by regular mash for the next 3 days. The medicated mash is fed again the sixth day. If bloody diarrhea is not completely checked, a third feeding of medicated mash for 1 more day is given following 3 days' feeding of regular mash.

To control intestinal coccidiosis, a disease not characterized by bloody droppings but by a steady decline in condition, medicated mash is fed for 3 days in succession, as soon as a correct diagnosis is made. Ordinarily a poultryman cannot make the diagnosis because it involves a careful postmortem examination of one or more birds in an affected flock and the finding of the causative organisms in sufficient numbers in scrapings of the intestinal lining.

THE AUTHOR

Benjamin Schwartz has been the head of the Zoological Division of the Bureau of Animal Industry since 1936 and has done parasitological research in the Department since 1915. He is the author of more than 100 scientific papers giving results of original investigations, and of many other papers dealing with various aspects of agricultural parasitology.

FOR FURTHER READING

Allen, R. W.: *Trials with Sodium Fluoride as an Ascaricide for Swine,* North American Veterinarian, volume 26, pages 661–664, November 1945.

Boughton, I. B.: *First Official Statement on Three Years' Investigation—Phenothiazine—Salt Mixture for Range Sheep,* Sheep and Goat Raiser, volume 34, pages 66, 68, December 1943.

Britton, J. W., and Miller, R. F.: *The Practical Application of Anthelmintic Medication of Lambs,* American Veterinary Medical Association, Journal, volume 104, pages 270–272, May 1944.

Cobbett, N. G., and Smith, C. E.: *The Eradication of Sheep Ticks, Melophagus Ovinus, by One Dipping in Dilute Derris-Water or Cube-Water Dips,* American Veterinary Medical Association, Journal, volume 103, pages 6–10, July 1943.

Enzie, F. D., Habermann, R. T., and Foster, A. O.: *A Comparison of Oil of Chenopodium, Phenothiazine, and Sodium Fluoride as Anthelmintics for Swine,* American Veterinary Medical Association, Journal, volume 107, pages 57–66, August 1945.

Farr, M. M., and Allen, R. W.: *Sulfaguanidine Feeding as a Control Measure for Cecal Coccidiosis of Chickens,* American Veterinary Medical Association, Journal, volume 100, pages 47–51, 1942.

Habermann, R. T., Enzie, F. D., and Foster, A. O.: *Tests with Fluorides, Especially Sodium Fluoride, as Anthelmintics for Swine,* American Journal of Veterinary Research, volume 6, pages 131–144, July 1945.

Olsen, O. W.: *Preliminary Observations on Hexachloroethane for Controlling the Common Liver Fluke, Fasciola Hepatica, in Cattle,* American Veterinary Medical Association, Journal, volume 102, pages 433–436, June 1943.

Schwartz, Benjamin: *Cattle Grubs and How to Control Them,* Proceedings Forty-sixth Annual Meeting, U. S. Live Stock Sanitary Association, Chicago, pages 173–178, December 2–4, 1942.

Spindler, L. A., Zimmerman, H. E. [jr.]: *Effect of Skim Milk on the Growth and Acquisition of Parasites by Pigs Under Conditions of Constant Exposure to Infection,* Helminthological Society of Washington, Proceedings, volume 11, pages 49–54, July 1944.

ALSO, IN THIS BOOK

Animal Diseases, by L. T. Giltner, page 81.
Advances in Feeding Calves, by Henry T. Converse, page 159.
Progress in Hog Production, by John H. Zeller, page 201.
Keeping Poultry Healthy, by Theodore C. Byerly, page 231.

THE SHAPE OF RESEARCH

e tools required for modern agricultural re-
rch are many and varied. To get worth-
ile results, experiments are carried on in
ny places and under all sorts of circumstances. Beltsville, Md., is but one of many
places in the United States where problems
are worked out that help the farmer, and contribute immeasurably to business and industry.

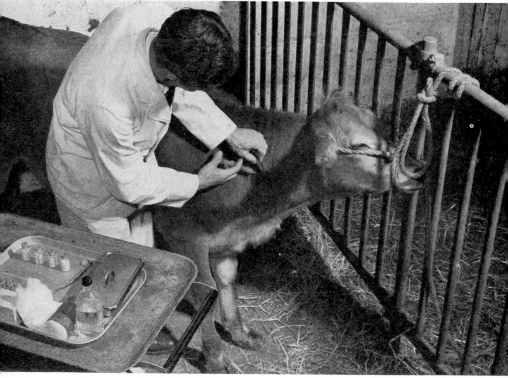

ause Bang's disease has been one of the
yman's worst enemies, more study has
n given to its control than any other disease. Department veterinarians have developed a vaccine for calves that insures a
high degree of immunity against this disease.

For 75 years the usual practice has been to feed calves whole milk for a month, then skim milk for 5 to 7 months. Tests indicate that calves can safely be weaned from milk much earlier than this. By using the methods scribed on page 159, some 40 million m pounds of butter and 8 billion pounds of m would be available, if needed, for huma

Crossbreeding and hybridization are important in animal research—with chickens as well as hogs, cattle, sheep, and horses. A hen used to lay about 86 eggs a year. These hens cross between inbred Rhode Island Reds a White Leghorns, average 225 eggs a ye

cooperating with nature, researchers have
nd ways to grow bigger flowers and vege-
.es—a common ambition of gardeners
everywhere. The process explained by S. L.
Emsweller on page 284, caused the Easter lily
on the right to grow to twice the usual size.

Department, in cooperation with State ex-
ment stations, has scientifically developed
1 varieties that resist hazards like insects,
drought, winterkill, and others. Seed of more
than 50 better varieties of wheat have been
made available to farmers in the past 10 years.

N.C.
1032

Heavy hangs the corn in this test planting of
North Carolina Hybrid No. 1032. It is one of
many varieties developed in cooperation with
experiment stations of the Southern States.

Adapted to the soil and climate of the Sta
outyields standard kinds by about 20 per
From 1942 to 1946 hybrid corn acreage ir
South increased from 1½ to 5½ million a

know the soil is a long step toward taking care of it. And, from its color, texture, depth, and other information a soil survey gives him, the farmer can be fairly sure as to what crops and practices are best for his farm. Soil surveys have been made in nearly 1,600 counties.

CLASS VII LAND
CLASS VIII LAND
CLASS VII LAND
CLASS VI LAND
CLASS IV LAND
CLASS II LAND
CLASS V LAND
CLASS I LAND
CLASS III LAND

Besides knowing what is under the surface of their land, farmers can now use a system of land classification—slope, fertility, and so on— that helps them fit each acre to its best use without robbing the land. There are eight classes of land approximately as shown here.

At Vincennes, Ind., work goes on to find a satisfactory insecticide to control the codling moth and other orchard pests. Experiments with DDT show encouraging results, not on against codling moths, but leafhoppers, orien fruit moths, pear thrips, and Japanese beet

Improved equipment for applying insecticides is important, too. This new machine can be used for dusts or liquid, or a combination of both. Chief advantage is to save weight of terials; a tree once needing as much as 40 lons may, with this machine, need only a qu

...t the Department's laboratory at Peoria, Ill., methods have been developed for stepping up production of penicillin. The result: A new outlet for farm products and another large industry. Peacetime uses of it include treatment of bovine mastitis and swine erysipelas of turkeys.

Agricultural chemists at the Peoria laboratory have perfected a way to use ground corncobs and rice hulls to clean carbon from internal combustion engines. This and other new uses offer a peacetime outlet for the some 16 million tons of corncobs once considered a nuisance.

The estimated time for harvesting an acre of peanuts by hand is 32 man-hours. With this tractor attachment the same operations—lifting, shaking, and windrowing—can be do[ne] in 3¾ hours. Similar machinery improv[e]ments are being studied by the Departmen[t]

During the war American housewives each year canned from 3 to 4 billion quarts of food. For some reason about 45 million containers of it spoiled. Here Katherine Taube of the [De]partment runs a test on string beans to aid [in] cutting down spoilage of home-canned foo[d]

EARCH to prevent, cure, or control dis-
of livestock is unceasing. Although much
ress has been made toward finding prac-
ways and means of cutting down livestock
s, test-and-slaughter is still the most effec-
method of controlling some of our most
us animal diseases—tuberculosis and brucellosis, for example. With the help of a new
tuberculin, developed by Department scientists
for detecting TB-infected animals, bovine tuberculosis is gradually reaching the vanishing
point. The following series of pictures shows
how tuberculin is prepared in the laboratories
of the Department's Bureau of Animal Industry.

first step is to prepare the culture medium
which the tubercle bacilli will be grown.
mixture consists of asparagin, glycerine,
rose, magnesium sulfate, potassium phosphate, and sodium and iron citrates. Large lots
are made up and poured into sterile flasks.
The flasks are then put into a steam sterilizer
to destroy any bacteria that might be present.

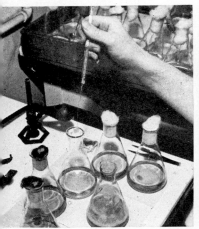

a glass-enclosed room, the culture is seeded
h tubercle bacilli (above) and placed in an
ibator where it is held at a temperature of
5° C. for 12 weeks. During this time the
teria will make a heavy growth and release
ducts of growth in the culture fluid. After
incubation the tubercle bacilli are completely
destroyed by steam sterilization. The dead
tubercle bacilli are strained from the culture
fluid (above), which is then transferred to an
evaporator and processed to a specified concentration to produce tuberculin, the final product.

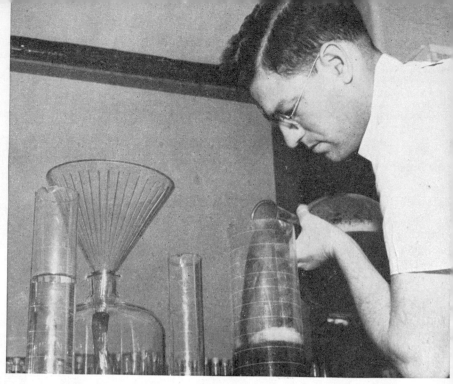

The evaporated tuberculin is measured out to be mixed with glycerine and phenol to make the fluid which, after further processing to re- move all bacteria of any kind, is used under-the-skin injections of cattle suspecte tuberculosis. L. A. Baisden does the measu

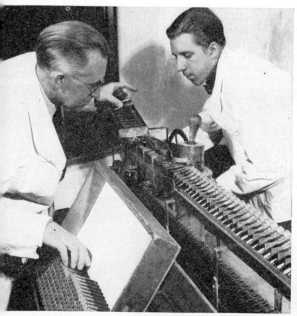

After the tuberculin has passed all tests for purity it is run into vials under the most sani- tary of conditions. Then they are hermetically sealed by a machine designed for the purpose by P. W. LeDuc (left) of the Bureau of Animal Industry. W. B. Buckman is assisting The sealed vials are labeled to show the and amount of tuberculin each contains. are packed in cartons (above) for distributio veterinarians in all parts of the United Sta

erinarian A. H. Frank tests a cow for tuber-
sis by injecting the tuberculin into the
cow's skin on the underside of the tail. These
tests are made on thousands of cattle each year.

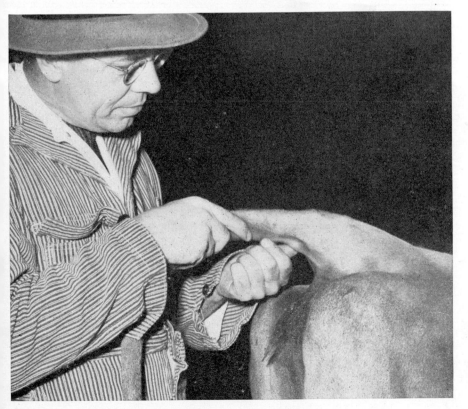

enty-two hours after the injection, Dr.
nk observes a small lump where the injec-
a was made, meaning that this cow is tuber-
ous. Despite all precautions there is still
some TB infection in nearly every State. For
a more complete word description concerning
the status of animal disease control see the article on page 81 of this volume by L. T. Giltner.

ANIMAL PARASITES EACH YEAR take a startling toll, not only in lives of animals, but in reduced quality and quantity of milk, meat, hides, and other livestock products. Some of the more recent developments on how to trol parasites with drugs is discussed on [71 by Benjamin Schwartz; a visual glimps the subject is presented in the next few pa

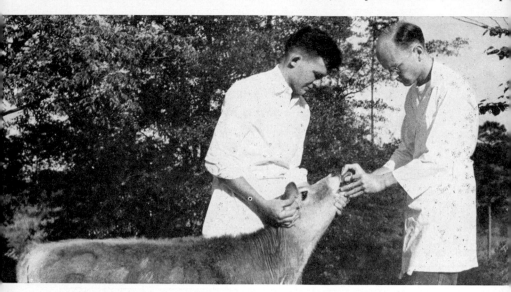

In an effort to find a better remedy for stomach worms in calves, John Bowling and Joseph Branson experimentally infect a calf with worms at the animal disease laboratory at Auburn, Ala.

In specially built equipment (below), wo are isolated from a culture medium. Ge E. Cauthen of the Auburn laboratory col the worms for research on drugs to control t

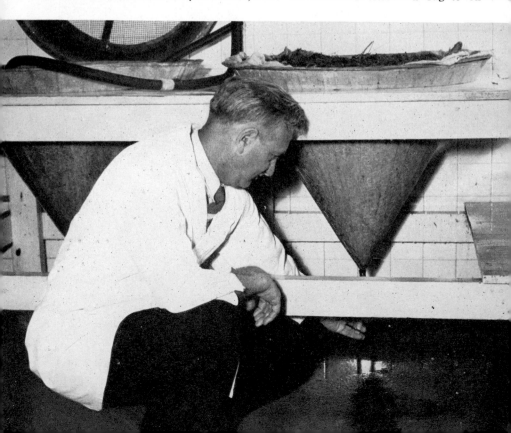

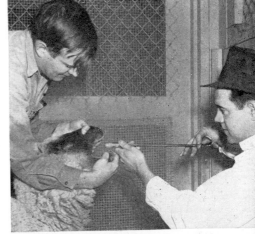

e of the most significant developments to
me from recent animal parasite research is the
e of phenothiazine in ridding sheep, cattle,
rses, and goats of stomach worms. The
elling on this sheep's lower jaw is a charac-
ristic symptom of stomach-worm infestation.

treatment consists of about 1 ounce of pheno-
iazine which, for adult sheep, is considered
full therapeutic dose. In this case (right) the
ug is administered in a soft gelatin capsule.

ineteen days after treatment the jaw swelling
as gone down and, although apparently not yet
ell, the sheep is on the road to better health.

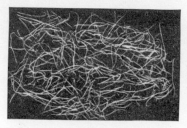

In a test with phenothiazine to remove nodular worms and hookworms from sheep, one therapeutic dose, as shown by a post-mortem examination, removed all but 2 of the animal's nodular worms (left), and 125 of its 134 hookworms. Worms are about one-half natural s

These two pigs are the same age. The larger one is normal size; the other was stunted by roundworms, one of the most serious parasites of swine. Recent research shows that sodium fluoride fed to pigs with their feed will result in 90 to 100 percent expulsion of roundworms.

Coccidiosis, a parasitic disease more perilous poultry than to other farm animals, sometin causes 50 percent mortality in chicken floc Extensive tests with sulfaguanidine has p duced satisfactory results in controlling ce coccidiosis, the most severe form of the disea

NOT ALL OF OUR LIVESTOCK LOSSES caused by specific diseases or parasites just mentioned. Recent research has definitely shown the need for some new ideas about nutrition for farm animals—cattle, sheep, swine— if they are to be healthy and produce efficiently.

use of vitamin A (carotene) starvation, this animal (above) has poor vision and appetite, is unsteady on his feet, and is sexually impotent; he has convulsions and anasarca. After 4 months of carotene therapy, the same animal (below) apparently has regained all of his faculties.

pregnancy disease is most common among heavily fed ewes. Studies indicate that the disease is associated with, or caused by, the animal's unsatisfied demand for feed of high caloric content. It can be prevented by proper flushing and by feeding carbohydrate-rich feed.

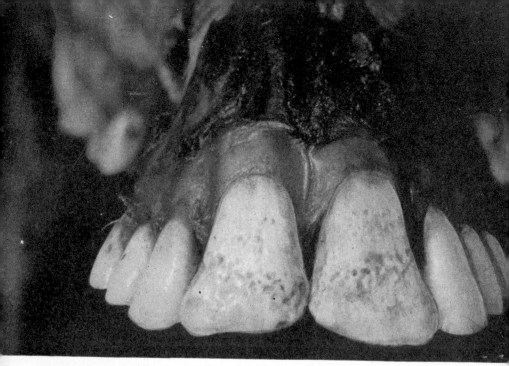

Mottled and irregularly worn teeth (above) are symptoms of fluorine poisoning in sheep, cattle, and swine. The intake of this element should not be permitted to exceed 0.003 percent o total dry ration for larger farm animals for poultry it should not exceed 0.015 per

Nicotinic acid is vital to the diet of swine as evidenced by these two groups of pigs. The above group was fed a purified diet that excluded nicotinic acid, while the group below had liberal amounts of the vitamin. As a of their feed both groups received thiam riboflavin, piridoxine, pantothentic acid, choline. For New Ideas in Feeding, see page

Animal Diseases

by L. T. GILTNER

VETERINARIANS and farmers have waged an aggressive fight against animal plagues in recent years. They have kept malignant ones like rinderpest and foot-and-mouth disease, a constant threat from abroad, out of the United States. The worst native diseases, anthrax, anaplasmosis, brucellosis, mastitis, hog cholera, swine erysipelas, tuberculosis, rabies, and pullorum disease, they held in check by applying approved control plans, including sanitation, vaccination, and treatment with drugs.

Some of the vaccines, notably those for preventing rabies and hog cholera, have been improved. All the biological products used in the control work have been maintained at a high standard of quality. Experimental studies on the sulfa drugs have done much to show which infections are amenable to treatment with them. Sulfanilamide, sulfathiazole, and sulfadiazine are useful in treating some types of streptococcal infections, but ineffective against some other bacterial infections. Sulfathiazole, sulfaguanadine, and sulfadiazine have value against some forms of dysentery. Sulfathiazole alleviates symptoms of coryza in chickens, although the symptoms reappear when treatment is stopped. Sulfamerazine acts somewhat the same against infectious sinusitis in turkeys. Sulfamerazine, although having a favorable influence against coccidiosis in chickens, is not effectve aganst lymphomatosis.

Penicillin is beneficial, experimentally and in practice, in treating the type of mastitis that is caused by *Streptococcus agalactiae*. It has shown marked curative effect on experimentally induced swine erysipelas infection in turkeys. It was not effective in treating infectious equine anemia, a virus disease, and so far has had no value in preventing or treating other virus diseases. Of course, the sulfa drugs and penicillin, like all

703830°—47——7

81

new drugs, should be used only as prescribed by a veterinarian; their indiscriminate use may be wasteful and actually harmful to the animal patients.

But all this is not to say that we have cured or are about to cure all diseases of animals. Much remains to be learned and done, as the following pages, in which I discuss some of the worst diseases, disclose.

Brucellosis of Cattle (Bang's Disease)

No disease of livestock has received greater attention from the standpoint of control measures than brucellosis of cattle, or Bang's disease, as it is commonly called. Years of research have been spent in developing methods of control, and these have been applied in practical field studies. The studies have definitely established that no one system of control is applicable to all herds, but that the choice of method depends on conditions such as size of herd, degree of infection, environment, and whether the herd is for dairy or beef.

As a consequence, the Department has approved the use of four methods of control in the Federal-State program for the control of Bang's disease, namely: Blood test and slaughter of all reacting animals; blood test and slaughter, accompanied by the vaccination of calves; blood test to determine the amount of infection, but retention of reactors until vaccinated replacements are available; whole-herd vaccination.

The first plan is the method of choice in small herds and in herds in which brucellosis has been of long standing, that is, where the storm of abortions has passed and the disease has taken on a chronic form. In herds from which certified milk is sold there is no alternative than test-and-slaughter, and this method also is used in the area-plan of control.

The second method adds calf vaccination to the first. It has the extra advantage of building a herd that eventually will be more resistant to reinfection, should it occur. Calf vaccination has proved to be a most desirable practice in all herds in which infection is present.

The third plan is a good one for herds in which such a large proportion of animals is shown on test to be reactors that their immediate removal, in the absence of suitable replacements, would work an extreme hardship on the owner. Calf vaccination is necessary in this plan and some owners prefer to vaccinate all animals up to breeding age. This plan applies especially to dairy herds in which the milk is pasteurized or sold to creameries, and in purebred herds where the preservation of valuable blood lines is involved. The retention of reactors should be considered only as a temporary expedient, to tide the owner over a period until vaccinated replacements can be raised and added to the herd. When replacements become available, the least desirable or profitable reactors should be removed from the herd first and this process continued until the herd is free of brucellosis. Three or four years should be enough to establish a negative herd.

The fourth plan, whole-herd vaccination, is one of last resort. There are a few herds, called problem herds, in which the infection is of so severe a type, or the animals are so susceptible, that the removal of reactors following repeated tests cannot check the infection. In such herds, vaccination of the whole herd has had some success. In some herds the procedure has stopped abortions abruptly, but in others no improvement is evident for 6 to 8 months. Whole-herd vaccination has its main advantage in infected beef herds, where a calf crop is a prime requisite.

There are several undesirable consequences of the vaccination of adult animals. The vaccinal blood titer, which cannot be told from that of actual infection, may persist for indefinite periods and thus interfere with sales or interstate shipment; in cows more than 4 months advanced in pregnancy it may cause abortion; and if practiced in dairy cows, a marked drop in milk production may be expected from 10 to 14 days following vaccination.

There is little reason to vaccinate all cows in a negative herd. The owner has little to gain, especially in view of the undesirable after-results. On the other hand, calf vaccination, preferably at 6 months of age, is good insurance in all types of herds, infected or negative, against the animal's subsequently becoming infected. The only drawback is that a small proportion of calves may be slow in losing the vaccinal blood titer, which may thus interfere with their interherd movement.

The rapidity with which brucellosis in cattle may be eradicated in an infected herd under any of the four plans depends largely on herd management and sanitation.

Brucellosis in Swine

Brucellosis is spread and perpetuated in swine mainly through the infected boar and aborting sow. Recently it has been proved that the causal germ, *Brucella suis*, is sometimes eliminated in the urine of infected sows. and thus further contaminates the premises. Under such conditions the most practical method is to dispose of the entire herd, especially if it is small or not too carefully developed, and make a new start in clean quarters.

Replacement animals should be most carefully selected from herds considered to be free from infection. All animals purchased should be negative in all dilutions to the blood test. If valuable blood lines are involved, or if the herd is large, success in developing a clean herd has resulted from separating weanling pigs negative to the blood test and rearing them in clean quarters as far away as possible from the infected herd. This method should be followed in each farrowing season, with the extra precaution that the separated pigs are tested at intervals of several months until bred. When a clean herd has thus been established, the infected herd should be disposed of and the old premises thoroughly disinfected. Herd boars should be selected with utmost care to avoid reinfection of the herd.

Other methods of control, including vaccination, have not proved practical. The infectiousness for man of the germ causing brucellosis in swine is another urgent reason for eradicating the disease.

Brucellosis in Goats

Except in some herds in the Southwest, goats are quite free from brucellosis. During the war, when all sources of food supplies were being utilized, cheese made from goats' milk in the infected sections was believed to have been the cause of several cases of brucellosis in man. Because of the extreme infectiousness for man of the type of brucella affecting goats (*Brucella melitensis*), all goats producing milk for human consumption should be blood tested. The immediate slaughter of all goats reacting to the test is the only method of control that should even be considered.

Mastitis of Cattle

Mastitis is undoubtedly the greatest scourge in the dairy industry. Each acute attack causes the loss of milk from the infected quarter until the condition improves, the graduated destruction of milk-secreting tissues and, thus, continued lower production during a lactating period until it no longer pays to keep the animal. Estimates are that at least a fourth of all dairy cattle in the United States have mastitis.

Until recently there has been no recognized cure for chronic mastitis. Control measures were of a practical nature—disposing of animals with badly diseased udders, segregating infected cows that were still milking profitably, and preventing the spread of infection to clean cows through strict sanitation in milking and handling the herd.

A few years ago drugs were developed that proved to be effective in curing many cases or a high percentage of cases of mastitis caused by *Streptococcus agalactiae,* the most common cause. The outstanding drugs are sulfanilamide, colloidal silver oxide, tyrothricin, and penicillin. They are infused into the udder through the teat canal.

Penicillin, the least irritating of the drugs, will cure a large proportion of streptococcal infections if infused daily in proper dosage for 4 or 5 days. Unfortunately, the drugs are much less effective against other types of infection, and are not easy to use. Samples of milk from the quarters of each cow's udder should be submitted for laboratory examination to determine which animals are infected and the type of infection. Each quarter showing the presence of germs should be treated by infusing it with a suspension of the drug selected. After treatment, further checks on the milk should be made as a basis for the disposition of the animals.

The control of mastitis calls for expert advice in herd management, sanitation, treatment, and disposition of affected animals, and should, therefore, be placed in the hands of a qualified practitioner. Drug therapy, even though effective, is only a helping factor in the control of mastitis; no dairyman should consider it as a substitute for proper sanitary practices and management. We suggest gentle, rapid milking, either by hand or machine; avoiding rough hand milking or improper regulation of the milking machine, which may cause irritation of the inner lining of the teat and afford a favorable atrium for infection; preventing injuries to teats and udder by providing clean, roomy, comfortable stalls; removing obstructions, such as high door sills and jagged stumps, which may injure teats and udders.

Tuberculosis of Cattle

All States are now in the modified-accredited status; that is, in no State is there an incidence of more than 0.5 percent of tuberculous infection in the cattle population. But some traces of infection remain in almost every State—it is impossible to give the tuberculin test annually to every animal in the country. A way of discovering foci of infection has been worked out with the Federal Meat Inspection Division. When postmortem examinations in abattoirs show animals to be tuberculous, their origin is traced, and the disease in the infected herd is eradicated by test and slaughter. The method, together with general testing, is slowly reducing bovine tuberculosis to the vanishing point.

Anthrax

Anthrax, one of the oldest and most destructive diseases of animals and man, is still a problem in some parts of the United States.

We obtained considerable necessary information on the history and incidence of anthrax in recent studies. Outbreaks of a disease believed to be anthrax occurred in Pennsylvania as early as 1834, in Louisiana in 1835, and in Mississippi in 1836. Outbreaks in New York were recorded in 1881, in Vermont and Massachusetts in 1887, and in California in 1888. Infected areas still exist in those States. Between 1915 and 1945 there was a gradual increase in the territory involved, with outbreaks of anthrax in livestock in 438 counties in 45 States. Large areas of recognized infection exist in South Dakota, Nebraska, Arkansas, Mississippi,

Louisiana, Texas, and California; small areas exist in Vermont, New Jersey, Delaware, Utah, Nevada, and Oregon. The disease in those areas can be largely controlled by annual preseasonal vaccination, strict quarantine, and prompt disposal of all infected material during outbreaks.

Experimental studies, observations in the field, and reports from practicing veterinarians indicate that anthrax spore vaccine of the proper strength administered between layers of skin is an effective type of preventive vaccination. It is gaining in favor in many parts of the country, and is widely used in Texas, Louisiana, Nebraska, and South Dakota;

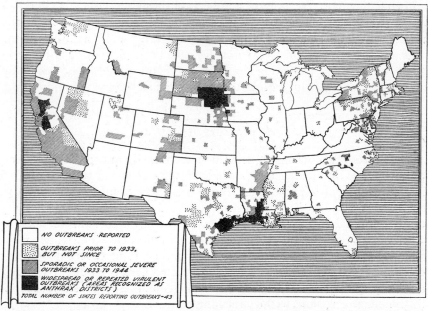

NO OUTBREAKS REPORTED

OUTBREAKS PRIOR TO 1933, BUT NOT SINCE

SPORADIC OR OCCASIONAL SEVERE OUTBREAKS 1933 TO 1944

WIDESPREAD OR REPEATED VIRULENT OUTBREAKS (AREAS RECOGNIZED AS ANTHRAX DISTRICTS)

TOTAL NUMBER OF STATES REPORTING OUTBREAKS—43

Anthrax still takes its toll of livestock in 43 States. Virulent outbreaks occur in South Dakota, Nebraska, Arkansas, Mississippi, Louisiana, Texas, and California.

in Nebraska, South Dakota, and small sections of Iowa and Minnesota, the number of herds quarantined for anthrax declined from 1,592 in 1937 to 20 in 1945. On the Indian reservations in South Dakota, where more than 45,000 cattle were vaccinated with intradermal spore vaccine from 1939 to 1945, only 16 animals were lost from anthrax.

Considerable information was obtained from recent studies on the tenacity of *B. anthracis* and its spores. Dry anthrax spores were killed by dry heat at 149° to 150° C. in 60 minutes, but not in 30 minutes. Spore suspensions in distilled water were destroyed in 3 to 5 minutes by vigorous boiling, in 5 to 15 minutes at 100° to 101° C., and in 5 to 15 minutes in the autoclave at 15 pounds pressure (120° C.), while several strains resisted heating at 90° to 91° C. for 60 minutes. Dry spores in dried

blood on cotton swabs from field cases held in glass vials at 25° to 30°
C. were both viable and virulent after storage for 8 years. Suspensions
of spores in normal saline resisted rapid shell freezing at −72° C. to
−78° C. and thawing at 37° C. for 45 successive times. Viable anthrax
spores were recovered from the vapors of heated anthrax-spore suspensions and from the distillate of anthrax-spore suspensions.

In the unopened carcasses of guinea pigs dead of anthrax, held at
28° to 30° C. for 80 hours, B. anthracis could not be isolated from the
blood, but when held in the ice box at 5° to 10° C. B. anthracis could be
recovered after 4 weeks in storage.

The spores that formed from vegetative forms in bone marrow and
muscle tissue from guinea pigs dead of anthrax were still viable after
the decomposing tissues had been held 6 months at room temperature
(28° to 30° C).

Newcastle Disease

Newcastle disease, a serious disease of poultry in many other countries,
has been identified in several widely separated areas in the United States.
Fortunately the disease has thus far caused relatively light losses here,
although extremely heavy losses have been suffered in the Dutch East
Indies, Korea, the Philippines, Ceylon, India, Kenya, the Middle Congo,
parts of the European Continent, and Palestine. England and Australia
have twice succeeded in eradicating the disease through rigid quarantines, prompt slaughtering of infected birds, and thorough cleaning of
infected premises. In other countries the disease has spread alarmingly.

In 1944, a comparatively mild disease in California that caused
symptoms resembling infectious bronchitis and laryngotracheitis, but was
frequently complicated by nervous symptoms such as paralysis, proved to
be a form of Newcastle disease. It spread rapidly and caused the greatest
mortality in chicks, but it affected birds of all ages, including turkeys.
Egg production in previously thrifty laying flocks suddenly dropped to
low levels.

The disease, referred to earlier as a "respiratory nervous disease," or
pneumoencephalitis, had apparently been present in California for several
years. Its true nature remained unidentified until samples of the virus
causing it were examined at Harvard University in 1944 by a group of
specialists working under the direction of a War Department commission.
Shortly thereafter the disease was identified in New Jersey and New York.
It is known to have occurred in about 27 States, and there are strong
suspicions of its existence elsewhere in the country. It cannot be said with
certainty that any section of the country has escaped.

The apparent spread of the disease, and its potential hazard to the
poultry industry led to several regional conferences of animal-disease

specialists, and a conference of poultry pathologists, State livestock sanitary authorities, and poultrymen from all parts of the country with Department officials in 1946. We decided to collect all the information we could about the disease and methods for its control. Poultrymen, veterinarians, and regulatory officials were warned to be on the alert.

Because of its similarity to other diseases, there may be considerable difficulty in making an exact diagnosis, which is possible only by technical examinations in the laboratory. Newcastle disease has certain aspects, however, that should arouse the poultryman's suspicions and lead him to report the facts promptly to a poultry pathologist and State veterinary authorities.

The incubation period may vary up to 2 weeks and sometimes longer. The average is generally placed at 5 days. The onset of the disease is usually sudden, and it spreads rapidly in the flock. In rare instances, death may occur before symptoms are observed. In the United States, the mortality rate has been less than 20 percent in most outbreaks, but in some instances the death rate, especially among young birds, has been alarming.

Respiratory symptoms, quite similar to those of infectious bronchitis and laryngotracheitis, are seen in Newcastle disease as it has occurred in the United States. Affected birds generally exhibit dullness, droopiness, weakness, slowness, lack of appetite, ruffled feathers, coughing, sneezing, rattling sounds in breathing, sleepiness, diarrhea, and fever. There may be a discharge of mucus from the nostrils; the accumulations lead to frequent swallowing and shaking of the head. A dark discoloration and swelling of the head may occur. Chicks usually emit a rapid, low, cheeping sound.

Egg production is sharply reduced. Affected flocks that survive generally seem to improve markedly after a week or 10 days, but decreased egg production continues for 4 to 8 weeks or longer. It has been reported that during this interval the laying of abnormal eggs, including some with soft shells, inferior quality of albumin, or bubbly contents, is not uncommon. At the same time, the birds are apt to go into a heavy moult. Younger birds, even though they appear to have recovered from the disease, are apt to develop poorly.

The nervous symptoms vary considerably. Sometimes they are absent. Weakness, progressing to paralysis, involves the legs and wings. Attacks like epilepsy may occur. Distortions of the neck, either downward, upward, or lateral, appear. Periodic shivering, twitching, incoordination, convulsive seizures, circling, backing up, and curling of the toes are common evidences of involvement of the nervous system. Such signs may develop abruptly or occur secondarily in birds that are apparently recovering. Paralyzed birds may live for several weeks, but most of them eventually die.

Post-mortem examination may reveal various changes, usually of little diagnostic significance. A catarrhal condition of the trachea, with accumulations of clear or yellowish mucus, or cheeselike material, occurs frequently. Cloudiness of the air sacs is common in chicks. Birds dying of the nervous type of the disease generally have no distinctive lesions.

Years have elapsed since Newcastle disease was last identified in either England or Australia. The procedure followed was the radical one of destruction of all affected birds, followed by thorough cleaning and disinfection of all infected premises before restocking was permitted. Rigid quarantines and control of all movements of chickens and other barnyard fowl were imposed. These means have also been used successfully in the United States in the eradication of European fowl plague. Such measures have been applied successfully with other highly contagious maladies when the diseases have been recognized early after their first appearance and before they have spread materially. The present situation is somewhat different in that the infection has been prevalent for a number of years and has apparently become widespread. Sanitary authorities have been reluctant to adopt the slaughter program as a general procedure, although they agree it may be the best procedure in isolated outbreaks.

Vaccination against Newcastle disease is still in the experimental stage, although rather extensive field trials have been carried out in California. Limited commercial production of vaccine was begun in 1945.

Some Methods of Control

Although exact methods of controlling the disease have not been worked out in detail, the following may be considered as objectionable and dangerous procedures that should be avoided:

Re-use of second-hand, unsterilized feed bags; admittance of unnecessary visitors to poultry premises; admittance of chick sexers, blood testers, cullers, or any necessary service personnel without proper precautions; the use of unsterilized bird crates; careless disposal of dead birds; performance of post-mortem examinations of poultry on the farm; shipment of sick birds in public conveyances to the laboratory; conducting egg-laying tests and poultry shows without authority from the livestock sanitary officials; failure to observe quarantine and other sanitary regulations; obtaining eggs, chicks, or any birds from infected or exposed flocks; failure to report sick birds immediately to the proper authorities; failure to sterilize or properly dispose of offal and other waste materials from slaughtered birds.

Additional information on the disease may be found in the Proceedings of the forty-sixth, forty-seventh, and forty-ninth Annual Meetings of the United States Livestock Sanitary Association in 1942, 1943, and 1945, the March 1946 issue of Nulaid News, the June 1946 issue of the

Journal of the American Veterinary Association, the July 1946 issue of the American Journal of Veterinary Research, and the April 1946 issue of the Cornell Veterinarian.

Hog Cholera

Hog cholera is still the most prevalent and devastating disease of swine. No herd in this country is absolutely safe from it, nor will be until the disease is wiped out. None of the methods that have been used successfully against some other diseases of livestock offers promise of success against hog cholera. Thus, the method used sometimes to eliminate foot-and-mouth disease—the slaughter of all infected and exposed animals—is not practical in the United States, although it is in Canada. The disease is too widespread in this country and too frequently is not recognized until it has spread throughout a community. Nor is the test-and-slaughter method, which promises ultimate eradication of bovine tuberculosis, applicable because no diagnostic test is known for the detection of hog cholera.

Although a method of eradication is not available, the swine raiser is fortunate in possessing a dependable method of control. The serum-virus treatment, developed by the late Marion Dorset, affords complete and life-long protection against cholera to all except an insignificant few of the treated hogs.

By its use, the great epidemics that once caused annual losses as high as 65 million dollars have been prevented, and any hog raiser willing to pay for the required treatment is relatively secure. But the method, since it involves the use of the live virus that causes the disease, offers no hope of eradicating hog cholera. Partly in recognition of that fact, scientists continued their search for a method of prevention that offered promise of being also a method of eradication.

A result of the search was the development of hog cholera vaccines. One of them, also developed by Dr. Dorset, is known as crystal violet vaccine. It seems incapable of causing the disease, but nevertheless it affords a marked degree of protection. It is the virus of hog cholera so treated that it has lost its ability to produce the disease, but it retains its antigenic properties, or ability to confer protection against the disease.

Field tests were begun soon after the vaccine was discovered. They have been continued on a graduated scale as confidence in its value has grown. These tests, although indicating the general dependability of the product, have also indicated the need of improvements.

One of these involved the purity of the product. The early crystal violet vaccines frequently contained contaminants, micro-organisms that had been derived from the virus donor or that had gained access during preparation of the vaccine. It was possible by animal test to determine whether the contaminants present would be injurious to hogs treated with the product. But it was also possible for the contaminants by their growth to produce spoilage in the vaccine and to cause a loss of potency that could not be detected. As soon as the need for a sterile product was recognized, attempts were begun to supply that need. It was found that the use of a glycerol solution of the dye, crystal violet, used in preparing the vaccine, instead of the formerly used water solutions of dye and phosphate, consistently afforded sterile vaccines. Under ordinary conditions of handling they remain sterile. The new method of preparing the vaccine was patented by Dr. F. W. Tilley, of the Bureau of Animal Industry, in 1945, and the patent was assigned to the Secretary of Agriculture.

The development of a sterile vaccine of satisfactory keeping qualities has been the chief recent advance in the product itself. A considerable advance also has been made in the recognition of the value of vaccines as a means of preventing hog cholera. As recognition grew, demand grew, and to supply the demand commercial establishments began preparing them. The use of commercially prepared vaccines was at first subject to certain restrictions imposed under the authority of the virus-serum-toxin act. By 1944, however, their merits had become so well demonstrated that the restrictions were withdrawn.

The production and use of the vaccines is not limited to this country. As a result of an extensive series of studies conducted by the British Ministry of Agriculture, crystal violet vaccine is being made available to farmers in England. Research workers in Venezuela also confirmed the value of the vaccine. Indeed, reports from all countries except Canada have been favorable. The degree of protection afforded by the vaccine in Canada was far smaller than elsewhere. Whether the results of tests by Canadian authorities are due to a peculiarly of Canadian pigs or to some other cause remains to be determined.

Swine Erysipelas

Swine erysipelas is now recognized to be second only to hog cholera in economic importance to swine growers of the United States.

It is not a consistent killer of swine, as is hog cholera, but causes losses by preventing normal rates of growth, altering tissues and organs to an extent that excludes their use for human food, lowering resistance of infected swine so that they readily fall prey to other diseases, and, in certain outbreaks, by actually killing.

Prevention by immunization of swine, with the simultaneous administration of anti-swine-erysipelas serum and live-culture vaccine, has been a subject of experimental study by several of the State livestock sanitary authorities, the State experiment stations, and the Department. The study has been conducted on a cooperative basis under restricted conditions for more than 8 years in 14 States where the disease is known to exist. Strict control over the production of the vaccine and serum has assured standard products of high quality for use in the work. This protective vaccination has been given nearly 7 million head of swine in 100,000 herds. The results have been satisfactory so far, but sufficient time to allow for complete evaluation of the sero-vaccination under all cyclic variations of the disease has not yet elapsed.

The organism that causes swine erysipelas is also dangerous to man. In humans, the disease is known as erysipeloid, and occurs generally through wound infection. Although erysipeloid usually localizes, in some cases general infection and death have resulted. Care should be exercised, therefore, in handling infected swine and their products.

The disease has also gained considerable economic importance for turkey growers. It manifests itself suddenly in turkeys around market time. The birds become droopy, sleeply, and depressed. Death usually occurs in about a day. There is a copious diarrhea in most cases. The wattles and caruncles become swollen and dark. On birds that recover, the caruncles may dry and drop off. Mortality ranges up to 50 percent, and the disease seems to affect young toms oftener than young hen turkeys.

Our preliminary investigations indicate that 10 cubic centimeters of anti-swine erysipelas serum (equine origin) introduced into the wattles of artificially infected turkeys will cure about 50 percent of birds so treated, but all untreated birds die. By repeated administration of oil suspension of penicillin into the wattles of similarly infected turkeys, mortality was reduced to 10 percent.

Rabies

Rabies as a disease of livestock has never ranked in economic importance with the other well known infectious diseases, but it is exceedingly serious because it may affect all warm blooded species, including man.

Although dogs are the main victims of rabies, human beings and many farm animals also die from it. From 1938 to 1945 rabies caused 70,201 deaths

Year	Dogs	Cattle	Horses	Sheep	Swine	Cats	Goats	Miscellaneous	Man	Total
1938......	8, 452	413	32	164	42	207	11	44	47	9, 412
1939......	7, 386	358	36	17	38	269	10	172	30	8, 316
1940......	6, 194	326	25	53	71	260	4	277	28	7, 238
1941......	6, 648	418	39	68	159	294	9	212	30	7, 877
1942......	6, 332	288	15	48	32	250	12	160	28	7, 165
1943......	8, 515	349	35	45	60	316	19	310	41	9, 690
1944......	9, 067	561	32	40	43	419	14	311	53	10, 540
1945......	8, 505	487	46	11	30	466	10	373	35	9, 963
Total...	61, 099	3, 200	260	446	475	2, 481	89	1, 859	292	70, 201

It is invariably fatal. Since 1938, the Department has gathered statistics on the incidence of the disease in the United States. In the 8 years from 1938 to 1945, a total of 70,201 cases was recorded, of which nearly 90 percent were in dogs and less than 7 percent in other farm animals.

Incidence of the disease gradually declined from 1938 to 1942, with a sharp rise during the following 2 years and a small decline in 1945. Even a slight increase in the spread of rabies in a community gives rise to grave concern among veterinarians, public health officials, and citizens. Consequently aggressive programs have been inaugurated in the past few years in certain affected areas. Particular emphasis was given to vaccination as a very helpful prophylactic measure. Large-scale vaccinations of dogs in a number of States and communities were carried out promptly. In Washington, D. C., approximately 35,000 dogs were vaccinated in about 2 weeks. The results of vaccination have been gratifying; in many instances the number of cases dropped sharply upon the completion of the vaccinations.

Each lot of commercial rabies vaccine must be subjected to the Habel test, an accepted method for determining its power to immunize, before being released for sale. In the test, white mice are vaccinated with some of the rabies vaccine and these animals, together with an equal number of unvaccinated mice, are inoculated with varying doses of rabies-fixed virus. The vaccine is not passed unless 50 percent of the vaccinated mice withstand at least a thousand fatal doses of the virus.

Despite the high quality of present-day rabies vaccine and the good results obtained through its use in many dogs, the control and ultimate eradication of rabies must include other recognized measures. In late years the fox has played an important role in the spread of rabies in some localities. Should the disease become established in these animals, a program of systematic reduction of the fox population will become necessary.

———

THE AUTHOR

L. T. Giltner is assistant chief of the Division of Pathology, in the Bureau of Animal Industry, where his work has included research on all of the animal diseases discussed in this article.

FOR FURTHER READING

Bunyea, Hubert, and Wehr, E. E.: *Diseases and Parasites of Poultry,* U. S. D. A. Farmers' Bulletin 1652, 1941.

Dorset, M., and Houck, U. G.: *Hog Cholera,* U. S. D. A. Farmers' Bulletin 834, 1939.

Eichhorn, A., and Crawford, A. B.: *Brucellosis of Cattle,* U. S. D. A. Farmers' Bulletin 1871, 1941.

Gochenour, W. S.: *Anthrax,* U. S. D. A. Farmers' Bulletin 1736, 1934.

Grey, Charles G., and Dale, C. N.: *Diseases of Swine,* U. S. D. A. Farmers' Bulletin 1914, 1942.

Schoening, H. W.: *Rabies and Its Control,* U. S. D. A. Yearbook, Keeping Livestock Healthy, pages 1109–1223, 1942.

Shahan, Maurice S., and Huffman, Ward T.: *Diseases of Sheep and Goats,* U. S. D. A. Farmers' Bulletin 1943, 1943.

Stein, C. D.: *Anthrax,* U. S. D. A. Yearbook, Keeping Livestock Healthy, pages 250–262, 1942.

Swett, W. W., Graves, R. R., Matthews, C. A., Cone, J. Frank., and Underwood, P. C.: *A Study of the Effectiveness of Sulfonamide Preparations in the Elimination of Bovine Mastitis,* U. S. D. A. Technical Bulletin 884, 1944.

ALSO, IN THIS BOOK

Men Who Went Before, by Ernest G. Moore, page 1.
Drugs to Control Parasites, by Benjamin Schwartz, page 71.
Progress in Hog Production, by John H. Zeller, page 201.
Developments in Sheep, by Damon A. Spencer, page 209.
Keeping Poultry Healthy, by Theodore C. Byerly, page 231.

New Ideas in Feeding

by N. R. ELLIS

W E HAVE had to revamp many of our old ideas about feeding livestock. War proved again the tremendous importance of food. We had to get all the milk, eggs, poultry, meat, pork, lard, beef, veal, lamb, and mutton we could and make every tittle of grain count in doing so. Chicken was compared with hog and hog with steer to see which yielded the most nutrients for humans in return for the least feed. Egg was measured against pork and pork against beef to determine relative food values. A dozen questions were raised that we thought we had answered pretty well before—the best weight at which to market swine, for example, and the amount of grain to feed to fattening steers.

We discovered that an animal's increase in live weight or the total quantities of eggs and milk were not exact enough measures of relative efficiency in converting feedstuffs into foods for human use. We had to consider the separate nutrients, the vitamins, minerals, proteins, and energy values, because one animal product may represent a highly efficient production of protein, and another of fat. Besides, supplies of common feeds were often scant, and new types of feed and sometimes entirely new feeds or feed byproducts were introduced. Out of this situation came extensive changes in diets and rations for livestock. Some of them are transient reflections of the war, but many may be permanent.

Early in the war, committees of the National Research Council undertook to state the nutritive requirements of different classes of livestock on a basis comparable to those for humans. They used the best available information on all the known essential nutrients in arriving at the figures, which were set up as guideposts for the rationing of livestock and served as indices of the research requirements to confirm or modify our information on the exact needs for energy materials, proteins, mineral elements, and vitamin factors necessary for a given purpose. Of the standards thus summarized, the ones of concern here are for swine, cattle, and sheep.

The relative proportions of forages and of concentrated feeds that yield the greatest financial return on the farm and at the same time satisfy the market demands for quality in beef have been a debated subject for years.

The need to conserve corn and other grains and protein concentrates for other livestock or for direct human use focused attention on methods of fattening cattle during the past few years. Considerable experimental work has been done on systems of feeding that utilize a maximum of pasture and harvested forages. As an example of the savings in concentrated feeds that can be made, the North Carolina Agricultural Experiment Station, in cooperation with the Bureau of Animal Industry of the Department, fattened yearling steers on varying amounts of barley and lespedeza hay with, usually, a small allowance of protein concentrates. The limitation of the allowance of barley, with corresponding increases in hay, has permitted the production of carcasses grading somewhat below the Choice level, yet very satisfactory.

Actually, the limitation of the amount of barley to two-thirds that of the full-grain group got the best results in terms of savings of grain for grade of carcass produced. Such a limitation, whether in the dry lot or on pasture, promises to yield beef produced almost as efficiently in terms of units of concentrated feeds as is pork or poultry meat. Such a favorable comparison is not often possible where beef animals are fed all the concentrates they will consume readily. It is evident that with a moderate sacrifice in grade, whereby the marketed product is classed in the upper brackets of the Good or Choice grades rather than top Choice or Prime grades, beef can be produced about as efficiently, in terms of concentrated feeds, as other classes of meat animals. At the same time, increased dependence is placed on forage crops, whose quantity and quality have been greatly improved in recent years.

While the maximum use of roughage in the form of pasture and harvested forages has been stressed in feeding horses under farm conditions, the transportation and use of bulky feeds may sometimes pose serious problems. Early in the war a possibility that horses might be used overseas by our armies prompted a study of the problem. We found that we could reduce the amount of hay fed both idle and working animals providing the allowance of concentrate was increased to make up for the nutrients in the hay. The tests indicated that 4 pounds or so of hay per 1,000 pounds of animal weight were adequate, compared with the normal allowance of 10 pounds. Decreases in the roughage content of the ration, we learned, permitted more complete digestion of the feeds as a whole. This effect was accordingly reflected in the feed allowance required to maintain weight, and necessitated a reduction in the amount of total feed as calculated according to the usual standards.

A further development has been the making of pellets or briquettes out of mixtures of chopped roughage and concentrated feeds. Several European nations used briquettes in various forms as horse feeds during the war. In experiments at Beltsville, briquettes weighing 1 to 2 pounds were made of a mixture of four parts of chopped alfalfa or timothy hay, four parts of crushed or whole oats, one part of beet pulp, and varying amounts of a binder, such as corn dextrin.

C. P. McMeekan and two colleagues in New Zealand applied to lambs a three-level system of feeding like the one McMeekan used some years ago in swine feeding. When lambs were fed at low, medium, and high planes to weights of 28.4, 38.2, and 49.6 pounds, respectively, there was little effect on skeletal growth. Muscle growth was moderately retarded when the level of feeding was lowered. Subsequent feeding on a high plane promoted rapid recovery in the low and medium groups, but the lambs never caught up with those in the high-plane group. The greatest recovery in comparative terms was in fat deposition.

H. M. Briggs, of the Oklahoma Agricultural Experiment Station, compared the value of feeds by comparing lambs that he fed for uniform gains. He used corn and alfalfa hay as base feeds. The method, originally proposed by F. B. Morrison, of Cornell University, calls for the production of uniform gains in terms of uniform fat and protein storage, a condition that not all rations will produce. For example, oats and barley did not produce the finish in the carcasses produced by corn. Net energy values of 72.8 and 70.3 therms per 100 pounds were obtained with the technique employed for oats and barley, respectively, when those feeds replaced all the corn, and 80.1 and 64.5 therms when they replaced half the corn. Prairie hay gave a value of 33.8 therms per 100 pounds, and alfalfa hay gave a value of 41.5.

E. J. Underwood and four Australian associates, in studies of pregnancy disease in ewes, made observations on the levels of serum calcium, blood glucose, liver glycogen, blood ketone, and liver vitamin A in late pregnancy on poor and medium planes of nutrition. A rise was observed in ketone bodies in the cases of toxemia that occurred within 7 weeks of lambing. There were more cases among the poorly fed than among the well-fed ewes. There was no definite evidence of hypocalcemia, and glycogen reserves dropped. It seems that the disease is associated with, or caused by, disturbed carbohydrate metabolism through low caloric intake and high demand. Prevention is achieved by feeding enough carbohydrate-rich feed to promote some increase in body weight. Other workers have reached the same conclusion; they recognize difficulties in diagnosis in some cases, but indicate that the disease is usually characterized by nervous symptoms, hypoglycemia, acetonemia, and fatty infiltration of the liver.

Considerable adjustment has taken place in feeding protein concentrates and in expressing protein requirements for various classes of animals. To meet the greatly increased demands of livestock feeders for protein feeds, the tonnage of soybean meal has increased considerably. Supplies of animal protein, however, were reduced by the curtailment in the production of fish meal and the diversion of milk byproducts to human consumption. A serious problem was thus created in changing the proportions of animal protein to plant protein that had to be used in diets. The change, of course, concerned mostly poultry and swine because they depend on the feed supply for the balance of essential amino acids most favorable for best performance.

Feeding experiments on growing and fattening pigs established that such animal protein supplements as tankage could be cut back to a level of about 3 percent of the diet by substituting properly heat-processed soybean meal. But calcium and other essential nutrients, otherwise supplied by the animal byproduct feeds, must be supplied from another source. Older pigs above 100 pounds and breeding stock can be fed successfully on rations lacking animal protein if care is taken to supply good green pasture or other good supplemental feeds, such as alfalfa. From a survey of available information, H. H. Mitchell, of Illinois, concluded that the value of protein supplements of animal origin, compared to those of plant origin, was not so much in superiority in amino acid make-up as in mineral and vitamin composition. This largely accounts for the need for a calcium supplement with soybean meal and the importance of green pasture and alfalfa hay for pigs fed all-plant diets.

How much total protein is needed by swine of varying sizes, particularly by pigs weighing 50 pounds or less? The table of daily allowances by the National Research Council gives an answer: The equivalent of approximately 22 percent of the total ration for 50-pound pigs. As weight goes up, the percentage drops, until at 200 pounds it is 13.3 percent.

Urea and other nonprotein nitrogen compounds, as substitutes for preformed proteins in the rations of ruminants, have been used most widely as ingredients of the concentrated mixtures fed to milking dairy cows. S. H. Work and associates found that urea can be fed fattening steers either on pasture or in dry lot at levels of 0.18 and 0.35 pound daily without causing damage to the kidneys and livers.

In experiments with yearling steers fed a basal ration of prairie hay, H. M. Briggs and others at the Oklahoma Agricultural Experiment Station found that urea made into pellets with hominy feed and molasses was as well utilized as cottonseed meal in terms of digestibility and storage of nitrogen. In fattening tests, a urea-containing mixture made to furnish the equivalent of 25-percent protein was considered better than a 50-percent formula and about equal to cottonseed meal. In some tests there was evidence of lowered palatability of the feed mixture because of the presence of urea, with consequent retardation in the rate of gain.

Tests conducted at the Illinois Agricultural Experiment Station with lambs showed good utilization of the urea as long as the level of total protein equivalent was kept on a medium plane of around 12 percent. The researchers conclude that lambs cannot utilize urea fast enough to meet their requirements for maximum growth. No evidence of kidney damage resulted even when the ration contained 3.16 percent of urea.

Results obtained by J. P. Willman, F. B. Morrison, and E. W. Klosterman at Cornell University on lambs fattened on a basal ration of yellow corn, corn silage, and hay showed that urea did not improve the rate of gain, as compared with the improvement obtained with linseed meal.

In seeking an explanation, J. K. Loosli and L. E. Harris tested the value of the amino acid, methionine, as an adjunct to the urea. The results, as measured in rates of gain and in nitrogen retention, showed that the methionine produced a decided improvement. The men suggest that the protein formed by micro-organisms from urea alone may be of inferior value, under certain conditions at least, but that the lack can be corrected by the methionine. Thus it seems evident that the use of urea in practical lamb-fattening rations requires further study to define the conditions under which the material can be depended upon to contribute the full value expected.

Mineral Requirements

We know quite definitely now the phosphorus requirements of swine, beef cattle, and sheep. Of the more recent studies, those of W. M. Beeson and others at the Idaho Agricultural Experiment Station emphasize that phosphorus deficiency decreases the utilization of feed of fattening lambs to a greater extent than it does the appetite. The minimum phosphorus requirement is placed at 2.4 grams of phosphorus per 100 pounds of body weight. This is somewhat higher than the figure for fattening steers, namely 2.0 grams, as given by the Idaho scientists. The phosphorus requirements, as stated in tables of the National Research Council, are adjusted to different classes and weights of animals. They also provide about a 25-percent margin of safety for beef cattle and sheep. The actual values, expressed on the basis of percentage of phosphorus of ration of 90-percent dry-matter content, are higher than the 0.13 figure given by W. H. Black, and others, in the 1939 Yearbook. Adding a 25-percent margin of safety to this 0.13 value gives a figure that is generally within the range of the recommendations of the National Research Council.

In areas where the range grasses are low in phosphorus, as in southern Texas, the low calf crops and retarded growth of the young stock can be remedied by supplying about 6.5 grams of phosphorus a day to dry cows and heifers and 14 grams to lactating cows, according to Black and his colleagues. Bonemeal and disodium phosphate were equally effective in preventing aphosphorosis and just as beneficial as a complex mineral mixture containing salts of iron, manganese, copper, cobalt, zinc, and boron in increasing the calf crop and the weaning weights of calves.

During the war the problem of meeting the national requirements for additional sources of phosphorus suited for feeding was met largely by working out methods for manufacturing defluorinated phosphates. In one procedure, fertilizer grade of superphosphate is utilized as the starting material. In another, rock phosphate is used. In both cases fluorine, the harmful element that is usually present at toxic levels in the starting materials, is largely driven off by heating the phosphates to high temperatures. Feeding tests on the defluorinated superphosphates and rock phosphates have been made by a number of investigators. We discovered some variation in utilization by animals of the phosphorus in the products produced in different manufacturing plants, much of it traceable to the temperatures of defluorination and the kind of phosphate compound formed, whether of the ortho, meta, or pyro type. A temperature of approximately 1,000° C., for example, was found to produce a defluorinated superphosphate superior to those made at lower temperatures and about as good as bonemeal.

The search for phosphates has served to reemphasize the dangers of fluorine in livestock nutrition and prompted H. H. Mitchell, working under the auspices of the National Research Council, to review the existing information in order to express the safe limits at which the element may be consumed. These permissible levels may be stated as 0.003 percent of fluorine in the total dry ration of cattle, sheep, and swine and .015 percent for poultry.

A further contribution by H. R. Seddon on the effects of fluorine in the water supply of sheep indicates that a content of 12 parts per million gradually leads to the characteristic mottling and irregular wear of the teeth. Under such conditions of borderline fluorine intake, the symptoms do not appear until the third and fourth years of life. Other effects of fluorine in the nutrition of sheep have been studied at the Indiana Agricultural Experiment Station by C. L. Shrewsbury and others. They fed breeding ewes and growing lambs on rations containing rock phosphate that supplied different levels of fluorine. Approximately 3 milligrams a pound of body weight was enough to retard the growth of lambs and to affect the metabolism of the thyroid gland, especially the iodine content.

The place of copper, cobalt, manganese, and other trace elements in the nutrition of livestock was reviewed in the 1942 Yearbook. Since then, we have obtained more evidence on their importance, and some new findings on their exact method of functioning. Both copper and cobalt are associated with iron in the building of hemoglobin and of red blood cells. Thus far, reports on the occurrence of sway-back disease, a form of anemia in sheep due to copper deficiency, have been largely confined to Great Britain and Australia. Mineral deficiency in animals can usually be traced to inadequate levels in the soil and the crops produced on the particular soil. That such is not necessarily always the case with sway-back disease is discussed by G. D. Shearer and E. I. McDougall, who point out that sheep in certain districts in England respond to copper therapy even though the grass the animals ate was of normal copper content. The possibility that some other element interferes with copper metabolism has been recognized; both lead and molybdenum have been mentioned. Considerable progress, however, has been made in controlling the disease by adding copper to the soil or feeding it directly.

Instances of cobalt deficiency, on the other hand, have been shown in several widely separated areas in this country and elsewhere. The occurrence of cobalt deficiency in cattle was observed some years ago in the Southeastern States, especially Florida. Later it was diagnosed in the Grand Traverse Region in Michigan, where the condition had been known for many years as "lake shore disease." More recently, unthrifty and emaciated cattle in Door County and nearby localities in northeastern Wisconsin have responded to treatment with 3 to 6 milligrams of cobalt a day. This amount has been supplied by adding to the grain mixture 1 percent of salt containing in each 100 pounds 1 ounce of cobalt sulfate, or by feeding 1 teaspoonful of a water solution containing 1 ounce of cobalt sulfate or cobalt chloride per gallon. The hemoglobin values on the blood and the appetite and gains of the cattle have improved markedly. Poor condition in sheep flocks also has been traced to cobalt deficiency. The deficiency exists in an extensive area in New Hampshire. There have been suggestions of its presence in sheep in Illinois, New York, and western Canada. Usually, the soil and the forage grown on it are suspected, or known to be deficient in cobalt. In New York, unthriftiness in fattening lambs was corrected by giving 4 milligrams of cobalt in a water solution of cobaltous chloride twice a week.

Technicians have established the needs of poultry and the laboratory rat for manganese, but the evidence on other farm animals is not so clear. What seemed like good proof of the needs of swine for this element has since been questioned by S. R. Johnson, of the Arkansas station, who has shown that pigs grow at a normal rate on a ration with less than 0.5 part per million and sows reproduce normally on 6 parts per million and even less. On the basis of this work, it appears that if manganese is essential for swine the requirement must be very low.

A troublesome disorder in sheep and cattle that seems to be associated in some way with mineral metabolism is that of urinary calculi formation. Investigations of feeding steers in west Texas have shown calculi involvement when the ration was made up of grain sorghum and sorgo products, along with cottonseed meal. The disorder is accentuated by increasing the magnesium content of the diet and relieved somewhat by using bonemeal, a calcium and phosphorus supplement, instead of limestone, which supplies only calcium.

Vitamin A therapy has been of no avail, but replacement of milo grain with corn in the concentrate feed has largely eliminated calculi. I. E. Newsom, J. W. Tobiska, and H. B. Osland, at Fort Collins, Colorado, studied the effects of different rations on calculi formation in lambs. It appeared that alfalfa and beet tops were protective feeds, but cane fodder, bran, and white corn seemed to favor calculi formation. In Australia, W. I. B. Beveridge has suggested that consideration be given to improper ratios of calcium, magnesium, and phosphorus, to vitamin A deficiency, to low water intake, and to highly alkaline urines as possible factors favoring calculi formation. Some of these are not in agreement with work done in this country, so the exact cause and the remedy, as far as feeding methods are concerned, still remain in doubt.

Vitamin Requirements

The vitamin A requirements, expressed in terms of carotene, for swine, beef cattle, and sheep as given in the statements of recommended nutrient allowances by the National Research Council reflect the newer findings. Selected values for milligrams of carotene per animal per day follow:

Swine:	Carotene (milligrams)	Beef cattle:		Sheep:	
50-pound pig	2. 0	400-pound calf	25	50-pound lamb	2. 7
200-pound pig	8. 0	800-pound year-		100-pound year-	
300-pound preg-		ling	45	ling	5. 5
nant gilt	20. 0	1,000-pound preg-		125-pound preg-	
400-pound lactat-		nant cow	55	nant ewe	6. 75
ing sow	40. 0	1,000-pound lac-		125-pound lactat-	
		tating cow	300	ing ewe	8. 10

It will be noted that for the growing and fattening animal, the allowances per unit of body weight are highest for beef cattle and lowest for swine, although the differences are small. In terms of practical feeding, when corn is the basic concentrated feed some interesting comparisons can be made between swine and beef cattle. When yellow corn is the only source of carotene (the forerunner of vitamin A), the average pig's requirements are met when the corn constitutes about one-fourth of the ration. In tests at Beltsville, we got full protection against blindness, nervous disorders, retarded growth, and other symptoms of vitamin A deficiency with such a level of yellow corn, which contributed approximately 4 milligrams of carotene per 100 pounds live weight a day, or the amount given in the National Research Council's table for Recommended Nutrient Allowances for Swine. On the other hand, steers on a fattening ration may not get enough carotene from a full feed of yellow corn of average grade to meet their needs. Fattening steer calves given a full ration containing 11 to 14 pounds of yellow corn, along with oat straw, developed symptoms characteristic of vitamin A deficiency, including stiffness, convulsions, blindness, and edematous swellings.

New information on the factors of the vitamin B complex is confined for the most part to the needs of pigs, ruminants having been shown to support synthesis of thiamine, riboflavin, nicotinic acid, and pantothenic acid. At Beltsville, we found that a pig's requirement for thiamine is related to its intake of carbohydrate and protein. In other words, the greater the proportion of fat in the diet the less the need for thiamine. We suggest a minimum of 0.61 to 0.64 milligrams per pound of carbohydrates and proteins consumed as necessary for normal growth, without much margin for building up the thiamine content of the body tissues. The figure, when translated to the average swine ration, is approximately 2.1 milligrams of thiamine per 100 pounds of live weight. Riboflavin is another of the vitamin B group essential for pigs. Without it, a pig cannot grow normally, and changes occur in its skin, hair, hoofs, and eyes.

We are not sure about the need for nicotinic acid. E. H. Hughes, of California, observed symptoms of poor appetite, vomiting, lessened growth, and unsteadiness in walking among pigs fed a purified diet composed of 81 percent sugar, 15 percent casein, and 4 percent of a salt mixture, supplemented with cod-liver oil, thiamine, riboflavin, pantothenic acid, and pyridoxine, but not with nicotinic acid. The addition of 10 milligrams of the vitamin, however, prevented the symptoms just described. Other investigators compared the growth of pigs fed a diet containing 10 percent of casein with one containing 26.1 percent. In the absence of nicotinic acid supplementation, the pigs on the low protein diet generally showed impaired nutrition, while those on high protein had better appetites and healthier appearance, and gained more nearly like the check group that received nicotinic acid. In work at Beltsville, however, we found that deficiency symptoms, such as impaired appetite, diarrhea, retarded growth, and necrotic lesions of the large intestine, occurred in most young pigs fed a purified diet lacking nicotinic acid and containing 25 percent of protein. Not all these symptoms developed in affected pigs, and the variability in growth was especially striking. Some pigs showed no effects of nicotinic acid deficiency.

The possible relationship of nutritional factors to necrotic enteritis in pigs has been studied for a number of years at the Michigan Agricultural Experiment Station. R. A. Rasmussen and associates have discussed results obtained by feeding cultures of *S. choleraesuis* to pigs and the subsequent development of necrotic enteritis in relations to dietary treatment. A combination of vitamins, including nicotinic acid, thiamine, riboflavin, pyridoxine, pantothenic acid, para-amino benzoic acid, and choline appeared to give more benefit than nicotinic acid alone. There was evidence, however, that when large doses of the organism culture were fed, complete protection could not be obtained either with vitamin mixtures or fresh liver to prevent death in the initial attack, but in the recovery period these substances were of distinct benefit.

The problem of nicotinic acid has been further complicated by observations of W. A. Krehl and other workers at the Wisconsin Experiment Station that corn in the diet tends to increase the apparent nicotinic acid requirements of the dog. Furthermore, growth retardation in the rat which was induced by a ration low in protein and containing 40 percent of corn grits could be counteracted by the addition of either nicotinic acid or tryptophane. More recently, G. M. Briggs reported that including gelatin in a chick ration also produced a depressing effect but was still capable of correction by the use of tryptophane. Our present evidence suggests that these relations hold true for swine, also.

In recent years unexpected deficiencies have appeared in swine fed on rations ordinarily considered adequate. For example, B. W. Fairbanks and associates at the Illinois Agricultural Experiment Station, while engaged in a study of protein requirements of pigs, observed poor growth, diarrhea, dermatitis, and other abnormalities on a ration of yellow corn, beef meal, soybean meal, alfalfa meal, and salt. A supplement of hulled oats was beneficial, but dry skim milk and dried corn distillers' solubles were not. Likewise, pigs fed a mixture of yellow corn, wheat flour middlings, soybean meal, fishmeal, tankage, minerals, and fortified cod-liver oil were benefited by the use of either a combination of B vitamins, dried corn distillers' solubles, or alfalfa meal. It was not possible to decide whether a new factor was supplied in the feeds, or whether the trouble was in a disturbance in the supply of the known vitamins.

The corrective value of alfalfa for the feeding of sow pigs has been stressed by O. B. Ross and associates at the Wisconsin Experiment Station. With only 5 percent of alfalfa meal present in a basal mixture of yellow corn, soybean meal, and minerals, the gilts farrowed pigs, many of which had congenital malformations of the feet and legs. During the suckling period, the surviving pigs were not very thrifty, and showed various abnormalities in locomotion and in condition of skin and hair. These disorders were eliminated by the use of 15 percent of alfalfa meal in the diet. Others have also attested to the high value of alfalfa meal as a corrective feed for gestation and lactation; some scientists used a basic ration of yellow corn, soybean oil meal, fishmeal, tankage, minerals, and cod-liver oil. As measured by condition and numbers of live pigs farrowed, alfalfa meal, along with dried corn distillers' solubles, and a mixture of the six better known B vitamins were effective in varying degrees as supplements to the basal diet, but alfalfa meal seemed the most reliable.

A troublesome disorder in young lambs known as stiff-lamb disease, which has baffled investigators for many years, appears to be of nutritional origin. The addition of wheat bran or wheat germ had a striking effect in preventing the disease. Proof that vitamin E is the factor required was obtained when six out of seven stiff lambs responded to treatment with an alpha-tocopherol compound.

Nutritional studies applicable to horses have been conducted by a number of scientists, including P. B. Pearson and associates of the Texas station. They have concluded from experiments with Shetland ponies that both riboflavin and pantothenic acid are essential factors. On the other hand, nicotinic acid is synthesized in the body. Without riboflavin, the appetites and growth of growing ponies were poor. Estimates of the requirements for adequate nutrition indicate a figure of approximately 20 milligrams per 1,000 pounds of weight.

Evidence that riboflavin deficiency is accompanied by cataract formation and other related degenerative changes in the eye in various animals and also the involvement of ascorbic acid in the nutrition of the eye tissues prompted T. C. Jones, F. D. Maurer, and T. O. Roby, of the Army Veterinary Corps, to study the disorder in horses known as periodic ophthalmia. They noted a strong similarity between the pathological changes in experimental riboflavin deficiency in experimental animals and those in periodic ophthalmia. While the ascorbic acid content of the ocular tissues has shown a decrease, the men suggest that low riboflavin intake may be the primary factor.

This idea is supported by the results of feeding crystalline riboflavin to horses at the Front Royal Remount Station. Among a total of 130 horses that were fed 40 milligrams a day of this vitamin, none developed periodic ophthalmia in contrast to the usual rate of 109 cases per thousand untreated animals. Supporting evidence from other sources has not been obtained thus far, but the results are striking enough to merit further careful study. It should be emphasized that the experiments have dealt with prevention; there is no published evidence to indicate that the disease can be cured once it has developed in an animal.

THE AUTHOR

N. R. Ellis is a chemist in charge of animal nutrition investigations in the Bureau of Animal Industry. His research has included the biochemistry of animal fats, swine nutrition, and vitamin requirements of animals. He is a graduate of the University of Wisconsin.

FOR FURTHER READING

Beeson, W. M., Bolin, D. W., Hickman, C. W., and Johnson, R. F.: *The Phosphorus Requirement for Growing and Fattening Beef Steers,* Idaho Agricultural Experiment Station Bulletin 240, 1941.

Beeson, W. M., Johnson, R. F., Bolin, D. W., and Hickman C. W.: *The Phosphorus Requirement for Fattening Lambs,* Journal of Animal Science, volume 3, pages 63–70, 1944.

Beveridge, W. I. B.: *Urinary Calculi in Sheep,* Australian Veterinary Journal, volume 18, pages 127–132, 1942.

Black, W. H., Tash, L. H., Jones, J. M., and Kleberg, R. J., Jr.: *Effects of Phosphorus Supplements on Cattle Grazing on Range Deficient in This Mineral,* U. S. D. A. Technical Bulletin 856, 1943.

Briggs, H. M.: *Some Factors Encountered in Experiments to Evaluate Feeds for Fattening Lambs,* Journal of Animal Science, volume 2, pages 336–355, 1943.

Ellis, N. R., and Madsen, L. L.: *The Thiamine Requirement of Pigs as Related to the Fat Content of the Diet,* Journal of Nutrition, volume 27, pages 253–262, 1944.

Fairbanks, B. W., Krider, J. L., and Carroll, W. E.: *Distillers' By-Products in Swine Rations,* Journal of Animal Science, volume 4, pages 420–429, 1945.

Johnson, B. C., Hamilton, T. S., Mitchell, H. H., and Robinson, W. B.: *The Relative Efficiency of Urea as a Protein Substitute in the Ration of Ruminants,* Journal of Animal Science, volume 1, pages 236–245, 1942.

McMeekan, C. P., Stevens, P. G., and Lambert R.: *The Effect of Plane of Nutrition on the Growth of Hoggets,* New Zealand Journal of Science and Technology, volume 24, pages 215–222A, 1942.

Mitchell, H. H.: *The Fluorine Problem in Livestock Feeding,* National Research Council, Reprint and Circular Series 113, 1942.

Mitchell, H. H.: *Is Animal Protein an Essential Constituent of Swine and Poultry Rations?* National Research Council, Reprint and Circular Series 117, 1943.

National Research Council: *Recommended Nutrient Allowances for Domestic Animals. No. II, Recommended Nutrient Allowances for Swine,* 1944.

Pearson, P. B., Sheybani, M. K., and Schmidt, H.: *The B Vitamin Requirements of the Horse,* Journal of Animal Science, volume 3, pages 166–174, 1944.

Rasmussen, R. A., Stafseth, H. J., Freeman, V. A., and Miller, M. J.: *Influence of B Vitamins, Liver, and Yeast on Induced Necrotic Enteritis in Swine,* Veterinary Medicine, volume 39, pages 421–423, 1944.

Ross, C. B., Phillips, P. H., Bohstedt, G., and Cunha, T. J.: *Congenital Malformations, Syndactylism, Talipes, and Paralysis Agitans of Nutritional Origin in Swine,* Journal of Animal Science, volume 3, pages 406–414, 1944.

Shearer, G. D., and McDougall, E. I.: *Some Observations on Swayback Disease of Lambs,* Journal of Agricultural Science, volume 34, pages 207–212, 1944.

Shrewsbury, C. L., Hatfield, J. D., Doyle, L. P., and Andrews, F. N.: *Some Effects of Fluorine in the Nutrition of Sheep,* Indiana Station Bulletin 499, 1944.

Underwood, E. J., Curnow, D. H., and Shier, F. L.: *Further Biochemical Studies of Pregnancy Toxaemia in Sheep,* Australian Veterinary Journal, volume 19, pages 164–173, 1943.

Willman, J. P., Loosli, J. K., Asdell, S. A., Morrison, F. B., and Olafson, P.: *Prevention and Cure of Muscular Stiffness ("Stiff-lamb" Disease) in Lambs,* Journal of Animal Science, volume 4, pages 128–132, 1945.

Wintrobe, M. M., Stein, H. J., Follis, R. H., Jr., and Humphreys, S.: *Nicotinic Acid and the Level of Protein Intake in the Nutrition of the Pig,* Journal of Nutrition, volume 30, pages 395–412, 1945.

ALSO, IN THIS BOOK

Thyroprotein for Cows

by L. A. MOORE and J. F. SYKES

THE THYROID gland affects milk production. If the gland is removed from a cow, her milk decreases 75 percent. If it is put back, in the form of dried thyroid tissue or the synthetic hormone, thyroxine, her yield returns to normal. Both substances stimulate normal cows to give more milk and fat. The difficulty has been that dried thyroid tissue is too costly to feed cows, and if the total supply of the tissue were made available for feeding cows, we would have enough for only a few animals. Lately, however, scientists have found a substitute.

German scientists in 1938 found that the addition of iodine to proteins under certain chemical conditions makes a product that acts like dried thyroid tissue. The next step was taken by E. P. Reineke and C. W. Turner of the dairy department of the University of Missouri; they ascertained that iodine could be added to skim milk or casein, the protein contained in milk, under certain conditions, with a similar result. Further work disclosed that the actual hormone, thyroxine, was produced by the process.

This material can be produced more cheaply and is even more active than dried thyroid. It does not lose potency in storage. It is known variously as iodinated casein, iodinated protein, thyrocasein, thyrolactin, thyroprotein, and by the trade name Protamone. Here we shall call it thyroprotein. Until recently it has been supplied only to experiment stations and similar research organizations for experimental purposes.

Professors Reineke and Turner tested thyroprotein on 9 cows in their herd. When they fed 50 to 100 grams (3 to 6 ounces) of thyroprotein to each animal for 3 days, they had increases of 6.09 to 22.6 percent (an average of 8.59 percent) in milk production. In six of the nine trials in which fat analyses were made, an increase in the fat percentage was

107

108 YEARBOOK OF AGRICULTURE

obtained, which, together with an increase in milk production, produced
a 13.9 percent increase in fat yield. In similar tests at the West Virginia,
New Jersey, and Louisiana stations, 10 to 15 grams daily were fed. These
amounts produced increases of 5 to 20 percent in milk production, 0.32
to 0.98 percent in fat percentage, and 25 to 50 percent in total fat yields.
The most extensive work with thyroprotein has been carried out in
England by K. L. Blaxter and his associates. Some of their findings are
given in the accompanying chart.

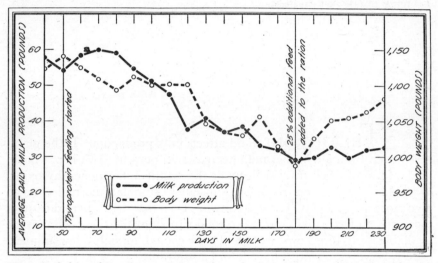

Extra feed favorably affects weight and production of cows getting thyroprotein.

A review of the data collected thus far indicates that on the average
and within narrow limits the response in milk production is proportional
to the quantity of thyroprotein fed. Because of limitations in the animal
itself, naturally this relationship would not hold where one feeds much
larger amounts of thyroprotein than shown in the chart for an extended
period. As a matter of fact, excessive amounts will lower milk production. The amount used must be carefully controlled.

The response of cows to thyroprotein feeding in terms of milk and
fat production appears to vary from cow to cow. Most of these variations we cannot yet explain. Several scientists, however, have found no
response if the material is fed to a fresh cow and none is noted until
lactation begins to decline. Likewise, very little response is evident during the last month or two of lactation; as a matter of fact, thyroprotein may tend to cause a cow to dry up late in the milking period. For
best results, therefore, the thyroprotein should be fed for only the middle 5 or 6 months of the lactation period.

Professor Blaxter and his colleagues suggest that in midlactation the
proportional response goes up as lactation declines, while the greater

the initial yield at the beginning of the feeding the greater the response in pounds per day. It seems likely, therefore, that good producers will generally give greater increases in milk and fat than poor cows. Whether a poor cow can be converted into a good producer merely by feeding thyroprotein is problematical, because the response obtained depends partly on her inherent ability to produce. Furthermore, increases in milk follow increases in the amount fed only within narrow limits.

Although thyroprotein can raise yields of milk and fat markedly, it also can create a condition of hyperthyroidism, with a higher heart rate, respiration rate, and body temperature, and a loss in body weight. These effects are to be expected, because the extra supply of thyroxine taken into the body steps up metabolism, or the rate at which the body of the cow utilizes food nutrients. In other words, she is using up food nutrients and the nutrients stored in her tissues somewhat faster than normal.

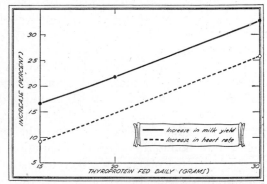

Here are the results obtained by Blaxter and associates on feeding thyroprotein to dairy cows.

We do not know whether these effects will harm the cow's health and reproduction if thyroprotein is fed from lactation to lactation. In the short feeding trials carried on at the various experiment stations, no permanent bad effects have been reported. The Bureau of Dairy Industry has started a long-time trial to learn more about this.

In the short-time tests carried out thus far, it appears that the heart rate increases approximately in proportion to the amount of thyroprotein fed. Similarly, as we have said, milk production increases in proportion to the amount fed. Thus, we may conclude that if a cow responds in milk production to thyroprotein feeding, the heart rate will be increased, and, conversely, if the heart rate is not increased, there will be no increase in production. Observations at Beltsville seem to substantiate this speculation.

Further data collected at Beltsville indicate that the heart rate of cows given thyroprotein is related to the level of feed intake. When the level of thyroprotein feeding is kept constant, the heart rate can be accelerated markedly by increasing the total feed intake 25 to 50 percent. If the high amount of feed is reduced, the heart rate then decreases. Also, after cows have been receiving thyroprotein for 4 to 8 weeks and there has been a considerable loss in body weight, and milk production has declined sharply, the heart rate will also decline. It would appear that the heart rate is governed by the amount of energy the body has available for use, whether from the body tissues or from feed, or both. These observations are preliminary; we are gathering further information on them.

A disturbing factor connected with the increased metabolism is the loss of body weight of cows fed grain at the usual level. Men at various experiment stations report definite losses of body weight where thyroprotein was used; such a loss may be particularly severe in hot climates and in summer.

The following changes appear to take place when thyroprotein is given for extended periods to cows fed at the usual level according to milk production: Milk production is markedly increased at the expense of body weight; after a period of 4 to 8 weeks, depending on the condition of the cow at the start of the feeding period and the amount of stimulation produced, milk production, and heart rate decrease, and when milk production drops to about 10 pounds a day, she will gain weight.

It would also seem probable that, if the cow were not able to make up the losses in body weight before the succeeding lactation started, milk production in the subsequent lactation might be adversely affected.

The English workers have therefore stated that for the best results, thyroprotein should be fed at a level that will raise milk yields about 20 percent, and that for this increase feed intake should be enlarged by about 20 percent. This practice largely eliminated the loss in body weight when thyroprotein was fed at the 15-gram level (one-half ounce). In one experiment these workers incorporated the thyroprotein into a grain mixture, which was cubed. Four pounds of these cubes contained sufficient thyroprotein to produce a 20-percent rise in production and at the same time supplied approximately the extra 20 percent of feed necessary to maintain body weight. The cubes were fed in addition to the regular allowance of grain.

In the Beltsville experiment, where the amount of thyroprotein fed for several months varied from one to one and one-half grams per 100 pounds of body weight, severe losses in body weight were noted. Because of the extremely poor condition of the cows and because it had been planned to continue the feeding of thyroprotein up to the last month of the lactation period, the total feed intake was increased 25 percent by grain feeding. As a result, the condition of the cows improved greatly. They gained weight, and their rapid decline in milk production was halted.

Obviously, if more feed must be fed to maintain body weight and milk production, the question arises as to whether the extra milk will pay for the extra feed. It is hard to give a definite answer on the basis of the data we now have. The Department's Technical Bulletin No. 815 points out that a 20-percent increase in the feed intake of a normally fed cow not receiving thyroprotein will increase milk production about 13 percent.

If by feeding thyroprotein, 20 percent more milk could be produced with 20 percent more feed, that would leave an increase of 7 percent in milk production to pay for the thyroprotein and the extra trouble of feeding it.

A few men have studied the effect of thyroprotein on the composition of milk. One effect we have mentioned: The percentage of fat is raised. Some investigators have noted a slight increase in the percentage of solids not fat, although others have not. J. G. Archibald, at the Massachusetts station, reported a decrease in casein and a roughly proportional increase for lactalbumin and globulin, with no change in total solids, ash, or lactose. Workers at the West Virginia station found that the ascorbic acid content of the milk was lowered to 33 percent below normal. English workers reported a considerable decrease in the phosphatase content.

It will also be necessary to settle the question as to whether sufficient thyroxine is secreted in the milk of cows fed thyroprotein to produce possible harmful effects when the milk is used by humans. Data collected at the Missouri station have shown that when guinea pigs were fed such milk no detectable thyroid effects could be observed, but data on human subjects are needed before this point can be established.

Officials of purebred breed associations express concern over the use of thyroprotein in making records. Such a practice is now banned, because by its use the record would not be an expression of the cow's inherited milk-producing ability. To guard against any possible unscrupulous use of thyroprotein to improve the official records of herds, methods of detection will be needed. Perhaps tests of the phosphatase content of the milk, which drops when thyroprotein is used, might be a tool in detecting the use of thyroprotein. Or, a study of some of the other enzyme systems in milk might be useful in this regard.

It seems doubtful that thyroprotein will ever be mixed into regular dairy grain mixtures, because it should not be fed except during certain periods of the lactation and because of the variation in effects produced in individual cows.

As previously stated, the effect of feeding thyroprotein for several lactation periods on the health and reproduction of cows has not been determined. Experiments are now in progress at Beltsville to answer these questions. Furthermore, when thyroprotein is fed for a long time it appears that extra feed should be fed. The amount of extra feed needed will probably vary with the condition of the cow, the amount of thyroprotein fed, and other factors. Until answers to these questions have been adequately settled, the general use of the material by dairymen is not recommended. If, however, it finally develops that feeding thyroprotein does not shorten the useful life of cows and does not adversely affect reproduction, it seems that this practice could be quite useful for increasing milk and fat production in commercial herds and where milk is sold on a basis of percentage of fat.

THE AUTHORS

L. A. Moore is in charge of the section of Dairy Cattle Nutrition of the Bureau of Dairy Industry. Before joining the Department in 1945 he was successively associated with the dairy departments of Michigan State College and Maryland University. For outstanding research relating to the nutrition of dairy cows, Dr. Moore in 1943 received the Borden Award.

J. F. Sykes is a physiologist with the Bureau of Dairy Industry specializing on problems of reproduction and lactation in dairy cattle. Dr. Sykes is a graduate of the University of Toronto and has been research associate in the physiology department of Michigan State College.

FOR FURTHER READING

Archibald, J. G.: *Some Effects of Thyroprotein on the Composition of Milk,* Journal of Dairy Science, volume 28, pages 941–947, 1945.

Blaxter, K. L.: *The Effect of Iodinated Protein Feeding on the Lactating Cow,* Journal of Endocrinology, volume 4, pages 237–265, 266–299, 1945.

Graham, W. R., Jr.: *The Effect of Thyroidectomy and Thyroid Feeding on the Milk Secretion and Milk Fat Production of Cows,* Journal of Nutrition, volume 7, pages 407–429, 1934.

Reece, R. P.: *The Influence of a Synthetic Thyroprotein When Fed to Dairy Cows Over a Three-Week Period,* Journal of Dairy Science, volume 27, pages 545–550, 1944.

Reineke, E. P., and Turner, C. W.: *Formation in Vitro of Highly Active Thyroproteins, Their Biologic Assay and Practical Use,* Missouri Research Bulletin 355, 1942.

Reineke, E. P., and Turner, C. W.: *Increased Milk and Milk Fat Production Following the Feeding of Artificially Formed Thyroprotein (Thyro-Lactin),* Journal of Dairy Science, volume 25, pages 393–400, 1942.

Reineke, E. P., and Turner, C. W.: *Nonpermeability of the Mammary Gland to Thyroid Hormone,* Journal of Dairy Science, volume 27, pages 793–805, 1944.

Seath, D. M., Branton, C., and Groth, A. H.: *Effect of Feeding Iodinated Casein on Production and Health of Milking Cows,* Journal of Dairy Science, volume 28, pages 509–517, 1945.

Spielman, A. A., Petersen, W. E., and Fitch, J. B.: *The Effect of Thyroidectomy on Lactation in the Bovine,* Journal of Dairy Science, volume 27, pages 441–448, 1944.

Van Landingham, A. H., Henderson, H. O., and Weakley, C. W., Jr.: *The Effect of Iodinated Casein (Protamone) on Milk and Butterfat Production and on the Ascorbic Acid Content of the Milk,* Journal of Dairy Science, volume 27, pages 385–396, 1944.

ALSO, IN THIS BOOK

What To Feed a Cow, by R. E. Hodgson and W. J. Sweetman, page 149.
Vitamin A for Dairy Cattle, by L. A. Moore, H. T. Converse, and S. R. Hall, page 133.
New Ideas in Feeding, by N. R. Ellis, page 95.

Artificial Breeding

by RALPH W. PHILLIPS

A BULL can cover 30 to 50 cows a year under average conditions. Each time he spends millions of sperms, any of which could fertilize an egg and beget a calf. To correct such profligacy of nature, careless with the individual however concerned she may be with the species, man has developed a technique called artificial insemination, whereby semen is obtained from the male, diluted considerably, and a part of it placed manually in the cervix or uterus of the female. Thus a bull can impregnate 500 or 1,000 cows a year, or even more in special circumstances. The usefulness of good bulls and other males is multiplied manifold. There is less chance of spreading disease. The semen of valuable males can still be utilized even when they become too big or too old for natural service.

Animal breeders in the United States became actively interested in the technique a decade or so ago, although actually it is much older. The Italian scientist Lazaro Spallanzani in 1780 artificially inseminated a bitch to show that semen alone was sufficient to start normal pregnancy. The Russian Professor Elie Ivanov in 1919, after 20 years of preliminary work, set up the Central Experimental Breeding Station in Moscow to further the method.

At first some failures resulted in the United States from improper handling of semen, mismanagement of bulls, and inadequate financing of associations, but the work was successful generally, and it has become well established. In 1939, six associations of dairy cattle breeders used artificial insemination; they had 646 members who owned 33 bulls and 7,539 cows. In 1946, there were 336 associations, with 73,293 members in 29 States. These members owned 579,477 cows and were using 900 bulls. The leaders were Wisconsin, Pennsylvania, Ohio, New York, and Iowa. Another

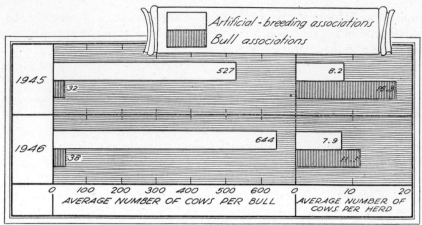

This chart, based on Dairy Herd Association data, shows how much artificial breeding can extend the use of good bulls over natural-mating bull associations.

interesting comparison: In 1946, cooperative bull associations and bull studs in which natural mating is practiced had an average of 11.1 cows to a herd and 38 cows to a bull; artificial-breeding associations had 7.9 cows to a herd and 644 cows to a bull.

Artificial insemination is used mostly among dairy cattle. An example of its use with beef cattle is in the purebred Hereford herd of the Apache tribe of San Carlos, Ariz. The herd comprises about 1,000 cows, which are kept in a pasture of approximately 10,000 acres. Bulls are kept at a central plant near one of two watering places. The plant has a laboratory, four corrals, a feed barn, and breeding and semen collection chutes, built especially to handle range cattle. Cowboys check cows for estrus, and the cows in heat are brought to the central plant, or to a subsidiary set of corrals and breeding chute about 5 miles from the central plant, where they are inseminated.

Horses and sheep also are bred artificially to some extent, primarily to meet the needs of individual breeders or experiment stations. Little use is made of the technique with goats and swine. Poultrymen employ it in experimental crossing and in studies that require controlled conditions of insemination. It is useful where birds are kept in individual laying cages, but commercial breeders find its cost is relatively high compared to the cost of roosters. Breeders of broad-breasted turkeys use it to maintain fertility, because many broad-breasted males are clumsy and unable to mate efficiently. Such use is of doubtful value, however, for breeding stock from flocks developed with the aid of artificial insemination may go to flocks where natural mating is the only economical procedure. Males that cannot give satisfactory service under these conditions are of little value.

Most artificial-breeding associations in the United States started as individual units, each having its own staff and bulls and operating in a small area. More recently, a trend began toward the more efficient federated type of organization, which functions in a larger area, such as a State or a part of a State.

Usually, a number of local organizations combine to form a federated organization, and members of the local groups belong to the central association that owns or leases the barn, laboratory, and all bulls, which are kept at the central barn. Semen is mailed or shipped to the local associations. The local associations usually employ their own technicians, manage local procedures, and elect directors of the central organization. The work is financed by an equitable division of income between the central and local associations. The local associations may be incorporated as affiliates or subsidiaries of the central association. After a central association is formed, local associations can become affiliated with it.

New Methods of Handling Semen

Investigations into the physiology of spermatozoa stand at the peak of the new research related to artificial breeding.

In the operation of breeding associations, it is usually necessary to ship semen some distance, and it was difficult to maintain it at a temperature of about 40° F. A simple method has been developed that is satisfactory for use within the radius in which most federated associations operate. The semen is sealed in a test tube with cork and paraffin, and labeled as to name and other identification of the sire, when the semen was drawn, its sperm count, rate of dilution, and any other pertinent information. Three thicknesses of heavy paper are placed around the test tube. The package is then wrapped, together with a container of ice, in an insulated paper blanket and placed in a corrugated cardboard box or carton. The box is securely sealed or tied and addressed, ready for shipment. If semen is to be in transit more than 12 hours, a second container of ice (which is a rubber toy balloon or a pint can) is added to the package.

Some of our most important new knowledge about the subject comes from several research workers at Cornell University, New York—G. W. Salisbury, Irvine Elliott, N. L. Van Demark, E. L. Willett, J. A. Zelaya, E. Mercier, and others. One of the problems they tackled was the extent to which semen can be diluted, thereby increasing the number of females upon which one ejaculate can be used. They studied bull semen diluted at the rate of 1 part to 8, 12, 16, 24, and 50 parts of yolk-citrate diluter. The average numbers of spermatozoa contained in 1 cubic centimeter were 150, 104, 80, 54, and 26 millions for the respective dilution rates. Results obtained in the use of this semen on large numbers of animals indicated that there were no statistically significant differences in the fertility of the semen diluted at these five rates.

H. H. Habibullin found that successful insemination resulted from

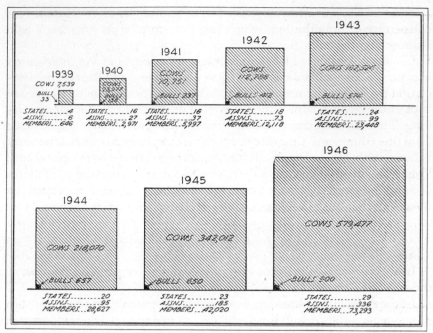

From 1939 to 1946 the number of dairy cows bred through artificial breeding associations went from 7,539 to 579,477. Above data are for January 1 of each year.

doses of 0.025 cc. of ram semen containing 80,000,000 spermatozoa. Seventy-five percent of the ewes became pregnant, compared to 78.2 percent in ewes receiving 0.05 cc. of semen containing 160,000,000 spermatozoa. Experiments with goats showed that doses of 0.05 and 0.025 cc. of semen stored for 6 hours before insemination were enough to insure a normal number of conceptions. (A cubic centimeter is about a thimbleful.)

Egg yolk is an important constituent of both egg-yolk-phosphate and egg-yolk-citrate diluters. Dennis T. Mayer and John F. Lasley, during research at the University of Missouri, isolated an active resistance factor from egg yolk that gives a water-clear solution in phosphate buffer and that has proved more effective than the original egg-yolk-buffer mixture in increasing the resistance of spermatozoa to adverse conditions. A. H. Frank, C. A. Smith, and A. Eichhorn, of the Bureau of Animal Industry, described promising results with a diluter manufactured from chick embryos for bull semen. Still other tests have been made by workers at Cornell University in which yolk citrate, incubated egg, and chick embryo were compared. In an experiment in which semen of better than average quality was used, no differences were observed in livability of the spermatozoa. When semen of somewhat poorer quality was used, a slight difference in favor of the chick-embryo diluting agent was noted, compared to the yolk-citrate diluter.

The addition of 58 to 116 milligrams of glucose per 100 cc. of bovine semen, diluted at the rate of one part of semen to four parts of yolk-citrate diluter and incubated for 1 hour at 46.5° C., or stored for 10 days at 5° C., results in increased livability, according to workers at Cornell.

Studies made by V. K. Milovanov to determine the possibility of storing semen under anaerobic conditions show that under these conditions— that is, the absence of oxygen—spermatozoa retained motility and fertilizing capacity for long periods. To preserve bull and ram spermatozoa outside the body, he recommended that inert gas, hydrogen or nitrogen, be blown through the undiluted semen, after which it should be sealed in small capsules and cooled.

How to evaluate semen accurately perplexes all who work with artificial insemination. Various methods are used. One way is to count cells to determine the concentration of sperms. Others are to score their motility, and to take into account the proportion of abnormal cells. Direct and indirect measures are made of the rate that the semen uses up oxygen.

Some associations use the methylene-blue reduction test routinely to test the quality of semen. In studies at Cornell, 116 ejaculates from 39 bulls were used; significant relationships were reported between the reduction time in fresh samples and semen volume, sperm concentration, motility, and lactic acid content. For routine prediction of semen quality, the Cornell workers recommend the use of the test, plus counts of spermatozoa and estimates of motility on fresh samples.

Various workers have determined the proportion of abnormal spermatozoa in semen as one way to check on fertilizing capacity. It has been customary to observe 300 to 500 cells per sample. Salisbury and Mercier believe that it is just as reliable to observe 100 cells as to make two slides and examine 500 cells on each.

A staining method to differentiate between live and dead ram spermatozoa is described by John F. Lasley, G. T. Easley, and F. F. McKenzie, on the basis of work at Missouri. An opal-blue stain is used, and the results indicate that dead or dying spermatozoa are stained, while active and potentially active sperm do not take the stain.

Three scientists at New Jersey, S. Margolin, J. W. Bartlett, and O. L. Lepard, studied the possibility of determining semen quality by observing its longevity. They diluted samples of semen with the egg-yolk-phosphate buffer. A portion was placed in a refrigerator at 45° F. and estimates of motility were made at 24-hour intervals until motion ceased. The remainder of each sample was used in insemination. The men observed significant positive correlations between longevity and the conception rate in six of the eight bulls they studied. In the other two, they found negative relations that they considered of no significance.

We have also learned much more about the equipment used for semen collection. L. V. Panyseva and T. M. Kozenko, of the Soviet Union, found that the artificial vagina for bulls, shortened to 15.8 inches, is best suited for medium-sized boars. The ordinary vagina for bulls can be used only for very large boars. They also found that pulsation of the artificial vagina when the semen was being drawn has no effect on the quantity and quality of semen.

An artificial vagina has been designed at Cornell for use with bulls to avoid subjecting the semen to too sudden a change in temperature. It is useful particularly in cold weather. The device has a water jacket made like the conventional artificial vagina, but has also a second inner lining of tubing. The tube is tapered at one end by cutting out a V-shaped piece and cementing the cut edges together with rubber cement, leaving an opening at the end small enough to hold the open end of the test tube. In cementing the edges, a small hole is left at the apex of the V-shaped cut to allow the escape of air when the bull thrusts his penis into the artificial vagina. The need for the small hole is questionable, however, because vaginas both with and without the opening have been used successfully. The large end of the inner lining is doubled back over the end of the water jacket. Water is poured through a hole in the outer hose located near enough to the end to be covered by the rubber tubing when doubled back. This device is used in the same way as the artificial vagina in common use. It is somewhat bulky to handle and requires a little more skill in its manipulation than the older model.

Waxed paper or cellophane capsules are being used extensively in Denmark and Russia for packaging semen. Each capsule contains one dose, and a gun of the type developed by Eduard Sörensen of Denmark is used for pushing the semen directly from the capsule into the cervix. This eliminates the use of glassware in storage and during insemination, and the procedure appears to be yielding satisfactory results.

Most artificial breeding associations maintain two or more bulls. These bulls may vary considerably in breeding merit, and a problem arises concerning the amount to charge for semen from each bull. Bartlett and E. J. Perry proposed a plan for charges based on performance of proved bulls and performance of ancestors of unproved bulls. Under this plan a basic charge is made per service from unproved bulls and a higher basic charge per service from proved bulls. Besides the basic rate, a charge is made on the basis of the production records of daughters of proved bulls. For unproved bulls, the basic rate is increased annually up to 5 years of age, and in addition a charge is made in accordance with the productivity of relatives of the bull, including dam, sisters, and half-sisters. Records are considered in relation to the breed average.

The possibilities of controlling certain diseases by using artificial insemination have been investigated. After experience with 12 herds in Missouri, H. A. Herman, E. R. Berousek, and E. W. Swanson suggested that artificial insemination can control vaginitis and trichomoniasis, besides reducing the number of repeated services, and the intervals between calving. Workers in Peru have encountered considerable difficulty with low fertility and sterility in rams at high altitudes. C. Monge and M. San Martin studied the semen of two rams imported from Chile to Peru and placed at 10,500 feet elevation. Both lacked spermatozoa at first. In one ram spermatozoa appeared later, and the pH (roughly, the degree of acidity), sperm concentration, and motility approached normal values. The semen of the other ram contained no spermatozoa after 5 months, but the animal at no time suffered any decrease in sexual drive. San Martin and J. Atkins compared the semen of imported rams kept at an altitude of 14,750 feet in Peru and of their offspring, with rams kept at sea level. Only 15 of the 58 rams studied at high altitudes had semen with optimal biological properties. Samples of semen showed a wider variation of pH, increased leucocytes and epithelial cells, decreased motility and viability, and the appearance of more juvenile forms, compared to that of rams kept at sea level. Of 59 ewes that supposedly were infertile at high altitudes, 51 became pregnant when they were artificially inseminated with semen of good quality. These workers concluded that reduced fertility at high altitudes is due to abnormalities in semen.

Similarly, F. Accame, Luis Monge, and J. C. Miller studied the effects of reduced barometric pressure on the semen of rams. No injurious effects of low pressure could be detected and the workers concluded that at high altitude fertility was impaired otherwise than by direct effects on the sperms.

L. Hansen Larsen and Eduard Sörensen conducted a series of experiments in Denmark to determine the importance of the amount and kind of protein in the diets of bulls. They concluded that the content of digestible protein in the ration regulates semen production. In all their experiments, a high content of digestible protein resulted in an improvement in the fertilizing capacity of semen. They could not determine, however, whether animal protein was more effective than plant protein. In this work the amount of digestible protein fed daily per animal ranged from 538 to 1,230 grams. The fertilizing capacity of the semen was evaluated by measuring the dehydrogenation activity of the spermatozoa, using the methylene-blue test.

The effect of size of dose has been studied by two Russians. I. I. Sokolovskaja and M. J. Solovei gave doses of semen containing varying numbers of spermatozoa to 12 Angora rabbits. Each produced 3 litters as a result of artificial insemination and a fourth litter from natural mating. These workers report that apparently normal results were obtained when the amount of semen contained 100,000 to 100,000,000 spermatozoa, but more or fewer sperms than that lowered the rate of conception and increased abortion. Solovei inseminated 4 female rabbits with 25,000 to 50,000 spermatozoa, but the does aborted or delivered young that were weak or dead. Two rabbits that for comparison received 500 million spermatozoa each produced normal litters. This dosage is considerably higher than the one that Sokolovskaja and Solovei report as giving normal results. Solovei also worked with swine. Seven sows were inseminated with 10,000 million or 20,000 million spermatozoa, and only two conceived. Five control sows received 70,000 million or 120,000 million sperms, and all conceived. These results are based on limited numbers and may be explained by factors other than those under investigation.

V. K. Milovanov reported great differences in the quality of offspring from female rabbits inseminated with semen that had been stored at 12°–18° C. under aerobic and anaerobic conditions—that is, with and without oxygen. In the latter group, 7.2 young were born in a litter, compared to 3.2 in the aerobic group and 8.0 in natural matings. Half of the young of the anaerobic group died in the first 4 months, but only 1 out of 13 young died in the aerobic group. Among the control animals, one-fourth died.

Solovei inseminated five groups of rabbits—which ovulate after copulation—10, 20, 25, 30, and 40 hours before ovulation. Half were killed and dissected at different times during pregnancy; the others went to term. In the first group, inseminated at 10 hours, all became pregnant and all the females that went to term produced seven to nine healthy young. In the second group, one female was barren, one had seven normal young, and the others had weak or dying offspring, or a reduced number of degenerating embryos. Similar results were obtained in the third group. Only two of the fourth group were pregnant and only two degenerating fetuses were found in one of them. None in the fifth group was pregnant.

The results summarized in the four preceding paragraphs were based on limited numbers and obviously need to be checked in further experiments on larger numbers of animals. They do indicate, however, the possibility that improper manipulation of semen may result in defective offspring and hence the need for very careful experimental work before drawing conclusions.

The Place of Artificial Insemination

What economic consequences can we expect from the expanding use of artificial insemination with dairy cattle? One result surely will be a reduction in the number of bulls on farms and correspondingly more cows on the farms where bulls are no longer required. Improved feeding and management practices will come through better keeping of records and contacts with technicians and other farmers. The health and fertility of animals should improve, along with the genetic make-up of herds. Regional specialization in the raising of dairy heifers is likely to be stimulated. There may be a tendency for a larger proportion of producers in deficit feed areas to buy replacements from areas where feed supplies are abundant, and buyers should be able to purchase heifers in carload lots from artificial breeding associations.

The various advantages of artificial insemination over natural mating, mentioned often enough, lead some persons here and abroad to be too enthusiastic about its use. But it cannot be said too often that the primary purpose of the technique is to speed up the rate of livestock improvement. To accomplish this, farmers must use sires that are genetically superior to the females to which they are to be bred.

Another point: These superior bulls must be used in a breeding program adapted to the farmer's locality. That means that adaptability must be considered when the technique is used in areas where the environment imposes limitations on livestock production. Sires well suited for use in New York or Wisconsin, for example, may not be adapted to use in some other areas where climate and feed supplies limit production. We have heard much discussion about possibilities of using artificial insemination to introduce improved stock quickly and on a large scale in countries or areas where the existing animals are relatively unproductive. If the animals are unproductive because of conditions imposed by nature, the widespread introduction of improved stock from more favorable environments may be a hazardous undertaking. Animals resulting from the first cross between improved stock and animals containing somewhat larger proportions of improved blood often perform satisfactorily under these conditions, while higher grade animals do not.

Any large-scale program involving the introduction of new types into areas of rigorous environment, employing either artificial or natural mating, should be based on experimental work designed to determine the amount of improved blood that may be safely introduced and the method of breeding best suited to those conditions.

THE AUTHOR

Ralph W. Phillips, who was formerly in charge of genetics investigations in the Bureau of Animal Industry, is now on the staff of the Food and Agriculture Organization of the United Nations.

FOR FURTHER READING

Anderson, James: *The Semen of Animals and Its Use for Artificial Insemination,* Published by Imperial Bureau of Animal Genetics, Edinburgh, Scotland, 1945.

Bartlett, J. W., and Perry, E. J.: *Rental Rate Plan for Bulls Used in Artificial Insemination,* Journal of Animal Science, volume 3, pages 283–286, 1944.

Beck, G. H., and Salisbury, G. W.: *Rapid Methods for Estimating the Quality of Bull Semen,* Journal of Dairy Science, volume 26, pages 483–494, 1943.

Dowell, A. A., and Winters, L. M.: *Economic Aspects of Artificial Insemination of Commercial Dairy Cows,* Journal of Farm Economics, volume 24, pages 665–676, 1942.

Frank, A. H., Smith, C. A., and Eichhorn, A.: *Preliminary Report on Prolonging the Viability of Spermatozoa in Vitro,* Journal American Veterinary Medical Association, volume 99, pages 287–288, 1941.

Herman, H. A., Berousek, E. R., and Swanson, E. W.: *Artificial Breeding as a Means of Controlling Genital Infections in the Dairy Herd,* Journal of Dairy Science, volume 26, pages 755–756, 1943.

Lasley, John F., and Bogart, Ralph: *Some Factors Influencing Reproductive Efficiency of Range Cattle Under Artificial and Natural Breeding Conditions,* Missouri Agricultural Experiment Station, Research Bulletin 376, 1943.

Lasley, John F., Easley, G. T., and McKenzie, F. F.: *A Staining Method for the Differentiation of Live and Dead Spermatozoa,* Anatomical Record, volume 82, pages 167–174, 1942.

MacLeod, John: *An Analysis in Human Semen of a Staining Method for Differentiating Live and Dead Spermatozoa,* Anatomical Record, volume 83, pages 573–578, 1942.

Margolin, S., Bartlett, J. W., and Lepard, O. L.: *The Relation of Longevity to Fertility of Bull Semen,* Journal of Dairy Science, volume 26, pages 983–985, 1943.

Mayer, Dennis T., and Lasley, John F.: *The Factor in Egg Yolk Affecting the Resistance, Storage Potentialities, and Fertilizing Capacity of Mammalian Spermatozoa,* Journal of Animal Science, volume 4, pages 261–269, 1945.

Phillips, P. H., and Lardy, H. A.: *A Yolk-Buffer Pabulum for the Preservation of Bull Semen,* Journal of Dairy Science, volume 23, page 399, 1940.

Salisbury, G. S., Elliott, Irvine, and Van Demark, N. L.: *Further Studies of the Effect of Dilution on the Fertility of Bull Semen Used for Artificial Insemination,* Journal of Dairy Science, volume 28, pages 233–241, 1945.

Salisbury, G. W., and Mercier, E.: *The Reliability of Estimates of the Proportion of Morphologically Abnormal Spermatozoa in Bull Semen,* Journal of Animal Science, volume 4, pages 174–178, 1945.

Salisbury, G. W., and Willett, E. L.: *An Artificial Vagina for Controlled Temperature Studies of Bull Semen,* The Cornell Veterinarian, volume 30, pages 25–29, 1940.

Salisbury, G. W., Zelaya, J. A., and Van Demark, N. L.: *Livability and Glycolysis of Bovine Spermatozoa in Yolk-Citrate, Incubated Eggs or Chick-Embryo Diluters,* Journal of Animal Science, volume 4, pages 270–276, 1945.

Sörensen, Eduard: *Insemination with Gelatinized Sperm in Paraffined Cellophane Tubes,* The Veterinary Journal, volume 102, pages 235–237, 1946.

ALSO, IN THIS BOOK

Hormones in Reproduction

by S. R. HALL and J. F. SYKES

NORMAL reproduction and lactation in domestic animals are regulated by hormones, a group of chemical materials that are secreted by the ductless or endocrine glands directly into the blood stream. The blood carries these chemical messengers to the parts of the body where they produce their effects.

Of the endocrine glands, the pituitary is the most important. In the cow it is about the size of an acorn and is located at the base of the brain. It has two main parts, the anterior and posterior pituitary. It is complex, the anterior portion secreting at least six hormones that affect sexual development and lactation; the posterior part secretes another hormone. The pituitary regulates the activity of the other endocrine glands. The ovary—an endocrine gland—secretes the female sex hormones, estrogen and progesterone. It also produces the egg, or ovum, that, when fertilized, develops into a new individual. The testis manufactures the sperm and the male sex hormone, testosterone. From the adrenal gland arises the adrenal cortical hormones. The thyroid secretes the hormone thyroxine.

A great deal of work has been done in recent years to determine the fundamental action of the hormones and to apply the findings to practical problems on the farm.

There are also synthetic—that is, laboratory-made—hormones. Two substances, known as diethylstilbestrol (or stilbestrol) and hexestrol and some of their derivatives, while not related chemically to estrogen, have the same general effect but are several times more potent. They are also much cheaper than natural estrogen and have been used to replace estrogen for several purposes. A material containing the thyroid hormone, thyroxine, has also been produced by adding iodine to casein under

123

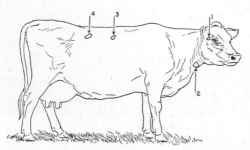

The endocrine glands of a cow: 1. Pituitary; 2. thyroid; 3. adrenal; and 4. the ovary.

controlled conditions. That material, usually called thyroprotein, is several times more active than dried thyroid gland and is cheaper to produce.

The growth of the ovaries and testes and their function after maturity is reached are determined by the secretion of the gonad-stimulating hormones from the anterior pituitary gland and by the interaction of those hormones with hormones produced by the ovary and testis. Successful pregnancy is also largely a result of hormone activity.

If the pituitary gland is removed from very young animals, the ovaries and testes fail to develop to normal size and do not produce eggs or sperm. If the glands are removed from mature animals that are producing eggs or sperm, those functions cease, and the ovaries and testes degenerate. Such effects may be prevented by injecting the gonad-stimulating hormones, FSH and LH, into the animals.

It is now known that the follicle-stimulating hormone (FSH), produced by the pituitary gland, is necessary for the formation of eggs in the ovary and for the production of sperm in the testis. It also stimulates the ovary to produce the female sex hormone, estrogen.

Glands and hormones affecting reproduction and lactation in domestic animals

Gland	Hormone	Function
Pituitary gland:		
	1. Follicle-stimulating hormone.	(FSH—gonad-stimulating hormone.)
	2. Luteinizing hormone....	(LH—gonad-stimulating hormone.)
	3. Prolactin, or lactogenic, hormone.	(Milk-secretion hormone.)
Anterior portion.....	4. Adrenotropic hormone...	(Adrenal-stimulating hormone.)
	5. Thyrotropic hormone....	(Thyroid-stimulating hormone.)
	6. Growth hormone.	
Posterior portion....	1. Oxytocin, or pitocin.....	("Let down" hormone.)
Ovary................	1. Estrogen..............	(Female sex hormone.)
	2. Progesterone..........	(Corpus luteum hormone.)
Testis................	1. Testosterone..........	(Male sex hormone—also called androgen.)
Adrenal cortex........	1. Adrenal cortical hormone.	
Thyroid..............	Thyroxine..............	(Thyroid hormone.)

The luteinizing hormone (LH), acting with the follicle-stimulating hormone (FSH), causes the follicle, which contains the egg, to rupture at the heat period and release the egg. It is also necessary for the growth of the corpus luteum, or yellow body, which forms after ovulation. Prolactin causes this structure to secrete progesterone. LH also stimulates certain cells in the testis to produce the male sex hormone, testosterone. Thus the production of eggs and sperm and the secretion of the male sex hormones are controlled by secretions of the anterior pituitary gland.

Both the male and female sex hormones produce marked effects on the reproductive organs and on the reproductive behavior of animals.

Estrogen causes the external signs of heat and is responsible for the female sex characters. It also produces changes in the lining of the uterus, which partly prepare it for pregnancy.

Progesterone, which is produced when the yellow body is present, further increases the changes in the uterus that were started by the estrogen, and it is by this combined action of estrogen and progesterone that the uterus is maintained in a highly active state during pregnancy so that the fetus can be nourished. Abortion usually occurs if the yellow body is removed during pregnancy.

The male sex hormone is similarly responsible for the male sex characters and for the sex urge. The seminal vesicles and the prostate gland, which produce fluids that combine with the sperm to form semen, are maintained in working condition under the influence of the male sex hormone.

In the nonpregnant female the secretion of the sex and pituitary hormones occurs in cycles rather than continuously, as is the case with the hormones concerned in reproductive processes in the male. The secretions occur in a regular order and in varying amounts in such a way that heat and ovulation occur at precise intervals. The regularity of this sequence is determined by the interaction of the sex and pituitary hormones with each other.

For instance, when estrogen is produced by the ovary under the stimulus of the follicle-stimulating hormone, its concentration in the blood increases to the point where it can keep the pituitary from secreting FSH. The amount of estrogen that prevents the release of the follicle-stimulating hormone by the pituitary, on the other hand, stimulates the pituitary to produce the luteinizing hormone, which, together with FSH, causes ovulation and growth of the yellow body. If enough estrogen is not present to cause release of LH, ovulation will not occur even though heat may be exhibited, and the animal cannot possibly conceive even though she usually accepts service to the male. When the yellow body is present and is producing progesterone, this latter hormone also affects the pituitary gland and prevents it from secreting LH in a manner similar to the way in which estrogen affects FSH. The whole cyclic nature and the normalcy of reproduction therefore depend on a delicate balance in the amounts of these hormones that are secreted at various times.

Success in treating reproductive disorders depends on recognition of this fact. Treatments that upset this balance are almost always failures.

During pregnancy much larger amounts of certain hormones may be produced than at other times. The extra hormones are not formed in the pituitary gland or the ovary but in the structures associated with the developing fetus. In all species studied, large amounts of estrogen appear in the blood and urine. That is particularly true of mares, whose urine, therefore, is the usual commercial source of estrogen.

Progesterone likewise increases during pregnancy. The blood of mares also contains very large amounts of hormones that have an action similar to the gonad-stimulating hormones of the pituitary gland. Mares can be bled several times during pregnancy, and the serum containing the hormones is processed by several companies and sold as pregnant-mare serum (PMS), which is used to treat sterility. A woman during pregnancy likewise secretes in her urine a hormone similar to the luteinizing hormone of the pituitary gland. This hormone is generally known as chorionic gonadotropin. It is sold under various trade names.

Hormones and the Treatment of Sterility

Treating sterility with hormones is not always successful. Failure is due sometimes to the fact that the exact amounts of the various hormones necessary for normal reproduction are not known, and the use of hormones has of necessity been largely on a trial and error basis. Some conditions are benefited, however, by treatment with appropriate hormones.

In males that fail to produce sperm in normal amounts or in females that fail to come in heat, the use of pituitary hormones is helpful. Pregnant-mare serum has been commonly used for such conditions. Most cows will come in heat after a 1,500-unit dose, and many will conceive. Similar doses given at intervals to bulls often increase the production of sperm. The treatment seems to be most successful with younger bulls. It is very difficult to restore sperm production in aged bulls, and in most cases no responses are obtainable with any treatment now available. Stilbestrol also has been used often to bring cows in heat. It is rare to have cows so treated conceive at such artificially induced heat periods, but after heat has thus been brought on once, some will show heat at regular intervals without further treatment.

Pregnant-mare serum has been used widely in attempts to induce out-of-season estrus and ovulation in animals, such as sheep and goats, that normally do not breed in the spring and summer. Efforts in this direction have met with some success, and out-of-season pregnancies and normal births have resulted. Uniformly good results, however, have not been obtained, an indication that not all the factors involved are clearly understood. The successful discharge and fertilization of several eggs from the ovary, followed by multiple births, have occurred as a result of hormone treatment in cows, mares, and ewes.

Some females show regular heat periods, usually of reduced intensity, but still do not settle. Young females exhibit this behavior oftener than older females. These animals develop follicles and eggs, but the follicle fails to rupture and release the egg so that it may be fertilized. Treatment with stilbestrol or chorionic gonadotropin containing luteinizing hormone is useful in such cases, because LH is apparently not produced in sufficient quantity to cause ovulation. Stilbestrol, an estrogen, stimulates the pituitary to release LH. Both materials have given successful results in many instances. In one experiment conducted with cows, chorionic gonadotropin was effective in 50 percent of the cases. Successful use of these hormones will depend on proper timing of the dose. A mature follicle—one that is ready to rupture—must be present at time of treatment and the hormones, therefore, should be given 2 to 3 days before the heat period is due.

Nymphomania, or constant heat, is another condition that is associated with sterility in many females. Multiple follicles or cysts of large size appear on the ovaries and produce sufficient estrogen to cause constant estrus. Even though these animals may be bred daily, they fail to conceive. The defect seems to be that there is too much follicle-stimulating hormone and too little luteinizing hormone. Workers at the Wisconsin Agricultural Research Station have found that, by injecting small amounts of a crude pituitary preparation into the blood of cows, they can correct the troublesome condition in a high proportion of cases. Research at the University of Pennsylvania has shown that similar good results can be obtained by injecting large doses of chorionic gonadotropin into the muscles. Our own results with a few cases are encouraging.

Lack of sexual desire in the male is often a troublesome condition in animals that are otherwise completely fertile. Two materials have been used in efforts to overcome the condition. The male sex hormone, testosterone, is often of definite benefit in such cases. The feeding of substances containing thyroxine may also be helpful.

The use of the hormones we have mentioned seldom brings lasting results. Often the treatment has to be repeated. One may well question the desirability of perpetuating such abnormal animals, as their offspring might suffer similar defects. But with certain valuable individuals and in emergencies where maximum livestock production is wanted, this kind of treatment may have its uses.

Both female sex hormones, estrogen and progesterone, influence the growth of the udder. Estrogen is responsible for the development of the tubular structures, the ducts and cisterns of the udder. These tubes branch out from the teat canal and hold the milk as it is secreted into the udder. Progesterone causes the development of the cells within the udder that actually secrete milk, and is not concerned with tubular development.

Little, if any, of the two hormones is produced until sexual maturity is reached, that is, until heat periods appear; no decided udder growth occurs until that time. After puberty, the female sex hormones are produced in greater quantity and there is a gradual growth of the udder until the first pregnancy occurs. During pregnancy, estrogen and progesterone are secreted in still larger amounts. Udder growth, therefore, proceeds much more rapidly and by mid-pregnancy all the structures that are destined to function in the first lactation are probably present. The apparent growth of the udder that occurs from this time on is apparently largely due to enlargement of cells already present and to accumulations of secretions.

Secretions from the pituitary gland also participate in the growth of the mammary gland. If the pituitary gland is removed from experimental animals, estrogen and progesterone produce very little mammary gland growth. However, if extracts of the anterior pituitary gland or if pure anterior pituitary hormones are given together with estrogen and progesterone to such animals, essentially normal growth is obtained. The anterior pituitary hormones that have been shown to be involved in mammary-gland growth include prolactin, the adrenal-stimulating hormone and possibly the thyroid-stimulating and growth hormones. Whether there are additional specific mammary-stimulating hormones (mammogens) produced by the pituitary gland is a disputed question.

The Initiation and Maintenance of Lactation

In general, the same anterior pituitary hormones that affect udder growth are concerned in milk secretion. If the pituitary gland is removed from pregnant animals, lactation does not commence when the young are born unless extracts or hormones from the pituitary gland are injected. This indicates that the pituitary hormones are necessary for the initiation of lactation. Prolactin is one of the hormones involved, but is not in itself capable of initiating lactation. The simultaneous administration of prolactin and adrenotropic hormone, however, is effective and it is possible that other pituitary hormones may also be involved.

The factors or hormone relationships that are responsible for the apparent sudden release of these hormones when pregnancy terminates are not fully known. It appears that the relative amounts of estrogen and progesterone present at that time are important in this regulation, because it has been shown that estrogen, at least, may alter the prolactin content of the pituitary gland. A solution of the interrelationship between estrogen and progesterone and the pituitary hormones as they occur before and after birth of the young may eventually be of considerable importance to the whole problem of the initiation of lactation.

Once lactation is established, the same group of hormones that are necessary for the initiation of lactation are responsible for its maintenance. Prolactin by itself cannot stimulate established lactation to any great extent. Other pituitary hormones when given singly are similarly incapable of markedly improving lactation, but if these hormones are given as a mixture substantial increases in milk yield can be obtained, particularly in the declining phase of lactation. In addition to the pituitary hormones, the synthetic estrogens and thyroxine, or materials containing thyroxine, will increase milk yield when given in suitable amounts.

The Use of Hormones to Stimulate Lactation

Several investigators have shown that it is possible to grow mammary glands and induce lactation in goats and cows by the use of hormones even though these animals were not pregnant. The synthetic estrogens, stilbestrol and hexestrol, have been most commonly used for this purpose. In virgin goats and heifers and in animals from which the ovaries have been removed, reasonably good udder growth and lactation, yielding up to 30 pounds of milk a day in cattle, has been obtained by implantation of these materials under the skin. Dry cows and freemartins do not respond so well to similar treatment and indeed the results are always quite variable. Several English workers have shown that the addition of pituitary extracts may in some instances improve the performance of estrogen in this regard.

Excessive amounts of stilbestrol or hexestrol will, however, lower or stop lactation, and the dosage necessary for best results must be carefully adjusted. While such animals are under treatment they are continuously in heat and may have to be segregated from other cattle; the English investigators found a high incidence of broken pelvises due to persistent mounting. Even though these animals are in heat they are sterile, and may remain so for long periods after treatment is stopped. We do not recommend the use of stilbestrol or hexestrol as a general practice, although it can be useful in salvaging some production from sterile cows.

Scientists have also investigated the use of anterior pituitary extracts for increasing lactation. Extracts containing a mixture of pituitary hormones will increase lactation when otherwise the cow would be drying up. The extracts must be injected frequently, however, and the cost and scarcity of suitable materials make the use of such extracts impractical. Through further research, however, we may find some cheap, practical means of stimulating the glands of cattle to produce hormones in increased quantities, and thus enable dairymen to increase production. Stilbestrol and hexestrol apparently partly exert their effects in this manner, and other similarly acting materials may be discovered.

When milk is secreted by the cells of the mammary gland, it is stored in the cisterns and ducts and finer spaces within the udder. The milk must be squeezed out of the spaces and forced toward the teat. At milking time, in response to such stimuli as washing the udder, the rattle of dairy utensils, or other barn practices that the cow ordinarily associates with milking, the posterior portion of the pituitary gland secretes a hormone that raises the pressure within the udder and forces the milk toward the teat and causes the cow to let down her milk. This hormone is destroyed relatively quickly in the body, and acts for only 3 to 5 minutes. As long as this pressure is maintained it is easy to obtain milk and the udder may be completely emptied.

Anything that disturbs the cow at milking time, such as unfamiliar noises in the barn, changes in milking or feeding routines, delay in milking after the udder is washed, or rough handling, may interfere with the secretion of this hormone or prevent it from being as effective as it should be. The result is that the cow does not let down her milk quickly, and adequate pressure may not be produced in the udder. The milk that has been formed since the last milking cannot be obtained under such circumstances.

Cows therefore can be milked more efficiently and completely if they are handled gently and quietly, if a regular routine is established, and if they are milked rapidly. Such facts are not new to good dairymen, but the explanation has only recently been brought to light, largely as a result of investigations conducted at the Minnesota Agricultural Experiment Station. The investigations also led to new ideas concerning the practical advantages of milking rapidly during the time that the "let down" reflex is operating at its peak.

The decline in milk production that occurs during the last several months of lactation is partly due to a gradual decline in the activity of the milk secreting tissue and to changes in the cells of the tissue. If milking is terminated suddenly, as is done when cows are being dried off, the milk left in the udder accelerates the changes until the tissue ceases to secrete milk. Even small amounts of milk left in the udder have a similar but less pronounced effect. The Minnesota workers showed that when cows are incompletely milked they decrease more rapidly in milk production than when they are milked dry at each milking. By properly stimulating cows to "let down" the milk and milking rapidly while the pressure in the udder is high, the rate at which cows drop off in production can, therefore, be decreased.

Valuable time can also be saved by taking advantage of the "let down" reflex. Most cows can be trained to let down their milk quickly and if they are then milked well all the milk in the udder can be removed by machine in 3½ or 4 minutes and hand stripping can be dispensed with. Fresh cows are more easily trained than others. The saving in time to dairymen who follow the technique of rapid milking reaches sizable proportions during the year.

Rapid milking has another advantage. As the udder becomes empty, the teat cups tend to creep up the teat and the delicate inner teat structures can be damaged. The opening into the teat may be partly closed because of such damage, and it becomes harder completely to empty the udder. Rough hand milking can produce similar damage. The damaged structures also provide a point where mastitis organisms could easily gain entrance to the udder. Milking should therefore not be continued beyond the point where the cups begin to creep.

In summary: The research we have discussed has brought a better understanding of the fundamental action of hormones in the processes of reproduction and lactation—facts that must be known before hormones can be used in a practical way.

The information has already been put to use with some success. Relief of certain types of sterility has been attained; reasonably good yields of milk have been induced in sterile cows and goats, and increased milk yields in poor-producing animals has been brought about by the use of hormones. The results with hormones in these regards, however, are far from being completely satisfactory. Apparently there are other factors that we must learn more about before best results will be attained. The present method of administering hormones is also not a practical procedure for the farmer, but if means can be found by which the secretion and activity of hormones may be controlled in a relatively simple manner, it may be possible to regulate reproduction and lactation more satisfactorily in farm herds and flocks.

In particular, more should be known of the interrelationships of hormones as they affect reproduction and lactation. Better methods of analysis for the various hormones concerned would be of an immense help in establishing such relationships. It should then be possible to determine at an early age which animals are potentially good producers and to develop better strains by breeding from such animals. Corrective measures, where desirable, could also be instituted more intelligently than is now possible.

The effect of various nutrients and the influence of environmental factors, such as light and temperature, on the secretion and activity of hormones needs further study. There is already some evidence that the actions of both vitamins and hormones are dependent on each other and that enzyme reactions in the body may be dependent on both. The level of nutrition may also be an important factor. Whether feed is efficiently used in making milk, meat, or wool depends finally on the proper functioning of all these processes. It has also been shown that the amount of light to which animals are exposed may, in certain species at least, affect hormone activity. Temperature may have similar effects. If such studies reveal that such factors importantly influence the activity of various glands, more practical means of regulating reproduction and stimulating lactation will be available.

Research of this type is already being undertaken in many laboratories, so that the future promises to yield information even more useful than that obtained in the past.

THE AUTHORS

S. R. Hall has been with the Bureau of Dairy Industry since 1936 and in that time has made important research contributions regarding physiology of reproduction and lactation. His work has included studies of the microscopic structure of the anterior pituitary gland, and the function, method of measuring, and distribution of the lactogenic hormone in cattle and other animals. Dr. Hall is a graduate of the University of Virginia.

J. F. Sykes is a physiologist in the Bureau of Dairy Industry. As a research associate in the Physiology Department of Michigan State College, Dr. Sykes studied the effects of hormones on lactation and reproduction.

ALSO, IN THIS BOOK

A Cow a Calf Will Be, by W. W. Swett, page 195.
Thyroprotein for Cows, by L. A. Moore and J. F. Sykes, page 107.
What to Feed a Cow, by R. E. Hodgson and W. J. Sweetman, page 149.
Vitamin A for Dairy Cattle, by L. A. Moore, Henry T. Converse, and S. R. Hall, page 133.
News About Goats, by Victor L. Simmons, page 217.
Developments in Sheep, by Damon A. Spencer, page 209.
Advances in Feeding Calves, by Henry T. Converse, page 159.

Vitamin A for Dairy Cattle

by L. A. MOORE, HENRY T. CONVERSE, and S. R. HALL

TOO LITTLE vitamin A in rations of dairy cattle leads to difficulties that sometimes a farmer cannot readily tell from ailments produced by other causes. Young calves that do not get enough vitamin A the first 3 or 4 months usually die of scours and pneumonia. If they survive early calfhood and their vitamin A intake is exceptionally low, they are apt to show poor condition, grow slowly, become blind, and have diarrhea and convulsions. Even though enough vitamin A is fed to produce good growth and apparently healthy calves, there still may be a partial deficiency; that can be detected only by directly examining the inside of the eye or by determining the vitamin A content of the blood plasma, which will be low. Cows that get too little of the vitamin reproduce poorly, as denoted by premature births, still-born calves, and retention of the afterbirth. The deficiency must be severe, however, to lower potency of bulls. Other symptoms of vitamin A deficiency are quite noticeable before semen quality and sexual urge are affected.

Except for the first few months of life, depending on the length of the whole-milk feeding period, dairy cattle receive most of their vitamin A in the form of carotene, a yellow pigment in plant material. Carotene is the same pigment that gives the yellow color to carrots and the natural color to butter. In hay and other roughages the yellow color is masked by the green pigments in the plant. The yellow pigment, carotene, sometimes called provitamin A, is changed by the animal body to the true vitamin A, which is almost colorless. The vitamin A in cod-liver oil is the same material as that formed from carotene in the animal body. Young calves receive a considerable supply of the colorless form of vitamin A in the cow's first milk (the colostrum), whole milk, or when their ration is supplemented with cod-liver oil.

133

At Beltsville calves getting 10 or fewer micrograms of vitamin A daily per pound of body weight died or were subnormal; those getting 17 micrograms were normal

Animal No.	Micro-grams vitamin A per pound body weight daily	Percent of normal weight at—					Result
		Birth	30 days	60 days	90 days	120 days	
136–H......	3. 4	85	69	......	......	......	Died at 75 days.
349–H......	3. 4	80	81	77	72	74	Died at 175 days.
431–J.......	4. 5	97	82	69	......	......	Died at 63 days.
1906–J......	4. 5	123	99	95	89	89	Deficiency symptoms.
348–H......	7. 0	116	90	85	85	85	Slow growth.
1909–J......	10. 3	80	74	65	55	42	Continuous scours
1758–H.....	10. 3	100	......	......	......	......	Died at 21 days.
246–H......	[1] 17 (25)	94	85	87	98	101	Normal.
247–H......	[1] 17 (25)	91	80	83	87	91	Do.
415–J.......	[1] 48 (110)	80	95	101	98	104	Do.
316–J.......	[1] 48 (110)	100	103	107	115	110	Do.

[1] Two calves, 246–H and 247–H, received 10 milliliters of cod-liver oil daily for an average intake of 17 micrograms of vitamin A per pound for 6 months or an average of 25 micrograms for the first 2 months; 415–J and 316–J received 20 milliliters of cod-liver oil daily in the same manner.

Quantities of vitamin A and carotene are usually expressed in terms of micrograms, a unit of weight that denotes one-millionth of a gram or about one twenty-eighth of a millionth of an ounce. One can readily appreciate the extremely small quantities of material with which we are dealing when we talk about vitamins. The term "International unit," abbreviated I. U., also is used. One I. U. equals about 0.25 microgram of vitamin A or 0.6 microgram of Beta-carotene in biological activity. A milliliter, another unit used in measuring volumes, equals about one-fifth of a teaspoon.

Calf Diets Have Changed

Present-day methods of raising dairy calves with limited amounts of whole milk have considerably altered the quality and quantity of food that a young calf receives, compared with what calves received in the wild state.

What happens is told in reports from several State agricultural experiment stations.

Maryland: When calves were fed limited amounts of whole milk, the vitamin A content of the blood plasma from birth to 4 months of age was in the deficient range, as judged by blood values of older calves that had too little vitamin A.

This table, based on studies at Beltsville, shows the amounts of vitamin A and carotene required to prevent losses from scours and pneumonia in calves, due to vitamin A deficiency. Also shown is the amount of cod-liver oil and average amount of alfalfa hay needed to meet the requirements. These values are based on the assumption that in cattle carotene is required in the ratio of 1 part of vitamin A to 4 parts of carotene on the weight basis or 1 to 2 on the International unit basis

| Age (months) | Weight | Vitamin A | | Carotene | | Cod-liver oil | No. 2 alfalfa hay |
		Total	Per pound of body weight	Total	Per pound of body weight		
				Holstein calves			
	Pounds	Micro-grams	Micro-grams	Micro-grams	Micro-grams	Milli-liters	Pounds
1...............	110	3, 780	34	14, 500	132	7. 0	2. 1
2...............	136	3, 276	24	12, 586	93	6. 0	1. 9
3...............	174	2, 945	17	11, 310	65	5. 5	1. 7
4...............	224	2, 310	10	8, 874	40	4. 3	1. 3
				Jersey calves			
1...............	64	2, 270	34	8, 680	132	4. 0	1. 3
2...............	85	2, 009	24	7, 714	93	3. 7	1. 1
3...............	111	1, 890	17	7, 250	65	3. 5	1. 1
4...............	147	1, 494	10	5, 742	40	2. 8	. 9

Michigan: The vitamin A content of the blood plasma of dairy calves getting limited quantities of whole milk was one-third lower than that of beef calves of the same age that obtained considerable whole milk by suckling.

Ohio: The incidence of pneumonia declined in calves that received 15,000 I. U. of vitamin A concentrate daily.

Minnesota: Less trouble from digestive disturbances was encountered in young calves fed cod-liver oil than in calves not receiving the supplement. Whole milk was fed at the rate of one-eighth of the body weight for the first 30 days, followed by skim milk to 6 months of age. While both groups had scours, some of the calves that had no supplement died.

Wisconsin: The administration of shark-liver oil, of high vitamin A potency, plus certain of the B vitamins, eliminated diarrhea and lowered the number of deaths from pneumonia.

Michigan: Young calves invariably died of pneumonia and scours when placed on a vitamin-A-deficient ration.

Beltsville: Calves on a low vitamin A intake all died before they were 100 days old.

The reports suggest that vitamin A may have something to do with the building-up of an immunity against bacterial infections in young calves.

H. T. Converse and E. B. Meigs, in studies at Beltsville, used a ration low in vitamin A, consisting of skim milk, grain, and late-cut brown timothy hay. Their results indicate that a minimum intake of between 10 and 25 micrograms of vitamin A per pound of body weight a day is necessary to maintain normal growth.

It is possible that vitamin A is more important to a herd in which the organisms that cause pneumonia and scours are present than to one where the organisms are absent or nonvirulent. In the latter case, a very low intake of the vitamin might cause no difficulty. In evaluating the tests and results, therefore, these points must be kept in mind.

It seems that the minimum quantity of vitamin A needed per pound of body weight to maintain good health, growth, and a normal level of vitamin A in the blood lies between 18 and 34 micrograms a day per pound of body weight. If an arbitrary average of 25 is chosen, and this figure doubled for optimum results under practical farm conditions, a 100-pound calf would require 5,000 micrograms of vitamin A or about 20,000 I. U. a day.

How can these requirements be met practically? First of all, because a cow's first milk after calving, or colostrum milk, is very high in vitamin A, calves should be left with the cow or fed the colostrum milk for the first 3 days. The following tabulation, based on studies at the Maryland Agricultural Experiment Station, shows the effect of colostrum on the blood-plasma vitamin A and carotene of newborn Holstein calves:

Age (days)	Number of animals	Vitamin A (micrograms)	Carotene (micrograms)
0 (birth)	17	3. 3+0. 48	1. 8+0. 11
1	17	15. 6+1. 80	14. 9+0. 64
2	16	16. 8+1. 34	17. 4+0. 63
3	17	15. 9+1. 32	18. 8+0. 59
4	16	15. 0+1. 44	19. 1+0. 77
5	15	14. 4+1. 47	18. 7+0. 56
6	16	13. 2+1. 26	17. 4+0. 44
7	13	13. 8+0. 84	16. 5+0. 41

The blood plasma is very low in vitamin A at birth, but the colostrum milk causes about a fivefold increase.

T. S. Sutton and H. E. Kaeser, of the Ohio station, report that colostrum milk furnishes the generous supply of 32,100 I. U. a day for the first 3 days of the calf's life. At Beltsville we found that the vitamin A content of colostrum milk varies with the carotene intake of the cow. Cows on pasture yielded colostrum milk up to 12 times richer in vitamin A than cows that had No. 3 grade of timothy hay. Many dairy farms discard the extra colostrum milk, a wasteful practice.

After the colostrum period, whole milk is usually fed at the rate of about 1 pound per 10 pounds of body weight, but this amount is gradually decreased after 30 days. Average winter milk contains about 640

This table shows the effect of feeding whole milk instead of colostrum for the first few days of a calf's life. One Holstein calf died when 10 days old; the Guernsey was sick at 2 days and died at 3 days of age. The data are based on studies at the Maryland Agricultural Experiment Station

Age in days	Amount per 100 milliliters of plasma					
	Holstein		Holstein		Guernsey	
	Vitamin A	Carotene	Vitamin A	Carotene	Vitamin A	Carotene
	Micro-grams	Micro-grams	Micro-grams	Micro-grams	Micro-grams	Micro-grams
0.......................	2. 7	2. 0	0. 6	1. 0	3. 6	4. 0
1.......................	3. 0	3. 0	1. 8	1. 0	3. 9	4. 0
2.......................	3. 3	4. 0	1. 5	3. 0	....	....
3.......................	3. 9	6. 0	3. 9	5. 0	....	....
4.......................	6. 0	8. 0	1. 8	4. 0	....	....
5.......................	4. 6	6. 0	1. 2	9. 0	....	....
6.......................	4. 5	8. 0	3. 0	7. 0	....	....
7.......................	6. 9	10. 0	2. 7	9. 0	....	....

I. U. a pound, according to a national survey by the Department. Thus, a 100-pound calf receiving a maximum of 10 pounds of whole milk a day would receive 6,400 I. U. a day. A calf up to 4 weeks of age consumes little hay, so that the intake of vitamin A from the whole milk would not appear to be adequate, when compared with a requirement of 20,000 I. U. If the calf is weaned or changed from whole milk to skim milk at 6 to 8 weeks of age, the total supply of vitamin A must come from the carotene in the roughage. If the roughage is of poor quality, it is doubtful whether the intake of vitamin A is adequate.

There may, therefore, be a need for supplementation of the young calf's ration if the quality of hay is low. The amount and method remain to be established. Conflicting data come from several States about the use of capsules containing 5,000 I. U. of vitamin A plus niacin and ascorbic acid. Until we get further information, then, it seems best to recommend 20,000 to 25,000 I. U. for young calves for the first 4 to 6 weeks where difficulty with scours and pneumonia is encountered. That amount is contained in about three-fourths of an ounce of ordinary cod-liver oil for animal feeding. Calves will consume sufficient hay of good quality (after the first or second month) to meet the requirements.

Of course, just giving a calf extra vitamin A will not overcome poor management. It is still as necessary as ever to have the pails clean, to feed regularly, and to give the calves the right quantities of milk at the correct temperature. Pens must be dry, bedding ample, and stalls free from draughts.

Some research workers suggest that young calves cannot utilize carotene efficiently. But among the calves raised at Beltsville without whole milk after the colostrum period of about 3 days were 50 calves that received no vitamin A as such, except from the colostrum. These calves, which made adequate gains, received skim milk with a carotene supplement starting on the third or fourth day after birth and continuing to at least 6 months of age. Thirty of them received carotene as carotene in oil, and 20 had grated or finely ground garden carrots as the source of carotene. Calves fed skim milk after the colostrum period but without any vitamin A or carotene supplement died before 100 days of age.

Carotene is the only natural source of vitamin A for growing dairy cattle after they no longer receive any whole milk. The minimum requirements as found by different investigators vary considerably depending upon the criteria used. A summary of these requirements is given in the table at the top of the next page.

Of course, the amount of hay or silage necessary to meet minimum requirements depends upon its carotene content. Several workers at Beltsville determined that various kinds of roughage differ widely between grades and have a wide range of carotene content within grades, as shown by the following tabulation, in which the carotene content is expressed in micrograms of carotene per gram as fed:

Kind of Feed	Average	Range
Alfalfa hay:		
Grade U. S. No. 1 in color	43	19–121
Grade U. S. No. 2 in color	15	12–20
Grade U. S. No. 3 in color	4	1–11
Timothy hay:		
Grade U. S. No. 1 in color	21	8–36
Grade U. S. No. 2 in color	9	8–11
Grade U. S. No. 3 in color	5	1–12
Corn stover (dry)	4	2–6
Corn silage	14	1–40

Under practical conditions the minimum carotene requirement should at least be doubled. If 30 micrograms of carotene per pound of body weight is considered about a minimum and this figure is doubled, the amount of hay of various grades to be fed to cattle of various weights can be obtained from the facing table. The carotene content of the average hay on dairy farms approximately equals that of No. 2 hay.

Vitamin A deficiency in growing dairy cattle under practical farm conditions probably does not occur often. But it has been observed when the dairyman feeds too much grain in proportion to roughage, in an attempt to get rapid growth; in drought years when the range is short and of poor quality; and in the feeding of poor or a limited quantity of roughage for a long time. A brown late-cut timothy hay, a 2-year-old hay, or No. 3 quality hay would fall in this classification.

We learned at Beltsville that cows that get 80 to 100 milligrams a day of carotene give birth to normal calves. A. H. Kuhlman and W. D. Gal-

Tests made at various stations show that growing calves need from 14 to 57 micrograms of carotene each day per pound of body weight. This table also shows the amount of average alfalfa hay needed to meet these requirements

Station	Required carotene per pound of body weight	Breed and criteria used	Pounds of average hay needed per 100 pounds body weight
	Micrograms		*Pounds*
California.......	14	Beef cattle (night blindness).............	0. 21
Texas..........	20	Beef cattle (physical condition)..........	. 29
Michigan.......	16	Holstein (night blindness)...............	. 24
Wisconsin.......	34	Holstein (blood vitamin A).............	. 50
Do........	57	Guernsey (blood vitamin A)............	. 84
Pennsylvania....	27	Guernsey and Holstein (blood vitamin A).	. 40
Maryland and	30	Holstein (spinal fluid pressure)..........	. 44
Michigan.			
Maryland.......	34	Guernsey (spinal fluid pressure).........	. 50

lup, working with Jersey cows at the Oklahoma Agricultural Experiment Station, considered a daily intake of 40 to 45 micrograms of carotene per pound of body weight about the minimum needed for normal calving. Large quantities of poor hay must be fed in order to meet the requirements, but only a small portion of good roughage is necessary. Good pasture furnishes an excellent supply of carotene and is the best roughage available for this purpose.

The possibility of a relationship between vitamin A intake and ascorbic acid metabolism and reproduction has been suggested. P. H. Phillips and

A good practice is to feed a growing dairy cow at least twice as much carotene as she must have. This can be done by feeding various weights of cattle these amounts

Grade of hay	Carotene content	Quantity of hay		
		200-pound animal	500-pound animal	800-pound animal
	Micrograms per gram	*Pounds*	*Pounds*	*Pounds*
No. 3.......................	2	13. 2	33. 1	52. 9
	4	6. 6	16. 6	26. 4
	8	3. 4	8. 2	13. 2
No. 2.......................	12	2. 2	5. 5	8. 9
	16	1. 7	4. 2	6. 6
	20	1. 3	3. 3	5. 3
No. 1.......................	24	1. 1	2. 8	4. 4
	30	. 9	2. 2	3. 5
	50	. 5	1. 3	2. 1

A cow needs an ample supply of carotene to produce normal calves. The amounts given here are double the minimum required, but are recommended for best results

Grade of hay	Carotene content	Quantity of hay			
		800-pound animal	1,000-pound animal	1,200-pound animal	1,400-pound animal
	Micrograms per gram	*Pounds*	*Pounds*	*Pounds*	*Pounds*
No. 3.................	2	106	141	159	185
	4	53	70	80	97
	6	35	44	53	62
No. 2.................	12	17	22	26	31
	16	13	17	20	24
	20	11	14	16	19
No. 1.................	24	9	11	13	16
	30	7	9	11	12
	50	4	5	6	7
Corn silage............	15	14	18	21	25
Grass silage............	50	4	5	6	7

his associates at the Wisconsin Agricultural Experiment Station reported lower blood plasma and urine ascorbic acid values in a calf on a vitamin-A-deficient ration than in a check animal that received 100 micrograms of carotene per kilogram of body weight. Later, they found that the feeding of a high potency shark-liver oil to certain dairy herds in a breeding cooperative caused the animals to maintain more nearly normal ascorbic acid values in the blood plasma. In studies conducted at the Maryland station it was found that ascorbic acid excretion was depressed in severe vitamin A deficiency, but not in moderate deficiency. These data raised the question of whether, under practical conditions, the vitamin A intake is not always sufficient to prevent any marked depressing effect on ascorbic acid synthesis. If there were a deficiency it would indirectly affect reproduction. Vitamin A deficiency does affect reproduction; severe deficiency will cause sterility or poor conception rates, but a study of the available scientific data does not lead to the conclusion that this would be true under practical farm conditions. The scientists at the Oklahoma station obtained a satisfactory conception rate when the carotene intake was at the same level as that required for normal calving. Data collected at Beltsville do not indicate that the conception rate was any lower for cows on poor hay than for those on good hay.

The need of bulls for carotene for proper reproductive performance has not been worked out in detail. Experiments with various species of animals, including the bull, have shown that vitamin A deficiency causes a degeneration of the germinal epithelium of the testicles. At Beltsville semen capable of fertilizing cows was produced by young bulls that had developed rather severe symptoms of vitamin A deficiency, such as blindness, incoordination, weakness, or diarrhea. The intake of these bulls was less than 10 micrograms of carotene per pound of body weight. Blindness will usually develop in growing bulls on an intake of 10 micrograms or less of carotene per pound of body weight. Although the semen of the bulls at Beltsville could impregnate cows, it did not maintain motility after storage, was low in concentration of sperm, and was in general of poor quality. Nor did the young bulls kept on these low intakes start to breed at the normal age. This sexual retardation appeared to depend on the age at which the bulls developed vitamin A deficiency.

According to data collected at the Maryland station, young bulls 12 to 14 months old reared on intakes of carotene varying from 10 to 34 micrograms per pound of body weight and kept outside during the heat of the summer showed marked histological alterations in the testicles. Increasing the intake of carotene to 100 micrograms per pound of body weight brought about marked improvement.

It seems unlikely, under practical farm conditions, that vitamin A will be a limiting factor of great importance in affecting the reproductive performance of bulls. It does seem likely that if hay were fed to them in the same quantities as for growing dairy cattle, the intake of carotene would be sufficient to maintain proper reproductivity in bulls.

THE AUTHORS

L. A. Moore, in the Bureau of Dairy Industry, has made several outstanding contributions in dairy cattle nutrition, his greatest being the correlation of increased cerebrospinal fluid pressure with vitamin A deficiency. He has also developed a method for determining the amount of carotene in hay and silage and has studied the effect of maturity on the carotene of some of the common hays and pasture plants.

Henry T. Converse, in the same Bureau, has investigated vitamin A requirements for growth, lactation, and reproduction in dairy cattle; calcium requirements for growth and milk production; and the role of some other vitamins than vitamin A in calf growth.

Among the important investigations made by S. R. Hall in the Bureau of Dairy Industry has been the effect of the low vitamin A in the ration on the anterior pituitary gland and reproduction in cattle.

FOR FURTHER READING

Converse, H. T., and Meigs, E. B.: *The Vitamin Requirements for Normal Growth in Young Dairy Cattle,* American Society of Animal Production, Proceedings, 32d Annual Report, pages 67–72, 1939.

Erb, R. E., Andrews, F. N., Bullard, J. F., and Hilton, J. H.: *A Technique for the Simultaneous Measurements of Semen Quality and Testes Histology in Vitamin A Studies of the Dairy Bull,* Journal of Dairy Science, volume 27, pages 769–772, 1944.

Gullickson, T. W., and Fitch, J. B.: *Effect of Adding Cod Liver Oil to the Rations of Dairy Calves,* Journal of Dairy Science, volume 27, pages 331–335, 1944.

Jones, I. R., Haag, J. R., and Dougherty, R. W.: *The Relation of Nutrition to Breeding Performance in Dairy Bulls,* Journal of Dairy Science, volume 25, pages 689–690, 1942.

Krauss, W. E., Monroe, C. F., and Hayden, C. C.: *The Value of Milk Fat Substitute-Skimmilk Combination for Raising Bull Calves for Veal and Heifer Calves for Replacement,* Ohio Agricultural Experiment Station Special Circular 57, 1939.

Kuhlman, A. H., and Gallup, W. D.: *Carotene Requirements of Dairy Cattle for Reproduction,* American Society of Animal Production, Proceedings, pages 67–73, 1940.

Lewis, J. M., and Wilson, L. T.: *Vitamin A Requirements of Calves,* Journal of Nutrition, volume 30, pages 467–477, 1945.

Lundquist, N. S., and Phillips, P. H.: *Certain Dietary Factors Essential for the Growing Calf,* Journal of Dairy Science, volume 26, pages 1023–1030, 1943.

Moore, L. A., and Berry, M. H.: *Effect of Colostrum on the Vitamin A and Carotene Content of Blood Plasma of New-Born Calves,* Journal of Dairy Science, volume 27, pages 867–873, 1944.

Moore, L. A., and Berry, M. H.: *Vitamin A and Carotene Content of the Blood Plasma of Dairy Calves from Birth up to Four Months of Age,* Journal of Dairy Science, volume 28, pages 821–826, 1945.

Nelson, H. F., Moore, L. A., Horwood, R. E., and Branaman, G. A.: *Vitamin A and Carotene Content of the Blood Plasma of Beef and Dairy Calves from Birth to Four Months of Age,* Michigan Agricultural Experiment Station Quarterly Bulletin, volume 27, pages 27–28, 1944.

Phillips, P. H., Boyer, P. D., Lardy, H. A., and Lundquist, N. S.: *Vitamin A Levels in the Blood Plasma of Dairy Cattle on Winter Rations and the Influence of Vitamin A Supplementation on Certain Constituents of the Blood,* Journal of Dairy Science, volume 24, page 522, 1941.

Phillips, P. H., Lundquist, N. S., and Boyer, P. D.: *The Effect of Vitamin A and Certain Members of the B Complex upon Calf Scours,* Journal of Dairy Science, volume 24, pages 977–982, 1941.

Sutton, T. S., and Kaeser, H. E.: *Some Physiological Effects of Extending the Colostrum Feeding Period of Dairy Calves;* Journal of Dairy Science, volume 29, pages 13–27, 1946.

ALSO, IN THIS BOOK

More Vitamin A in Milk

by R. E. HODGSON, H. G. WISEMAN, and W. A. TURNER

THE COW normally gets her vitamin A as carotene, which she obtains mostly from pasture and other forages. Part of the carotene is secreted in the milk unchanged and part of it is secreted as vitamin A. The total vitamin A value of milk, therefore, is due to both materials because the human body also converts some carotene into vitamin A. The carotene accounts for about 15 to 25 percent of the total vitamin A value of milk in the lower testing breeds, like the Holstein; it may account for about 30 to 40 percent in the higher testing breeds, like the Jersey. The amount of the vitamin in the milk varies according to the amount of carotene in the feed. When large amounts are fed, the value is high. When small amounts are given, it is low.

Under all conditions, the proportion of ingested carotene that is recovered in the milk by the cow averages about 5 percent or less. The reason for this poor utilization is not clear. The explanation awaits further research, which also may offer a means of increasing the vitamin A value of milk by a more efficient use of the available carotene. It is worth while to study the matter. Milk is a desirable source of vitamin A, and because it is so widely accepted as an essential food it is to the interest of all of us, particularly producers, to increase the amount of the vitamin in milk.

The greatest opportunities for doing so lie in providing uniform, adequate, year-round amounts of feed rich in carotene. Under average conditions the supply of carotene varies tremendously. In summer, when cows are on good pasture, the amount consumed is large. In winter, particularly when only roughage of poor quality is fed, it is small. The greatest effort, therefore, should be directed toward improving the winter milk. It is true, however, that efforts at improvement are slowed

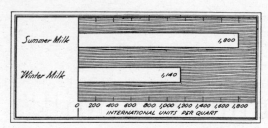

Under average conditions, the kinds of feed a cow gets in summer or winter is directly reflected in the vitamin A content of her milk as shown by data obtained in cooperation with some 20 States.

by lack of economic advantages. Feeding large amounts of carotene does not of itself increase milk production, a l t h o u g h farming practices that tend to preserve carotene in roughages also save other valuable feed nutrients.

The carotene content of pasture and other roughage varies with the species and with the stage of maturity; it generally decreases rapidly after the plants mature, particularly after bloom. To produce milk of high vitamin A value, then, the forage should be utilized when relatively immature and growing vigorously. Fertilization with nitrogen promotes vigorous growth and increases the carotene in forage.

But even in summer, when pastures are relatively immature and milk has a high vitamin A value, the amount of the vitamin in milk varies, depending on the availability and condition of pasturage. Pasture-management practices that provide a continuous supply of immature grass will effectively maintain the vitamin A in the milk at high levels.

Harvested forages put up as hay or silage provide carotene during the nonpasture periods. Partly because they usually are harvested at a

Changes in vitamin A value of milk of cows on pasture at Beltsville in 1943

Date	Type of feed and pasture the cows received	Vitamin A content	
		Holstein	Jersey
		International unit per quart	International unit per quart
Apr. 21	Barn feeding, average-quality alfalfa hay......	888	1, 239
May 8	Excellent pasture for 2 weeks; grass young, green, and succulent.....................	1, 698	1, 970
May 26	Very good pasture; grass maturing but green and succulent........................	1, 815	2, 190
June 23	Good pasture, grass fairly mature...........	1, 648	1, 887
July 11	Fair pasture, rainfall deficient, grass browning and mature............................	1, 372	1, 854
July 25	Fair pasture, grass short, browning and not succulent	1, 581	1, 904
Aug. 8	Good pasture, abundant rain, growth of grass improving	1, 980	2, 252
Aug. 22	Good pasture, grass green and succulent......	2, 019	2, 155
Sept. 6	Good pasture, abundant green, succulent grass.	2, 534	3, 053
Sept. 19	Good pasture, abundant green, succulent grass.	2, 582	3, 072

later stage than pasture, they are lower in carotene. The manner in which forage is harvested and preserved greatly affects the quality of the resulting feed. Carotene is easily destroyed or lost through bleaching, oxidation, leaching, and leaf shattering. The degree of loss depends on factors like length of time the forage is left in the field, the amount of handling, weather during harvesting, the length of the storage period, in the case of hay, and the extent of fermentation that takes place in the silage. We recommend harvesting practices that favor rapid moisture evaporation with a minimum exposure of the forage to the weather, s u c h a s windrowing shortly after cutting, cocking, using machinery that minimizes leaf shattering, a v o i d i n g overcuring, using forced-ventilation barn drying when making hay, or making the forage into silage.

Field curing, especially in places where uncertain curing weather exists, is not conducive to producing hay of high carotene value. In forced-ventilation barn drying, the forage is taken from the field when about half dry and

703830°—47——11

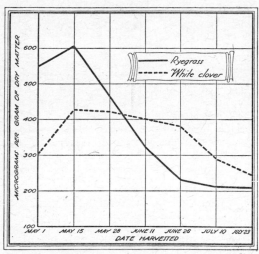

The carotene content of pasture varies according to species and stage of maturity. Ryegrass has much more carotene than white clover when very young but content decreases with increasing age.

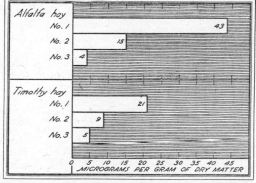

This chart, based on data obtained by H. G. Wiseman and others at Beltsville, shows the carotene content of three grades of alfalfa and timothy hay.

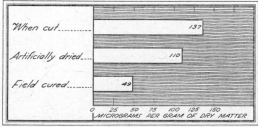

Forage when cut has most carotene; and from data obtained by O. M. Camburn and others at the Vermont station artificially dried hay is richer in carotene than similar forage when field cured.

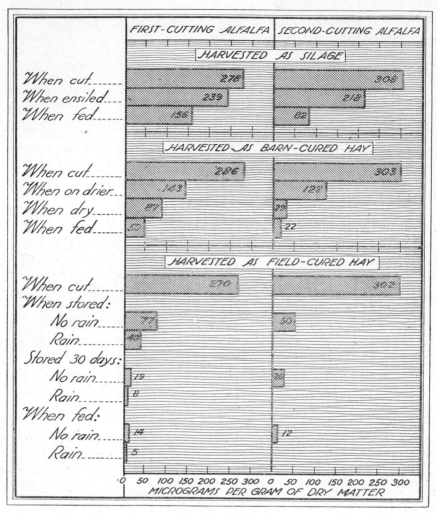

Here are the results of tests made to determine the effect of the method of harvesting on the preservation of carotene in alfalfa for first and second cuttings.

before the leaves shatter, and placed in a mow over a system of air ducts. The drying is completed by forcing air through the mass of hay. The method offers possibilities of producing hay of higher quality and probably of higher carotene content. The extent of loss of carotene in barn drying probably depends on the length of time it takes to bring the hay to a sufficient degree of dryness so that it will keep.

A method of producing harvested forage of high carotene content is by artificial dehydration, with the use of high temperatures to evaporate rapidly the moisture in the green crop.

The quality of the newly made hay, at least as far as the color and leafiness are concerned, is a good measure of its carotene value. Hay of high carotene content loses some of it during storage under average conditions, while hay in storage for a long time has lost a large part of its carotene.

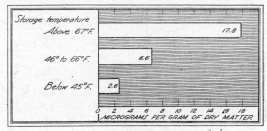

Immediately before and during the war much work was done at Beltsville and at several State experiment stations to de-

Hay of high carotene content will lose some of it in storage. Temperature is a strong factor, as shown by this chart based on tests made by Wiseman and others at Beltsville on baled hay.

velop practical methods of making silage from forage crops that ordinarily are made into hay. The crop is taken off the field soon after it is cut, and much carotene is saved. It is ensiled with or without a preservative to promote fermentation.

At Beltsville we made comparisons during harvesting and preservation of the carotene in alfalfa that was being put up in three ways: Silage, by the wilting method developed at our station; hay, by the forced-ventilation barn-drying method; and field-cured hay. Considerably more of the carotene was saved for feeding by making the crop into silage. In the first crop, the carotene in the barn-dried hay was quite high, compared to that of the second crop. This was because the air forced through the

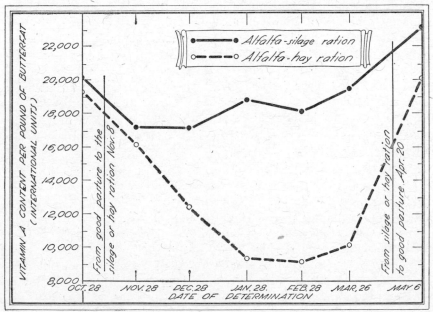

Here are comparative data on the effect of feeding wilted alfalfa silage or alfalfa hay with corn silage and concentrates on the vitamin A content of butterfat.

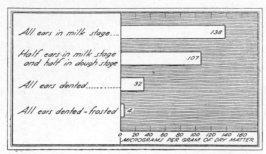

Corn silage is high in carotene if harvested when the ears are in the milk or half-dough stage. Dented or frosted corn is very low in carotene.

wilted forage to dry it was heated as it entered the duct system, and the drying was completed in 3 days as against 13 days needed to dry the second crop when the air was not heated. Also, the part of the first crop of field-cured hay that had been rained on lost considerably more of its carotene than that taken in in sunny weather—an important point in making hay.

We have fed silage and field-cured hay made from the same crops of alfalfa to milking cows and have determined the vitamin A value of the milk produced throughout the winter months. Our results demonstrate that the alfalfa silage when fed with corn silage and grain maintains the vitamin A value of winter milk at a high level, so that it more nearly approaches that of summer milk. Thus we have a practical method of preserving large amounts of the carotene that is present in the growing crop for use by the cow in producing high vitamin A milk throughout the winter when it is most needed. Feeding experiments in which we have compared the value of alfalfa silage with alfalfa hay in the ration of milking cows indicate that slightly greater milk production also is obtained on the silage ration. The cows like the silage and consume it in large quantities. Thus it may be an economic advantage to the farmer to make at least part of his hay crop (the first cutting) into silage.

Corn silage also can be an important source of carotene, provided the corn is harvested at the proper stage of maturity. Data collected at Beltsville indicate corn harvested when the ears are in the milk stage may be three times higher in carotene than if harvested when they are dented.

THE AUTHORS

R. E. Hodgson is assistant chief of the Bureau of Dairy Industry. During 1942–43 he conducted a survey of dairying in seven Latin-American countries and in 1939 was awarded the Borden award for outstanding research in dairy production.

H. G. Wiseman is an associate chemist in the Bureau of Dairy Industry. He is a graduate of the University of Maine.

W. A. Turner, now deceased, was also an associate chemist in the Bureau of Dairy Industry.

FOR FURTHER READING

United States Department of Agriculture, *Vitamin A in Butter,* U. S. D. A. Miscellaneous Publication 571, 1945.

Wiseman, H. G., Shenn, L. A., and Cary, C. A., *The Carotene Content of Market Hays and Corn Silage,* Journal of Agricultural Research, volume 57, pages 635–669, 1938.

What to Feed a Cow

by R. E. HODGSON and W. L. SWEETMAN

THE GOOD dairyman knows that the difference between just any feed and good feed is profit—that his cows produce milk efficiently only when their ration gives them enough of all the nutrients they need. Just filling their stomachs is not enough.

Cows use nearly half their feed to maintain body weight, repair worn tissues, and get energy for all vital processes. The rest is used for production. During the cycle of lactation-reproduction, the cow needs feed to produce milk; to grow, if she is immature; to develop the fetus, if she is pregnant; and to lay on fat. The important point is that good dairy cows use more nutrients for making milk than for other production purposes, and must be adequately fed if they are to produce as much as their inheritance permits.

Several standards giving the amounts of protein and total digestible nutrients have been proposed as guides to feeders. One of them, drawn up by the Committee on Animal Nutrition of the National Research Council, gives a list of recommended allowances, which is reproduced in table 1 as a guide for the feeder. Cows fed the suggested rations, including roughage of high quality and concentrates that provide the various needed substances, thrive and produce well. But feeding at even higher levels, particularly total digestible nutrients from which energy is derived, may result in greater production. Many farmers have found that under certain economic conditions such a practice is profitable. Lack of energy-giving feeds limits production oftener than any other deficiency. The only way to correct it is to provide enough feed.

Of course other nutrients may be lacking. In some areas, like the Great Lakes region and the Pacific Northwest, soils and water may contain too little iodine, and iodized salt or some other form of iodine must supple-

149

1. Dairy cows need a well-balanced diet for growth, maintenance, to develop the fetus when pregnant, and to give milk. Here are recommended feed allowances

Condition and weight of animal (pounds)	Expected gain		Daily allowance per animal [1]					
	Jersey	Holstein	Di-gestible protein	Total digest-ible nutri-ents	Calci-um	Phos-phorus	Caro-tene	Vita-min D
Growth:	Pounds	Pounds	Pounds	Pounds	Grams	Grams	Milli-grams	Interna-tional units
50..........	0.5	....	0.30	1.0	4	3	([2])	150
100.........	1.0	0.8	.45	2.0	8	6	6	300
150.........	1.3	1.4	.60	3.0	12	8	10	450
200.........	1.4	1.6	.70	4.0	13	9	12	600
400.........	1.2	1.8	.80	6.5	14	11	25	1,200
600.........	.8	1.4	.85	8.5	15	12	35	....
800.........	1.1	1.2	.90	10.0	15	12	45	([3])
1,000.......	....	1.3	.95	11.0	14	12	60	....
1,200.......	....	1.2	1.00	12.0	12	12	70	....
Maintenance: [4]								
700.........	....	....	.45	6.0	7	7	40	([3])
1,000.......	....	....	.60	8.0	10	10	60	....
1,200.......	....	....	.70	9.5	12	12	70	....
1,400.......	....	....	.80	11.0	14	14	80	....
Pregnancy (per 1,000 pounds) last 6 to 12 weeks.........	....	....	1.2	14.0	22	17	90	([3])
Lactation (per pound of milk):								
3 percent fat.	....	....	.040	.28	1	.7	([5])	([5])
4 percent fat.	....	....	.045	.32	1	.7	....	....
5 percent fat.	....	....	.050	.37	1	.7	....	....
6 percent fat.	....	....	.055	.42	1	.7	....	....

[1] Thiamine, riboflavin, niacin, pyridoxine, pantothenic acid, and vitamin K are synthesized by bacteria in the rumen and it appears that adequate amounts of these vitamins are furnished by a combination of rumen synthesis and natural feedstuffs. Manganese, iron, copper, and cobalt are clearly essential, but the amounts needed are not known. For growth, 0.6 gram magnesium is needed per 100 pounds of body weight.
[2] Calves should receive colostrum the first few days after birth as a source of vitamin A and other essential factors.
[3] While vitamin D is known to be required, data are inadequate to warrant specific figures for older growing animals and for maintenance, reproduction, and lactation.
[4] When calculating the allowances for lactating heifers that are still growing, it is recommended that the figure for growth rather than maintenance be used.
[5] When adequate amounts of vitamins A and D are fed for normal reproduction, extra amounts will probably not stimulate milk production but will increase the vitamin content of the milk.

ment the regular ration. Phosphorus, cobalt, and possibly iron and copper may be insufficient in several regions; special precautions must then be taken to provide the elements, either by adding them to the soil as fertilizers or feeding them directly as mineral supplements. Wheat, wheat millfeed, and oilseed byproducts included in the concentrate mixture will provide phosphorus. A farmer who suspects such mineral deficiencies in his animals should seek the advice of his State college dairy specialist. Cows fed roughage of poor quality a long time may not get enough vitamin A, and therefore may be subject to night blindness and diarrhea, and fail to drop normal calves. Vitamin A deficiency can be avoided by feeding good green roughages high in carotene.

Meeting Feed Requirements

Pasture and harvested roughages are highly important. They furnish the biggest part of the nutrients for the dairy herd, and are the cheapest source of feed. They supply specific needs like calcium, other mineral elements, and carotene. They are soil-conserving crops: The wise dairy farmer, then, is essentially a "grassland farmer," and his crop rotations, while favoring perennial forage, also include corn for silage and small grains that have the double value of being nurse crops for new seedings and providing energy-rich concentrate feeds to supplement the roughage.

Under most conditions we recommend that a farmer keep only as many animal units as the land he has available for pasture and harvested forage will adequately support. Only in special areas where market conditions permit—as in the fluid milk regions of the Northeast—is it ordinarily profitable to depend on purchased hay and concentrates. In planning the cropping program and the size of the herd that a farm will support, it is helpful to know what are the yearly feed requirements of cows. In table 2 we give examples of feeds and acres needed for a year by cows of different sizes and producing ability. The requirements are based on average conditions, including a pasture season of 6 months. They have worked out satisfactorily in many areas. The acre yield of the various feeds, of course, will vary with factors such as soil fertility and climate. Young stock require from about one-half to three-fourths as much feed and pasture as do milking cows.

Feeding Cows on Pasture

Because pasturage is the best and cheapest feed for dairy cows, the efficient dairyman takes the best possible care of his pastures. He develops them on good land, not any old field. He seeds them to productive grasses and legumes, fertilizes them to maintain high yields, manages them so that the herbage is grazed uniformly and thereby is kept growing well, irrigates wherever necessary and possible, and removes clumps, weeds, and brush. He uses the several types of pasture—permanent, rotational, and temporary—in combination, where practicable, to supplement one another; thus he provides abundant grazing all season. In

2. Based on average conditions, including 6 months of pasture, this table gives the yearly feed allowance for a dairy cow and the acreage needed to grow it[1]

Weight of cow	Butter-fat production	Hay[2]	Land required for hay or hay silage		Corn or sorghum silage	Land required for silage	Grain[3] to be allowed	Land required[4]	
			If alfalfa is raised	If clover and timothy is raised				Corn	Oats
Pounds	Pounds	Pounds	Acres	Acres	Pounds	Acres	Pounds	Acres	Acres
900	200	3,000	0.75	1.15	5,400	0.34	410	0.09	0.11
900	300	3,000	.75	1.15	5,400	.34	1,470	.33	.38
900	400	3,000	.75	1.15	5,400	.34	2,530	.56	.66
1,200	200	4,000	1.00	1.54	7,200	.45	400	.09	.10
1,200	300	4,000	1.00	1.54	7,200	.45	1,580	.35	.41
1,200	400	4,000	1.00	1.54	7,200	.45	2,760	.62	.72

[1] Based on yields per acre as follows: Alfalfa hay, 2 tons; clover and timothy, 1.3 tons; silage, 8 tons; corn, 40 bushels; and oats, 40 bushels.
[2] Multiply the number of pounds by 3 to convert the hay to hay silage.
[3] If the roughage is of low quality or contains little legume, some high-protein concentrate may have to be fed in addition to the farm grains. One can estimate this amount at one-fifth that of the farm grains.
[4] An additional 2 acres of medium-quality permanent pasture is required for each cow.

many places it is wise, also, to renovate old established permanent pasture.

Pasture is high in feeding value, but because it is succulent and bulky, the best milkers cannot eat enough total nutrients to meet their needs. Under good conditions they will consume as much as 150 pounds of grass daily or about 30 pounds of dry matter—enough for maintenance and the production of about 1¼ pounds of fat. But for higher production good pasture must be supplemented with feeds rich in energy like corn or barley. When pasturage is not abundant, hay or silage or both should be fed in addition. Cows relish a little dry hay along with pasturage; hay fed to cows before they go on legume pasture helps prevent bloat.

How much supplemental feed should a dairyman give his cows when they are on pasture? That depends upon the relation of the cost of the feed to the amount of extra milk obtained beyond the production obtained on pasture alone. When cows are on poor or scarce pasture, however, they should not be allowed to get in poor condition because it will then be hard to get them back in high production when more pasturage is available. In table 3 we give the approximate amounts of milk of different fat content that good cows should be expected to produce on pastures of different qualities and the amount of concentrates that should be fed for each additional 5 pounds of milk daily that the cows will produce. This schedule has been followed with success and will help a farmer

3. To produce more milk, cows need varying amounts of concentrates, depending on the quality of their pasture. This table can be used as a feeding guide

Milk butterfat test (percent)	Pounds of milk daily that pasture alone might produce		Pounds of concentrate needed to produce each 5 additional pounds of milk daily [3]
	Good pasture [1]	Average pasture [2]	
3.............................	40	20	2. 0
4.............................	30	15	2. 2
5.............................	25	12	2. 5
6.............................	20	10	2. 8

[1] Good pasture is young and succulent and abundant enough so that cows can graze their fill in 1 to 1½ hours several times daily.

[2] Average pasture is short and young or of somewhat advanced growth and is not palatable or abundant enough to permit cows to graze their fill in 2 to 3 hours several times daily. Poor pasture will no more than maintain the weight of cows. Some grain or hay may be necessary for cows to maintain weight if the pasture is very poor.

[3] If hay or silage is fed, reduce the grain by 0.6 pound for each pound of hay and 0.2 pound for each pound of corn silage consumed.

determine when and how much supplemental feed he should provide. To illustrate: Suppose a cow will produce 45 pounds of 4-percent milk when grazing on good pasture, provided she is adequately fed. The pasture should provide for the production of 30 pounds of milk. To enable her to produce the extra 15 pounds, it is necessary to feed 6.6 pounds of concentrate (2.2 pounds × 3) or its equivalent in the form of roughage. Good pasture is rich in protein, and it is not necessary to feed extra protein unless the pasturage is limited and poor.

Feeding Cows Not on Pasture

Roughage is the basis of the winter ration. However, if a farmer depends on roughage for most of the ration, it must be of good quality so that the cows will eat enough to furnish the necessary nutrients. Emphasis should be given to growing legumes or legume-grass mixtures, because they are richer in protein, minerals, and carotene than are grasses alone. The crops should be harvested when they are in the early-bloom or early-head stage because then they have more protein and total digestible nutrients than more mature forage.

Forage that is made into hay varies greatly in quality, depending on its stage of growth when it is cut, conditions of curing and storing, and so on. Every effort should be made to save the leaves, because they contain most of the protein, minerals, and carotene. A good way to put up forage of this kind, particularly the first cutting, in areas where haying weather is not good, is to make it into silage. In this way the crop can be gotten off

4. Hay crops vary considerably in protein and nutrients, depending on the time of harvest. Early bloom stage gives best results as shown in this table [1]

Stage of maturity when harvested	Alfalfa		Red clover		Timothy	
	Digestible protein	Total digestible nutrients	Digestible protein	Total digestible nutrients	Digestible protein	Total digestible nutrients
	Percent					
Prebloom or prehead......	14. 2	53. 2	12. 0	56. 4	5. 6	50. 2
Three-fourths bloom.......	9. 9	49. 7	....	....	4. 2	51. 6
Full bloom................	....	....	7. 8	53. 4	3. 2	48. 0
Past full bloom...........	8. 6	44. 9	7. 3	51. 7	2. 4	44. 4

[1] From *Feeds and Feeding*, by F. B. Morrison (20th edition; 1936), table 1, appendix. The Morrison Publishing Company, Ithaca, New York.

the field more or less independently of weather conditions when it is in the right stage, with a small loss of nutrients. By harvesting the first cutting quite early, where that is possible, silage of high protein content is produced. Such silage, fed liberally with corn silage and good hay made from later crops, supplies most of the protein needed.

Cows eat large amounts of roughage when it is good. Tests have shown that animals maintained on good roughage alone produce about 70 percent as much milk as when fed concentrates in addition.

When plenty of high-quality roughage is available and the price of milk is low compared to the price of concentrates, it probably is economical to feed only roughage. Usually it is profitable, however, to feed concentrates, particularly where a home-grown supply is available. When the demand for milk is strong, it is profitable to feed concentrates liberally, particularly to the good cows.

5. If fed concentrates, in addition to certain amounts of roughage, dairy cows will produce more milk. This feeding schedule for concentrates is recommended

Milk test (percent)	Pounds of milk daily that may be expected from roughage consumed at rate of 1½ pounds hay and 3 pounds silage per 100 pounds weight daily, by cows of the following weights:				Pounds of concentrate needed to produce each additional 5 pounds of milk daily
	700	1,000	1,200	1,400	
3.0..........	12	18	22	25	2.0
4.0..........	10	15	19	22	2.2
5.0..........	9	13	17	19	2.5
6.0..........	8	12	14	17	2.8

6. These concentrate mixtures are good for feeding with different roughages

Roughage	Approximate protein content needed in concentrates	Concentrate mixture [1]			
		Corn, barley, or kafir	Oats or wheat	Wheat bran	Linseed, soybean, or cottonseed meal
First-quality legume hay or silage (alfalfa, clover, soybeans), or pasture............................	*Percent* 12–13	*Pounds* 500	*Pounds* 200	*Pounds* 300	*Pounds* ....
Average-quality legume hay or silage and corn or sorghum silage or first-quality mixed hay and corn or sorghum silage.....................	14–15	300	300	200	200
Average-quality mixed hay and corn or sorghum silage...............	16–17	300	200	200	300
Grass hay and corn silage [2].........	18–20	200	200	200	300

[1] One percent of iodized salt should be added to each mixture. In phosphorus-deficient areas, add 1 percent bone meal or other fluorine-low phosphorus supplement.
[2] Add 1 percent ground limestone or calcium carbonate.

The total digestible nutrients in good hay average about 50 percent; those in grass or legume silage, about 18 percent; and those in corn silage, about 20 percent. These are convenient figures to use in estimating the energy value of roughages. The protein in these feeds varies considerably more than does the total digestible nutrient content. The amount of protein that is fed in the concentrates should be governed by the protein content of the roughages. Tests have shown that when high-quality legume hay is fed in unlimited amounts, home-grown grains like corn or mixtures of corn and barley or wheat are perfectly satisfactory supplements for liberal production. Cows will eat about 1½ pounds of good hay and 3 to 3½ pounds of silage daily per 100 pounds of weight when the average amount of concentrates is fed. If no concentrate is fed, they will eat 2 to 2½ pounds of good hay. Small cows may eat less. Large cows may eat more. When 1½ pounds of hay and 3 pounds of silage are used as the daily consumption of roughages, they will provide enough nutrients for maintenance and several pounds of milk, depending on the test of the milk. This is indicated in table 5, which lists the number of pounds of concentrate needed for each additional 5 pounds of milk the cow will produce. If the concentrate mixture used properly balances the roughage, as shown in table 6, that schedule will meet the requirements for protein and total digestible nutrients given in table 1.

We have learned from experiments that under average conditions cows will produce more milk when fed more total-digestible nutrients. This should be done whenever it is profitable to do so. The cow's capacity is limited, and heavy feeding should be done with concentrates because they are richer in energy per unit of weight.

The profitableness of feeding more heavily than the standards call for depends upon the relation between the price of a pound of concentrate and the value of the additional milk produced. The most important time to feed heavily on concentrates is in the first half of the lactation period, when the urge to produce is greatest. It also is important to feed so that the cows may be in good flesh when they calve. If that is done, they are better able to meet the heavy demands for milk secretion at that time and will "milk off" the reserve energy stored in their body fat.

The Most Profitable Feeding Level

Experiments by colleagues in the Department have shown the relative increases in production by good cows fed liberally on roughages and concentrates at various levels above those suggested in feeding standards: As the feeding level is increased the production also is increased, but at a progressively smaller rate. A cow fed at 110 percent of the standard may be expected to yield 0.8 pound of milk for each additional pound of concentrate. Thus by heavier feeding of concentrates, more milk can be obtained from the same number of cows. The extent to which heavier feeding can be practiced profitably depends entirely on the feed-milk price ratio. This ratio, obtained by dividing the price of a pound of feed by the value of a pound of milk, should be followed closely for best results. When the value of the extra milk obtained from feeding an additional pound of concentrate is worth more than the

7. By calculating the feed-milk price ratio, the dairy farmer can select the most profitable level of feeding from this table

Production ration in percent of Haecker requirements [1]	Increase in pounds of 4 percent fat-corrected milk for each additional pound of concentrate fed	Production ration in percent of Haecker requirements [1]	Increase in pounds of 4 percent fat-corrected milk for each additional pound of concentrate fed
90	1. 4	120	0. 6
100	1. 0	130	. 5
110	. 8		

[1] Haecker standard for total digestible nutrients is very slightly higher than those indicated in table 1.

concentrate, then it is profitable to feed at the heavier rate. With each additional input of concentrate, the output of milk per unit of input decreases.

Cows can utilize large quantities of roughage because they have a large paunch, the rumen, where the material is stored as it is eaten and until it is returned to the mouth for masticating. It has another important function. The rumen contains micro-organisms like bacteria, yeasts, molds, and protozoa, some of which break down the fibrous portions of foodstuffs into material the animal can use. The organisms also make certain vitamins like the B-complex vitamins. It is therefore unnecessary to include these vitamins in the ration. Certain micro-organisms also make usable and digestible protein from the nonprotein nitrogen that is naturally in the feed or is added to the feed in the form of urea or ammonium carbonate, and from nitrogen that becomes available through protein and amino acid decomposition. This newly made protein apparently has high biological value.

Use of Urea as a Protein Feed

This knowledge that rumen micro-organisms utilize inorganic nitrogen to build protein has made it possible to use substances like urea as part of the cow's protein supply.

The amount of urea that should be used depends on the protein content of the rest of the feed supply. One pound of urea feeding compound contains enough nitrogen to make about 2.6 pounds of protein. The micro-organisms take the nitrogen and combine it with carbohydrate material, which must come from the regular feed supply, to form protein. For each pound of protein made from urea, about 0.9 of a pound of carbohydrate feed is used. Since natural high-protein feeds contain considerable energy, which urea does not furnish, additional carbohydrate feed is needed when the urea is used to replace the natural feeds.

Urea usually is added to the concentrate mixture to increase the protein content. Thus, by adding 2 pounds of urea to 100 pounds of a 10-percent protein concentrate mixture, the protein equivalent is increased to 16 percent. When a mixture contains as much as 18 to 20 percent protein, however, added urea is poorly utilized. Most of the urea used for feeding dairy cattle has been mixed in commercial feeds. It can be used in amounts up to 3 percent of the mixture without harmful effects to the animals. Large amounts make the feed unpalatable and it may be toxic. For this reason, it is important to limit the amount used and to make sure that it is thoroughly combined throughout the mixture. The use of urea as a source of protein for cows, of course, should be limited to its economic advantages compared with other sources of protein.

THE AUTHORS

R. E. Hodgson is assistant chief of the Bureau of Dairy Industry. During 1942–43 he conducted a survey of dairying in seven Latin-American countries; in 1939 he received the Borden award for outstanding research in dairy production. Dr. Hodgson is a graduate of the University of Wisconsin.

W. J. Sweetman is associate dairy husbandman in the Bureau of Dairy Industry. He is a graduate of Michigan State College.

FOR FURTHER READING

Dawson, J. R., Watt, A. L., McIntyre, C. W. Leighton, R. E., and Graves, R. R.: *Single Grains and Grain Mixtures as Supplements to Alfalfa Hay and Silage for Milk Production,* U. S. D. A. Circular 696, 1944.

Graves, R. R., Dawson, J. R., Kopland, D. V., Watt, A. L., and Van Horn, A. G.: *Feeding Dairy Cows on Alfalfa Hay Alone,* U. S. D. A. Technical Bulletin 610, 1938.

Jensen, E., Klein, J. W., Rauchenstein, E., Woodward, T. E., and Smith, R. H.: *Input-Output Relationships in Milk Production,* U. S. D. A. Technical Bulletin 815, 1942.

Morrison, F. B.: *Feeds and Feeding,* The Morrison Publishing Company, Ithaca, New York, 20th Edition, 1936.

National Research Council: *Recommended Nutrient Allowances for Dairy Cattle,* A Report of the Committee on Animal Nutrition, No. 3, 1945.

Woodward, T. E.: *Feeding Dairy Cows,* U. S. D. A. Farmers' Bulletin 1626, 1940.

ALSO, IN THIS BOOK

Vitamin A for Dairy Cattle, by L. A. Moore, H. T. Converse, and S. R. Hall, page 133.
More Vitamin A in Milk, by R. E. Hodgson, H. G. Wiseman, and W. A. Turner, page 143.
New Ideas in Feeding, by N. R. Ellis, page 95.

Advances in Feeding Calves

by HENRY T. CONVERSE

SOMETHING like 5 million heifer calves are raised every year in the United States for replacements in dairy herds. Many males are also raised for herd sires. They all need tremendous amounts of milk for which, in times of shortage, they compete with humans.

For 75 years—at least for so long that the practice has gained the force of habit or tradition—authorities have recommended feeding the dairy calf whole milk for a month or longer before changing to skim milk. It has been recommended also that heifer calves that are to be kept for milkers be fed skim milk to 6 or 8 months of age, leastwise when there is plenty of it. Now and then somebody or other experimented and learned that dairy calves could be safely weaned from milk at 2 or 3 months, but few people paid them much heed, the suggestion being that revolutionary.

The accepted way of feeding new calves whole milk and older ones skim milk takes about 200 pounds of whole milk, besides the colostrum, and at least 1,900 pounds of skim milk for each calf. If the feeding of this whole milk could be dispensed with, at least 8 pounds of butter would be saved per calf, or 40 million pounds for the 5 million calves a year. If calves could be weaned from skim milk at 2 months of age, instead of at 6 months, there would be a further saving of 1,600 pounds or more of skim milk per calf, or 8 billion pounds in all.

In 1933, Edward B. Meigs and I started feeding some calves skim milk only (except colostrum) at Beltsville. The first calves were fed skim milk properly supplemented with vitamin A, usually 2 to 4 teaspoonfuls of cod-liver oil starting usually on the fourth day—that is, after three full days on colostrum. The skim milk was continued to at least 6 months of age. Since then, 98 male calves have been reared by this schedule to 6

Female calves fed skim milk after the colostrum period compare favorably with those fed whole milk for 30 days. The calves used for this test were similar ones from the same Holstein and Jersey herds. All had skim milk until 6 months old

Calves	Average weight, in pounds, at different ages (in months)										
	Birth	1	2	3	4	5	6	9	12	18	24
13 Holsteins fed whole and skim milk..............	83	107	135	177	223	279	337	478	601	776	944
26 Holsteins fed skim milk after the colostrum period.	84	101	135	181	233	288	346	483	607	821	986
6 Jerseys fed whole and skim milk...................	48	65	87	116	151	191	238	347	448	628	764
8 Jerseys fed skim milk after the colostrum period.....	48	57	78	108	145	186	230	341	454	613	787

months or older, and 33 Jersey and Holstein females have been similarly reared to producing age. The growth rates of Holstein heifers at least have not been adversely affected. The Jersey heifers did not make quite such good gains as those receiving some whole milk, at least during the first few months. However, as we shall see later, we have obtained satisfactory results by feeding Jersey heifers without whole milk, except colostrum, and weaning them at 2 or 3 months, rather than at the usual age of 6 months.

To conserve milk for human use, a war-emergency experiment was begun at Beltsville in 1942 to find out how much earlier than 6 months calves could be weaned from milk. Calves were fed colostrum for about 3 days and then changed to skim milk with 2 to 4 teaspoonfuls of cod-liver oil daily. At first we weaned calves at 90 days and later at earlier ages. The calves were induced to eat generous amounts of a suitable grain mixture and hay as early as possible. The results of weaning calves from skim milk at 90 days were satisfactory.

Subsequently, 6 Jersey heifer calves were weaned from skim milk at 60 days, 10 Jersey steers were weaned at 60 days, and 18 at 45 days. Two Holstein heifer calves were weaned at 60 days, 2 at 45 days, and 3 at 30 days. Eight Holstein steers were weaned at 60 days, and 19 at 30 days. Ten crossbred steers were weaned at 60 days, and 9 at 30 days.

These 87 calves were fed no whole milk except colostrum and were weaned from skim milk at 2 months of age or earlier. In no case did we use dried skim milk, dried blood, tankage, fish meal, or any other high-protein feeds of animal origin that are usually used in dry calf starters.

The feeds other than milk fed to the calves in these milk-saving experiments were the same as those fed to milking cows in the nutrition herd at Beltsville. The grain mixtures comprised corn meal, wheat bran, and linseed oil meal—sometimes with and sometimes without soybean oil meal.

This table shows the weights of different groups of calves weaned at various ages, as compared with normal weights for other similar calves at the same ages. Note that the group of 5 Jersey steers, weaned at 60 days, averaged only 239 pounds at 6 months while another group, weaned at the same age, averaged 303 pounds at 6 months. The reason: The heavier steers were encouraged to eat large amounts of dry feed before and after weaning. The table also shows that although calves may be underweight at 6 months, they usually make greater-than-average gains and reach normal or nearly normal weight at 9 or 12 months

Number of animals	Weaned (days)	Weight of calves, in pounds, at different ages (in months)									
		Birth	1	2	3	4	5	6	9	12	18
Jersey steers											
7.....................	90	58	65	87	122	160	210	266	[1]378	....	....
5.....................	60	51	60	78	100	139	184	239	[1]396	....	....
7.....................	60	61	70	96	131	174	226	303	[1]384	....	....
9.....................	45	59	71	86	117	160	210	265	398	....	....
Normal for males [4].....	....	60	78	104	141	184	233	282	410	....	....
Holstein steers											
4.....................	90	97	105	139	195	261	333	417	....	....	....
8.....................	60	93	96	125	164	218	288	363	[2]504	....	....
11....................	30	96	109	132	179	239	308	381	[3]579	[3]739	....
Normal for males [4].....	....	94	125	164	214	269	336	399	563	741	....
Jersey females											
3.....................	90	51	57	78	103	146	177	228	353	473	664
2.....................	60	53	66	90	120	152	204	256	382	477	613
Normal for females [4]....	....	53	67	90	121	158	199	243	360	450	601
Holstein females											
2.....................	60	84	91	117	156	215	295	366	499	615	823
2.....................	45	73	91	124	164	211	265	323	478	614	....
1.....................	30	90	107	139	189	255	314	370	525	708	....
Normal for females [4]....	....	90	112	148	193	243	297	355	509	632	845

[1] 1 animal only. [2] 2 animals only. [3] 7 animals only. [4] Normal according to A. C. Ragsdale

The hay was mostly good alfalfa hay. Timothy hay was fed in a few instances.

All calves weaned at 90 days and at 60 days survived. One of the 20 Jersey calves weaned at 45 days died when it was 49 days old. Two of

162

YEARBOOK OF AGRICULTURE

the 13 crossbred calves weaned at 30 days died at 52 and 59 days of age, 1 of pneumonia and 1 of scours. Five of the 26 Holstein calves weaned at 30 days died at 35 to 57 days; 4 of the 5 cases had either pneumonia or scours.

We do not believe that early weaning caused the deaths. All these deaths occurred either just before or during the period when dependence for the control of calf scours was placed on the Wisconsin "scour prevention capsules," described later. Since these deaths, 15 Jersey males and 3 Holstein females weaned at 45 days of age have been reared without loss; and 14 Holstein males, 7 crossbred males, and 3 Holstein females weaned at 30 days have been reared without loss. Calves that safely reach 60 days of age usually survive.

It seems that the proper age to wean calves from milk is largely an economic question. If skim milk is plentiful and cheap, it might well be fed to 6 or 7 months of age, but if it is scarce or expensive, as compared to the cost of grain and hay, or if it is plentiful and is needed for hogs or poultry, calves may advantageously be weaned at quite early ages.

If calves are to be safely weaned from milk at 60 days, and particularly if they are to be weaned at 30 or 45 days, they must be trained to eat generous amounts of hay and grain before weaning. Grain and carefully selected hay should be available by the time the calf is 10 or 12 days old. Grain should be rubbed on the nose or placed in the mouth of the calf at convenient times, or a little may be dusted into the bucket just as the milk is nearly finished. The feed boxes should be carefully observed to be sure the calves are eating dry feed before weaning completely from milk.

A few calves in these experiments voluntarily ate as much as a half pound of grain at 20 days of age, and when a handful of grain was mixed into the milk three Holstein calves ate a pound and a half, and two others ate a pound at this early age. At 40 days, several Holsteins—some weaned from milk and some not yet weaned—voluntarily consumed from 1¼ pounds to 3 pounds of grain daily, and in several cases where grain was added to the milk the daily grain consumption was 2 to 3½ pounds—in one case, 4 pounds. Jersey calves seldom eat more than half as much grain as Holstein calves, at least until after 40 days of age. These experiments indicate that, while Holstein calves can almost always be safely weaned by 45 days, and with extreme care at 30 days of age, Jersey calves should be allowed milk for an extra 15 days as a safety measure.

Energy Additions to Skim Milk

Skim milk contains only about half the energy value of whole milk. It is not safe, however, to feed too much skim milk during the first month, because of the danger of causing scours. Therefore, when skim milk is fed immediately after the colostrum period, the energy intake for the first month or so is apt to be somewhat low and the gain in weight not so large as on whole milk. Calves usually make up this slower early gain.

In recent experiments at Beltsville, added energy has been fed in the skim milk for about 2 months, or fed in warm water if the calf has been weaned from milk. Corn meal, ground soybeans, oatmeal gruel, flaxseed jelly, or the same grain mixture as fed dry was fed mixed into the skim milk to different groups of calves. Starting usually with a quarter of a pound daily at from 5 to 12 days of age, the extra feed was mixed into the skim milk. The amount of feed was usually increased to a half pound in a few days and continued usually to 60 days and sometimes to 90 days.

The soybeans proved particularly unpalatable. The oatmeal gruel formed a pasty feces that stuck all over the calf. The corn meal was not very well cleaned out of the bucket, particularly when fed in warm water after weaning from milk, and there seemed to be more tendency to scour. Mixing into the skim milk the same grain mixture that was fed dry proved quite successful. In a few cases, as much as a half pound of the grain mixture was added to the milk before the calf was 10 days old, but we usually did not add as much as a half pound of grain daily until the calf was 15 to 20 days old. Usually, too, a half pound daily was as much grain as was added at any time to the milk or to the water after weaning from milk. However, the last three Holstein calves fed grain in milk were fed more than a half pound daily. With these three calves, the half pound fed in the milk by 15 days of age was increased to about a pound daily before 30 days of age. At 40 days, when these three calves had been weaned from milk for 10 days, they were eating a pound of grain daily mixed in the warm water and 2, 2½, and 3 pounds respectively, as dry grain.

Twenty-three calves have been fed grain in milk as an energy supplement. Flaxseed cooked to a jelly in a little water, although more expensive, appeared to be the best energy supplement for skim milk.

Thirty-nine calves in the Beltsville experiments received about a half pound daily of dry flaxseed cooked to a jelly in water. With Holstein calves, a half pound of the dry flaxseed made into a jelly was usually safely added to the skim milk before the calves were 10 days old. Smaller calves seemed to do better if the increase to a half pound was not made until 12 to 15 days of age. The groups of calves fed either flaxseed jelly or a grain mixed with the skim milk made somewhat better average gains in body weight during the first month than did those calves that had in addition to skim milk only such amounts of grain and hay as they would voluntarily eat from the manger. The gains of the calves fed the flaxseed jelly averaged a little better than the gains of the calves with the grain added to the milk. We found that the average gains of the group fed corn meal in the skim milk for added energy were almost as large as the gains of the group fed a grain mixture in the skim milk. Nevertheless, the corn meal is considered less satisfactory for the purpose than a grain mixture.

During their first month, calves will gain weight faster if an energy supplement
is added to their skim-milk diet. Flaxseed jelly ranks high for this purpose

Energy supplement	Holstein		Jersey	
	Number of animals	First-month gains (pounds)	Number of animals	First-month gains (pounds)
No energy supplement..............	13	7. 6	15	6. 1
Corn meal.......................	4	12. 5	5	9. 6
Grain in milk....................	15	12. 8	8	10. 9
Flaxseed jelly...................	22	15. 6	17	11. 6

Is Added Calcium Needed for Early-weaned Calves?

Fourteen pounds of skim milk contains about 7½ grams of calcium, a
generous contribution to the needs of the calf for this element. In the
Beltsville experiments, the first calves weaned from skim milk at 60 days
of age or earlier were fed a grain mixture containing 3 percent of bone
meal when alfalfa as well as when timothy hay was fed. The excellent results, even when timothy hay (which is low in calcium) was fed, indicates
that the calcium from bone meal satisfactorily replaces the calcium of
the milk which is usually fed.

Calves weaned at 30 to 40 days of age and fed timothy or grass hay
and a grain mixture without a calcium supplement showed rachitic or
calcium-deficiency symptoms (not vitamin D deficiency, for the calves
had cod-liver oil) within 2 months. More recently, 40 calves have been
weaned from skim milk at 45 days or earlier. They received alfalfa hay
with a grain mixture without a calcium supplement. Two or three of
these calves ate very little hay during the first month after weaning and
might possibly have been benefited at this period by the addition of
calcium, but this is not at all certain. Blood-calcium analyses were
made on several of the calves weaned at 30 to 45 days and fed alfalfa
hay without a calcium supplement. In only one case was there any
decided lowering of the blood calcium after weaning. Calves weaned
much before 6 months and fed grass hay definitely should be fed some
added calcium until 6 months, when the calcium can be discontinued.

Protein

The grain mixtures fed to most of the calves weaned at an early age
were grain mixture No. 75 (2 parts corn meal, 2 parts wheat bran, and
1 part linseed oil meal) and grain mixture No. 65 (3 parts corn meal,

2 parts wheat bran, 2½ parts linseed oil meal and 2½ parts of soybean oil meal.) Grain mixture No. 75 contained about 17 percent protein and about 0.14 percent calcium. Mixture No. 65 contained about 25 percent protein and about 0.20 percent calcium.

The calf's needs for protein are quite high and, of course, are amply supplied by the milk in the usual milk-feeding program. When milk is discontinued at an early age, a high protein grain mixture is necessary. In the few cases tried, the 17-percent mixture with alfalfa hay seemed adequate. Most of the calves fed alfalfa hay, as well as those fed grass hay, however, were fed the higher protein grain mixture because the calves seemed to eat larger amounts of this mixture during the first and second months, possibly because it was a little less bulky. While these experiments do not cover the point, probably even with early weaning from milk, farm-grown grains could replace the higher protein grain mixture when the calves are 4 or 5 months old, at least when alfalfa or other legume hay is fed.

Vitamin D

Some conservative investigators suggest that some vitamin D supplement might well be fed during the milk-feeding period or during the winter months. Several experiments, however, indicate that supplementary vitamin D is seldom needed. I. W. Rupel, G. Bohstedt, and E. B. Hart, working at the Wisconsin Agricultural Experiment Station, reported that calves on rations devoid of vitamin D, but exposed to all available sunlight both summer and winter, gained nearly as much weight as calves fed a vitamin D supplement. S. I. Bechdel, K. G. Landsburg, and O. J. Hill at the Pennsylvania station reported that 2½ pounds of sun-cured alfalfa hay supplied an adequate amount of vitamin D.

At Beltsville 50 calves received carotene and skim milk after 3 or 4 days of colostrum feeding, and therefore had to depend from birth on sun-cured hay in the ration and exposure to sunlight for their supply of vitamin D. Most of these calves had very little exposure to sunlight during the first 6 months of life and several of the calves had very little exposure to sunlight during the first full year. Some four or five of the calves kept for a full year out of all direct sunlight showed only mild rachitic symptoms—slightly roached backs—during a period when they were eating little hay, but the symptoms disappeared when they ate more hay.

Cod-liver oil, which supplies both vitamins A and D, was fed experimentally to calves in the Holstein and Jersey breeding herds at Beltsville. These calves are always fed whole milk until about 30 days old and skim milk for at least 6 months. A suitable grain mixture is fed, with a limit of 3 pounds daily. Alfalfa hay, usually of U. S. No. 2 grade, was fed free choice in hayracks. Alternate calves in each breed, 70 in all, were fed 20 cubic centimeters (4 teaspoons) of cod-liver oil daily. The addition of the cod-liver oil showed no advantage in gains in body weight at 3 months or at 6 months of age. Monthly observations showed no difference between the two groups as to thickness, mellowness, and flexibility of the hide, or as to the animal's health, vigor, or condition.

If dehydrated or barn-dried hay or grass silage constitutes the only roughage, while the calves are kept out of the sunlight, growing animals will probably require a vitamin D supplement. If heavy grain feeding materially lessens the amount of hay consumed, they might get rickets. In other words, it appears that additional vitamin D is needed by the growing calf only under unusual conditions of feeding or management.

Vitamins B and C and Nutritional Scours

Several experiments have indicated that the cow manufactures vitamins B and C in adequate amounts, and that the calf receives enough of them in the milk until its capacity to synthesize them is sufficiently developed to take care of its own needs. Paul H. Phillips, at the Wisconsin station, reported that the calf at birth was deficient in vitamin A, ascorbic acid (vitamin C), and niacin (nicotinic acid). He reported also that 90 percent of calf scours was due to nutritional deficiencies and could be prevented by feeding these substances during its first 2 weeks of life. As a result of this report, many drug houses now are advertising, for the preventions of scours, capsules containing the Wisconsin recommendation—vitamin A, 5,000 International units; vitamin D, 500 International units; vitamin C (ascorbic acid), 250 milligrams; and niacin (nicotinic acid), 50 milligrams.

The rather startling claims concerning the efficacy of these supplements for the control of calf scours led several investigators in Ohio, Michigan, and Cornell University to initiate rather extensive check experiments with more than 1,200 calves. The trials were made in experiment station and university herds, in other State institution herds, and in New York in some private herds. Alternate calves in each herd were fed the supplements, and the other calves served as controls. Capsules of two colors were usually used. Capsules of one color contained the supplement and capsules of the other color contained an inert oil. The herdsmen were not told which capsules contained the supplements. The reports, by W. E. Krauss, for Ohio and Michigan, and A. A. Spielman, for New York, did not indicate any favorable effect on the control of scours from feeding the "scour-prevention capsules."

Calf-feeding experiments in the nutrition herd at Beltsville were being continually disrupted by deaths from scours, pneumonia, and other ailments, when the hopeful reports on the control of calf scours were being made by the Wisconsin station. No division of animals into experimental and control groups was made, but nearly all the calves on feeding experiments from December 1943, to March 1945, received the supplements recommended to control "nutritional scours." During this period of about 15 months, 64 calves received capsules containing ascorbic acid (500 milligrams), and niacin (100 milligrams). Each day the calves also received 20,000 to 40,000 International units of vitamin A from cod-liver oil. Eighteen of these calves, or 28 percent, died before 65 days of age. Eleven of the 18 died before 30 days of age. We did not keep a careful record of the condition of the feces during the first part of the period but of the 18 that died, autopsy reports of the station veterinarian showed scours as the cause of death in 13 cases, scours and pneumonia in 2 cases, and pneumonia in 3. Thirteen of the calves that died had received two capsules daily for the first 5 days and one capsule daily for the next 10 days if they lived that long. Thus, the calves that died had more than twice the amount of each of the supplements included in the capsules reported by the Wisconsin station as capable of controlling 90 percent of "nutritional scours" in calves.

Very few of the calves fed "scour-prevention capsules" at Beltsville were treated with sulfa drugs or any other therapeutic agents; however, one such calf might be cited as a specific case. A Jersey steer received colostrum for 3 days and then skim milk. Starting the day after birth 20 cubic centimeters of cod-liver oil or about 36,000 International units of vitamin A were fed daily. For 4 days starting the day after birth, the calf received two of the capsules daily or a daily dose of 1 gram of ascorbic acid and 200 milligrams of niacin. For the next 11 days the calf was fed one capsule. Although this dosage was much more generous than the Wisconsin recommendations, the calf started scouring on the fifth day after birth. The calf scoured from the fifth to the thirty-fourth day except for the eleventh, twelfth, and thirteen days, when the feces were soft. From the thirty-first day combined sulfaguanidine and sulfathiazole treatment was administered for 8 days. Scours were not observed after the fourth day of this treatment.

Sulfa Drugs for Calf Scours

The use of sulfa drugs began in March 1945, when we realized that the "scour prevention capsules" were not preventing deaths from scours of dairy calves. While there was some variation in dosages, all calves received at least 2 grams daily of either sulfaguanidine or sulfathiazole. These protective doses of sulfa drugs were usually started within 2 or 3 days after birth (sometimes on the day of birth) and were continued for 30 days or longer. If scours developed the dosage was increased for a few days until the scours subsided or the calf died. The severity of scours and the number of deaths was much less during the sulfa drug period than when "scour-prevention capsules" were fed.

From March 23, 1945, to January 19, 1946, 46 calves were placed on feeding experiments. Nearly all were taken from the maternity barn before 3 days of age. Of the 46 calves, 5 died. This gives a mortality rate of 10.6 percent, as compared with the loss of 28 percent among 64 calves fed "scour capsules." Of the 5 calves that received sulfa drugs that died, 1 seemed unable to swallow and consumed less than 1 pound of milk daily for the 6 days that it survived; 1 died at 1 month of age while running to the scales to be weighed, apparently in perfect health. Of the 5 calves that died only 3 had any history of scours.

Those responsible for the feeding of calves should be cautioned not to rely on the use either of sulfa drugs or large doses of vitamin A to prevent scours, pneumonia, or other infections among calves kept in unsanitary quarters. Calf pens should be kept clean and dry and they should be thoroughly disinfected frequently. The intensity of infections among calves is apt to be greater where large numbers of calves are continuously housed together than when only a few calves are kept.

THE AUTHOR

Henry T. Converse is a dairy husbandman in the Division of Nutrition and Physiology, Bureau of Dairy Industry. For 20 years Mr. Converse has conducted research in nutrition of dairy cows and calves, including energy requirements for growth and milk production and the calcium and vitamin A requirements of calves.

FOR FURTHER READING

Bechdel, S. I., Landsburg, K. G., and Hill, O. J.: *Rickets in Calves,* Pennsylvania Agricultural Experiment Station, Technical Bulletin 291, 1933.

Converse, H. T., and Fohrman, M. H.: *Cod-Liver Oil as a Supplement for Dairy Calves When Fed Alfalfa Hay,* American Society of Animal Production, Proceedings, pages 82–83, 1940.

Krauss, W. E.: *Vitamins for Calves,* Feedstuffs, pages 40–44, February 2, 1946.

Ragsdale, A. C.: *Growth Standards for Dairy Cattle,* Missouri Agricultural Experiment Station Bulletin 336, 1934.

Rupel, I. W., Bohstedt, G., and Hart, E. B.: *Vitamin D in the Nutrition of the Dairy Calf,* Wisconsin Agricultural Experiment Station, Research Bulletin 115, 1933.

Spielman, A. A.: *Do Calves Need Vitamin Supplements?* Feedstuffs, pages 38–40, January 5, 1946.

Stewart, Elliott W.: *Feeding Animals,* The Courier Company, Buffalo, N. Y., 1883.

ALSO, IN THIS BOOK

Breeding Better Cows

by M. H. FOHRMAN

IT WOULD be possible to raise our national level of dairy production from four thousand five hundred-odd pounds of milk a year to 7,500 or more and from 185 pounds of butterfat to at least 300. The ways and means of doing it are at hand, but there is reason to believe that little measurable progress in breeding better dairy cattle has occurred in the past decade.

Let us first consider some background details. Cows in Dairy Herd Improvement Association herds showed an average increase of 319 pounds of milk and 14 pounds of butterfat between 1935 and 1945; in 1944, the 561,587 cows on test gave an average of 8,296 pounds of milk and 336 pounds of butterfat. Such figures, however, do not truly measure progress in breeding, because the averages are subject to the influence of markets, prices of milk and feeds, and labor conditions. Besides, the admirable responses to incentives offered to enlarge wartime production must be considered in the light of what would have been produced in a normal situation. We cannot assume that the increase is to be attributed entirely to genetic improvement through better breeding practices.

Much more significant are records that compare the production of daughters with that of their dams. We analyzed such records of 29,598 cows in 708 good herds and found that the dams averaged 452 pounds of butterfat, against 451 pounds for the daughters. These were above-average animals: Their owners were employing their best judgment in selecting herd sires and were culling out the poorer cows, yet the final results were disappointing as far as improvement through breeding was concerned.

It is true that the benefits of any advance in teaching better breeding would come only after a long time because of the slow growth of dairy

Production records of Holstein and Jersey herds at Beltsville show the effectiveness of good inheritance. Records were taken on July 1 for each of the years given

Year	Holsteins				Jerseys			
	Number of cows	Milk (pounds)	Percent (fat)	Fat (pounds)	Number of cows	Milk (pounds)	Percent (fat)	Fat (pounds)
1926.....	25	18, 936	3. 55	672	36	11, 564	5. 49	632
1931.....	39	19, 727	3. 47	684	46	12, 644	5. 45	683
1936.....	24	18, 915	3. 62	686	21	11, 992	5. 17	620
1937.....	24	19, 302	3. 69	712	24	12, 520	5. 17	647
1938.....	29	20, 009	3. 71	742	25	13, 603	5. 16	702
1939.....	34	20, 177	3. 85	776	25	13, 648	5. 22	713
1940.....	40	19, 945	3. 94	785	33	13, 523	5. 41	732
1941.....	38	20, 648	3. 94	814	34	13, 313	5. 61	749
1942.....	35	20, 633	3. 97	818	33	14, 517	5. 35	777
1943.....	44	21, 267	3. 93	837	34	14, 097	5. 47	772
1944.....	52	21, 143	3. 93	829	38	13, 907	5. 74	791
1945.....	56	22, 114	3. 89	856	35	14, 233	5. 73	812

cattle and the vast number of animals that comprise the national dairy herd. Any improvement in the upper levels, however, will gradually filter down through the cattle population as better bred stock becomes available from these top herds. That, of course, throws a large responsibility for better breeding on the owners of the herds that supply bulls to be used in farm breeders' herds, so that the breeders, in turn, will be passing on better breeding stock from their own herds.

Which procedures offer the greatest assurance of this continuous progress? We believe the experience of the Bureau of Dairy Industry gives the answer. Since 1919, our various experimental breeding herds have been following a program of breeding that calls for the continuous use of sires that have already proved their transmitting ability, as determined by comparing the production records of their daughters with those of the dams of these daughters.

Our logic is sound. We know that the ability to produce milk and butterfat is inherited from both parents. When a sire's daughters demonstrate that they are better producers than their own dams, it is a safe conclusion that what they inherit from their sire is better than what comes to them from their mothers. When the increased ability is great enough to be indicative, and a large proportion of the daughters outproduce their dams, then we have the proved sire with which to work. Used in sequence, each of these sires makes a contribution toward the betterment of the germ plasm of the females in the herd. The system replaces the older idea that the only helpful guide to selection of breeding stock was the production record of the individual cow, and that, in the case of young sires, most of the emphasis was to be put on the record of the dam.

Many practical breeders have experienced the success that follows the use of an outstanding sire, but they have been slow to realize that such sires can be properly evaluated only after they have daughters in production, and that means proved-sire breeding. Objections are voiced to the use of older bulls in the herd; good proved sires are hard to find and difficult to handle, and perhaps not so fertile as younger bulls. But none of these objections is tenable if one is willing to put forth the earnest effort needed to breed better cattle.

This method of breeding may have been classed as theoretical a generation ago, but we have used it long enough at Beltsville to offer it now as a successful way to build a high level of production. Our herds have all been handled under uniform conditions, and the results can be interpreted in terms of genetic improvement. A series of 7 unrelated sires have been used in the Holstein herd, and 15 in the Jersey herd. The figures illustrate the effective way that the good inheritance has influenced the average production level of the females in the herd; they do not express the average production in the year indicated, but are a production inventory of the animals in the herd on July 1 of each of these years. No culling has been practiced to influence the averages; all females have been kept in the herd as long as they were useful. In all cases, a total has been made of the highest milk and butterfat record on a mature-equivalent basis of each cow in the herd; this total is divided by the number of cows to give the average shown.

The figures tell their own story: In both breeds, the herd cows in 1945 averaged almost 200 pounds more butterfat than those of 1926. The decline in numbers in 1936 was due to an outbreak of tuberculosis that forced the disposal of many of the older animals. All records were made on three milkings daily for a 365-day lactation period, and the feeding and handling were always uniform. Therefore, it was the good germ plasm contributed by the proved sires that effected the increase in producing ability. The figures may be compared with records of the Dairy Herd Improvement Association, given in the second table.

Outbreeding and linebreeding have been used in both Jersey and Holstein herds at Beltsville, and with bulls of satisfactory transmitting ability there has been no measurable difference in the results. It is not the system of mating that is important, but the quality of sires. Inbreeding may be helpful in concentrating the superior qualities found in good males or females, but its use may be accompanied by a loss in size, and the animal may not be able to express a good inheritance. Experience has shown that inbreeding to certain animals has worked successfully, but it must be tried in the case of any particular individual, and may result in loss of animals and time if the results are unsatisfactory. Hybridizing from inbred strains within a breed takes a long time and many animals in order to establish anything approaching purity; besides, the combination of such

The average production in Dairy Herd Improvement Association herds

Year	Number of herds on test	Number of cows on test	Average production of cows on test		
			Milk (pounds)	Test (percent)	Butterfat (pounds)
1935...................	15, 573	364, 218	7, 977	4. 0	322
1936...................	17, 344	404, 412	7, 012	4. 0	319
1937...................	20, 772	496, 562	7, 923	4. 0	320
1938...................	23, 701	558, 993	7, 831	4. 0	317
1939...................	25, 949	625, 284	7, 977	4. 1	323
1940...................	27, 948	676, 141	8, 133	4. 1	331
1941...................	31, 381	763, 502	8, 225	4. 1	335
1942...................	32, 957	816, 117	8, 323	4. 1	339
1943...................	24, 155	616, 972	8, 325	4. 1	338
1944...................	20, 825	561, 587	8, 296	4. 1	336

inbred strains offers nothing more than a return to the level of production from which the original lines were derived.

One recent development has added much to the value of the proved-sire system. It is the policy of most well organized artificial-breeding associations to use proved sires as much as possible. If the procedure is followed closely, many members of such associations ultimately will have progeny in their herds from a series of good sires.

Proved-sire breeding stands now as a demonstrated method of uninterrupted improvement in the producing ability of dairy cattle, and the measure of this development in the females in the Beltsville herd is a clue to the value of the males produced under this system of breeding when they are used as herd sires. Their inheritance is the same as that of the females, and this is borne out by the results which have come in from herds that have used such young bulls in cooperation with the station where they were bred.

The part of the breeding program carried on with cooperating dairymen and herds at several institutions has yielded a large amount of data in the course of proving the young bulls from our various station herds. This now furnishes abundant proof that these young sires carry the same quality of germ plasm as their half sisters that are developed and tested in our own herds.

Of the 332 proved bulls, 264 sired daughters that averaged better than their dams. This is nearly 80 percent of the bulls, compared to about 48 percent proved in Dairy Herd Improvement Association herds. The 4,619 daughters of these bulls produced an average of 690 pounds more milk and 30 pounds more butterfat than their dams. Proved-sire breeding has thus demonstrated its value as a means of breeding young bulls capable of raising production levels in most dairymen's herds.

Records from station herds show that a large majority of sons of proved bulls
will beget daughters with higher milk-producing ability than that of their dams

Station	Number of sires	Number of daughters	Daughters' production			Dams' production			Number of sires [1]
			Milk (pounds)	Percent (fat)	Fat (pounds)	Milk (pounds)	Percent (fat)	Fat (pounds)	
Holstein									
Woodward.......	27	286	11, 300	3. 43	387	10, 084	3. 40	341	25
Mandan.........	18	153	12, 071	3. 54	427	12, 294	3. 52	432	11
Ardmore.........	5	86	10, 908	3. 59	392	9, 626	3. 57	344	5
Huntley..........	97	1, 111	11, 504	3. 61	415	10, 606	3. 56	378	77
Beltsville.........	85	1, 548	13, 066	3. 55	462	12, 365	3. 49	429	65
All Holstein	232	3, 184	12, 256	3. 56	436	11, 469	3. 51	401	183
Jersey									
Jeanerette........	17	297	6, 845	4. 79	328	6, 246	4. 73	296	13
Lewisburg........	12	110	8, 266	5. 06	418	7, 769	5. 11	397	9
Beltsville........	71	1, 028	8, 215	5. 32	427	7, 778	5. 19	407	59
All Jersey......	100	1, 435	7, 935	5. 19	406	7, 460	5. 09	384	81
Grand total.....	332	4, 619	10, 914	4. 07	426	10, 224	4. 00	396	264

[1] Sires whose daughters produced more milk than their dams.

The supply of good dairy sires has always been limited. The policy of
raising and selling only a part of the young bulls dropped in most herds
has further restricted the number. The result is a price level out of reach
of many dairymen who need better bulls. These factors no doubt have had
a part in holding down the national level of milk production. Good germ
plasm is wasted also by keeping meritorious bulls in service in single herds.

To alleviate this situation and provide service by good sires on a wider
basis, there has been a tremendous development during the past 6 years
in the organization and development of artificial-breeding associations.
The idea first took hold in New Jersey and has now spread to most of the
dairy States. The type of organization varies from the small local unit
owning its own bulls, to the central bull stud plan, where the bulls are
located in one place and semen is drawn and processed for distribution to
the inseminators in a large number of local units. It has been particularly
helpful to the owner of a small herd, as his breeding fees for artificial

insemination total less than the cost of keeping a herd sire. It also relieved him of the problem of purchasing a new and satisfactory bull every 2 or 3 years, and in most cases it has made available to him service from bulls of better quality than he could afford to buy.

Starting with a few thousand cows a year impregnated by this method, the total quickly climbed to about half a million, and at the rate of expansion anticipated by some associations, a million cows a year will soon be bred artificially. Single bulls have sired thousands of calves, and most astonishing of all is the number of females inseminated from the diluted semen had in one ejaculate. During the busy breeding season, 150 cows bred from a single service is not uncommon.

Production figures compiled by the New York Artificial Breeders' Cooperative, Inc., at Ithaca, N. Y., tell a story well worth considering. Twenty-seven of the sires used in that cooperative now have one or more daughters in milk from dams which also had production records. The report lists a total of 178 daughters sired by these bulls with average production of 11,984 pounds of milk and 442 pounds of butterfat. The dams of these daughters produced 11,656 pounds of milk and 418 pounds of butterfat, a net increase of 328 pounds of milk and 24 pounds of butterfat. The sample is small compared to the vast number of cows bred, but it is a fair criterion of what has happened in all herds whose owners were fortunate enough to have had the use of these bulls. It is also a splendid testimonial to the judgment of the committee responsible for selecting sires. An estimated 80,000 cows were bred in the cooperative in 1946—40,000 heifer calves born in a single year with an inheritance to produce 24 pounds more butterfat annually than their dams is bound to lift average production. Then, too, sons of those proved bulls will join lesser herds, there to spread their good qualities.

Similar encouraging results are reported from New Jersey and Maine; altogether, there is much to anticipate from artificial insemination. A note of caution: The men who pick out the bulls should not be pushed too hard by desires to expand operations to the extent that they feel obliged to lower their standards of selection.

More testing is required to furnish a broader foundation for constructive breeding. Membership in Dairy Herd Improvement Associations is still only a small percentage of those who own dairy cows. Herd improvement testing has grown in scope, but still only a small part of the herds of registered cattle have an over-all testing program. Sixteen thousand bulls have been proved in association herds since bull proving was started, but fewer than half of them had daughters with average production better than their dams; of the bulls that proved to be desirable, only a small number were still alive when the proof came in.

Keeping bulls until the proof is in is an important part of cow testing. Artificial breeding associations are always on the lookout for good proved sires, and the quality of the sires holds the key to expansion and development of the associations. It would be well to consider offering more pay in order to get testers who measure up to the demands for adequate cow-testing work. This includes the job of sending in the records for proving bulls and setting up the records in the owners' herds so that they tell the story of his own breeding progress.

Better methods of selling young bulls likewise are worth consideration. In Michigan a plan was inaugurated of pricing young bulls in herds of Dairy Herd Improvement Association members so that value was established at an early age and the bulls could be sold before the cost of feeding made them too expensive for small dairymen. Owners of registered stock might well give thought to the plan, in order that more good bulls can be raised and sold for breeding.

Open Herd Books

Another point: All our dairy cattle breed associations operate with closed herd books, and thereby limit the possibilities of improvement of the breed to only the animals that are eligible to registry. But the laws of heredity operate without regard to whether an animal is numbered and entered in a book. Good combinations of germ plasm often are made in matings of unregistered animals; that plasm is now lost as a source of betterment for the breed. An appendix to the regular herd register would make it possible to bring such hereditary material into use as part of the germ plasm of the registered stock. Necessary precautions could be taken to exclude animals that do not conform to the established color or other characteristics of the breed.

The open herd book would give hope to men who have labored to develop high-producing grade herds by using good registered bulls and already have cows so meritorious that even experts cannot distinguish them from cows in registered herds. Consider the case of a son who inherits such a grade herd. He wants to breed registered cattle, but to satisfy his ambition his only course is to replace his grade animals with the registered stock he can afford. If the approach to a registered herd were open, through a stud-book appendix, he could work toward his goal immediately. He would also have the benefit of the improvement that had been bred into his herd over the years.

The idea of the open herd book is not new. All registry societies abroad permit the entry of good animals through the appendix, and ultimately to full registry. The proposal to adopt the open herd book was made to the Holstein-Friesian Association of America at their annual meeting in 1929. A similar proposal was considered by the Ayrshire Breeders' Association at their annual meeting in 1942. In both instances the members disapproved the suggestion. Nature works slowly, and we need to take advantage of all her fortunate combinations that come in and out of registry.

THE AUTHOR

M. H. Fohrman is a dairy husbandman in charge of the Division of Dairy Cattle Breeding, Feeding, and Management, Bureau of Dairy Industry. Since joining the Department in 1921 he has carried on breeding work with Holstein and Jersey herds at Beltsville to demonstrate the value of using only outstanding proved sires. Mr. Fohrman is a graduate of the University of Missouri.

ALSO, IN THIS BOOK

ARTIFICIAL BREEDING

▲ (North Eastern Pennsylvania) Artificial
ing Cooperative, one of five such organi-
s in Pennsylvania, is an association of
al units, to which belong 2,950 dairymen,
owned 25,882 cows on Nov. 1, 1946)
ne counties. Headquarters is in the re-
led buildings of the former Wyoming
ty Fair just outside Tunkhannock. A
of one of the buildings and one of two
pens—about to be enlarged with addi-
fencing—are shown above. NEPA
or leases a total of 27 bulls of four
dairy breeds.

m F. Schaefer, Jr., has been the manager
cooperative since it was formed in Feb-
1945. In the picture overleaf, his assist-
rank Horrocks, is shown leading a Hol-
bull, Penstate Inka Paul, registry No.
1, to the breeding rack along a passage-
uilt, like the stalls for the bulls, of heavy
.

st part of the success of the cooperative
chaefer attributes to the careful records
re kept of all phases of the work. Each
e 10 technicians employed, all of them
d under supervision of workers at Penn-
ia State College, keeps a breeding record
ch member, as in A, on the third page.

A similar chart, showing when and how often
the cows are bred and the sires, is kept on a
cardboard form in the member's barn for ready
reference when the inseminator visits the farm.
Another important record, not shown here, is
the technician's receipt from a service; it is the
source of information for the records and is
the means whereby members register offspring
from artificial breeding.

Another chart, reproduced as B, third page,
gives data on each sample of semen drawn:
The date drawn, the number of ejaculations,
the amount and quality of the semen, the
clearing time for the methylene blue test, the
degree of dilution with egg yolk-citrate
diluter, and the motility of the sperms. Examinations of motility are made about three
times each week until the sperms show no
life—usually 3 weeks later. The longevity of
the sperms, thus ascertained, has a direct bearing on the expected efficiency of the sample.
To insure that the technicians do not mis-
takenly use the wrong semen, all samples are
colored with a safe coal-tar color when they
are prepared for shipment. Semen from Holstein bulls is colored green; that of Jerseys, red;
and Ayrshires, purple. The semen from the
Guernsey bulls remains yellow from the egg
yolk used in the diluter. Chart B, among

other details, shows that semen was drawn four times (two ejaculations each time) from Penstate Inka Paul in April; a total of 51.5 c.c. of semen, which was diluted to 976 c.c. and used for 473 inseminations. If natural mating had been practiced, Penstate Inka Paul would have served eight cows that month.

Chart C gives Penstate Inka Paul's Individual Sire Efficiency Record for a part of 1946. The cumulative figures show that 31 drawings were made from him January through July; the semen, properly diluted, was used for 3,062 inseminations, of which 2,071 were first services; 710, second services; 213, third; and 68, fourth to cows hard to get in calf. In January and February of 1946, as shown in the right-hand column, 67 percent of cows that received Penstate Inka Paul's semen became pregnant after one insemination. This rate of conception compares very well with natural mating. Charts like C are kept for each bull on the basis of receipts issued by the 10 inseminators and submitted once a month to headquarters.

Altogether, about 40,407 cows have been inseminated in 21 months.

A committee for each breed recommends the purchase of a bull, after close scrutiny of its pedigree and past performance.

The cooperative's balance sheet on June 30, 1946, showed total assets of $54,186.71, including buildings and improvements, $15,438.10; office equipment, $404.86; laboratory equip-

ment, $563.06; barn equipment, $16,4 and bulls owned, $6,410. Revenues fc month were $5,316.15, including $5,1 service fees. Expenses for the month to $2,004.83 (leaving an operating marg $3,311.32). The major expenses were lease ($101.75); feed and hay ($321.66 aries for 4 men ($783.35); shipping the s ($80.32); and depreciation expenses ($32

The cooperative has 21 directors, chos local units on basis of one director for 1,000 cows or major fraction. They me monthly. The technicians meet at least a year to consider suggestions for impr their work, discuss plans and projects, a talk things over with workers at Pennsy State College, among them Joe S. Taylo R. H. Olmstead, extension dairy spec John O. Almquist and C. B. Knodt, c dairy research staff, and others. The dir and the manager also attend State confe of artificial-breeding cooperatives.

Caution in every detail of handling the a has meant that there never has been a s accident at the headquarters. A s stanchion is used to tie each bull every mo until operations are complete. All bull curried every day before releasing. Doc tween inside and outside pens are control an overhead rope and operate on an in track. The doors can be opened and without entering the bull's pen.

NEPA Artificial Breeding Cooperative
MEMBER'S BREEDING RECORD

Name Herbert F. Hunter Address Falls, Pa. Phone S. Winola 2268 Year 1946

Cows in Herd 11 Breed Holstein D.H.I.A. Yes Bangs OK No. Cows Entered 11 $22 advance

NAME AND NUMBER OF COW No.	Date Bred	Bull	Date Re-bred	Bull	Date Re-bred	Bull	Date Re-bred	Bull	Date Re-bred	Bull	Date Re-bred	Bull	Asst's	Service Fees Paid	Remarks
#2443955														1st 4th 5th	
Bessie War Lathrop Star #2351729	1-8	H1												5.	
Pietje Denver Bessie War #2360062	1-14	H1	6-7	H1	6-24	H8	7-15	H6						5. 2	
War Korndyke Denver #2351726	1-17	H8												5.	
Skyline Bessie War #2443954	1-17	H8	1-27	H5										5.	
Bessie War Lathrop Star 2d #2360061	1-26	H5												5.	
...by Denver Star Canink #2443953	1-28	H1												5.	
Bessie War Lathrop Star Onyx #2346813	4-30	H4												5.	
Skyline	5-7	H8												5.	
...2														5.	
Bessie ?														5.	
Skyline														5.	
...72															

Semen record of Penstate Inka Paul Code No H5 #735351

Date 1946	Ejaculations	C.C. Semen	Concentration	M&R Minutes	Dilution	Motility by days 1 2 3 4 5 6 7 8 9 10 11 12 13 14 15 16 17 18 19 20 21 22 23 24 25 26 27 28 29 30
Mar 30	2	7	G	4½	1:16	80 - 70 - 50 - 40 - - - 20 - 30 - 30 - - 5 - 2 - 2 - 2 - - 1 - d
Apr. 6	2	8½	G+		1:20	80 - 60 - 50 - 50 - - 20 - 10 - 2 - 2 - 2 - 2 - 1 - d
Apr.13	2	7	G+	3¾	1:16	80 - 60 - 50 - 50 - - 30 - 10 - 5 - 2 - 2 - 2 - - d
Apr.20	2	7½	G	5	1:16	80 - 60 - 50 - 30 - 30 - 10 - 10 - 5 - 2 - 2 - - 1 - d
Apr.27	2	6½	G+		1:16	80 - 60 - 50 - 40 - 30 - 30 - 20 - 10 - 2 - 2 - 2 - - d
May 4	2	9	G+	3	1:20	75 - 70 - - 40 - 20 - 10 - 10 - 5 - 10 - 3 - 5 - 5 - d
May 11	2	8½	G+	4½	1:14	70 - 60 - 50 - 40 - 25 - 20 - 10 - 2 - 2 - 2 - 1 - d
May 18	2	5	G+	4:30	1:20	75 - 20 - 40 - 30 - 20 - 5 - 10 - 5 - 2 - 2 - 2 - - 1
May 25	2	6½	G+	3½	1:20	70 - 60 - 50 - 30 - 10 - 5 - 2 - 2 - 2 - 2 - - d
June 1	2	5½	G	4½	1:20	70 - 60 - 40 - 40 - 10 - 5 - 5 - 2 - 1 - 2 - d
June 8	2	6½	G		1:24	70 - 50 - 40 - 40 - 5 - 10 - 10 - 2 - 2 - d
June 15	4	6	G+	3½	1:17	60 - 40 - 30 - 10 - 5 - 10 - 10 - 2 - 2 - - 2
June 20	2	6½	G	4½	1:20	80 - 60 - - 50 - 40 - 20 - 20 - 5 - 2 - - d
June 27	1				1:17	70 - - 40 - 40 - - 5 - 5 - c

NEPA ARTIFICIAL BREEDING COOP.
Tunkhannock, Penna.

INDIVIDUAL SIRE EFFICIENCY RECORD
Bull Penstate Inka Paul #735351

1946 Month	No. of Markings	No. of Services 1st 2nd 3rd 4+ Total	Returns 30 days 1st 2nd %Ret	Returns 60 days 1st 2nd %Non-Ret	Returns 180 days 1st 2nd 3rd 4+ Total	% Non-returns 180 days 1st service 2nd service Aver.
Jan.	4	301 73 15 5 394	59 19 79%	82 27 71%	95 33 7 2 137	69% 55% 66%
Feb.	4	270 91 30 12 403	63 22 76%	85 29 68%	92 34 6 4 136	66% 63% 65%
Total	8	571 164 45 17 797	122 41 78%	167 56 70%	187 67 13 6 273	67% 59% 65%
Mar.	5	320 108 33 7 468	67 28 78%	86 34 72%		
Total	13	891 272 78 24 1265	189 69 78%	253 90 71%		
Apr.	4	331 105 29 8 473	70 29 77%	96 32 71%		
Total	17	1222 377 107 32 1738	259 98 78%	349 122 71%		
May	4	369 141 35 11 556	90 33 77%	106 42 71%		
Total	21	1591 518 142 43 2294	349 131 78%	455 164 71%		
June	5	317 126 34 11 488	73 22 79%			
Total	26	1908 644 176 54 2782	422 153 78%			
July	5	163 66 37 14 280				
Total	31	2071 710 213 68 3062				
Aug.						
Total						

MAY 1946

Breed Holstine

SIRE EFFICIENCY

NEPA ARTIFICIAL BREEDING COOP.
Tunkhannock, Penna.

(A) Handwritten sire-efficiency tally sheet with columns for each sire — H1 Aggie, H2 Pixie, H3 Dollar, H5 Paul, H6 Design, H7 McCoy, H8 Burke — each with "Services" (tally marks) and "Ret." columns, plus a final "All Services" section. Rows numbered 1–10 by Date.

All Services	1st	2nd	3rd	4+	Total
1	50	23	4		77
2	64	15	1	3	83
3	48	10	5	2	63
4	46	14	5	3	68
5	44	19	2	1	71
6	60	18	5	2	85
7	53	17	1	2	73
8	35	15	5		55
9	39	19	4	4	66
10	49	19	6	1	75

SIRE EFFICIENCY — ALL BREEDS 1946

NEPA ARTIFICIAL BREEDING COOP.
Tunkhannock, Penna.

(B) Monthly summary table.

1946 Month	No. of Drawings	No. of Services 1st	2nd	3rd	4+	Total	Returns 30 days 1st	2nd	% Non-ret	Returns 60 days 1st	2nd	% Non-ret	Returns 180 days 1st	2nd	3rd	4+	Total	% Non-returns 1st Ser	2nd Ser	after 2nd Ser	two Ser	Probable No. of Cows in calf 180 days	Inseminations required per Non-return 180 days
Jan.	65	1940	543	134	51	2698	466	137	76%	596	188	69%	665	209	41	22	938	66%	63%	65%	87%	1750	1.53
Feb.	57	1580	541	164	49	2334	400	124	75%	508	169	68%	576	199	56	12	843	64%	63%	63%	86%	1491	1.57
Total	122	3520	1104	298	100	5022	866	261	76%	1104	357	68%	1244	406	97	34	1781	65%	63%	64%	87%	3241	1.55
Mar.	62	2001	629	202	72	2904	489	159	76%	622	193	69%											
Total	184	5521	1733	500	172	7926	1355	418	76%	1726	550	68%											
Apr.	61	2014	619	210	61	2904	495	153	75%	671	206	67%											
Total	245	7535	2352	710	233	10830	1850	571	74%	2397	756	68%											
May	67	2439	759	227	97	3520	639	205	74%	762	241	68%											

MONTHLY EFFICIENCY OF LOCALS — JANUARY 1946

C

Local	No. of Cows Bred 1st	2nd	3rd	4th	Returns in Jan	No.	30 Days Returns in Feb — No.	% Non Ret.	60 Days Returns in Mar — No.	% Non Ret.	Returns after 60 Days Apr May June July	180 Days No.	% Non Ret.
Jumbo #1 1st	316				‖‖‖	30	47	76.7%	91	71.6%		97	69%
2nd	81				‖	6	21	74%	32	59%	None	33	59%
3rd	19					1	4		6			7	(67%)
4th	10						4	(75%)	4	(64%)		4	(67%)
Jumbo #2 1st	193				‖‖‖	12	41	79%	54	72%		62	68%
2nd	52					1	10	91%	13	75%		14	73%
3rd	14					1	1		2			3	

MONTHLY REPORT and EFFICIENCY WAYNE LOCAL 1946

Clifford Eno — Inseminator
Clifford Erk — Assistant

D

1946 Month	No. of Services 1st	2nd	3rd	4th	Total	Series of Receipts Used	No. Receipts voided	New Cows No.	Members added No.	Payments Service Fees	Assessment	Returns 30 days 1st ret.	2nd ret.	% Non Ret.	Returns 60 days 1st	2nd ret.	% Non Ret.	Returns 180 days 1st	2nd	3rd	4th	Total	% Non Returns 180 days 1st ser	2nd	3rd	4th	Total Calf	Probable Insem. No. of required Cows per Ten return in 180 days
Jan	283	92	22	7	404	2013 to 2416	-	10	95	$513.00	$142.50	61	23	78%	97	30	63%	105	34	7	5	151	63%	63%			2.53	1.58
Feb	218	76	29	6	329	2417 to 2730	-	9	42	442.00	63.00	45	18	79%	54	28	70%	65	30	8	1	104	70%	61%	68%		2.25	1.46
Total	501	168	51	13	733	2731 to 3041	2	19	137	1015.00	205.50	106	41	78%	141	58	70%	170	64	15	6	255	66%	62%	65%	78%	4.78	1.52
Mar	304	91	26	7	428	3042 to 3052	2	15	118	615.00	177.00	61	28	77%	81	32	71%											
Total	805	259	77	20	1161			34	255	1630.00	382.50	167	69	77%	222	91	70%											

When the receipts are received at the central office from the local technicians, they are tabulated according to date of service, bull used, and whether first, second, third, or fourth service under the heading "services" (chart A, above.) An asterisk denotes the date semen was drawn from each bull, and the figures above it indicate the motility at time of drawing (70 percent in the case of Inka Paul) and (32 days) the length of time that semen showed life in the refrigerator. As any of these services are repeated, the receipt carries the informa-

tion as to date of original service, and the bull that failed to get the cow pregnant. The failures are tabulated opposite, under the heading of "Returns," and the number of returns are counted at the end of 30 days, 60 days, and 180 days, and transposed to the monthly record of the Individual Sire Efficiency Record as of Penstate Inka Paul.

Chart B (page 4), shows how information on all bulls of all breeds is collected from the records of individual bulls and individual breeds. It shows, for instance, that in January 65 samples of semen were obtained from the bulls at Tunkhannock and were used for 2,688 inseminations; probably 1,750 cows were gotten in calf (although a few cows required as many as five services), and the average number of inseminations per cow was 1.53.

Chart C is part of the record that tabulates the efficiency of the 10 local groups for January 1946. It shows, for example, that 426 cows belonging to members of Tunkhannock Local No. 1 were bred that month; of that number, 76 were rebred within 30 days; 133 were rebred in 60 days, and 141 rebred by the end of 180 days. As shown in the right-hand column, 67 percent of the cows bred never returned for service. The information for this record is collected from receipts of the corresponding month.

Chart D is the technician's monthly record of work at one local unit, the one in Wayne County, Pa. It gives data on inseminations and payments by members. Information is

added as it becomes available from the l[...] monthly records.

Above, Schaefer and Horrocks are shown w[...] ping test tubes of semen for shipment to [...] technicians. Each technician is sent a p[...] termined portion of the diluted semen (b[...] upon his estimated needs) from the parti[...] bulls from which semen had been coll[...] that day—enough to inseminate 15 to 30 c[...] although, of course, the technician may [...] have that many calls from dairymen men[...] that day. The semen is first diluted with [...] yolk-citrate, then cooled in a refrigerator i[...] laboratory, put in tubes, packed with cans o[...] wrapped securely, and sent on its way, by a[...] mobile, special delivery mail, and sometim[...] airplane. Most of the members live w[...] 100 miles of Tunkhannock; some live as f[...] 150 miles away.

Artificial breeding has developed into on[...] the greatest advances in the field of dairy [...] bandry. It is making available the use of [...] of proved ability to dairymen who other[...] would have to depend upon bulls of a n[...] poorer quality. It should improve our c[...] cattle at a rate which could never be ac[...] plished with natural breeding. Some [...] have now been used in the artificial bree[...] of more than 10,000 cows each, and the[...] every reason to believe that in the near fu[...] many times this number will be bred to a si[...] bull during his lifetime. It now appears [...] if proper care is exercised, artificial bree[...] will be valuable in preventing the sprea[...] certain types of diseases.

TLE FOR HOT CLIMATES has been a sub-
f study at the Iberia Livestock Experiment
at Jeanerette, La., for a number of years.
have demonstrated that animals having
icient heat-regulating system like the zebu
e) are more apt to survive and perform
satisfactorily in the subtropics than our local
breeds. Cattle of the zebu strain also are superior to European cattle so far as ability to
withstand warm humid climate is concerned.
The animal pictured below, Bull No. 7G1, is
the first cross of zebu × Aberdeen Angus.

A. O. Rhoad, formerly in charge of the Iberia experiment farm, checks the amount of sweat under the discs strapped around each of the two cows shown above, both of which have been exposed for the same length of time to the Gulf Coast sun. The animal at left is a zebu cow, the other is half zebu and half deen Angus. The zebu showed less evider perspiration. Experiments have also s that cattle with Africander blood are h than Angus in the subtropics. The yea below is a halfbreed Africander × Angus

CROSSBRED DAIRY CATTLE

til recently little conclusive work had been ne to prove the merits of cross-breeding dairy tle. Some experiments have now been completed at Beltsville that have included the ossing of Holstein with Jersey and Guernsey, d Dane with Jersey and Guernsey, and Jer- with Holstein. Encouraging results have en obtained. The animal shown above may considered a good example of a crossbred hybrid. She was sired by a proved Red Dane bull on a Guernsey dam. Her record at 1 year and 11 months, milked 3 times a day for 365 days, is 14,055 pounds of milk with 4.79 percent or 674 pounds of butterfat. The following series of pictures includes groups of cows on which production experiments have been run. Unless otherwise indicated, all data are actual first-lactation records for 365 days, three milkings daily. An article on the cross-breeding of dairy cows begins on page 177.

Jersey × Holstein, from left to right:

Cow No.	Pounds of milk	Percentage of butterfat	Pounds of butterfat
X–41	12,453	4.63	576
X–42	9,417	4.90	461
X–47	12,189	5.13	625

X–41 and 42 sired by Jersey bull No. 1114.

Holstein × Jersey, from left to right:

Cow No.	Pounds of milk	Percentage of butterfat	Pounds of butterfat
X–11	12,584	4.82	606
X–20	12,383	5.13	636
X–38	11,929	5.09	607
X–51	13,800	4.44	613

All were sired by Holstein bull No. 966.

Holstein × Guernsey, from left to right:

Cow No.	Pounds of milk	Percentage of butterfat	Pounds of butterfat
X–16	14,577	4.68	683
X–33	11,363	5.53	629
X–44	15,284	4.10	627
X–45	11,341	4.95	561

All were sired by Holstein bull No. 966.

Red Dane × Guernsey, from left to right:

Cow No.	Pounds of milk	Percentage of butterfat	Pounds of butterfat
X–21	14,614	4.12	602
X–52	14,044	4.30	603
X–53	14,055	4.79	674
X–61	12,463	4.35	542

All were sired by Red Dane bull No. D–501.

Red Dane × Holstein, from left to right:

Cow No.	Pounds of milk	Percentage of butterfat	Pounds of butterfat
X–22	16,949	3.60	611
X–56	16,100	4.08	657
X–58	13,956	4.27	596
X–63	14,030	3.79	532 (279 days)

All were sired by Red Dane bull No. D–501.

Red Dane × Jersey, frcm left to right:

Cow No	Pounds of milk	Percentage of butterfat	Pounds of butterfat
X–10	12,561	5.03	631
X–18	13,315	5.06	674
X–29	12,691	4.56	579
X–70	9,295	4.25	395 (268 days)

All were sired by Red Dane bull No. D–501.

Some tests have also been run on 3-breed crosses that were the result of mating 2-breed females to males of a third breed. The 10 animals shown above have been used in these experime... Their rather complex parentage and milk pr duction records are discussed on page 1

These bulls were used in the dairy cross-breeding experiments at Beltsville. Top to bottom: Jersey bull No. 1114; Holstein No. 966; and Red Dane No. D–501.

THE UDDER of a dairy cow (left) is made up almost entirely of glandular tissue. That of a beef-type cow (right) is mostly fat, and under the best of conditions could not yield much m Why some cows give more milk than othe discussed in an article beginning on page

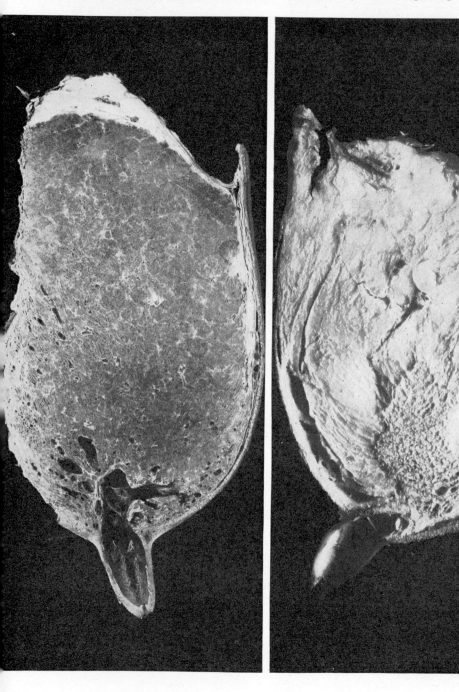

EXAMINATION of the mammary glands calves at 4 months of age or younger, it is sible to foretell whether or not they will be h producers of milk. The upper photo shows the mammary glands of a calf 2½ months old; center, 3½ months old; and lower, a calf 5 months old. An article on the subject, with other illustrations, begins on page 195.

REMARKABLE RESULTS have come from research on the stimulation of udders by hormones to bring about lactation in female animals that might otherwise be sterile. The effect of a synthetic estrogen, stilbestrol, is shown by these two yearling does. The (above) is untreated; the other had been trea with stilbestrol for 3 months. She gave a m imum of 2.7 pounds of milk a day. See art on page 123 by S. R. Hall and J. F. Sy

Cross-Breeding Dairy Cows

by M. H. FOHRMAN

W E WONDERED whether the spectacular vigor of hybrid corn could be matched in dairy cattle—whether we could cross purebred, efficient Jerseys and Holsteins, for instance, and get an increase in milk that we could say was due to hybrid vigor. We started such an experiment in 1939, and our first results lead us to believe that a part of the gain we got might have come from the extra vitality.

We had some examples to follow. Breeders of poultry, swine, and beef cattle, and of corn and several other plants had had practical, even startling, results with crosses of different breeds. But little conclusive work had been done with dairy cattle. Nearly 30 years ago experiments in crossing Holstein-Friesian, Jersey, Guernsey, Ayrshire, and Aberdeen-Angus cattle were reported from Maine. Most of these experiments were made with mixed dairy and beef breeds and not dairy cattle alone. A study in the crossing of Guernseys and Holsteins was started in Massachusetts in 1911. At the University of Wisconsin some crosses were made with Jerseys, Holstein-Friesians, and Aberdeen-Angus. In most of the experiments, however, the level of the primary function of dairy cattle—milk production—and the transmission level of the bulls of the dairy breeds were not clearly established.

When the Bureau of Dairy Industry began to explore the field of cross-breeding of dairy cattle at Beltsville, we brought in foundation females from the proved-sire bred herds at our field stations—Holsteins from Huntley, Mont., and Mandan, N. Dak., Jerseys from Lewisburg, Tenn., and Guernseys from the Sandhill station in South Carolina. Females of the Red Danish milk breed were available at Beltsville, as well as proved Holstein, Jersey, and Red Danish sires. All foundation females were from production-bred herds—the bulls had proved they

177

could beget heifers that surpassed their mothers. We felt that the blending of these proved stocks would bring forth any hybrid vigor that might be expected to result from interbreed matings.

The project differed from the usual pattern of crossing breeds in that it called for continuous introduction of new genes, the units of inheritance, through the use of proved sires of different breeds. We proposed to have only a limited number of interhybrid matings. Females resulting from mating Holsteins and Jerseys, for example, are mated to Red Danish sires for the three-breed crosses; such females, in turn, are mated to either Holstein or Jersey proved sires in a second round of the three breeds involved.

The Holstein sire, No. 966, was bred at Beltsville, and proved in a cooperating herd before he was used in cross-breeding. Thirty-one of his daughters, milked three times daily for 305 days, had an average mature equivalent of 18,416 pounds of milk and 645 pounds of butterfat, compared to an average of 17,772 pounds of milk and 619 pounds of butterfat for their dams. This sire also proved to be heterozygous for color and had sired several red and white calves.

The Jersey sires were herd bulls bred at Beltsville and proved in co-operating herds. Most of the Jersey matings were made to No. 1114. The Red Danish bull had been proved in the herd at Beltsville, and all Red Danish matings until April 1944 were made to him.

All the females were weighed and measured periodically. Their ability to produce was determined in the first lactation period under uniform conditions. All were milked three times daily for a 365-day lactation period and were bred about $4\frac{1}{2}$ months after calving. During the milking period, all were barn-fed, because pastures at Beltsville vary and their beneficial effects would not appear with all cows at the same stage of lactation. The cows were fastened in stall ties and were turned out in a dry lot for a short time after milking, when weather permitted.

We crossed four breeds, and tried to keep all combinations in numerical balance. No reciprocal or reverse crosses with Guernseys were made because we had no proved Guernsey sire. Only a few matings of Jerseys and Guernseys were made because we thought they are too much alike. With the Holstein, Jersey, and Red Danish breeds, the plan was to make reciprocal crosses, but the matings of Holstein and Jersey bulls to Red Danish females were held up for a while in order that we could increase the size of the Danish herd. (A reciprocal cross is one that is the opposite of a previous mating; for example, the mating of a Red Danish bull and a Holstein cow would be the reciprocal of one between a Holstein bull and a Red Danish cow.) Some of the groups were upset by unbalanced sex ratios, but we are trying to bring the group to equal numbers.

The accompanying table shows the records of the crossbred cows that completed one lactation period or progressed far enough to afford an estimate of their ability. All cows that came into milk are listed—no culling was practiced. To help in making comparisons, let me point out that the average production of all cows in the Dairy Herd Improvement Association herds in 1945 was 8,592 pounds of milk and 346 pounds of butterfat and in 1941, 8,225 pounds of milk and 335 pounds of fat on two milkings daily; and 226 junior 2-year-old Holsteins included in the Advanced Register test for 1945 averaged 13,833 pounds of milk and 493 pounds of fat on three milkings daily. The average of this class has been close to 500 pounds of fat since 1933.

Production records of the cows used in cross-breeding experiments at Beltsville

No. of cow	Pounds of milk	Percentage of fat	Pounds of butterfat	Age (years and months)	Remarks
		JERSEY BULL × GUERNSEY COW			
X–13........	10, 653	5. 27	562	2–2	
		JERSEY BULL × HOLSTEIN COW			
X–1.........	9, 784	4. 85	475	2–0	
X–3.........	13, 065	4. 71	615	1–11	
X–17........	13, 837	3. 85	533	2–3	
X–32........	13, 728	3. 94	540	1–11	
X–35........	10, 508	5. 24	550	2–1	Mastitis.
X–41........	12, 453	4. 63	576	2–5	
X–42........	9, 417	4. 90	461	3–3	
X–47........	12, 189	5. 13	625	1–8	
		HOLSTEIN BULL × JERSEY COW			
X–5.........	13, 032	4. 62	602	2–4	
X–11........	12, 584	4. 82	606	2–4	
X–20........	12, 383	5. 13	636	1–11	
X–30........	11, 867	5. 60	664	2–0	
X–38........	11, 929	5. 09	607	2–1	
X–40........	13, 690	4. 74	649	2–8	
X–51........	13, 800	4. 44	613	2–5	
		HOLSTEIN BULL × GUERNSEY COW			
X–16........	14, 577	4. 68	683	2–5	
X–26........	11, 717	4. 84	567	2–0	
X–28........	14, 052	4. 63	651	2–3	
X–33........	11, 363	5. 53	629	2–0	
X–43........	11, 990	4. 12	494	2–4	Mastitis.
X–44........	15, 284	4. 10	627	1–11	
X–45........	11, 341	4. 95	561	2–9	
X–59........	8, 471	4. 70	398	2–9	231 days, incomplete.

Production records of the cows used in cross-breeding experiments at Beltsville—
Continued

No. of cow	Pounds of milk	Percentage of fat	Pounds of butterfat	Age (years and months)	Remarks
		RED DANE BULL × HOLSTEIN COW			
X–14.........	13, 643	4. 05	552	2–2	
X–22.........	16, 949	3. 60	611	2–2	
X–23.........	14, 636	3. 77	552	2–0	
X–46.........	11, 103	4. 05	449	1–11	Mastitis.
X–56.........	16, 100	4. 08	657	2–0	
X–58.........	13, 956	4. 27	596	2–4	
X–63.........	14, 030	3. 79	532	2–4	279 days, incomplete.
		HOLSTEIN BULL × RED DANE COW			
X–15.........	12, 730	4. 04	514	2–3	
		RED DANE BULL × JERSEY COW			
X–7.........	12, 228	4. 80	586	2–7	
X–10.........	12, 561	5. 03	631	1–11	
X–18.........	13, 315	5. 06	674	2–2	
X–29.........	12, 691	4. 56	579	1–11	
X–70.........	9, 295	4. 25	395	1–11	268 days, incomplete.
		RED DANE BULL × GUERNSEY COW			
X–21.........	14, 614	4. 12	602	2–1	
X–52.........	14, 044	4. 30	603	2–2	
X–53.........	14, 055	4. 79	674	1–11	
X–61.........	12, 463	4. 35	542	1–11	
X–73.........	7, 066	3. 98	281	2–0	196 days, incomplete.

Some footnotes to the records are needed. One Jersey × Guernsey heifer died in her first lactation period. The Jersey-Holstein crosses X–17 and X–32 were sired by Jersey bulls other than No. 1114, and are considerably below the other six in percentage of butterfat. The early calving of X–47 came about because she was bred by a young bull in the calf barn. Five more Holstein × Red Dane heifers, sired by No. 966, were under production age when this tabulation was made. All the Red Dane × Jersey heifers were sired by D–501. Four heifers from Red Dane cows, sired by Jersey bull No. 1114, were born, but two died and two were under calving age when we compiled our records. Two more Red Dane × Guernsey heifers are in the herd; six of the seven are by sire D–501. Analyses of birth weights and growth and comparisons of daughters with their dams await results of further work and tests.

In all, 38 females of the various two-breed combinations completed production records. Their average production was 12,904 pounds of milk and 588 pounds of butterfat; the average test was 4.60 percent of butterfat, and average age at calving, 2 years and 2 months. Four incomplete records not included in the average should not materially alter it. Ten heifers had not come into milk; they will bring our total of two-cross animals to 52; in breeding large animals, that is a sizeable group, and when handled under carefully controlled conditions the results are indicative. A few records have been interfered with by mastitis, but on the whole there has been a free expression of inheritance in these cattle.

The average production of the different combinations varied somewhat, but the numbers in each group were relatively small, and a few additional animals in each group might bring the production more in line. There is a possibility of some genetic difference in the sires, however, but at this stage it appears that the heifers sired by the Holstein No. 966 and Red Dane D–501 are about equal and somewhat better than those sired by Jersey No. 1114 and the two other Jersey bulls used.

Most of the 38 crossbred heifers produced better than their dams. Since they are daughters of proved sires, it was to be expected that they would outproduce their dams. We carefully analyzed the production records of their ancestors and calculated the amount of the average increase that we could expect. We found that the actual increase in production of the daughters over dams was more than the increase we had expected. This may be due to hybrid vigor.

The answer to the question of breed intermating is slowly evolving, as more of the three-breed combinations come into production, and the limited information now available is here tabulated.

Fourteen more three-breed hybrids were sired by No. 966. Seven are from Red Dane × Jersey dams, three from Red Dane × Guernsey dams, one from a Jersey × Guernsey dam, and the other three are from dams which resulted from crosses of three breeds. This is the beginning of the second cycle of three breeds.

Thirteen other three-breed heifers were sired by Red Danish bulls, one by D–501, four by D–540, an inbred son of D–501, seven by D–508, and one by D–507. Five are from Holstein × Guernsey dams, six from Holstein × Jersey dams, and two from Jersey × Holstein dams.

Three other three-breed heifers were sired by Jersey No. 1114, two from Red Dane × Holstein dams, and the other from a dam representing three breeds.

Only eight of these three-breed animals have completed 365-day lactation records; their average is not conclusive, but it is impressive. The eight averaged 14,927 pounds of milk and 641 pounds of butterfat—average test 4.32 percent—at an average age of 2 years. The incomplete records available at this time do not indicate that this average

182					YEARBOOK OF AGRICULTURE

Three-breed crosses sired by Holstein Bull No. 966

No. of cow	Parentage of dam	Pounds of milk	Percentage of fat	Pounds of butterfat	Age (years and months)
X–50.....	Red Dane × Jersey.......	16, 186	3. 97	643	1–11
X–62.....	.......do	16, 862	3. 92	661	2–0

Three-breed crosses sired by Red Dane bulls

No. of cow	Parentage of dam	Pounds of milk	Percentage of fat	Pounds of butterfat	Age, years and months	Remarks
X–39...	Jersey × Holstein	13, 992	4. 35	609	1–11	
X–54...	.......do...............	16, 500	4. 16	686	1–11	
X–55...	Holstein × Guernsey.......	15, 284	4. 47	684	2–1	
X–60...	.......do...............	15, 036	3. 98	598	1–11	
X–65...	Holstein × Jersey	12, 896	4. 67	602	1–11	
X–66...	Holstein × Guernsey.......	11, 037	4. 30	475	2–3	240 days, incomplete.
X–68...	Holstein × Jersey	6, 605	4. 78	316	2–3	177 days, incomplete.
X–71...	.......do...............	7, 788	4. 42	345	2–0	208 days, incomplete.
X–75...	.......do...............	6, 170	4. 94	305	1–11	182 days, incomplete.

Three-breed crosses sired by Jersey Sire No. 1114

No. of cow	Parentage of dam	Pounds of milk	Percentage of fat	Pounds of butterfat	Age, years and months	Remarks
X–48...	Red Dane × Holstein.......	12,668	5.07	643	2–0	
X–77...	Holstein × Red Dane.......	5,858	4.11	240	2–0	164 days, incomplete.
X–81...	Red Dane × Holstein......	5,175	4.67	242	1–11	152 days, incomplete.

will be greatly reduced, and it is significant that all but one of these three-breed heifers exceeded their two-breed dams in production of butterfat.

One of the striking characteristics shown by all of these crossbred animals is their persistency in milk production. Often the monthly butterfat production varies less than 10 pounds from the high month to the low month. This is perhaps one of the factors that adds to the production potential of the proved sires used in this study and in our other proved-sire breeding.

Some intermating of hybrids has already been worked into the project. That is being done in a limited way in order to check the transmitting ability of males bred like the females listed above. Cross-bred bull X–120 was a son of Red Dane D–501 and his dam was a Holstein foundation cow. He was kept a while for use on heifers that might be difficult to settle and two of his daughters are in the herd. The first of these is X–49; her dam was a Holstein × Jersey female, and she is therefore a three-breed cow with Holstein in both sire and dam. She freshened at 2 years of age and produced 14,082 pounds of milk and 658 pounds of butterfat, testing an average of 4.68 percent. Her dam freshened at 2 years and 4 months and gave 12,584 pounds of milk and 606 pounds of butterfat with an average test of 4.82 percent. One case proves nothing but is an indication that the inheritance for milk and butterfat production should be the same in these males as has been demonstrated by the females of similar breeding.

Two other bulls have been sampled. X–179 is a son of D–501 and his dam is a Jersey × Holstein. He has three daughters in the herd—all from three-breed dams. X–191 is also sired by D–501, and his dam is a Holstein × Guernsey. There are six of his daughters in the herd, four from three-breed dams and two from two-breed dams.

A summary of the records completed by 38 two-breed and 9 three-breed cows shows an average of 13,273 pounds of milk and 599 pounds of butterfat—average test 4.55 percent; average age 2 years 2 months.

We are conducting this cross-breeding project in order to develop exact knowledge on the subject. Results obtained so far may warrant a few speculations as to the applications.

First, we must emphasize that production-bred foundation stock and production-proved sires were used almost entirely. It can be said, therefore, that similar results can be expected only where proved stock is used in making the crosses. This emphasizes the value of proved sires in breeding for milk and butterfat production. Factors that control those yields appear to be similar in the different dairy breeds. Numbers are large enough and we have enough combinations to indicate that we can repeat our good results if good sires are used.

The standard warning against cross-breeding is that "if Holsteins and Jerseys are intermated the resulting animals will produce Jersey quantity and Holstein quality of milk." This may be true with random-bred animals of the two breeds, but actually we can normally expect that the chances for Holstein quantity and Jersey quality of milk are as likely as the reverse, and that most of the offspring will produce at an interbreed level in both milk and percentage of butterfat.

This type of cross-breeding holds possibilities for expanding the usefulness of our registered cattle because proved sires of the different breeds must be used in all crosses—at the start and in later matings—to maintain the high level of production and add hybrid vigor.

Commercial application awaits the demonstration of the hybrid's superior ability. Many commercial milk herds lack facilities for raising their own replacements, and are always in the market for dairy cows and heifers. Cross-breeding fits well into the latest advances that are being made in dairy cattle-breeding practices. Artificial insemination, for example, permits of the expansion of cross-breeding work without the necessity of keeping extra herd sires. Let us assume that a dairyman in a region with good pastures and an abundance of cheap home-grown roughage has followed a practice of selling about 10 or 12 extra heifers each year from a herd of 50 milking animals. This represents the surplus females above his requirements for herd replacements. If he is a member of an artificial-breeding association he can order semen from proved bulls of other breeds than the one he owns to impregnate 20 or 25 cows in his herd, and these crossbred calves will be sold as surplus. When the market appreciates the value of well-bred hybrid heifers, they should bring a premium price and will cost no more to raise than straight-bred heifers.

Hybridizing may also appeal to the man who has spent 10 or 15 years building up a good producing grade herd, only to find that the closed herd book is a bar to his ever having any of his good cows registered. To become a breeder of registered stock he must sacrifice his good grade cows and purchase registered females, even though his herd may have been bred entirely from registered bulls. His surplus cows are sold for dairy purposes and the basis of their value should be their production records. If cross-breeding can raise the level of production of cows in his herd, their value when sold should be increased correspondingly.

THE AUTHOR

M. H. Fohrman, head of the Division of Dairy Breeding, Feeding, and Management of the Bureau of Dairy Industry, has been in charge of the Department's dairy-cattle breeding work at Beltsville since 1921.

ACKNOWLEDGMENTS

Cooperating with Mr. Fohrman in the preparation of this article were: R. A. Hilder, dairy husbandman, who supplied production and other data; and John Confer, herdsman, who supplied information on the feeding and care of cattle.

FOR FURTHER READING

Fohrman, M. H., and Graves, R. R.: *Experiments in Breeding Holstein-Friesian Cattle for Milk- and Butterfat-Producing Ability, and an Analysis of the Foundation Cows and of the First Out-Bred Generation*, U. S. D. A. Technical Bulletin 677, 1939.

The Inside of a Dairy Cow

by W. W. SWETT and C. A. MATTHEWS

THE DARKEST place in the world, William Dempster Hoard once remarked, is the inside of a cow. The former Governor of Wisconsin was referring to the lack of facts about the significance of body form in dairy cattle—how a farmer, that is, can identify a good producer on the basis of her appearance, since he cannot see inside. The question vitally concerns dairymen, who succeed or fail as their cows give milk and butterfat: Only 3 or 4 percent of the milk cows in the United States are actually tested for producing ability, and at least 96 percent of the time, therefore, a dairyman has to rely on the looks of an animal when he buys onc for his herd.

For generations the problem has puzzled and challenged cattle breeders, who select and mate their best animals in constant efforts to get cows that give more milk, and then study the results of their handiwork in the hope of determining the basic reason why one cow produces more than another. Formerly, as now, some breeders accomplished more than others; their herds grew better, looked better, and gave more milk.

The owners and their neighbors speculated as to why these animals were superior. The keen observers among them found certain points more or less common to superior animals, came to look upon those points as associated with the desired performance, and, on that basis, started to imitate the successful breeders. Progressive cattlemen took pride in showing off their better animals and, as time went on, competition developed; they began to bring their cattle together for comparison—probably by a disinterested judge. So, cattle shows and judging developed one hundred fifty-odd years ago. Later, agricultural societies and breed associations put out scales of points and score cards for judging, revising the criteria as new theories were advanced or abandoned. Then came livestock judging

185

as a classroom subject and at fairs, national dairy cattle shows and expositions, and interscholastic judging contests.

Undoubtedly all these activities do much good. They stimulate thought, bring exchanges of ideas, create a more uniform ideal of dairy cattle type, and establish goals for less experienced dairy farmers. But the fact remains that many details commonly considered important pertained largely to the beauty of the animals. Logical explanations are given for desiring certain body characteristics, yet there is little scientific information to support some of them. Besides, little credit has been given to the two vital points, the recorded ability of cows to give milk and butterfat and the proved ability of sires to transmit high production to their daughters.

The ideas and ideals of the show ring have set the pattern for most teaching of subjects pertaining to dairy type and for competitive judging among boys and girls, college students, and farmers. Show-ring activities, consequently, should be conducted so as to emphasize known performance as well as excellence of body form.

To increase the educational value of the show ring, and thereby instruction in judging and selecting dairy cattle, we made a plan that recognizes both type and records of production in arriving at a final placing for a class of animals in the show ring, or in selecting animals for any purpose.

The plan, which has been used successfully, covers the judging of cows on the basis of combined ratings for type and production performance; for judging sires on the basis of the type-production rating of their daughters; for judging cows by groups; and for conducting judging contests in which the combined-rating system is used. It obviously cannot be applied to heifers or bulls that do not have daughters with records of production. Under the system, a class of cows is first judged on the basis of type and lined up in the usual manner. Each cow is assigned a numerical rating for type; this represents her relative position in the line. She is also given a numerical rating that represents the relative position of her production among the cows in the class. The two ratings are combined, and the cows are realigned according to their combined ratings for type and production.

The procedure differs from the so-called production shows, in various parts of the United States, in which a minimum production record is usually required for every cow entered for competition on the basis of type. Such a requirement serves only to limit competition to cows with moderate milking records. It gives no consideration to differences in production—a cow with a record of 1,000 pounds butterfat in a year receives no more credit than one that barely meets the requirements for entry.

Although the plan was developed primarily for judging individual cows, it has been adapted to the Danish system, which consists simply of placing the cows in groups representing well-defined degrees of excellence in type. Cows meeting established standards for any particular group are placed in that group, and all cows in the group receive identical awards.

Thus, one need not split hairs over minor points for cows of similar type, and one can recognize all breeders who have attained certain standards of excellence, rather than a few with top-ranking individual animals. The judge need not award first prize to a mediocre animal when classes do not contain superior individuals.

Herd sires are rated on the basis of the type and performance of their daughters. Each sire's daughters are treated as a group. Each group is judged for type and given ratings for it, for butterfat production, for increase or decrease in butterfat production as compared with their dams, and for the percentage of the daughters that are better than their respective dams in butterfat yield. The sires themselves are not rated on the basis of their own type, consequently they need not be exhibited—a costly and sometimes dangerous practice for valuable, old, and heavy animals. The method is essentially similar to the procedure followed in the selection of a herd sire. Our plan was worked out with the current conceptions of type unaltered, although we believe numerous ideas of type are based largely on suppositions that may have little scientific support.

Build and Performance

Judging in this way does not settle all the problems in choosing a cow or bull, especially in everyday farming operations. The solutions would come if all milk cows were tested for ability to produce, and sold and handled on that basis. But in all probability it will be many years before most milk cows are so tested. It is important, therefore, to obtain every bit of information that may be used to provide the soundest possible basis for selecting animals by their appearance, body form, or physical characteristics.

As a start toward getting this knowledge, all available information about the relation between build and performance in several species of animals was studied. The investigators learned, for example, a great deal concerning the mechanics of the horse and the relation of its form to its strength and adaptability. Some data were obtained pertaining to the form of meat animals and its significance as to carcass value. Leading anatomists, physiologists, athletic directors, and other specialists were asked for precise information that would indicate, for instance, whether a specific shape among humans would indicate a better constitution or stamina than some other form. Medical colleges had records of thousands of autopsies, but in most cases pathological conditions were involved, and their data helped little. Veterinarians offered many ideas and opinions, but none of those interviewed could supply specific data to clarify the subject.

Theories taught in the show ring and classroom implied that there were certain relationships between the external form and proportions of the dairy cow and the size of her body cavities and chest and abdominal organs. They also implied that large cavities and internal organs were essential for strong constitution and good feeding capacity, and thus for efficient and high production.

Soon after our studies began, we made arrangements with Swift & Co. to obtain measurements of cows purchased for slaughter, and to weigh and measure their internal organs and carcasses. Ante mortem and post mortem data were obtained on nearly 400 cows. Most of the cows, selected for the study at the time they were bought in the yards, showed indications of being identified with one of the dairy breeds and of having been kept for dairy purposes. No record of their producing ability was obtainable, but our data provided ample material for our study, which was published in 1939.

In the meantime, a similar study was started at Beltsville, where cows in the experimental breeding herd were slaughtered when they had fulfilled their purpose of demonstrating their producing capacity and leaving offspring for comparison with themselves.

Before slaughter, each cow was photographed and her form measured. At the time of slaughter, internal organs and endocrine glands were weighed. The dimensions of the chest cavity were measured for length, depth, and width at every rib or vertebra. Thirty-seven ante mortem and eighty-two post mortem items were included for each cow. Since every cow had a record of production, the data thus obtained provided a basis for determining not only the relationship between external form and internal anatomy, but also the interrelationships between external form, size of organs and body cavities, and capacity for milk production.

The study had not long been under way when a number of the State agricultural experiment stations became interested, and a cooperative arrangement was made with more than 20 of them to handle in the same way the cows to be discarded from their herds. The information was catalogued according to the plan followed at Beltsville.

When approximately 600 cows had been studied in this way, a report was prepared on the average body form and anatomy of cows of the more prominent dairy breeds studied, and how much the form and anatomy of individuals and breeds varied. It has served as a useful guide in subsequent anatomical studies. Correlation studies are planned when data on a sufficiently large number of cows are available to justify statistical analyses.

· Pregnancy is a disturbing factor in interpreting results of many studies of inheritance, growth, nutrition, physiology, lactation, body form, and anatomy of animals. More specific information is needed on what takes place in the pregnant uterus. In the course of the anatomical studies of more than 900 cows, pregnant animals have sometimes been slaughtered. In such cases, records were kept of the weight of the uterus and its contents, the fetus, the amniotic fluids, and the fetal membranes. An analysis of these records, which are available for 115 pregnancies, has shown the rate of growth of the various parts and their relation to one another. It has shown the changes in body form of the fetus during successive stages of gestation, and the breed and sex differences in weight of fetus. The results are particularly valuable from a scientific point of view.

Study of the Udder

Because the udder is so important, major attention was focused on that organ. Early in the study—even before the program of slaughtering cows was launched—regular examinations were made of the udders of cows in the Beltsville herd to detect individual differences and changes through lactating life in an effort to learn more about the qualities and characteristics of the udders of superior cows. With such a lifetime history as a background, we obtained more detailed information about the structure of the mammary glands at slaughter and afterwards.

When a cow was killed at Beltsville, her udder was removed and suspended from a frame in a natural position. It then was filled with a formalin solution by injection under pressure through the teats. The quantity of fluid held by the individual quarters was measured as a means of determining the capacity of the secretory system of the udder.

After the udder was filled and distended, it was placed in a low-temperature chamber and frozen. Then it was cut with a band saw into vertical cross-sections approximately an inch thick, care being taken to have one cut follow the long axis of the front teats and one the long axis of the rear teats. The sections were thawed, washed, and photographed. Various studies were started to determine the comparative physical characteristics of the tissues of individual udders to show variations and, if possible, the relation between such characteristics and production records of the cow during life. The results—particularly with regard to the characteristics of mammary tissue—are not sufficiently complete yet to warrant conclusions. We have, however, determined the weights and capacities of udders of cows of different breeds, ages, stages of lactation, and levels of producing ability.

Individual variations were great. The udders of lactating Holsteins held an average of more than 60 pounds and the Jerseys more than 51 pounds of formalin solution. In both breeds the measured capacity was nearly one and a half times the weight of the udder.

The udder tissue is like a sponge. Blocks of tissue that have been treated with formalin and frozen can be subjected to pressures of 300 pounds for several minutes until they have yielded nearly all of the moisture they contained and become like thin wafers. When again placed in water or weak formalin they quickly become restored to their original thickness

The secretory systems of more than 400 amputated udders have been measured at Beltsville

	249 Holsteins		191 Jerseys	
	Lactating	Dry	Lactating	Dry
Number of cows.........................	134	115	110	81
Average age ....years—months..	5–11	6–1	6–7	6–8
Average time since last calving.months—days..	5–14	13–15	4–11	15–1
Average weight of udder............pounds..	43.05	25.49	36.09	24.58
Average capacity of udder............do....	60.74	36.40	51.43	29.13
Average relation of capacity to weight of udder.........................percent..	149.51	143.92	145.54	117.67

and appearance and pick up fluid to the extent of about four times their pressed weight.

These facts have an important bearing on the results of experiments, begun at Beltsville in 1926, that proved to be revolutionary and provided a basis for much of the work since performed by research workers in the physiology of lactation. Before the experiments were made, it was taught that only a small amount of the milk obtained from a cow at a milking— perhaps a pint for each quarter—was present in the udder when milking began. People supposed that the stimulating effect of milking brought a sudden rush of blood to the udder and that the milk was manufactured rapidly during the brief time the cow was being milked. But it was found that a large part of the quantity regularly obtained at a definite milking time could be obtained from the same udder that had been amputated from a cow slaughtered just before her regular milking hour.

In 11 trials it was found that 70 percent of the average quantity obtained at regular milkings before slaughter was obtained from the amputated udders. In one case the post mortem yield was more than 100 percent of the average at corresponding milkings during the previous 10 days. When we cut open the udders, after we had removed as much milk as we could, we found that most of them contained a considerable quantity of milk—the milk was there, but the dead cow could not aid in its removal. We concluded that milk secretion is essentially a continuous process and that practically all of the milk obtained at a milking is present in the udder when milking is begun.

This emphasized the desirability of large udders, or udders with large storage capacity, and raised the question of how the udder of a cow producing 50 to 75 pounds of milk on two milkings or 100 pounds on three milkings daily could hold so much. This question has since been answered by the measurements of udder capacity. At the same time, it emphasized the importance of milking high-producing cows more than twice daily, because secretion undoubtedly is slowed down and finally stops as pressure in the udder is built up by the accumulation of milk. The more frequent milking tends to keep the pressure down and permits unrestricted milk secretion at a maximum rate.

In a comparison of a highly specialized dairy cow and a highly specialized beef cow, body measurements were made, the internal organs were weighed and measured, the skeleton of each was completely mounted for purpose of comparison by measurements and photographs, and the udders were filled, frozen, and sectioned. Although the cows differed greatly in form, we found no differences in their internal organs big enough to indicate significant differences in function, and in most respects their skeletons were surprisingly similar. Aside from their external form, the most striking difference found was in the quantity of secretory tissue in their udders. The dairy cow's udder consisted almost entirely of glandular tissue, while that of the beef cow contained little except a mass of fat. The dairy cow was 19 years old, had been a regular breeder until she reached old age, and for nearly 5 years held the world's record for the Jersey breed in butterfat production. The beef cow had borne eight calves. She was said to have been a good milker for a beef cow, but in view of the almost complete lack of glandular tissue in her udder, it does not seem possible that she could have produced a large amount.

In another investigation of the differences between beef and milk cows, four Herefords were put in a dairy herd some 2 months before calving, so they could get used to being handled regularly. They were maintained through a lactation period in the same way a dairy herd is managed. Although they were milked up to the time that the milk yield was less than a pound a day, their lactation periods averaged only 211 days and production for the entire period averaged only 557.45 pounds of milk and 27.66 pounds of butterfat. One cow produced only 80.6 pounds of milk.

In skeletal structure, the Herefords were not greatly different—except for body size and weight—from the Holstein cows with which they were compared. The udder and some of the glands—particularly the thyroid and the pancreas—were comparatively small in the Herefords, both in actual weight and in relation to net body weight. The total quantity of mammary-gland tissue and the measured udder capacity of the Herefords were deficient. These results indicate that cows of the specialized beef breeds are relatively poor producers because they do not inherit a mammary development sufficient to enable them to be liberal milkers. The significance of the smallness of some of the endocrine glands is a point that needs further study.

An udder that showed an extreme case of pitting edema after calving was also studied. In this condition, the pressure with the tip of a finger leaves a dent in the surface that persists for several minutes after the pressure is removed. We found that the intense swelling did not appear to invade or to affect the secretory tissue of the udder to any appreciable extent, but was confined chiefly to the space between the glandular tissue and the skin. Opinions differ as to whether the occurrence of the condition is desirable in a dairy cow.

The unsoundness of a practice sometimes followed of making allowances for lost quarters of an udder and adjusting the production upward in proportion to the number of quarters lost, when comparing production records of individual cows, was emphasized in a study of an udder that failed entirely to yield milk from the two rear quarters.

The cow was a Jersey that calved at $2\frac{1}{2}$ years. She produced, entirely in the front quarters, 7,223 pounds of milk and 410 pounds of butterfat in 365 days during her first lactation period. Research by us and others shows that the front quarters of an udder produce on an average about 40 percent of the total milk yield. On that basis, one might figure that, since only 40 percent of her udder was functioning, this cow's producing ability as a 2-year-old was 18,057 pounds of milk and 1,025 pounds of butterfat. Further correction for age would have raised her estimated mature equivalent capacity to 23,294 pounds of milk and 1,282 pounds of butterfat. A cow like that would be worth a lot of money, but we had no reason to believe she possessed an inheritance for production that even approached that high level. When she was slaughtered, it was found that the secretory tissues of the front quarters had expanded backward and occupied most of the area above the rear teats normally occupied by rear-quarter tissue. She gave us evidence that nature sometimes compensates in large measure for the loss of one or more quarters, particularly when the quarters are lost early in life.

Occasionally, infections occur in one or more quarters of a young calf's udder. In one instance, the infection was first noted at 18 days of age. In another case the calf was a month old. Others have been 3 to 5 months old when the infection was first noted. In every case on record where pus discharge from the teat occurred in the young calf, the affected quarter has failed to yield milk from the beginning of lactation. Usually these quarters filled out like the others before calving, but after calving no milk could be obtained, and soon the affected quarter became shrunken to a fraction of the size of the opposite quarter. Post mortem examination of some of these udders showed that the secretory tissue of the affected quarter developed and probably secreted milk but scar tissue in the region of the cistern prevented the passage of any milk. As a result, involution quickly followed and the quarter became permanently "blind."

In hundreds of udders sectioned for post mortem anatomical studies, none has been found to contain a cancerous growth. This is in agreement with other findings that cancer is virtually nonexistent in the cow's udder. While it is difficult to understand why mammary cancer, a disease of such high incidence in humans and other species, should be so nearly nonexistent in the cow, it is gratifying to know that this is true of the gland in which one of our most important foods is produced.

The yield and rate of milking of each of the four quarters of the udder, in cows milked by machine, has been determined for 94 cows. The front quarters yielded 41.8 percent and the rear quarters yielded 58.2 percent of the total. Rates of milking varied during the course of a milking, and from one milking to another if there were differences in total milk yields. Higher milk yields resulted in higher rates in pounds a minute. However, higher milk yields—whether from separate quarters or for the entire udder—required a little longer milking time, but the percentage increases in time were much less than the percentage increases in milk yield. These results have an important bearing on fast-milking procedures now being advocated in many places as desirable from the standpoint of economy of time and good dairy-herd management.

The importance of an abundant blood circulation through the udder of lactating cows has long been stressed. A thorough study of the course of arterial and venous circulation has been made. The results indicate that the internal veins are adequate in size to take care of the return of blood from the udder. In this connection, it was found by studying 106 Holstein and 89 Jersey cows that neither an abundance of veining on the abdominal wall or on the surface of the udder nor the presence of large "milk wells" indicated high milk-producing ability.

Fundamental information has been obtained with regard to the structures by which the udder is suspended from the body. This information has made it possible better to understand why the udders of high-producing cows—especially udders that are fleshy, or edematous—may overtax the structures by which they are supported, and become broken down and misshapen. If inherited weaknesses in the suspensory apparatus and excessive weight of the udder and its contents are the chief factors contributing to the broken-down condition, the selection of breeding stock with an inheritance for well-supported udders, and frequent milking of heavy producers, should be the most effective preventives.

THE AUTHORS

W. W. Swett is a dairy husbandman in the Division of Dairy Cattle Breeding, Feeding, and Management of the Bureau of Dairy Industry. He has been in charge of the Bureau's research pertaining to the interrelationships between body form, anatomy, and udder structure in dairy cattle since its beginning in 1922.

C. A. Matthews, also a dairy husbandman in the same Division, has assisted in most of the studies and has been responsible for carrying out a number of them.

FOR FURTHER READING

Craig, John A.: *Judging Live Stock*, Des Moines, 1901,

Gow, R. M.: *The Jersey, an Outline of Her History During Two Centuries, 1734–1935*, New York, 1936.

703830°—47——14

Matthews, C. A., Swett, W. W., and Graves, R. R.: *Milk Yields and Milking Rates of the Individual Quarters of the Dairy Cow Udder*, U. S. D. A. Technical Bulletin 827, 1941.

Swett, W. W., and Graves, R. R.: *Judging Dairy Cattle on the Basis of Type and Records of Production*, U. S. D. A. Miscellaneous Publication 409, 1941.

Swett, W. W., Matthews, C. A., and Graves, R. R.: *Injury or Infection in Udders of Heifers May Terminate in Blind Quarters*, Journal of Dairy Science, volume 22, pages 993–1006, December 1929.

Swett, W. W., Matthews, C. A., and Graves, R. R.: *Extreme Rarity of Cancer in the Cow's Udder: a Negative Finding of Vital Interest to the Dairy Industry and to the Consumer*, Journal of Dairy Science, volume 23, pages 437–446, May 1940.

Swett, W. W., Matthews, C. A., and Graves, R. R.: *Early Recognition of the Freemartin Condition in Heifers Twinborn with Bulls*, Journal of Agricultural Research, volume 61, pages 587–624, Oct. 15, 1940.

Swett, W. W., Matthews, C. A., Miller, Fred W., and Graves, R. R.: *Nature's Compensation for the Lost Quarter of a Cow's Udder*, Journal of Dairy Science, volume 21, pages 7–11, January 1938.

Swett, W. W., Miller, Fred W., Graves, R. R., and others: *Comparative Conformation, Anatomy, and Udder Characteristics of Cows of Certain Beef and Dairy Breeds*, Journal of Agricultural Research, volume 55, pages 239–287, Aug. 15, 1937.

Swett, W. W., Matthews, C. A., and Graves, R. R.: *Nature of the Swelling in the Udder of a Cow at Calving Time*, Journal of Dairy Science, volume 21, No. 11, pages 713–723, November 1938.

Swett W. W., Underwood, P. C., Matthews, C. A., and Graves, R. R.: *Arrangement of the Tissues by Which the Cow's Udder Is Suspended*, Journal of Agricultural Research, volume 65, No. 1, pages 19–43, July 1, 1942.

A Cow a Calf Will Be

by W. W. SWETT

A DAIRY calf takes about 3 years to develop into a milking cow and prove her worth as a producer. That means 3 years or so of her owner's time, labor, feed, barn space, money, and worry, and all the while he has little knowledge as to whether she will be a profitable milker or whether she will be fit only for the butcher. If he could know that when the calf is a few months old he would make tremendous savings—in fact, if all American dairymen could foretell the future of the calves they plan to add to their herds, they would save much of the 250 million dollars they spend each year in raising the heifers that turn out to be unprofitable producers.

There are other reasons why the information would help. The chances are that half of these money-losing culls have left daughters that will prove to be no better. If the farmer could identify potentially high producers early enough, he could better plan a program of herd replacement and improvement. Persons who choose calves for boys' and girls' club members could buy younger animals at lower prices and be assured of getting animals of which their young owners might be proud. Cattle breeders would be able to evaluate roughly the transmitting ability of young herd sires at least 2 years earlier than is now possible.

After years of research, we have a promising basis for prejudging a calf by examining the glandular development in her udder when she is only 4 months old.

To start with, too much attention has been paid to the external size and appearance of the udder. It has long been a common practice to favor a large udder in the young dairy heifer; in the show ring, the judge is apt to take a general look at the udder, maybe pass his hand over its surface, and, other factors being equal, give the top award to the heifer with

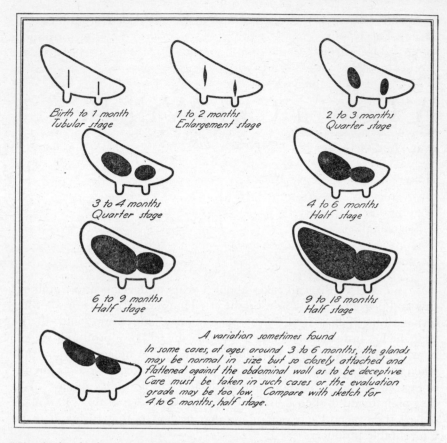

Birth to 1 month
Tubular stage

1 to 2 months
Enlargement stage

2 to 3 months
Quarter stage

3 to 4 months
Quarter stage

4 to 6 months
Half stage

6 to 9 months
Half stage

9 to 18 months
Half stage

A variation sometimes found

In some cases, at ages around 3 to 6 months, the glands may be normal in size but so closely attached and flattened against the abdominal wall as to be deceptive. Care must be taken in such cases or the evaluation grade may be too low. Compare with sketch for 4 to 6 months, half stage.

Here is shown the mammary gland development of a calf from birth to 18 months of age. Following through from upper left to right: At birth the udder is in the tubular stage, each quarter containing a string-like formation that extends from the teat up toward the body wall. Enlargement begins at about 1 month; at 6 weeks or so a bulge can be felt near the center of each tubular formation. Between 2 and 3 months these bulges develop into firm, oval-shaped bodies and is called the quarter stage. At the 3- to 4-month stage, note that the quarters are shaping up to fit the abdominal wall. From 4 to 6 months the front and rear glands usually make contact and grow together at the base and continue to develop in all directions and fuse together more and more. Although the front and rear quarters appear to be completely fused together at the later half stage, they actually remain as four separate milk secretion systems for the cow's lifetime.

the deep, broad, level udder that is carried well forward and to the rear. Yet there seems to be little evidence that these prize-winning yearlings develop into superior milkers; there is some indication that they do not.

A careful examination of the udders of a number of young heifers by feeling through the skin with the fingers demonstrated that external appearances may be deceptive. Some udders that appeared to be well developed contained little glandular tissue. Others that seemed to be small and undeveloped when viewed externally contained well-developed glands. Fat deposits and the relative position of the glandular formations in the udder affected its external appearance. Marked variations were found among individual calves with regard to mammary development at a given age—in other words, some were advanced, and some were retarded.

To determine the significance of these individual variations, to learn whether advanced development indicated superior production, we began examining the mammary glands of every heifer calf in the Beltsville herd periodically at ages from a month to 18 months. When approximately 100 Holstein and 100 Jersey calves had been examined at each of these ages, an average or standard for each breed was established as a basis for grading other calves in the herd as they reached any given age.

Then analyses were made to determine the relation between the grades assigned to represent the relative degree of advancement and the amount of milk they were able to produce as cows. Fifty-two Holstein and 45 Jersey cows that had been thus graded as calves had completed records of production for at least one lactation period. We found that the calves that were advanced in mammary-gland development at about 4 months of age could produce in the neighborhood of 4,000 pounds more milk, on an average, than those that were retarded in mammary-gland development at the same age. We believe these preliminary findings may offer the indicator dairymen have been looking for.

Our diagrams illustrate the various stages of development to be expected at specified ages. It is of interest that all of the rudiments of the mammary glands are present in calves only 3 months old. The teat canal, the cistern, and the ducts leading from the cistern are definitely formed and can be seen in dissected specimens without magnifying them.

Up to 1 year there is little difference between Holsteins and Jerseys. The Jerseys appear to reach a given stage slightly younger, but there is no significant difference in the size of the glandular formations of the two breeds. Only a limited number of observations have been made on calves of other breeds, but there does not seem to be any marked breed difference

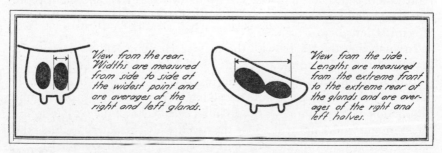

Mammary gland development is measured from front to rear and from side to side.

Average dimensions of mammary glands at various ages. Data based on 2,000 examinations of 200 Holstein and Jersey calves at ages ranging from 14 days to 18 months

	Straight-tube stage (percent)	Enlargement stage (percent)	Quarter stage			Half stage			
			Percent	Width, front	Width, rear	Percent	Length	Width, front	Width, rear
Holsteins:				Inches	Inches		Inches	Inches	Inches
14 days.......	100	6	......	......	......	......	......	......	......
1 month......	99	7	2	0.22	0.27	......	......	......	......
2 months......	62	29	49	.33	.37	......	......	......	......
3 months......	17	9	78	.44	.52	17	1.79	0.63	0.72
4 months......	5	4	44	.56	.66	55	2.33	.77	.83
5 months......	......	......	19	.63	.80	81	2.78	.93	.94
6 months......	......	......	6	.63	.88	95	3.33	1.04	1.04
9 months......	......	......	......	......	......	92	4.73	1.29	1.22
12 months....	......	......	......	......	......	100	5.56	1.40	1.32
18 months....	......	......	......	......	......	99	7.09	1.45	1.35
Jerseys:									
14 days.......	100	8	......	......	......	......	......	......	......
1 month......	99	9	2	.50	.50	......	......	......	......
2 months......	56	31	53	.31	.36	3	1.50	.47	.47
3 months......	12	7	66	.45	.53	32	1.77	.64	.67
4 months......	2	1	31	.51	.59	74	2.23	.75	.78
5 months......	......	......	7	.60	.72	94	2.78	.86	.86
6 months......	......	......	......	......	......	100	3.35	.99	.98
9 months......	......	......	......	......	......	99	4.73	1.19	1.15
12 months....	......	......	......	......	......	100	5.83	1.32	1.26
18 months....	......	......	......	......	......	100	8.26	1.47	1.41

The percentages show the proportion of the total number represented in the various stages at each age. In some cases as many as three different stages may be found in an udder at one time (a "half" on one side, with a "quarter" and either a "tubular" or an "enlargement" stage 'on the other side). This explains why percentages total more than 100.

in the form or in the rate of their mammary development. Until the breed standards were available, there was no satisfactory basis for evaluating these variations. These yardsticks make it possible to establish a systematic basis for grading individual calves at any age. Nine grades are used, in which nine represents the extreme of advancement, one the extreme of retardation, and five the average. Grades of six, seven, and eight represent degrees of advancement, and four, three, and two represent degrees of retardation.

In analyzing the results with the first 52 Holstein and 45 Jersey cows for which the required data were available, we adjusted the production records of the first lactation to a mature-age basis so as to overcome the effects of differences in age at first calving. We determined separate milk production averages for cows that had received each of the various grades for mammary development when they were calves; that is, animals that were given a grade of one were put in one group, those graded two in another, those graded three in another, and so on. In this way we ascer-

Here are shown differences in production of cows that were advanced and those that
were retarded in mammary gland development when graded as 4-month-old calves

Grade for mammary development in the calf	Average milk production [1]			
	Holstein		Jersey	
	Animals	Milk	Animals	Milk
	Number	*Pounds*	*Number*	*Pounds*
A (advanced).....................	5	19, 639	6	14, 634
B (average)......................	34	18, 369	33	12, 707
C (retarded).....................	13	16, 243	6	10, 243
Difference between A and C ..	....	3, 396	....	4, 391

[1] Unweighted averages for first lactation period corrected to a mature-age basis.

tained the average milk production of cows that were in each of the different degrees of advancement in mammary development as calves.

The increase in average production with successive grades (one, two, three, four, etc.) was marked but somewhat irregular for Holsteins. For Jerseys, each grade had a higher average than the one next below.

The practical test of the significance of degree of advancement of mammary development in calves is to determine whether the animals that are potentially low, medium, or high producers can be identified as calves rather than to attempt to draw fine lines of distinction between those that are good and those that are slightly better or between those that are poor and those that are slightly poorer. Thus it probably is enough to classify calves into three groups—the advanced, the average, and the retarded. The calves that were given grades of seven, eight, and nine for mammary development (advanced development) were put in one group, those with grades of four, five, and six (average development) in another, and those with grades of one, two, and three (retarded development) in still another group. The average milk production for the Holsteins that were advanced in mammary development as calves was 3,396 pounds higher than the ones retarded. The corresponding difference for Jerseys was 4,391 pounds.

Separate analyses of grades given calves at various ages indicate that the relative degree of mammary-gland development at from 3 to 5 months is more significant of potential producing ability than the relative degree of development at any other age. Grades given after 6 months were of little significance.

It should be borne in mind that the so-called breed standards and the results shown were based on studies made in one herd—the one at Beltsville. In this herd the continued use of sires proved for their ability to transmit high production to their daughters has resulted in an extremely high and uniform level of production. In this connection it should be pointed out that even the cows graded in the retarded group as calves had production averages that would be considered profitable in most herds. The question is whether the relatively low and the relatively high producers in any herd can be identified while they are calves regardless of the producing level of the herd.

The present need is to give the method a rigid test in other herds. It should be tried in herds where the inheritance for milk production may be at different levels, and where wide individual variation in producing capacity exists. In making such a test it would be necessary to obtain grades on calves in herds that are regularly tested for production. The animals would have to be kept through one lactation period—those that were retarded as well as those advanced in mammary development as calves. Otherwise, it would be impossible to establish the level of their producing ability and the test of the method would fail.

In making such a test, the development of each heifer calf in the herd would be examined by palpation when she is 4 months old. The examination takes only about 10 minutes, and is not difficult. Unfortunately, the method is not readily explained, except by demonstration. The various stages of development can be detected and identified easily by the beginner, without previous experience. Some practice is needed to enable one to evaluate consistently their degree of advancement, but experience in conducting demonstrations in many places has proved that there is little disagreement on whether a calf is to be graded A, B, or C.

The widespread interest of dairymen in the method is indicated by the response from 38 States and several foreign countries, including 800 requests for information and expressions of desire to try the plan. Some breeders already have started to keep records of the mammary development of their young calves.

We must emphasize again that the results are not conclusive, because of the limited number of animals tested, and because all of the results were obtained from one excellent herd. Encouraging as they appear to be, the results must be proved in the field. But the idea is worth the effort— worth, if it is proved to be perfect, 250 million dollars a year.

THE AUTHOR

W. W. Swett is a dairy husbandman in the Division of Dairy Cattle Breeding, Feeding, and Management, Bureau of Dairy Industry. He is a graduate of the University of Missouri and taught dairy husbandry there for 6 years.

ALSO, IN THIS BOOK

Progress in Hog Production

by JOHN H. ZELLER

FARMERS keep asking three questions about hogs: What is the best type and breed? How do parents pass their distinct features on to their offspring? How can we improve production? Another question was added a few years ago when it became plain that the usual kind of pig had too much lard, which, because of the growing competition of fats of plant origin, depressed the price of live hogs. Swine breeders and workers in agricultural experiment stations agreed that if the hog business were to stay profitable, they would have to develop a leaner animal— one that would grow well on the available feed and under American production methods.

One sign that the questions are being answered is the record made during the war. In 1943, for example, more than 121 million pigs were raised, more than ever before, and 66.4 percent above the average in the decade before that.

Research before the war indicated that an intermediate type suited the needs of the American producer and consumer better than extremes, particularly in the Corn Belt—a hog that could be finished at 200 to 240 pounds or, on farms with plenty of feed, at 300 pounds or more. This kind promises to be adaptable to a wide range of production and marketing conditions.

To develop this meat type the Department, in cooperation with the Iowa Agricultural Experiment Station, imported 23 head of Landrace hogs from Denmark in 1934 for use in experiments in breeding and feeding. The Danish Landrace had been bred under testing-station methods for many years, and was producing carcasses that were favored by the London bacon market.

Some of the Landrace were crossed with domestic breeds to determine

201

whether we could improve the meat of domestic stock and perhaps reduce lard yields. Several strains were started from the various crosses. From them, strains similar in type to the Landrace are being produced. They are a little longer of body and shorter of leg than the domestic breeds that were used in the crosses, and the carcasses compare favorably with those of the domestic breeds.

We believe that some of the strains may ultimately aid in improving domestic stock through systematic crossing. Cross-breeding has been practiced generally by many hog producers for years, because of the hybrid vigor usually obtained. These and other studies should ultimately point a way for obtaining the maximum in hybrid vigor from systematic crossing and perhaps eventually get better carcasses than are now had.

At the Regional Swine Breeding Laboratory at Ames, Iowa, an institution established in 1937 by agricultural experiment stations in the Corn Belt and the Department, experiments are in progress to explore possibilities for using inbred lines to improve the seed-stock value of pure breeds, and improve the performance and the carcasses of hogs produced for market. Methods of selection also are being investigated. Progress is being made. Some day inbred lines may be used not only to improve pure breeds, but also, when used systematically, may yield more pork per litter than the established practices.

The methods being tested in the various experiments have demonstrated that inbred lines can be produced within any of the pure breeds, and that the very best of the lines may have a place in future hog production. Likewise, useful lines can be formed from crosses of breeds. There is some evidence that lines from crossbred foundations may give more hybrid vigor in crosses than lines formed within breeds.

Today, swine breeders emphasize performance records as a means of improving the herd. The usefulness of such records in the dairy and poultry industries has been demonstrated by years of testing and proving superior stock.

Performance records for sows require earmarking of pigs and weights of pigs at weaning time. More thought is being given to final selection of boars and gilts for the breeding herd and how they can be used to increase feedlot efficiency and yield high quality carcasses.

Feeding Hogs

The American farmer did a first-rate job of feeding hogs during the war. Feed takes 70 to 85 percent of the cost of production and it was necessary to get as much efficiency as possible out of the feed on hand in order to meet the need for the large increase in numbers of hogs. Farmers realized that protein feeds saved corn or cereal grains in the swine ration, and could speed up gains so that hogs would be ready for market earlier.

A combination of feeds of both animal and plant origin are more efficient supplements to grain than either one used alone as a supplement. On the other hand, a protein feed of animal origin should be part of the ration of sows during the gestation and suckling periods and for the young pig until it reaches at least 75 pounds. Consequently, when the supply of animal protein feeds, like tankage and fishmeal, is limited, they should be fed to the animals that need it most for proper development.

For growing and fattening pigs, over 75 pounds in weight, feeds of plant origin, like meals of soybean, linseed, cottonseed, peanuts, and alfalfa, used in various combinations to supplement the grain ration, will produce satisfactory results if the supply of protein feeds from animal sources is low or lacking. During this period, however, hogs receiving some animal protein in the supplement will gain faster than those on an all-vegetable supplement.

Wartime shortages of protein feeds of animal origin led to a series of tests at Beltsville on the value of plant proteins. We found that a good all-vegetable protein supplement can be used during the gestation period, but that a ration containing some animal protein is necessary to increase growth rate in growing and fattening pigs. In the tests, the sows and litters were handled under conditions similar to those found on many hog farms. Pasture crops were fed during the gestation and suckling periods. Considerable corn and other grains were saved when high-protein supplements were used to provide a well-balanced diet.

We think a farmer will do well to grow his own protein supplements so that he need buy little extra feed. Skim milk is a valuable supplement of animal origin. Soybeans are good in small quantities, when combined with other supplements and minerals. The practice of exchanging whole soybeans for soybean meal, which can be used safely in large quantities, is often profitable. For fattening hogs over 100 pounds in dry lot, a mixture of three parts soybean meal and one part ground alfalfa hay may be self-fed in one compartment of a feeder with corn and a mineral mixture in separate compartments.

Legume hays and hay meals, like alfalfa, soybean, red clover, Ladino clover, and lespedeza, provide proteins, minerals, and vitamins of excellent quality. They may be fed separately, as hay, or ground and mixed with concentrates.

The hog's stomach is small and requires feed in concentrated form. The bulkiness and relatively high fiber content of hay and hay meals limit the amount that can be fed profitably. In general, 5 to 10 percent of good legume hay, either ground or unground, has been considered the most desirable level, although more may be fed with good results. A growing and fattening hog can tolerate as much as 8 percent fiber; that permits the use of as much as 20 percent of a hay of 30 percent fiber content in a mixture of corn, tankage, and linseed meal.

Tests at the Wisconsin Agricultural Experiment Station show that brood sows fed only 5 percent alfalfa in a ration made up largely of corn and soybean meal did not produce enough milk to suckle their litters satisfactorily. On the other hand, sows that received 15 percent alfalfa had strong litters. The addition of 15 percent of alfalfa hay was also favored in a ration containing tankage as well as those with only vegetable-source protein feeds. Rations containing 15 percent ground alfalfa hay also gave excellent results for growing and fattening pigs.

It is not necessary to use ground legume hays in rations where pigs have access to good pasture. If pigs are fed in dry lot or in fields where the pasture is poor, ground hays are valuable in the ration. The winter ration for fall-farrowed pigs should contain liberal amounts of good hay to promote general health and rapid and economical gains.

Pastures for Pigs

Green pastures furnish proteins, vitamins, and minerals, and when they are properly rotated are the basis of a good sanitation program and save as much as one-fourth of the grain ration and one-half of the protein supplement ordinarily fed to pigs.

Scientists at the University of Illinois, after experiments in which pigs were grazed on excellent alfalfa pasture, credited the pasturage with about 1,000 pounds of pork an acre, besides the gain credited to the corn that was fed.

At the same experiment station, rye pasture furnished excellent grazing for sows and March-farrowed pigs. An acre of good rye pasture carried 100 early pigs and their dams until alfalfa was ready to graze about May 1. In those tests, an acre of rye pasture saved almost 100 bushels of corn and 560 pounds of protein supplement. In another instance, sows and pigs fed only corn on rye pasture made more gain with less feed per 100 pounds gain than sows and litters fed corn and supplement in dry lot.

Winter oats is an excellent grazing crop for sows and early spring litters. An acre of winter oats pasture ordinarily furnishes pasture for four sows and their litters during the suckling period. In sections of the country where it can be planted early to get a good fall growth it is one of the best early spring pasture crops.

Year-Round Grazing

In the South, soil and climate make it possible to produce a variety of crops that can be hogged off almost the year round. Under such systems, litters can be farrowed so as to provide a more uniform supply of market hogs throughout the year.

The Georgia Coastal Plain Experiment Station began a series of tests in 1936 to determine the value of different crops in a year-round grazing program. Only grain crops were used that could be harvested by the hogs. A sufficient acreage was planted so that each crop would carry a given number of hogs until the succeeding crop was ready. Over an 8-year period, data were obtained on the value of 14 feed and grain crops to determine their place in such a program.

The sequence of crops found best for the Coastal Plains area of Georgia was: Mature oats, to be hogged off in May and June; early dent corn to furnish feed in July, August, September, and October; either runner peanuts or sweetpotatoes for feed in November, December, and January; and field corn for February and March. Early dent corn, which returned $2.59 for each dollar of cost, was the most profitable of the crops tested. Only two crops, sweetpotatoes and sunflowers, failed to return enough pork per acre to cover expenses. The average amount of pork produced to the acre ranged from 542 pounds for corn and Spanish peanuts to 305 for corn and soybeans. On the average, it required approximately 0.4 of an acre of fattening crops to grow out and fatten a pig from weaning to market weight.

The year-round hogging-off program saves labor in harvesting the crop, increases soil fertility, distributes labor and income more evenly through the year, establishes good sanitation practices to control parasites, and uses soil-building crops that could not be harvested economically and fed to hogs.

Going to Market

What is the best weight at which to market hogs in relation to feed costs per unit of gain? At Beltsville we tried to determine the amount of feed required for each 50 pounds of gain between 75 and 375 pounds of live weight. Hogs of the intermediate type were self-fed, with these results:

Pounds	Number of hogs on test	Average daily gain in pounds	Pounds of feed per 50 pounds of live-weight gain
75–124	42	1.62	167
125–174	42	1.75	190
175–224	34	1.71	206
225–274	26	1.65	223
275–324	18	1.46	252
325–374	9	1.31	276

We found that 275 pounds is about the limit to which the in-between hogs can be fed profitably under normal conditions. Beyond that, the rate of gain dropped significantly, and the feed needed for each succeeding 50 pounds of gain increased appreciably. Therefore, unless lard is needed, it is desirable from the standpoint of feed utilization to market hogs at live weights of 200 to 225 pounds, because it requires less feed to produce lean meat than it does to produce fat.

The use of distillers' dried grains with solubles as a feed for swine grew out of war conditions. The shortage of protein feeds and the large quantities of distillers' dried grains resulting as a byproduct of alcohol production led to tests at Beltsville to determine the value of the product. Besides their high protein content, the products contain the B vitamins.

Dried distillers' grains with solubles were fed to pigs at different levels as protein supplements. The distillery product made up 9.4 to 12 percent and from 18 to 26 percent of a ration composed of corn, tankage, soybean meal, alfalfa meals, and minerals. The tests, in which the hogs were fed to market weights of approximately 225 pounds, showed that at the level of 9 to 12 percent of the ration, rate and economy of gains were comparable to those of pigs in the check lot without distillers' grains. However, when the dried grains with solubles were fed at the second level, the rate of gain was slowed up by about 30 percent while 40 percent more feed was required per 100 pounds of gain. It was apparent that the added high fiber content of the ration at higher levels hindered normal gains.

Tests conducted at the Kentucky Agricultural Experiment Station confirmed our results and indicated that the distillers' feed products do not contain all the essential amino acids at a level required to promote satisfactory growth. Further tests at Kentucky, and some at the Illinois Agricultural Experiment Station, show that when distillers' dried solubles were used as a supplement to certain basic rations, an improvement in quality was obtained, with an increase in rate and economy of gains. It seems likely that this improvement is due to vitamin factors contained in the distillers' solubles. Results to date indicate that growing pigs receiving distillers' products in the ration, nevertheless may be expected to produce more economical gains when given access to good pasture than when fed these products in dry lot.

Self-Feeding of Sows During Gestation

Self-feeding of sows and litters during the suckling period and of pigs during the growing and fattening periods is common in swine management. Bred sows fatten so easily that the practice of self-feeding grains and concentrates during the gestation period until recently was not considered advisable. Comparisons of self-feeding and hand feeding of bred gilts have been made at the Minnesota Agricultural Experiment Station. Preliminary results show that self-feeding during gestation is practical, but there should be enough bulk to the ration to keep the sows from getting too fat. A ration of 43 parts of ground corn, 25 parts of ground oats, 25 parts of alfalfa meal, and 7 parts of tankage, plus a mineral mixture, proved satisfactory.

An adequate ration for self-feeding can be made up largely of home-grown grains and good legume hay; only an animal protein supplement, if skim milk is not available on the farm, need then be bought. Other preliminary results show that the average number of pigs farrowed and weaned and the weights of pigs at both farrowing and weaning were practically the same for the self-fed and hand-fed groups. The milk production of the sows did not seem to be adversely affected by either method. The cost of feed per sow was slightly higher in the self-fed group. Self-feeding, however, lightens the work of morning and evening feeding.

Reducing Death Losses

The big economic loss in the swine industry is due to the failure to raise and market a higher percentage of pigs farrowed. An average of 35 to 40 percent of the total pigs farrowed never reach market. It is estimated that approximately a seventh of all hog feed is fed to pigs that never get to market.

Where electric current is available, the use of electric heat in the farrowing pens pays well. An ordinary 150- or 200-watt electric lamp is enough. The cost of installation of hover and light will pay for itself the first season in pigs saved. At Beltsville we saved approximately 5 percent more pigs in the spring of 1940 by using home-made electric hovers than we did without them. The comparison was made in a heated central farrowing house. Similar experience was had at the Purdue Agricultural Experiment Station. The sows in a group with supplemental heat saved 82.8 percent of live pigs farrowed, compared to 65.7 percent in the group without heat. The death loss of pigs from chilling was reduced from 10 percent in the lot without heat to 2.2 percent in the lot with heat. The difference of 17.1 percent in pigs saved is of economic importance. If a similar saving could be had in a State or the whole country, it would mean greatly increased production with the same number of sows, or fewer sows would be needed to maintain a normal swine population.

Uremia in Young Pigs

A post mortem examination of young pigs that died during the suckling period in the herd at Beltsville revealed that most of the pigs lost in the first 2 weeks of life had uremia. The condition shows up in the excretory ducts of the kidneys, and is characterized by crystalline deposits, a marked increase in urea, uric acid, and other compounds in the blood, kidneys, and liver.

The condition apparently is not associated with the so-called baby pig disease, as the blood sugar content is within normal range. A similar condition was produced experimentally in young pigs by withholding food, an indication that the cause may be the failure of the sow to come in milk normally after farrowing, faulty feeding or management, or failure of the pigs to suckle soon after birth. Proper attention to the diet of the sow before and after farrowing should be helpful, although the definite cause of the condition is not yet fully understood.

THE AUTHOR

John H. Zeller is from Franklin County, Pa. He is in charge of swine investigations at the Bureau of Animal Industry. Except for time out to serve in the naval aviation service during the war, he has been continuously active in swine research for the Department since 1917.

FOR FURTHER READING

Craft, W. A.: Swine Breeding Research at the Regional Swine Breeding Laboratory, U. S. D. A.   Miscellaneous Publication 523, 1943.

Fairbanks, B. H., Krider, J. L., and Carroll, W. E.: Distillers' By-Products in Swine Rations, Journal of Animal Science, volume 4, pages 420–429, 1945.

Foster, G. H., and Vestal, C. M.: The Use of Electric Heat in the Farrowing Pens of Young Pigs, Purdue University Experiment Station Bulletin 494, 1944.

Hankins, O. G., and Zeller, J. H.: Hogs of Danish Origin Imported for Breeding Studies in This Country, U. S. D. A. Yearbook, pages 231–233, 1935.

Madsen, L. L., Earle, I. P., Heemstra, L. C., and Miller, C. O.: Acute Uremia Associated with "Uric Acid Infarcts" in the Kidneys of Baby Pigs, American Journal of Veterinary Research, volume 5, number 16, pages 262–273, 1944.

Oberholtzer, J. W., and Hardin, L. S.: Simplifying the Work and Management of Hog Production, Purdue University Experiment Station Bulletin 506, 1945.

Peters, W. H., and Ferrin, E. F.: Can Winter Rations For Brood Sows Be Self-Fed, Hog Breeder, volume 19, number 11, pages 22–23, 1944.

Southwell, B. L., and Treanor, K.: Hogging-Off Crops in the Coastal Plain, University System of Georgia, Bulletin 41, 1945.

Winters, L. M., Comstock, R. E., and Dailey, D. L.: The Development of an Inbred Line of Swine (Minn. No. 1) from a Crossbred Foundation, Journal of Animal Science, volume 2, pages 129–137, 1943.

ALSO, IN THIS BOOK

FEEDING CALVES

er the traditional methods of feeding dairy s, each one of them during its first 6 to nths of life drinks about 200 pounds of e milk and 1,900 pounds of skim milk. rch to determine how early calves can be weaned from milk is reported by H. T. Converse on page 159. Of course as a calf's milk diet is reduced, it must be trained to eat more hay and grain. The following pages present some results of calf-feeding tests at Beltsville.

These Holstein steers are 6 months old; their average weight is 381 pounds. None had any whole milk except colostrum, nor any skim milk or other animal protein after 1 mont[h] age. They had had an average of 234 po[unds] of milk at the time their pictures were ta[ken]

These Jersey and Holstein heifers (above) are 9 months old and, reading from left to right, were normal weight at 8, 3, 6, and 7 months, respectively. None of them had any whole milk except colostrum and no skim milk or other animal protein after 2 months of age. They consumed an average of 461 pounds each.

Below, a Jersey heifer calf as she looke[d] monthly intervals from 2 to 6 months. [She] was weaned from skim milk at 2 months o[ld] and never had any whole milk except c[olos]trum. She consumed a total of 491 poun[ds] milk; weight normal at 3 months. The [com]posite pictures were made by W. A. Stenh[olm]

ese four Holstein heifers were a year old n their pictures were taken. From left to it, they had no milk after 1, 2, 6, and 6 ths, respectively. The first three had no le milk except colostrum; the fourth had no n milk, but at 6 months had drunk 2,377 nds of whole milk. The skim milk con-ed by the first three was 278, 427, and 2,590 pounds, respectively. The weight of each of the calves, in pounds, at different ages, was:

6 months	370	386	400	396
12 months	708	593	641	655
18 months	857	853	844	838

The first calf was under weight at 6 months, but exceeded the others at 12 and 18 months.

ts at Beltsville indicate that vitamin D sup-nent is not absolutely necessary in a calf's . This young bull had never been exposed to sunlight and had no vitamin D except what he got from sun-cured hay. At 6 months, when the picture was taken, he weighed 354 pounds.

CROSSBRED SWINE

With increasing competition from fats and oils of plant origin, swine breeders realize the need for a leaner hog that is adapted to American methods of production. In cooperation with several State experiment stations, good progress has been made, as illustrated in these pages. An article on swine breeding and management appears on page 201. Above, John Zeller inspe a group of pigs selected at random from litter at weaning time. The purpose is to termine record of performance as to rate gain and economy of feed per unit of ga

In 1934 the Department, in cooperation with the Iowa Agricultural Experiment Station, imported some Landrace hogs (left, above) from Denmark for crossing with local stock. From this white breed there have been developed strains that are black or red in color. A sult is the Landrace-Poland China inbred g (right), at 9 months of age. They are 75 perc Landrace and 25 percent Poland China and h longer bodies and shorter legs than U. S. bree

ese older Landrace-Hampshire inbred sows
ove) are of a black strain. They were bred
he U. S. Range Livestock Experiment Station
Miles City, Mont., in cooperation with the
ntana Agricultural Experiment Station at
eman. They are 60 percent Landrace
and 40 percent unbelted Hampshire. The
8½-month-old gilts (right, above) are from
Landrace and Berkshire stock. They are 63 percent Landrace and 37 percent Berkshire, and
were bred at Blakeford Farms, Queenstown,
Md., in cooperation with the Maryland station.

foundation stock of the 8½-month-old gilts
ove) are Landrace from Denmark and Large
k from England. They are a black strain
at Beltsville and are 75 percent Landrace
and 25 percent Large Black. Some Landrace-
Duroc, a red strain, are also being developed. The 9-month-old gilts (below) are about
75 percent Landrace and 25 percent Duroc.

The 8-month-old gilts (above, left) are red and are being developed from a three-breed cross. They are 77 percent Landrace, 15 percent Duroc, and 8 percent unbelted Hampshire. Those at the right, above, are of four breeds: 60 percent Yorkshire, 33 percent Duroc, 3 percent Landrace, 3 percent unbelted Hampshire. They are a red strain at Beltsville, 8½ months

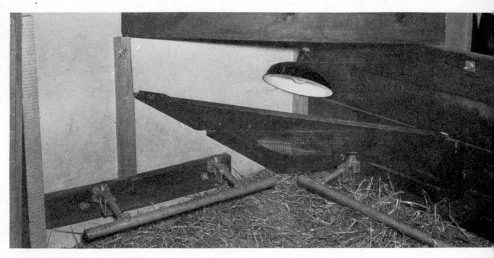

PIG LOSSES CAN BE REDUCED where electric current is available to provide warmth in this type of home-made hover. This equipment has helped reduce pig losses at Beltsville. Attracted to the light and warmth of the hover (below) almost as soon as they are born, these little pigs are cozy and, under the protecting guard rail, are fairly safe from being trampled

PICAL SHEEP COUNTRY is the setting for headquarters of the U. S. Sheep Experiment :ion, and Western Sheep Breeding Labora-, at Dubois, Idaho. In these barns, corrals, and laboratories, and on the sagebrush range, research goes on to develop better breeding and feeding methods and thus better sheep. A general article on the subject begins on page 209.

Sheepmen usually breed their ewes at 18 months, but tests with purebred Hampshire sheep at the U. S. Belle Fourche Field Station, Newell, S. Dak., indicate that lambs born early in the spring, and with proper feeding and c can be bred the following fall with no appar bad effect on them. Both the lamb-bred yearling-bred ewes are in the above fl

The Columbia breed (above, left) is a product of the Dubois station and is considered by some sheepmen as the perfect sheep. This ram, a plump, square, rugged specimen, is a typical Columbia sheep. The Targhee ewe (above, right) is shown in every-day range condit She carries a good half-blood fleece of med fineness that is usually in strong demand manufacturers of apparel fabrics. She ha square mutton form, open face, no skin fo

Below, left, is a modern Rambouillet ram, and (right) one that not long ago was considered a prize-winning type of animal. The large folds at the neck and wool over the eyes are now considered as serious drawbacks by p tical producers. The ideal modern ram has n of these bad features but produces a heavy y of wool in high demand for fine dress go

pical yearling Navajo ram (left, above), a second-generation yearling crossbred ram uced at the Southwestern Range and Sheep ding Laboratory in New Mexico. Fleece from the crossbred ram (right) is a long staple quarter-blood type of wool good for either hand-weaving or commercial use. The Navajo ram produces a carpet-type wool of low value.

b feeders send thousands of lambs to feed uch as this (below) in Colorado, Wyoming, Nebraska, where much good lamb-fatten- ing feed like alfalfa, corn, oats, and barley is grown. Most of the feeder lambs from the western ranges are fattened in these open feed lots.

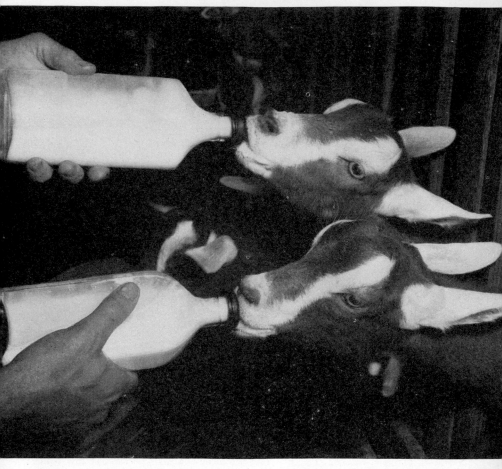

MILK, MOHAIR, AND CHEVON are produced by goats. Interest in raising them for these purposes is increasing in the United States. Research is under way to develop breeding and management methods that will give the raiser higher returns. Progress made in re years is discussed on page 217. The above p shows a common method of feeding young g

Selective breeding based on performance is one phase of efforts to obtain higher milk yields. An example of improved breeding is Supreme Security No. 44784 (left), a purebred Saanen buck, who has proved his ability to trar high milk production. One of his daugl U. S. D. A. 105 (right), gave 2,303.5 poun milk and 73.51 pounds of butterfat in 306

does ordinarily breed only in the fall,
-round supply of goat milk is somewhat of
blem. Partially offsetting this drawback is
ct that they usually give birth to two kids
me, as the above Toggenburg doe No. 607;
ently they have three and even four.

Experiments indicate that it pays to add some
grain to a milk goat's diet. This Toggenburg
doe No. 971 gave 1,551.9 pounds of milk and
60.52 pounds of butterfat in 301 days on a ration
of 1 pound of grain to each 4 pounds of milk.
During subsequent lactations, without grain,
she gave an average of only 886 pounds of milk
and 28.03 pounds of butterfat in 231 days.

ra goats are the only source of mohair, a
llion-dollar industry in the Southwestern
. The best mohair comes from Angora
that carry a dense, fine-quality fleece that
s in ringlets rather than as straight hair.
specimen at right is a doe of high quality.

platform and stanchion arrangement (be-
is adapted to goats. It not only prevents
oat from wandering around, but is sanitary
brings the milker's work closer to him.

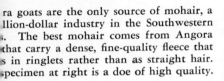

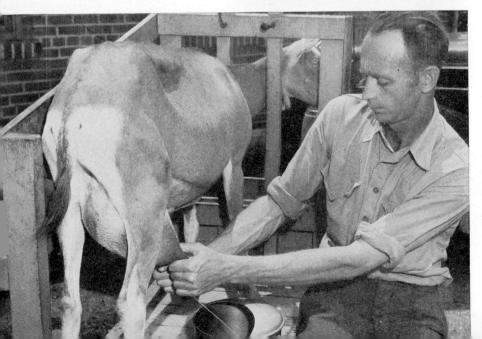

HIGHER QUALITY MEAT AND EGGS from poultry, and greater efficiency in feeding and taking care of domestic fowl, are some of the objectives of research by the Department in cooperation with several State experiment sta- tions. On page 225 T. C. Byerly discuss breeding of better poultry, and on page 2 reports results of work on how to keep try healthy. The next few pages show the work is done and some of the re

The development of new strains to meet specific needs is a phase of poultry work at Beltsville. Here M. W. Olsen (left) and J. P. Quinn display a Rhode Island Red hen, a Sussex rooster, a White Wyandotte hen, the three breeds cre to get the Columbian poultry strain (be

Fast-feathering chicks are better for table use because they have fewer pinfeathers when ready for market. Of the two same-aged chicks (left), a strain of the new Columbian chicken, the upper one has well-developed tail and wing feathers. This is done by selective breeding.

as a result of selective breeding and testing the Beltsville Small White turkey has become a well-established type. It is a relatively small bird with lots of white meat, and thus meets very well the needs of smaller families.

A good egg has a strong nonporous shell, no blood spots, keeps well, and retains its weight in storage. Here eggs are being tested for shell strength and weight. Research continues to develop a hen that combines these qualities.

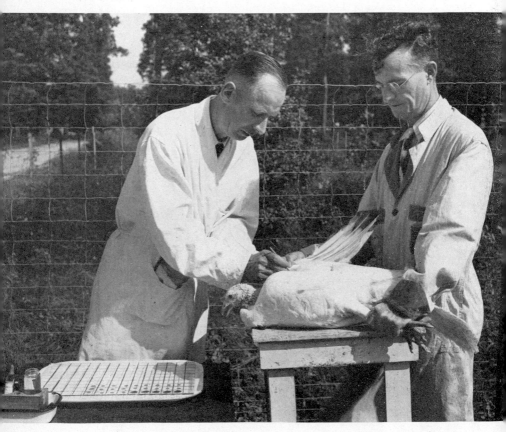

Department pathologists have found a faster way to determine whether or not a turkey has pullorum disease. A drop of blood taken from the turkey's wing is mixed with a drop of solution called antigen. If the antigen shows curdled spots, the turkey is afflicted; if it remains cloudy throughout, the turkey is free of the disease. The process takes about 3 minutes.

POULTRY FEEDING RESEARCH at Beltsville has proved that a concentrate of cow
manure aids growth in chickens. Proof of this
is shown by the two chicks being weighed by
H. R. Bird. They are 6 weeks old; both were
fed the same diet except that the chick a[t]
left received 23 grams of cow-manure co[ncen-]
trate per 100 pounds of feed. Its effe[ct on]
growth is due to an unknown dietary facto[r. The]
article on Feeding Poultry begins on pag[e]

The diet of a hen, if she is to produce hatchable eggs and strong chicks, apparently must
contain some animal protein. Of 100 fertile
eggs laid by hens fed an adequate diet, except
for animal proteins, 34 failed to hatch; chicks
from 19 died during the first week of life.
another 100 fertile eggs from hens fe[d an]
adequate diet but including fish-meal su[pple-]
ment (below), 15 eggs failed to hatch and [only]
4 chicks died before they were a week [old.]

EAST A DOZEN STATES are carrying on ~ch to develop horses that are better ~ed to farm and general use. The U. S. ~rtment of Agriculture, at its Morgan Horse Farm in Middlebury, Vt., and at its Range Livestock Experiment Station at Miles City, Mont., has made studies that indicate the need for improvement in breeding and management.

SENTING Mentor 8627, a 4-year-old Mor- stallion, used by the Department in its breeding program at the Morgan Horse Farm. He stands 15.1 hands high; weighs 1,040 pounds.

~ries of tests has been devised for measur- ~he performance and endurance of a horse, ~of which is a 11½-mile cross-country ride ~r saddle carrying 20 percent of its body weight. Another test is a 5-mile trot hitched to a cart. Walking and trotting speed and length of stride are recorded over a measured mile, th~ animal pulling 60 percent of its body w~

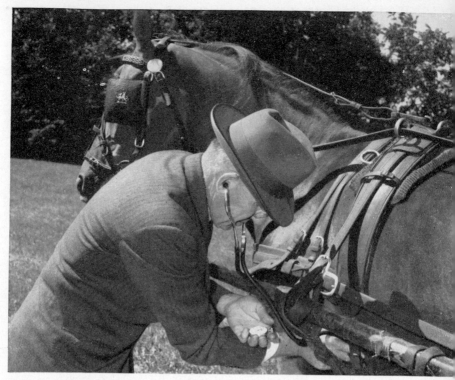

For the 5-mile test, respiration and heart rates are taken before the test and 5, 10, and 15 minutes afterwards. Each horse is given a for signs of fatigue and ease of gait for ri

The Michigan station developed the handy-sized farm horses shown above. They are crossbred fillies sired by an Arabian stallion from a r of Percheron x grade Clydesdale breec

Developments in Sheep

by DAMON A. SPENCER

THE PIONEER phase of our sheep industry has passed. There are no more free grazing lands. Most sheep now graze on owned or leased pastures or ranges or national forests. Stock and equipment and operating expenses are so high that any wasteful method means failure; success comes only through the best scientific practices.

For much of the newer science in sheep raising we now look to a comprehensive program of research and improvement like the one in progress at Dubois, Idaho. Near that community, in the heart of the sheep country, President Wilson in 1915 withdrew from settlement 28,160 acres of sagebrush land for use by the Department for experiments in breeding and grazing sheep. President Harding withdrew 16,650 acres of high summer-grazing lands in Montana, about 40 miles northeast of Dubois, in 1922 for a similar purpose. Other smaller areas and parts of the nearby Targhee and Salmon National Forests are also used in the work. In 1937 the agricultural experiment stations of the 11 Western States and Texas and the Department organized the Western Sheep Breeding Laboratory. Its headquarters and primary facilities are on the lands of the United States Sheep Experiment Station near Dubois. Julius E. Nordby, of the Department, directs activities of the station and laboratory. Rambouillet sheep are used in the work of the laboratory; the flocks at the station include Columbias, Targhees, and Corriedales.

One of the earliest and most important accomplishments at Dubois was the development of the Columbia breed, which some sheepmen consider the perfect sheep. It was an answer to the growing demand for mutton and lamb at a time when the costs of sheep production were rising, a situation that created a need for animals efficient in producing both meat and wool. Cross-breeding was employed in various ways, including the mating of fine-wool ewes of the Merino and Rambouillet breeds to coarse long-wool mutton rams of the Lincoln, Leicester, Cotswold, and Romney breeds to get rapid-growing market lambs and whitefaced ewe stock.

In 1912 the Department started experiments in cross-breeding range sheep at Laramie, Wyo. Lincoln × Rambouillet crossbreds were selected as the most promising for sheep and wool production in the Rocky Mountain region. Both ewes and rams of this cross were mated, and thereafter their descendants were also mated without backcrossing to either parent stock. Sheep resulting from this cross-breeding were the foundation of the Columbia breed, which is now liked in both range and farming areas.

Other useful new breeds developed during the same period include the Panama and the Romeldale. The Panama was founded by James Laidlaw, of Muldoon, Idaho, through cross-breeding Lincoln ewes and Rambouillet rams; the Romeldale was originated by A. T. Spencer, of Gerber, Calif., through his cross-breeding of Rambouillet ewes with Romney rams. Both breeds were established by mating the crossbred ewes and rams and their descendants without backcrossing to either parent stock.

Later, at Dubois, the Department began the development of a fixed strain to satisfy the need for animals suited to ranges intermediate in their production of forage. Excellent ewes resulting from the crossing of Lincoln × Rambouillet ewes and Corriedale rams and inbreeding of their descendants, also some selected Lincoln × Rambouillet ewes, were mated with choice Rambouillet rams. The offspring resulting from that breeding and their descendants were then inbred to form the Targhee strain, named after the Targhee National Forest. The Targhees produce good wool that grades uniformly as Half-Blood. They are relatively plump and are good producers of lambs under range conditions.

Rambouillets for Western Ranges

Breeding sheep for the western ranges has depended largely on the Rambouillet, the breed that the State and Federal sheep-breeding specialists agreed to concentrate on when they organized the laboratory at Dubois and began the program of improving sheep for the West. The program includes systems of breeding aimed at locating strains in the Rambouillet that possess combinations of genes that will improve strains of Rambouillets with which they are crossed. Such breeding is between strains of the same breed; Rambouillets are not crossed with other breeds. In these efforts we have found that size and body weight are directly associated with satisfactory weights of lambs. At the Dubois laboratory, under range conditions, 303 Rambouillet ewes were studied for lifetime lamb production over a period of 5 years. Ewes that averaged 119 pounds during their lifetime produced an annual average of 55 pounds of weanlings. Ewes that averaged 125 pounds produced 60 pounds of live lambs, and ewes averaging 135 pounds produced 69 pounds of live weaned lambs. In other words, Rambouillet ewes of good size and weight are needed for maximum production of lambs under range conditions.

We found it important to increase the length of staple in fleeces of Rambouillet sheep. This we accomplished by selecting rams and ewes of especially good length of staple. Mr. Nordby reported that their yearling progeny have consistently produced fleeces measuring one-third of an inch longer and averaging 0.45 pound more in clean wool than have progeny of the flock as a whole. What the improvement means in money is indicated by the fact that in 1943 Strictly Combing fleeces averaged $5.87 and the shorter French Combing fleeces brought only $5. All fleeces were grown under the same conditions at Dubois.

J. M. Jones and co-workers of the Texas Agricultural Experiment Station reported that smooth "C" type Rambouillet ewes produced a longer wool staple than did the wrinkled "B" type ewes of similar ages. They found that the staple length of 2,274 fleeces from "C" type averaged 2.28 inches, compared to 2.05 inches for 365 fleeces from "B" type ewes. Wool manufacturers, especially those making worsted goods, are willing to pay extra for fine wools having good staple length.

Two other desirable qualities that sheep breeders work for are open faces (that is, not excessively covered with wool), and absence of skin folds, which are unprofitable and a nuisance.

Open-faced Rambouillet ewes at Dubois have each produced more than 10 percent more pounds of live lambs a year than wool-blind ewes. In 1942 about 17 percent of the Rambouillet lambs had open faces, 40 percent had partly open faces, and 43 percent had wool over their entire faces, compared to 11, 40, and 49 percent, respectively, in 1941. The open-faced ewes weighed about 5 pounds more after shearing than those that were wool-blind. When open-faced rams were mated with open-faced ewes, about half of the offspring were opened-faced, and the rest had partly covered faces.

The Texas Agricultural Experiment Station and the Department have cooperated in analyzing the inheritance of the skin-fold character in Rambouillets. The results of that project show that culling the wrinkled sheep and selecting for mating only the animals without excess skin folds can be effective in gradually eliminating this monstrosity. The workers at Dubois have been successful in similar efforts. The average score for skin folds on the necks of all the Rambouillet weanling offspring from inbred lines changed from 2.2 to 1.7 in about 4 years, a score of 1 representing complete absence of skin folds and a score of 5 indicating maximum skin-fold development. Rambouillet lambs with practically no skin folds increased from 28 to 58 percent between 1938 and 1944.

Another example of what can be done through selective breeding is the research on the inheritance of defective jaws. In experiments conducted from 1937 to 1944 with Rambouillets having overshot jaws, the workers at Dubois found that when one or both parents were defective, 16.4 percent of the progeny were defective, compared to 1.4 percent of the progeny in a flock in which all the sheep of breeding age were normal. Sheep breeders, therefore, can best cope with the problem by not mating sheep having bad jaws.

Feeding and Management

Sheep get most of their feed from pastures and ranges that supply a variety of forage plants. It seldom pays to feed grain to breeding sheep or even to suckling lambs when they can have enough succulent herbage. On plenty of good forage, sheep can be kept thrifty and lambs can be raised to a market finish without grain. If grain is fed, about 100 pounds a year for a ewe and her lambs is the most that is likely to be profitable. Feeding sheep from stack, mow, and bin may be necessary during deep snows and extreme droughts, or when pastures and ranges are overstocked, or other conditions adversely affect grazing. Research in the use of grazing forage has been going on since 1923 at Dubois.

We have learned how important it is to detect range deterioration before it becomes far advanced. Studies with flocks on fenced pastures and with large bands on ranges in Idaho have yielded signs by which we can detect range depletion early enough to make corrections in management. The condition of the sheep may not accurately reflect the condition of the range. Deterioration of forage cover and soil may be noticeably progressing before the weights of ewes and lambs decline. Reseeding ranges, along with sagebrush eradication, is a way to increase forage twofold to tenfold on spring-fall ranges. As with stands of native forage species, correct grazing management of reseeded stands is imperative. These studies are providing valuable information on intensity of use and methods of grazing reseeded stands, as well as information on where, when, and how getting sufficient phosphorus from their feeds or grazing forages.

In various sheep-producing regions, the level of phosphorus in the blood of sheep has been noted as an important element in their nutrition. Lack of phosphorus is associated with unthriftiness in sheep and low profits from their production. The question arose concerning the availability of phosphorus in the forages of the western ranges, where about two-thirds of our sheep are produced. A project to investigate this problem was initiated in 1938 by the Idaho Agricultural Experiment Station and the Department. In 4 years, blood samples were collected from about 40 Columbia ewes that were kept by the Department at Dubois under intermountain conditions providing typical spring, summer, fall, and winter grazing. The ewes were wintered on alfalfa hay and fed some grain after lambing. Blood samples were taken from the jugular veins of the ewes at the close of the fall-range, winter-range, winter-feed-lot, lambing, spring-range, and summer-range periods. The samples were centrifuged and the plasma was analyzed at the University of Idaho.

We learned that seasonal trends in blood phosphorus level were fairly definite and that variations between seasons were significant. The highest levels were found on the winter and spring ranges; the lowest levels were at lambing time, in the late summer and fall, and in the winter feed lot. Supplemental feeding of cottonseed cake or oats on the winter range or feed lot increased the phosphorus in the blood. Ewes that had lambed had lower levels of blood phosphorus than those that had not yet lambed. Dry ewes had higher blood phosphorus than ewes that were pregnant or were suckling lambs. Ewes that were losing weight tended to have higher blood phosphorus than those that were maintaining their weights or were gaining. Blood phosphorus tended to decrease with the age of the ewes. No definite evidence of phosphorus deficiency was found, except the low blood-phosphorus levels that were associated with factors of season of the year, stage of pregnancy, the number of lambs the ewes were suckling, changes in weight, and advancing age.

The normal levels of blood phosphorus were found to be from 4 to 5 milligrams of inorganic phosphorus per 100 milliliters of blood plasma. The percentages of ewes having blood phosphorus values of 3.5 milligrams or below for the various seasons were 5.3 percent for the fall range, 2.5 percent for the feed lot, 20 percent at lambing, 2.7 percent for the spring range, and 10.0 percent for the summer range. The most critical time for supplying plenty of phosphorus in the diet of breeding ewes is at lambing time. Phosphorus can be fed free choice in a mixture of 2 parts of bone meal and 1 part of common salt by weight, when it appears they are not getting sufficient phosphorus from their feeds or grazing forages.

When feed is scarce and prices high, the producer must practice every economy in his methods of wintering sheep, particularly ewe lambs that are to be replacements in the breeding flocks.

In southern Utah many ewes are somewhat undersized at 18 months, the usual age for their first breeding. Feed is relatively scarce in that locality and lambs are sold as feeders or raised as breeding ewes. The usual practice there is to use the best ranges for ewes and lambs during the summer. After weaning, the ewe lambs go directly to the winter range. The following spring the best ranges are again used by ewes and lambs and the yearling ewes are placed on the less productive and drier ranges. In the following fall the yearling ewes go to the winter range as a part of the breeding bands. Although they are usually in thrifty condition at that time these yearling ewes are somewhat undersized.

The Utah Agricultural Experiment Station investigated the effects of feeding ewe lambs during the first winter of their lives, rather than keeping them on the winter range. In each of the 3 years of the experiment,

125 ewe lambs were obtained from a range operator. Seventy-five of them were fed in the feed lot and 50 were handled like other range sheep. The feeding periods each winter lasted about 6 months. The 75 lambs were fed at a level to insure satisfactory growth without fattening, and the other 50 ewe lambs were subjected to the variations and hazards of the ranges of southwestern Utah.

The lambs that got special feed their first winter made significantly greater gains in body weight (although most of the advantage was lost when the lambs were put on the range the following summer) and in weight of wool, unscoured and scoured, with fleeces of significantly longer staple. There were fewer deaths among them. Further, the percentage of ewes lambing at 2 years, of those alive at breeding age, was 64.7 in the groups that were fed and 45.5 in the range groups—in all, an increase of 42.6 percent more ewes lambing as a result of a little extra winter feed.

Fluorine in Phosphates for Fattening Lambs

Fluorine may be toxic when present in considerable quantities in the rations of animals. J. D. Hatfield, C. L. Shrewsbury, and L. P. Doyle, of Purdue University, fed western fattening lambs rock phosphate containing 3.85 percent fluorine as a mineral supplement, in amounts furnishing 1.5, 3.0, and 6.0 milligrams of fluorine per kilogram of body weight a day. The investigators found that the consumption of grain declined and growth was depressed in the lot receiving 6.0 milligrams. As the fluorine intake was increased, the breaking strength per gram of bone went down proportionately, and the percentages of ash and fluorine in the bone increased. The weight of the thyroid gland declined as the amount of fluorine went up.

The Department also made laboratory studies of the problem. The manufacture of defluorinated phosphates on a large scale began in the midst of the war, and the Department undertook feed-lot tests on fattening lambs at Beltsville in an effort to aid manufacturers in standardizing their products. Earlier tests had shown that the temperature of defluorination was important in determining the availability of phosphorus in the product to the animal. In the feeding tests three commercial defluorinated phosphates were found to be nearly as good as bonemeal in availability. The chief measure of phosphorus availability of a product was the level of inorganic phosphorus in the blood serum, although gain in weight, bone composition, and carcass quality were also considered as indices.

Phenothiazine is one of the most important discoveries ever made for keeping sheep healthy. Parasites and parasitic diseases have troubled sheep seriously from time immemorial. Copper sulfate and nicotine sulfate have been used to control several of the internal parasites, but since phenothiazine became available, soon after its discovery was announced in 1938, it has been more widely used for that purpose than any other drug. Workers in the Bureau of Animal Industry have found that sheep will consume sufficient quantities of a suitable mixture of phenothiazine and salt to result in reasonably effective control of stomach worms and intestinal roundworms. A satisfactory mixture consists of one part, by weight, of powdered phenothiazine and nine parts of loose granular salt. This method of administering the drug saves labor and expense.

Breeding Hampshire Ewe Lambs

Sheepmen generally breed their ewes for the first time when the ewes are about 18 months old, so they will lamb at 2 years of age. Because many ewes born early in the spring come in heat in the fall, it has been reasoned that lifetime production may be increased by breeding them then. Hampshires, which develop early, seemed well suited for a test of the idea.

The Department and the South Dakota Agricultural Experiment Station collected data on 119 pairs of Hampshire ewes born at the Belle Fourche Field Station at Newell, S. Dak. The lambs were paired on the basis of age, weight, and family relationship. One of each pair was mated as a lamb at the age of 9 or 10 months, and the other was bred at the age of 18 or 19 months. Eighty-four conceived, and were designated as group A. The 35 that failed to conceive as lambs were put in group B. Their pair mates were classified as groups C and D, respectively. Performance was followed for 5 years. Group A lambs were lighter in weight at 2 years, but they made it up by the third year. Group A produced 89 lambs at 14 to 16 months of age. The total numbers of lambs born in groups A, B, C, and D were 427, 135, 370, and 140, respectively, and the totals raised to weaning age were 305, 92, 255, and 102. Average weaning weights of lambs in the four groups were 67.0, 68.2, 70.1, and 69.0 pounds, respectively. The average weaning weight of lambs from group A in the first year was 54.3 pounds, the lightest of any group of lambs. Group A produced a total of 2,572 pounds more lambs at weaning time than group C. The average annual fleece weights of the ewes in these groups were 7.9, 8.3, 8.2, and 8.0 pounds, respectively.

Breeding these Hampshire ewes for the first time as lambs resulted in a material increase in total lamb production, with only a very slight decrease in wool production. Early breeding appears to be economical and profitable under conditions where ewe lambs can develop adequately and where Hampshire or similar breeds can be given extra feed and care at reasonable cost.

State experiment stations and the Department have under way many other research projects that will help solve new problems of great importance to producers of lamb meat, wool, and the fur of sheep and lambs.

Specifically, emphasis is placed on investigations having to do with improving the manufacturing properties of wool, in preparation for the competition between natural and synthetic fibers, and on greater efficiency in the production of lamb meat and wool in all regions that raise sheep commercially and among all important breeds. Research men hope for the same kind of progress in these studies that has been made in producing more wool. The average annual fleece weight of wool in the United States is now about 8 pounds. A century ago it was only 2 pounds.

THE AUTHOR

Damon A. Spencer, as senior animal husbandman in the Bureau of Animal Industry, has been in charge of the Bureau's sheep, goat, and animal-fiber investigations since 1920. These investigations have included 40 research projects, involving the use of about 10,000 sheep and lambs, about 100 goats and kids, and about 50,000 pounds of wool each year. This research program has included cooperation with nine Federal bureaus and 42 State experiment stations, in finding scientific solutions for practical problems in the sheep, goat, and animal-fiber industries.

FOR FURTHER READING

Beeson, W. M., Terrill, Clair E., and Bolin, D. W.: *Some Factors Affecting the Blood Phosphorus Level of Range Ewes,* Journal of Animal Science, volume 3, No. 2, pages 175–182, May 1944.

Esplin, Alma C., Madsen, Milton A., and Phillips, Ralph W.: *Effects of Feeding Ewe Lambs During Their First Winter,* Utah Agricultural Experiment Station Bulletin 292, October 1940.

Hatfield, J. D., Shrewsbury, C. L., and Doyle, L. P.: *The Effect of Fluorine in Rock Phosphate in the Nutrition of Fattening Lambs,* Journal of Animal Science, volume 1, No. 2, pages 131–136, May 1942.

Jones, J. M., Dameron, W. H., Davis, S. P., and others: *Influence of Age, Type and Fertility in Rambouillet Ewes on Fineness of Fiber, Fleece Weight, Staple Length, and Body Weight,* Texas Agricultural Experiment Station Bulletin 657, August 1944.

Jones, J. M., Warwick, B. L., Phillips, R. W., and others: *Inheritance of Skin Folds of Sheep,* Journal of Animal Science, volume 5, No. 2, pages 154–169, May 1946.

Nordby, Julius E.: *Improving Rambouillet Sheep for Western Ranges,* The National Wool Grower, volume 33, No. 3, pages 12–17, March 1943.

Nordby, Julius E.: *Stabilizing Wool and Body Type in Whitefaced Crossbreed Sheep,* The National Wool Grower, volume 33, No. 7, pages 15–17, July 1943, and No. 8, pages 16–18, August 1943.

Nordby, Julius E., Terrill, Clair E., Hazel, Lanoy N., and Stoehr, John A.: *The Etiology and Inheritance of Inequalities in the Jaws of Sheep,* The Anatomical Record, volume 92, No. 3, pages 235–254, July 1945.

Terrill, Clair E., and Stoehr, John A.: *The Importance of Body Weight in Selection of Range Ewes,* Journal of Animal Science, volume 1, No. 3, pages 221–228, August 1942.

News About Goats

by VICTOR L. SIMMONS

GOATS, being useful and personable animals, are attracting more and more interest among Americans. Consumers want to know more about goat milk, mohair, and chevon. Breeders look for guidance to develop better animals and better products.

As with other animals, progress in breeding milk goats depends upon selecting and mating animals that inherit the ability to give more milk and butterfat. Physical appearance alone is an unreliable index. A newer and better method is genetic selection by basing the choice of breeding stock on records of individual performance and progeny and on the pedigree, if other records are unavailable. Data of this kind will enable breeders to develop constructive breeding programs and to identify individuals most likely to improve their herds.

Through a Star Milker award, introduced by the American Milk Goat Record Association, new opportunity is provided for obtaining performance records for does tested at Official Milking Competitions. This 24-hour test is particularly important to goat owners who keep does only for the family milk supply or as a hobby. Such animals may now be tested without the expense of the usual Advanced Registry 10-month testing. Goat raisers may obtain information about entering their does in official milking competitions or qualifying them for "Star Milker Certificates" by getting in touch with the American Milk Goat Record Association, Sherborn, Mass.

Most does breed only in the fall and early winter, and a way to spread the period over which they come in milk is greatly needed by dairymen and others who must have a regular supply of milk. The simplest and most practical plan at present, provided there are enough does in a herd, is to breed some of them early and some late in the breeding season. A relatively large number of dry does may result, however, from their failure to come in heat as regularly or to breed with as much certainty during the latter part as in the early months of the breeding season.

Research with Hormones

The selection of does that tend to breed out of season gives some opportunity to develop strains that breed at all times of the year. But such natural methods take time, so scientists have been exploring the chances of artificially inducing lactation and stimulating extraseasonal breeding. Work by A. A. Lewis and C. W. Turner at the University of Missouri, and S. J. Folley, F. G. Young, and F. H. Malpress, at the University of Reading and the National Institute for Medical Research, London, first pointed to the possibility of inducing lactation in virgin goats by injections of stilbestrol, a synthetic chemical product having the properties of the natural estrogenic hormones. Later the scientists found that lactation induced in virgin and dry does by stilbestrol could be augmented with treatments of anterior pituitary gland extracts. This combination gave quicker results than injections with estrogen alone. In some cases, in which estrogen failed to induce lactation, the injection of anterior-pituitary extract was followed by heavy milk secretion. These experiments indicate that artificial induction of lactation depends on the maintenance of the proper relation of the estrogen level in the circulation to the activity of the anterior pituitary.

Research with hormones in their relation to lactation has suggested a rather peculiar phenomenon. The administration of estrogens and stilbestrol in certain amounts may effectively stimulate the initiation of milk secretion in virgin or dry animals but at the same time established lactation may be seriously depressed by the same hormones. J. P. Mixner, J. Meites, and Turner, working at the University of Missouri, initiated lactation in yearling virgin Toggenburg goats by daily subcutaneous injections of 0.25 milligram of stilbestrol, but in milking goats doses varying from one to four milligrams a day reduced the milk yield, apparently in proportion to the dosages given. The lactation-stimulating effects of small dosages of the hormone are explained as due to its stimulation of the anterior pituitary to the secretion of lactogenic hormone, while the lactation-inhibiting effects are thought by one group of workers to be the result of an overstimulation of the adrenal cortex.

The importance of hormones in udder growth and development has been shown experimentally. Mixner stimulated the mammary glands of virgin females to extensive lobule-alveolar growth by daily injection of estrogen (stilbestrol) and progesterone and indicated the need for both of these in causing complete mammary growth. Similarly, the British researchers found that either natural or synthetic estrogen will cause teat growth in virgin females.

The theory that goats breed normally in the fall because the days (periods of light) are becoming shorter may have much practical logic. T. H. Bissonnette, in experiments at Trinity College, Hartford, and at Hillshire's Goat Farm, Killingly, Conn., has shown that breeding cycles in goats may be induced by artificially shortened days or inhibited by lengthened days. He also concludes that the annual "temperature cycle is not a major factor in environmental control of sexual or breeding cycles in goats."

Stimulation of extraseasonal breeding in does by use of gonad-stimulating hormones has been emphasized in experiments by Department workers at Beltsville. In a preliminary test, Ralph W. Phillips, Ralph G. Schott, and I found that a dose of 200 rat units, or four cubic centimeters of pregnant mare serum (PMS) was without effect, but a dose of 400 rat units was enough to bring dry does into estrus. Lactating does were more difficult to bring in heat than dry does. We made a second experiment with similar treatments, but followed by an examination of the ovaries; it revealed that follicular growth and ovulation were frequently produced without visible estrus. If this condition occurs naturally, it may explain the difficulty in getting some does bred.

The inconsistency of inducing estrus in anestrous does indicates a need for study of the physiological mechanisms controlling estrus in the goat. Dr. Phillips, R. M. Fraps, and A. H. Frank report that very small doses of estradiol benzoate (0.05 milligram) will induce estrus in spayed does. The duration of estrus increases as the dosage of estrogen increases, but the latent period (hours from injection to estrus) does not vary consistently with the dosage of estrogen. For full estrous response in laboratory rodents, estrogen should be followed with progesterone, but there is little evidence that this procedure gives the same reaction in the doe. On the contrary, progesterone seems to shorten the duration of estrus induced by estradiol benzoate. Once the factors involved in the production of estrus are clearly understood, the induction of estrus and ovulation properly synchronized in anestrous does will have practical possibilities.

Control of Hermaphrodism

Hermaphrodism or intersexuality occurs more frequently in milk goats than in any other farm animal. It is usually possible to recognize hermaphrodite kids at birth, but sometimes positive indications are not evident for several months. A colleague, O. N. Eaton, found in anatomical examinations that not only their external genitalia but also the internal structures resemble those of both sexes. Since hermaphrodites will not breed, failure to recognize the external manifestations of this character results in disappointment and economic loss to breeders. Dr. Eaton and I, in several years of observation of the Department's herd, calculated that 11.1 percent of the kids produced in the Saanen breed and 6 percent in the Toggenburg breed were intersexual.

Horned hermaphrodites are rare. In purebred herds where attention is given to the breeding of polled animals, the possible existence of a relation between the polled condition and the birth of hermaphrodites has economic significance. Eaton's analysis of breeding data confirms the inheritance of intersexuality as a simple recessive and of hornlessness as a simple dominant. Close agreement was found between the observed number of horned and hermaphrodite animals and those expected if there is linkage between the genes for the hornless and hermaphroditic characters. If this genetic theory is correct, it suggests that breeders have been increasing the gene frequency for hermaphrodism. More important, it indicates that the elimination of hermaphrodism from goat herds should be fairly easy by the use of one horned parent in each mating. The rare occurrence of horned intersexes is believed to be due to the crossing over between the closely linked genes for hornlessness and hermophrodism.

Feeding Milk Goats

Individual goats differ in their ability to turn feed into milk or growth. The variations may be due largely to individual differences in appetite and inherited ability to utilize feed. In the Department's herd, milking does are fed at the rate of one pound of grain for each 4 pounds of milk produced. Thus, a doe that increases milk production with increased grain fed is permitted to demonstrate her maximum ability.

Because feeds vary considerably in composition, the nutritional requirements of animals can be more accurately expressed in terms of digestible nutrients than by pounds of feed in the ration. W. L. Gaines of the University of Illinois reports the development of a standard equation for calculating the feed requirements of milking goats. The equation is given as $DN = 0.016W \div 0.3$ FCM, in which DN equals the daily digestible nutrients intake in pounds, W equals the live weight of the doe in pounds, and FCM equals the daily milk energy yield in pounds of 4-percent milk. The milk production of a doe may be corrected to a butterfat basis of 4 percent by use of the Gaines-Davidson formula: FCM (fat corrected milk) $= 0.4M + 15F$, in which M represents the weight of milk and F the weight of fat. By converting milk yields to a FCM basis more accurate comparisons of the productive abilities of individual does is possible.

To provide succulent feeds for milking does in winter, technicians at the New Jersey Agricultural Experiment Station stored green lawn clippings by thoroughly packing them in tight barrels with molasses as a preservative. With 100 pounds of molasses to 1 ton of clippings, they prepared a silage on which does thrived.

We also know more about the need for proper mineral balance in rations for goats. Besides common salt, the minerals most likely to be deficient in feeds are calcium and phosphorus. The cereal grains and high-protein byproducts, such as wheat bran, linseed, soybean, and cottonseed meals, are relatively rich in phosphorus. Feeding cereal grains and protein concentrates with legumes of alfalfa, clover, lespedeza, or soybean hay that furnish calcium gives a ration that provides enough calcium and phosphorus. If necessary, mixtures of limestone or bonemeal one part, and salt, two parts, may be given to goats free choice. There have been no developments to indicate that vitamins other than A and D are needed in goat feeding.

About Goat's Milk

Investigators recently have confirmed and added to many of the findings of J. A. Gamble, N. R. Ellis, and A. K. Besley. These Department workers found in 1939 that the milk of Saanen and Toggenburg goats resembles Holstein cow's milk in percentage of water, lactose, fat, protein, and ash, although subject to greater variation with the advance of lactation than milk of either Holstein or Jersey. The percentage of total solids in goat's milk ranged from 13.05 in February to 10.78 in August.

Goat's milk shows a soft curd, small fat globules, and a rather high buffer index. It contains a high ratio of albumin and globulin to casein and greater quantities of the fatty acids, caproic, caprylic, and capric, than cow's milk. Milk of both goats and cows is low in iron and copper, and in feeding tests nutritional anemia developed on the unsupplemented milk diets. The calcium and phosphorus content of the milks appeared satisfactory. In feeding trials with rats and guinea pigs, Gamble, Ellis, and Besley found goat's milk similar to Holstein milk in vitamin A and D values, relatively high in vitamin B_1 (thiamine), and lacking in vitamin E. They also noted that spring and summer milk had more ascorbic acid (vitamin C) than did fall and winter milk, and that the exposure of milk to air and light materially reduced the ascorbic acid content. Both goat and cow milks were inadequate sources of ascorbic acid.

Because pasteurization of goat's milk distributed for human consumption is now required by public-health authorities in many localities, its effects on nutritive values are important. According to Ellis and others, the solubility of calcium and phosphorus is slightly increased and the curd tension is reduced by pasteurization. This process improves the keeping quality more than the flavor of fresh goat's milk. Pasteurization by holding the milk at not less than 142° F. for 30 minutes caused a decrease of from 33 to 45 percent in the content of reduced ascorbic acid. The phosphatase test, for the detection of improper pasteurization, is not applicable to goat's milk, as this enzyme is inactivated sufficiently to pass the test when the milk is heated only 5 minutes at 143° F.

Angora Goats

Texas, New Mexico, Arizona, Oregon, Missouri, Utah, and California lead in raising Angora goats. Because these animals can utilize certain types of vegetation that other livestock do not like, farms and ranches make millions of dollars annually from the production of mohair. A major part of the industry is concentrated in Texas, particularly the Edwards Plateau in the Southwest.

Mohair has luster, fineness, strength, and excellent spinning and dyeing qualities. In recent years many breeders have sacrificed quality (fineness) for large fleece weights; consequently, manufacturers contend that too large a percentage of coarse mohair is being produced. Despite this trend there is still a relatively large number of goats that yield mohair of fine quality that might be used more in breeding for finer quality mohair, provided breeders are encouraged to do so.

Selection of herd bucks with fine fleeces, free of kemp, is an important step in breeding for improved mohair quality. Kemp, a coarse, chalky white, stiff hair, will not take a dye, and the trade discriminates against it. Angora does selected for breeding should be well developed, carrying dense fine-quality fleeces relatively free from kemp, and showing distinct ringlets or flat locks, as contrasted to straight hair, which indicates a lack of fleece character. More attention needs to be given to constitution and development in selecting foundation stock, for without sturdiness there is no foundation upon which to breed.

Studies on the inheritance of type in Angora goats by the workers at the Texas Agricultural Experiment Station indicate that equally fine-quality mohair fleeces may be produced by flat-lock and ringlet types; also that fleece weights need not be sacrificed at the expense of average fineness. The average fleece weight per head produced during 12 months' growth by registered Angora does ranging in age from 1½ to 10 years was 7.8 pounds, and for doe kids was 4.7 pounds. Fleeces produced during the fall and winter are reported to be finer in quality than those produced on lush ranges during the spring and summer.

The Angora goat has not yet received full recognition as a meat-producing animal. Surplus animals in many herds could undoubtedly be utilized for meat purposes. On many southwestern ranches, goat meat, known as chevon, is eaten extensively and for years has been a popular barbecue dish.

Feed-lot and carcass studies of Angora goats made by the Texas station are probably the first of their kind. J. C. Miller, J. M. Jones, and

C. R. Burt report the feeding of Angora wethers in dry lot for 100 days. Average daily gains by yearlings, 2-year-olds, and 3- and 4-year-olds were 0.19, 0.12, and 0.16 pound, respectively, as compared with 0.31 pound by choice Rambouillet feeder lambs. The dressed yield of the wether goats ranging from 48 to 53 percent on an unsheared basis compared favorably with good to choice Rambouillet lambs. The goat carcass was surprisingly similar to fat lamb carcasses in the percentage of edible meat and bone. However, even the best goat carcasses lacked the thickness and plumpness found in medium to good lamb carcasses. The fat was lacking in uniformity of distribution. In palatability tests, chevon was rated favorably in juiciness and flavor.

It has been estimated that before the war 80 percent of all mohair grown in the United States was used in the manufacture of upholstery and wall and floor coverings. The rest went into yarns and fabrics for clothing. During the war, considerable quantities of the fiber were used in making sweaters, neckties, and socks. New markets for mohair may open: Upholstery for the new automobiles, airplanes, trains, and busses, in the new, modern homes, and in woven and knitted fabrics for clothing.

THE AUTHOR

Victor L. Simmons is an associate animal husbandman in the Bureau of Animal Industry. He has been engaged in research in the breeding, feeding, and management of sheep and goats since 1928. His long experience has given him an understanding of both the scientific and practical aspects of raising sheep and goats.

FOR FURTHER READING

Bissonnette, T. H.: Experimental Modification of Breeding Cycles in Goats, Physiological Zoology, volume 14, pages 379–383, 1941.

Eaton, O. N.: The Relation Between Polled and Hermaphroditic Characters in Dairy Goats, Genetics, volume 30, pages 51–61, 1945.

Folley, S. J., Scott Watson, H. M., and Bottomley, A. C.: Studies on Experimental Teat and Mammary Development and Lactation in the Goat, Journal of Dairy Research (London), volume 12, pages 241–264, 1941.

Folley, S. J., Malpress, F. H., and Young, F. G.: Induction of Lactation in Goats and Cows With Synthetic Oestrogens and Anterior Pituitary Extracts, Journal of Endocrinology, volume 4, pages 181–193, 1945.

Frank, A. H., Schott, R. G., and Simmons, V. L.: Response of Anestrous Does and Ewes to Pregnant Mare's Serum During Two Consecutive Seasons, Journal of Animal Science, volume 4, pages 317–324, 1945.

Gaines, W. L.: Feeding Standard Equations for Cows and Goats in Milk, Journal of Animal Science, volume 2, pages 304–313, 1943.

Gamble, J. A., Ellis, N. R., and Besley, A. K.: Composition and Properties of Goat's Milk as Compared With Cow's Milk, U. S. D. A. Technical Bulletin 671, 1939.

Haller, H. S., Babcock, C. J., and Ellis, N. R.: The Effect of Pasteurization on Some Constituents and Properties of Goat's Milk, U. S. D. A. Technical Bulletin 800, 1941.

Holmes, Arthur D., Lindquist, Harry C., Jones, Carleton P., and others: *The Vitamin Content of Commercial Winter Goat's Milk,* New England Journal of Medicine, volume 232, pages 72–75, 1945.

Miller, J. C., Jones, J. M., and Burt, C. R.: *Angora Goat Produces Excellent Meat—Feedlot and Carcass Studies of Angora Wethers Indicate Economic Significance of This Meat Animal,* Sheep and Goat Raiser, volume 24, pages 9–11, 45, 1944.

New Jersey Agricultural Experiment Station: *How Can the Dairy Goat Producers Provide for Silage During the Winter Months?* Science and the Land, 62d Annual Report, 1940–41.

Phillips, Ralph W., Simmons, Victor L., and Schott, Ralph G.: *Observations on the Normal Estrous Cycle and Breeding Season in Goats and Possibilities of Modification of the Breeding Season With Gonadotropic Hormones,* American Journal of Veterinary Research, volume 4, pages 360–367, 1943.

Richmond, Martha S., Grinnells, C. D., and Satterfield, G. H.: *Ascorbic Acid in Goat's Milk, Blood, and Tissues,* North Carolina Agricultural Experiment Station, Technical Bulletin 68, 1942.

ALSO, IN THIS BOOK

Breeding Better Poultry

by THEODORE C. BYERLY

THE AVERAGE hen on our fathers' farms laid 86 eggs a year. Today the average is 118 eggs, and in some flocks it is about twice that. Changes in management, systematic trap-nesting, and selective breeding brought about the improvement. The amazing wartime yield of eggs and meat, far exceeding all peacetime records, shows what a well-organized industry, aided by research, can accomplish.

But we are not satisfied: Experimental flocks and progressive breeders of poultry demonstrate how we can get even more eggs and more profits. For, as egg production increases, the income over feed costs rises more rapidly, and higher production is had at a lower cost per dozen eggs. In the better flocks, also, more eggs are laid in the winter months, when prices normally go up. Hard economics like this underlie the experiments directed toward improved blood lines.

Many poultry breeders have developed strains of chickens of the more popular kinds that lay 200 to 250 eggs during the first laying year—provided, of course, feeding, management, health, and sanitation are of the best. A breeder develops these outstanding strains by mating selected birds—selected because of proved ability to lay, pedigree, handsome appearance, and, finally, family proof that they can pass on to their offspring the genetic factors necessary for high egg production.

We have found by analyzing many records that selection and mating in this way enable many poultrymen to maintain high production and that the method is effective also in flocks that are not so good. In other words, rigorous selective breeding will improve a flock in a few years to a peak that can be maintained, but not heightened, by further selection. But if selection stops, production drops. Improvement through selective breeding is directly proportional to the correlation between individual and family performance on the one hand and genetic make-up on the other. To find out whether by developing and crossing inbred families we could boost average egg production beyond the level reached by such family selection and line-breeding, we have made comparisons of the two methods at Beltsville each year since 1940. Inbreeding (that is, the mating of closely related stock), followed by matings between unrelated families, parallels the production of hybrid corn, which greatly outyields its parent stock. The results of thus crossing inbred stock of two different breeds, as well as of the same breed, promise much.

The offspring of inbred families of the Single-Comb Rhode Island Red variety that we mated to inbred Single-Comb White Leghorns have steadily exceeded the average of the family-selected purebred parental strains by about 25 eggs a pullet during the first laying year. These incrossbred pullets were relatively nonbroody; many crossbred pullets are excessively broody. Incrossbred pullets may be excellent layers, but their records do not exceed those of the best purebreds, and it remains to be determined whether they are consistently superior to all family-selected strains of purebred chickens.

Hatcherymen and poultrymen who raise chickens for meat may improve the quality of their breeding stock by selecting birds for three main characteristics—fast feathering, rapid growth, and superior conformation. This plan of selection, which begins with young chicks, does not affect egg production and does not greatly increase management costs.

Fast feathering is desirable partly because it reduces the number of pinfeathers in market birds. Indications of fast feathering in day-old chicks are the length and number of the wing-feather sheaths. The best chicks for broiler stock have well-developed primary feathers—the large outer wing feathers—and well-developed secondaries, which number six or more and lie next to the primaries. Slow-feathering chicks have fewer secondaries and primaries that are not so well developed. You can easily find the feather sheaths in the down at the outer edge of the wings. If you select chicks of the desired type for next year's breeding flock, you should raise them by themselves or mark them in some way, by a wing band or leg band, for instance.

You can best judge the ability of chickens to grow rapidly by their body weight when they are 1 to 2 months old. Those that have made the most satisfactory gains should be kept for the breeding flock. You can make another check for growth at the age of 5 months, when you can remove from the special group any birds that are below expectations.

Superior conformation for meat production is indicated by good development of the breast when chickens are about a month and a half old, and not later than 3 months. Because the breast meat is the most valuable part of a broiler, only birds with well-meated breasts should be kept for use as breeders.

In producing broilers, the practice of crossing certain breeds or varieties has been popular and successful. Crossbreds commonly produce more meat for feed consumed than the purebred parents, they feather more satisfactorily, and fewer die during the growing period. Crossbred pullets and hens, however, tend to be broody oftener than the parent stock. Birds from Barred Rock roosters and New Hampshire or Single-Comb Rhode Island Red females are especially popular for meat production. Cross-breeding is less widely used for laying stock, although one advantage in crossing between certain breeds is that one can identify the sex of chicks at hatching time because of differences in the down color or feathering. For this purpose, nonbarred red, buff, or black roosters and barred hens may be used, or roosters with gold in their plumage may be bred to silver females.

In experiments covering 3 years, we made two- and three-way crosses of Rhode Island Red, White Wyandotte, and Light Sussex. We found that the crossbred progeny generally outgrew standardbred Rhode Island Red pullets up to 10 and 20 weeks of age, and matured somewhat earlier. Those of the two-way cross were 6 to 10 percent more viable, and the progeny of the three-way cross were even better in this respect. The crossbreds were no better than standardbred stock, however, in annual egg production, egg weight, hatchability, and weight of mature birds.

We bred by genetic selection a strain of rapid-feathering and fast-growing silver chickens with Columbian pattern from the offspring of these crosses. This strain now breeds true in major characteristics. After a few more years of improvement in egg production and meat type, it will be useful for broiler production. Its advantage over good rapid-feathering Barred Plymouth Rocks is that the progeny of Columbian males in both pure matings and crossbred matings with New Hampshire or Single-Comb Rhode Island Reds have light colored pinfeathers. Housewives accept the barred feathers of the purebred or crossbred progeny of Barred Plymouth Rock males as a mark of quality. Now that more broilers are marketed dressed, and often drawn and cut up ready to cook, the dark pinfeathers are a serious disadvantage.

Turkeys

We have also been successful in breeding operations designed to get a small turkey of good conformation that is more suitable for family use than the larger kinds. The type of such a bird has been reasonably well fixed. The new turkey is named Beltsville Small White, so called from its place of origin, small size, and white color. Several thousand such birds of acceptable quality have already been produced. Hatching eggs have been distributed through State experiment stations to commercial breeders and considerable commercial production has resulted.

Beltsville Small White young toms weigh 12 to 17 pounds alive at market age. Young hens weigh 7½ to 10 pounds—roughly about two-thirds the weight of mature standard-size birds. The body is compact, with much breast meat. The legs and neck are relatively short.

Artificial insemination has scientific and commercial possibilities in breeding chickens and turkeys. Department workers developed a simple way to obtain semen from chickens and turkeys and to inseminate the females. Fertility has proved high, and many breeders have shown interest in the method; but, except in turkeys, its commercial use has been limited. Research workers, however, use the technique to effect fertilization when birds cannot or will not mate naturally—to make crosses between bantams and larger varieties of chickens, for example.

Some researchers in nutrition employ the practice to fertilize the eggs of hens kept in batteries, so they can get information on experimental diets, fertility, and hatchability. A few poultrymen also use it for hens kept in batteries. Breeding hens are not usually kept in batteries, however, and many poultrymen prefer to mate a proved sire naturally with an unusually large number of hens, risking some infertility, rather than to undertake the additional effort.

Turkeys, particularly the Broad-Breasted Bronze, have shown considerable infertility, and some turkey raisers breed them artificially to overcome the fault. Other growers, encouraged by experiments at the Texas Agricultural and Mechanical College, have improved the reproductiveness of Broad-Breasted Bronze turkeys through genetic selection for well-balanced body conformation.

Broodiness in turkeys, as in chickens, cuts egg production, causes extra labor, and increases costs of producing poults. We believe we can develop relatively nonbroody strains, and have started working toward that goal at Beltsville.

The Improvement Plan

Persons who prefer not to breed poultry but rather to purchase stock, either as day-old or larger birds, can do so now with prospects of obtaining much better stock than was available several years ago. Coordinated Federal, State, and commercial activities have been directed toward a wider use and better supervision of improved breeding methods. Examples of this trend are the National Poultry Improvement Plan for chickens and a similar plan for turkeys.

Use of males from bred-to-lay strains has been one of the principal factors responsible for the increase of 25 eggs a hen in course of the 10 years the National Poultry Improvement Plan has operated. A further increase is probable, because only about 30 percent of hens in hatchery-supply flocks are mated to males one or both of whose parents were officially pedigreed. Besides, as farmers get better stock they feed and manage their flocks better so as to get the most from their improved birds.

Bred-to-lay stock of chickens, representing any one of four progressive breeding stages, can be had from hatcheries and breeders. The stages, each with successively higher requirements, are: U. S. Approved, U. S. Certified, U. S. Record of Performance, and U. S. Register of Merit. The turkey plan stresses efficiency in meat production. For both species of birds, official flock and hatchery inspections and other forms of supervision provide reasonable assurance of obtaining the degree of quality desired.

As a further guide to persons seeking superior chickens, the Department of Agriculture now issues an annual directory of birds that have qualified for U. S. Register of Merit, the highest breeding stage.

Recognition is given to sires and dams on the basis of the productivity of their daughters, of which at least a third of those entered in the third-highest stage of the plan must have annual records of 200 eggs or more. Other requirements cover acceptable size of eggs and physical characteristics of the birds. More than 14,644 birds have thus far met the specified high standards. As evidence of the egg production to be reasonably expected from daughters of U. S. Register of Merit dams, officials in charge of the National Poultry Improvement Plan report that the average production of 28,248 such daughters was 208 eggs in 1944.

The use of airplanes for transporting hatching eggs long distances has prompted experiments to find out if high altitudes affect hatchability. They apparently do not. In our investigations we used reduced air pressures to simulate altitudes of 7,000 feet, 12,000 feet, and more, and discovered that the eggs under test, when incubated in the usual way, hatched after 3 days' exposure to a rarefied atmosphere equal to that at 15 miles above the earth.

Improving Egg Quality

Consumers prefer eggs with better shells, substance, and keeping quality; poultrymen like them because they cut marketing costs and losses.

We did some research on the thickness, porosity, and related characteristics of eggshells, as shown by shrinkage of their contents during storage; and found indications that the characteristics are inherited. Our studies, made with two different lines of chickens, also point to the improvement of shell quality by selecting families of breeding birds on the basis of blood lines that produce eggs that shrink little in storage.

Studies on the interior quality of eggs have shown that blood spots in eggs come from inherited faults. Poultrymen, therefore, are wise to cull their breeding flocks of hens that lay eggs containing blood spots, which cause great loss to producers, market agencies, and consumers. Our studies showed us the falsity of the common belief that handling birds, moving them about, or frightening them cause their eggs to contain blood spots. We found also that because many blood spots are very small (less than a thirty-second of an inch in diameter) candling is only about 50 percent efficient in detecting them—another reason for culling birds that are known to produce eggs with blood spots.

We also selected families of chickens on the basis of the rate at which the albumen in eggs deteriorates. One line developed in this way produces eggs which, when infertile, remain fit for table use after being held 2 weeks at 99° F. The albumen remains fairly thick in these eggs after such mistreatment, but another line of hens lays eggs that have no visible thick white after similar treatment. Poultrymen can use this method of selection in order to supply housewives with eggs of outstanding quality even if refrigerated transportation and holding facilities are lacking.

THE AUTHOR

Theodore C. Byerly is in charge of poultry investigations in the Bureau of Animal Industry. He is a graduate of the University of Iowa and for several years taught poultry husbandry at the University of Maryland. In 1943 Dr. Byerly received the Borden award for outstanding work in poultry research.

FOR FURTHER READING

Barott, H. G.: *Effect of Temperature, Humidity, and Other Factors on Hatch of Hens' Eggs and on Energy Metabolism of Chick Embryos,* U. S. D. A. Technical Bulletin 553, 1937.

Burrows, William H., and Quinn, Joseph P.: *Artificial Insemination of Chickens and Turkeys,* U. S. D. A. Circular 525, 1939.

Godfrey, Albert B.: *Poultry-Breeding-Stock Selection for Desired Characters,* U. S. D. A. Circular 715, 1944.

Quinn, J. P.: *Selecting Hens for Egg Production,* U. S. D. A. Farmers' Bulletin 1727, 1934.

ALSO, IN THIS BOOK

Keeping Poultry Healthy

by THEODORE C. BYERLY

BECAUSE average death losses among growing chickens and laying hens add about 2 cents a dozen to the cost of producing eggs, poultry owners make money by keeping their flocks in good health. It is not easy to do, for more than 50 different diseases and parasites constantly threaten poultry. The first step in dealing with an unfamiliar ailment is to determine the cause as a basis for applying appropriate cures.

Pullorum disease, one of the most insidious and devastating of all poultry maladies, no longer takes the heavy toll it once did. The National Poultry Improvement Plan, established in 1935 and now operating in 47 States, contains specific provisions for its control. Similar provisions are contained in the National Turkey Improvement Plan, now active in 42 States. The plans have four progressive pullorum-control classes, which represent different stages in the suppression of the infection in breeding stock and deal with related steps to protect hatcheries, eggs, and chicks against infection by pullorum organisms. The key to most of the work is the simple stained-antigen rapid whole-blood test, developed by Department scientists for diagnosing the disease in breeding stock. On the basis of the current volume of testing and relative survival rates of chicks in tested and untested flocks, it saves poultrymen millions of dollars.

The chief precaution in dealing with this highly infectious malady, which breeding flocks transmit through the eggs, is to be sure that new stock—either mature birds or newly hatched chicks—are from properly pullorum-tested sources. One of the newer research contributions to pullorum disease control, announced in 1943, was the use of an improved medium for producing the stained antigen used in the test. The new medium consists of colloidal sulfur suspended in glycerol, and gives a greatly increased yield of the bacteria needed for preparing the antigen.

231

The practice of culling all hens at the end of their first laying year and thus keeping only pullets in laying flocks helps prevent transmission of several diseases, especially respiratory diseases and avian tuberculosis, from old birds to young ones. All-pullet laying flocks lay more winter eggs than hen flocks, and are generally more profitable. The plan is being adopted widely, especially among owners of flocks of the heavy breeds.

For coccidiosis, a parasitic disease, medication with sulfaguanidine, one of the sulfa drugs, is effective. It prevents, to a large degree, severe coccidiosis in chickens. It also permits a sufficient number of the infective organisms to develop to immunize the birds against the highly fatal form of cecal coccidiosis. Indications are that sulfaguanidine will help prevent severe outbreaks of intestinal as well as cecal coccidiosis.

Continued heavy losses from fowl paralysis and other forms of the avian leukosis complex have stimulated both State and Federal research, which is actively in progress. Paralysis and other nerve involvements, although frequent expressions of the disease, represent only one type. The inclusive term "avian leukosis complex" is appropriate because of the varied manifestations of this disease. Practically all tissues, organs, and other parts of the body have been found to be involved. Thus far no drug, vaccine, feed, or other product has been found that can cure it.

Recommended preventives are sanitation and quarantine measures. The use of breeding stock from families of high viability offers promise of reducing losses from this group of diseases. Research at the Regional Poultry Laboratory at East Lansing, Mich., and at Cornell University has indicated that brooding chicks in clean quarters separated by several hundred feet from any adult poultry is another way to cut losses. Apparently chicks are most susceptible when hatched and grow increasingly resistant to the disease with age.

Many other details affect the earning power and general well-being of poultry, among them housing, equipment, and exercise. Research and practical experience have worked together to give us several improved and profitable practices. Some of these differ from those advised and followed even as recently as 1940. I list several of the recommendations that are typical or that research workers believe have value:

Move portable brooder houses to clean ground before the chicks arrive, as a defense against coccidiosis, roundworms, and tapeworms. The term "clean ground" refers to land that has not been used by chickens or turkeys or been fertilized by poultry droppings within 2 years. As an added precaution against the same dangers, do not permit chicks or poults to mix with older birds, and do not permit visitors to enter brooder houses or yards.

For litter in the brooder house, use deep, absorbent material. Begin with at least 2 inches and add new litter each week until the total depth is about 4 inches. Crushed corncobs, shavings, dry sawdust, or a good commercial litter is suitable, but not straw alone unless cut into lengths of 2 inches or less. For the first 5 days, while the chicks are learning what and where to eat, keep the litter covered with sacks or building paper. Stir the litter at least three times a week. Unless an infectious disease occurs, the litter need not be changed during the brooding season.

A good litter is advised also in laying houses; begin with a depth of 3 inches and increase to about 6. Besides reducing disease hazards, litter helps insure against lowered egg production. House pullets in buildings or laying shelters by themselves—never add pullets to a flock of old hens even though the hens have been carefully examined and appear to be in perfect health. The reason is that adult birds, even though showing no visible symptoms, may transmit several infectious diseases.

Litter reduces the danger of coccidiosis. As another protection against it, fill in low places around brooder houses with clean gravel. Also helpful in lowering mortality of chicks is ample light in brooders. Without good light many chicks will not learn to eat and drink, and losses will be high. The color of the light is much less important than the intensity. Studies show, however, that neither color of light nor its intensity during the first 16 weeks has any effect on the final live weight, egg production, or the fertility or hatchability of eggs.

The use of artificial lights to supplement natural daylight, especially in winter, has been the subject of much discussion among poultrymen. Artificial lights have been observed to affect both molting and egg production of mature stock. Most molting hens resume egg production under the stimulus of artificial light. During a 3-month molt period (December, January, and February) the rate of production of experimental birds receiving artificial light was about 40 percent—signifying an average of four eggs in 10 days. By contrast, the rate for control birds that received only natural winter daylight during the same period was about 15 percent. No known light stimulus, however, affects the normal one-egg-a-day limit to a hen's egg production.

Turkeys also respond well to artificial lighting, and by its use they can be made to produce hatchable eggs during the fall and winter, thus lengthening the egg-producing season.

Poultrymen have learned to hatch chicks in January, February, and March so that they reach sexual maturity in September, October, and November, the period of shortest egg supply. Day length is sufficient to support egg production in well-grown pullets during these months.

Many pullets that start to lay in early fall molt during the short winter days. These pullets and molting hens in good flesh can be kept in production by lengthening the day with artificial light if their feed intake and body weight are normal. Hens that lose weight do not respond readily to increased light.

Regulating the time of hatch is important with respect to egg weight, too. Pullets 5 months old in July sometimes start laying heavily before they are big enough to produce eggs of good market size. There is a negative relation between length of day at sexual maturity and age and body weight at sexual maturity. Pullets that begin to lay in December without artificial light are older, heavier, and lay larger eggs than those that start to lay in September. We do not know whether sexual maturity of early hatched pullets can be delayed by artificially shortening day length during the summer months until they reach a good body weight.

Light is one of the external factors regulating the hen's hormone secretion. Physiological processes involved in egg formation are under direct hormonal control. Thus, the pituitary gland, at the base of the brain, is stimulated by light acting through the eye to produce certain hormones. These hormones are carried by the blood that goes to the ovary or testis, causing them to grow and ripen eggs or sperm. The ovary, or testis, is also stimulated by these pituitary hormones to produce sex hormones, which cause the comb and oviduct to grow and regulate the amount of lime in the blood, so that eggshells may be formed.

Several other organs are involved in the complex hormone relationships necessary to egg and sperm formation. The thyroid, for example, reaches maximum activity in February at about the time maximum body weight is attained. Maximum egg production follows a month or so later. The thyroid and egg production decline together during the summer. Research at the Missouri Experiment Station with iodine-containing proteins fed to laying hens indicates that these may supplement declining thyroid activity in the summer months and thus maintain a high rate of egg production. These proteins are not yet available for farm use.

Several chemicals have been found to act similarly to the female hormone. At the Oklahoma Experiment Station it was learned that certain of these chemicals, added to the feed for a few days, cause males, even old cocks, to assume characteristics of the capon, such as plump, soft flesh. We must postpone practical application of these results until we have removed the remotest possibility that the flesh of such treated birds, when eaten by men, will have a feminizing effect on them.

THE AUTHOR

Theodore C. Byerly is in charge of poultry investigations in the Bureau of Animal Industry. He is a graduate of the University of Iowa.

FOR FURTHER READING

Bunyea, Hubert: *Use of the Rapid Whole-Blood Test for Pullorum Disease,* U. S. D. A. Miscellaneous Publication 349, 1941.

Bunyea, Hubert, and Wehr, E. E.: *Diseases and Parasites of Poultry,* U. S. D. A. Farmers' Bulletin 1652, 1941.

Feeding Poultry

by H. R. BIRD

HALF a poultryman's expenses go for feed. More than half his worry and moil go into it. When feedstuffs are scarce, he must use them more efficiently. When they are expensive, their formulas might be changed, and he is not sure of their value. One of his main problems always is how to provide enough protein.

From studies at Beltsville of the protein needs of growing chickens, we found that the birds make their greatest gains, in proportion to feed consumed, when their ration contains about 21 percent protein. A diet containing much more or less than that is definitely less efficient. But when the birds are full-grown, the proportion of protein may be reduced, with satisfactory results, to about 16 percent for laying stock, and to as little as 13 percent in a maintenance ration for male chickens. Feed-consumption records of experimental birds show that chickens generally need more pounds of feed per pound of gain as they grow.

The war meant shorter supplies of high-quality protein supplements of animal origin. We found, however, that in well-balanced diets proteins of vegetable origin may constitute up to about 80 percent of the total proteins for chickens that produce hatching eggs, and 90 percent of the total for other mature chickens and for growing chickens and turkeys. Successful growing diets in which all of the protein is of vegetable origin have been devised for turkeys more than 8 weeks old that have access to good range. These percentages are a good bit higher than were once considered practicable. Because vegetable proteins are generally cheaper than those of animal origin, this knowledge bears directly on economy of production. Properly cooked soybean meal is an excellent feed for poultry.

Considerable progress has been made at the California Agricultural Experiment Station in expressing the protein requirements of growing

235

chicks in terms of amino acids, which constitute proteins. More information on this vital subject and on the distribution of amino acids in feeds will help us to predict the feeding value of feedstuffs and feed mixtures from the results of chemical analyses. It is too much to expect, however, that the value of the usual protein supplements will be predictable entirely on the basis of their amino acid content, because they also contain vitamins that poultry need. The amino acids and vitamins, furthermore, do not exert their effects independently, but are interrelated. For example, work at the Wisconsin and Maryland experiment stations reveals that when growing chicks consume relatively large quantities of corn or gelatin, they have increased requirements either for tryptophane, an amino acid, or for nicotinic acid, a vitamin.

Also, we have discovered that for growing chicks a practical diet containing soybean meal as the only protein supplement is effectively supplemented either by an amino acid named methionine or by two vitamins: Pantothenic acid and choline. It is also interesting to note that such diets are effectively supplemented by 2 to 4 percent of fish meal, which does not supply enough methionine, choline, or pantothenic acid to account for such an effect. The ability of these chemically dissimilar materials to substitute for one another probably is due to their role as intermediaries in metabolism, rather than as constituents of body tissues.

Research at the Wisconsin, New York, and Ohio experiment stations has yielded much valuable information about the need for the B-complex vitamins by different classes of poultry. The information has been useful as a basis for experiments on the utilization of byproducts, such as those of the fermentation industries, and of synthetic vitamins, to obtain nutrients formerly supplied by animal products.

As a result of research it is now possible to recommend quantitative allowances of the following nutrients for growing chickens. Six amino acids: Glycine, arginine, methionine, cystine, lysine, and tryptophane. Ten vitamins: A, D, K, thiamine, riboflavin, pantothenic acid, nicotinic acid, pyridoxin, biotin, and choline. And nine mineral elements: Calcium, phosphorus, sodium, manganese, iodine, potassium, magnesium, iron, and copper.

Another discovery is that cow manure is a valuable source of vitamins for chickens and turkeys. This subject was first investigated because it had been shown that bacteria in the rumen (the first and largest stomach of cattle) can synthesize thiamine, riboflavin, and several other vitamins. Our experiments showed that the addition of cow manure (dried at 45° C.) to a low-grade diet enhanced the growth of chicks and stimulated comb growth. Its addition to a low-grade diet for laying hens decreased egg production but increased hatchability. Drying the cow manure at 80° C. destroyed the factor that stimulated comb growth and decreased egg production, but did not destroy the factor that improved the growth of chicks and increased hatchability. We did not find these favorable effects when we added the manure to an already adequate diet. The low-grade diets contained no animal protein supplements. They were improved to about the same extent by adding either dried cow manure or fish meal as 5 percent of the diet.

This new knowledge interested us tremendously. Besides its own basic, practical value, the discovery exemplifies a truth about the nature of modern science: Farmers had no need to give it thought during the centuries that chickens ran freely in barnyards, eating what manure they wanted; now, when countless broilers are raised in batteries and never even touch the ground, we see the merit of an old practice.

We went on experimenting. We learned that the growth-promoting effect of cow manure was due to an unknown factor in it, not to the presence of any of the known vitamins. We also demonstrated that this mysterious factor is synthesized in the digestive tract of mature chickens and is present in their excrement in about the same concentration as in cow manure. Hence, the rumen is not essential to its synthesis.

Cow manure was used as a starting material for the preparation of concentrates of the growth-promoting factor. The most potent concentrates thus far prepared were effective when fed as 0.004 percent of the diet, and thus were about 1,000 times as effective as dried cow manure or fish meal. Tests on both the white and dark meat of chickens whose feed was up to 10 percent dried manure failed to disclose any undesirable odors or flavors. Notwithstanding the encouraging results obtained, the use of cow manure as a source of vitamins is not yet advised by the Department, pending further research. We must know more about the possibility of spreading diseases.

To go back to soybean meal: In studies of hatchability, we found that, without animal protein, the hatchability and viability of chicks go down as the level of soybean meal in the hens' diet goes up. This effect of soybean meal is overcome by feeding the hens animal protein of high quality, such as fish meal and dried-milk products, and also by feeding dried cow manure. When adequately supplemented with these materials, the total diet of breeding birds may contain 10-percent soybean meal.

We wanted to know how the amount of feed a hen eats affects the number of eggs she lays. When we cut the quantity of feed to 87.5 and 75 percent of the normal consumption, the hens cut their production 25 and 50 percent, respectively. Cutting down on feed this way, however, did not affect the size of eggs or the live weight of the birds. But since efficiency of egg production depends so largely on rate of production, it follows that reducing the feed for laying hens cuts their efficiency.

Other experiments indicate that increasing the fiber content of diets of laying hens from about 2½ percent to about 6 percent decreases by about 16 percent the efficiency with which hens utilize feed.

Artificial incubation and brooding, increasingly popular systems that keep large numbers of chicks together, are apt to cause more feather picking, toe picking, and cannibalism, vices that sometimes cause heavy losses. They can usually be stopped by giving the chicks more salt in their feed. Adding 2 percent of salt to an all-mash diet or 4 percent to a mash fed with a grain or grain mixture for 2 or 3 days is recommended.

A high proportion of corn in the diet increases the chicken's need for nicotinic acid. That seems true also of human diets, since pellagra, the disease due to deficiency of nicotinic acid, is likely to occur among people who subsist largely on corn. Meats are good sources of nicotinic acid; chicken meat has been found to be outstanding in this respect. The light meat and liver contain as much nicotinic acid as beef and pork liver, which are often recommended as the best sources of the vitamin; dark chicken meat contains slightly more nicotinic acid than beef and pork.

In feeding turkeys, fish oils of all kinds should be omitted from the diet after the birds reach 8 weeks of age. When such oils appear to be necessary in the diet of turkeys older than 8 weeks, the quantity should not exceed one-eighth of 1 percent. The quality of the oil should be high and it must not be rancid. Fish meals also should be omitted or sharply restricted in the diet of turkeys older than 8 weeks.

Color has little bearing on the nutritive value of poultry products. But it does affect their appearance and must be considered as a quality factor. The yellow pigments of egg yolk and of the shanks and skin of chickens are related chemically to vitamin A, but the pigments present in greatest quantity have no vitamin A potency. It was demonstrated some time ago at Beltsville and the University of Maryland that some feedstuffs contain substances that interfere with the laying down of yellow pigment. More recent work showed that vitamin A itself produces such an interfering effect when present in large quantities. Vitamin A is practically always present in poultry feeds and in egg yolk, but whether it interacts with the yellow pigments when present in the usual quantities remains to be investigated.

In the case of feather pigmentation, researchers at the University of California and in industrial laboratories found that pantothenic acid and folic acid are needed for the development of black pigment; scientists at the University of Maryland learned that deficiency of vitamin D increases the production of black pigment.

THE AUTHOR

H. R. Bird is a biochemist in charge of Poultry Nutrition Investigation at the Bureau of Animal Industry. For approximately 5 years prior to 1944 he was associae professor of poultry nutrition at the University of Maryland. Dr. Bird is a graduate of the University of Wisconsin.

Horses and Mules

by WILLIAM JACKSON

IN 1947 Americans owned 8 million horses, the smallest number in 75 years. Nevertheless, those of us who believe there will always be a place for horses in the rural scene have gone ahead with tests and experiments to breed better horses and to learn more about them. Institutions that have taken the leadership are the agricultural experiment stations in California, Michigan, Mississippi, Missouri, Indiana, Montana, Tennessee, Wisconsin, Utah, Kentucky, and Minnesota; the Army Remount Service; and the Department of Agriculture, chiefly at the United States Morgan Horse Farm at Middlebury, Vt., and its Range Livestock Experiment Station at Miles City, Mont.

Interesting experiments have been started at the Michigan station to produce a handy-size farm horse for comparison with heavy draft horses in adaptability to general farm work, market demand, and size. Mares of draft breeding, mainly Percheron and Belgian, are being bred to Arabian, Thoroughbred, and Morgan stallions. The fillies from these crosses will be bred back to stallions of the same light breeds, respectively, and later mated with draft stallions.

Another aim of the work in Michigan is to find cheaper ways to produce horses by using pastures as much as possible and eliminating feeding of grain, chore labor, and housing. Results indicate that both draft and light-type colts can be raised satisfactorily by keeping them out-of-doors on pasture in summer, and on uncut meadows and stacked hay in winter. Such colts reach full mature weights, and have better legs and feet than similar colts housed in stalls. When sold as yearlings or 2-year-olds, they are in somewhat rougher condition than stall-fed colts, and consequently tend to sell at slightly lower prices, but bring a higher net profit because of their lower cost to produce. Four fillies

239

raised outdoors have produced 12 colts in the 3 years since they were first bred as 3-year-olds, thus giving 100-percent colt crops for three successive seasons—an achievement in any stud.

Attention also has been given to developing practical means of measuring equine performance and utility. A series of preliminary tests with light horses at the Morgan Horse Farm developed a useful background of experience for such measurements, which Ralph W. Phillips, G. W. Brier, and W. V. Lambert have summarized in this way: The tests of speed and length of stride demonstrated significant differences between horses; horses tend to increase the length of stride during a test, indicating that records must be taken under similar conditions if individuals are to be compared; normal respiration and heart rates are difficult to obtain. A slight disturbance resulted in an increase. If normal rates at rest are to be obtained, they will probably have to be taken in the stall, at complete rest, and by someone with whom the horse is familiar. The extent to which respiration and heart rates rise during exercise and the rate of return to normal vary with the amount of exercise and also with the individual horse.

Tests at Middlebury

Based upon these observations, a series of tests has been devised through which all progeny of the Department's Morgan stud are measured in harness and under saddle at 3 years of age. Speed of walking and trotting and length of stride are recorded over a measured mile when the animal is pulling 60 percent of its body weight under harness and hitched to a two-wheel training cart, and again under saddle carrying 20 percent of its body weight. Endurance is measured by a trot over a 5-mile course, the horse being hitched to the cart, and, on another day, over an 11½-mile cross-country ride under saddle, during which each animal covers measured and marked portions of the ride at three different gaits, which add up to 4.7 miles at a walk, 5.7 miles at a trot, and 1.1 miles at a canter. For the 5-mile test, respiration and heart rates are taken before removing animals from their stalls, at the end of the test, and 5, 10, and 15 minutes thereafter. After these endurance tests, the animals are scored for signs of fatigue, ease of gaits from the standpoint of the rider, and other factors.

These tests should help us discover some correlation between characteristics like temperament and conformation, on the one hand, and speed, endurance, and other important performance qualities on the other; and help us to use the geneticist's tools of inbreeding and rigid selection to produce animals that can perform as we want them to.

The tractive dynamometer, an electrical instrument in which the pointer is deflected as a result of a force exerted between fixed and moving coils, is still the most practical instrument for measuring performance in draft animals. It was first developed at Iowa State College. Its use has shown that the weight of a team is the most important factor in determining how much it can pull. But no reliable specific correlation has been found between body type and the animal's pulling ability.

After 9 years of observing pulling contests in Utah and southern Idaho, Milton A. Madsen, Harry H. Smith, and Ralph W. Phillips reported that the average body weight of all teams performing in nearly 2,500 entries was 2,872 pounds, and their average tractive pull was 2,385 pounds. These workers also summarized data from various sources on the amounts of tractive pull required to do different jobs on the farm, and discussed the relationship of results of the study to the ability of the horse to do farm work. Since dynamometer contests are almost all conducted for teams, to measure maximum pull rather than ability to work day after day, and are participated in by relatively few highly trained teams, these men concluded that the results now available are of little use in guiding breeding operations. They suggested that tests should measure walking speed, length of stride, and increase in heart and respiration rates of horses while doing definite amounts of work.

At the Missouri station, H. H. Kibler and Samuel Brody, working in cooperation with the Department, are attempting to establish indices for obtaining those measures. They are based on the assumption that heart and lung capacity are important factors, that temperament and will to work make a big difference, and that—on a given day—temperature, humidity, air movement, feeding, and handling vitally influence the animal's ability to work. The men at Missouri, using mules for experimental animals, have constructed an ergometer with a weight and pulley system mounted on a trailer. It measures the amount and speed of work done and eliminates the variables of grade and irregularities of surface on which the animal performs. Within the automobile pulling this trailer is mounted an open-circuit respiration apparatus that enables the animal being tested to breathe normal outdoor air and at the same time to be measured with respect to significant physiological responses.

New Knowledge About Feeding

Studies at a number of stations provide new information on the feed horses need. In tests with Percheron geldings, A. L. Harvey, B. H. Thomas, C. C. Culbertson, and E. V. Collins, of the Iowa station, showed that horses weighing about 1,700 pounds at light, medium, or heavy work probably do not receive enough calcium and phosphorus either in a maintenance ration of 3 pounds of oats and 20 pounds of timothy hay, or in the same ration plus sugar and dextrinized starch, which give energy.

At the University of California, C. E. Howell, G. H. Hart, and N. R. Ittner found that rations commonly fed to horses in areas where yellow corn is not available are apt to be deficient in vitamin A, a deficiency that leads to night blindness. Accompanying that condition they also found a joint ailment that causes lameness, which they later discovered is not due to vitamin A deficiency. In speculating on the significance of that finding, Dr. Hart pointed out that green feed may contain a vital dietary factor that helps prevent lameness. He recalls that in the days of horse cars, the car horses had to be taken out of regular service for a rest on summer pasture from 2 to 7 weeks, and that British horse trainers provide green feed near their training stables to prevent lameness, which is so fatal to success in racing.

Tests at the Army Remount Veterinary Research Laboratory at the Front Royal Remount Depot in Virginia showed that the use of riboflavin in rations effectively prevented periodic ophthalmia, or moon blindness, a malady responsible for more blindness in horses than all other causes combined. Forty milligrams of crystalline riboflavin, a member of the vitamin B complex, was fed to each horse daily with the grain ration, at a cost of a cent a day. From November 1943 to June 1944 no cases of moon blindness occurred among 130 horses that received the supplement, but new cases occurred annually at the rate of 109 per thousand horses among those not receiving it. Riboflavin is now given all horses at the depot. Whether ophthalmia is purely a nutritional disease is still an open question, however. Further research is needed.

We have also learned a great deal about reproductive processes in stallions and mares. V. R. Berliner, at the Mississippi station, reported that stallion and jack sperm cells stay alive inside the female for only a day or so, and for only a matter of hours in storage without the addition of some life-prolonging and diluting medium known as a diluter. Bull sperm survive 2 days or more in the female, and longer outside. The differences in longevity between the stallion or jack sperm cells and bull sperm cells are apparently due to the high glucose content of bull semen that the sperm convert into lactic acid. The acid depresses the life processes of the spermatozoa and brings about a resting stage from which they can later be restored to motility. Semen of stallions has a relatively high salt content, which acts as an overstimulant to the sperm and causes their rapid exhaustion and death.

Dr. Berliner evolved a gelatinized glucose-tartrate egg-yolk diluter with which it was possible to effect pregnancies in mares with 48-hour-old semen. However, he advocates the use of semen preferably not more than 6 to 8 hours old. The requirement that semen be fresh would limit the practice of artificial insemination of mares to relatively small areas, or to points having good air-transport connections.

Dr. Berliner points out further that artificial insemination, although sometimes useful, cannot increase pregnancies over the natural capacities of the mare and the stallion, and that the highest percentages of pregnancies are probably obtained by turning stallions and mares together on pasture or range. He found also that sperm production by stallions and jacks declined when the animals became overfat, and that sperm produced by sires fed on corn were of low viability, thus verifying an old saying, "There are no foals in corn." In his experiments, good pasturage overcame the bad effects of an overfattening grain ration, which was also low in vitamin content and in mineral balance.

Experiments at the Michigan station throw light on at least one of the qualities of pasture that make it a valuable feed for breeding animals. It was found that blood ascorbic acid values for good breeders, in mares of both heavy and light breeds, were significantly higher than those of poor breeders, and that the ascorbic acid content of the blood of mares varied directly with their access to good pasturage. In the spring before the mares were turned on pasture, .09 mg. of ascorbic acid was found per 100 ml. of blood plasma. This value rose to .17 mg. on spring pasture, fell to .11 mg. on summer pasture, rose again to .14 mg. on fall pasture, and fell to .11 mg. during the winter. Injections of ascorbic acid (vitamin C) into a 3-year-old Belgian stallion whose semen showed almost an absence of sperm and no sperm motility, raised the sperm count to between 2 billion and 4 billion and the motility to approximately 70 percent activity. Later this same stallion was fed ascorbic acid by capsule, at the rate of one gram daily, with equally good results.

Good results were had at the Mississippi station from using the synthetic estrogen stilbestrol in inducing heat in mares that were shy breeders. The treatment induced heat 5 days after injection. Ovulation followed in 4 or 5 days. The treated mares were bred on the second and fourth day of heat, and became pregnant.

Many horse breeders believe that the surest time to get a mare with foal is to breed her during foal heat, which occurs on about the ninth day after foaling, and lasts 1 day. Dr. Berliner strongly advises against this practice on premises where breeding diseases resulting in abortions and losses of newborn foals have occurred. At this time, the mare's uterus usually has not had time to recuperate from parturition, and is much more vulnerable to infection. Records kept at large breeding farms show higher percentages of navel ill, joint ill, and other prenatal diseases in newborn foals when the pregnancies occur during foal heat than when the mares are bred at later heat periods.

Other findings also confirm that only strong, healthy mares should be bred during foal heat. Dr. Hart and his colleagues in California learned that pregnancies that required a large number of services per conception were followed by long gestations and resulted in high percentages of foals born dead—another indication that the mare's sex organs may not be entirely sound for some time after parturition. A competent veterinarian should examine the placenta of each foaling mare to determine the best time to mate her, especially if there are any signs of infection or other abnormal conditions.

Foalings in winter and early spring were found to follow longer gestation periods than did summer and fall foalings, probably because of the lower nutritive value of feed during the seasons of scant pasturage at the time the fetus is at a rapidly growing stage. A healthy foaling mare is one that shows no important necrotic lesions of the placenta, has not retained her placenta longer than 6 hours, has a healthy vigorous foal, and has not carried her foal longer than 340 days when foaling from December to May, nor longer than 334 days for June-to-November foalings.

THE AUTHOR

William Jackson is assistant chief of the Animal Husbandry Division in the Bureau of Animal Industry. Among his more recent publications is a textbook on *Livestock Farming* prepared specifically for men who chose to study the subject while in the armed forces. He is a graduate of Purdue University.

FOR FURTHER READING

Andrews, F. N., and McKenzie, F. F.: *Estrus, Ovulation, and Related Phenomena in the Mare,* Missouri Agricultural Experiment Station, Research Bulletin 329, 1941.

Berliner, V. R.: *Artificial Insemination for Horse and Mule Production,* Book 283 of the Horse and Mule Association of America, Inc., 1945.

Britton, J. W., and Howell, C. E.: *The Physiological and Pathological Significance of the Duration of Gestation of the Mare,* Journal of the American Veterinary Medical Association, volume 52, June 1943.

Harvey, A. L., Thomas, B. H., Culbertson, C. C., and Collins, E. V.: *Effect of Work on the Calcium and Phosphorus Retention of Percheron Geldings,* Journal of Animal Science, volume 2, May 1943.

Hudson, R. S., and Good, Byron: *Factors Affecting Farm Horse Power,* Michigan Agricultural Experiment Station, Quarterly Bulletin, volume 28, February 1946.

Kelser, R. A.: *Preventing and Controlling Disease Among Horses and Mules,* Book 287 of the Horse and Mule Association of America, Inc., 1946.

Kibler, H. H., and Brody, Samuel: *Field Studies on Cardio-Respiratory Functions and Energy Expenditure During Work and Recovery in Mules,* Missouri Agricultural Experiment Station, Research Bulletin 394, September 1945.

Phillips, Ralph W., Madsen, Milton A., and Smith, Harry H.: *Dynamometer Tests of Draft Horses,* Utah Agricultural Experiment Station, Circular 114, 1940.

ALSO, IN THIS BOOK

Genetics and Farming

by E. R. SEARS

THE SCIENCE of genetics, which deals with the manner in which characteristics are passed on from generation to generation, is only about 50 years old, but already it has made many contributions to agriculture. The most spectacular undoubtedly is hybrid corn, whose value is even greater than the millions of dollars it has added to American farm income.

Hybrid corn is truly epochal in and of itself, but a greater good is the example, the impetus, and the key that it has given to all scientific breeding. It is at once a fruit and root of the discovery by the Austrian monk Gregor Mendel that characters are determined by unit factors, called genes, which remain unchanged in hybrids and which segregate out in succeeding generations to give new combinations of characters.

Because of Mendel's discovery, we can use nature's laws to produce more productive, better adapted, and healthier plants and animals. Many of our present-day crops and certain of our breeds of livestock owe some of their most desirable or even vital characteristics to the scientific breeder. For example, resistance to the deadly black stem rust was bred into our common wheats through a planned program involving crosses with related species.

Mendel made his basic studies almost a century ago (they remained unnoticed until the turn of the century), and the genetic experiments that led to hybrid corn were completed some 30 years ago. Since that time our knowledge of genetics has increased greatly, carried forward by man's intense interest in his own heredity and in that of other animals and of plants. Now, in 1947, we can confidently look ahead to a wide and profitable use by American agriculture of some of the more recent advances in genetic knowledge.

Hybrid corn owes its superiority in yield to hybrid vigor. When strains or varieties of corn are self-fertilized, or inbred, for a few years, the plants become progressively smaller and poorer yielding. In fact, many lines become so weak that they die out. Each surviving line becomes more and more uniform from year to year, however, with less and less further reduction in size and yield, and eventually becomes a constant, true-breeding type. When two such inbred lines, not closely related, are crossed with each other, the resulting "single-cross" hybrid is usually larger and higher yielding than the original strains or varieties. This increase in size and yield is called hybrid vigor. Besides their higher productivity, hybrids of this sort are remarkably uniform, thus contributing to easier cultivation and harvest. Also, many undesirable characteristics, such as susceptibility to disease and lodging, may be eliminated in the process of inbreeding.

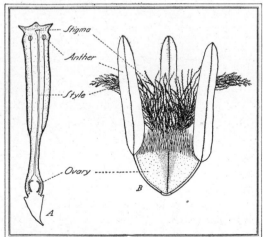

INHERITANCE IN PEAS

P_1 Round green   ×   Wrinkled yellow

F_1 Round yellow

F_2 9 Round yellow   3 Round green   3 Wrinkled yellow   1 Wrinkled green

This chart on the inheritance of peas is a good example of the basic laws of heredity in plants.

Thanks to genetic studies, we are now able to use hybrid vigor in other crops. We can do this because we have overcome the difficulties of crossing, or mating, plants that are normally self-fertilized.

In corn the female flowering organ, the ear, is separated from the male flowering organ, the tassel. Consequently, a plant may be self-fertilized or cross-fertilized at will, simply by shielding the ear until it is ready for pollination, and then applying pollen from a tassel on the same plant (for selfing) or from another plant (for crossing).

In almost all of the other common crops, male and female organs do not

Here are two examples of perfect flowers: A, the flower of a tobacco plant cut in half lengthwise; and B, the essential parts of a wheat flower. In them, the pollen grains from the anthers fall upon the stigma and each puts out a pollen tube. The tubes grow down the style to the ovary, carrying with them the male elements to fertilize the eggs.

occur separately, but are found together in the same flower. Each flower is "perfect," possessing both male and female parts, and self-fertilization normally occurs. In order to prevent self-fertilization, we remove the male organs from each individual immature flower—a process, called emasculation, too laborious for commercial use.

There are, however, some crops in which each plant, while possessing normal male and female organs, is infertile to its own pollen. The self-sterile plants include tobacco, rye, buckwheat, and certain fruits, vegetables, forage grasses, clovers, and flowers. In them cross-pollination is quite readily obtained, simply by growing the desired parental lines near one another. But in order to obtain the maximum vigor and uniformity in hybrids, one must have inbred lines for crossing each year—lines that have been self-fertilized for several generations. And in some self-sterile crops no satisfactory way has been found of selfing to obtain inbreds. In certain other self-sterile plants, pseudo self-fertility occurs, and these plants can be selfed successfully. In tobacco, for example, a plant may be self-sterile throughout the entire flowering season, except for the last few days. In this period of end-season fertility, self-fertilization occurs readily. Also, bud fertility occurs in various self-sterile plants, including tobacco and some members of the cabbage group, in which selfed seed may be obtained by opening an immature flower by hand and applying pollen from another flower of the same plant. By either of these methods the plant breeder can get inbred lines for use in production of commercial hybrid seed.

Actually, the inbreeding process may successfully be dispensed with in certain self-sterile crops, of which alfalfa is one. H. M. Tysdal and T. A. Kiesselbach, working in Nebraska, found that in alfalfa substantial increases in yield sometimes resulted from crosses between ordinary, noninbred plants. The hybrid offspring were not so uniform as if inbred parents had been used, but uniformity is not particularly important in a forage crop. Since alfalfa is a perennial plant, desirable crosses can be repeated year after year, and commercial quantities of seed can be had following vegetative propagation of the parent plants.

Most crop plants do not have separated sexes, like corn, and are not self-sterile; hence they are largely self-fertilized, and each variety is in effect an inbred line. Crosses between these inbred varieties often show hybrid vigor, but the necessity of making the crosses laboriously by hand prevents commercial use of the hybrids. Within recent years, however, a way has been found of simplifying the making of crosses—namely, the use of male-sterile types—and hybrid vigor in many additional crops can now be used commercially.

The known instances of male sterility may be divided into several classes according to the way in which they are controlled genetically. Best known, perhaps, is the so-called cytoplasmic male sterility, in which

The method of inheritance of three different types of male sterility are illustrated here: *A*, cytoplasmic-genetic; *B*, cytoplasmic; and *C*, genetic. Letters in the inner circles represent genetic factors; letters in the outer circles show cytoplasmic factors; the S means male-sterile; the F male-fertile. The gene F is dominant to gene S. The cytoplasmic factors are transmitted only by the female parent.

the sterility depends wholly or partly on a particular type of cytoplasm. Cytoplasm is material transmitted through the egg only; therefore, an individual's cytoplasm is always like that of its mother, whereas its genes are derived equally from mother and father.

One type of cytoplasmic male sterility depends upon the interaction of a particular gene with a particular cytoplasm. Here, neither the genetic factor nor the cytoplasmic factor alone is enough to cause male sterility; male-sterile plants must have both. This type of male sterility occurs in onions, and is used by H. A. Jones and his colleagues in the production of hybrid onions of superior yielding ability. The program is essentially the same as that used for corn, with the commercial crop being grown from seed produced each year from crosses of inbred lines. The chief difference from hybrid-corn practice is that, since the male-sterile strain cannot by itself produce any seed, a special line must be maintained to keep the male-sterile strain going. This line has the genetic factor but not the cytoplasmic factor for male sterility, and hence is male-fertile. When it is used to pollinate the male-sterile strain, male-sterile plants only are produced. Those male-steriles are then pollinated by an unrelated inbred line to produce vigorous hybrids.

Male sterility due to interaction of cytoplasmic and genetic factors has been discovered, too, in the sugar beet, where, as in onions, it promises to be of outstanding importance for the production of vigorous hybrids. That type of male sterility has been found also in flax and in the commercially unimportant group Epilobium. Dr. D. Lewis, an English investigator, believes that this cytoplasmic-genetic sterility is to be expected frequently following hybridization of species or races.

In a second type of cytoplasmic male sterility, no genetic factor is involved. The offspring of all male-sterile plants are male-sterile, regardless of the male parent used. M. M. Rhoades, in experiments at Cornell University, found this condition in corn. Various naturally occurring plant species exhibit it. This kind of male sterility might easily be used in producing hybrids in much the same way as the cytoplasmic-genetic type.

Male sterility that depends upon a single genetic factor, with no cytoplasmic effect involved, is found in several plants, notably corn, barley, sorghum, and tomato. Genes causing this type of male sterility are ordinarily recessive, that is, noneffective when the corresponding gene (allele) for male fertility is also present, as a contribution from the other parent. In practice, male-sterile plants are obtained by crossing male-steriles with carrier plants. The male-sterile parent is pure (homozygous) for the gene concerned, while the carrier plant is impure (heterozygous), with both the sterility gene and its normal counterpart. The offspring of the cross consist of male-steriles and carriers in approximately equal proportions. If the male-fertile plants are removed as soon as they appear, the remaining male-steriles may be used in crosses with some other line to produce vigorous hybrids for commercial use. Maybe this is most easily done by growing the other line and the line yielding the male-steriles in alternate rows. Then, if the pollen is carried by wind or insects, the cross will be made automatically. Hand pollination will be necessary in some crops, such as barley and tomato, but is not unduly difficult to do. The male sterility eliminates the really laborious step in crossing—that of removing the male organs from the immature flowers.

Male sterility due to simple recessive genes arises spontaneously in some plants—tomatoes, for example—and can easily be induced by X-rays in many other crops. Its use in programs that employ hybrid vigor for greater production is likely to increase greatly.

New developments in methods of corn breeding are of particular interest, not only because corn is an important crop, but because workers with other crops customarily look to corn breeding for refinements in the hybrid-vigor technique.

D. F. Jones and W. R. Singleton, of the Connecticut Agricultural Experiment Station, report the occurrence of spontaneous changes, or mutations, in lines of corn that have been inbred continuously for many generations. The mutated lines have reduced vigor, but when they are crossed with the pure lines from which they arose, the resulting hybrids

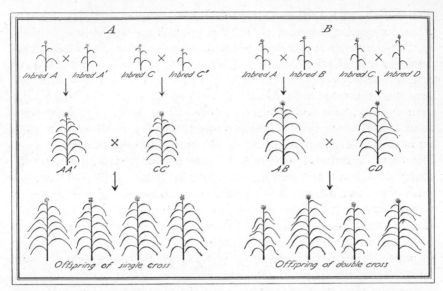

Two methods of producing commercial corn hybrids are shown here: *A*, the use of mutated lines for crossing to their parental inbreds, and *B*, the standard double-cross method. Lines A' and C' are derived from inbreds A and C by mutation. Of the two methods, *A* produces more uniform plants than *B*.

frequently are stronger than the parental pure lines. This remarkable finding does not by any means disprove the prevailing theory that hybrid vigor is due primarily to the action of dominant favorable-growth genes. It does suggest, however, that at least a part of the vigor may be due to something else—namely, to the complementary action of different forms of the same gene. It suggests also the practical possibility of using in the seed-production program the comparatively vigorous hybrids produced by crossing the mutated lines to their parental inbreds. Since a small number of genic differences (possibly only one) are involved in these crosses, the "hybrids" are actually pure lines in most respects. Crosses between two of these "hybrids" would be essentially single-crosses, with greater uniformity than possessed by "double-crosses" (crosses between two single-cross hybrids). Double-cross hybrids are now used by farmers almost to the exclusion of single-crosses, because seed for the latter is produced on low-yielding inbreds and is therefore very expensive.

A second recent contribution to corn breeding is the "gamete selection" technique originated by L. J. Stadler at the Missouri Agricultural Experiment Station. His plan emphasizes the greater genetic variability among gametes (unfertilized sex cells) than among plants, and hence the greater chance of recovering an exceptionally good gamete than an exceptionally good plant. Gametes from open-pollinated varieties are recovered by crosses to existing inbred lines; and performance tests of these hybrids indicate which received superior gametes. These best plants are then inbred, with further performance tests to insure retention of the genes for high yield. Gamete selection seems to be particularly well adapted to the replacement of individual inbreds in existing double-cross combinations. There is no theoretical reason, however, why the inbreds obtained through gamete selection could not be combined into valuable, new, double-cross combinations.

Another recent development in genetics is concerned with polyploid plants—how they behave genetically and how to produce them artificially. Polyploidy means the possession of some multiple of the so-called basic number of chromosomes, the minute bodies that carry the genetic factors, of the group to which the particular plant or animal belongs. For example, the basic number of chromosomes in the wheats is seven pairs—each kind of chromosome is present in duplicate, one being maternal and one paternal. That basic number is possessed by the einkorns, the diploid wheats. Another group, the emmers and durums, with 14 pairs, are the tetraploid wheats. The common wheats, with 21 pairs, constitute the hexaploid group.

Two different types of polyploids are recognized, autopolyploids and allopolyploids (or amphidiploids). In autopolyploids the increases in the number of chromosomes are the result of doubling the chromosomes of a single species, so that in the tetraploid, for example, each chromosome is present four times instead of only twice. In allopolyploids the doubling of chromosomes is preceded by hybridization between two different species, so that, as in the diploid, no chromosome is present more than twice.

By use of the drug colchicine or certain other chemicals, plants with doubled chromosome number are now easily obtained. By treating seeds, or the growing tips of established plants, with colchicine in solution or in a paste mixture, polyploid sectors or entire polyploid plants are produced. Recently, Department scientists have simplified colchicine treatment of large numbers of plants by developing an aerosol, a sort of chemical fog, containing colchicine.

When A. F. Blakeslee and A. G. Avery, of the Carnegie Cold Spring Harbor station in New York, first announced the effectiveness of colchicine in doubling chromosome number, it was immediately obvious that here was an important new tool for plant research. Plant scientists immediately sensed its practical applications. Subsequently many polyploids have been produced, the majority of them being autotetraploids. For crops where the setting of seed is an important factor, few, if any, autopolyploids have proved of practical value, for seed set is usually considerably lower than in the diploid. Furthermore, while some autopolyploids may attain a final size greater than that of their diploid parent, this is not true of all; and autopolyploids tend to grow more slowly than diploids. Consequently, higher yields of forage can be expected only infrequently from autopolyploids.

But in some respects autopolyploids commonly excel diploids, and flower size is perhaps the most conspicuous of these characteristics. Flower gardeners have taken advantage of this circumstance, with the result that there are now on the market tetraploid marigolds, snapdragons, and pinks. Tetraploid lilies have been produced experimentally. Autopolyploids, too, frequently show an increased proportion of special substances. L. F. Randolph and D. B. Hand, of the Department of Agriculture and Cornell University, found, for example, an increased vitamin A content in tetraploid corn; and the content of gums and essential oils is known to be higher in autotetraploids of certain plants.

Allopolyploids appear to offer greater promise than autopolyploids in plant breeding. In general, they are much more fertile and more nearly true-breeding. Allopolyploidy provides a means of conferring fertility upon hybrids between different species, while retaining all of the hybrid vigor. It thereby provides for the synthesis of new species almost at will, within the limits of cross-fertility. Some of the new species thus produced will certainly have practical value.

Perhaps the best known allopolyploid involving crop plants is wheat × rye (that is, wheat crossed with rye). This new species (called Triticale, from *Triticum* for wheat and *Secale* for rye) has been produced by a number of investigators, and has several desirable characteristics.

Here is a potentially useful allopolyploid in the wheat group: Heads of *A, Triticum dicoccoides,* one parent; *D, Aegilops speltoides,* the other parent; *B,* the sterile hybrid between *A* and *D*; and *C,* the same hybrid with chromosome number doubled by colchicine treatment and now allopolyploid and fertile. The use of this or a similar allopolyploid would seem to furnish the best chance of transferring to wheat the high resistance of *Ae. speltoides* to the wheat rusts. The allopolyploid, itself highly resistant, can readily be crossed to common wheat, whereas *Ae. speltoides* crosses with common wheat with difficulty and sometimes not at all.

Triticale is relatively infertile, however, and thus has not proved useful. Other allopolyploids involving wheat have been produced, such as macaroni (durum) wheats × Timopheevi (a recently discovered wheat highly resistant to various diseases), which are quite fertile. Some of these are highly regarded, particularly in Russia. The perennial wheats reported by Russian breeders are not allopolyploids, but are segregates from crosses of wheat with Agropyrons. It is doubtful that perennial wheats would be acceptable to American farmers, because growing wheat for two or more successive years on the same land is contrary to good crop-rotation practice.

Aside from their possible value as new species, many allopolyploids are useful as breeding material. Turning to the wheats again, we find certain diploid species of the related group Aegilops that possess desirable characteristics, particularly resistance to disease. The direct transfer of these characteristics to hexaploid wheats is difficult or impossible because of the failure of the crosses to set seed, or because of extreme sterility of the hybrids. But by first add-

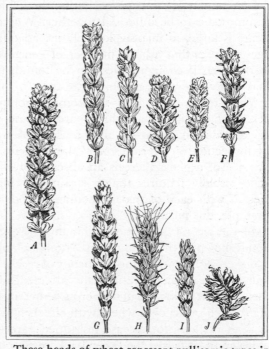

ing the diploid Aegilops species to a tetraploid wheat through allopolyploidy, we can obtain a plant with 21 pairs of chromosomes that can be crossed readily with wheat. Furthermore, the resulting hybrid has a fair degree of fertility.

The problem of polyploidy involves much more than just the artificial production of new types. Many of the common crop plants are polyploid— wheat, oats, tobacco, and cotton, to name a few. The genetic analysis of polyploids is difficult, because the effects of a particular pair of genetic factors may often be concealed by other similar or identical genes located on a different pair of chromosomes. In wheat,

These heads of wheat represent nullisomic types in common wheat. *A* is normal with 21 pairs of chromosomes; *B* to *J* are nullisomics I, II, III, V, VI, VII, X, XV, and XVI, each with only 20 pairs of chromosomes. The nullisomics indicate on which chromosomes certain genetic factors are located. For example, the longer awns on nullisomic X show that the missing chromosome X carries a gene that shortens the awns.

although many genetic studies have been carried out, the total genetic situation is much less clearly understood than in many nonpolyploid plants that have received considerably less attention. Hence, breeding of wheat has not proceeded on so precise a basis as plant breeders would like. •

Recent research with tobacco and wheat shows the possibility of obtaining whole-chromosome deficiencies and using them in genetic studies. In tobacco, an allotetraploid with 24 pairs of chromosomes, 24 different types of monosomic plants have been obtained, each deficient for a different chromosome. In common wheat, a still more extreme type of deficiency has been obtained—namely, nullisomics. These completely lack one pair of chromosomes; that is, they have only 20 pairs of chromosomes instead of 21. Of the 21 different nullisomics possible in wheat, each deficient for a different pair of chromosomes, 18 have been obtained.

Monosomics and nullisomics are extremely useful for determining on which chromosomes particular genetic factors are situated. The ordinary method of locating genes on the chromosomes is based on the determination of "linkage"—that is, the tendency of genes on the same chromosome to be inherited together. Where the number of chromosomes is large, as in polyploid plants, adequate determination of linkages requires that a large number of genes be available with which to work. Even if enough genes can be found, the linkage studies require that many crosses be made and tested.

With monosomics and nullisomics, comparatively few crosses are necessary to determine which chromosome carries a particular gene. In fact, dominant factors may be located without any crosses, simply by inspection of the nullisomic plants themselves, for in the complete absence of a gene, there is an absence of effect. Location of recessive genes usually requires that a strain carrying the dominant allele be crossed with each of the nullisomics or monosomics, but in wheat, for example, this means only 21 crosses.

In the second generation following these crosses, the recessive condition is shown by the normal proportion of plants (one out of four), except in one cross. In this one the frequency of recessives is much less than one in four, only nullisomic plants being affected; and the chromosome which was deficient in this particular cross is thereby identified as the one carrying the gene. Genes in wheat with effects hard to classify precisely (such as most of those for disease resistance) are located by crossing to the nullisomics, as before, and then backcrossing to the nullisomics for a few generations. Lines are eventually obtained, each of which has one known pair of chromosomes from the resistant variety, and the other 20 pairs from the standard variety. Tests of these lines show which chromosomes of the resistant variety carry the resistance factors.

A program for the use of nullisomics in cataloguing the genetic factors for disease resistance in wheat has been in progress since 1942 at the

Missouri Agricultural Experiment Station and at Beltsville. In this program, in which H. A. Rodenhiser and I are collaborating, resistance to the widely destructive disease, black stem rust, has received most attention. The objective of the study is to find the major genes for rust resistance in wheat, and to learn on which chromosome each of these genes is located. The information obtained should enable breeders to put together new varieties with superior resistance to disease and to improve the resistance of existing varieties. In the building up of these new varieties the nullisomics and monosomics will again be useful, since they may be used to increase the ease and precision of transferring chromosomes and genes from one variety to another.

Genetics of Micro-Organisms

Finally, a few words about the recent active interest of geneticists in the micro-organisms, especially molds, yeasts, bacteria, and viruses. Some of the research being done is of the utmost significance to genetics, because of the information obtained on how genes act in the living cell. The results with bacteria and viruses are of considerable importance in the field of medicine. For example, a mutant strain of Penicillium mold has been obtained, following X-ray treatment, that is much more productive of penicillin than any previously known type. The findings of M. Demerec of the Carnegie Cold Spring Harbor Station in New York, on the way in which bacteria, through mutations, may adapt themselves to tolerance of high concentrations of penicillin, have far-reaching implications in medicine.

As concerns agriculture, some persons have supposed that new varieties of yeasts and fungi might be bred that would largely replace present soil-grown plants as sources of food, but there is very little indication that this development will soon, if ever, take place.

The most important application to agriculture of the genetic work with micro-organisms will probably be the creation by geneticists of new strains and races that can profitably utilize various farm products, including waste materials. This will mean increased demand for the farmer's wares.

THE AUTHOR

E. R. Sears, a geneticist in the Bureau of Plant Industry, Soils, and Agricultural Engineering, has been a member of the Department since 1936. Stationed at Columbia, Mr., Dr. Sears works with wheat and related grasses. His research on nullisomics in common wheat, each with a pair of chromosomes missing, provides a new approach to the genetics and breeding of wheat. With E. S. McFadden of the Department he has shown the way in which our common wheats probably arose in nature. Dr. Sears is a graduate of Oregon State College and Harvard University.

Plant Growth Regulators

by JOHN W. MITCHELL

A LITTLE more than a decade ago scientists learned that
they could change the way some plants grow by putting a chemical on
the stems. The substance they used was one that they had just isolated
from human urine, but they found out later that some of the crystals they
had so laboriously purified were those of indoleacetic acid, a substance
that had been known for years and had been made in the laboratory.

They discovered that plants, somewhat like animals and humans, are
sensitive to chemical stimulants that can be made readily in the laboratory
and factory. Because plants respond by changing their rate or type of
growth, the chemicals are called growth-regulating substances, or growth
regulators. So far they have been produced synthetically, only; they have
not been found in green plants.

There are, however, some regulators of growth that plants do produce.
They are properly called plant hormones. They are not secreted by special
glands, as animal hormones are; these natural growth regulators are made
in certain parts of the plant, such as leaves and buds. They are often
moved through the plant from one part to another. Scientists believe
they govern growth in plants much as animal hormones regulate growth
in animals. The true plant hormones have not yet been made in the laboratory; in fact, only small amounts of them have ever been isolated from
plants. But we are trying to extract some of them in larger amounts, so
we can learn whether plants treated with true plant hormones will behave
in a way that might be useful in the production of some kinds of crops.

Since the first discovery, scientists have found that plants are stimulated
to respond in various ways by more than a hundred different organic
chemicals that are not found in plants but that can be made in the
laboratory. The way plants behave when treated with the chemicals

depends on the kind of growth regulator used and on the amount and way it is applied. For instance, if only a speck, about one-millionth of an ounce, of 2,4–D (chemically called 2,4–dichlorophenoxyacetic acid) is put on one side of the stem of a bean seedling, the cells along the treated side grow faster than those on the untreated side, and the plant will bend sharply in a direction away from the treated surface.

If, however, about 2,000 times that amount of 2,4–D (about as much of the powder as can be held on the flat side of a toothpick for a distance of an eighth of an inch from the blunt end) is mixed with a little lanolin and the mixture rubbed on a tender section of the stem, the plant responds differently. Food materials within the plant are moved from other parts of the stem, and possibly from some of the leaves, into the treated section, where many new cells are formed. The new cells finally become organized and arranged so that they form new roots inside the stem. The young roots, called root primordia, later push their way to the outer surface of the stem, and if that part of the stem is covered with moist soil the primordia will grow out into it and function as ordinary roots do in supplying the plant with water and nutrients.

If, on the other hand, the above-ground parts of the plant are sprayed or dusted with 2,4–D, the response is yet different, for leaf growth ceases, the rate of respiration of the plant is increased, and its reserve food materials are broken down and subsequently burned up. As a result the plant generally dies within 1 to 3 weeks after treatment, or the length of time required for its reserve food materials to be depleted.

How plants respond also depends upon what kind of chemical is applied. For instance, many growth regulators (indoleacetic acid, naphthaleneacetic acid, and others) will cause the stems to bend, but others (2,3,5–triiodobenzoic acid and related benzene derivatives) do not cause bending. Instead, they greatly alter the shape and rate of growth of the leaves located some distance from the part of the stem to which they are applied. The reactions of the treated plants, then, might include bending, rooting, increased respiration and growth, chemical changes and movement of food materials within the plant, and the production of new cells.

Already we have put the discoveries to many practical uses in agriculture; in fact, few other fields of plant research have progressed so fast or affect so many branches of farming and gardening as this one.

Most of the practical uses have come from experiments that you might consider to be of minor importance. An instance: A scientist experimented with holly flowers, which generally fall off unless they are pollinated. When sprayed with a growth-regulating substance, even the unpollinated flowers remained on the plant and produced berries. From this beginning, a practical application of considerable importance to fruit growers has developed—the use of growth regulators to prevent apples and pears from dropping to the ground before they are ready to pick.

As most kinds of fruits ripen, they generally become less firmly attached to the branches. That is because a small section of the stem of the fruit close to the branch serves a special purpose and, as the fruit ripens, it gradually becomes a weak link, finally breaks, and allows the fruit to fall. Difficulty arises when this weakening process proceeds too rapidly in a crop such as apples; the stems no longer can support the weight of the fruits and the apples fall before they are ripe. Many of the fruits are injured as they hit the ground, their quality is lowered, and the grower loses money.

Reasonably good assurance against such loss to apple and pear crops can be had by spraying the trees with one of several growth-regulating substances. You can buy them under fully descriptive trade-marked names at hardware or seed stores in a form ready for applying in a water spray. They should be applied according to the manufacturer's directions. After spraying, the section of stem that ordinarily would weaken and allow the fruit to fall remains surprisingly strong for a week or two. Few fruits do fall; the rest remain on the trees until ripe enough to be picked.

The harvest sprays generally remain effective long enough to prevent much loss from dropping, but some orchardists find it hard to judge the exact time at which the substance should be applied, because if the trees are sprayed too early, the effect of the chemical runs out before picking.

We are testing new growth regulators, however, to find the compound that gives the longest effective period during which the sprayed fruit will remain on the tree. One compound, 2,4–D (2,4-dichlorophenoxyacetic acid) shows promise. Trials made in 1944 by L. P. Batjer and P. C. Marth near Beltsville indicate that Winesap apples sprayed with 2,4–D (a 0.001 percent water mixture) stayed on the trees about twice as long as did comparable fruit sprayed with naphthaleneacetic acid, the first substance widely used to prevent fruit drop.

In experiments by C. P. Harley and others, Stayman Winesap apples sprayed with 2,4–D a month before harvesttime also remained on the branches well past the commercial picking date. At the end of the experiments, 19 days after the commercial harvest, the stems were still firmly attached, although the fleshy parts of many apples had rotted and fallen away. The experiments lead one to believe that the effective period of harvest-drop sprays can be extended through the use of 2,4–D, in place of the earlier naphthaleneacetic compound on Winesap and Stayman Winesap trees, and perhaps other varieties.

The work by Harley and his colleagues illustrates a characteristic of plants that, in the case of fruit drop, somewhat limits the usefulness of certain of these chemicals. That is that different varieties behave in different ways when growth regulators like 2,4–D are applied. Delicious, Golden Delicious, and York Imperial apples respond favorably to harvest sprays of the naphthalene type (naphthaleneacetic acid and naphthaleneaceta-mide). When sprayed with 2,4–D, however, their fruit fell as though the trees had not been sprayed at all.

In fruit-drop sprays, as in insect sprays, a spreading agent is often added to the mixture. The choice of the spreader is important. The addition of a water-miscible waxy substance known as Carbowax 1500 to the sprays containing naphthaleneacetic acid has significantly extended their effective period.

Growth Regulators and Greenhouse Tomatoes

Growers who specialize in growing tomatoes in greenhouses in the winter have, besides the usual problems of soil fertility and disease control, the additional problem of how to make the young tomato fruits hang on the vines and grow vigorously. Because there are few insects or air currents in greenhouses in winter to do it for them, the growers must pollinate the tomato flowers by shaking the individual flower clusters. But even carefully hand-pollinated flowers often fail to set a high percentage of fruit, especially when the weather is cloudy. Often that failure is due to the failure of the flowers to produce enough good pollen. Vigorous pollen, the kind that is generally developed during the summer by field plants, serves to fertilize the fruits so that seeds develop, and also apparently contains substances that stimulate the young fruit to grow rapidly—something the weak winter pollen often does not do.

Growth-regulating substances are the answer. With them, the young fruit can be artificially stimulated and often made to stick on the vines and grow vigorously. Not all of the fruits, of course, will develop seeds, because some of the flowers are not pollinated, but in size and flavor the sterile ones often surpass the pollinated fruits. The safest and most widely used way now to apply the chemicals for this purpose is to spray the flowers, when they are fully open, with an emulsion containing 1 to 2 percent lanolin (fat from sheep's wool) and 0.2 percent of indole-butyric acid. If entirely seedless fruit is wanted, it is necessary to cut off the stamens, the male flower parts, at the time of treatment.

Indolebutyric acid is relatively mild in its effect as a growth regulator. A number of compounds (naphthoxy and phenoxy) are many times more active than indolebutyric acid in effecting some kinds of plant responses. These have been tested for use in the production of greenhouse tomatoes. Of the more potent ones, naphthoxyacetic acid holds some promise, especially when mixed with indolebutyric acid. Most of the other active compounds cause outer parts of the fruit to grow faster than the inner parts. As a result, pockets form in the fruit and remain unfilled, and the fruit is of lower quality.

At first, small amounts of a mixture of growth regulator and lanolin were rubbed by hand on each tomato flower. A time-saving improvement is the use of a small atomizer with which an emulsion or solution of the hormone can be sprayed on the flower clusters. The most recent method, still in the experimental stage, is the aerosol bomb, a small metal tank that is partly filled with the growth regulator together with a liquid (such as dimethyl ether or Freon) that produces high pressure inside the container.

Frequently, the flowers of tomato plants grown in the field also fail to set satisfactorily. That may be due to factors other than poor pollen—such as relatively high night temperatures or cloudy weather that cause flowers of plants grown in very fertile soil to drop. So far we have had no consistent success in using the chemicals for improving the set under such field conditions.

Of course, the growth regulators, effective as they are, cannot replace sound cultural practices like good soil, proper temperature, and sunlight.

Rooting Cuttings

The stems of many kinds of plants can easily be stimulated to produce roots. For example: If the stem of a tomato vine is bent so that it rests in a horizontal position near moist ground, it will produce many roots along its lower surface. Or, stems of some climbing plants, like ivy, can be made to root by simply fastening them close to a building or tree trunk.

On the other hand, some plants of considerable economic importance, among them apple trees and pines, can be rooted only with great difficulty and under exacting conditions. Because the multiplication of many such plants is most quickly and cheaply done through the use of cuttings, it is important to improve methods of propagating them in this way.

The young stems of many kinds of plants have been stimulated by growth regulators to produce roots. Growth regulators are of considerable value to the plant propagator, since cuttings that root readily can often be made to root even faster by means of such treatments. Those that root with difficulty can often be made to produce a sturdy root system in less time than would be required without the chemical treatment. Indolebutyric acid and naphthaleneacetamide are the compounds most commonly used for the purpose.

Cuttings can be treated by dipping their basal ends in a solution of one of the substances, or by dusting the ends with talc that contains them. Formulations to be used for this purpose are available at most stores that handle farm supplies.

W. D. McClellan and Neil W. Stuart, working at Beltsville, found that growth regulators stimulated the rooting of lily scales, which are used as cuttings. Lily scales, like some other kinds of fleshy cuttings, sometimes rot in the ground. To prevent such loss, succulent cuttings are generally treated before planting with a fungicide, which prevents the growth of some kinds of molds. Drs. McClellan and Stuart added the growth-regulating substances to the fungicide and thereby decreased mold infection and also stimulated root production at the same time.

Growth regulators, as we have seen, can be stimulants when they are used in minute amounts. But when they are applied in larger doses the chemicals create so strong a reaction in many kinds of plants that they are severely injured. In fact, only a small amount of a growth regulator such as 2,4–D is needed to kill some plants. There are others that show little injury when the chemical is applied to them. For reasons yet unknown, most kinds of grasses are of the resistant type. Scientists are now busy trying to find out how growth regulators kill plants; the more thoroughly the technicians understand the effects of the chemicals, the more intelligently they can put them to work killing weedy plants.

Killing Weeds

In testing growth-regulating substances as weed killers, scientists learned first that when a compound like 2,4–D was placed on the leaves or stems of a plant its effect showed up several inches or even a foot or two away in another part of the plant. That discovery meant that 2,4–D was an entirely new type of herbicide; its effect traveled through the plants both upward and downward from the place where it was applied. Next, they learned that the presence of 2,4–D on a young leaf prevented it from expanding, and that the new leaves curled up and became distorted so that they were of little value to the plants.

Finally, the scientists found that some plants treated with 2,4–D were stimulated to burn up a large part of their reserve food supply, so that the sprayed plant actually starved to death. That is the reason why some weeds, including dandelions, plantain, and annual morning glory, can be killed by spraying their leaves with a water mixture of 2,4–D. The effect of the chemical results in a quick check in growth of the leaves already there, while the stimulus travels through the plant and prevents the formation of new leaves and causes the plant to burn up the food reserves in its leaves, stems, and roots.

Department scientists found that by judicious use of 2,4–D it is possible safely, easily, and cheaply to kill many kinds of weeds that grow on lawns, pastures, golf courses, or other grassy areas without noticeably hurting the grass. Various formulations that contain 2,4–D are on the market. The manufacturer's directions should be carefully followed.

A Department scientist, J. W. Brown, found an easy and inexpensive way of cleaning 2,4–D from spray tanks. The spray tank is first rinsed with water and then filled almost to capacity with hot water (under boiling or about 180° F.), and household ammonia is added at the rate of about 2 teaspoonfuls to a quart of water. The filling with water is then completed, the ammonia solution stirred, and the sprayer closed. A small portion of the solution is then sprayed through the nozzle and the remainder allowed to remain in the sprayer for about 18 hours or overnight. The equipment is then drained and rinsed twice, a portion of each spray being sprayed through the nozzle.

The killing effect of 2,4–D is gradual. When it is sprayed on a weed, some time is required for the effect to travel to the roots and some additional time is needed for the 2,4–D to cause the plant to burn up its food reserves. In summer, it generally takes about 1 to 3 weeks before the sprayed plants die and rot away. In this respect it differs from the better-known plant poisons, such as sodium chlorate or arsenical preparations, which generally kill the above-ground parts of plants quickly.

Little is gained by using 2,4–D with one of the more common plant poisons because the latter generally kill the tops of plants so quickly that the 2,4–D does not have time to take effect and kill the roots as well as the above-ground parts of the weeds. The addition of a conventional plant poison to 2,4–D, therefore, merely dilutes the effect of the plant growth regulator.

Although old and relatively mature weeds can sometimes be killed with 2,4–D, more rapid and complete effects are had when the plants are sprayed during or just after an active stage of growth, after they have all their leaves or just before the flower buds open. Low temperatures and low soil moisture reduce to some extent, however, the effectiveness of 2,4–D as a weed-killer.

Tests on some farm animals showed that 2,4–D was not poisonous to cows and sheep even when the animals were fed the acid, or when they ate pasturage sprayed with it. The acid is considered to have little, if any, bad effect on humans. I stress, however, that pure 2,4–dichlorophenoxyacetic acid was used in the tests; they do not prove that all 2,4–D formulations on the market are nontoxic to animals and humans because they contain materials other than the acid.

The presence of 2,4–D in soil can seriously retard the germination and growth of crop plants. Cotton and tomatoes, for example, are extremely sensitive to soil in which there is 2,4–D. As little as one part in four and a half million parts of soil has reduced the germination of mustard seeds. So care should be taken in applying 2,4–D to crop areas.

On the other hand, some scientists believe 2,4–D may be useful in killing some kinds of weeds in soil. On this point, though, we need more information. In experiments we found that as little as 9 millionths of a pound of 2,4–D (about the amount that can cover an eighth of an inch of the flat end of a toothpick) in a pound of soil reduced the germination of mustard seeds by 90 percent. The chemical soon becomes inactive in moist soil. After moist soil containing that amount of 2,4–D had lain fallow for a period of from 2 to 6 weeks, seeds of crop plants germinated as soon, and grew as vigorously, as they did in uncontaminated soil. The productivity of moist soil that is contaminated with 2,4–D may be reduced for a few weeks, but in dry soil the chemical may seriously reduce productivity for a year or longer.

P. C. Marth and I looked into the possibility of fertilizing grassy areas as they were being treated with 2,4–D to kill weeds. We used both liquid spray and solid mixtures of 2,4–D and fertilizer—enough urea to make a 3-percent water mixture of urea in a 0.1 percent 2,4–D spray. The spray killed plantain, dandelions, and other weeds, and at the same time the nitrogen in it stimulated the grass. Five gallons of the spray were applied to 1,000 square feet of lawn.

Fungi sometimes attack grass grown in a moist place. Fungicides, such as Fermate, can also be added to the 2,4–D spray mixture without lessening its weed-killing properties, but with a saving of time and labor.

Marth and I performed some experiments in which we applied mixtures of 2,4–D and a mineral fertilizer of the kind commonly used on lawns and pastures. We found that the mixtures enriched the soil so that lawn grass grew vigorously and at the time time killed common weeds such as plantain and dandelion.

It was learned that under some conditions 2,4–D can apparently be used to advantage in the production of Kentucky bluegrass seed. The acid was mixed with a commercial fertilizer (a commonly used one containing 10 percent nitrogen, 6 percent phosphorous and 4 percent potassium) and applied in a dry state evenly over areas of lawn that were infested with narrow-leaved plantain, sheep sorrel, and other common lawn weeds. The amount of seed produced by bluegrass on these treated areas greatly exceeded the amount produced by bluegrass on adjacent unfertilized areas and it also exceeded that produced on nearby plots that received fertilizer but no 2,4–D. The effect of the 2,4–D was twofold. It eliminated the weeds, and thus allowed the grass to obtain more of the fertilizer that was added to the soil; it was possible to harvest from the 2,4–D-treated areas a crop of bluegrass seed that was practically free of weed seeds, since practically all weeds in the area were killed before they produced seeds.

We started other experiments to study the usefulness of 2,4–D fertilizer mixtures in the production of other kinds of grass seeds.

2,4–D will not kill grasses that occur as weeds, such as crabgrass, quackgrass, and others, without injuring also the desirable grasses (bluegrass, fescue, or red top) present in the turf. It is simple enough to rid a lawn of common broad-leaved weeds, like dandelion and plantain, by spraying the area with 2,4–D, but after those weeds have been killed the task is only partly done, because as the broad-leaved weeds die and rot away, bare areas are exposed. In most localities the bare spots will soon become infested with weeds of the grass type that cannot be controlled with 2,4–D. We recommend therefore, that the control of lawn weeds be undertaken in the season (usually autumn) that is most favorable to the growth of lawn grass and that bare areas that result from killing the weeds in the turf be replanted to grass within 2 weeks or a month after the area is treated.

Research regarding 2,4–D has been under way only a short time; already it is considered to be one of the most successful weed killers we know. After further research, it will no doubt take its place as a safe and useful method of controlling many kinds of noxious weeds—but it is not a cure-all for all weeds.

British scientists have reported that two chemicals (ethyl and phenyl carbamate and isopropyl phenyl carbamate) have been successfully used on an experimental basis to kill grass-types of weeds without injury to certain garden crops. Those and related substances are being studied to determine their usefulness in controlling weeds of the grass type.

Other Effects

Scientists have found other potential uses for growth regulators. Bananas have been made to ripen faster by spraying them with a mixture of 2,4–D and water. Experimentally, scientists have made pears and Grimes Golden apples ripen more evenly, and parsnips to cure in a relatively short time after harvest, by spraying or dipping the fruits and vegetables in water mixtures of the chemical.

It is possible also that the keeping qualities of apples may be improved. The skins of stored apples often develop brown patches soon after they are removed from storage and placed on the market. The disease is known as apple scald. Drs. H. A. Schomer and Marth found that some kinds of apples scalded much less severely after the fruit was dipped in a lanolin emulsion containing naphthaleneacetic acid than when untreated.

Tests have been made to determine whether other kinds of fruit can be stimulated as greenhouse tomatoes are. On an experimental basis, Drs. Marth and E. M. Meader stimulated the growth of fruit of some varieties of blackberries by spraying the flowers when they open with the water mixture of naphthaleneacetic and naphthoxyacetic acids. This practical use of growth regulators is being subjected to further tests, and shows promise as a means of improving yields.

Growers of pineapples find that too many of the fruits ripen at about the same time, and sometimes the facilities for processing are thereby taxed to capacity. It has been found that pineapples can be made to flower and ripen at an early date by spraying them with naphthaleneacetic acid or 2,4–D. Some growers spray plants in part of their fields with these chemicals so as to make the fruits mature at different dates, and they can stagger the harvest periods for the different sections of the planting.

In Puerto Rico, Dr. J. van Overbeek discovered that plant growth regulators can be used to advantage there in the production of pineapples. The Red Spanish variety, the principal one grown in Puerto Rico, produces a large percentage of flowers during the winter when the days are relatively short. Even immature plants of the variety often flower and bear small and inferior fruits. But plants of the Cabezona variety are relatively slow to flower. They may even grow for 5 years before they produce fruit. Puerto Rican scientists found that Cabezona pineapples can be stimulated to produce flowers and fruit during any month of the year by spraying the center of the plant with minute amounts of naphthaleneacetic acid or 2,4–D. Fruits of especially high quality can be produced in this way since the plants can be made to flower after they have produced a full number of leaves and reached the most suitable growth.

In the preparation of Christmas decorations, difficulty is sometimes experienced in shipping wreaths made of holly because the leaves fail to remain on the branches until they reach the market. In experimental work by J. A. Milbrach and H. Hartman this difficulty has been lessened by spraying the leaves with a water mixture of 0.01 percent of naphthaleneacetic acid.

In experiments at the University of Wisconsin by T. C. Allen and E. Fisher, the yield of wax beans and of Refugee beans was increased by dusting the plants with talc containing naphthaleneacetic acid. The reason: The dusted plants retained most of their flowers, while the untreated plants lost many flowers because of insect injury or adverse weather conditions. The experimenters found that the insecticides rotenone and pyrethrum could be added to the dust containing the growth-regulating substances so as to control some insects without impairing the effectiveness of the dust mixture in increasing bean yields.

Natural fertilizers like manure are sometimes used for top dressing on areas seeded to grass. Weed seeds, usually found in manure, are a problem because they germinate and sometimes make it difficult for the grass to become established. Department and other scientists applied 2,4–D to shredded manure on an experimental basis, and thus prevented subsequent growth of most of the weed seeds that it contained. By such a pretreatment, it may be possible to kill or prevent the subsequent growth of some kinds of weed seeds in manure that is used as fertilizer.

In the laboratory scientists have learned that the chemical composition of some kinds of plants changed rapidly after the plants were sprayed with growth-regulating substances. The leaves of bean plants, for instance, contained nearly twice as much sugar on the fourth day after they had been treated with naphthaleneacetic acid as did unsprayed ones. Although no practical use has yet been made of this type of response, scientists are experimenting further in an attempt to learn how growth regulators can be used to control the chemical composition of plants.

In growing useful kinds of molds, it is sometimes difficult to prevent some kinds of bacteria from interfering with the cultures, the growing colonies. Scientists have found that the growth of some kinds of bacteria can be retarded by adding 2,4–D to media upon which the molds are growing. They believe that in this way it may be possible to protect mold cultures against infection from some kind of bacteria.

THE AUTHOR

John W. Mitchell is a physiologist in charge of the work on plant-growth-regulating substances at the Bureau of Plant Industry, Soils, and Agricultural Engineering. Dr. Mitchell has done research on the composition of plants and the effect of growth-regulating chemicals on them. He is a graduate of the University of Chicago.

FOR FURTHER READING

Allen, T. C., and Fisher, E.: *Increase Yields of Wax Beans with "Hormones" Insecticide Dusts,* The Canner, pages 12–13, May 1, 1943.

Batjer, L. P., and Marth, P. C.: *New Methods for Delaying Fruit Abscission of Apples,* Science, volume 101, pages 361–364, 1945.

Hamner, C. L., Moulton, J. E., and Tukey, H. B.: *Effect of Treating Soil and Seeds with 2,4–Dichlorophenoxyacetic Acid on Germination and Developments of Seeds,* Botanical Gazette, volume 107, pages 352–361, 1946.

Marth, P. C., and Meader, E. M.: *Influence of Growth-Regulating Chemicals on Blackberry Fruit Development,* American Society for Horticultural Science, Proceedings, volume 45, pages 293–299, 1944.

Marth, P. C., and Mitchell, J. W.: *Period of Effective Weed Control by the Use of 2,4–Dichlorophenoxyacetic Acid,* Science, volume 104, pages 77–79, July 1946.

McClellan, W. D., and Stuart, Neil W.: *The Use of Fungicides and Growth Substances in the Control of Fusarium Scale Rot of Lilies,* Phytopathology, volume 34, pages 966–975, 1944.

Milbrach, J. A., and Hartman, H.: *Holly Defoliation Prevented by a Naphthaleneacetic Acid Treatment,* Science, volume 92, page 401, 1940.

Schomer, H. A., and Marth, P. C.: *Effect of Growth-Regulating Substances on the Development of Apple Scald,* Botanical Gazette, volume 107, pages 284–290, 1945.

Templeman, W. G., and Sexton, W. A.: *Effect of Some Arylcarbamic Esters and Related Compounds upon Cereals and Other Plant Species,* Nature, volume 156, page 630, November 1945.

Thompson, A. H., and Batjer, L. P.: *The Use of the Airplane in Applying Hormone Sprays for the Control of Pre-Harvest Drop of Apples,* American Society for Horticultural Science, Proceedings, 1945.

ALSO, IN THIS BOOK

Short Cuts for the Gardener

by F. C. BRADFORD

THE RELATION of invention to necessity is proverbial. This matriarchal view implies that paternity is inconsequential. In matters pertaining to plant culture, however, where there are so many ways of doing the wrong thing, the genealogy of invention should include experience, despite its kinship to routine.

Necessity, under the guise of labor shortage and higher wages, often changes the relationship between cost of material and cost in labor. At the Plant Introduction Garden at Glenn Dale, Md., a case in point is presented by resort to "plunging" of potted plants, that is, sinking them to the top of the pot in soil, gravel, or a similar material. The practice has been known to gardeners a long time, but rarely used in greenhouses. It had been used occasionally at Glenn Dale with some plants whose culture in pots was difficult; uniformity in moisture supply was the principal end in view. Plant growth was so greatly improved by plunging and the labor involved in watering—a task for the best men available—so reduced that systematic study of the processes involved was begun. The practice was extended, as a labor-saving device, to plants of less difficult culture.

Careful study showed that the term "porous" when applied to flowerpots is an understatement. When plants were "staged"—placed on a thin layer of sand or gravel—in the usual way, the walls of the pot acted as wicks, and water passed outward through their sides faster than it passed through the soil itself. Under these conditions, many soils contract as they dry, and the ball of soil pulls away from the pot wall, leaving a channel down which subsequent waterings pour with little benefit to soil or plant. Conversely, the porosity of the pot walls permits the passage of moisture, when plants are plunged, from the plunging medium to the soil within the pot. Therefore it is possible to water the medium rather

267

than the pot, thus avoiding the compacting of the topsoil, and, since the water moves inward rather than outward, also avoiding the leaching of nutrients from the soil within the pot.

The net result of these processes, in one lot of plants, was the use by plants plunged in peat of less than one-tenth the water required by staged plants, while plants plunged in sand used roughly one-fourth. In this lot the plants plunged in peat, with their small ration of water, grew significantly more than the staged plants. Salvias plunged in peat averaged one watering in 5 days through the summer. Fertilizer applied to the plunging media penetrated the pots in quantities sufficient to benefit the plants.

Carefully handled, coarse peat has proved to be a satisfactory plunging medium. The chief danger in using it is overwatering. When that occurs, its prodigious ability to hold water becomes a detriment. Restoration of the proper moisture content becomes almost impossible. Teaching proper restraint in use of water on a peat plunging medium to a man accustomed to watering staged plants is hard. For that reason, sand or washed gravel, though considerably less effective, may be the safer plunging medium. Even with them, the saving in labor is great.

Potted plants staged in autumn on an open bench in an unheated pit require considerable attention. Atmospheric moisture is dissipated rapidly during the brief periods of sunshine. Frequent watering of plants in low temperature tends to encourage root rot, particularly with deciduous and heather-like plants. Plants plunged in peat under similar conditions require little attention, an occasional application of water to the peat being enough to keep plants healthy.

The need of constant watchfulness of seed flats before, during, and shortly after germination takes most of an experienced man's time, if the sowings are at all large. Since overwatering of soil in flats is likely to be disastrous, he must water sparingly and often. He must manipulate shades even more frequently.

The use of shredded sphagnum moss as a medium for sowing seed greatly reduces the amount of time needed for proper care of seed flats. For some years before the war, most of our sowing had been done on shredded sphagnum, usually in flats. Live sphagnum had been used for sowing seed of certain plants, like azaleas and tropical plants, at various places in past years, but lack of live sphagnum had prevented wide use.

Experience at Glenn Dale showed that dried sphagnum could be shredded and used satisfactorily. Though perhaps the greatest advantage obtained in germinating seed on sphagnum is freedom from damping-off, the saving of labor is no small item. The chief danger seems to be lack of recognition of the need of keeping the surface of the sphagnum moist, to forestall development of a waterproof surface while the seedlings are still turgid. Fortunately, overwatering does no harm, and in case of doubt watering is always safe. Despite the need to watch the surface, the work of watering seedlings in sphagnum is much less than the work of watering them in soil. Under conditions that require watering of seedlings in soil twice a day, those grown in sphagnum require watering once in 2 or 3 days. Between the watering of the flats at sowing and the germination of the seed, screening or glass is placed over the flats and no water is applied. Subirrigation of sphagnum has not been satisfactory.

All these uses of sphagnum refer to the commercial dried product, sold in bales by florists' supply houses. Small quantities are prepared by rubbing, while dry, through a screen that has three meshes to the inch. Large quantities are run through a hammer mill, using a 1-inch diamond screen. When it is used in the open bench, the lower layers may be of peat or sand and the upper 2 inches of sphagnum. It is used alone in pots and in flats. In cold frames a layer 2 inches deep is usually ample.

Growing plants in sphagnum moss, in place of soil, has permitted economies of several sorts. The practice had been used occasionally for many years, but plants so grown had evoked suspicion in the minds of people receiving them, and little use was made of it for some time. Under the stress of war conditions, when dispatch of plants of cinchona, a strategic item, in great numbers by airplane was imperative, this forgotten practice was revived, slightly modified, and used extensively.

In previous years, half the cinchona plants that had been grown in soil and forwarded by surface ships to Caribbean points had died. Tests showed that plants grown entirely in shredded sphagnum, with considerable quantities adhering to the roots, would grow perfectly well when transplanted to ordinary soils. In one lot of 90,000 plants grown in sphagnum, forwarded by plane, and handled properly at the destination, the mortality was less than 2 percent. These plants were larger than those formerly shipped, but their shipping weight per plant was only one-seventh of that of plants grown in soil. Packing costs in time and labor were greatly reduced, and the plants were forwarded in pasteboard cartons rather than wooden cases.

Plants of many kinds have been grown in shredded sphagnum, in pots, entirely without soil. No plants tested have reacted unfavorably; even succulents and cacti have thrived under this treatment. Root systems developed on plants potted in sphagnum fill the pot more uniformly, with much less tendency to seek the edge of the pot than they show in soil. When plants thus grown are removed from the pots for shipment, the ball of roots remains intact; a plant may be dropped on a concrete floor and the pot be shattered without injury to the root ball.

In lining out plants grown in sphagnum, the only special care necessary is to mound the soil around the stem or to set the plants in loose soil without compacting. The roots grow into the soil readily enough, but for a brief period the ball of sphagnum may become in effect a well into which water drains if the surrounding soil is compact. In ordinary or dry weather no difficulty arises, and the precautions mentioned seem necessary only in unduly wet weather.

The use of mechanical humidification is another recent development that reduces greatly the labor and attention necessary in greenhouses.

Several different systems have been tried at various institutions; at Glenn Dale, most of the experimentation has been done with centrifugal atomizers. These are essentially a metal or plastic disk that is rotated inside a baffle plate at a high speed by an enclosed electric motor. A suitable device is provided to lift the water to the surface of the disk from a reservoir below. The water is discharged as a fine mist that drifts through the air of the propagating greenhouse. If desired, this device need be operated only during the daytime on sunny summer days. In winter, on the other hand, humidification is particularly useful at night when the humidity is lowered by the radiation from heating pipes. The humidifiers, however, may be operated continuously. Contrary to expectation, mechanical humidification causes less, rather than more, disease in the cutting bench. The rooting of many kinds of cuttings is improved; sometimes even cuttings difficult to root by any other means can be handled.

Expanded Vermiculite as a Rooting Medium

Our work at Glenn Dale demonstrated that expanded vermiculite is usable as a rooting medium for cuttings and has some exceptional properties that probably place it close to the ideal in rooting media. Experiments were conducted with a species difficult to root, *Chionanthus retusus;* by far the best results were obtained with vermiculite. We got similar results for tests with many other kinds of plants. The rooting of cuttings is usually somewhat more rapid in vermiculite than in other materials, and the root systems are noticeably heavier.

Vermiculite is an insulating material sold by dealers in building supplies. It is a mica-like mineral composed of hydrated silicates and has the property of expanding into a light fluffy material when heated. Many of the properties of the expanded material are valuable. It is inert, sterile when fresh, and has many adsorbent pore spaces and inner surfaces that retain water for long periods and hold large amounts of air. The medium or coarser grades combine in a unique way the ability to provide excellent aeration and to retain large amounts of water.

With vermiculite one need not water so often; on the other hand, if drainage is adequate, large amounts of water may be applied frequently without harming the cuttings. This material may be used alone or mixed with sand. Mixtures of vermiculite and peat have given good results with plants that need acid soil.

Recent work at Glenn Dale in the use of opaque propagating houses or miniature propagating cases represents a new and radically different approach to the ideal of propagating structures that are nearly or completely automatic and therefore require little labor or skill. The opaque structure, combined with the use of modern types of fluorescent lighting, has given results as good as those obtained wtih more effort in conventional greenhouses.

The construction cost can be low. The structure can be partly or, preferably, completely underground. Temperature thus can be controlled in winter and summer. If the insulation is good, the reduced heating cost offsets much of the cost of the current for illumination. In the absence of sunlight, the humidity can be kept constant at a high level, without mechanical apparatus. Because artificial light is used, the space required and consequently the construction and heating costs can be cut sharply by a vertically tiered arrangement of the cutting beds.

Various types of small propagating cases with fluorescent lamps and thermostatically controlled units for providing bottom heat have also been used at Glenn Dale. The results equal, we believe, those obtainable in any glass-covered propagating house or frame. Small units of this type should be helpful to the amateur who wishes to start plants for the garden in a basement or spare room. In certain types of units, many kinds of cuttings will root before watering again becomes necessary.

The possibilities of controlling the quality of radiation in opaque structures are most interesting. The modern fluorescent lamps, with their high efficiency and low heat production, made the use of opaque structures practical. They are available in a variety of colors, some of them definitely superior to natural daylight in promoting the rooting of cuttings. Results of many trials have all shown that rooting is usually more rapid and heavier in light that has a relatively high proportion of the orange-red end of the spectrum. Rooting is usually inferior under blue light.

The color range available in high-voltage cold cathode tubes is much greater. The rooting obtained under the fluorescent tubes (orange, rose) invariably has been exceptionally heavy. Under these colors, cuttings of a somewhat tender unripened growth become firm and turgid long before those under other colors, including white or daylight. After a few weeks under the fluorescent tubes, the leaves of the cuttings often have a firm, leathery quality that make them distinguishable from those under argon-mercury cold cathode tubes of various colors.

The surprisingly low intensities needed for satisfactory rooting under favorable colors of light augur well for the possibilities of commercial application of this system of propagation. Intensities between 100- and 200-foot candles have been used most frequently, but excellent results have been obtained with lower strengths. Two miniature propagating cases that have given outstanding results have provided intensities of 80- and 110-foot candles on the cuttings. With cold cathode tubes, normal rooting was often obtained under only 40-foot candles. In one experiment, using helium-filled, nonfluorescent cold cathode tubes, moderate rooting resulted in the normal period of time with only 10-foot candles. Cuttings root well under 16 hours of light a day or continuous light.

Well-insulated opaque structures provide an easy control of humidity that will usually balance naturally at a relatively high level. They also require very little heat in winter. A semiunderground shed, 10 by 36 feet, constructed of cinder blocks was operated during the winter as a propagating house for both cuttings and seedlings. Although the insulation was not perfect in many respects, the lowest temperature recorded inside after subzero nights was 58° F., and usually the temperature ranged from 60° to 68°. Aside from the lamps, no heat was provided other than a small 1-kilowatt electric heater, which was operated as needed. A brief check-up once a day by one man was the only attention given.

The requirements for producing good seedlings under fluorescent lamps are considerably different. Much higher light intensities are needed; most seedlings require at least 600- or 700-foot candles for proper development. This amount of light will produce excellent seedlings if temperatures are kept from exceeding those proper for growing. Raising the temperature may increase the light requirement above that which can be supplied from several fluorescent tubes. Distances of less than 1 foot from several 40-watt tubes in a reflector are most useful for growing seedlings, and for best results the seedlings can be placed so they almost touch the lamps. Fifteen or so hours of light a day is satisfactory with seedlings.

The quality of light is most important in growing good seedlings. Too much red will produce somewhat soft, blanched, sickly growth. But a predominance of blue light tends to produce short-jointed, stocky plants. Thus the type of seedling produced can be varied somewhat by changing the spectral balance of the light. The daylight and the soft white tubes produce excellent seedlings. Combinations of white and daylight tubes and also combinations of 3,500° white and blue tubes are useful.

Both seedlings and cuttings have been grown for long periods under artificial light of good spectral balance, like that provided by mixtures of white and daylight tubes, and have performed normally when moved into conventional greenhouses.

THE AUTHOR

F. C. Bradford is a senior horticulturist in the Division of Plant Exploration and Introduction, in the Bureau of Plant Industry, Soils, and Agricultural Engineering. He is a graduate of the University of Maine and has taught horticulture and has done research on that subject at the University of Missouri and at Michigan State College. He is the co-author of two books: *Fundamentals of Fruit Production* and *Orcharding*.

ANTS RESPOND to chemicals about the
e as animals and humans do. Scientists
e developed proof of this during the past
ade which promises to be of great value to
truck gardeners, orchardists, and farmers in
general. John W. Mitchell discusses the subject on page 256; some examples of what plant-growth regulators will do are shown here.

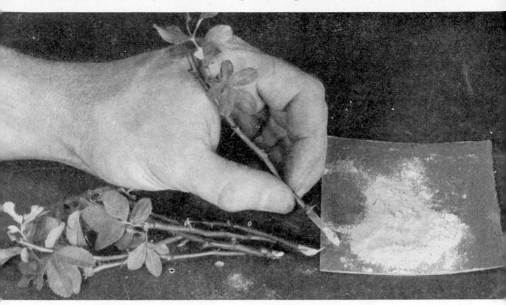

tings can be stimulated to grow roots faster
noistening and then dipping the basal ends
plant-growth regulating chemical (above)
taining 0.05 to 0.2 percent indole butyric
. The same results can be obtained by
<ing the bottom ends of the cuttings from 1
to 3 hours in about an inch of water containing
0.005 percent of the acid. After this treatment,
the cuttings are set in moist sand for rooting.
The picture below, taken 3 weeks after the untreated (left) and treated cuttings had been set
out, shows the effect of the growth-regulator.

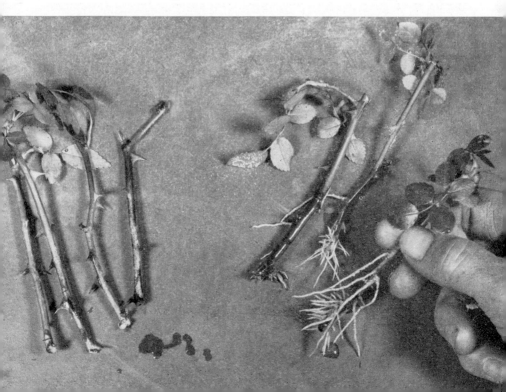

Growers of greenhouse tomatoes have had the problem of making young tomatoes hang on the vines and grow vigorously. At the left, above, is a hand-pollinated tomato plant ~ only one fruit. The one at right was tre with indole butyric acid, 100 p. p. m. in w

Even more graphic, perhaps, is this comparison of the amount of tomatoes that were produced from the same number of flower clusters untreated and treated greenhouse tomato pl.

the chemicals that stimulate plant growth also be used to destroy unwanted plants. ꜱod example of this is the use of 2,4–D in ng buckhorn plantain, one of our most common lawn pests. The picture below was taken 6 weeks after 2,4–D spray was applied. For reasons yet unknown, most types of grasses are resistant to the harmful effect of 2,4–D.

Apple growers lose money if the fruit falls to the ground before it has reached the best stage of ripeness. The untreated Rome Beaut ple tree above dropped a lot of its fruit b

sttime; another (above), also a Rome   naphthaleneacetic acid 8 days before the usual
y, was treated with a water mixture of   time for picking; few apples will be lost.

GARDENING SHORT CUTS have resulted from recent research at the Department's Plant Introduction Gardens at Glenn Dale, Md. Experiments with fluorescent lamps and cold cathode tubes in plant propagation permit the use of opaque or underground structures in which temperature, lighting, and humidity can be controlled. A propagating case is shown above using the cold cathode lighting, and at right a case in which fluorescent lighting is used.

Other tests at Glenn Dale have proved that the use of shredded sphagnum moss in seedbeds has many advantages over soil. Less labor is required and, however the seed is planted, there is greater assurance of a good stand and no damping off. For an article by F. C. Bradford on various gardening short cuts, see page 267.

en plants do not get a proper balance of
ients, such as nitrogen, potassium, magne-
, or calcium, they give visual distress sig-
Scientists have learned much in recent
s about the meaning of these signals and,
knowing what is wrong, can apply the correct
remedy. Here, C. P. Harley, of the Bureau of
Plant Industry, Soils, and Agricultural Engineering, examines the blotched leaf of a Lodi
apple tree, a sign of magnesium deficiency.

NEMATODES—hundreds of different kinds of them—are known to reduce seriously the yields of many important tree, truck, and field crops. Efforts to find ways of controlling them have been successful as shown by the pictures on this page. Above is a small section a plot used to test a soil fumigant called D (not DDT or 2,4-D) on squash. The soi the left was treated, at right untreated. Pict was taken 4 weeks after the squash was plan

Below are the roots of some of the treated and untreated plants shown above. Those from the treated plots, photographed when 6 weeks were completely free of nematode infecti

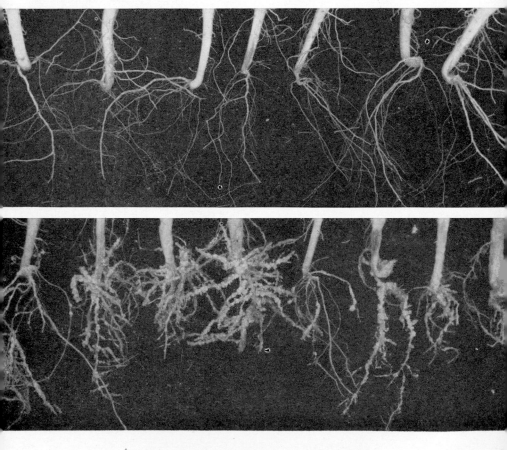

length of day, or photoperiod, affects the ering, rate of development, and time of rity of many plants. Varieties of the same ies often differ widely in their day-length irements. Studies to compare the day-th needs of varieties are made in light-tight partments (above) in which the photope-can be artificially controlled. The effect of daylight on soybeans is illustrated in the photographs below. The plants at left, grown with 13½-hour photoperiods, were about a foot high at harvest and produced mature seed. The group at right, in the same number of days but with 14½-hour photoperiods, were 2 feet high at harvesttime and were still immature. This is explained more fully on page 273.

Although the growing of crops without soil has its limitations, it did have practical use during the war and, under certain circumstances, is of real benefit to seed producers. Above, left, is a soilless culture garden on Iwo Jima that produced fresh vegetables for U. S. Army Air Forces. Windbreaks protect crops from den squalls. Lettuce and other garden c (above, right) were produced in bitumi macadam beds and lava cinders on Ascen Island. Below, onions and carrots (right) grown for seed in sintered shale at Beltsv

ew years ago it was discovered that treating
[s] with a drug called colchicine produced
[ ]vigor in the plants. Above, S. L. Ems-
[ ]er examines some double-chromosomed
snapdragons that were produced with this drug.
Neil Stuart (below) attends to some tetraploid
selections of snapdragon (*Antirrhinum majus*
L.) perfected in greenhouses at Beltsville.

Not long ago red stele root disease threatened to wipe out strawberry production in parts of eastern Maryland. In a cooperative effort to combat the disease, the Department and the Maryland experiment station originated the Temple variety, now important in eastern Maryland, Virginia, and Delaware. Above, George M. Darrow examines roots of seedli that have been grown in soil infested with stele fungus. Those in his left hand show sistance to the disease, a step toward succ This process has been repeated many, ma times to find bigger, better, and healthier b ries, adapted to various parts of the coun

At left, Dr. Darrow displays some hybrid bl berry fruits, the result of crosses with the lo bush blueberry of Maine and other North States. The plants are most vigorous and p duce large berries of high flavor. The clus at left, below, is a newer highbush select as compared with the Wareham at rig

earch is under way at the Department's sta-
n at Orlando, Fla., to determine and improve
palatability and food value of citrus fruit.
ove, P. L. Harding runs a test to determine
soluble solids in grapefruit juice. The
er right picture shows Dr. Harding titrating
the juice to determine its acidity. But the
final test is in the tasting (below). The group
samples grapefruit from different rootstocks,
groves, and areas; careful records are kept
to find out the relationship between eating
quality of the fruit and the laboratory tests.

An important goal of the peach breeder is to develop varieties for specific purposes such as seasonal ripening, high yields and quality, attractive appearance, and resistance to diseases. A first step in "reaching" for a new variety is to transfer the pollen from one parent variety to the flower stigma of another (above, left). The offspring from this process is planted and grown to about 18 inches in the greenhouse during early spring (above, right). W danger of frost is past, the young trees planted in the field (below, left). The fruit is usually borne the third summer, w selections are made and only the most pro ing trees are kept for further testing. At ri below, F. P. Cullinan, of the Plant Indu Station at Beltsville, examines a new peach shows promise of making a name for it

arkable results have been obtained through idization and cross-breeding of onions. have new lines that are resistant to thrips various diseases and are of more uniform and better eating quality. In the above pic- Henry A. Jones, in charge of onion breed- at Beltsville, prepares the male, pollen- ing onion plants for transfer across the to pollinate male-sterile female parent plants. The flower heads of the parent plants are placed together in cages (below). At left, A. E. Clarke ties cloth around a cage while Charles Green releases house flies into a cage to assure transfer of the pollen from one plant to another. The selection Italian Red No. 13–53 has been important in the onion-breeding work of the Department as explained by Jones and Clarke in an article beginning on page 320.

The annual farm value of our tomato crop, exclusive of home gardens, is about $166,000,000. This volume has resulted largely from breeding for better quality, higher yields, and for resistance to disease. Above, left, W. S. Porte holds in his hand the Pan America tomato; its parents are the Marglobe and berrylike South American species directly in front of him. At right, above, 30-day-old tomato plants are inoculated with fusarium wilt fungus. Their resistance to wilt is indicated below. Left to right are: Pan America; U. S. 24; Rutgers; and Bonny Best. At right is the wilt-resistant Pan America tomato on a staked greenhouse plant.

Day Length and Flowering

by H. A. BORTHWICK

ABOUT 30 years ago a problem of the kind that has concerned farmers for centuries was put up to two scientists in the Department of Agriculture: How could one get the new Maryland Mammoth tobacco to flower and produce seed in the latitude of Washington, D. C.?

The answer, found by W. W. Garner and H. A. Allard, was that the length of darkness and light each 24 hours regulates the flowering of this variety of tobacco and of many other kinds of plants as well. This fundamental law of nature tells us why some plants blossom in the spring, or in the Tropics, or in specific zones, and not in others. It is an example of basic research with wide economic uses.

Garner and Allard submitted the tobacco to all the known factors that govern the growth of plants. One by one, they eliminated differences in soil moisture, temperature, fertilization, and intensity of light as reasons for the failure of the plants to mature properly. But, regardless of treatment, the tobacco grew vegetatively that summer and fall.

To save the tobacco plants from freezing, several were cut back, potted, and moved into the greenhouse for further study. At the same time, tobacco seedlings were also started in the greenhouse. In a few weeks, old plants and seedlings alike began to bloom. Blooming continued through the winter, but, with the beginning of spring, nonflowering shoots were produced again, and these continued to grow vegetatively—without producing seed—throughout the summer. To the two scientists, the fact that old and young plants bloomed simultaneously meant that neither size nor condition of the plants was the limiting factor.

Because blooming started in late autumn and ended in the early spring, there was little doubt that the length of winter days in Washington was what limited the blooming period of these plants. Allard and

703830°—47——19   273

Garner tested this conclusion further the following season, the summer of 1918, by growing the tobacco and the Biloxi soybean, another plant that did not mature its seed in the latitude of Washington, D. C., in pots, and exposing them to 7 hours of sunlight a day. This was done by placing the plants in dark chambers from 4 p. m. to 9 a. m. daily. Both tobacco and soybean promptly bloomed. This simple experiment answered their problem.

The two men, who worked in what is now the Bureau of Plant Industry, Soils, and Agricultural Engineering, extended their studies to include other kinds of plants. They discovered that some flowered sooner when the days were shortened, and others blossomed only when the days were lengthened. The flowering of still others was apparently not influenced at all by the length of day. They identified these groups of plants as short-day, long-day, and indeterminate types. They also observed that many other responses were influenced—the formation of bulbs and tubers, the coloration and abscission of leaves, and the branching and growth habit of plants. In brief, they recognized, and in 1920 reported, that the variable environmental factor of day length profoundly influenced plant development. This response that an organism makes to relative length of day and night the discoverers called photoperiodism.

Studies of photoperiodism since have been numerous in every part of the world where plants are studied scientifically. In increasing the economy of crop production the studies have been profitable. From the theoretical viewpoint, they have stimulated much basic research in plant physiology that has given new insight into many physiological processes.

How can agriculture profit from studies of photoperiodism? Even though day length does control plant development, man cannot control day length over any considerable area—so what practical advantage could result from his studies of photoperiodism? Such questions are often the first ones asked when people are introduced to the subject.

It is certainly true that it is impractical or impossible to attempt to change the length of day in a region in which field crops are to be grown, but is is quite possible to change the crop to suit the day length of such a place. Farmers have followed this procedure for generations with respect to temperature requirements of their crops.

They know, for example, that winter cereals will winterkill if grown too far north, and will fail to flower because it is not cold enough if grown too far south. Peaches need different amounts of low temperature in the winter to break their rest periods so they can resume growth when spring temperatures are right. Peach varieties requiring the least low temperature in the winter are therefore grown farthest south, while those requiring most low temperature must be kept in the north.

The same principles apply with even better results to crops that are affected by photoperiod, because seasonal variations in length of photoperiod are exactly the same from year to year, while the seasonal variations of temperature are always different.

Some of the most important practical results have thus come about through understanding that day-length requirements of a variety often determine whether it can be grown successfully in a particular region. If the day-length requirements of a variety do not fall within the range of day lengths that occur in the locality, there is little use in attempting to modify other environmental factors to compensate. Such attempts seldom succeed. Since the natural day length cannot be changed, the only solution is to select a variety whose day-length requirements are satisfied by those prevailing in the locality in question.

Although the photoperiod requirements of certain kinds of crop plants tend to restrict their usefulness to relatively narrow ranges of latitude, there is usually enough difference between varieties so that the crop can be grown over a wide region. The soybean, for example, grows well from the Gulf coast to southern Canada, but the north-south range of individual varieties is rather narrow, and is determined largely by the length of photoperiod.

In investigations of soybeans, it has been convenient to divide the country into nine zones, the southernmost along the Gulf coast, and the northernmost in the latitude of North Dakota. The average depth of these zones is somewhat less than 150 miles. Department scientists have found that varieties can be grouped according to their adaptation to these regions, and that relatively few do equally well in more than one zone. The rather narrow limits of the zones are probably determined more by the photoperiodic requirements of the varieties than by any other factors; they point up the fact that small differences in environment may mean significant differences in the crop.

The onion is another plant in which the geographic distribution of kinds is set largely by photoperiodic response. Varieties adapted to the North, like Sweet Spanish and the Southport Globes, cannot be grown successfully in the South, because the days are short and they produce a vigorous top growth, but fail to form bulbs that reach maturity. Varieties like Crystal Wax, Yellow Bermuda, and Creole, which are adapted to the photoperiods of the South, cannot be profitably grown from seed in the North, where, because of longer days, they bulb nearly as soon as they come up, and produce small unmarketable onions.

Rather small differences in day length can have important effects. Volstate soybeans, for instance, blossomed 15 days later when grown with 14½-hour photoperiods than when grown with 14-hour ones. This difference of 30 minutes is less than the difference in day length of Washington, D. C., and Charleston, S. C., on the first of July, and is only slightly more than the difference in day length of the two cities in the middle of August. But in its effect on the soybeans that difference could easily determine the success or failure of the crop.

A knowledge of the photoperiodic requirements of plants is important to a farmer when frost or flood makes him replant much later than customary. When crops like soybeans are planted in April or early May, the seedlings are subjected to lengthening photoperiods until the end of June; flowering may be retarded or even stopped because the days are too long. The plant then grows vegetatively to some size and can therefore produce a large crop of flowers and fruits when the flower-inducing stimulus of short photoperiod finally expresses itself. If it is necessary to seed late in the season, however, the plants have fewer weeks of long days in which to grow before flowering is induced by the natural shortening of the day. The plants are smaller when flowering starts and they yield less. The growers make up for it by seeding more thickly or by choosing an earlier maturing variety, or both.

Photoperiodic principles are also involved in producing seed in kinds of soybeans normally grown for forage. The forage types tend to produce excessive quantities of vines when planted early, and they are hard to thresh. If planted several weeks later, however, the vines are smaller. Because the plants started late are subjected to short photoperiods much sooner after they come up than when planted early, they begin flowering when they are small and their growth habit is more bush-like as a consequence. Yields per plant are reduced, but yields per acre can be maintained by increasing the rate of seeding. Thus, the grower can take advantage of the photoperiodic response of the plant through selection of planting date, get a good yield of seed, and modify growth habit so the plants are easy to harvest and thresh.

Plant breeders and other experimenters often use photoperiodic procedures to facilitate the handling of plants, for example, to induce simultaneous blooming of varieties that are to be crossed, and to increase the number of generations that can be produced a year, thus speeding up the breeding of new varieties. Photoperiodic tests of strains or varieties produced in breeding experiments give preliminary indications as to the regions where they will grow well.

Numerous questions arise: What part of the plant is sensitive to photoperiod? Do the effects of treatment of one part of a plant affect the development of an untreated part? Does the plant seem to produce some chemical substance in response to a certain photoperiod that can be translocated elsewhere to regulate development? Is the plant sensitive to the length of day or night, or to some combination of each? Are long-day and short-day plants fundamentally different, or is the same basic photoperiodic mechanism operative in both? We have answers to some of the questions.

We have known for several years that plants receive the stimulus of photoperiod through their leaves. J. E. Knott of the University of California at Davis discovered this fact by exposing the leaves of spinach to long photoperiods while the stem growing point and very young leaves in the center of the rosette received short photoperiods. These plants produced seed stalks, as did the controls that received long days. Other lots that received long photoperiods on the growing points and short photoperiods on the leaves remained vegetative, like the short-day control plants.

Garner and Allard were the first to recognize that the effects of photoperiodic treatment could be expressed by parts of plants that had not received the treatment. They found that part of a cosmos plant kept in continuous darkness produced flower buds following treatment of other parts of the same plant with photoperiods favorable to flowering. With many plants, however, they found that production of flowers resulting from favorable photoperiod remained localized on the treated parts and did not occur on parts that received unfavorable photoperiods. It is known now, however, that flower buds often will form on such untreated parts if the leaves are removed from them. These leaves seem to interfere with transmission of the flower-inducing stimulus to the area from the part of the plant that had a treatment that was favorable to the formation of flowers.

Dr. Knott's discovery made it evident that the effects of photoperiodic treatment can be expressed by untreated parts of a plant. The spinach flowers were produced by the stem tips that were subjected to short days, so it is obvious that some stimulus must have been moved from the leaf, where it is originated, to the stem growing points, where its effects were expressed in flower formation. This strongly indicates that a chemical regulator of some kind is involved, but I shall postpone discussion of that until several other points have been considered.

Flowering of short-day plants after treatment with short natural photoperiods and the inhibition of flowering of long-day plants under the same conditions occur because the dark periods in such 24-hour cycles are long, not because the photoperiods are short. This is proved by experiments in which each long dark period was made into two short ones of approximately equal length by inserting a very brief period of light. With short-day plants, dark-period interruptions of less than 1 minute prevent flowering, while with certain long-day ones, 1-minute interruptions promote flowering. Reversal of response is thus induced in either type by a break in a chain of reactions occurring in the dark period.

Those experiments are the same in principle as those in which natural photoperiods are extended with artificial light added to one end of the dark period or the other. The light energy required to prevent flowering, however, can be measured much more accurately if it is applied in the middle of the dark period; in certain greenhouse applications it saves current to use the light for a few minutes at that time, rather than for several hours at the beginning or end of the dark period.

The importance of the length of the dark period in the flowering of short-day plants is also shown by growing them with artificial light on photoperiodic cycles differing in length from the natural 24-hour ones. When the cycles consisted of short photoperiods and short dark periods, flowering failed, but when they consisted of long photoperiods and long dark periods flowering occurred. Flowering required the long dark periods, not the short photoperiods. In similar experiments with long-day plants, flowering took place with photoperiodic cycles consisting of short photoperiods and short dark periods. Failure of long-day plants to flower on short natural photoperiods would therefore seem to be caused by the presence of the long dark periods, not the short photoperiods.

That is not to imply that the photoperiod has no special function. Photoperiods are essential to the process, but with short-day plants it is the light intensity during the photoperiods, not the length of photoperiods, that is critical so long as they are associated with long dark periods. Biloxi soybeans will flower in response to three or four photoperiodic cycles consisting of 10-hour photoperiods and 14-hour dark periods if the light intensity during the photoperiods is high enough. Various experiments show that flowering of short-day plants in response to short-day treatment requires that a period of active photosynthesis occur during each photoperiod.

Experiments also indicate that the photoperiodic mechanism of long and short day plants is probably the same basically, although the two kinds respond differently to the same photoperiodic treatment. First, the characteristic photoperiodic response of both types, when grown on short photoperiods and long dark periods, depends upon reactions during the dark periods. Second, in both types, the effects of these reactions during the dark periods can be nullified by brief durations of light of relatively low intensity. Third, experiments in which leaves of long-day plants are grafted to short-day plants are reported to have induced flowering of the latter under conditions of long photoperiod. Fourth, the wave lengths of light that most effectively inhibit flowering of short-day plants when used to interrupt the dark period are the ones that most effectively promote flowering of long-day plants under similar conditions.

Most investigators agree that a flower-inducing substance is produced in leaves of plants that are sensitive to photoperiod and that this substance is transmitted to the stem growing points, where it produces flowering. The possibility that a flower-inhibiting substance might be produced in short-day plants grown on long photoperiods and that it causes the plants to remain vegetative has been shown experimentally not to occur.

According to that hypothesis a soybean growing on long photoperiods would remain vegetative because its leaves were producing flower-inhibiting substances. We have found in experiments that all but one leaf of such a plant may be removed, and the plant will continue vegetative as long as it receives long photoperiods. This could be interpreted, by the hypothesis, to mean that a single soybean leaf produces enough flower-inhibiting material to maintain the plant in vegetative condition. We have also found experimentally that if all leaves are left on the plant and one leaf is subjected to short photoperiods while all others receive long photoperiods, the plant forms flower buds. This should not happen if the flower-inhibiting proposition is correct. Because all leaves but one are available to produce flower-inhibiting compounds, the plant should remain vegetative. Since it produces flower buds instead, we must conclude that the one leaf that receives short photoperiod must produce a flower-inducing stimulus. The long-day leaves do not supply a flower-inhibiting substance; they merely fail to supply a flower-inducing substance. The vegetative condition might therefore be considered as the natural one from which the plant departs whenever, because of photoperiodic stimulation or for other reasons, it produces proper amounts of flower-inducing substances.

Although there is much evidence that flower-inducing substances are produced in plants, there is no evidence as to their chemical nature. Many investigators have attempted to extract, purify, and identify such substances, but none has succeeded. One difficulty is that no method is available by which an investigator can be certain that he has extracted an active substance. A test would require that such an extracted material cause flowering when reintroduced into a plant. Reintroduction of the substance, however, presents difficulties. As a consequence, failure of such a test may indicate either that the extract was not active or that it was not successfully reintroduced. Rapid progress in identifying the flower-inducing substance therefore does not seem probable.

Although nothing is known about the nature of the flower-inducing substance, it is possible to design experiments that reveal certain facts about the reactions in which it is produced. We have conducted experiments of this kind at Beltsville since 1944. They were based on the fact that very brief exposures of short-day plants to white light during the middle of the long dark periods prevent flowering. In these experiments, we substituted various wave-length bands of light for white light, and determined the energies required to prevent flowering when the dark periods were interrupted with light from such wave-length bands. These experiments have disclosed certain characteristics of a pigment involved in the photoperiodic reaction.

A prism spectrograph was designed and constructed for the work. The light source was a 12-kilowatt carbon-arc lamp, necessary because of the high intensities of blue light required. The spectrum produced was about 3 inches high and the visible region was about 6 feet long. With the instrument the energies in the red region of the spectrum were so high that exposures of soybean leaves for less than a half minute in the middle of the long dark periods were enough to inhibit flowering. Even with the least effective regions of the spectrum exposures of less than an hour were adequate.

The plants studied with this equipment were Biloxi soybean and cocklebur, two short-day plants with which several scientists have conducted extensive photoperiodic studies in the past. We followed a procedure of growing plants in the greenhouse until a size suitable for the experimental work was attained. During that time the Biloxi soybean and cocklebur plants were subjected to long photoperiods, which kept them from flowering. Then they were transferred to growth chambers that had carbon-arc and incandescent-filament lamps, which supplied about 2,000 foot candles of light.

In these rooms, the soybeans received photoperiods of 10 hours each for 6 days, and the cockleburs photoperiods of 12 hours each for 3 days. Experimental treatments consisting of brief dark-period interruptions were applied near the middle of each long dark period. After the experiments, the plants were returned to long photoperiods for about a week. Records of the presence or absence of tiny flower buds were made then.

The plants were defoliated at the beginning of the treatment, only a single leaflet being left on a soybean and one leaf on each cocklebur. Thus we reduced the amount of foliage that had to be irradiated on each plant, so we could use larger numbers of plants in each experiment. This amount of defoliation did not change the photoperiodic response.

Several plants were irradiated with light from rather narrow wave-length bands of the spectrum as near the middle of the dark period as possible. The plants irradiated in each region usually consisted of at least five groups of four plants, each group receiving a different amount of energy. Variations in energy were got by varying the duration of irradiation.

This range of energies for each experiment was calculated from results of preceding experiments so that flowering would fail in lots that received most energy and would succeed in lots that received the least. Some intermediate lot would thus be subjected to just enough radiant energy to stop flowering. From such experiments the energy requirements to prevent flowering were determined for each wave-length region. Such results from many experiments with Biloxi soybean and cocklebur have been summarized and expressed as action spectrum curves that show the approximate energy required at any wave length of the visible spectrum to prevent flowering of either plant. The wave lengths of the visible spectrum are measured in several kinds of units. The Ångström unit (A.) used here is 0.003937 inch in length. The human eye recognizes radiation of about 4000 A. as violet and 7000 A. as red.

The most effective region of the visible spectrum was found to be a rather broad band extending from about 6000 A. to 6800 A. and a second somewhat less effective region was found in the blue near 4000 A. The least effective region was near 4800 A. and a sharp limit in the red occurred near 7200 A. The curves for the two plants were qualitatively alike in all of these characteristics but differed quantitatively in energy requirements at certain points. Cocklebur, for example, required more than seven times more energy than Biloxi soybean at 4800 A. to prevent flowering. Energy differences between the two in other regions were less.

Since radiation in the region of 7000 A. is effective in preventing flowering, it follows that carotinoid pigments are not responsible, except possibly in their screening action at shorter wave lengths. Several characteristics of the action spectra of the two plants indicate that chlorophyll, the only other common leaf pigment, may be the active agent. These are the occurrence of a long wave-length limit near 7200 A., the presence of two regions of maximum effectiveness, one in the red and the other in the violet, and general effectiveness of radiation throughout the visible spectrum. These results do not prove that chlorophyll is the effective pigment in the photoperiodic reaction but they suggest that it is involved in the series of reactions which lead to the formation of a flowering substance.

Besides these investigations into the effects of light of different spectral constitution on the photoperiodic reaction, studies have also been made of the interactive effects of various environmental factors with photoperiod. It has been found, for example, that rather wide differences in nitrogen concentration may influence the time and place of formation of flower buds on certain soybean varieties if the plants are grown at photoperiods that slightly retard flowering; at somewhat shorter photoperiods more favorable to flowering these differences do not occur.

The bulbing of onions was also found to be influenced by concentration of nitrogen in the nutrient solution if the photoperiod was held in the proper range. In the case of onions, bulbing took place at certain photoperiods if nitrogen concentration was low, but failed if it was high. At slightly longer photoperiods, bulbing occurred regardless of nitrogen concentration.

In both experiments, relatively small differences in photoperiod made considerable differences in the response of the plants to variations in nitrogen nutrition, and in both cases the effects were greatest when photoperiods were of such a length that the plant response concerned, flowering in one case and bulbing in the other, was slightly retarded.

The seasonal shift in length of photoperiod produces just this condition for many types of plants during the course of their development. Soybeans planted in late spring grow vegetatively because of the long days then prevailing, but as the season progresses there is a gradual shift to photoperiodic conditions favorable to flowering. During this period of transition, differences in nitrogen nutrition may cause differences in time of formation of flower buds.

Studies were also made of the effects of variations in concentrations of calcium, potassium, and magnesium ions in the nutrient solution upon floral initiation in soybeans. Variations in potassium resulted in small but significant differences in time of flower-bud formation with certain varieties but not with others.

New practices that can be used in breeding hemp have resulted from recent photoperiodic studies. Hemp is a short-day plant. It flowers promptly when day lengths are less than 14 hours and very slowly or not at all when day lengths are greater than 14 hours. Under average field conditions about half of the plants are female and half are male. Under some circumstances, however, female plants, each of which may produce a very large number of female flowers, will also produce a few typical male flowers. The opposite condition occurs in the males; that is, a male plant will form an occasional female flower in addition to a great number of male flowers. This tendency for hemp plants to produce these extra flowers of the opposite sex is increased by subjecting them to photoperiods of 14 hours or less and to cool nights when flowers are being formed.

Most rapid progress in breeding plants can be made with those that can be self-pollinated. Hemp, obviously, can be self-pollinated only when it produces these occasional additional flowers of the opposite sex. The advantage of being able to increase their tendency to form these flowers is apparent.

Dr. Hugh C. McPhee of the Department made use of this behavior of hemp several years ago. He used the pollen of the male flowers that were produced in small numbers on certain of the female plants to self-pollinate those plants. When he grew the resulting seeds he made the important discovery that all of the plants were female. We have recently produced several thousand seeds in this way and have not obtained a single male plant, thus thoroughly confirming Dr. McPhee's observations.

Under greenhouse conditions, with proper control of temperature and day length, a very high percentage of female plants produced enough male flowers so that self-pollination could be effected, and in certain experimental lots of female plants produced out-of-doors in late summer when days were short and nights were cool, enough male flowers were formed so that natural pollination occurred and a quantity of pure "female" seed was produced. These results suggest that a locality can be found in which the conditions are favorable to the formation of these intersex male flowers on female plants in sufficient quantity that a good crop of seed could be obtained. If this could be done, a means would be at hand to produce commercial quantities of "female" seed, thereby enabling growers to produce a pure stand of female plants. Such pure stands would result in a more uniform fiber crop and eliminate certain harvest problems. The basis for developing such a procedure lies in finding in nature a combination of environmental factors similar to that which, under experimental conditions, has resulted in formation of abundant male flowers.

In the course of our studies we have also obtained certain results that have found immediate application in crop production. An example is the work with dark-period interruptions to prevent flowering.

For many years chrysanthemum growers have extended the natural photoperiods of late summer and autumn to delay flowering of certain varieties. To do so they used artificial light for several hours each night, either immediately following sunset or just before sunrise. By beginning this treatment in the middle of the summer, and continuing it regularly the remainder of the summer and early fall, they found they could keep their chrysanthemums in greenhouses from flowering until late fall or early winter.

Just as brief dark-period interruptions prevented the flowering of Biloxi soybean, so it seemed probable they might have a similar effect on chrysanthemums. The method was tested and was found better in certain respects than the previous method of applying several hours of artificial light at the beginning or end of the day. With this method of delaying flowering by dark-period interruption, the stems of the plants did not elongate so much as with the former method. When the plants were finally permitted to bloom, following discontinuation of the interruptions, the flowers produced were of exceptionally fine quality. The individual flower stalks were short, so that the entire inflorescence was compact, a feature that added to the beauty of the flowers. Florists have used the procedure to postpone the flowering of several varieties of chrysanthemums, for many weeks. Because some early varieties are more desirable than the late ones, the procedure served to make them available at times of the year when there would otherwise be no equally satisfactory types. The practice also allows growers to time the dates of the flower harvest to synchronize with special holiday markets.

Indeed, several growers of chrysanthemums have started work on a plan whereby they can grow chrysanthemums the year around. Such a development depends upon the photoperiodic response of the plants; it will involve dark-period interruptions to delay blooming under some conditions, and artificial shortening of the day by shading to accelerate blooming under other conditions.

THE AUTHOR

H. A. Borthwick, a graduate of Stanford University, is a senior botanist in the Bureau of Plant Industry, Soils, and Agricultural Engineering. He has concentrated on studies of photoperiodism for about 10 years.

Flowers as You Like Them

by S. L. EMSWELLER

FOR SOME reason or other the average gardener likes his flowers big. He boasts about his giant pansies and petunias, or gladiolus spikes 6 feet tall with flowers 6 inches across. At the flower shows the accolade goes to the mammoth amaryllis or the colossal zinnias. Vegetable gardeners also know this urge to achieve greater size—taller corn, giant radishes, 4-pound onions, turnips as big as pumpkins, and pumpkins as big as a house. The truth is that as a rule the very large vegetables are inferior in quality, but the public likes size, and size is what flower and vegetable seedsmen are trying to give them.

The size of a flower or vegetable is something over which the gardener has considerable control. The old discussion over heredity versus environment has been laid to rest, and now we talk of heredity plus environment, with each playing an important role in determining size and quality of both flowers and vegetables.

The good gardener is one who obtains the maximum of growth and yields from the seed and plants available to him. He accomplishes this by using the best growing practices: Adequate fertilizers, moisture, and good tillage. As a result of flower-breeding work by the seed companies, amateurs, and State and Federal workers, there has been a steady advance in the quality and quantity of varieties available to the gardener. Many of these improvements have resulted from hybridization between two varieties. Thus we have been able to reshuffle their characters and combine good qualities from both. The better of the new types are fixed (that is, made to come true from seed) by selection and then become available to the gardening public. It has also been found that when crosses are made between certain strains or varieties of flowers, the resulting hybrids exhibit greater vigor than either of the parents. We have

284

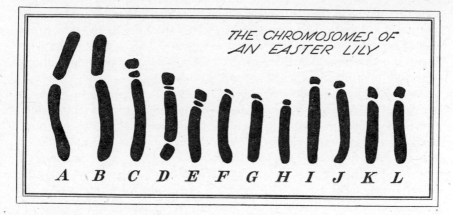

THE CHROMOSOMES OF AN EASTER LILY

A B C D E F G H I J K L

taken advantage of this hybrid vigor to develop greater size and yield in corn, onions, tomatoes, squash, cucumbers, and snapdragons. The seed of such hybrids cannot be used since it will not produce plants like the hybrid parent—an important warning.

About 9 years ago A. F. Blakeslee and A. G. Avery, of the Carnegie Cold Spring Harbor Station in New York, and B. R. Nebel and M. L. Ruttle, of the New York Agricultural Experiment Station, described a method by which one type of mutation could be produced at will. They found that treatment of seed or young seedlings in a water solution of the drug colchicine usually produced increased vigor and larger flowers. Colchicine, by the way, is extracted from bulbs of the fall-blooming crocus and, strangely enough, has no effect on the crocus chromosomes. Examinations of the cells of such affected plants revealed striking changes from the normal. The plant cells were larger and the number of chromosomes had been doubled. The chromosomes are the carriers of the heredity of a plant. They determine whether a plant will be tall or dwarf, perennial or annual, bear white, red, or some other colored flower. Such characters as size of flowers and fruits are also determined by them.

The chromosomes occur in pairs, that is, there are two of each type present. An Easter lily plant has 24 chromosomes, two each of 12 types. It is relatively easy to distinguish among all 12 except those labeled in the illustration I and J, and K and L. All normal Easter lily plants have two each of the A, B, C, and the nine other types. No other plants so far studied by anyone have exactly the same types of chromosomes as the Easter lily. Thus, if we had only a small piece of a plant and found the chromosomes shown in the picture in its cells, we would know it was a piece of an Easter lily.

A plant with twice as many chromosomes as it should have is called a tetraploid. Such plants do appear spontaneously in plantings now and then. Almost always they are more vigorous and bear larger flowers than the other plants in the same group. Since the chromosomes control such qualities as vigor and size of flower, the tetraploid with twice as many should be more robust and bear larger flowers. This is not always true, however, since some plants are already tetraploids and further doubling of the chromosome number may result in dwarfing.

As a rule, hybrids between species of plants set little or no seed. In many instances this is because the hybrid cannot form viable pollen and ovules. When a hybrid is formed, it receives half its chromosomes from one parent and half from the other. But there are exceptions: When a species with 24 chromosomes is crossed with one that has 12, the hybrid will have 18. It will get 12 from one parent and 6 from the other. If this were not the case, the hybrid would have the sum of the chromosomes of the two parents. In fact, the pollen grains and ovules of plants normally contain only one of each type of chromosome present in the parent. Since there are always two of each kind of chromosome, these special cells (pollen and ovules) always contain half the chromosome number of the parent.

Frequently, the inability of hybrids to set seed may be overcome by doubling the chromosome number. This has happened spontaneously to several sterile hybrids. One of these was a hybrid primrose made by crossing the species *Primula floribunda* Wall. (buttercup primrose) and *P. verticillata* Forsk. (Arabian primrose). The hybrid was grown for several years and always failed to set any seed. Finally one of the hybrid plants produced a side branch that was more vigorous than the others and bore flowers larger than any yet seen on the hybrids. These larger flowers set some seed from which seedlings were grown. When the unusual branch was examined it was found to have twice as many chromosomes as it should have had.

Doubling the chromosome number of sterile hybrids is one of the most promising fields for the use of colchicine. Many hybrids are discarded because they are completely sterile. They should be treated with colchicine before a final decision is made regarding their value.

Splitting of the chromosomes is accomplished just as if each one had a zipper holding two equal halves together. When colchicine is present in the cell the zipper acts as if it were stuck, and by the time it is ready to operate again the cell has given up the idea of dividing. The zipper action is then complete and the two halves of each chromosome have to remain in the same cell, which now has twice as many chromosomes as it should have. This figurative sticking of the zipper does not usually occur at the next division, which behaves in a normal manner. If the cell or cells now having the double number of chromosomes form a branch it will be tetraploid.

Colchicine, then, is effective only when cells are dividing. This means that treatments should be applied to actively growing plant tissues. The part of the plant treated should be the portion that eventually will produce flowering stems or branches.

Young germinating seedlings also respond well to treatment. A method for treating seedlings that we have used successfully at Beltsville is: The seeds are sown about 1 inch apart each way so that each seedling can be treated and observed carefully. As soon as true leaves have formed, the temperature of the greenhouse is raised for several days to speed up growth and cell divisions. The colchicine is applied to the growing point by means of a medicine dropper. Treatments may be repeated several times, with an application every other day.

As soon as affected seedlings resume growth they should be transplanted to pots so they will have ample room to develop. If the chromosomes were doubled in all the cells of the growing point, the main stem and all its branches will be tetraploid.

Frequently only a sector of the growing point is affected, and only a portion of the growth is tetraploid. Usually the tetraploid branch will have larger, thicker leaves and a sturdier stem. It is advisable to cut off the unaffected parts in order to concentrate all growth in the affected branch or branches. It is advisable also to keep several untreated plants for comparison, especially of the flowers. Such plants also furnish pollen in the event the tetraploid proves to be completely self-sterile.

Some plants reproduce by forming buds on bulb scales, cuttings of leaves, or stems. Among these are lily bulbs, African violets, and some types of begonias. Easter lily bulbs are made up of scales attached at the base only. When scales are removed from the bulb they soon form small bulblets on the basal end. In order to double the chromosome numbers of lilies, the scales should be soaked, as soon as detached, in a colchicine solution for about 2 hours. They should then be dried, dusted in either Arasan or Fermate, to protect against rot, and planted. If this is done in the North, by the middle of August the scales can be planted outdoors. They can be handled relatively later in the South, but treatment should not be delayed much beyond late October.

It is advisable to plant the scales about 1 to 2 inches deep and at least 3 inches apart so the plants coming from each scale can be identical and examined. A scale may produce both tetraploid and normal bulblets. It is relatively easy to distinguish the affected bulblets as soon as they produce leaves. Such bulblets are greatly retarded in growth and their leaves are usually rather narrow and very thick. Usually the difference in thickness between leaves on normal and affected bulblets can be detected by merely feeling the leaves between the fingers. Eventually the affected individuals start to grow and usually they produce large plants by maturity. If lily scales are handled in this manner, the small bulblets may be dug and replanted in September of the year following treatment, or left in the soil for 2 years. In cold sections it is advisable to place some sort of mulch over the scales and bulblets; about 2 inches of straw will do. It should not be applied until the ground freezes.

A fairly high proportion of the bulblets formed on such treated scales will be tetraploids. Some freak bulblets also will form. In these, some of the cells may have a double chromosome number and some a normal. These types may continue to grow and even flower. Usually their flowers are distinctly abnormal.

The Easter lily tetraploids so far made demonstrate the importance of treating as many different varieties as possible. All have larger flowers than normal, but some have a much greater increase in size than others.

When a tetraploid lily has been secured, it should be propagated by scaling. Even if it is fertile it can only be reproduced true to type by scales, since Easter lilies do not come true from seed.

The chromosome number of African violets has also been doubled by colchicine treatment. This plant is easy to propagate by leaf cuttings. The leaves are removed with about an inch and a half of stem attached. Several leaves may be bunched together and the bases of their stems set in a colchicine solution for about 2 hours. They should then be removed and dried and the bases dusted with either Arasan or Fermate to prevent rotting. The cuttings should then be placed in sand. This is best done by setting the stems in a slanting trench with the base of each leaf just touching the sand. New plants are formed at the bottom of the stem, and usually some will have the doubled chromosome number. The few tetraploid African violets we have developed did not show any improvement over the normal.

The concentration of colchicine giving best results may vary considerably for different plants. In lilies, good results have been had with a 0.2-percent solution. African violets responded well to both 0.01-percent and 0.1-percent solutions; snapdragon chromosomes were doubled with a 0.2-percent solution. The colchicine comes in a powdered form and is easily dissolved in water. It is also advisable to add a wetting or penetrating agent, such as Santomerse, which may be added to the colchicine at about the rate of a few drops to 10 liquid ounces of the colchicine. If you prepare a stock solution of 1-percent colchicine, it is then easy to dilute it to a 0.1-percent or any other concentration up to 1.0-percent. The colchicine solution should be stored in a refrigerator.

THE AUTHOR

S. L. Emsweller, as principal horticulturist in the Bureau of Plant Industry, Soils, and Agricultural Engineering, has been in charge of the investigations on floricultural and ornamental plants since 1935. Before joining the Department he did research at the University of California on various floricultural crops, including the development of rust-resistant varieties of snapdragons. Dr. Emsweller specializes in genetics and cytology, and at present is developing improved types of hardy chrysanthemums and new Easter and garden lilies, including the tetraploid lilies described in this article.

About Hydroponics

by NEIL W. STUART

THE IDEA of growing plants in water or sand without soil has fired almost everyone's imagination at some time or other. Whether it is called hydroponics, soilless culture, water culture, nutriculture, or whatever, many an American has dreamed of using it to become rich or self-sufficient when he gets out of the Army, or retires from the office, or gets his little place in the country. But the truth is that soilless culture, a practice of great value to students of plant nutrition, has been overpublicized and overpopularized, so that many persons have false impressions as to its real possibilities and limitations.

It was a technical tool in plant nutrition for more than a century, and helped researchers find out what kinds and amounts of food plants need. It came out of the laboratory as a practical, but restricted, means of commercial production primarily for a specific economic reason. The first trials were made in greenhouses on ornamental crops and the growing of vegetables in winter. In those instances, the difficulties of obtaining and handling large quantities of soil and manure, besides watering, weeding, fertilizing, and sterilizing, led to attempts to replace them with other systems of production.

Another use was exemplified during the war. The United States Army Air Forces used soilless culture to produce vegetables at several isolated air bases where vegetables could not be grown in the available soil or with the natural water supply.

Three general methods of crop production with nutrient solutions, collectively termed nutriculture, are in use. These are sand culture; water culture, sometimes called hydroponics; and subirrigation culture, also called gravel culture, or cinder culture.

In sand culture the soil in beds or benches is replaced with fine sand, which is watered with a nutrient solution applied to the surface. Workers at the New Jersey Agricultural Experiment Station have developed and improved the method. It is simple and, with proper control, can produce good crops. It is useful for experimental studies, but is not well suited for large-scale crop production because it wastes water and nutrients.

The water-culture method has received the most publicity, but is frequently not well understood. The plants are grown with their roots suspended in a nutrient solution contained in shallow tanks. The plants are supported above the water by wire netting or hardware cloth, which is covered with straw, wood shavings, or rice hulls in order to exclude light from the solution and maintain a high humidity around the upper roots. The solution must be aerated in order to supply sufficient oxygen to the roots; that is done by circulating the solution with a pump so that air is mixed with it or by letting air bubble into it through perforated pipes. The need for aeration and the difficulty of supporting the plants are disadvantages of the method. Control of the composition of the nutrient solution is also somewhat more exacting than in the other systems. Workers at the California Agricultural Experiment Station have done much toward developing this method.

In the subirrigation method, watertight beds or benches are filled with gravel or other suitable aggregate, which is irrigated from the bottom of the bed. Subirrigation overcomes some of the limitations of the sand and water culture systems. It was developed in 1934 at the New Jersey and Indiana Agricultural Experiment Stations. Subirrigation is accomplished by pumping the nutrient solution from the tank or cistern into the bottom of the bench, which is slightly lower at the middle than at the sides. Inverted half-round clay tiles or boards nailed together to form an inverted V are placed end-to-end at the middle of the bench and serve as a channel for the solution. When the solution has nearly filled the bench, the pump is stopped either manually or by an electric time switch and the solution drains back to the tank by gravity. This type of installation is known as the direct feed system and is useful in greenhouses, propagation units, or other small systems. In the newer benches built for subirrigation the solution channel is made a part of the bench by depressing the bottom of the V. The channel thus formed is covered with bricks or slabs of concrete that are provided with drainage holes at the sides. To facilitate rapid drainage these holes are covered with coarse gravel.

For larger installations it is more economical to employ the gravity feed system. The beds or benches are divided into three or four sections, each on a higher elevation and slightly longer than the one following it. Two solution tanks are used in this system. The larger one is located at the end of the beds and is below ground. It is connected with a somewhat smaller tank above the level of the beds by means of a flume. The capacity of the second tank should be approximately one-half the volume of the first sections of the beds. This tank is filled from the larger or sump tank before an irrigation is planned. The nutrient solution flows into the first bed sections by gravity and then successively through the other sections, finally emptying into the sump tank. By this means only the solution for irrigating the first sections of the beds has to be pumped, gravity flow irrigating the rest of the beds. The system was used by the United States Army Air Forces in their operation of soilless-culture gardens at Ascension Island, Atkinson Field in British Guiana, and Iwo Jima.

Benches or beds intended for subirrigation are usually built of reinforced concrete. They should always be coated on the inside with nontoxic petroleum asphalt that is applied hot, as an emulsion, or cut-back in a volatile solvent. The asphalt waterproofs the beds and protects them from the slightly acid nutrient solution. Ground beds of asphalt macadam can be constructed by mixing hot asphalt with sand and molding it into shape while hot. This type of bed was used on Ascension Island.

Prefabricated bituminous surfacing (PBS), consisting of burlap saturated with asphalt, was used successfully for constructing subirrigated beds in the Iwo Jima garden. The material comes in rolls 3 feet wide and has the advantage of being tough, flexible, waterproof, and easily laid. If it becomes generally available, PBS should be satisfactory for waterproofing existing wooden benches for subirrigation.

Several naturally occurring aggregates have been used in the soilless culture of a number of plants. Lava cinder was screened and used in the beds on Ascension and Iwo Jima. Gravel washed free of sand and clay has been widely used in the United States. Sintered shale, a commercial product used in making low-density concrete, is porous, light in weight, and has a higher water-holding capacity than gravel. Calcareous aggregates (coral limestone) have produced satisfactory crops experimentally after pretreating them with phosphate solutions to stabilize the pH (acidity). In tests at Beltsville, we got good results by using expanded vermiculite, a mica-like, hydrated magnesium aluminum silicate used industrially as an insulating material, as an aggregate. Sintered shale and vermiculite contain calcium and potassium and tend to take up phosphates from the nutrient solution that are later available to the plants growing in them; consequently, the pH and nutrient balance of solutions used on them do not fluctuate so rapidly as when the aggregate is gravel.

The size of the particles of the aggregates should be between one-sixteenth and one-half inch in diameter. The frequency of irrigation is determined partly by the water-retaining capacity of the beds. This in turn depends to a considerable extent upon the size of the particles and the porosity of the aggregate.

The nutrient solution supplies water and oxygen as well as mineral elements to the plant roots. Much effort has been expended in attempts to determine the best combination of nutrients for various plants. While many combinations have been proposed, it is now generally recognized that rather wide limits of solution composition can produce equally good growth with many plants. Climatic factors of temperature and the intensity of sunlight, as well as the part of the plant that the grower wants, that is, leaf, root, fruit, or flower, also are determining factors in the composition of solutions for optimum growth.

It should also be recognized that the total volume of the solution in relation to the number of the plants, the particle size of the aggregate, the frequency of irrigation and replenishment of absorbed nutrients, as well as the initial composition of the solution are important factors that govern growth. With small installations the nutrient solution can be replaced at frequent intervals. In larger systems it is more economical to replenish the elements as they are absorbed.

Some technical training and considerable experience are necessary for the efficient management of soilless-culture crop production. Its future development in the United States will probably be confined to the production of crops having a relatively high unit value—ornamentals, out-of-season vegetables, or seedlings for transplanting.

Under favorable conditions, yields may be expected to equal or surpass similar yields in soil, but so far the differences have not been outstanding. The method is also well adapted for specialized studies in plant nutrition, phytopathology, and plant breeding where growth under standard conditions is desired. The indications are that soilless-culture techniques will be more widely employed in the future.

THE AUTHOR

Neil W. Stuart is a physiologist in the Bureau of Plant Industry, Soils, and Agricultural Engineering, specializing in research work on effect of light, temperature, and nutrition on floricultural crops. Dr. Stuart is a graduate of Michigan State College.

ALSO, IN THIS BOOK

Finer Strawberries Ahead

by GEORGE M. DARROW

IN 1938 E. F. Farlow, like many of his neighbors in eastern Maryland, had to give up growing strawberries. Each spring his plants died soon after growth started. By harvesttime only plants on the higher ground were alive. Growers clear across the Northern States were having the same trouble, and the losses were serious.

Research workers who tackled the problem found first that a fungus was the cause. It rotted off the roots of the strawberries. It spread rapidly in cool, wet weather, but not in well-drained soil or in summer. Next, by testing many varieties, men at the Illinois Agricultural Experiment Station discovered that the Aberdeen strawberry was highly resistant to the devastating disease, which was called red stele disease. Never was a crop failure of Aberdeen due to the red stele disease—but the fruit of Aberdeen was too soft to sell in any but local markets, and it usually lacked flavor. The Department and the Maryland Agricultural Experiment Station joined forces. The Aberdeen was crossed with the Fairfax, a firm, high-flavored kind, and with other varieties. We raised thousands of seedlings on red stele-infested soil, retested those that were least affected, and tested the best of the survivors a third time.

On Mr. Farlow's place one selection proved to be productive; it had high flavor and it shipped well. It was named the Temple in 1943. Three years later it had become an important early variety in eastern Maryland, Virginia, and Delaware. Farlow and research workers want still better varieties. So now Farlow is growing several acres of Temple, an acre of seedlings, and about 100 other selections for the Department and the Maryland station for further testing. He and his neighbors have again become strawberry growers. The project is indeed a cooperative one: Research workers in Scotland, where the red stele disease is also serious, others in Illinois, and a research group in Oregon have exchanged both breeding material and ideas with those working in Maryland, all with the same objective, to originate varieties resistant to the red stele disease and adapted to each section of the country.

Another example also will illustrate the aims and methods of plant breeders. For 40-odd years, up to 1940, Klondike, because of its adaptation to the South, was almost the only strawberry grown in Louisiana. But during that time the leaf spot disease had become more and more injurious, until the plants had to be sprayed several times a year. Then research workers at the Louisiana Agricultural Experiment Station crossed Klondike with Blakemore, and got thousands of offspring, which they raised. These seedlings the scientists sprayed with leaf spot spores. All seedlings that developed much leaf spot were thrown away. Only those not injured were retested. But to be a good variety in southern Louisiana, a plant must throw out many runners. Therefore, in the second test, only good producers of runners were saved. They were fruited, and one, later named Klonmore, was found to produce large crops of firm, bright berries of good flavor. Only 4 years after its introduction, more than half of the crop in Louisiana was Klonmore. No spraying was necessary, for leaf spot has left Klonmore alone up to now.

Thus, when the cause of low yields has been determined or when growers need a variety better suited to preserving, shipping, freezing, or another use, or require one with better flavor, we survey the problem and determine which is the best method of breeding to obtain the desired end.

In California, for instance, virus diseases have been especially serious, and varieties healthier than the Marshall have been bred, named, and introduced by the California Agricultural Experiment Station workers.

In the Great Plains none of the older varieties is fully hardy, but the wild native strawberries are. So, crosses were made at the United States Horticultural Field Station at Cheyenne, Wyo., between the hardy wild kinds and the best cultivated varieties. The seedlings were planted in the field, and only those that survived the severe winters without protection were saved. Three selections far hardier than older kinds have been introduced for home gardens in that region—the Early Cheyenne 1, which is early; Cheyenne 2, midseason; and Cheyenne 3, a late kind.

For long-distance shipments from the South, much firmer berries than the Missionary were needed. The losses between the field and consumer were sometimes as high as 75 percent. Now, as the result of breeding, the Blakemore and Massey are grown, and losses have dropped considerably. In Tennessee, the Tennessee Shipper, still firmer than Blakemore, was obtained as a cross of Missionary and Blakemore and has been introduced. Berries as firm as the Tennessee Shipper—ones that will not bruise easily and are not so subject to decay as present varieties—are needed for each section of the country. Breeders have set out to get them.

Twenty years ago we had several kinds that were far above run-of-mine strawberries in flavor, but they could be grown only in a few localities. The aim of breeders since then has been to obtain high-flavored varieties that could be raised in all sections. We have been fairly successful. Among the flavorful new kinds are Fairmore, Dorsett, Fairfax, Narcissa, Redheart, Massey, Midland, Fairpeake, and Suwannee.

Flavor, even in the best varieties, is affected greatly by weather conditions. Sunny days and cool nights are necessary for berries of the best flavor. Some varieties occasionally have high flavor; in Maryland, for example, Aberdeen, under the most favorable conditions, has high flavor, but it has favorable conditions for high flavor perhaps only once in a hundred times. Missionary has high flavor oftener than Aberdeen, although generally it is too acid to be a good dessert berry. Of the newer varieties, Fairfax, Dorsett, Midland, Fairpeake, Fairmore, Narcissa, Redheart, and Massey are usually high-flavored, although in cloudy weather with hot nights, their flavor is not always what we would like. The Suwannee, introduced in 1945-46 as a home-garden variety by the Department and the Mississippi Agricultural Experiment Station, has very high flavor oftener than any other sort. It has good flavor even when the days are cloudy and the nights warm, and can be widely grown from Maryland to Georgia, and west to Texas and Kansas. It is too soft to be a good shipping variety, but it is usually well adapted to the home garden, and it may be the forerunner of commercial varieties of just as high quality.

To understand best the differences in varieties, let us rate them in the way that breeders score the selections they make. For each characteristic, breeders give a berry a mark from 0 to 10, with 10 the best. If a variety is rated as low as 5 for any characteristic, it is not considered worth growing in a particular section. A variety may have good flavor in one section, but not in another. Or, it may be soft, and be adapted to local markets but not for shipping. Thus:

Variety	Location	Pro-duc-tion	Firm-ness	Flavor	Color	Resistance to—	
						Spot	Scorch
Howard 17 (Premier)...	Maryland.....	9	4	6	7	9	9
Howard 17 (Premier)...	Massachusetts..	10	6	8	8	9	9
Missionary............	Florida........	10	8	6–9	8	7	7
Missionary............	North Carolina.	8	5	6–9	7	6	6
Marshall.............	Oregon.......	9	6	9	8	7	9
Marshall.............	Maryland.....	1–3	3	3–5	5	3	7

Among the important differences in the three varieties in different locations are: The firmer, better flavored berries of Howard 17 grown in Massachusetts, as compared with the same variety grown in Maryland; the greater firmness of Missionary ripening under short days in midwinter in Florida, as compared with the way it ripens in North

Carolina in the longer spring days; and the greater productiveness, flavor, and freedom from leaf spot in Oregon of Marshall, as compared with Marshall grown in Maryland.

In any one location, as in Maryland, the great differences among varieties may be shown similarly. So:

Variety	Size	Produc- tiveness	Firm- ness	Flavor	Color	Resist- ance to Spot	Season: Earli- est = 1; latest = 10
Blakemore	7	8	8	7	9	7	2
Suwannee	7	8	5	10	8	7	3
Midland	10	10	7	9	7	9	2
Fairpeake	8	9	8	9	8	7	9
Redstar	8	7	7	7	8	9	10
Tennessee Shipper	5	8	10	5	7	7	3

In this comparison, the Tennessee Shipper is shown to have too small a berry to be a good commercial variety, while Midland has the largest berry and the most productive plant. Suwannee is too soft to be a commercial variety, while Tennessee Shipper is the firmest variety. Tennessee Shipper is too tart to be a dessert strawberry, but Suwannee has the highest flavor oftener than the others. Thus, the breeder's ideal is to combine the size, productivity, and leaf spot resistance of Midland with the firmness of Tennessee Shipper, the flavor of Suwannee, and the appearance of Blakemore, plus whatever seasonal factors the grower desires. The special qualities of each of these varieties have all been bred into them by previous crossings. In the same way, further crossing may result in still finer varieties—a Midland, for example, that keeps its good size and productivity, and inherits Tennessee Shipper's firmness, Suwannee's flavor, Blakemore's appearance, and Redstar's late maturity or Maytime's early maturity.

But, furthermore, other characteristics must be sought for special conditions. In much of California, aphid- or virus-resistant varieties are necessary. In Oregon, resistance to mildew is important. In Florida, varieties must be able to grow and fruit during the short days of winter. In eastern North Carolina, resistance to leaf scorch is an important character. In all areas of the United States, drought resistance, abundant pollen in the flowers, bright color, and smoothness of fruit are needed. How can we get them? Extensive tests and an intimate knowledge of scores of varieties and scores of characteristics of each variety and of the inheritance of characters are essential for intelligent and effective breeding.

The objectives of the present work may be illustrated by the character of the seed collected from crosses made in the greenhouse at Beltsville in January and February 1946 by F. L. Goll and the writer. Other

crossing was done by George F. Waldo at Corvallis, Oreg., and by Prof.
E. B. Morrow of the North Carolina Experiment Station at Raleigh for
the objectives of the breeding work in those States. Although not all
the individual crosses are given in the following summary, a study of the
list of varieties with superior qualities given above will suggest suitable
parents for each objective. The crosses made at Beltsville in 1946 include:

Objective and kind of cross—	Number of crosses	Number of seed—calculated by weight	
For red stele-resistant plants:			
Aberdeen x varieties_____	2	26, 130	
Auchincruive #9 x varieties_____	3	17, 300	
USDA 3374 x varieties_____	6	58, 406	
Temple selfed and x variety_____	2	16, 254	
For large-sized berries:			118, 090
Massey x varieties_____	3	29, 139	
For firmness and freezing quality:			
Tennessee Shipper x Midland_____	1	4, 655	
For high-flavored berries:			
Fairpeake x variety_____	1	19, 930	
Suwannee x varieties_____	2	7, 978	
For chromosome study and aroma:			27, 908
Fragaria vesca 4x x Midland_____	1	223	
Do do 2x x do.___·_____	1	852	
			1, 075
Total_____			180, 867

A small part of this seed was sent to others for growing. The seed for
red stele resistance was sowed on sifted sphagnum in July and about
50,000 seedlings transplanted during the fall to greenhouse benches filled
with red stele-infested soil for a resistance test. The rest of the seed was
held for later sowing.

In the field at Beltsville for fruiting are more than 7,000 seedlings,
grouped as follows:

Purpose of crosses	Number of seedlings
To obtain hardy flowers resistant to severe frosts_____	480
To obtain the earliness, vigor, hardiness, and productiveness of selected wild octoploid species____	745
To obtain aroma of the "alpine" in cultivated varieties_____	180
For higher flavor_____	2, 700
For larger size_____	2, 000
An inheritance study of vitamin C_____	750
To test the value of selfing as a method of breeding_____·_____	275
Total_____	7, 130

These seedlings were set in early summer. Runners were kept off
most of them, and the plants grew large enough for the first selections to
be made in May and June 1947.

In the following summary, I list varieties that are notably superior for
certain qualities, although in some instances they are definitely inferior
in other ways.

SUMMARY LIST OF VARIETIES

(A=highest rating; B=next highest; C=third highest)

PLANT CHARACTERISTICS

1. Hardiness of plant to cold and to drying winds. — *Fragaria ovalis* (western North American strawberry) and Cheyenne 1, 2, and 3. *F. virginiana* from N. Dak.

2. Drought resistance_____ *Fragaria ovalis,* Suwannee, Blakemore.

3. Vigor in South_____ A. Missionary, Klonmore, Fairmore, Massey, Blakemore, Suwannee.
   B. Klondike, Southland, Ranger.

4. Large leaves_____ Redstar, Starbright, Southland, Massey.

5. Red stele resistance_____ A. Aberdeen, *F. chiloensis* selections in Oregon.
   B. Md.–683, US–3374, Temple.
   C. US–3205, US–3203, Pathfinder.

6. Leaf spot resistance_____ A. Klonmore, Fairmore, Southland, Fairfax, Midland, Howard 17
   B. Starbright, Redstar.
   Susceptible: Marshall, Klondike, Catskill, Dresden, Maytime, Robinson.

7. Scorch resistance_____ A. Southland, Fairfax, Howard 17, Dorsett, Redstar, Maytime, Fairpeake, Starbright, Fairmore.
   B. Midland.
   Susceptible: Klondike, Klonmore, Redheart, Julymorn, Konvoy, Robinson, Redwing.

8. Mildew resistance_____ A. Marshall, Rockhill.
   Susceptible: *F. ovalis.*

9. Yellow-plant resistance_____ A. Klondike, Fairmore, Marshall.
   B. Missionary (some seedlings turn yellow).
   Susceptible: Howard 17, Blakemore.
   Slightly susceptible: Chesapeake, Tennessee Beauty, Bellmar.

10. Virus resistance_____ A. Blakemore, Klondike, Howard 17, Brightmore.
    Susceptible: Marshall, Catskill.

11. Productiveness_____ A. Howard 17, Catskill, Midland, Fairpeake.
    Unproductive: Starbright, Northstar.

FRUIT CHARACTERISTICS

12. Earliness_____ Maytime, US–2259, Blakemore, Klonmore, Howard 17, Narcissa, Dorsett, June Rockhill, *F. ovalis* selections.

13. Lateness_____ Redstar, Fairpeake, Gandy, Massey, *F. chiloensis* selections.

14. Frost resistance of flower buds__ A. US–3405, Ill.–77–41, US–2249, US–3032, Mo.–446, US–2100, US–2830, Northstar, Howard 17, *F. virginiana* from Fairmont, N. Dak., NC–1012.
    B. *F. virginiana* from Sheldon, N. Dak.
    Susceptible: Daybreak, Southland.

15. Large size_____ Massey, Midland, Eleanor Roosevelt, Marshall,
                                 Howard 17, Tennessee Beauty.
                                 Small: Tennesee Shipper.

16. Firmness_____ NC–1022, Tennessee Shipper, Fairpeake, NC–
                                 1053, Fairmore, Starbright, Redheart, Fair-
                                 fax, Blakemore.
                                 Soft: Marshall, Howard 17, Catskill, Dorsett,
                                 Southland.

17. Color _____ Light: Blakemore, Massey, Suwannee.
                                 Dark: Fairmore, Fairfax, Marshall, Redheart.

18. Flavor_____ Fine: Suwannee, Fairpeake, Massey, Fairmore,
                                 Marshall,   Fairfax,   Rockhill,   Starbright,
                                 Dorsett.
                                 Poor: Lupton, Pathfinder, Dresden, Aroma.
                                 Acid: Tennessee Shipper, Klondike, Blakemore,
                                 Missionary.

19. Freezing for preserving_____ Blakemore, Brightmore.

20. Freezing in packages_____ Midland, Brightmore, Redheart, Corvallis,
                                 Julymorn, Klondike, Dorsett, Joe, Tennessee
                                 Beauty, Tennessee Shipper.

21. Canning_____ Redheart, Corvallis.

22. High vitamin C content_____ Fairpeake, Fairmore, Gandy, Catskill.
                                 Low content: Aberdeen.

23. Adapted to short days of winter Missionary,   Klonmore,   Fairmore,   Konvoy,
    and early spring.   F. virginiana var. grayiana of La., Blakemore,
                                 Massy, F. chiloensis varieties of Mexico and
                                 Peru.

THE AUTHOR

Much credit for many of the better berry varieties we have today is due to George M. Darrow, principal pomologist, Bureau of Plant Industry, Soils, and Agricultural Engineering. Except for time out during the First World War, he has been with the Department since 1911. Among the strawberry varieties he has originated in that time are Blakemore, Fairfax, Dorsett, Redheart, Redstar, Fairpeake, Midland, Massey, Maytime, and others; also to his credit are Sunrise red and Potomac purple raspberries, and rabbiteye blueberries. Through Dr. Darrow's work on strawberries we know more about the factors that govern their yields and varieties that are adapted to different regions of the United States. He made studies on polyploidy and the botany of blackberries, blueberries, and strawberries.

FOR FURTHER READING

Darrow, George M., and Waldo, George F.: *Strawberry Varieties in the United States,* U. S. D. A. Farmers' Bulletin 1043, 1946.

Demaree, J. B.: *Diseases of Strawberries,* U. S. D. A. Farmers' Bulletin 1891, 1941.

Fisher, D. F., and Lutz, J. M.: *Handling and Shipping Strawberries Without Refrigeration,* U. S. D. A. Circular 515, 1939.

ALSO, IN THIS BOOK

New Varieties of Blueberry

by GEORGE M. DARROW

THE VARIETIES that have made possible a cultivated blueberry industry in the United States consist of some 14 sorts bred by F. V.
Coville of the Department, and one variety selected from the wild when
he was collecting breeding material for his work.

Since Dr. Coville's death in 1937, three varieties have been named
and introduced from the selections being tested at the time of his death.
These consisted of two late sorts, Atlantic and Pemberton, and one very
late variety, the Burlington. All three have been propagated and widely
tested, and are proving to be worth while.

Atlantic is still liked for exactly the superior qualities that were observed when it was named. It has a large, vigorous plant that is very
productive. The berries have good flavor, a fine, light-blue color, very
large size, and good picking and shipping qualities. Also, of the varieties
tested by the New Jersey Experiment Station, it has been the best of all
for quick freezing. At one location in North Carolina the berries have
been of largest size, but at a second location they were no larger than
the Jersey. In the North their size equals that of the Dixi and is larger
than that of the Jersey.

The Pemberton, in the Northern States, has proved to be even better
than it seemed when it was introduced. It has superior vigor and productiveness, and good flavor and size of berry. Although in New Jersey
its color does not seem better than that of Weymouth, in Massachusetts
its color is much lighter. There, too, the scar (where the berry separates
from the stem) is better than in New Jersey. It is considered promising in southern New England. Both Atlantic and Pemberton are well
adapted to home gardens.

The Burlington is the latest to be introduced. It has a vigorous, large

300

bush that resists the mite, a miscroscopic pest that is serious on some varieties. The color of the berry is light blue, its flavor is good, and it picks easily and ships well. Although not so large as Atlantic and Pemberton, it is of good size. This is a promising sort.

Dr. Coville and his associate, O. M. Freeman, left many unnamed selections that they considered worth testing. They also left about 30,000 seedlings, from which many additional selections have been made. Because those seedlings represented the accumulated experience of more than 25 years of breeding work, there are likely to be finer seedlings among them than the ones Dr. Coville named and introduced. We think there are, and are propagating several of them for extensive testing and study. Dr. Coville realized the needs of the industry, and among the crosses he left were some for better early-ripening varieties to replace the Weymouth, and for late-ripening varieties to extend the season after that of the Jersey. Seedlings having those qualities were found, and are being propagated for testing for their hardiness, disease resistance, vigor, productiveness, picking qualities, shipping qualities, and other characteristics that determine the value of a variety. The breeding work has been continued especially to obtain hardy and late-ripening varieties in the North, early canker-resistant varieties for North Carolina and neighboring States and varieties better for shipping, canning, and freezing.

Besides the northern highbush blueberry, the southern rabbiteye seems promising. It is much more drought- and heat-resistant than the northern highbush and can be grown on higher land. It can be grown from southern Arkansas and Louisiana to northern Florida and eastern North Carolina. Several varieties are being propagated; among the best are Myers, Clara, and Owens. Myers and Clara have fairly blue berries; the Owens has black fruit. In shipping and storage tests the Myers and Clara hold up well.

W. M. Walker, of southeastern Georgia, has for many years had fishing as a hobby. Much of his fishing has been along the Satilla River, where the rabbiteye blueberry is abundant. He selected many of the best wild plants and planted them in his garden. Neighbors were allowed to pick the surplus fruit. One of them reported the superior quality of his selections to the Department. Sure enough, when a visit was made to his place, among his selections were found better light-blue ones than anywhere else. Three of the best were named Walker, Ethel (for Mrs. Walker), and Satilla (for the Satilla River). These have already been extensively hybridized with the best varieties from other sections and with the best selections from the breeding work previously undertaken. Mr. Walker has wanted others to have his selections and placed no restrictions on them. He gave the Georgia Coastal Plain Station at Tifton propagating wood so that others might enjoy his selections. They are now being propagated for distribution.

The remarkable vigor, productivity, and tolerance of drought and heat of the rabbiteye make it a superior horticultural plant. Full-grown bushes have averaged more than a bushel of berries each. The varieties already being propagated are good enough to form a commercial blueberry industry, but the new selections seem very much better than the older named varieties. Myers, Clara, Owens, Walker, and Ethel, selected from the wild, correspond to the Rubel, Adams, Sam, and other varieties selected from the northern wild highbush, while the new selections from breeding work correspond to the first varieties of the highbush from Coville's breeding work—Pioneer and Cabot. The more recent varieties of the northern highbush, such as Atlantic and Pemberton, are better than the Pioneer and Cabot. Likewise, crosses of the best selections of the present rabbiteye blueberries are expected to produce still finer sorts.

The highbush and rabbiteye are just two of the many blueberry species that possess fine horticultural characters. Others, such as Constables blueberry of the high mountains of western North Carolina, and the dryland blueberry of the southern Piedmont region, bear fine berries as they grow unselected in the wild. An evergreen blueberry grows vigorously in barren, dry soils and the hot climate of Florida even south of Miami. Preliminary hybrids with these and other kinds of wild blueberries indicate that they can be of value in developing a great blueberry industry.

The extent of the breeding work now being carried on is illustrated by the work of 1945. The following list includes the crosses made:

Kind of cross	Number of crosses	Approximate number of seeds
Rabbiteye crosses and hybrids:		
Varieties × varieties	14	62,000
Varieties × Constables blueberry	5	12,000
Varieties × (varieties × Constables blueberry)	4	21,000
Varieties × highbush	3	4,000
Varieties × *Vaccinium tenellum*	2	100
Florida evergreen hybrids:		
Varieties × highbush	5	500
Varieties × (Florida evergreen × highbush)	4	5,500
Highbush crosses:		
Varieties × varieties	29	54,000
Dryland hybrids:		
(Dryland × highbush) × highbush	3	1,000
Deerberry hybrids:		
Deerberry × blueberry	2	70
Total	71	160,170

The crosses were made on potted plants brought into a warm greenhouse from outside in January. The crossing began February 5, was at its height about the middle of the month, and continued through March. The berries ripened during April, May, and June and a few in July. The seed was extracted from the berries and stored for "after-ripening" in a household refrigerator until planting time. A large part of the seed was sent to cooperators at experiment stations. The seed kept at Beltsville was sowed on sifted sphagnum moss October 4. In January 1946 the first seedlings were placed in 2½-inch rose pots and later through the winter additional plants were potted up. In April the following seedlings were in the greenhouse:

Kind of cross	Crosses planted	Approximate number of seed planted	Number of seedlings
Rabbiteye crosses and hybrids:			
Varieties × varieties....................	10	6, 430	2, 469
Varieties × Constables blueberry.........	4	3, 120	1, 020
Varieties × (varieties × Constables blueberry).............................	4	3, 000	1, 268
Varieties × highbush...................	3	2, 500	635
Varieties × V. tenellum..................	2	100	14
Florida Evergreen hybrids:			
Varieties × highbush...................	1	50	24
Varieties × (Florida evergreen × highbush)................................	1	200	52
Highbush crosses:			
Varieties × varieties...................	8	5, 300	3, 592

Because the germination was not high, the seed flats have been kept over for a second year to see if more seedlings would appear. The seedlings grow large enough for field planting in late fall and early winter and are large enough for testing their fruit qualities 2, 3, or 4 years later.

THE AUTHOR

George M. Darrow is principal pomologist in the Bureau of Plant Industry, Soils, and Agricultural Engineering.

FOR FURTHER READING

Darrow, George M.: *The Atlantic, Pemberton, and Burlington Blueberries,* U. S. D. A. Circular 589, 1940.

Darrow, George M., Wilcox, R. B., and Beckwith, Charles S.: *Blueberry Growing,* U. S. D. A. Farmers' Bulletin 1951, 1944.

Better Peaches Are Coming

by LEON HAVIS, J. H. WEINBERGER, and C. O. HESSE

THE ELBERTA has long been the standard of comparison in peaches, like sterling in silver. Elberta yields bountifully, looks attractive, has a free stone, and flourishes in different climates. It is not perfect, however, and for more than a decade we have been breeding new peaches to get one that will surpass Elberta in resistance to several diseases, hardiness of tree and flower bud, and value for canning, freezing, and eating fresh. Our results indicate that many of the characters lacking in the Elberta can be bred into new varieties—but perhaps not all of them into one variety. In the future the grower, the processor, and the consumer will be able to a greater degree than ever before to select varieties to suit his requirements.

Peach growing as an industry should not be based largely on one variety such as Elberta, but should be able to choose from a number of varieties suited to different seasons of ripening, different requirements of hardiness, and different eating, canning, or freezing requirements. Varieties are needed that resist diseases prevalent in certain localities.

Basic objectives in experiments with peach varieties have been to increase the size of fruit and the average yield. More and more there is a demand for higher colored fruit. A lengthening of the peach season with productive freestone varieties is desirable. A lengthening of the canning-cling season has been an important objective in California. Never before has there been so much emphasis on improvement in peach flavor for canning, freezing, and preserving as there is at present. Varieties that have especially high quality for these purposes are being bred.

In the central and southern regions, hardiness to spring frost is a special problem. In Massachusetts, New York, and Michigan, hardiness of tree and flower bud is of prime importance. In regions such as south-

304

ern California, Texas, and Georgia, a tree with a low winter-chilling requirement to break the rest period of buds is essential for dependable production. Shipping quality is first in importance in some regions that are far from markets, but in other places the local markets do not require so firm a fruit. Freestones are preferred throughout the season for eating fresh and for home canning. Perhaps that will always be true.

Consumers now prefer varieties that have a bright red skin, although there is no actual relationship between the amount of red skin color and dessert quality. Yellow-fleshed peaches are in greater demand generally than white ones. This choice of the highly colored, yellow-fleshed peach may change sometime, however, and peach breeders keep in mind the possible and most likely requirements 25 years from now.

Recent Basic Information on Breeding Peaches

Several varieties were introduced during the war period. Thousands of seedlings resulting from crosses made before the war have been gone over and the most promising ones selected for further trial. The actual crossing of varieties and the detailed work connected with that process have not been conducted on so extensive a scale as was done just before the war. Lack of workers and demand for work of more immediate war value reduced the breeding program in the Department as well as in most State experiment stations. Through the study of progeny of crosses made previously much has been learned that should aid in selecting parents to obtain the desired characters in future seedlings.

The development of superior varieties in the future should be more sure and rapid as a result of our knowledge of inheritance of characteristics of parents. Several years ago investigators at the New Jersey Agricultural Experiment Station found that pollen fertility was a dominant character in peaches and evidently controlled by a single pair of genes. Now, because of the large number of individual progeny records made, we can classify a great many varieties on the basis of how they transmit pollen sterility to their progeny. We also know that varieties vary considerably in the transmission of the chilling required to break their rest period. For example, Halehaven gives a wide variation in chilling requirements among its offspring. This is an important character in Southern peach areas, and until recently it was largely a matter of chance whether an improved variety could be grown successfully in the southern parts of Georgia, Texas, and California, or anywhere in Florida.

Genetic studies have recently been made on the inheritance of such characters as bud set, time of ripening, size and shape of fruits, firmness, color of flesh and skin, amount of fuzz on the skin, and freedom at the stone. We can select parents with more and more confidence in obtaining the desired combination of characters.

We now know that when certain parents are used in crosses there will be a wide variation in some characters among the offspring; when others are used the variation is much less. Thus we can estimate the number of progeny desired to obtain the character or combination of characters desired. In some crosses several thousand offspring seem none too many, whereas in others only 25 may be enough.

A modern method of peach breeding can be illustrated by the development of the Dixigem by the Department. The first peaches to reach Northeastern markets in fairly large quantities have long been those from southern and south-central Georgia. Some of the more popular varieties have been Mayflower, Uneeda, Early Rose, and Early Wheeler (Red Bird). Because of their earliness, these white varieties have been in demand by consumers and have been profitable to the peach grower during certain years. Those who eat peaches prefer the larger, yellow-fleshed varieties and higher quality. Those who grow them want more dependable bearing, higher yielding, firmer fleshed varieties, and of course they want varieties that as nearly as practicable fulfill the consumer's ideal. When the peach-breeding work at Beltsville was started in 1936 by F. P. Cullinan, one of his major objectives was to breed better peaches for the South. One of the major problems faced that first year was which parents to use in their crosses. Much less was known then than now about the merits of different varieties as parents. About 75 crosses were made in 1936 and several varieties were self-pollinated. Among the many parents used were Halehaven, South Haven, and an unnamed seedling selection of a cross between Admiral Dewey and St. John. This last selection was a result of some of the earliest peach breeding by the Department, a cross made by W. F. Wight in 1920 at South Haven, Mich.

Peach breeding was started in 1936 at Fort Valley, Ga., the center of the major peach regions that specialize in the production of early peaches. When J. H. Weinberger began the work there, he took with him the peach seeds resulting from the crosses made at Beltsville the previous spring. The seeds were germinated and grown in pots in the greenhouse during the late winter, and early spring of 1937. In April 1937, when the danger of frost was over, the trees, then about 18 inches high, were transferred to the field. There they were planted 3 feet apart in rows 12 feet apart. Next came the years of selection of the best progeny. In the meantime other crosses were made at Beltsville, Fort Valley, and in California.

Among the progeny of the 1936 crosses were several that seemed superior to the early-ripening commercial varieties of the same season grown in central Georgia. They could not all be named, but the best one for a particular season and purpose had to be selected through trial year after year. A few trees of each of the more promising progeny were tested on the grounds of the United States Horticultural Laboratory at Fort Valley, some were sent to State experiment stations, and some to the Plant Industry Station at Beltsville. Large tests were made in cooperation with fruit growers in Georgia.

As the testing progressed, some of the selections were discarded each year because of one or more faults. Finally, in 1944, the one tested under the number FV 8—35, resulting from a cross of the unnamed seedling of Admiral Dewey × St. John with the South Haven variety, seemed best for its season. It was named Dixigem, and whatever budwood was available was furnished those who wanted to propagate it. The popularity of Dixigem is indicated by the 50,000 trees budded in 1944 and 100,000 in 1945. Dixigem is far from being the perfect peach, but it seems superior to other early varieties in the South, where it has been tested most.

California and Texas

Several public institutions and private individuals are engaged in peach improvement in California. The development of freestone varieties of good quality, attractive appearance, and suitability for market and processing purposes is fostered. There is considerable interest in developing cling varieties that ripen earlier and later than the standard midsummer group. The origination of both freestone and cling varieties for southern California, where many standard sorts fail to bear because of lack of enough winter cold, is also a major field of peach improvement.

The University of California has breeding programs at Davis and Riverside. Guy L. Philp, in charge of the peach-breeding work at Davis, is studying the inheritance of the nonoxidizing factor in peaches in connection with the development of varieties especially adapted to freezing; and L. D. Davis is studying the inheritance of high and low gum content of clingstone peaches, since high gum content is associated with gumming and splitpit in certain varieties.

Peach breeding at Riverside is primarily concerned with the origin of peach varieties suitable to the mild winter climate of southern California. J. W. Lesley is responsible for the work at Riverside, and several varieties (Rosy, Golden State, Ramona, Hermosa, and Sunglow) were introduced in 1939. More recently Bonita, a yellow-fleshed freestone maturing before Elberta, has been introduced.

G. P. Weldon, at Chaffey Junior College in Ontario, Calif., has also been breeding varieties for mild winters. The Chaffey, Fontana, and Weldon were introduced in 1938. The Welberta, named in 1946, is a cross between Weldon and Elberta. It resembles Elberta, but it has a shorter chilling requirement and ripens 10 days to 2 weeks earlier. The Armstrong Nurseries, also of Ontario, Calif., have about the same objectives as those described for Riverside and Chaffey Junior College. Their more recent introductions are Robin, Redwing, Meadowlark, and Flamingo. Curlew and Golden Blush were chance seedlings recently introduced by Armstrong Nurseries.

F. A. Dixon made several promising peach selections. Fred Anderson of Merced recently introduced the LeGrand Kim and Kim nectarines. Grant Merrill of Red Bluff made several promising selections of early shipping peaches.

Efforts at the Texas Agricultural Experiment Station, under the direction of S. H. Yarnell, are directed primarily toward obtaining superior, early, yellow freestones of dependable production and suited to a mild climate. Particular emphasis has been placed on varieties with desirable fruit and tree characteristics suited to districts where there is not enough winter cold to break completely the rest period of many peach varieties. Five promising selections are being tested for introduction in southern Texas for home use.

The Middle West

The goal of the work at the University of Illinois has been better varieties that ripen earlier and later than Elberta in order to spread the period of harvest. Attention is given to hardiness, firmness of flesh, type of tree, productiveness, disease resistance, and dessert quality in the selection of parents for the different crosses.

The most promising selections—about 100 out of more than 10,000 seedlings that have fruited—are given further tests in selected orchards in Illinois and in some Eastern States. Tests of storage and freezing qualities also are made of the most promising selections.

As a result of this program, which is under the direction of M. J. Dorsey, seven promising selections were named in 1946: Prairie Dawn, Prairie Sunrise, Prairie Daybreak, Prairie Rose, Prairie Schooner, Prairie Clipper, and Prairie Rambler.

Hardiness of the tree and flower buds to low temperatures is the chief objective in breeding peaches for Iowa. Several large yellow freestone selections resulting from fourth- and fifth-generation seedlings of Hill's Chili seem promising, and budded trees have been put under test. T. J. Maney, who was in charge of the peach breeding until his death in 1945, also obtained several promising hardy yellow-fleshed peaches by crossing peaches with *Prunus davidiana,* although the flavor and the size of fruit are not ideal. Approximately 1,000 hybrid seedlings have been planted at the Iowa Agricultural Experiment Station; about 10 of them have been propagated for a second orchard test.

Objectives of the program at the Michigan Agricultural Experiment Station, under the direction of Stanley Johnston, are: To combine the excellent appearance and firm, fine texture of Redhaven in a series of varieties with larger size than Redhaven; to obtain in these new varieties a greater resistance to winter cold than is found in present commercial varieties; to originate a series of varieties having the characteristics mentioned above and ripening over a period of 5 weeks before Elberta and 1 week later, and to obtain superior clingstone varieties for use of the commercial canning industry in Michigan. Between the introduction of Redhaven in 1940 and the introduction of Fairhaven in 1946, none has met the standard the station has set for a new peach.

Peach breeding at the Missouri State Fruit Experiment Station, at Mountain Grove, is under the direction of P. H. Shepard. The principal objectives are: To obtain superior varieties with winter bud hardiness and late blooming; to produce early and medium-early freestone varieties that will stand shipping and that have good quality, production, and texture; to produce an early cling variety that has high quality, firmness, and attractive color; and to obtain better freezing varieties than are now available.

About a dozen medium-early freestone selections are now being tested intensively, and two, the Loring and the Ozark, both of which resulted from the crossing of Frank with Halehaven, were named in 1946. They are medium-early, firm freestones with good color, quality, and texture.

The Frank and Japan Giant Cling have been used extensively in crosses to obtain a better early cling variety. The Japan Giant Cling has transmitted its characteristic of high sugar content to all its offspring.

The East

Peach breeding under J. S. Bailey and A. P. French at the Massachusetts Agricultural Experiment Station has been largely a study of the inheritance of characters, such as types of flowers, glands, and flesh, rather than to develop new varieties. Recently, however, a few seedlings were selected from a selfed Oriole group for further testing.

Some of the main aims of the work at the New Jersey Agricultural Experiment Station are to study the inheritance of characteristics, develop superior canning and freezing varieties, develop a succession of early commercial varieties, obtain varieties with fruit of low acid and tannin content, and get stronger varieties for rootstock purposes. A special effort is also being made to develop better nectarines. During the war the maintenance of the large collection of species and varieties was of primary concern. During this period selection and breeding were also continued on a limited scale, and several new selections are now ready for more extensive trials. Approximately 35 peach varieties have been developed there since the breeding work started in 1914. The Laterose, a promising white freestone ripening just after Elberta, was named in 1945. Two early yellow-fleshed varieties ripening before Golden Jubilee, the Early-east and the Jerseyland, and a yellow freestone midseason one, the Redcrest, were named and released for propagation in 1946. M. A. Blake directs the work at the New Jersey station.

Richard Wellington, G. D. Oberle, and John Einset conduct the peach breeding at the New York State Agricultural Experiment Station. The main purpose is to obtain commercial varieties that will be relatively resistant to low winter temperatures, with fruit of high quality and firm flesh. In a latitude like that of New York, winter hardiness of flower buds is extremely important. Another objective is to obtain nonoxidizing or nondarkening varieties for freezing. Efforts to develop superior nectarines are also being made.

The main objective in the breeding work at the Virginia Agricultural Experiment Station is to obtain a variety similar to Elberta, plus greater hardiness, larger fruit, and higher quality; and high-quality, yellow-fleshed, early-season varieties. Another ideal is a larger fruited, yellow-fleshed nectarine. W. S. Flory, Jr., and R. C. Moore use selected seedlings as well as named varieties as parents to obtain their objectives in the offspring. Several outstanding selections are being backcrossed or crossed with each other, where this appears feasible from the standpoint of character recombinations. Along with the breeding work, studies are made of genetic characters, determination of "marker" character, and cytological problems in breeding.

The Department of Agriculture

One object of the Department's breeding program is to obtain varieties that yield more bushels of larger peaches than the present varieties, which show considerable genetic difference in this respect. Another objective is to improve the dessert quality of fruit for all purposes and seasons. Freestone peaches with an attractive color are desired. Peaches are bred and tested for resistance to low winter temperatures in the Northern States, for resistance to spring frost in the Central States, and to rapid changes in temperature in the Southern States. Varieties with low winter chilling requirements are being bred for such places as southern areas of Georgia, Texas, and southern California. One of C. O. Hesse's special objectives in California is to extend the canning-cling season with high-flavored varieties. They should have no red in the flesh and should be resistant to pit splitting and gumming. Resistance to such diseases as bacterial spot and mosaic is an objective for peaches to be grown in areas where these diseases are common.

The Department now has by far the largest breeding program ever carried on. Approximately 36,000 seedlings of controlled crosses were fruited between 1939 and 1946. In 1946 approximately 650, or fewer than 2 percent, of these had been selected as worthy of further trial.

Since 1942 several new varieties have been introduced by the Department. They are described briefly here. The cross that produced the new variety is given in parentheses in each case.

Corona (Libee × Lovell) is a canning-cling variety named in 1942. It ripens just after Phillips Cling. The flesh is firm and fine-grained and the flavor excellent. It was introduced as a result of the breeding work of W. F. Wight in cooperation with Stanford University.

Carolyn (Libbee × Lovell), introduced in 1942, also resulted from the work of Mr. Wight. It is a canning cling and ripens with Gaume. It appears superior to that variety in color and texture of flesh.

Amador (Elberta × Ontario), named and introduced in 1942, also originated from the breeding work at Palo Alto. It is a freestone. It ripens just before Elberta and has an attractive yellow flesh. Its fairly low chilling requirement makes it promising in the southern peach regions.

Cortez (Paloro × Halford I) is a canning clingstone peach named in 1944. The original cross and early trials of the selection were made by Mr. Wight at Palo Alto. The fruit seems excellent for canning, and ripens just before Paloro or with Walton. The fruit is of good size and the flesh is firm and fine-grained with very little red at the pit.

Dixigem ((Admiral Dewey × St. John) × South Haven) was introduced in 1944. The cross was made at Beltsville but the seed was planted and the selection made at Fort Valley. Dixigem ripens about a week before Golden Jubilee. It is almost a freestone, is yellow-fleshed, firm, and attractive. The quality is excellent. It freezes and cans well.

Dixired (Halehaven selfed) is a yellow, medium-sized, melting-fleshed cling introduced in 1945. Like Dixigem, this pollination was also done at Beltsville and the selection made at Fort Valley. It ripens with Uneeda, or about 2 weeks ahead of Golden Jubilee. The flesh is especially firm for its season, the color is attractive, and the flavor good.

Southland (Halehaven selfed), named in 1946, is a yellow freestone variety especially suited to southern regions. It also originated from seeds produced at Beltsville in 1936, but grown at Fort Valley. The Southland is a medium-to-large, firm-fruited peach that ripens at the same time as the Hiley and has a moderate chilling requirement, to break the winter rest period.

THE AUTHORS

Leon Havis is a senior pomologist in the Bureau of Plant Industry, Soils, and Agricultural Engineering, stationed at Beltsville. He is in charge of stone-fruit production and breeding research of the Department.

J. H. Weinberger, a pomologist in the same Bureau, is stationed at Fort Valley, Ga. He is in charge of the United States Horticultural Field Laboratory there.

C. O. Hesse, an associate geneticist of the Bureau, is stationed at Davis, Calif. His work is mainly concerned with fruit breeding investigations which the Department carries on in cooperation with the California Agricultural Experiment Station.

Healthier Tomatoes

by WILLIAM S. PORTE and C. F. ANDRUS

THE TOMATO is a native tropical American plant, but for a long time it was without honor in its own hemisphere. Jefferson grew tomatoes in Virginia in 1781 and Washington is said to have used them in his army rations, but about a half century elapsed before they became generally regarded as a food in the United States.

Now tomatoes are grown on more than 800,000 acres in the United States, and the crop is valued at 166 million dollars, not counting the tomatoes grown in home gardens.

At first, when tomatoes were grown only in small patches, diseases were no problem. The few varieties planted had been brought from England and France. The early breeding, done by amateurs, was devoted to improving the size, shape, color, and production of the fruit. But at the beginning of this century the commercial tomato industry was concentrated in definite regions in which the incidence and severity of diseases were continually increasing. The Department recognized that the control of tomato diseases had become a national problem, and in 1915 started a project for breeding disease-resistant varieties.

The work was under the leadership of F. J. Pritchard, whose name all tomato growers know. His first job was to do something about fusarium wilt, which is caused by a soil-infesting fungus. During the next 10 years a series of wilt-tolerant varieties enabled growers to produce profitable crops on soils lightly infested with the fungus.

The new kinds and the practice of crop rotation reduced damages from wilt. But the disease was still causing an estimated annual loss of more than a million dollars to commercial crops and uncalculated losses in home gardens before the war—because of the expansion of the crop and the gradual infestation of more soil areas and because of the natural

312

development of more virulent races of the fusarium fungus. At the same time, the foliage blights and virus diseases also were taking a graduated toll of the crop, despite a program of field sanitation that had been developed in the Department to control leaf spot diseases.

Field sanitation programs are not very successful because the measures are not generally and properly applied. On the other hand, any disease resistance or immunity bred into a variety of tomato becomes available to all growers wherever the resistant line is used. That is the great advantage of breeding for disease resistance over other methods of disease control, and is a reason why the Department has increasingly emphasized and expanded its breeding work for disease control. For such efforts we must have varieties possessing the genetic factors for immunity or high resistance to all the important diseases.

Plant explorers, in recent years, have searched Peru and adjacent South American countries in which the tomato is native, and have imported hundreds of varieties of *Lycopersicon esculentum* (the edible tomato) and numerous lines of related species such as *L. hirsutum, L. peruvianum,* and *L. pimpinellifolium.* They have also obtained a large number of exotic varieties from Europe, Asia, Africa, and Australia, in their search for new and superior genetic factors for disease resistance.

The introductions are tested by breeders in the Department and in the State and Territorial stations. The tests determine the resistance of each strain to various diseases, so that the breeders can isolate superior resistant plants for use as parents in the development of stronger varieties. Because varieties that tolerated fusarium wilt were not entirely satisfactory when cropped on soils heavily infested with the wilt fungus, the introduction of new parental material stimulated a search for stocks that showed definitely higher degrees of resistance to the wilt. From 1935 to 1941 a project at Beltsville was directed chiefly to the development of commercially acceptable varieties possessing higher resistance to wilt than those already in use.

Pan America

Foreign stocks of *Lycopersicon pimpinellifolium,* a wild, small-fruited species known as currant tomato, have been a fertile source of parent lines that are immune, resistant, or tolerant to wilt and other important diseases, including leaf mold, foliage blights, and mosaic.

One of these stocks, P. I. 79532, was discovered growing in a cane field near Trujillo, Peru, within sight of the Pacific Ocean. It was tested on soil that had been artificially loaded with the fusarium wilt fungus, and its healthy green foliage stood out like an emerald in the bright September weather in contrast to hundreds of browned, wilt-sick varieties. Repeated inoculation tests established the practical immunity

of this tomato from attack by the fusarium wilt fungus. A series of reciprocal crosses was made between inbred lines of Marglobe, a widely used
canning and shipping variety, and the almost immune wild line of Red
Currant.

The fruits of Red Currant are only about a quarter of an inch in diameter. They are thin-walled, usually two-celled and filled with greenish
watery pulp and numerous seeds. The breeding problem involving this
cross was the isolation and development of a line combining the wilt
resistance of Red Currant with the large, fleshy, heavy-walled, scarlet
Marglobe fruits. The size of fruit in the progeny of the new hybrid
was increased by successively backcrossing it three times to the Marglobe
parent. Each backcrossed generation and the subsequent generations
of line selections were rigidly tested to determine their complete resistance
to attack by a highly virulent strain of the fusarium fungus.

In all the wilt tests of parent lines selected in 1938 or later, 95 to 100
percent of the samples tested were entirely free from any evidence of
fusarium wilt infection. The variety Pan America, developed from
this cross, was released by the Department in 1941 by distributing stock
seed to commercial tomato seed growers and all interested research institutions. It is widely used by tomato breeders as a wilt-resistant parent in
developing varieties that withstand two or more diseases and are adapted
to special regional conditions. Commercial growers and home gardeners, especially in localities having soils heavily infested with the
fusarium wilt fungus, are successfully producing crops practically free
from wilt by using Pan America.

Essential Techniques Devised

Before a breeding program can be carried to a successful conclusion,
technical procedures must be developed that will produce essentially
uniform results in all successive tests conducted with the same variety or
strain. In order to test effectively the resistance of a tomato line to a
disease, the organism causing the disease must be thoroughly studied.
The more the breeder knows concerning the life history of the agent
causing the disease and the nature of the inheritance in the tomato of
resistance to its attack, the more effectively he can breed resistant varieties. In recent years workers in the Department and in State research
institutions have devoted much of their time and effort to this phase of the
work. Several workers have studied cultures of the tomato wilt fungus,
Fusarium oxysporum f. *lycopersici,* from diverse regions of the United
States and found striking differences in their capacity to produce wilt in
tomato plants. They have isolated the most virulent strains and these
are now used in testing the resistance of tomato lines.

F. L. Wellman, working at the Plant Industry Station at Beltsville, devised a laboratory and greenhouse technique for the study of both the capacity of the tomato wilt organism to produce tomato wilt and the relative wilt resistance of tomato strains and varieties. By maintaining a greenhouse soil and air temperature of about 80° F., he obtained conditions that enable tomato breeders to test the wilt resistance of a population of 3,000 tomato plants each month during the fall and winter with only 72 square feet of bench space. In previous field tests, usually fewer than 3,000 plants per acre were tested each year and the breeder could grow and test only one generation of tomato plants a year.

Similarly, workers at the United States Regional Vegetable Breeding Laboratory at Charleston, S. C., developed an effective laboratory and greenhouse technique for testing large populations of tomato seedlings for resistance to tomato leaf spot diseases. They also determined the nature of inheritance of resistance to the collar rot phase of *Alternaria solani* and to septoria leaf spot. These are important contributions in speeding up breeding for resistance to these damaging tomato foliage diseases.

Organization for More Effective Breeding

Because of the greater need to get varieties adapted to all regions of the country, the Department has undertaken research at the Cheyenne Horticultural Field Station in Wyoming, the laboratory at Charleston, and a number of other field stations and laboratories.

Since 1938 the workers at these institutions have been testing a large group of wild tomatoes and related species from South America in addition to unfamiliar varieties from other parts of the world. From this group of varieties and species they have isolated original sources of resistance to several important diseases including collar rot (*Alternaria solani*), gray leaf spot, (*Stemphylium solani*), septoria leaf spot, (*Septoria lycopersici*), and mosaic. They have also found new sources of resistance to fusarium wilt, leaf mold, and root knot. Through information from other sources, stocks of tomatoes with resistance to anthracnose (*Colletotrichum phomoides*) have also been accumulated. With few exceptions, the original resistant sources have been commercially worthless types. Long breeding programs involving carefully designed cross pollinations, selection for many generations, and repeated disease tests are necessary before the new disease-resistant varieties will approach acceptable size and quality.

The foliage disease called early blight, caused by the fungus *Alternaria solani*, is considered by tomato growers and research men to be one of the most generally harmful diseases of tomatoes, perhaps second only to fusarium wilt. It attacks both stems and foliage of tomato plants. When this fungus infects young tomato stems at the soil line, it produces a black lesion or canker known as collar rot, which either stunts the growth of the plant or causes it to break off entirely. The foliage infections of early blight cause spotting, withering, and dropping of leaves when humid weather favors the spread and growth of the fungus.

Starting in 1938, the workers at the laboratory at Charleston vigorously attacked the problem of breeding early-blight-resistant tomatoes. While no tomatoes were found to be outstandingly resistant to this disease, two very hopeful factors emerged. One is that, in many localities, early blight often has been confused with damage caused by other diseases, and the development of resistance to other foliage diseases such as septoria leaf spot, gray leaf spot, and leaf mold, will definitely reduce losses that formerly might have been entirely attributed to early blight. The second factor is the discovery of a high degree of resistance to the collar rot or stem canker phase of infection by *Alternaria solani* and the knowledge that tomatoes resistant to the stem canker phase, while not highly resistant to leaf infection, are significantly less susceptible to it.

Resistance to collar rot was found in several wild types from South America, in a number of western European forcing varieties, and in a few of the less familiar domestic varieties. The domestic varieties contributed size and the European forcing varieties productivity, in crosses with Rutgers and Marglobe, and the collar rot problem was found to be relatively easy of solution. Several new tomato lines of commercial grade have been produced, among which probably could be found one or more with a range of adaptation equivalent to that of such popular varieties as Rutgers and Marglobe. However, we believe resistance to collar rot in a new variety is no longer sufficient in itself because it is evident that new varieties should also possess Pan America's resistance to the fusarium wilt fungus.

Fortunately, the combination of resistance to collar rot and Pan America's kind of resistance to fusarium wilt also proved to be relatively simple to accomplish. A large number of tomatoes resistant to both diseases have been produced, but none has yet been released as a new variety. After extensive field trials, one or more of these tomatoes will probably be found to be qualified for commercial production.

Other Breeding Projects

A similar breeding program is being followed in the combination of practical immunity to fusarium wilt with resistance to gray leaf spot, to septoria leaf spot, and to leaf mold, respectively.

Gray leaf spot resistance was found primarily in the South American collections of currant tomato, *Lycopersicon pimpinellifolium,* and the slow incorporation of large fruit size has retarded this program. However, several tomatoes resistant to gray leaf spot and to fusarium wilt and of acceptable commercial size have already been produced. Some of these carry a combination of earliness and productivity that is popular in certain commercial varieties.

Resistance to septoria leaf spot is now known to occur in many collections of the wild species *Lycopersicon hirsutum* and *L. peruvianum,* but at the Regional Vegetable Breeding Laboratory, resistance to septoria was originally found in a primitive type segregated from the Australian variety Targinnie Red, which proved to be wholly fertile in crosses with domestic varieties. These crosses are well advanced, but none of the lines is sufficiently fixed as to the factors of productivity, size, and quality.

Leaf mold, caused by *Cladosporium fulvum,* is a serious disease on greenhouse tomatoes. Four physiologic races of this fungus that have been isolated exhibit distinct differences in pathogenicity. All varieties of the common tomato are more or less susceptible, but Red Currant is highly resistant. Resistance to one strain of the leaf mold fungus is already available in the forcing varieties Globelle, Bay State, and Vetomold. Breeders are progressing in their development of other varieties resistant to other races of the leaf mold fungus. The cross Vetomold × Pan America has yielded some promising types at Charleston.

During the winter of 1946 an epidemic of late blight caused by *Phytophthora infestans* on field tomatoes in southern Florida provided an exceptional opportunity for a field test of resistance to this disease. All of the commercial varieties observed were very susceptible, but among 15 advanced breeding lines from the Vegetable Breeding Laboratory under propagation at Homestead three were highly tolerant to late blight. All of the blight-resistant lines possess near-immunity to fusarium wilt; one of them is also resistant to collar rot and to early blight.

The Department breeders working at various locations, and State investigators, have devoted much effort toward using the resistance to various diseases found in *Lycopersicon hirsutum* and *L. peruvianum* species, which are closely related to the common tomato and possess high resistance to a number of tomato diseases, but have no economic value unless their resistance can be combined with other desirable characters by hybridizing them with horticultural varieties. A selected clonal line of *L. hirsutum* possessing high resistance to the ordinary tobacco mosaic virus has been crossed with several commercial varieties at Beltsville. Some of these progeny lines have shown high tolerance when subjected to heavy inoculations with mosaic virus.

Hybrids have also been made between *Lycopersicon peruvianum* and *L. esculentum.* Although they are practically sterile in the first hybrid generation, they have been outcrossed to several popular canning varieties. These outcrosses are now under test by both Federal and State breeders to determine their resistance to tomato leaf spot, to leaf mold, to root knot, and to late blight caused by *Phytophthora infestans.*

Work is in progress in cooperation with the Utah Agricultural Experiment Station to develop tomatoes resistant to curly top and to verticillium wilt, two very serious diseases in certain western regions. Curly top, also known as western yellow blight, is caused by a virus which is disseminated by the sugar-beet leafhopper, a native of the wastelands of the semiarid West. Literally thousands of tomatoes, including all available commercial varieties and wild related species, have been extensively tested by Department workers in regions where curly top is prevalent.

More than 30,000 tomato plants are tested each year at Hurricane, Utah, where the curly top disease regularly occurs in severe form. From the vast population of tomato lines tested, only three wild species, *Lycopersicon glandulosum, L. peruvianum var. dentatum,* and *L. peruvianum var. humifusum* have exhibited any very marked resistance to the disease. These species have been crossed with varieties stemming from *L. esculentum* in many combinations of backcrosses and outcrosses. Some progress has already been made in the development of commercial varieties that are resistant to curly top but much work yet remains to be done before a good resistant variety can be released for commercial use.

Verticillium wilt is known to be a cool climate disease as contrasted with fusarium wilt, which thrives in relatively high temperatures. Therefore, verticillium wilt causes severe damage to tomato crops principally in those Western States where the growing season is generally cool.

Since verticillium wilt is caused by a soil-borne fungus, the best solution to the problem is the development of wilt-resistant varieties. Wilt-resistant wild tomatoes from South America have been successfully crossed with commercial varieties and lines have been selected from the progenies possessing a degree of resistance superior to that of the wild parent. Some of these lines produce fruit of excellent size and color but field trials have indicated that these selections are too late in maturity and the yields are too low. The best of these lines are being outcrossed to free-fruiting earlier varieties in an effort to combine earliness and good fruit production with disease resistance.

At the Cheyenne Horticultural Field Station, breeders are developing tomato varieties with capacity to set a good crop of fruit under adverse climatic conditions that prevail in certain areas in the West and Southwest. They are also cross breeding to incorporate in these varieties resistance to bacterial canker, leaf mold, tobacco mosaic, and fusarium wilt.

The Department is by no means alone in the program of breeding tomatoes for disease resistance. Many State or Territorial experiment stations have active tomato breeding projects with disease resistance an important goal. An outstanding example of success in developing multiple disease resistance and superior yield for unusually difficult growing conditions is the work of the Hawaii Agricultural Experiment

Station. W. A. Frazier and associates have developed individual varieties that are resistant to fusarium, spotted wilt, and gray leaf spot and also are far more productive in the Territory than any varieties that originated on the mainland. Also active in the field of tomato disease resistance are some commercial seed firms and food processors who have shown a universal willingness to cooperate with the Federal and State laboratories.

One of the ultimate goals of tomato breeders is the development of varieties combining resistance to the principal diseases of each region in one variety. The Charleston laboratory is already working on the combination of resistance to fusarium wilt, collar rot, gray leaf spot, leaf mold and septoria leaf spot. However, many generations of cross breeding and testing will be required before a finished variety possessing all these superior attributes will be available to the tomato industry.

THE AUTHORS

William S. Porte is a pathologist in the Bureau of Plant Industry, Soils, and Agricultural Engineering. He has been doing research on disease resistance of tomatoes in the Department for more than 25 years.

C. F. Andrus, a pathologist in the same Bureau, has been with the Department 18 years and at present is handling vegetable disease work and tomato breeding at the Regional Vegetable Breeding Laboratory at Charleston, S. C.

FOR FURTHER READING

Andrus, C. F., Reynard, G. B., and Wade, B. L.: *Relative Resistance of Tomato Varieties, Selections, and Crosses to Defoliation by Alternaria and Stemphylium,* U. S. D. A. Circular 652, 1942.

Andrus, C. F., and Reynard, G. B.: *Resistance to Septoria Leafspot and Its Inheritance in Tomatoes,* Phytopathology, Lancaster, Pa., volume 35, pages 16–24, 1945.

Blood, H. L.: *Curly Top, the Most Serious Menace to Tomato Production in Utah,* Farm and Home Science, Utah Agricultural Experiment Station, volume 3, number 1, pages 8–9, 11, 1942.

Blood, H. L.: *Tomato Wilt Studies in Utah,* Seventh Annual School for Canning Crop Growers and Canners Field Manual, Proceedings 1946.

Doolittle, S. P., Porte W. S., and Beecher, F. S.: *High Resistance to Common Tobacco Mosaic in Certain Lines of Lycopersicon Hirsutum,* Phytopathology Abstracts, 1946.

Porte, W. S., and Walker, H. B.: *The Pan America Tomato, a New Red Variety Highly Resistant to Fusarium Wilt,* U. S. D. A. Circular 611, 1941.

Porte, W. S., and Wellman, Frederick L.: *Development of Interspecific Tomato Hybrids of Horticultural Value and Highly Resistant to Fusarium Wilt,* U. S. D. A. Circular 584, 1941.

Wellman, F. L.: *Differences in Growth Characters and Pathogenicity of Fusarium Wilt Isolations Tested on Three Tomato Varieties,* U. S. D. A. Technical Bulletin 705, 1940.

The Story of Hybrid Onions

by H. A. JONES and A. E. CLARKE

SCIENTISTS have succeeded in crossing suitable inbred lines of onions and obtained excellent results. One hybrid was more than three times heavier than either parent. Other hybrids were outstanding in shape, size, uniformity, and time of maturity. Even more significant: The results showed great possibilities for using hybrid seed for commercial crop production.

Between these encouraging results and the first development of the methods that make possible the production of hybrid seed of all types and in quantity lay a good deal of painstaking, tedious work—work that some of us believed could never succeed.

In the ordinary onion, male and female parts are in the same flower (the perfect flower), and thus each plant is capable of pollinating itself. To get hybrid seed it is therefore necessary to remove the pollen-containing anthers of the female parent, a procedure known as emasculation. Emasculation is not so easily performed with the onion as with corn, whose male and female parts are entirely separate. In corn, emasculation consists merely in removing the tassel. In the onion, the male and female parts are close together, and emasculation is tedious and difficult, because the pollen-bearing anthers must be carefully snipped out with tweezers—a process entirely too expensive for commercial production.

This obstacle, however, has been surmounted. Onion plants are now available whose flowers are not perfect, as they contain no fertile pollen. They are solely female as far as breeding is concerned, and emasculation is unnecessary. In 1925 a plant of this nature was found in the breeding plots at Davis, Calif., in the variety Italian Red. It was given the pedigree number 13–53. It cannot pollinate itself and thus cannot be carried along by seed, but, fortunately, it usually produces

320

large quantities of head sets or bulbils, and these are used to preserve and increase this line.

Two somewhat different methods are now in use to produce hybrid onion seed, but in each case the hybrid seed is produced on naturally female plants that have been crossed with desirable males. These methods are not difficult to understand, but they are different from those used for any other crop. In the first the female line Italian Red 13–53, which is propagated by top sets, is used. Hybrid seed is produced on the female plants when crossed with pollen-bearing plants. In this method only two lines need to be carried along, the female line and a selected male parent.

The second way is slightly more complicated, but has greater potentialities. Female plants have been produced in other varieties of onions and are perpetuated through seed and not vegetatively by bulbils, as is 13–53. Consequently, we can make innumerable combinations in our quest for the best hybrids. Three lines must be carried along instead of two. Just why this is necessary will be shown. We shall tell the advantages and disadvantages of the two methods, and because of the singular part played by the Italian Red 13–53 selection, we believe that a record of its discovery and history is important.

In the early fall of 1924, 63 Italian Red bulbs were selected from a commercial lot and planted in the vegetable-breeding plots of the University of California at Davis. The plants were grown through the winter, and the following spring the flower heads were enclosed in manila paper bags to aid self-pollination and prevent crossing. The bags were tapped several times each day to distribute the pollen inside the bag and to facilitate pollination. On August 8, 1925, the seed heads were harvested. The weather was satisfactory for seed setting, and most of the plants gave a good supply. An especially good plant, Italian Red 13–52, produced 5,866 seeds. On 15 plants, however, no seed was produced. Some of this sterility may have been due to seed-stem rot. One of the seedless plants, the one with the pedigree number 13–53, differed from the other sterile ones in that the seed heads were packed with small sets or bulbils. Its 5 seed stems had 136 sets; the ability to produce head sets saved it from extinction. Its designation, 13–53, should not be forgotten, for it is probably destined to be the most important onion bulb selection ever made.

From 1925 on, 13–53 was propagated vegetatively by use of small head sets. As the bulbils can be held in storage for only a few weeks, they are usually planted in the nursery soon after harvest. They are then transplanted to the field in late fall or early winter and over-wintered as growing plants. When they are planted on productive soil, the foliage grows luxuriantly, and the large, spindle-shaped bulbs usually mature in late June or July. Because of their poor keeping quality,

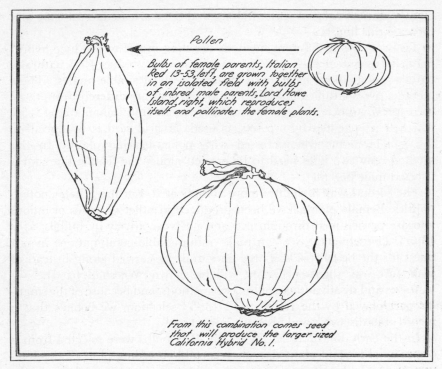

How two onions are crossed to get the California Hybrid Red No. 1. It combines the early maturity of Lord Howe Island and delayed bolting habit of 13–53.

these large bulbs are again planted back into the field in September and overwintered in a mild climate as growing plants.

Since its discovery, 13–53 has been grown under a wide range of climatic conditions. During this time, seed has never been produced when the flower heads were properly protected from pollen by bagging or by isolation. When the flowers are well pollinated, however, they give a heavy set of seed. Even when loaded with seed, the flower heads continue to produce bulbils almost as though no seed had been produced.

In 1934, crosses were made between the female line 13–53 and red varieties like Lord Howe Island, Red 21, Italian Red, Southport Red Globe, and Red Wethersfield. In 1935 and later comparative yield tests were made in California between these hybrids and standard varieties. Some of the crosses looked promising from the very beginning, especially those made with Lord Howe Island and Red 21.

In September 1944, the hybrid of 13–53 × Lord Howe Island was introduced cooperatively by the California Agricultural Experiment Station and the Department as California Hybrid Red No. 1. It combines the early maturity of Lord Howe Island and the delayed bolting habit of Italian Red. It is adapted to the Southwest, where the seed is planted in early fall and the plants grow throughout the fall, winter, and early spring. Under these conditions, plants grow to a large size, which seems to be essential for the production of large bulbs and high yields. In California, a yield of 73,100 pounds to the acre has been reported, but it is not adapted to the North when seeded directly in the field.

The limitations of 13–53 as a source of hybrid seed are recognized, but breeders work with what they have and not with what they would like to have. We needed female plants in white and yellow varieties, in the early and late varieties, and in the storage types so that hybrids of all commercial types would be available. The method of developing female lines in all types of onions was finally worked out.

We shall not attempt to tell here how the character that permits a potentially perfect flower to perform only female functions is inherited, but we should like to show how this character has been introduced into many types of onions in order to expand greatly its usefulness. This leads us to the second method of producing hybrid onions, whereby the female character is perpetuated through the seed.

When a plant of almost any of the commercial varieties is crossed with the female plant 13–53, the offspring will be one of three kinds: All plants will have perfect flowers, or some plants will have perfect flowers and some female flowers, or all of the plants will have female flowers. In producing hybrid onions, we are especially interested in the crosses that produce all female offspring. Fortunately, in almost all of the important varieties we have been able to get a few crosses that produce only female plants.

These female offspring, when backcrossed to the same male parent, continue to produce all females. With each backcrossing the female plants look more and more like the male parent, and after four or five generations there is no difference in appearance. For the production of hybrids, it is necessary to perpetuate these female lines, and this is done by continually backcrossing to the proper male parent. A single female or a field of female plants under isolated conditions will fail to produce a single seed. They cannot be perpetuated alone. Under certain conditions, however, observed so far only in the greenhouse, plants of these female backcross lines may provide a little good pollen and a few seeds may be obtained. But if rows of the proper male plants are interplanted with the females, insects, such as flies and bees, carry pollen to the female plants, and all the seeds produced on them will be female. As the male parents have perfect flowers, they will pollinate one another and set seed in abundance. So the propagation of the male parent is very easy. Thus, male parent and the female line are carried along in the same plot.

We have now introduced female plants into nearly all the commercial varieties. These include Yellow Globe Danvers, Brigham Yellow Globe, Early Yellow Globe, Sweet Spanish, Southport White Globe, Crystal

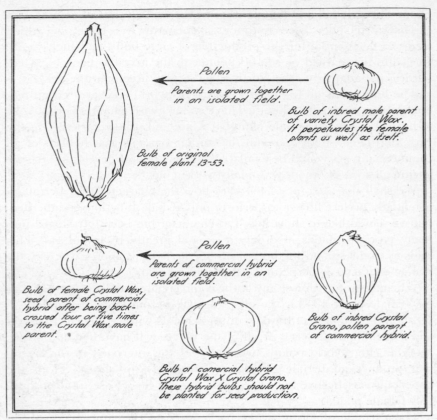

By planting a male onion parent in the same field with a female, the male perpetuates itself as well as the female, as shown in the upper section of this chart.

Wax, Yellow Bermuda, Creole, and Stockton G36. Female lines and the necessary male parents have been distributed to a number of seed companies and to experiment stations in most of the important onion-producing States. After female lines have been established, the next step is to find desirable pollen parents to cross with the female lines for the production of commercially acceptable hybrids. We can determine the combinations that produce the best hybrids only by actual field tests.

For this method of producing hybrid seed it is necessary to carry along three separate lots of onions for each hybrid. A female line and a male parent are needed to give continuity to the females, and a second male parent is needed to cross with the females in order to produce types of onions that are desired commercially. In other words, seed from the male parent reproduces the male parent. Seed from the female line reproduces the female line and provides plants for crossing with a third lot of onions to produce seed for the commercial hybrid onion crop.

We have made numerous crosses in the greenhouses at Beltsville. The cooperating State agricultural experiment stations have made others. Some of them show great promise. One hybrid, a cross between Crystal Wax and Crystal Grano, was developed cooperatively by the California Agricultural Experiment Station and the Department. Hybrids used to produce the commercial crop will not reproduce hybrid seed so they should not be planted for seed production.

Breeding work is under way to incorporate into the hybrids resistance to two major diseases, downy mildew and pink root, and to one insect pest, thrips. Though sporadic in appearance, the downy mildew is probably our most destructive disease of onions. In the North, damage is done chiefly to the bulb crop. On the west coast, it is particularly serious on the crop grown for seed; much of the seed acreage, therefore, has been shifted to other areas where the disease is less prevalent. No entirely satisfactory control method by the use of sprays or dusts has been developed. Apparently the only satisfactory means of control will be by the use of resistant varieties.

In breeding for resistance to downy mildew, Italian Red 13–53 has again come to our aid. Its high resistance to this disease was first observed in 1934 in the breeding plots at Davis. Under California conditions, infection is usually confined to the tips of the leaves, and the spread toward the base is slow. The seed stalks of 13–53, however, are immune. Lesions have never been found even during the most severe epidemics. Now you can begin to see why we consider that 13–53 may be the most important onion selection ever made. Besides its contribution to hybrid onions, it has also given us the best source of resistance to downy mildew. To produce hybrids resistant to downy mildew, it will be necessary to incorporate resistance into the female lines, as well as into the pollen parents.

Pink root is also a major disease in most areas, but it is especially destructive in the South. As the organism lives and multiplies in the soil, chemical control is not practical. Again, we think the use of resistant varieties is the only permanent solution. Resistant lines of Yellow Bermuda are being developed by the Department in cooperation with the experiment stations of Wisconsin and Texas. At the Wisconsin station, the young seedlings are given a severe test. Those surviving are grown to maturity and the bulbs are sent to Beltsville. The resistant plants are used for crossing with female plants, and the various progenies are tested in the South for yield and other desirable characters.

Breeding is also being done to develop lines that resist smut, purple blotch, and yellow dwarf.

The onion thrips—not a disease, but an insect—is without question the most destructive pest on the onion crop the world over. They puncture the surface cells of the leaves and suck out the contents, causing local injury. In severe cases the plants are killed prematurely, and the yield is greatly reduced. Satisfactory chemical control has only recently been developed. DDT is the first insecticide that has given commercial control. Resistant varieties would require less spraying or dusting and thus reduce cost of growing.

Breeding for resistance to thrips has been under way for some time. Characters have been determined that either reduce the number of thrips per plant or cause the plant to show less injury, but the character that can be used most advantageously in breeding for resistance is glossy foliage. Most onion plants secret a waxy layer, or "bloom," on the surface of the leaf, a deposit that gives a grayish cast to the leaf. It is easily rubbed off. When this waxy covering is absent, the foliage has a glossy appearance. In all field tests, glossy plants show considerable resistance to thrips. This glossy character, derived from a single plant selection from a field of Australian Brown onions and from the variety White Persian, which was obtained in Persia by W. E. Whitehouse of the Department, is being bred into our commonly grown varieties and into the lines that are being developed for the production of hybrid seed. Here, too, it is necessary to have two resistant glossy male parents for the production of resistant hybrids: One to perpetuate the female line; the other to combine with the female line for the production of hybrid seed.

This hybrid work makes possible the combining of those lines that are resistant to the attack of thrips and various diseases, and it provides a method for attaining great uniformity of shape, color, time-of-maturity, and edible quality in the onion and at the same time gives a means of obtaining the greatest amount of vigor. The production of hybrid seed opens up an almost unlimited field for the production of improved onion varieties. We now have unusual opportunties for accomplishment. Excellent tools are available, but improvements will be made only in proportion to the efforts put forth.

THE AUTHORS

H. A. Jones, olericulturist, is in charge of potato and onion investigations at the Bureau of Plant Industry, Soils, and Agricultural Engineering. He was head of the Division of Truck Crops at the University of California for 14 years, previous to 1936, when he joined the Department. In 1944 Dr. Jones was awarded the William Herbert medal by the American Plant Life Society in recognition of his important contribution to onion breeding. He is a graduate of the University of Nebraska and the University of Chicago.

A. E. Clarke is a cytologist in the Bureau of Plant Industry, Soils, and Agricultural Engineering and has carried on cytogenetic and breeding investigations with potatoes and onions since 1936. After graduating from the University of Alberta and the University of Wisconsin, Dr. Clarke was awarded a National Research Fellowship in the Biological Sciences and continued his studies at the University of California and the California Institute of Technology. In 1943, for their study of male sterility in onions, Jones and Clarke received the Vaughan Research award offered by the American Society for Horticultural Science.

Breeding Healthy Potatoes

by F. J. STEVENSON and ROBERT V. AKELEY

OUR standard kinds of potatoes are hard to beat in yield and quality. Our problem is how to overcome diseases and insects.

The diseases are commonly caused by fungi, viruses, and bacteria. Fungous diseases include late blight, early blight, and common scab. The worst of the virus diseases are mild mosaic, latent mosaic, rugose mosaic, leaf roll, net necrosis, yellow dwarf, and spindle tuber. Of the bacterial diseases, the most troublesome are ring rot, brown rot, and black leg.

Any one of them could eliminate the potato as a leading food crop of North America. We have control measures that allow us to grow even the most susceptible varieties, but the cost of the preventives and cures amounts to many millions of dollars a year, and they have by no means eliminated all losses. If a small fraction of the expense and effort now consumed in fighting disease had been put into the production of disease-resistant varieties, potato growing would be much more profitable.

State experiment stations and the Department organized the national potato-breeding program in 1929 and have distributed to growers 25 new varieties of potatoes. Some of them resist late blight, or virus diseases, or common scab. Much has been done, but there is much more to do.

Potato plants are propagated asexually and sexually. In commercial practice, the new crop is grown from tubers or pieces of tubers. That is a vegetative or asexual method of reproduction. A variety can be grown vegetatively for years without visible change, and any attempt to make a selection within it is usually futile. Occasionally bud mutations occur, and a few new potato varieties have been obtained by selecting bud sports. When such changes do occur they are for the most part of minor importance, because most of them have been color changes, for example, from red tubers to "splashed" or to white. Changes from white to red or from white to russet have also been known to occur. Even though only a few varieties have come as the result of bud mutations, this is still a source of variation that the potato breeder cannot ignore. But because it is quite impractical to make much improvement by selecting tubers of a variety with the hope of getting something new, the plant breeder must use true seed and seedlings to get more variations and combinations of characters.

True seed is the result of the fusion of male and female gametes, or germ cells; that is the first step in sexual reproduction. The seed is found in the fruits or seed balls that grow on the potato vines and look very much like small tomatoes. A seed ball may contain 200 or more seeds which will produce plants that are quite different from each other. Most seedlings are undesirable from the commercial standpoint, but occasionally a new variety is produced that excels the old in one or more important characters. Many people who live in the South or where the climate is hot and dry have never seen a seed ball growing on a potato plant, and not a few are quite surprised when they first discover one. In cool, long-day climates, on the other hand, some sorts produce many seed balls.

The first potato-breeding work in this country started nearly 100 years .ago, when late blight was destroying potato crops in many European countries and causing large losses in this country. Blight was the cause of the famine in Ireland in 1845, which, because of the failure of the potato crop, brought sickness and distress to many people and caused the death of at least a million persons. The cause of the disease was not known then, but many persons thought it was the result of a loss of vigor in the plants, brought about by growing the crop year after year from tubers. They also believed that the vigor could be restored and the disease eliminated by growing plants from true seed.

Acting upon this belief, a number of people in Europe and the United States began growing seedlings. As a result, many new varieties were produced. A few of them are among the best varieties we have today.

The blight problem remained unsolved, however, because the trouble was not a result of the loss of vigor but was due to a parasitic fungus that attacks the leaves and stems of the potato plants and often kills them before they have a chance to mature. Susceptible seedlings are just as severely attacked as the commonly grown susceptible varieties.

In 1910, when potato breeding was actively undertaken by the Department, resistance to late blight was still considered the most important character for which to work, but the project was just under way when the virus diseases took first place in the breeding work, and blight resistance was once more thrown into the background. It was not until 1932 that Department workers could again attend to the problem.

Varieties of potatoes showing different degrees of resistance to blight were introduced from foreign countries and used as parents of new seedlings. A few seedlings with an intermediate type of resistance were produced by crossing two susceptible American varieties. A much larger proportion of intermediates was obtained when moderately resistant varieties, like Ekishirazu from Japan or President from Holland, were used as parents. Selections from the so-called *W* races, which were introduced from Germany, showed resistance to late blight, but were low in yield and market quality.

When some of them were crossed with American kinds and seedlings, a number of selections from the resulting family lines retained the blight resistance of their foreign parents and were much more desirable from the commercial standpoint. Several of the selections were in turn selfed, backcrossed, and outcrossed to various commercial varieties and promising seedlings. From this second series of progenies, selections have been made that are highly resistant to late blight. They have been subjected to blight epidemics by spraying them with blight spores in the field under conditions favorable for the spread of the disease, and many of them have escaped infection over a period of years. In the same tests, the Green Mountain, which was planted at frequent intervals throughout the field, was frequently killed by blight 30 to 40 days before it would mature normally.

In preliminary trials some of the blight-resistant selections have produced yields and dry-matter content of tubers equal to the best commercial varieties that are grown in Maine. Several of the most promising of these are being increased for distribution, and a limited amount of seed of two, B69–16 and B70–5, should be available soon.

Some of the seedlings that are resistant to late blight in the vines also show tuber resistance to rot caused by the late blight fungus. In the same family line some seedlings will be resistant, others susceptible. In a test for reaction to blight the tubers are covered with spores of the fungus and placed in a moist chamber and kept cool—conditions that favor rot.

While the Department, in cooperation with the Maine Agricultural Experiment Station, was producing blight-resistant varieties by using commercial types and foreign introductions closely related to our cultivated forms, Donald Reddick, of Cornell University, was attacking the problem by the use of species hybrids. It has been known for many years that some strains of *Solanum demissum* are immune to blight. This species is distantly related to our cultivated potatoes, however, and is deficient in almost all characters of economic importance. For one thing, it is almost nontuber-bearing in the ordinary potato-growing season in Maine. When crosses are made between it and cultivated varieties, some of the resulting progeny are immune to blight, but are still quite poor in other characters. Each cross to cultivated varieties shows some improvement, and, after four generations, Dr. Reddick has succeeded in combining the immunity to late blight of the species *S. demissum* with the desirable horticultural and culinary characteristics of the commercial varieties commonly grown in the Northeastern States.

Another fungous disease, common scab, causes losses in every section where potatoes are grown, and in some places its attacks have become so severe that potatoes can no longer be produced profitably. The organism causing this disease lives over in the soil and is carried also on the tubers. Soil treatments have been tried, but they are costly and not reliable. Treatments that will kill the organism on the seed potatoes have been recommended, but these are often of questionable value because if clean seed is planted in scabby ground the resulting crop of tubers will be scabby. In its effects on yields, scab is not so noticeable as late blight, but it affects the market quality and, hence, the value of the tubers.

In our program a comparatively large number of varieties and seedlings have been tested, and different degrees of resistance to scab have been found. Resistant varieties, such as Hindenburg, Jubel, and Ostragis, have been imported from Europe, but none of these is adapted to conditions in this country. They produce low yields of tubers and have poor market quality. Crosses have been made between these resistant types and American varieties and seedlings, and some of the resulting family lines have shown a high degree of resistance to scab, combined with other characters of commercial importance. None of them has reached the high standard of excellence for which we are striving, but they can be grown successfully in scabby soil where at present it is unprofitable to grow other commercial varieties. Four of these, Menominee, Ontario, Cayuga, and Seneca, have been distributed to growers for use in scabby lands.

As a group, the virus diseases are perhaps the most widespread and the most baffling. They occur in every potato-growing region of the United States, and it is probable that not a single field of the old varieties could be found entirely free from one or more of them. They are not new. Their effects have been observed by growers for many years, but for a long time it was thought that they were due to "running out" or "degeneracy" brought about by growing potatoes year after year from the same tuber stock—the same belief that was held concerning late blight. Not long ago it was discovered that degeneracy is due to virus infection and that insects spread the most common of the virus diseases.

Ways were soon devised to hold these diseases in check. Diseased plants are rogued out of the seed plots, and early harvesting is sometimes practiced in an effort to get away from late infections, because the insect vectors, especially aphids, are usually most plentiful during the latter part of the growing season. Seed-certification programs have been organized in the principal potato-growing States in an effort to provide growers with seed that will produce satisfactory yields.

In the earlier studies, it was observed that some varieties did not degenerate so quickly as others or, as we now say, some varieties are more resistant to viruses than others. Knowing that such differences must be heritable, we have undertaken a rather extensive program to produce new varieties that resist the commoner virus diseases, mild mosaic, latent mosaic, rugose mosaic, leaf roll, and net necrosis. We have produced large numbers of seedling varieties that are immune to mild mosaic under field conditions, latent mosaic, and rugose mosaic.

It is doubtful whether any of the kinds we now have are immune to leaf roll, but some have been produced that under severe tests have not shown leaf roll for 4 or 5 years, although in some of the same tests more than 90 percent of the plants of the control varieties, Green Mountain and Chippewa, became infected with the virus in a single season. Current-season infection with the leaf roll virus frequently causes net necrosis in the tubers of such varieties as Green Mountain, and losses to growers are large. Many varieties have been produced, and some of them, like Katahdin and Chippewa, which are apparently immune to net necrosis, have been released to growers and have been increased rapidly.

A bacterial disease, ring rot, has recently come into prominence as a widespread menace to potato production. Sanitary measures and the insistence of State authorities that no seed be certified that has even a trace of ring rot in it have done much to keep this disease under control. However, outbreaks are frequent despite precautions.

Cooperating in the program of breeding for resistance to ring rot are the Maine, Michigan, and Wyoming Agricultural Experiment Stations. We have tested large numbers of varieties and seedlings and have found resistance in only a few lines. It is interesting to note, however, that resistance was obtained from widely separated sources. It was found in the varieties Friso and President from the Netherlands and in a number of seedling varieties produced in the United States.

The seedling U. S. D. A. 47102, tentatively called Teton, has shown a high degree of resistance in the tests in Maine and Wyoming. It has also produced high yields and has satisfactory market and cooking quality, compared with standard varieties grown under the same conditions. It is not immune to ring rot, but has shown only a small amount of the disease in tests over a period of years; control varieties, like Triumph and Green Mountain, usually show 80 to 100 percent infection in a year.

Since problems and objectives in the production of disease-resistant varieties of potatoes are not confined to a single State but involve large regions of the country, potato breeding was organized in 1929 as a national project. The work is conducted cooperatively by 35 State experiment stations and the Department. The practice under the program is to send seedlings produced by the Department or by any of the cooperating State experiment stations to other States for trial. After sufficient tests, if any seedling variety shows superiority to the standard varieties in at least one important character, such as yield, market quality, or resistance to a disease that is difficult to control, it is named and released to growers. Since 1932 more than 25 varieties have been released. Several of these have increased rapidly in yearly production; others increased more slowly.

In some of the new varieties the important objective for which they were bred has been reached. Sebago, Empire, Placid, Virgil, Chenango, and Ashworth are resistant to late blight; Menominee, Ontario, Cayuga, and Seneca are resistant to common scab; Katahdin, Chippewa, Warba, Houma, Earlaine, Sebago, Red Warba, Mohawk and Menominee are resistant to one or more virus diseases; and Teton is resistant to ring rot.

How well the new varieties have been received by the growers is shown by the fact that in 1945 about 26 percent of all the certified seed in the United States consisted of varieties that have been released since 1932. None of these will meet the needs of the growers in all the cooperating States, and it is doubtful if such an ideal variety will soon be produced. However, a sectional demand existed for each one, and because of their disease resistance and other characters of economic importance they have been increased under severe competition and critical evaluation.

A beginning has been made, and the new varieties that have already been released have been a factor in increasing the yield of potatoes in the United States from a little more than 100 bushels an acre 25 years ago to about 150 bushels an acre in 1945. The results indicate much greater possibilities in breeding. We have available a large number of important characters that have not yet been combined in one variety, and each new combination should give us a new variety more valuable to some of the growers than any we now have. These characters include wide adaptation; early, medium, and late maturity; smooth, desirable shapes; shallow eyes; high yielding ability; and high dry-matter content. Besides, we have seedlings that resist one or more of the following diseases and insects: Mild mosaic, latent mosaic, rugose mosaic, leaf roll, net necrosis, yellow dwarf, late blight of the vines, tuber rot initiated by the late blight fungus, common scab, potato wart, brown rot, ring rot, hopperburn, flea beetle injury, and aphid injury.

THE AUTHORS

F. J. Stevenson is a geneticist in the Bureau of Plant Industry, Soils, and Agricultural Engineering, where he conducts research in potato breeding with special emphasis on the inheritance of disease resistance in potatoes. Before joining the Department in 1930, Dr. Stevenson was successively an instructor in plant genetics at State College of Washington, and assistant professor at the University of Minnesota, College of Agriculture. He is a graduate of the State College of Washington.

Robert V. Akeley is a plant breeder in the Bureau of Plant Industry, Soils, and Agricultural Engineering. His work deals with potato breeding and genetics with special reference to color, dry-matter content, yield, and disease resistance.

Control of Bean Diseases

by W. J. ZAUMEYER

GROWERS who plant two new varieties of pinto beans and use sulfur dust as a control measure have less need to fear the ravages of bean rust caused by the fungus *Uromyces phaseoli typica* Arth.

The rust, like the cereal rusts, can ruin a crop in a few weeks if the weather is right. It did tremendous damage in 1927 and 1928 in northeastern Colorado. It appeared again in 1938; in 1942, in epidemic proportions, it caused a loss of a million dollars in a county where 50,000 acres of pinto beans are grown and heavy losses also in other parts of Colorado. Severe and costly outbreaks occured in 1944 and 1945 in fields of Great Northern beans in Wyoming and Montana.

The losses were particularly bad because they came when there was heavy demand for dry beans by the armed services and farmers were expanding their acreages—in Colorado, from 421,000 acres to 595,000 acres in 1943; in Wyoming and Montana, from 49,000 and 21,000 acres, respectively, to 124,000 and 66,000 acres. Plant diseases are usually more severe where a concentration of acreage of any crop occurs, especially if environmental conditions favor the development and spread of the causal organisms. Because of the increase in acreage, farmers did not follow crop rotation as carefully as they did in previous years, and the rust was more destructive in fields that had grown beans the previous year than where another crop had been grown.

The two rust-resistant varieties became available to growers in 1946. They were developed by the Department of Agriculture in 8 years of breeding and selection at Beltsville and the Department's Field Station at Greeley, Colo. They are called Pinto No. 5 and Pinto No. 14.

As with the cereal rusts, races or strains of the bean rust occur. Before 1937 little was known about them, but since then scientists in the De-

333

partment have identified 24 races. Because there are so many races and they show different degrees of infecting ability, the problem of breeding resistant plants is complicated. Before making crosses for the ultimate production of a rust-resistant pinto bean, a variety that resisted as many of these races as possible had to be found. After several years of testing, a white-seeded Kentucky Wonder type that could withstand most of the races of rust was found. In 1937 it was crossed with several pinto varieties. Pinto No. 5 and No. 14 were both derived from a cross between Idaho Pinto, an early, rust-susceptible type, and the resistant white-seeded Kentucky Wonder.

The early generations were tested in greenhouses at Beltsville by inoculation with practically all the rust races. Only the resistant plants were saved. These were grown in Colorado, where selections were made for an ideal pinto type. This process of elimination was continued until 1943, when we conducted a large field test and grew 110 different hybrid lines under commercial conditions. Rust was widespread, and all the commercial varieties of pinto in the test proved to be completely susceptible, but most of the hybrid lines were resistant. Sixteen lines were chosen for commercial tests at six locations in 1944. Rust was again widespread, but the two new sorts were immune.

Besides resisting rust, the two varieties are tolerant to common bean mosaic, a virus disease that causes considerable loss in the present commercial pinto beans. No. 5 and No. 14 are also highly tolerant to a bacterial blight of beans known as halo blight (*Pseudomonas phaseolicola* Dow.), which is rather widespread in many western areas.

They resemble commercial pintos in most characteristics. They are less viny and about 2 weeks earlier in maturity than the old Colorado strain, but are slightly more viny and a little later in maturity than the Idaho and Wyoming strains. Their seed-coat pattern is practically identical with that of the commercial varieties, except that it is somewhat brighter and has a clearer white background and darker brown markings. The new pintos require approximately 96 days to reach maturity, a few days later than the Idaho and Wyoming Pintos, but about 10 days to 2 weeks earlier than the Colorado strain. Thus in many western areas they can be threshed before other row crops, like sugar beets, are harvested.

Like the Idaho and Wyoming commercial strains, Pinto No. 5 and No. 14 are primarily adapted to irrigation. Under dry-land conditions they may not yield quite so well as the Colorado strain, which is primarily a dry-land type, but No. 5 and No. 14 are fairly well adapted to those conditions, and dry-land farmers may want to grow them in preference to the Colorado strain because they mature earlier.

When we started the breeding work we realized that we would need several years to produce a rust-resistant pinto. Besides, rust was becoming a serious menace to the Great Northern beans in Wyoming and Montana, and no variety or strain resisted the disease. So it seemed desirable to devise chemical spraying or dusting methods of control. We tried many different chemicals, both sprays and dusts, with success; but in cost, ease of obtaining materials, and efficiency, sulfur dust appeared to give the best results under field conditions in Colorado.

Bean rust overwinters as resistant black spores which germinate in the spring about the time the beans are planted. Each spore produces four smaller spores, which are spread by the wind and may infect the young bean plants. If a smaller spore lights on a bean plant, and conditions are right, it germinates and grows into the leaf. In about 10 days, small white flecks appear on the under side of the leaf; soon they break through the leaf surface, and the rust spots or pustules appear. Each pustule contains hundreds of a third kind of spore, the brown summer spores, the ones that farmers first notice. They also are blown about by the wind and spread infection to other beans. Each single spore may produce another rust spot with hundreds of spores. If the humidity is high enough, from either rain or dew or irrigation, the rust fungus produces a crop of spores in 10 days from first infection. Unless something is done to control the disease, a severe epidemic may occur.

Tests under field conditions in Colorado have proved that when sulfur is applied to beans fairly early in the season, before rust spots become visible, the control is excellent. The sulfur destroys the comparatively few rust pustules that are present at that time. The secondary spread from these spots is stopped and the formation of other infection centers is prevented. If dusting is done after the rust is rather advanced and widespread throughout the field, more applications of sulfur dust are needed and the control is not so complete. If rust is widespread in an area, two or three dustings are usually necessary, even though the first one was applied early in the season, because spores from undusted fields may later be blown to fields that were dusted. Since sulfur is effective for only about 10 days, another application is necessary if viable rust spores are present.

The ideal time to dust is when the atmosphere is quiet and the plantings are not wet with rain or dew. The sulfur should be applied at the rate of 20 to 25 pounds to the acre. If two dustings are made, 15 pounds can be applied the first time, when the plants are small, and approximately 20 pounds at the second dusting. Naturally, care should be exercised in getting as good a coverage as possible.

In parts of Colorado the Mexican bean beetle (*Epilachna varivestis* Muls.) is frequently a serious pest. Entomologists have found that basic copper arsenate controls this insect in Colorado and does not injure beans. A mixture of 25-percent basic copper arsenate and 75-percent sulfur dusted on beans at the rate of 20 to 25 pounds to the acre is recommended to control both rust and the Mexican bean beetle at the same time.

The cost of the materials is relatively low. The basic copper arsenate and sulfur mixture costs about $2 an acre for materials for a single dusting. The sulfur alone costs about 75 cents per acre, and the cost of application is about $1 an acre for each dusting. We consider this to be reasonably cheap insurance for a crop, even in years when rust is not a menace.

In northeastern Colorado most growers of pinto beans have been dusting their fields with sulfur alone or the basic copper arsenate and sulfur mixture. In 1944, even though rust was serious, many farmers controlled it in excellent fashion. Some did not apply control measures until the disease was widespread; even then it was fairly well controlled, but two and sometimes three applications of sulfur were necessary. Some undusted fields were so severely damaged that they yielded only 6 to 10 bushels an acre, while most of the sulfur-dusted fields yielded 30 to 35 bushels an acre. By using sulfur the farmers reduced the production of overwintering spores, thus lessening the chances of a heavy rust infestation the following year. In 1945, although conditions were ideal for rust, only a single dusting in most cases was necessary for almost perfect control. The percentage of overwintering spores was so reduced that one thorough sulfur dusting early in the season killed the few rust infection centers and no secondary spread occurred. With cooperation from growers, the disease was nearly eliminated in 2 years.

In Wyoming and Montana, control measures for rust were not applied in 1944, and the disease was serious. In 1945 only a small proportion of farmers dusted with sulfur. Where this was done, the yield increases were outstanding.

In Wyoming, fields dusted twice yielded on an average of 1,600 to 1,800 pounds of seed to the acre; undusted fields averaged 800 to 1,000 pounds.

In Montana, dusting with sulfur was extremely successful. The fields dusted twice produced almost 1,000 pounds more seed to the acre than the undusted fields, and 610 pounds more than those dusted once. The best producing field, which was dusted twice, yielded 2,369 pounds an acre; the poorest undusted field gave only 380 pounds.

Several new disease-resistant snap beans have been developed by workers in the Department and State experiment stations.

Pioneer, released to growers in 1943, resists curly top and common bean mosaic. Its pods are dark green, short, round, straight, and stringless in the early stages. It is recommended only as a home-garden variety in sections where curly top usually causes severe injury to standard varieties.

Florida Belle is a green-podded snap bean that is adapted to the South, especially to Florida. It was introduced in 1943. It resists rust, powdery mildew, and common bean mosaic, and is tolerant to heat and drought. The plants are of the bush type, large and sturdy, and produce long, almost flat, light-green pods. It is used principally as a market or shipping variety.

Logan is another new green-podded snap bean, somewhat like Tendergreen. It withstands powdery mildew and common bean mosaic. It is hardy and can set pods under adverse conditions, such as hot weather at blooming time. Its pods are round, long, straight, and stringless. It is well adapted to most bean-growing sections.

Several disease-resistant bush wax beans also have been released to growers since 1943. Florida White Wax is resistant to mildew, common bean mosaic, and some forms of rust. Cooper Wax, a market-garden type, resists common bean mosaic and tolerates powdery mildew. Ashley Wax, a canning type, is somewhat similar to the Refugee varieties, but has a shorter bush. It is resistant to common bean mosaic and tolerates powdery mildew.

Work on the production of varieties resistant to common and halo bacterial blights of beans is under way. Before long we can expect varieties resistant to these diseases.

THE AUTHOR

W. J. Zaumeyer, a pathologist, joined the Department in 1928 and since that time his work has dealt particularly with bacterial blights, rust, and virus diseases of beans, and root rot and leaf-spotting diseases of peas. At present his main job is to develop bean varieties that are resistant to disease and to find other ways to control certain diseases of this crop. Dr. Zaumeyer is a graduate of the University of Wisconsin.

FOR FURTHER READING

Dana, B. F.: *The Pioneer Bean Resists Curly Top,* Seed World, volume 55, pages 46–47, 1944.

Harter, L. L., and Zaumeyer, W. J.: *Differentiation of Physiological Races of Uromyces phaseoli typica on Bean,* Journal of Agricultural Research, volume 62, pages 717–732, 1941.

Harter, L. L., and Zaumeyer, W. J.: *A Monographic Study of Bean Diseases and Methods for Their Control,* U. S. D. A. Technical Bulletin 186, 1944.

Townsend, G. R., and Wade, B. L.: *Close-Up of Something New in Snap Beans,* Southern Seedsman, volume 6, pages 9, 40, 1943.

Wade, B. L.: *New Wax Beans Have What it Takes,* Southern Seedsman, volume 5, pages 9, 18, and 26, 1942.

Wade, B. L.: *Logan, A New Hardy Snap Bean,* Seed World, volume 53, pages 12, 13, 40, and 41, 1943.

ALSO, IN THIS BOOK

Genetics and Farming, by E. R. Sears, page 245.

703830°—47——23

Soybeans for the South

by PAUL R. HENSON

SEVERAL new varieties of soybeans have been developed that strengthen the position of soybeans as an oil crop for industrial use in the South. The new kinds are of wide adaptation, and the southern farmer now has a much better opportunity to select a high-yielding variety suited in his own cropping practices.

And, looking to the future, breeding programs are going forward all over the South. Large numbers of new strains and hybrid lines are being tested, or are under observation at many of the southern experiment stations. Crosses have been made and promising early strains having a high oil content are being selected from crosses between high-yielding, high-oil northern varieties and adapted southern varieties. Several non-shattering hybrid lines that appear to have good yielding ability are under test. Lines resistant to bacterial pustule have been selected from crosses with CNS and other southern varieties. Crosses between high-yielding grain types are expected to bring us productive strains better adapted to the lower Coastal Plain section of the Southeast.

It is not unreasonable to expect that from all this material many new strains will soon be developed, fully capable of meeting the needs of the southern farmer for an oil bean and of overcoming several circumstances that have been handicaps to growing soybeans there: The lack of adapted varieties, the conflict with cotton for labor during the harvest season, and adverse climatic conditions during the late fall and winter.

Two areas produce more than 90 percent of the soybeans grown in the South for industrial use: The Coastal Plain soils of North Carolina and Virginia and the Mississippi Delta sections of Arkansas, Tennessee, Mississippi, and Louisiana. Only 17.5 percent of the total soybean acreage in the South was harvested for beans during the 10-year period, 1934 to

1943. The average yield then was 11.1 bushels an acre. In 1945, after several better kinds became available, 27.6 percent of the total acreage was harvested for beans, and the average yield, 13.8 bushels an acre, was 24 percent above that from 1934 to 1943.

To meet the demand for more oil during the war and to encourage an expansion of soybean plantings in the South by developing varieties adapted to the section so it, too, could help fill the need, the facilities of the United States Regional Soybean Laboratory at Urbana, Ill., were expanded in 1942 to include 12 Southern States in a cooperative soybean improvement program. Southern headquarters for the region were located at the Delta Branch Experiment Station at Stoneville, Miss.

To achieve the chief aim of the program—the development of adapted higher-yielding sorts for industrial uses—varieties must be developed that not only yield more, but resist shattering, lodging, and diseases, and have a content of oil and protein most desirable for industrial uses. Such new varieties, besides, must fit into the varied rotations and cropping practices characteristic of the different sections of the South. Cotton farmers of the Delta section of Arkansas, Mississippi, and northern Louisiana want a high-yielding variety that will mature in August or early September so they can better use their labor supply. Others want a kind that will mature in September or early October, so that winter grains or alfalfa may be planted after the soybeans are combined. Possibly a somewhat different type is needed in the East and Southeast, where soybeans are often planted after oats or, as in southern Alabama, after early potatoes. The farmers of Oklahoma and Texas want a productive, drought-resistant variety that will develop and mature seed during dry summers. All these factors had to be considered.

The principal varieties that were being grown for beans when the southern soybean program was initiated were Arksoy, Arksoy 2913, Ralsoy, Mamredo, and Macoupin in the central and upper South; Wood's Yellow, Herman, and Tokyo, in the East; and Palmetto, Mamloxi, Clemson, and Nanking in the South and Southeast. Two new strains, Ogden and Volstate, had been developed and released by the Tennessee Agricultural Experiment Station, but had not been grown to any extent over the South at that time.

Breeding and selection work to develop better adapted varieties are under way at most of the southern experiment stations in the cooperative program. New strains are entered in the uniform tests across the region as rapidly as they are developed. The varieties are grouped by maturity, in conformity with the system established by the Regional Soybean Laboratory in 1938. The varieties and strains of the Uniform Tests, groups O to IV, are adapted to the Northern States. The southern varieties are entered in the progressively later maturing groups of VI, VII, and VIII. Through the mid-South, the strains of group VI normally

Except for oil content, the new soybean strain, S100, measures up well against standard varieties of the same maturity group in the uniform variety test

Two-year average, 1944–45	S100	Gibson	Patoka	Macoupin	Boone
Yield per acre [1]......bushels..	22. 7	19. 8	19. 4	19. 0	18. 4
Lodging [2]....................	2. 0	2. 0	1. 3	1. 9	2. 0
Maturity date................	Sept. 21	Sept. 12	Sept. 10	Sept. 9	Sept. 8
Plant height..........inches..	36	29	25	34	33
Seed quality [3]................	2. 8	2. 7	3. 0	2. 6	3. 2
Seeds per pound.....number..	3, 370	3, 520	2, 990	3, 330	3, 460
Protein..............percent..	42. 0	39. 8	42. 5	39. 7	41. 1
Oil....................do....	19. 7	21. 5	21. 3	22. 2	21. 5
Iodine number of oil..........	128. 6	128. 3	128. 4	126. 2	124. 1

[1] Two-year average yields from the following locations: Baton Rouge and Opelousas, La.; Stoneville and Tunica, Miss.; Coweta, Fairland, Miami, and Stillwater, Okla.; Columbia, Crossville, Knoxville, and Jackson, Tenn.; Lubbock, Tex.; Orange and Blacksburg, Va.

[2] Lodging notes were recorded on a scale of 1 to 5 as: Nearly all plants erect; plants leaning slightly; plants leaning moderately or 25 to 50 percent down; plants leaning considerably or 50 to 80 percent down; and 80 percent or more of plants down.

[3] Seed quality was recorded on a scale of 1 to 5 as: Very good; good; fair; poor; very poor. Based on development of seed wrinkling, damage, and color for the variety.

Note: The standards given here for measuring the degree of lodging and seed quality also apply to the succeeding tables.

mature from October 1 through October 15, those of group VII, October 16 to 30, and group VIII, November 1 and later. The maturity of these groups is a few days later across the upper South and earlier in the lower South. Varieties of late September maturity, group V, have not yet been developed. Because of the interest in very early maturing beans, the varieties and strains of group IV are being grown at a number of locations across the upper South. Cooperators in the region carefully note yields, with other agronomic and morphologic data. Seed samples from the tests are sent to the Urbana laboratory for chemical analyses. All data on new varieties are taken from the regional variety tests. Because the varieties in the tests were regrouped in 1944, only 2-year averages are given.

The new, early-maturing strain, S100, has consistently yielded above the commercial varieties of this maturity. It is a rogue out of Illini, and was developed under the direction of B. M. King, agronomist of the Missouri Agricultural Experiment Station. The seeds are yellow and medium in size. S100 is tall-growing, with gray pubescence and white flowers. The principal objection to it is its low content of oil. It yields well and is well adapted along the northern rim of the southern region, but excellent yields of good quality beans have been obtained from it as far south as Stoneville.

Ogden is the most productive soybean of midseason maturity for the South. It was developed from a selection from the cross, Tokyo × P. I.

The uniform variety test shows the Ogden variety of soybean to have higher yields and oil content, and to resist lodging better than similar maturity types

Two-year average, 1944–45	Ogden	Arksoy 2913	Mamredo	Ralsoy
Yield per acre [1].............bushels..	27. 1	20. 3	19. 1	18. 8
Lodging [2].............................	1. 3	1. 8	2. 2	1. 7
Average date matured..................	Oct. 11	Oct. 10	Oct. 13	Oct. 10
Height........................inches..	29	25	32	28
Seed quality [3].......................	2. 2	2. 0	2. 4	2. 0
Seeds per pound..............number..	2, 980	3, 500	3, 250	....
Protein.....................percent..	40. 6	42. 9	40. 9	42. 5
Oil.........................percent..	21. 3	20. 3	20. 0	20. 5
Iodine number of oil..................	132. 7	132. 0	127. 6	131. 5

[1] Two-year average yields from the following locations: Fairhope and Auburn, Ala.; Clarkedale, Hope, Marianna, Stuttgart, and Winchester, Ark.; Watkinsville, Ga.; Baton Rouge and Opelousas, La.; Holly Bluff, Stoneville, and Tunica, Miss.; McCullers and Plymouth, N. C.; Coweta, Heavener, and Stillwater, Okla.; Monetta, S. C.; Columbia, Crossville, Jackson, and Knoxville, Tenn.; and Lubbock, Tex.

[2] Lodging notes recorded on scale of 1 to 5.

[3] Seed quality recorded on scale of 1 to 5.

54610, by the late H. P. Ogden, associate agronomist of the Tennessee Agricultural Experiment Station. Ogden is erect, bushy, and medium tall. It has gray down on leaves and stems—pubescence—and purple flowers. The seeds are olive yellow, medium in size, and high in quantity of oil. It is more resistant to leaf diseases, particularly bacterial pustule, than the other kinds of the same maturity. But under very dry conditions Ogden will shatter shortly after maturity. Shattering appears to be more severe on light-textured, infertile soils. Ogden is well adapted to the central and upper part of the South; it has led all varieties of group VI maturity in yield in 19 out of 23 tests where 2-year average yields are available—an outstanding record in view of the wide variation in soil and climatic conditions across the South. Breeders of soybeans have made many crosses of Ogden with nonshattering varieties, and a number of promising nonshattering, high-yielding, hybrid lines from the crosses have been put under test.

Two other new kinds, Volstate and Roanoke, of late October maturity, group VII, are distinctly superior to the old varieties. Volstate, also of Tennessee origin, was selected by H. P. Ogden at the same time from the same cross (Tokyo × P. I. 54610) as Ogden. It is medium tall, with gray pubescence and white flowers. It matures 10 days to 2 weeks later than Ogden and produces high yields of excellent yellow seed.

Roanoke was selected as a single plant from a mixed seed lot in the fall of 1941. The strain was developed under the direction of J. A. Rigney, associate agronomist of the North Carolina Agricultural Experiment Station, in cooperation with E. E. Hartwig of the Department. It was

Volstate and Roanoke, two new late-maturing soybeans, produce more beans and oil in the middle and upper South than other varieties of their group

Two-year average, 1944–45	Roanoke	Volstate	Wood's Yellow	CNS	Palmetto
Yield per acre [1] (middle and upper South)..........bushels..	26. 9	25. 9	20. 8	17. 5	16. 3
Yield (lower South and Southeast) [2]......................	15. 4	15. 7	15. 0	19. 3	17. 0
Lodging [3].....................	1. 8	1. 8	1. 6	3. 0	2. 9
Average date matured..........	Oct. 28	Oct. 26	Oct. 30	Oct. 29	Oct. 26
Height...............inches..	34	33	34	32	50
Seed quality [4].................	1. 9	1. 8	2. 4	2. 0	2. 1
Seeds per pound.....number..	3, 000	2, 990	2, 070	3, 400	3, 750
Protein.............percent..	39. 9	39. 9	42. 6	45. 0	44. 8
Oil................percent..	21. 9	21. 5	19. 4	18. 5	18. 0
Iodine number of oil...........	132. 4	133. 1	128. 9	129. 5	129. 9

[1] Two-year average yield from the following locations: Clarkedale, Marianna, Hope, Fayetteville, Stuttgart, and Winchester, Ark.; Experiment and Watkinsville, Ga.; Stoneville, Holly Bluff, State College, and Satartia, Miss.; McCullers, Plymouth and Willard, N. C.; Florence and Monetta, S. C.
[2] Two-year average yield from the following locations: Auburn and Fairhope, Ala.; Tifton and Richmond Hill, Ga.; Blackville, S. C.; and Baton Rouge, La.
[3] Lodging notes recorded on a scale of 1 to 5.
[4] Seed quality recorded on a scale of 1 to 5.

entered in the Regional Variety Test, group VII, in 1944. Its excellent showing the first year in the tests and in other tests in North Carolina left little doubt as to its superiority. It resembles Volstate in appearance, with gray pubescence, and yellow seed of medium size. Roanoke is higher in oil and has yielded slightly more than Volstate. Both varieties are superior to Wood's Yellow in yield, resistance to shattering, and content of oil. Seed stocks of Roanoke were increased in 1945. Approximately 500 bushels of certified seed were available for further increase in 1946.

Volstate and Roanoke are adapted to an area that includes the lower half of Arkansas and the upper third of Louisiana, extending eastward through the mid-South, the Piedmont, and Coastal Plain areas of North Carolina; neither is adapted to the lower South and Southeast.

A third promising variety, CNS, is like Roanoke and Volstate in maturity. CNS was selected out of the Clemson variety by J. E. Wannamaker of St. Matthews, S. C. Plants of CNS are of medium height, with tawny pubescence and purple flowers. The yellow, medium-size seeds number approximately 3,400 to the pound, compared to Palmetto's 3,700 seeds to a pound. The oil content of CNS is low, but it is higher than that of Palmetto. CNS is well adapted to the Coastal Plain soils of South Carolina, Georgia, and Alabama and is resistant to bacterial pustule, a serious leaf disease. Breeders have used CNS in crosses to get resistant varieties adapted to other regions.

The new late-maturing varieties, Pelican, Acadian, and L. Z., appear to be promising for the lower South. All three were selected from crosses made by John P. Gray, associate agronomist of the Louisiana Agricultural Experiment Station. Their seed is yellow, with dark-brown or black hilums, and medium small to small in size. Acadian has 3,520 seeds to the pound, L. Z. 3,890, and Pelican 3,950. The oil content of each is much higher than Wood's Yellow and Mamloxi. All 3 are tall-growing types, but lodge very little in the lower Coastal Plain area. They hold their seed well and shatter much less than established varieties. Pelican, Acadian, and L. Z. have been tested for 3 years in the Uniform Variety Test, group VIII. They have yielded equally well through the southern half of the region, but are particularly well adapted in southern Louisiana and to the Coastal Plain soils in southern Alabama and Georgia.

THE AUTHOR

Paul R. Henson is an agronomist at the U. S. Regional Soybean Laboratory, Stoneville, Miss., in the Bureau of Plant Industry, Soils, and Agricultural Engineering.

ACKNOWLEDGMENTS

Several men helped plan and conduct the investigations in the southern soybean program. Among the collaborators and other workers of southern experiment stations who assisted are: H. R. Albrecht, E. F. Schultz, and Otto Brown of Alabama; C. K. McClelland and E. M. Cralley of Arkansas; George E. Ritchey of Florida; R. P. Bledsoe and U. R. Gore of Georgia; John P. Gray of Louisiana; J. F. O'Kelly, H. A. York, and Robert B. Carr of Mississippi; J. A. Rigney and S. G. Lehman of North Carolina; H. W. Staten of Oklahoma; W. R. Paden and E. E. Hall of South Carolina; John B. Washko of Tennessee; E. B. Reynolds, R. C. Potts, K. F. Manke, J. R. Quinby, W. L. Jones, P. J. Lyerly, Harold D. Lynn, and P. B. Dunkle of Texas; T. B. Hutcheson, M. H. McVicker, G. D. Jones, and R. P. Cocke of Virginia.

FOR FURTHER READING

Johnson, Howard W., and Koehler, Benjamin: *Soybean Diseases and Their Control*, U. S. D. A. Farmers' Bulletin 1937, 1943.

Morse, W. J., and Cartter, J. L.: *Soybeans: Culture and Varieties*, U. S. D. A. Farmers' Bulletin 1520, 1939.

Zeleny, Lawrence, and Neustadt, M. H.: *Rapid Determination of Soybean Oil Content and of Iodine Number of Soybean Oil*, U. S. D. A. Technical Bulletin 748, 1940.

Progress With Sugar Sorgo

by E. W. BRANDES

SORGO IS grown extensively for table sirup. If it could be made to yield better, it might be used to make sugar. Sorgo is the name of convenience applied to the juiciest, sweetest-stemmed variants found in many species of the genus *Sorghum*. Between sorgo and grain sorghum, which commonly has dry, pithy stems, there are many intermediate types with few sharp distinctions in stem characters.

There is nothing new in the idea of using sorgo to make granulated sugar. All previous efforts, beginning when sorgo was first introduced about the middle of the past century, miscarried because of low yields, complicated by practical difficulties in processing the juice. Because of excessive amounts of starch and glucose in the juice, only a fraction of the sugar would crystallize. These early attempts were made before the principles of genetics were applied to plant breeding and when the conception of plant introduction and adaptation was in the "cut and try" stage, from which only now it is beginning to emerge. Although the purpose for which the plant was brought to America was not realized, sorgo became an important crop plant. During the Civil War and afterwards, it provided "long sweetenin' " in the form of thick sirup. More important, as a forage crop, sorgo occupies about 2 million acres in subhumid parts of the Great Plains.

An active revival of studies of sorgo for sugar production, based on new conceptions of plant introduction, modern plant-breeding methods, and improved sugar-processing techniques occurred in 1941, in cooperation with The South Coast Co., and the American Sugar Cane League, Inc. We cannot say yet whether the studies will lead to practical use of sorgo for sugar manufacture, but in any event the development of better varieties for sirup production, an integral part of the project that already

344

is on the road to accomplishment, will justify the whole effort. The general breeding program for greater yields of better quality sorgo has assurance of success, the time of reaching that objective depending upon intensity of the program. Confidence in achieving the modest objective of specialized varieties for sugar production, yielding 20-ton crops of acceptable quality, is based on scientifically sound considerations of plant adaptation and upon progress made in following them.

There is little prospect of developing a sorgo-sugar industry independently of the already established sugar crops, beets and cane. The harvesting and processing season for sorgo would be far too short to justify the required large investment in processing machinery, which for efficient operation must be elaborate and therefore expensive. Production costs would be prohibitive. The sorgo harvesting season, however, does not overlap those of beets and cane, and an off-season supply of sorgo of good quality would be a welcome addition to keep beet factories or cane mills operating longer. The advantage to farmers and processors in leveling out their labor requirements is obvious. With a longer harvesting season attained by following sorgo with sugarcane, or sugar beets with sorgo in the areas where such sequence may be found possible, all operations may be conducted more efficiently and economically.

Another advantage of growing sorgo around central factories is that it would permit more economical use of valuable byproducts, like bagasse, the mass of material that remains after the juice has been pressed out of the stalks and is used in making lumber substitutes. The comprehensive resurvey of sorgo as a source of sugar and byproducts was prompted by the ever-present need for reducing sugar-production costs.

In general, the potential dispersal areas of domesticated plants are restricted to areas not drastically different in climate from their geographic centers of origin or the points of origin of their wild prototypes. This is especially true of the plants that must rely on seed production for their perpetuation. To the more familiar climatic requirements of plants, including appropriate levels of temperature, light, and water supply during a frost-free growing season, must often be added appropriate photoperiod. Photoperiod is the relative duration of day and night, which differs at different latitudes and at different times of the year and profoundly influences the development of most plants, especially their production of flowers and seed.

Another fundamental requirement is the photothermal balance, which demands that at given temperatures there must be appropriate quotas of light. The complex, exacting, and usually interrelated requirements of plants determine where the plants will grow. Unless the plants can be made to hybridize with related plants outside of the natural dispersal area, it is extremely unlikely that the area will be materially extended. There are exceptions in the case of short-lived annuals not sensitive to photoperiod (day-neutral forms), but in general the colonizing or re-settlement of domesticated plants is limited by these considerations.

There is no real acclimatization of plants as the term is generally understood. What passes for acclimatization in horticulture is merely the survival of adapted elements of heterogeneous plants in a new dispersal area. The environment of the new area must be compatible with some element already present in the plant, or that can be incorporated in the plant by crossing it with another plant. The dictionary definition of acclimatize, "to become habituated to a foreign climate," is misleading. But easy acceptance of that idea is the rule, fostered no doubt by apparent exceptions like the partial compensation of altitude for latitude and vice versa, "off-season" growing of plants in new areas, or artificially providing requirements such as shade, irrigation, and many others.

Africa the Center of Sorgo Origin

The center of origin of domesticated sorgo is on the continent of Africa. Satellite centers were established centuries ago in anterior Asia, India, China, and Malaya, and more recently in southern Europe, the Americas, Australia, and other parts of the world. The recognized wild prototypes of domesticated sorgo (and of all cultivated sorghums) are limited to Africa south of the Sahara, and range far down into the Temperate Zone of South Africa. Sorgo is one of the domesticated plants for which the geographic place of origin is well defined. In common with similar, well-defined centers of origin and distribution of cultivated plants, the situation may be likened to a target in which the greatest number and diversity of varieties is in the bull's-eye, and successively decreasing numbers are found in the concentric rings from the bull's-eye to the outer edge of the target. The situation is not quite so simple, because there are secondary centers, some quite far removed from the primary center, but essentially the situation holds true. The evidence of location of wild prototypes and the relative concentration of diverse varieties show that for sorgo the equatorial part of Africa is the bull's-eye.

It is plain that the plant breeder will not be content with a meager sampling of the forms or varieties available on part of the target, but will try to assemble representative forms from locations on lines bisecting the bull's-eye and extending from the northern to the southern edges.

The first introductions of sorgo into the United States were from the edges of the area of origin and the dispersal areas. About 1850 a variety was obtained from an island in the mouth of the Yangtse River in China, about 31° 30′ north of the Equator, at sea level, and 15 varieties from Natal in South Africa, about 30° south of the Equator, at elevations up to 4,000 feet. In mid-continental United States at latitudes 30° to 35° north, this limited sampling of varieties from the fringes of the natural range encountered conditions not incompatible with those of their native homes. The greatest concentration of sorgo in the United States is now precisely in that area.

Later, many races of sorghum were brought to the United States and among them were representatives of the solid-stemmed type with sugary juice. For sugar production none of the latter has proved superior to the original introductions or varieties selected from the original introductions. The significant point is that, in general, the later introductions from points closer to the center of origin in equatorial Africa grew to large size at an astonishing rate but failed to produce flowers and seed. When the imported seed was used up, these desirable forms unfortunately were lost. It is a safe assumption that among them were varieties that varied in quality of juice as well as in size and rate of growth.

We know now that the development of the influoresence in many sorgos is powerfully influenced by photoperiod and that under our conditions the short-day forms of the Tropics must be grown farther south, or planted "off-season," or the daily exposure to light shortened artificially in order to induce blooming. To make use of the short-day forms in breeding, it is now comparatively simple to manipulate the environment so that short-day and long-day forms will bloom simultaneously and produce hybrids.

Quite recently this has been accomplished with sugarcane, a case in which the problem was essentially similar to the sorgo problem. Long-day forms of sugarcane from the North Temperate Zone normally blooming in July–September were crossed with short-day tropical forms normally blooming (north of the Equator) in November–January by artificially advancing the blooming date of the latter. This was accomplished by growing the tropical varieties in flat cars that could be pushed into a large, light-tight photoperiod house on a daily schedule that simulated the tropical short day. Another device used successfully was to ship the pollen across the Equator by air in specially designed refrigerated containers, taking advantage of the reversed seasons. The short-day and long-day forms bloom simultaneously on opposite sides of the Equator.

In some cases, but not all, less expensive methods can be used to induce simultaneous blooming. The simple expedient of planting short-day forms in winter in the greenhouse or at subtropical stations can be used to cross them with intermediate and day-neutral forms. This device has already been used to cross tropical sorgo varieties with certain temperate-zone varieties in southern Florida. The important fact is that by new techniques an obstacle to hybridizing the numerous and important short-day sorgos with other sorgos has been removed and many desirable crosses that formerly seemed impossible now can be accomplished and valuable hybrids can be obtained.

With that background of old objectives and new techniques, a fresh attack was begun in 1941 on the problem of improving sugar and sirup sorgos. Three lines of investigation were started: Intensive exploration for varieties in the Old World and establishing the introduced plants, as a reservoir of breeding material, at stations in the New World where they would complete a normal life cycle with production of viable seed; assembling all sorgo varieties available in the United States at a central breeding station for study and segregation of the best sugar lines; and widespread test plantings of sorgo, including tests in all important sugar-beet and sugarcane districts.

Establishing Introduced Varieties

The exploration for suitable breeding varieties and their importation (or reimportation) was considered the foundation of the investigation, but within a few months, while plans were being perfected, that part of the project was interrupted by the outbreak of war. It was not re-sumed until late 1943, but during the interim some progress was made in obtaining seed from Africa and India by correspondence. The re-sumption of plans for original collecting in Africa during the war was stimulated by the developing need for large quantities of industrial alco-hol in the manufacture of explosives. Sorgo of available varieties had been planted around Louisiana sugar factories in 1942 for that purpose and about a quarter million gallons of alcohol were produced, but the acre yield of fermentable raw material was not up to expectations. The rapid development of higher yielding varieties adapted to the local conditions and suited to the less exacting requirements for alcohol production in contrast with sugar production was believed possible.

With the objective of obtaining seeds for the dual purpose of emer-gency alcohol production and long-term investigation of sugar produc-tion, the writer left Washington December 9, 1943, and arrived at Addis Ababa, Ethiopia, 5 days later.

Many other countries in Africa have well-organized departments of agriculture able to furnish information and technical assistance, but in Ethiopia the agricultural explorer is entirely on his own scientifically and must dig out independently all information and collections of plants.

The head of agricultural services in Addis Ababa gave assurance that there were indeed two kinds of mashela (sorghum) in Ethiopia, the red and the white. But the peasants of the "out back," who sometimes had to be interviewed through a chain of interpreters, knew of many different kinds and were mines of information on them. Eighty distinctly different varieties of sorghum, including two that grow wild, were obtained in Ethiopia during the winter of 1943–44.

Seed of the 80 varieties were shipped by air to Washington and dis-tributed to five stations ranging from the Panama Canal Zone, 9° north, to Beltsville, 37° north. At Beltsville, where they were planted in the greenhouse on March 25, the majority grew to a height of 15 to 20 feet by the end of July and produced seed heads. In contrast, the growth rate at the Meridian, Miss., station was somewhat retarded by drought. Growth rate at Canal Point, Fla., and Summit, C. Z., was about the same as that in the greenhouse at Beltsville. The average growth rate and total growth of many varieties were actually greater at these stations than in Ethiopia, but the average quality of juice was not up to that of the best quality, low-tonnage local varieties.

A succession of plantings of the latter was started on different dates in Florida in an attempt to synchronize the flowering of the local and the newly imported varieties, and it was possible to make the desired crosses with a small part of the Ethiopian varieties in the first year, 1944. The first-generation (F_1) hybrids were planted at Meridian in 1945 and were first analyzed in August and September. Although the hybrids will segregate into different forms in future generations, the F_1 results give a good index of the future breeding possibilities of a cross and the first analyses were encouraging in stalk weight and sugar content. Two progenies of the cross Straightneck M. N. × Saragie M. N. 684 gave the following results, in which the sugar content is fair and weight of stalk is two and one-half times that of the domestic parent:

	Stalk weight	Sucrose in juice	Purity of juice
	Pounds	Percent	Percent
Average	4. 72	11. 92	71. 9
Range	1. 75–5. 80	9. 60–13. 27	63. 3–77. 4
Average	5. 60	12. 58	73. 5
Range	5. 10–6. 80	11. 07–14. 35	68. 9–80. 9

The unfinished job of assembling varieties from equatorial Africa was resumed in September 1945, when Carl O. Grassl started collecting in the Sudan, and progressed through Kenya, Tanganyika, Nyasaland, Northern Rhodesia, and Uganda. With splendid cooperation from agricultural departments and other agencies that aided in original collecting and also furnished seed from their own collections, he has added more than 1,000 accessions of seed to the rapidly growing African collection established in the United States. Only a few of these appear to duplicate varieties previously collected.

Besides the personal collecting, which is always preferable and sometimes indispensable, many accessions of seed have been obtained by correspondence. By persevering effort, more than 200 packets of seed were obtained during 1942–44 from 16 countries, a gratifying testimonial to the cheerful cooperation of foreign colleagues during that time of interrupted and difficult communications. Of the number received, including many important ones, 131 came from India and the rest from countries in Africa. A possibly important source not represented in the recent collections is that part of China extending from 110° to 120° E. in approximately the latitude of Shanghai. The Indian and Chinese sources in which we have interest correspond to ancient dispersal areas that have become secondary centers of origin of domesticated sorgos. They are important for new and more thorough investigation because of the chance that some varieties may possess one or more qualities desired in our present project and, by their location, may be assumed to be reasonably well adapted to our conditions.

Sugar Lines from Available Varieties

During the 90 years since the first group of 17 varieties were introduced from China and Africa, an immense number of variant forms were evolved by selection or by planned hybridization and by new introductions. Moreover, much confusion of names was injected in the first years by promoters who took advantage of the widespread interest in the new crop by rechristening varieties so as to enjoy temporary advantage by selling seed of "new and improved" varieties. The result was that the same variety was known by many names and they, superimposed on many legitimate new names, resulted in a formidable list. The process of coining new names, both legitimate and illegitimate, was carried on to the point where it was difficult to untangle the confused nomenclature and assay the existing material in a methodical way. No less than 389 "domestic varieties," or at least plant materials with that many designations, have been assembled at the Meridian, Miss., station.

Because of the systematic studies of competent agronomists, including C. R. Ball, and the late H. Vinall, C. V. Piper, and H. B. Cowgill, many of the more or less true-to-seed sorts in that assemblage are recognizable, but it requires a specialist to determine varieties with any degree of certainty. Every year since 1941 thousands of chemical analyses and studies of various kinds, genetic, pathological, and agronomic, have been conducted on the mass of plant material in an effort to sift out the best "sugar lines" and "sirup lines" suitable as beginning points for breeding and to continue breeding and selection with combinations already made.

Fourteen crosses of domestic varieties considered promising as sugar lines have been made. They comprise various combinations of Honey, Collier, Rex, Hodo, and White African with Cowper, Sourless, Straightneck, Hodo, S. A. 287, and Early Folger 9097. Sirup lines are represented by crosses of Hodo, S. A. 287, White African, Coleman (M), S. A. 108, and Iceberg in various combinations with C. P. Special, Early Folger 16154, Cowper, and Straightneck. All of them have now been carried to the F_6 generation. The best results have been obtained from Hodo × Early Folger 9097. More recently, exploratory crosses were made to find parents that would transmit high yield and disease resistance; they represented 43 combinations of Rox Orange, S. A. 183, M. N. 60, M. N. 61, Texas Blackhull Kafir, Sugary Feterita, Dawn, Blackhull Kafir, Georgia Blue Ribbon, Straightneck, Iceberg, M. N. 51, and M. N. 352 with S. A. 287 C, Sumac, Coleman Y, McLean, Silvertop, Saccaline, Leoti, S. A. 107, Rex, Honey, Hodo, Atlas, and Early Folger 16154.

The results indicate that the only good domestic parent varieties for intercrossing are Collier, Rex, Honey, Early Folger 9097, White African, and Hodo. Combinations of these are not likely to produce high-yielding varieties for sugar production, but because Hodo is rank-growing there is a good possibility of increasing sirup yields.

Rex, Collier, and Honey were used in 1944 for more than 200 crosses with a number of the large, robust varieties obtained from Ethiopia and India. Promising parents among the latter include M. N. 414, 423, 531, 534, 543, and 684. The F_2 generation was grown in 1946. Although its progenies will be actively segregated, it is probable that there will be enough material to permit selection of parents that may produce the type wanted. As indicated before, this line of breeding—crossing of the promising large tropical varieties with domestic varieties—is the main hope for success. At this stage it is only well begun.

The third main phase of the sorgo investigation, consisting of widespread indicator, or test, plantings, was started in 1942 and continued through 1945. Obviously the tests were restricted to the so-called domestic varieties because hybrids resulting from fresh importations were not available. The purpose was to get an indication of comparable expected yields especially in districts where farmers grow beets and sugarcane commercially to determine possibilities of growing the crops in combination. A representative selection of sorgos was used, including one or more varieties known to grow reasonably well in each district. The pattern of the test and the varieties were identical in each of the districts, which were in Michigan, Minnesota, Nebraska, Utah, California, Louisiana, Mississippi, Georgia, and Florida.

The test plantings almost everywhere confirmed that the old-established varieties are not promising for sugar production, the yields per acre and quality of juice being unsatisfactory. But the plantings permitted evaluation of the different sections of the country for sorgo-sugar production. The lower latitudes and lower elevations are, generally speaking, superior for the purpose. With present varieties, and presumably with varieties improved to the extent that can be visualized, the Middle West and Intermountain areas are not suitable. The assumption is made on good grounds that the tropical hybrids now in process of development will be even more definitely restricted to the lower latitudes and elevations. In climatic and environmental requirements they will doubtless demand conditions intermediate between those suitable for the present sirup varieties and subtropical conditions existing farther south. Prospects for the Gulf States are reasonably good. Under irrigation in the sugar-beet areas of southern California the most promising indications for sorgo-sugar production were obtained. The results of test plantings in the Imperial Valley were:

Variety	Tons of stalks per acre	Indicated 96° sugar per acre (in pounds)
Straightneck	16. 7	4, 297
Rex	15. 4	3, 097
Saccaline	17. 3	3, 775

In this report of progress, no definite forecast can be made as to the outcome of investigations on using sorgo to make sugar. The performance of sorgo in the test cited is impressive. The prospects are brighter with the promise of better adapted varieties now in process of development. Sugar beets and sugarcane yield more sugar per acre and there is a temptation to compare harvest results directly, but it should be emphasized that in terms of sugar increment per month, sorgo even now compares favorably with the other sugar plants that require much longer crop seasons.

THE AUTHOR

E. W. Brandes was one of the organizers of the International Society of Sugar Cane Technologists in 1924, and has directed various scientific explorations in Central and South America, Asia, Africa, and the Pacific islands. At the present time he is in charge of the Division of Sugar Plant Investigations of the Bureau of Plant Industry, Soils, and Agricultural Engineering.

FOR FURTHER READING

Brandes, E. W., and Lauritzen, J. I.: *A Required Photothermal Balance for Survival and Growth of Sugarcane,* The Sugar Bulletin, volume 18, No. 23, pages 3–5, September 1, 1940.

Lauritzen, J. I., Brandes, E. W., and Matz, Julius: *Influence of Light and Temperature on Sugarcane and Erianthus,* Journal of Agricultural Research, volume 72, pages 1–18, 1946.

Leukel, R. W., Martin, John H., and Lefebvre, C. L.: *Sorghum Diseases and Their Control,* U. S. D. A. Farmers' Bulletin 1959, 1944.

Ventre, E. K., and Paine, H. S.: *Making Sugar Out of Sorgo,* Seed World, volume 53, No. 6, pages 12–13, 1943.

Walton, C. F., Jr., Ventre, E. K., and Byall, S.: *Farm Production of Sorgo Sirup,* U. S. D. A. Farmers' Bulletin 1791, 1938.

New Kinds of Sugarcane

by GEORGE B. SARTORIS

PROGRESS in improving sugarcane has been in the direction of increasing yields and developing varieties that can be harvested more easily and economically by machines. Higher yields were obtained by producing disease-resistant varieties especially adapted to the various regions where sugarcane is grown in the United States. The primary objectives in developing machine-type sugarcanes are to lower the cost of production and to eliminate back-breaking tasks, without losing the precision and quality of hand harvesting.

For a long time new varieties have been needed. Most of the varieties grown commercially used to be soft, large-stemmed noble varieties belonging to *Saccharum officinarum,* although several harder and slender-stalked varieties of *S. sinense* and *S. barberi* were also used. Only a few of these natural varieties (although each was known by several different names) attained commercial prominence. With modern methods of breeding, many new varieties were produced by hybridization. Most of the first breeding was with the noble varieties, but it was soon learned that they could not bequeath disease resistance and increased yields. Breeders then turned to crossing varieties of *S. officinarum* with varieties of the widely distributed wild cane, *S. spontaneum,* and with the Temperate Zone varieties of *S. barberi* of India. Species crosses have produced the high-yielding, disease-resistant varieties now grown almost universally.

The crossing of natural varieties from the Temperate Zone (Chunnee) and *Saccharum spontaneum* of India with tropical varieties has enabled the breeder to produce varieties especially adapted to the temperate climate of the United States. These new trispecies hybrids have replaced the tropical noble canes. Here we shall not be interested in all the C. P.— that is, Canal Point, Fla.—varieties, but only in those that have been

703830°—47——24   353

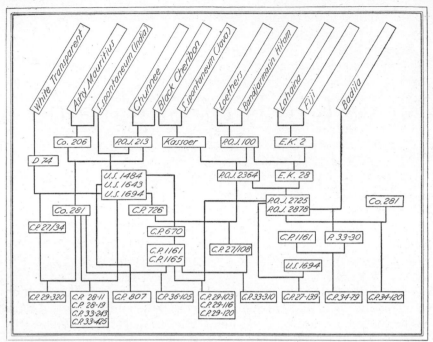

This geneological diagram shows the lines of descent of the Canal Point, Fla., sugarcane varieties now grown commercially in the United States. The boxes across the top show the original varieties and species. There are two varieties of *S. spontaneum,* one of *S. barberi* (Chunnee), and eight noble cane varieties (*S. officinarum*). The commercial C. P. varieties are shown in the bottom row of boxes. Note that all are trispecies hybrids, since each has some noble blood, some Chunnee blood, and some wild blood. The varieties given in the box with C. P. 29/103 and all those to the right have wild blood from two sources, India and Java.

released for general culture since 1941, and with two somewhat older varieties that are especially adapted to the new methods of harvesting.

Most of the new C. P. varieties are resistant to red rot, root rot, and mosaic. All are susceptible to chlorotic streak, but this disease is controlled by hot-water treatment of seed cane or by rogueing.

C. P. 29/320 and C. P. 29/120 already are old-timers, although both varieties are still in their teens. They merit consideration because they possess the essential characteristics that adapt them to machine harvesting. C. P. 29/320 is the dominant variety in the northern section of the Louisiana Cane Belt, and also is grown extensively in the Bayou section of southern Louisiana. Although it may continue to be a prominent commercial cane, its importance is historical; it was the guinea pig for the harvesting machines. Much of the early experimental work with cane harvesters was done in fields of C. P. 29/320.

C. P. 29/120 was almost a failure. It lacks eye appeal. The trash clings to the relatively short stalk. Its straight stalks of uniform height, however, are admirably adapted to machine harvesting, and with the development of practical harvesters its merits were soon recognized. Here was a variety tailored to the machine. During the war years the acreage of C. P. 29/120 was expanded rapidly.

Since 1941 six varieties have been released for commercial planting in the United States. Two of these—C. P. 33/310 and C. P. 33/425—are specialty canes adapted to small areas in Louisiana, and it is improbable that either of them will ever occupy larger areas.

C. P. 33/243 is a good type, but it is susceptible to red rot and moderately susceptible to mosaic. In 1945 it occupied only 1 percent of the Louisiana acreage.

Two varieties—C. P. 36/105 and C. P. 34/79—were released in 1945. C. P. 36/105 has a wide range of adaptability in Louisiana. Because of its erect growth and resistance to lodging, it can be harvested by machines.

C. P. 34/79 was bred in 1934 and released to growers of southern Florida in 1945. It compares well with present varieties in the Everglades in yield of sugar per ton and tonnage of cane per acre. It also appears to be well adapted to the sand and the muck soils near Fellsmere, Fla. It is an early to midseason variety, with stalks of medium size that remain erect, except under the most adverse conditions. It is one of the few varieties grown in Florida that can be harvested by machine. It is not recommended for other areas.

The outstanding variety released during the war years was C. P. 34/120. It is grown successfully throughout the Cane Belt of Louisiana. It grows vigorously, with tall, erect stalks; the trash is easily removed, and it is adapted to machine harvesting. Because of its resistance to inversion after cutting, it is rapidly replacing Co. 281, a poor yielder that was continued in culture because it was the only good windrowing variety available. Farmers liked C. P. 34/120 and expanded it rapidly immediately following its release.

C. P. 36/13 was released to sugarcane farmers of Louisiana in July 1946. It compares favorably in yield and quality of cane with the leading commercial varieties. The stalks are of medium thickness and usually erect enough for machine harvest. It stubbles satisfactorily and has good windrowing qualities. In fiber content and juice extraction it equals C. P. 29/116. The outstanding characteristic of C. P. 36/13 is its high resistance to inversion of sucrose after cutting. In this respect it is probably superior to any variety thus far released.

C. P. 36/13 has an interesting origin. It was selected from a progeny of the cross P. O. J. 2725 × Honey sorghum. Its morphological characteristics and chromosome number show that it is not a hybrid of sugarcane and sorghum. P. O. J. 2725 does not have fertile pollen and it has never produced any selfed seedlings at Canal Point, but in most crosses with sorghum some seedlings that are not hybrids are produced. It is very probable, therefore, that the sorghum pollen induces development of seed (eggs of P. O. J. 2725) without fertilization, a process known as apomixis or apogamy.

C. P. 36/13 is similar to P. O. J. 2725 in color of stalks and resistance to inversion of sucrose. It differs in that stalks are somewhat smaller, earlier maturing, and with a higher sucrose content.

A large acreage of low-yielding, mosaic-susceptible P. O. J. varieties is still being grown for sirup. In the sirup section of Florida, Georgia, Alabama, Mississippi, Louisiana, and Texas, these should be replaced by the higher yielding varieties C. P. 29/116 and Co. 290. Co. 290 is susceptible to mosaic, but it can readily be kept free of disease by rogueing. C. P. 29/116 resists mosaic; in most places, it stubbles better than Co. 290, and produces a slightly greater yield of cane and sirup to the acre.

The superiority of the new varieties is shown by the definitely upward trend of yields since 1926 when the P. O. J. varieties were introduced to commercial culture in the United States. The first C. P. variety was released in 1930. From then on the acreage planted to C. P. varieties was expanded each year and by 1945 they occupied about 71 percent of the acreage planted to sugarcane in Louisiana. The annual yield of sugar per acre also increased 394 pounds more from 1936 to 1944 than from 1899 to 1908, when the old noble varieties gave their highest yields. In the period 1919 to 1926, following the incidence of mosaic, the yield from the noble varieties was only about 57 percent of present yields.

The increase was not due alone to the greater yield of cane by the new varieties; the quality of the new canes also was improved. The new kinds yield 26 pounds of sugar more per ton of cane than the old noble types.

Another advantage is that less seed cane is required for planting. When the noble varieties produced their highest yields (1899–1908), 11.1 percent of the total acreage grown was used for seed, but with the introduction and spread of red rot and mosaic diseases, the figure rose to 23.1. In contrast, during the period from 1931 to 1944, only 9.8 percent of the total acreage of new varieties was required for seed.

THE AUTHOR

George B. Sartoris has been in charge of the sugarcane-breeding project of the Bureau of Plant Industry, Soils, and Agricultural Engineering for 20 years and is an authority on the wild and cultivated sugarcane varieties of the world. Most of the commercial sugarcane varieties now grown in the United States were developed by Dr. Sartoris.

FOR FURTHER READING

Arceneaux, George, Hebert, Leo P., and Mayeux, Louis C.: *Results of Sugarcane Variety Tests in Louisiana during 1945*, Sugar Bulletin 24, number 18, pages 139–142, 159–161, June 1946.
Sartoris, G. B.: *Longevity of Sugarcane and Corn Pollen—A Method for Long-Distance Shipment of Sugarcane Pollen by Airplane*, American Journal of Botany, volume 29, pages 395–400, 1942.

Saving Our Sugar Beets

by EUBANKS CARSNER and F. V. OWEN

ONLY 30 years ago curly top of sugar beets seemed an insurmountable barrier to progress of the beet-sugar industry in much of the West. One authority at that time even advised the abandonment of infested and susceptible areas. Had that been necessary, we would not have the sugar and sugar-beet seed now produced in a vast territory in 12 Western States, and their settlement and development would have been retarded.

But now, in retrospect, curly top appears to have been a blessing in disguise. The need to conquer it prompted much research, which led to the development of varieties adapted to American conditions and the establishment of a new industry, growing sugar-beet seed. The two results completed the integration of the American beet-sugar industry and made it independent of Europe.

The violent vicissitudes through which sugar-beet growing and the beet-sugar industry in the Western States passed before curly-top-resistant varieties were produced can be brought out best in the record of a representative region. Farmers in the Burley area of southern Idaho started growing sugar beets in 1912. Average yields were low at first but gradually improved with increasing experience, and the acreage was expanded because of the sugar shortage during the First World War. In 1919 came the first outbreak of curly top. From then until 1935 yields dropped recurringly to disastrous levels—in 1924, 1926, 1931, 1934. Areas in Arizona, California, Colorado, Nevada, New Mexico, Oregon, Texas, Utah, and Washington suffered in much the same way.

The deep dips in the curve of average yields in southern Idaho indicate only a part of the losses that curly top caused in those years. Average

357

yields of 5 to 6 tons an acre meant heavy losses to processors and the growers who carried their beets through harvest. Besides, a big acreage was plowed up. The average yield in 1934 was 4.88 tons an acre from 2,754 acres harvested—but in that season, of 21,389 acres planted to beets, 18,635 were abandoned. Contrast with this the record for 1941, a season in which damage from curly top also caused a conspicuous decline. It would have been a disastrous year if varieties of relatively high resistance had not been used. That year 22,005 acres were planted, 21,418 were harvested, and the average yield was 13.45 tons an acre.

The progress that has been made in the control of curly top through breeding resistant varieties can be indicated by results obtained in 1941 on experimental plots. Under the drastic disease conditions of that season a standard European variety once widely used in this country failed completely; U. S. 1, the first resistant variety to be released to growers, gave 6.31 tons to the acre, and the latest commercial variety, the second release of U. S. 22, yielded 16.61 tons. The test plots were purposely planted late to get more severe exposure to curly top. There was a good deal of curly-top damage that year in the commercial fields and, even with the resistant varieties now in use, curly-top losses of economic importance occur under some conditions. However, it can be stated with assurance that crop failures of sugar beets due to curly top need no longer be feared anywhere. It is not uncommon now to have the resistant varieties yield 25 and 30 tons an acre even when exposed to curly top, under conditions that cut the production of the old susceptible varieties to unprofitable levels.

Mass selection has been used to breed the varieties thus far released for commercial use. But the method involves much more than it did when breeding for curly-top resistance was started 29 years ago. We used to depend on naturally occurring epidemics to differentiate degrees of resistance. Now we regularly induce epidemics artificially in the breeding field regardless of the severity or mildness of the injury in the surrounding territory.

We introduce an abundance of the curly-top virus into the breeding field early in the spring. There are several ways to do it. In the first place, as many viruliferous leafhoppers (carriers of the curly-top virus) as possible are held over winter on hardy food plants, like annual mustards, spinach, and sugar beets, which are planted late in summer next to the field to be used for the sugar-beet plots the following spring. Leafhoppers held over in this way move into the young beets in the spring and inoculate beets here and there.

A second important measure is setting out in the field infected mother beets that have been carefully stored over winter. We usually also introduce virus into the experimental field by releasing viruliferous beet leafhoppers that are reared in insectaries. The newly infected young plants or the transplanted, diseased mother beets serve as reservoirs of curly-top virus. From these reservoirs the spring-brood leafhoppers invading from natural breeding grounds in the desert obtain a supply of virus which they then pass on to the healthy beets they feed upon. The presence of an adequate source of virus in the experimental field at the time of the spring invasion accelerates the rate of development of the curly-top epidemic in the field because many of the invading leafhoppers carry no virus with them.

Planting the breeding plots late is another way we use to bring about severe epidemics. Beets generally are more susceptible to infection and injury when they are small. The leafhopper vector is more active under warm temperatures. And the curly-top virus multiplies more rapidly under relatively high temperatures when the beets are growing rapidly. Plants that withstand such severe epidemics give rise to highly resistant varieties.

But besides resistance to curly top, extensive areas, especially in California, require sugar beets that do not bolt and that resist downy mildew. Some varieties like that have been bred and are in wide use. Better adapted varieties are needed in several districts, however, and efforts are being directed toward producing them.

New Breeding Methods

Methods of breeding sugar beets, other than mass selection, have been investigated while that method was being used to produce and improve better kinds. The investigations open new vistas of progress.

We discovered lines of self-fertile beets that in their sexual reproduction would not follow the general pattern of cross-fertilization. The usefulness of these highly self-fertile beets for breeding purposes was increased when beets were discovered that produced no pollen themselves and hence needed pollen from other beets for their fertilization. These male-sterile plants can be fertilized by pollen from self-fertile beets, and so produce pedigreed hybrids. With the way thus open to produce self-fertile or inbred lines with characteristics that can be determined, the possibility has arisen that many desirable combinations of characters can be bred in pedigreed hybrids. Inbred lines must be produced and evaluated before desired combinations can be planned and developed.

An indication of the promising possibilities from pedigreed hybrids is afforded by the performance of one such hybrid that has been studied. S. L. 4108 was produced by crossing a vigorous inbred line with a male-sterile beet of fair quality and high resistance to curly top. Under conditions entirely free from curly top, S. L. 4108 yielded 513 pounds more sugar to the acre than the average of seven other leading mass-selected kinds. This excellence was due partly to high vigor and partly to greater resistance to a parasitic disease that affects the petioles and roots. Under very severe exposure to curly top, S. L. 4108 proved as resistant as the most resistant variety now in commercial use.

We have another significant indication of the possibilities of pedigreed breeding. By studying the reaction between certain inbred lines of beets and the different strains of the curly-top virus, it was discovered that some of the inbred lines are immune to some of the virus strains. We hope that the same immunity will be found in hybrids made with these immune inbreds. None of the best commercial varieties now in use has such immunity.

Also possible is the production of varieties that have single-seeded, or unilocular, seedballs and kinds having bilocular seedballs. Inbred lines have been found with a high proportion of bilocular seedballs. These characteristics can be reproduced in pedigreed hybrids. Two-seeded seedballs would be inferior to single ones, but would be a big improvement over the mechanically segmented seed now generally used.

Certain inbred lines have shown a noticeably low bolting tendency. This fact brightens the prospect for breeding for general adaptation to conditions where nonbolting varieties are required, as with early fall and early winter plantings in California. Such plantings are necessary. In the Imperial Valley, for example, the summer heat is so intense that in this extensive, highly productive area sugar beets must be planted in the fall, grown through the winter, and harvested in the spring. The winters are cold enough, however, that varieties very low in bolting tendency are necessary. Varieties of higher bolting tendency were extensively planted there by mistake one year and in the spring the fields looked more like plantings for seed than for sugar production.

Greater uniformity in size and shape of beets and consequently better adaptation to harvesting machinery seems a likely possibility through pedigreed breeding.

Another approach to the control of curly top is unique, and perhaps has a point for many other farmers. It is through an ecological study of the vegetation in desert range lands where disturbances of the natural plant cover encourage weedy areas that serve as breeding grounds for the beet leafhopper. A large-scale disturbance of that kind occurred in several regions under the stimulus of high prices for food during the First World War. Later, many of the areas that had been under cultivation were abandoned and they were immediately invaded by annual mustards, Russian thistle, and other hosts of the beet leafhopper. Bad practices prolonged those objectionable early stages of the plant succession.

The factors in the restoration of the natural plant cover, plants like sagebrush and grasses on which the beet leafhopper does not breed, were sought in the investigation. We found that with adequate protection from destructive agencies—temporary farming and abandonment, fire, and excessive grazing—a grass cover will replace the leafhopper weed-hosts in 5 years. Cattle, incidentally, are not the only animals that may overgraze: The persistent, year-round feeding of large numbers of jack rabbits destroys more vegetation than we had realized. Large experimental plots in the desert, portions of old abandoned farms, protected from fire and the grazing of domestic animals, continued to produce crops of mustards and Russian thistle and consequently large numbers of beet leafhoppers—until jack rabbits were excluded. Then the desired change in plant cover began. Rodents sometimes thwart efforts to reseed the ranges with perennial grasses; such failures often are wrongly attributed to too little rain.

Good management of range land and farm land, besides helping to control curly top of sugar beets, by keeping the population of beet leafhoppers below dangerous levels, is highly important to several other commercial crops. Tomatoes and a good many varieties of beans, for example, would be produced in a number of areas if it were not for the frequent heavy invasion of beet leafhoppers and the consequent damage from curly top.

Establishing the Seed Industry

Sexual reproduction in sugar beets depends on two environmental factors of primary importance, prolonged low temperatures that permit only very slow growth, and long days or long daily periods of light exposure. Varieties vary genetically in these reproduction requirements. Only those high in bolting tendency gave good seed yields in the warmer areas first developed. And if they were repeatedly reproduced there, natural selection eliminated those individuals that did not go to seed and the bolting tendency of the resulting varieties increased to a degree unacceptable in fields of beets grown for sugar production.

Research overcame the difficulties. The factor of temperature required most attention. Early planting, proper fertilization, and right irrigation gave large growth of leaves in the fall to shade the soil and keep the beets comparatively cool through the winter. Deterioration of varieties in bolting tendency was avoided by growing the stock seed under climatic conditions of other regions that afforded complete reproduction. Such stock seed is used to produce only a single generation of commercial seed in the warmer areas.

The regions better adapted climatically were also found to reproduce satisfactorily the varieties so low in bolting tendency as to merit the designation "nonbolting varieties."

Thinning or spacing beets, a laborious, expensive operation in producing sugar, is undesirable in seed-growing areas where winter days are often warm. Leaving the plants thick to shade the soil and each other helps reduce the temperature. The process of thermal induction of flowering goes forward slowly under favorable low temperatures, but under high temperatures it is rapidly reversed. Spacing may prove economically practicable in seed districts where daytime winter temperatures are seldom high enough to reverse the reproductive processes. Better light relations for photosynthesis and more economical use of nutrients and water in the soil result if there is not too much crowding.

Disease factors have been encountered in the seed-growing areas, too. Curly top in the interior regions, several fungus diseases, and one bacterial disease in the coastal regions have required attention. Breeding for resistance to all these diseases offers the best control.

The production of seed was firmly established in the United States as a result of the need for multiplying American varieties resistant to curly top. The foundation for the method of growing seed generally used in this country was laid some years before we had varieties that resist curly top. In Europe, the beets are grown one season, dug, stored over winter, and set out in the spring. Our method is much less laborious. The seed is planted in late summer or early fall, the plants allowed to grow slowly over winter in place, usually without thinning, and the seed harvested the following summer. The method permits mechanized operations that eliminate much of the hand labor required in the transplanting method.

Growing beet seed has benefited the agriculture of the areas where the industry has been established. The soil fertility has been improved as a result of research on the soil requirements for sugar-beet seed production and by the residual effect of fertilizers applied for the beet seed crop.

THE AUTHORS

Eubanks Carsner is a pathologist in the Bureau of Plant Industry, Soils, and Agricultural Engineering. He has been a field leader of sugar beet curly-top investigations since 1917.

F. V. Owen is a geneticist in the Bureau of Plant Industry, Soils, and Agricultural Engineering. He has had an important part in breeding sugar beets for curly-top resistance since 1930.

FOR FURTHER READING

Cook, W. C.: The Beet Leafhopper, U. S. D. A. Farmers' Bulletin 1886, 1941.

Owen, Forrest V., Abegg, Fred A., Murphy, Albert M., Tolman, Bion, Price, Charles, Larmer, Finley G., and Carsner, Eubanks: Curly-top-resistant Sugar Beet Varieties in 1938, U. S. D. A. Circular 513, 1939.

Tolman, Bion: Sugar-beet Seed Production in Southern Utah, With Special Reference to Factors Affecting Yield and Reproductive Development, U. S. D. A. Technical Bulletin 845, 1943.

Wallace, James M., and Murphy, Albert M.: Studies on the Epidemiology of Curly Top in Southern Idaho, With Special Reference to Sugar Beets and Weed Hosts of the Vector Eutettix tenellus, U. S. D. A. Technical Bulletin 624, 1938.

New Kinds of Tobacco

by E. E. CLAYTON

DURING THE 300-odd years that tobacco has been culti-
vated intensively in this country disease problems have multiplied. They
are not little problems. Root rots, blue mold, and leaf blights plague
every producing area. Some of them cause the leaf to ripen too early and
force growers to harvest much tobacco while it is still green. Diseases
also lower the yield and compel growers to rest their best fields 3 to 5
years and to grow the crop on land that is not so well adapted to tobacco.

To meet this situation we need new varieties of good quality that can
withstand the common diseases. But the work of breeding for disease
resistance can go forward only as rapidly as adequate sources of resistance to the major diseases are established. The discovery of a new type
of disease resistance rarely receives much attention except in the scientific
world. Once discovered, the new kind of disease resistance is combined
with desirable yield and quality through hybridization and selection.
The final products are spectacular new varieties. Before 1920 we had
plants resistant only to black root rot. During the next 10 years plants
that could withstand black shank were developed. A little later mosaic
resistance was obtained.

Beginning in 1934 the Department of Agriculture undertook an extensive search for new types of disease resistance. Collections were
made throughout Mexico, Central America, and South America—more
than 1,000 of them. They were tested systematically, and those that
showed promise of disease resistance were tested further at field stations.

A major object was to find a tobacco that would not be attacked by
the Granville (bacterial) wilt disease. Four years of searching and testing revealed the first wilt-resistant tobacco ever found, and it has been
designated as T. I. (for Tobacco Investigations) 448. T. I. 706, from

which selections were obtained that were highly resistant to both root knot and nematode root rot, was obtained in the same manner. The two collections thus provided resistance to three major diseases. To get them took a year of laborious travel by two trained collectors and 6 years of intensive testing and selection by scientists and other skilled workers. The work of testing and selection was conducted at five locations simultaneously. Adequate resistance was now available to black root rot, black shank, mosaic, bacterial wilt, root knot, and nematode root rot, diseases that are estimated to cause an annual loss of at least 10 percent of the crop, or about $23,000,000 in 1940 values.

The search for healthier varieties of tobacco led ultimately to the many wild relatives of tobacco, some distant and some rather close, that offer types of immunity that do not exist in the cultivated tobacco. Blue mold and wildfire resistance were the two most important additional needs. Fortunately, some of the wild species proved immune to blue mold; still others were immune to wildfire. Crosses between separate species present many complications; the discovery of resistance to wildfire and blue mold in species related to tobacco represents only a small start toward the solution of these problems. However, the opportunities from crosses between cultivated tobacco and the wild species of *Nicotiana* are not limited to disease resistance. It is probable that desirable quality characters, such as better color, aroma, and leaf composition may also be had from the wild tobacco.

In breeding tobaccos resistant to disease, it is important to understand the inheritance of the resistance, the way the resistant plants react to the parasite, and the degree of resistance. In many diseases we find all degrees of resistance, from high susceptibility to practical immunity. Black root rot is a good example. Roots of various genotypes were grown in the same infected soil; all the roots of one, the highly susceptible T. I. 706, were destroyed, whereas none of the roots of T. I. 89 were diseased. In between were several commercial varieties that graded from the slightly resistant variety 400 to the distinctly resistant Havana 211.

Even a slight amount of disease resistance often has great practical value. The 400 variety in an area such as western North Carolina, where only weak strains of the root-rot parasite exist, is a valuable root-rot-resistant variety. Obviously, it is desirable to use in breeding work the highest degree of disease resistance available. Resistance to one disease does not mean resistance to other diseases. T. I. 706, which is so susceptible to black root rot, is our best source of root knot resistance at the present time.

Most resistant tobaccos are invaded by the parasites, but for reasons not clearly understood the parasites are not able to grow freely after they are inside the resistant plant. A good example is T. I. 448, which often shows slight wilt symptoms early in the season; later it recovers and shows no further signs of disease. Susceptible plants are invaded and killed. The root knot nematodes penetrate the roots of T. I. 706, but, once inside, the nematodes literally starve to death.

Different breeding methods are suited to different crops. With tobacco, the good quality of the present disease-susceptible varieties must be preserved—any changes that are made should clearly be improvements. In many instances we want to keep the leaf size and shape of present varieties because they are adapted to machinery or to special uses. The general breeding procedure followed, consequently, has been to pick the susceptible type into which it is desired to introduce disease resistance, and to pick the best source of that resistance. The two are crossed, and in subsequent generations, lines are selected that possess the full resistance of the original resistant parent. In rare instances it is possible also to obtain suitable growth characters and quality in combination with this resistance at this stage. Usually it is necessary to backcross to the quality parent and go through the process of selection again. This backcrossing may need to be repeated anywhere from two to ten times before the desired combination is obtained. The secret of rapid progress in breeding disease-resistant varieties is an abundance of facilities in greenhouse and field for the critical testing of much material, and the careful elimination of all but the most highly resistant plants and lines.

New Flue-cured Varieties

The variety 400 is a selection made in the Old Belt flue-cured area. It is not highly disease resistant, but it has slight resistance to a number of diseases: black root rot, root knot, nematode root rot, bacterial wilt, southern stem rot, and leaf spot. That combination of resistance, plus a natural vigor of growth, causes 400 frequently to outyield older, more disease-susceptible flue-cured varieties by as much as 300 pounds of cured leaf to the acre; 400 is well adapted to the heavier soils of the old and middle flue-cured belt areas, and it also does well on occasional more fertile soils of the Coastal Plain area. On these more productive soils, 400 will produce good cigarette tobacco to the top of the plant; it is important, however, to allow the leaf to mature fully before it is harvested; it should not be planted on light soils, like those in South Carolina and Georgia, as the tobacco produced usually lacks enough body to be of desirable quality. Yellow Special is another new variety quite similar in origin and qualities to 400.

Variety 401 is a selection from a cross of 400 with Cash. Like 400, it is slightly resistant to root knot and leaf spot. It yields better than the older varieties. If the leaf is allowed to mature well before it is cured, it produces a cigarette tobacco of good quality to the very tip of the plant. The cured leaf has more body than 400 and therefore is well suited to the more sandy soils of both the New Belt of eastern North Carolina and the South Carolina Belt. It does not seem to be adapted to Georgia.

The variety 402 is another selection out of a cross with 400. It is a high yielder, and resembles 400 in quality, but is better adapted to eastern North Carolina.

Oxford 1 is a black-shank-resistant type developed by crossing good-quality but susceptible flue-cured varieties with Florida 301, which is highly resistant to black shank. Oxford 1 does not have the full black-shank resistance of 301 and it does not have the resistance to black root rot than 400 has, and the combination of black-shank and root-rot resistance is needed in the Old Belt flue-cured area. Oxford 1 does fill an immediate need and through its use losses from black shank have been greatly reduced in the Reedsville-Winston-Salem region. The cured leaf quality of Oxford 1 is entirely satisfactory. Oxford 2, 3, and 4 are other selections that resist black shank.

Oxford 26 is the first commercial variety that withstands bacterial wilt. It is the result of a world-wide search begun in 1934 to find wilt resistance. T. I. 448, obtained in Colombia, was the answer. T. I. 448 was a vigorous type that produced cured leaf of fair color and had no distinctly objectionable qualities. It was crossed with a number of good wilt-susceptible flue-cured varieties, including 400, and a selection was made that possessed the full resistance of T. I. 448 and had excellent flue-cured quality. It was named Oxford 26. It is outstanding for the uniformity of its cured leaf color, and has an oiliness and elasticity that appeals strongly to buyers. Many experts think it has better smoking quality than any of the common varieties. Oxford 26 proves that it is possible to combine improved quality with improved disease resistance.

Other New Varieties

Ky. 16, and more recently Ky. 41A, are black-root-resistant Burley varieties that yield well and produce cured leaf of good quality. They are planted extensively throughout the Burley area.

Ky. 19 sometimes yields slightly more than Ky. 16 or Ky. 41A. Its quality is not exceptional, but it does well on fertile lands. It resists black root rot.

Ky. 33 is resistant to fusarium wilt and it is recommended to growers in the Burley area who are troubled by the disease. It yields as much or more than Ky. 16 in favorable seasons, but may yield much less in a dry season. It is easily blown over in wet weather.

Ky. 34 tolerates black root rot, fusarium wilt, and mosaic. It is not recommended for general use because the leaves are very close and hard to cure and it blows over badly.

Ky. 52 is resistant to black root rot and mosaic and is of excellent quality. It is particularly recommended to farmers who have a serious mosaic problem. It is light-colored and should be allowed to mature fully before it is cut. It is about 1 week earlier than Ky. 16.

Ky. 22 is a recently introduced variety more highly resistant to black root rot than previous introductions. Under farm conditions it has proved to have exceptional quality. The yield seems to be somewhat less than Ky. 16 but higher than Ky. 52.

Ky. 150 and Ky. 160 are dark-tobacco varieties that are resistant to mosaic disease. Ky. 150 and Ky. 160 are similar in appearance to Brown Leaf and One Sucker, respectively.

During the 1920's the shade tobacco producing industry of Florida and Georgia was threatened with destruction by the appearance and spread of black shank. The situation was saved by the development of Florida 301, and subsequently R. G., the latter being equally resistant and an improved type.

Conn. 15. In New England growers of shade tobacco are making increasing use of this new variety, which is highly resistant to black root rot. It produces 20 to 25 marketable leaves, compared to 15 to 18 for the ordinary shade variety and has other desirable characteristics. It represents an improvement in both quality and yield of cured leaf.

Havana 142, 211, 307, and 322. The production of cigar binder in Wisconsin is being improved through the introduction and use by growers of these new varieties. All are highly resistant to black root rot. Havana 142 is now grown on about three-fourths of the Wisconsin acreage. Havana 211 is used to a limited extent in Wisconsin and quite extensively in the Connecticut Valley. Havana 322, developed from a cross between Havana 142 and Havana 38, is indistinguishable in the field from the Old Comstock Spanish, which, except for its susceptibility to root rot, has long been regarded as the best type of binder tobacco.

Disease Resistance Yet To Be Introduced

Throughout the entire Coastal Plain cigarette tobacco-producing region of Virginia, North Carolina, South Carolina, Georgia, and Florida, root knot and nematode root rot diseases are prevalent. They cause the roots of the tobacco plant to swell and decay. Affected crops are reduced in size and ripen prematurely. The search for resistance to these diseases has involved the testing of hundreds of seed collections. Out of these, T. I. 706, a collection from Central America, proved to be the best. From it, selections that resist both root knot and nematode root rot were obtained. T. I. 706, aside from its resistance, was a poor type and much work has been required to combine this resistance with suitable characteristics of growth and quality. Lines have been developed that have the full root-disease resistance of the T. I. 706 parent and that grow and cure like flue-cured tobacco. Further improvement is necessary before we will have commercial varieties, but these are definitely in prospect. When produced they will solve a disease problem that each year affects some 600,000 acres of tobacco.

Wildfire is a disease that is extremely destructive in Pennsylvania, middle Tennessee and Kentucky, and in some other areas. Satisfactory resistance to wildfire has not been found in any variety of N. tabacum. Some wild species of Nicotiana, however, are immune to wildfire. One such species is N. longiflora. After extensive efforts, successful crosses were made between cultivated tobacco and N. longiflora. As the result of this cross, and subsequent work, plants have been obtained that look and grow like cultivated tobacco, but are immune to wildfire.

Blue mold is a disease that has caused tobacco growers much grief since it became widespread in this country in 1932. Plant breeders have tried hard to find resistance to it, but without success in collections. Again, certain of the wild relatives of the cultivated tobacco were immune to this disease. One of them, N. debneyi, was successfully crossed with tobacco. This cross was even more difficult than the one previously described because the N. debneyi chromosomes—those small units of heredity—were so different from the tobacco chromosomes that the breeders' problem was greatly complicated. Most of the hybrid seedlings died, but a few survived, matured, and produced a few seed. To facilitate their work, plant breeders built a special temperature and light controlled chamber in which plants were tested for blue mold resistance during the heat of the summer, instead of merely during the cooler months, when the disease was normally active. Progress is being made, and blue-mold-resistant lines have been obtained that at least look much like cultivated tobacco and cross with it readily.

THE AUTHOR

E. E. Clayton is a pathologist in the Bureau of Plant Industry, Soils, and Agricultural Engineering, where he does research on tobacco. Dr. Clayton is a graduate of the University of Wisconsin.

FOR FURTHER READING

Bullock, J. F., and Moss, E. G.: Strains of Flue-Cured Tobacco Resistant to Black Shank, U. S. D. A. Circular 683, 1943.

Clayton, E. E.: Resistance of Tobacco to Blue Mold (Peronospora tabacina), Journal of Agricultural Research, volume 70, pages 79–87, 1945.

Mathews, E. M., and Henderson, R. G.: Yellow Special Tobacco, a New Flue-Cured Variety Resistant to Black Root Rot, Virginia Agricultural Experiment Station Bulletin 346, 1943.

Smith, T. E., Clayton, E. E., and Moss, E. G.: Flue-Cured Tobacco Resistant to Bacterial (Granville) Wilt, U. S. D. A. Circular 727, 1945.

ouraging results have been obtained from ...arch to develop hybrid corn that is adapted ...ie climate and soil of the South. The above ...ts are a single cross between T13 and T61 ...he Tennessee Agricultural Experiment Sta- .. Tennessee Hybrid No. 10 (below, left), another contribution from the Tennessee station, is the most popular white hybrid of the Neal Paymaster type. Good husk protection to prevent weevil damage (lower, right) can be inherited from a parent plant, a quality that should be bred into corn for Southern States.

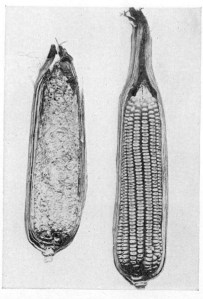

American wheat growers have constantly faced the need for new varieties so as to reduce losses from drought, disease, insects, and other hazards. A few of the improved varieties are pictured here. Upper left is a field of Pawnee being grown for seed increase at Lincoln, Nebr.; it resists leaf and stem rusts, loose smut, and hessian fly. Comanche (lower left), also a hard red winter wheat, resists stinking s. Both Pawnee and Comanche mature fro to 6 days earlier than Tenmarq. A new bun sistant wheat for the Columbia Basin is O (below, right). It yields high, resists smut, stiff straw that combines well, and it ca seeded in fall or spring. At upper right is Le a new spring variety for land under irriga

EARCH ON COTTON has proved that
:rent varieties of it behave alike in some
:s, but there are differences in structure,
igth, fineness, and uniformity of the fiber
ifferent varieties and species. Soil moisture,
berature, fertility, and other factors also
: a bearing, but variety is by far the most
ortant factor in cotton. In some cases, the
igth of 22s yarn from different selections of
it the same length and staple differ as much
) percent.

ufacturers are now buying cotton on the
: of variety and they select varieties that
: their specific needs. To help cotton breeders select and increase seed for a desired purpose,
the Department makes available to them a fiber
and spinning-test service. The breeding work
and studies of inheritance by the Department
in cooperation with State experiment stations
have produced strains that surpass many now
being grown. In the above picture, a plant
breeder selects individual plants from the breeding plot for yield, quality, and other superior
characteristics.

A new strain developed at the Shafter, Calif.,
Experiment Station yields fiber 50 percent
stronger than the variety now widely grown
in that area. Another, developed at State College, N. Mex., is 35 percent stronger than other
local strains. Other good, strong strains are
being perfected elsewhere and will go into production when they have been proved well
adapted and better than common varieties in
yield, resistance to diseases, insects, and so on.
In the photo at left, J. B. Dick of the Stoneville, Miss., station, studies the characteristics
of new varieties of cotton.

The place where cotton is grown also affects its
quality. Tests have demonstrated that the
variety of cotton that produced the strongest
yarn when grown at Florence, S. C., also produced the strongest yarn when grown at Stoneville, Miss., and College Station, Tex. Likewise,
the kinds that produce weak yarn at one location will produce weak yarn when grown elsewhere.

In order to get mass production of the better
varieties of cotton, a one-variety community
plan was initiated by the Department some
years ago under which large supplies of seed

are made available to all growers in a community or area. All growers in a neighborhood agree to plant the same kind of cotton so that the community gin (below) can limit its operations to the adopted variety. Thus, there is no mixing of seed or lint at the gin; it is easy to maintain pure seed stocks and at the same time supply a large volume of uniform cotton. In 1945, over 5½ million acres of the more than 7 million acres in one-variety production were limited to only four types.

Breeders of cottonseed are also cooperating in the one-variety program. They are reducing the number placed on the market and sometimes keep the original variety names even when the kind is improved.

Another step toward reducing the number of varieties is the breeding of new high-yielding strains of medium-length staple, good spinning quality, and equal adaptation to wilt or non-wilt soils. Thus, the same variety can be used for standardized production in much larger areas than heretofore in the eastern area,

regardless of the presence of wilt; higher y[i] and better cotton are produced.

Almost 40 percent of our acreage and n than 45 percent of the production in 1945 v in one-variety communities. As communitie combined into larger areas growing a si kind of cotton, the cotton trade and man turers can obtain increasingly large pure lo cotton of the same variety. In Georgia Alabama, where careful estimates have I made, the extra income to growers above v they make under usual methods averages u $11 an acre.

The cotton breeding work of the Departr is under the direction of H. W. Barre, hea the Division of Cotton Crops and Dise Bureau of Plant Industry, Soils, and Agr tural Engineering. Other phases of this portant American crop are being studie the Department and elsewhere—marketin cotton, for example, the pests that attac new uses, fertilization, and economics of c production.

COTTON-TESTING EQUIPMENT

to the cotton breeder and grader are
uments that quickly and accurately measure
on fiber for length, strength, and structure.
ve, left, Chester Chew measures fiber length
the fibrograph. At right Marion Simpson
a test on the Pressley fiber-strength machine, while (lower, left) Martha Chamblin
measures fiber structure with the X-ray diffrac-
tion unit. Earl E. Berkley (lower, right) tests
resiliency of cotton to determine its ability to
resist injury from packing or crushing. An
article by Dr. Berkley appears on page 369.

On the coastal Gulf prairies of Louisiana and Texas many farmers graze beef cattle on rice stubble (upper photo). This system helps control weeds, maintains soil productivity, and provides two sources of income. The application of straw on rice land is also a good practice (middle picture); at Crowley, La., 3 tons of straw per acre increased yields by 5 bushel acre. The bottom photo shows rice growin the Rice Field Station at Biggs, Calif., w tests showed that nitrogen fertilizer with ammonium sulfate carrier, applied at rate of 150 pounds to the acre, upped age rice yields to about 100 bushels an

FLAX INVESTIGATIONS

SELECTION AND CROSS-BREEDING FOR DISEASE
RESISTANCE, YIELD, OIL CONTENT AND QUALITY.

THIS IS PLOT 30—IT HAS BEEN UNDER CONTINUOUS
FLAX CROPPING SINCE 1890.

(NO FERTILIZERS EVER APPLIED)

ONLY THOROUGHLY RESISTANT FLAX CAN SURVIVE HERE.
FROM THIS PLOT WAS TAKEN THE FIRST PURE CULTURE OF THE
FLAX WILT FUNGUS, FUSARIUM LINI, JULY 4, 1900.

HERE WERE ORIGINATED THE FIRST VARIETIES OF
T-RESISTANT FLAX: N.D.R.—52, N.D.R.—73, N.D.R.—114.
DEN, BUDA AND BISON.

more than half a century flax research has
n under way at the North Dakota Experi-
t Station (above). Development of varieties
stant to a fatal wilt disease, *Fusarium lini*,
been one of many accomplishments. Below,
Richard Heising at the North Dakota sta-
carefully harvests a new disease-resistant

hybrid. In 1927 flax was first tried in California;
the variety was Punjab (lower, right). Under
irrigation yields run up to 35 bushels an acre.
From 1939 to 1944 California and Arizona
produced nearly 21 million bushels of flaxseed.
An article entitled Flax Moves West, by A.
C. Dillman and L. G. Goar, begins on page 385.

Although the Victoria oat (above) has little value as a field crop, it resists crown rust and smut and is the parent stock of about 30 improved varieties of oats. The Department brought it from South America in 1927. (See p. 395.) Fulgrain (above, right), when crossed with Victoria, acquired resistance to crown rust and is now the earliest red oat grown extensively in the South. Another progeny of Victoria is Vicland which, in 1945, constituted about ⌐ fourth of our total oat production. It re⌐ rust and smut and, as shown to the right of lower left photo, it does not lodge. Another proved oat is Clinton (lower, right), wh⌐ parentage is Iowa D69 and Bond. Develope⌐ Ames, Iowa, it has a high yield and test we⌐ and resists crown rust, stem rust, leaf s⌐ *Helminthosporium* blight, as well as lodg⌐

Nearly 50 improved varieties of barley have been distributed to farmers in the past 10 years. A few of them are shown above: 1. Arivat—Has a stiff straw, matures early, yields 10 percent more than Vaughn in Arizona; 2. Compana—A spring type popular in Montana, has high test weight and resists loose smut, grasshoppers; 3. Rojo—Outyields other varieties in California by 12 percent, resists scald and net blotch; 4. Mars—Yields well and matures early in Minnesota, resists stem rust and stripe but not scab, loose smut, or leaf rust; 5. Tregal—Outyields other kinds in North Dakota, resists loose smut; 6. Velvon 11—Adapted to Intermountain irrigated area, combines well, good for feeding and bedding; 7. Flynn 37—Resists drought, combines well, good for hay in Columbia River Basin; 8. Flynn 1—Popular on the Great Plains, outyields other kinds, resists grasshoppers and greenbugs but is subject to smut; 9. Munsing—Has high test weight and yield on Great Plains, livestock like its straw; 10. Wong—Derived from China and now adapted to Atlantic Coast States, resists mildew, outyields other common types; 11. Reno—A winter barley that withstands the cold, matures early, does well in Kansas and nearby States; 12. Wintex—Grown mostly in Texas and although subject to winterkilling and greenbugs, it outyields other kinds and is good for grazing.

By adapting grain sorghums to machines and machines to sorghums, farmers during the war years greatly increased their acreage of this crop. The crossing of one variety with another to get a desired result is a delicate process as indicated above, left, by C. L. Lefebvre. At right, above, is a head of Midland. It is an early variety for Kansas and Nebraska; its stiff, disease-resista stalks make it good for combining. Below i field of Martin, named after the Texas farm who found it; since 1943 it has been the leadi variety in the United States. It matures ea dries quickly and thus combines well, and c be grown from South Dakota to southern Tex

research on sugarcane has several objectives: reduced cost of production through varieties that can be harvested by machine; increased yields from kinds that resist diseases and insects; and development of kinds that will prevent the spread of noxious weeds. An example of sugarcane that combines well is C. P. 29/320 (above) at Bunkie, La., growing on Yahola soil. At left, below, Entomologist Ralph Mathes at Houma, La., holds a tall stalk of cane, C. P. 33/409, that resists the sugarcane borer; the other stalk, variety C. P. 29/103, does not. The tall, wide-topped plants shown below, C. P. 34/120, crowd out noxious weeds along ditch banks.

The goal of tobacco research is to develop varieties that resist diseases and are of good quality. The third row from the left, above, has been developed to resist black shank. The two groups of plants below were inoculated wi blue mold; the group at left represents progre in getting resistance to this disease. The resis ance comes from the wild species N. *debne*

The photo below shows varying degrees of resistance to black root rot. Left to right are T. I. 706, 400, Kentucky 16, Harrow Velvet, Hava 211, and T. I. 89, which is almost immur

otatoes, one of our leading food crops, is sub-
ct to many diseases. Therefore, the potato-
eeding program of the Department, in co-
eration with State experiment stations,
esses disease resistance. Painstaking work is
quired. Above, left, F. J. Stevenson puts bag-
ng around potato fruits to prevent them
om breaking off. In making crosses, another
ep (above, right) is to collect the pollen from

the potato flower. When a new variety is ready
for testing it is sent to cooperating State experiment stations. Below is the Menominee
potato shown at left in each pair in comparison with check varieties at nine stations. The
lower row, from left to right, represents Maine,
South Dakota, and Wyoming; the middle row,
Wisconsin, New York, and Indiana; the top
row, Michigan, Massachusetts, West Virginia.

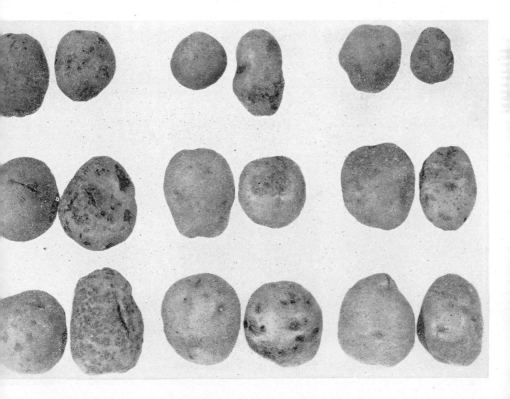

New varieties of soybeans are being develop
for the South which promise to increase the
importance as an oil crop. Above, a good sta
of soybeans in the Delta section of Mississip

The Ogden variety (left) is well adapted to
the South; its yield is high as is the oil content.
Volstate (lower, left), a later maturing variety,
yields well in certain parts of Arkansas, Louisiana, and North Carolina. An article by Paul
R. Henson about soybeans begins on page 338.

Many southern farmers interplant corn and sc
beans (below) and find it a profitable practi

:terial wilt disease, winterkilling, and harm-
insects are among the most serious enemies
alfalfa. Breeding to overcome these hazards
produced encouraging results. Above, left,
M. Tysdal shows off the broad, spreading
wn of a 2-year-old selected alfalfa plant.
for other plant-breeding work, cross pollinating must be done carefully by hand (above,
right). The hope is that the hybrid seed that
develops in the tagged pods will combine the
disease resistance of one parent and the more
desirable features of the other. Below is an example of wilt resistance in 5-year-old alfalfa—
Ranger at the left, and Grimm at the right.

More than 700 million acres of western range land are producing less forage than they could; much of the topsoil on them is being lost because of inadequate plant cover. About 4 million acres have been reseeded by modern methods. The pictures on this page give an idea of what can and is being done. Heavy growth of sagebrush (top, left) usually indicates a good reseeding site; heavy wheatland plows (top, right) kill the sagebrush and condition the l for reseeding. Where the soil is rocky, a he harrow (center, left) will kill brush and ot noxious plants. In some areas, where there no rocks or heavy vegetation, disc drills (abo do an efficient job without other preparati The picture below shows the same area upper right. By reseeding it to crested wh grass, grazing capacity was increased tenfo

What Makes Cotton Good?

by E. E. BERKLEY and H. D. BARKER

THE FARMER who has an indifferent local market will say that quality in cotton means a high yield and ease in picking. To the cotton broker, quality may mean above-average classer's grade and staple length. The technologist may define it as a strong, reasonably long, and fine cotton. The spinner's definition may include a smooth running, uniform cotton that produces a nep-free, strong yarn. The finisher looks for something that will bleach and dye uniformly. The consumer wants a product that will survive repeated washing and ironing.

All these are abstractions that are difficult to measure, but even so the cotton breeder has been able to perfect new, productive varieties that embody these diverse and poorly defined qualities.

The starting point is the development of rapid and reliable instruments and techniques to measure the properties of fiber and relate them to use value. Studies of the past decade have centered around cooperative regional plantings that would give us material for investigating the way in which fibers are formed, the period of fiber elongation, and how the cell wall develops. The investigations have aided greatly in interpreting influences of heredity and environment on the properties of fiber and how they affect the quality of the finished product.

At least four characteristics have a major bearing on quality of cotton: Length, strength, fineness, and structure of the fiber wall. The cotton breeder and the industry can now measure these factors quickly. Laboratory technicians can compile accurate data that will show the relation of specific qualities to the strength and appearance of yarn, and other manufacturing needs; evaluate the influence of heredity and place or condition of growth on the development of these properties; help the cotton breeder or the cotton grower make improvements in these quali-

703830°—47——25

ties, and guide the manufacturers in choosing and using such properties to make goods of desired quality. The cotton breeder must study thousands of selections to obtain the best combinations of agronomic and fiber quality factors. He can now get accurate information on the fiber properties of these selections; in the past he had to depend on "feel," judgment, and guess.

Fiber length is quickly measured by a photoelectric instrument known as the Fibrograph. Fiber strength is measured by the Pressley strength tester. Fiber fineness up to now has been measured tediously by weighing fibers of known lengths. A new instrument, the Arealometer, provides a rapid way to measure fineness, expressed as specific surface or cm^2/mgr. The cell-wall structure is measured by X-ray technique and expressed as X-ray angles: The greater the angle between the fibrils or cellulose strands and the long axis of the fiber, the lower the fiber strength, and vice versa.

Cotton fiber is made up of a multitude of fine, threadlike strands of crystalline cellulose glued together by other cellulose molecules that are not a part of the crystals, that is, amorphous cellulose. These threads are placed in the cell walls in a spiral like the strands of a rope. The cellulose strands reverse their spirals at intervals along the fiber, and the pitch at which they are deposited in the fiber can be determined by the X-ray. The angle between the long axis of the strands and that of the fiber is indicated by the size of the arc that is measured as the X-ray angle.

There are other properties, largely subdivisions of the four major ones listed. They cannot yet be measured so quickly, or they lack definite end points or precision of determination. Hence their exact importance in fiber quality is not so clearly established. For example, cell-wall thickness, one of the attributes of fineness, is hard to measure, and is reported unsatisfactorily as "percent of fiber with a given lumen-wall ratio." To some extent, the extremely thin-walled fibers and perhaps the oversized thick-walled fibers influence the processing, finishing, and wearability or utilization of the product. New and improved methods of measuring fiber wall thickness and fiber perimeter are needed before their effects can be accurately evaluated.

The flexibility and toughness of the fiber are undoubtedly among the more important factors in the processing, finishing, and use of many garments and fabrics, but they are difficult to measure and are usually measured directly only where their effects are pronounced, such as, for example, in tire cords. Fortunately, however, cell-wall structure as interpreted from the X-ray angle seems related to flexibility and toughness.

We have found that a significant correlation exists between X-ray angles and the percentage of increase in skein strength of 36s, two-ply yarn, over twice the skein strength of 36s singles yarn. This, together with other preliminary data on flexibility, fatigue resistance, and the response of certain varieties in tire cord, indicates that a fiber that has good tensile strength and a large X-ray angle would be preferred to one with a higher tensile strength but a small X-ray angle.

Cell-wall structure as measured by the X-ray angle is closely associated with fiber strength as measured by the Pressley index. In fact, X-ray measurements can be substituted for directly obtained fiber-strength measurements in predicting spinning performance except where weather damage occurs to the fibers. Peculiarly enough, deteriorated fibers that have little strength can still be used for reliable X-ray measurement for cell-wall structure. Advantage is taken of this fact to evaluate the potential fiber strength of the cotton breeder's selections when bad picking weather has made direct fiber-strength measurements valueless to the breeder in informing him whether or not he has succeeded in obtaining desired fiber-strength combinations. Primarily, however, X-ray measurements are of greatest value when used together with fiber-strength measurements, not in place of them.

Norma L. Pearson, of the Department, has shown that varieties that characteristically produce long fiber tend to produce fine fiber—that is, the greater the inherited fiber length, the smaller the fiber. If, however, the length of a given variety is increased by the growing conditions such as unusually rich, moist soil, the relationship is reversed—the longer the fiber, the coarser it becomes. Similarly, above-average inherited fineness and length tend to give neppy yarns of poor appearance, whereas environmentally induced fineness, usually associated with reduced fiber length, results in smooth yarn of good appearance. There are exceptional conditions where environmentally induced fineness has nothing to do with reduced length and good-yarn appearance. If the fibers are thin-walled, because of frost or other damage to the plant or boll after the fibers have fully elongated, but before the fiber wall is mature, such fineness may or may not be associated with shorter fiber and good-yarn appearance.

It is evident that the use value—that is, the quality of the textile fabricated from cotton—depends on the interaction of fiber properties. The size of the yarn is determined mostly by the length and size or fineness of the fiber, while the use value is in turn influenced by the fiber strength and structure. Strong fabrics must be made of reasonably strong fiber, whatever its length, but fabrics, like tire cord, that are flexed a great deal, may require fibers that can stand bending. The strength of coarse to medium-sized singles yarns can be largely accounted for by two properties, fiber length and strength. In the finer yarns and those where appearance of the yarn is important, fiber fineness is of increasing importance. In plied yarns requiring strength, toughness, and flexibility, added significance is attached to cell-wall structure as measured by the X-ray.

Within a variety, stronger yarn may be expected from a shorter fiber if the shorter length is induced by stress during growth. When comparing one variety with another under varying conditions of growth, the skein strength is usually greater as the length increases, although unusual fiber strength may overcome length differences, reversing this relationship. For certain varieties, Pima and S × P cottons, for example, there exists a negative relationship between fiber length and skein strength because the shorter S × P cotton is stronger; therefore, it is not surprising that the shorter but stronger fibers produced by stress during growth give a stronger yarn than the longer but weaker fibers from the same varieties. Thus, while fiber quality research has demonstrated that fiber properties are modified by growth conditions and other environmental conditions, varieties are characterized by distinctive combinations of fiber properties that should be recognized in marketing and manufacturing operations.

Recent research has by no means unlocked all of the secrets of cotton quality, but much has been done to help further improve the quality of the world's dominant fiber, to utilize more effectively varying fiber properties, and to improve the competitive position of American cotton.

THE AUTHORS

E. E. Berkley is a West Virginian who, for the past 10 years, has done research for the Department on the structure and strength of plant fibers. At present he is a fiber technologist in the Bureau of Plant Industry, Soils, and Agricultural Engineering. Dr. Berkley is the author or co-author of numerous articles on the structure of cotton fiber and related subjects. In 1945 he was appointed associate editor of the Textile Research Journal, and in 1946 he was elected to the Executive Committee of the Division of Cellulose Chemistry of the American Chemical Society.

H. D. Barker, a pathologist in the Bureau of Plant Industry, Soils, and Agricultural Engineering, has devoted most of his life to cotton research in the Department. He has spent about 12 years in Haiti making scientific studies of cotton and other plants of that country.

FOR FURTHER READING

Anderson, Donald B., and Kerr, Thomas: Growth and Structure of Cotton Fiber, Industrial and Engineering Chemistry, volume 30, pages 48–54, 1938.

Hertel, K. L.: Cotton Fiber-Length Determination Using the Fibrograph, American Society for Testing Materials Bulletin, pages 25–27, August 1942.

Pearson, Norma L.: Neps in Cotton Yarns as Related to Variety, Location, and Season of Growth, U. S. D. A. Technical Bulletin 878, 1944.

Pressley, E. H.: A Cotton Fiber Strength Tester, American Society for Testing Materials Bulletin, pages 13–17, October 1942.

Sisson, W. A.: X-ray Analysis of Textile Fibers: Part V, Relation of Orientation to Tensile Strength of Raw Cotton, Textile Research, volume 7, pages 425–431, 1937.

Sullivan, R. R., and Hertel, K. L.: Surface per Gram of Cotton Fibres as a Measure of Fibre Fineness, Textile Research, volume 11, pages 30–38, 1940.

New Rices; New Practices

by JENKIN W. JONES

A GOOD many things have happened to rice in the past few years. New and better varieties have replaced the old stand-bys on four-fifths of the million-odd acres used to grow rice in the United States. Consumers get a tastier grain. Growers have received higher prices. Yields have been increased or fully maintained. Five improved varieties grown on nearly half of the southern rice acreage in 1945 yielded about 13 percent more than the older varieties, and added 10 million dollars to farmers' incomes.

The higher production helped out materially in the war. Normally, Burma, French Indochina, and Siam supply 90 percent of the rice that enters international trade. When Japan took those countries, a serious food problem arose for several Allied countries that depend upon imports of rice. To help meet the critical situation, production in the Western Hemisphere was expanded from a prewar average of 153 million bushels to more than 225 million in 1945. The largest increases were in Brazil and the United States.

The United States grew an average of 46.6 million bushels of rice on 950,000 acres, or 49 bushels an acre, in the 1930's. In 1945, the production was more than 70 million bushels on 1½ million acres—an all-time high. But because of continuous cropping of old lands and the use of lands less well suited to rice, our average yield went down 2 bushels an acre during the war.

Rice cannot be grown under nearly so many conditions as other cereal crops. It grows well in sections of Arkansas, California, Louisiana, and Texas where other small grains do not do so well because of soil types, excessive moisture, and high temperatures. Rice is the main cash crop of many counties of the four States.

In each of the States, extensive research to breed better types is carried on. The rice breeder's ideals are kinds that mature early, late, and in between, have stiff straw, are healthy, taste good, yield and mill well, and are suited to various climates and methods of culture.

The most serious fungus diseases of rice in the South (but not in California) are the brown, narrow brown, and blast leaf spot diseases and stem rot. White tip, a physiological disease, is another enemy. In severely infected fields, they all cut yields and lower milling quality. The best controls, as for most other cereal diseases, are the use of resistant varieties.

Before 1912, Shinriki, a short-grain rice, and the long-grain Honduras were the main varieties in the South. Shinriki was introduced by the Department from Japan in 1902. Honduras was introduced by commercial agencies in 1890. Shinriki is late-maturing, short, and stiff-strawed. It tillers freely and produced high yields of good milling quality. Honduras, which matures early, produced well on virgin lands.

Shinriki and Honduras were largely replaced by the more productive Blue Rose and Early Prolific, which have a medium grain, and the long-grain Edith and Lady Wright, all of which S. L. Wright, of Crowley, La., distributed. But they succumb to leaf spot diseases and white tip. Healthier replacements in the South include the long-grain Rexoro, Fortuna, Nira, Texas Patna, Bluebonnet, and Prelude, and the medium-grain Zenith, Blue Rose 41, and Arkrose. Federal and State agencies cooperated in developing and distributing them.

In California, the late, short-grain Wataribune, popular from 1912 to 1920, gave way to the earlier-maturing Colusa and Caloro, short-grain varieties developed and distributed by the Biggs Rice Field Station. They were grown on about 95 percent of the California acreage in 1945.

Of the new kinds, Rexoro and Texas Patna were grown on a fourth of the total rice acreage in 1946. Fortuna and Arkansas Fortuna were grown on 9 percent, Prelude on 5 percent, and Nira and Bluebonnet on about 6 percent. Varieties with smooth hulls are preferred to those with rough hulls for harvesting by the combine-drier method because the smooth-hulled types disperse much less dust during drying. Rexoro, Texas Patna, Nira, and Bluebonnet all have smooth hulls.

Rexoro matures late and has stiff straw. It has long, slender grain, and yields and mills well for a rice of that type. It was selected at the Rice Experiment Station at Crowley from a variety introduced by the Department of Agriculture from the Philippines. Rexoro resists white tip and several forms of narrow brown leaf spot, and is of good table quality. Because of its late maturity, it is grown only in Louisiana and Texas, where the growing season is long.

Fortuna matures late and has stiff straw. It yields well in Arkansas, Louisiana, and Texas. It was selected at Crowley from seed brought by the Department from Formosa. Fortuna resists white tip and several forms of the narrow brown leaf spot. Arkansas Fortuna, selected at the Rice Branch Experiment Station at Stuttgart, Ark., is from 7 to 10 days earlier than Fortuna. It is better adapted to the shorter seasons in Arkansas. Fortuna and Arkansas Fortuna thresh easily, a characteristic appreciated by growers who harvest with combines.

Texas Patna was selected at the Texas Substation No. 4 at Beaumont from the cross Rexoro × C. I. 5094—"C. I." referring to the accession number of the Division of Cereal Crops and Diseases. It is a long, slender grain variety, similar to Rexoro in disease resistance, yield, and table quality, but it matures 10 days earlier. Texas Patna is inclined to lodge more readily than Rexoro on rich land. Its earlier maturity, compared to Rexoro, appeals to growers, and the acreage sown to Texas Patna has increased in Louisiana and Texas.

Nira is late maturing and has long, slender grain. It yields and mills reasonably well. It was selected at Crowley from a variety brought from the Philippines. Nira is resistant to white tip and narrow brown leaf spot, and is of good table quality. It is the tallest variety grown commercially in the South, and although it does not tiller freely, it usually yields well in the South on old rice lands.

Bluebonnet, a midseason type with long, slender grain, was selected from the cross Rexoro × Fortuna at Beaumont. Bluebonnet tillers freely, matures quickly and evenly, threshes easily, and yields well. It resembles Rexoro and Texas Patna in table quality and in resistance to white tip and to narrow brown leaf spot, but it matures much earlier. Bluebonnet is well suited for harvesting by the combine-drier method.

Prelude is an early-maturing variety selected at Stuttgart from the cross Improved Blue Rose × Fortuna. It grows vigorously, has stiff straw, and withstands white tip and narrow brown leaf spot better than the older Edith and Lady Wright. Prelude produces much higher yields in Arkansas than Lady Wright, and has much better table quality.

Of the improved medium-grain varieties, Zenith was grown on 16 percent of the total rice acreage in 1946. Blue Rose 41, Arkrose, and Blue Rose were grown on 12 percent of the acreage. Calady 40 occupied a small part of the acreage in California.

Zenith, selected from Blue Rose, was tested and increased at Stuttgart. It is more uniform in heading and in ripening, and also is more resistant than Early Prolific and Blue Rose to white tip, the narrow brown leaf spot, and blast diseases. The kernels of Zenith are smaller, clearer, and of better quality than those of Early Prolific.

Blue Rose 41 was selected at Crowley from Blue Rose. It resists one form of the narrow brown leaf spot disease and white tip, and resembles its parent in growth habit, grain type, maturity, and milling and table qualities. Its resistance to diseases, however, makes it preferable to Blue Rose in the South.

Arkrose, a late-maturing variety, was produced from the cross Caloro × Blue Rose at Stuttgart. It is prey to the narrow brown leaf spot diseases and white tip, which do not, however, reduce its yield or affect its quality as much as they do that of Blue Rose. In grain shape and quality, Arkrose is like Blue Rose, but in Arkansas it produces higher yields.

Calady 40 was selected from the cross Caloro × Lady Wright at Biggs. A late-maturing, high-yielding variety, Calady 40 has stiff straw, a rather compact head, a clear, medium grain, and good milling quality. In California it yields as well as Caloro and is of better quality.

Plant breeders think the improved varieties described are pretty good, all factors considered. But that does not mean the breeder's job is completed, for new diseases or new races of old diseases appear unexpectedly. Methods of tillage and processing change, and changes in market demands create new problems.

New Production Methods

Either application of fertilizer or additions of soil organic matter can make rice grow better. A combination of the two makes rice try to jump out of its roots.

The reason is that rice is mostly grown on poorly drained land where other cash crops give mediocre yields; consequently, it is almost impossible to use the rotations that are so successful elsewhere. The virgin soils of our rice-growing regions contain fair amounts of organic matter, but it decomposes rapidly in the warm, humid climate that rice likes. Farmers generally agree that the humus must be restored after a few years of growing rice. But how? Heavy soils deficient in organic matter are usually compact, rather impervious to water, and hard to work. Rice grown on them, moreover, often fails to respond well to commercial fertilizers or to rotations with legumes.

An attempt to correct the shortcoming is being made in Louisiana and Texas, where more than 950,000 acres of rice were grown on the coastal prairies in 1945 and where some farmers grow only rice. Other growers have both rice and beef cattle, a logical combination that controls weeds, maintains soil productivity, and provides two sources of cash income. They plant rice usually in alternate years, or once in 3 years, on land that otherwise is fallowed or left in stubble pasture. The stubble comprises volunteer red rice, native grasses, some legumes, and weeds—not very good grazing for cattle during late winter and early spring.

Few farmers use improved pastures. They, as we shall see, can solve the problem, although each farmer must decide for himself whether it will pay him.

Yields of rice in coastal Louisiana average 40 to 50 bushels an acre. At the Rice Experiment Station at Crowley, La., the average in 2-year rotations ranged from 47 bushels, following red clover, to 35 bushels an acre, following cotton which had been dusted until residual arsenic was in the soil. The average following the usual practice of alternate pasture was 45 bushels. Similar yields followed Italian ryegrass, fallow, soybeans and bur-clover, and crotalaria.

Notable results have been had in experiments with improved pastures at the station at Crowley. A mixture of Dallis grass, lespedeza, white clover, and California and southern bur-clover are sown; volunteer native grasses are allowed to stand 4 years before the land is plowed up and planted to rice. A complete fertilizer is applied at the rate of 400 pounds an acre every other year. The pasture is clipped now and then during the growing season, but the clippings are not removed. When rice is planted, 400 pounds an acre of a complete fertilizer that contains phosphorus from three sources are applied. The average yield on unfertilized plots is 57 bushels. The average on the fertilized plots, following improved pasture, is 72 bushels.

Thus, the usual system of rice and native pasture gives an average yield of about 45 bushels. Fertilizers increase that figure 5 bushels; 4 years of improved pasture between rice crops raises the yield about 12 bushels more, and fertilization, in addition to improved pasture, lifts the yield about 27 bushels. Besides, on such pastures, organic residues are returned to the soil and cause the rice to respond better to fertilizers.

Agronomists at the Louisiana Agricultural Experiment Station learned from experiments that the production of beef per acre is two to four times as much on improved fertilized pastures as on unfertilized native pastures. Improved pastures also have at least 50 percent higher carrying capacity and supply good grazing for a longer period each year. The calf crop on improved pastures is said to be a fifth greater than on ordinary pasture. Obviously, then, a more extensive use of improved pastures for grazing, with rice, promises well for the Gulf Coast section.

Further evidence on the benefits to the rice crop from additional organic matter is given in the larger yields obtained from the application of straw in preparation for a succeeding rice crop. At Crowley, the average yield of unfertilized rice, grown in alternate years, was 47 bushels an acre. Plots on which three tons of straw were turned under in the fall yielded 52 bushels an acre; plots on which three tons of straw were turned under, plus 400 pounds of complete fertilizer (half applied with the straw and half at seeding time), gave a yield of 62 bushels. Thus, application of straw alone in alternate years increased the yield 5 bushels. Fertilizer alone usually increased the yield by the same amount. The application of both straw and fertilizer increased the yield 15 bushels, or 32 percent. The increases for the same treatments on land cropped each year, with a yield of 38 bushels for unfertilized rice, were again 5 bushels for straw alone, and 15 bushels an acre for straw plus fertilizer.

The combine-drier method of harvesting, which is replacing the binder-thresher, leaves the straw on the fields. This is desirable, but straw stacks for winter roughage are not available to cattle grazing on stubble pastures. Thus, on combined stubble fields it is advisable to provide better winter pastures and some hay for supplemental winter feeding.

Average rice yields in California are relatively high, but on the older rice lands ammonium sulfate increases yields. Recent studies indicate, however, that the time is approaching when it probably will be necessary to use both phosphates and nitrogenous fertilizers to maintain yields.

Fertilizer experiments at the Biggs Rice Field Station in California showed that rice responds well to applications of nitrogen. Ammonium sulfate was the most profitable nitrogen carrier tested. At first, 100 pounds an acre of ammonium sulfate appeared to give the most profitable returns. Later, rates of 150 to 200 pounds were found to be more profitable. Increases in the yield of Caloro rice from the application of ammonium sulfate have averaged about 22 bushels for the 150-pound rate, bringing the average yield up to 100 bushels an acre. The early-maturing Colusa variety gave an average increase of 30 bushels an acre for the 200-pound rate, or from 64 to 94 bushels an acre, and gave a net return of about $30 an acre on the fertilizer applied. In more recent experiments on less fertile land, the average increment has been about 26 bushels for the 200-pound rate and 42 bushels for the 350-pound rate.

A vital point that the farmer weighs carefully is the relative cost of developing improved pastures and the value of the increased yields of rice and beef. When the costs of pasture development and fertilizers are high and the prices of rice and beef are low, the extra yields of rice and beef may not result in a profit. But high prices for these products and relatively low costs of improved pastures should make the practices pay. Because costs and prices vary from year to year, it usually is good practice to apply fertilizers liberally when they are relatively cheap and rice and beef cattle high.

THE AUTHOR

Since 1931 Jenkin W. Jones has been in charge of rice investigations in the Bureau of Plant Industry, Soils, and Agricultural Engineering. From 1912 to 1931 he was successively the superintendent of the Cheyenne Field Station at Archer, Wyo., superintendent of the Nephi Substation in Utah, and then in charge of the Biggs Rice Field Station in California. In 1925 he went to Japan, Korea, China, Java, and the Philippines to collect rice varieties and study methods of production and improvement. Mr. Jones is the author of various scientific publications on dry-land crops and rice.

FOR FURTHER READING

Davis, Loren L., and Jones, Jenkin W.: *Fertilizer Experiments with Rice in California*, U. S. D. A. Technical Bulletin 718, 1940.

Walker, R. K., and Sturgis, M. B.: *A Twelve-Month Grazing Program for the Rice Area of Louisiana*, Louisiana Agricultural Experiment Station Bulletin 407, 1946.

New Varieties of Wheat

by B. B. BAYLES

MORE THAN 50 improved varieties of wheat have been distributed to American farmers in the past decade. They resist rust, smut, other diseases, drought, insects, or winterkilling, major hazards that threaten crops always in one place or another. They increased our total wheat production by more than 800 million bushels in the years 1942 to 1946.

Most of them were developed at State agricultural experiment stations in breeding and testing work in which the Department of Agriculture cooperated and which is closely coordinated in each of the four main wheat-growing regions — hard spring, hard red winter, soft red winter, and western. All varieties developed in these programs are carefully tested to determine where they are adapted for growing and to insure that the grain quality of those released is satisfactory.

Varieties resistant to stem rust, released for growing in the preceding decade, occupied more than 12 million acres of the 15,700,000 acres of hard red spring wheat grown in 1944. This class of wheat predominates in the northern Great Plains and Prairie States, where stem rust formerly caused losses as high as 100 million bushels in some years. Approximately two-thirds the total acreage was sown to varieties resistant to both stem and leaf rust in 1946. Some of them also resist stinking smut and loose smut and one of them withstands the hessian fly.

Thatcher, the first extensively grown hard red spring wheat that is highly resistant to stem rust, was developed in cooperation with the Minnesota Agricultural Experiment Station and released in 1934. Because of its spectacular performance during the stem rust epidemic of 1935, when other varieties were badly damaged, it increased rapidly. By 1939 it was grown on an estimated 14.5 million acres in the United States

379

and Canada. The acreage continued to increase until it was partly replaced by varieties resistant to both stem and leaf rust. In 1944 the acreage of Thatcher in the United States had decreased to 4.5 million but had increased in Canada to nearly 17 million. Before the distribution of Thatcher, stem rust had caused such heavy losses to Marquis and later to Ceres, the susceptible varieties then grown, that the damage from leaf rust was scarcely apparent. But when the stem-rust-resistant but leaf-rust-susceptible Thatcher was grown on large acreages the plants undamaged by stem rust were attacked by leaf rust.

Wheat breeders had foreseen this possibility and had been developing adapted varieties that could also withstand leaf rust. The first of these— Renown, a beardless variety—was developed at Canadian experiment stations and distributed in 1937. Pilot and Rival, two high-yielding bearded varieties, were distributed from the North Dakota Experiment Station in 1939. These are resistant to both stem and leaf rust as well as bunt; Pilot is also resistant to mildew. By 1944 Rival was grown on 4,050,000 acres and Pilot on 1,216,000 acres.

Regent, another beardless variety distributed in Canada in 1939, resists stem rust and bunt, and is fairly resistant to leaf rust. It was grown on about 1,334,000 acres in the United States in 1944.

Four other hard red spring varieties were distributed between 1944 and 1946. All merit special mention. They are Mida, in North Dakota; Newthatch, in Minnesota; Henry, in Wisconsin; and Cadet, in North Dakota. Mida is bearded, medium early, high-yielding, and highly resistant to stem rust, leaf rust, and bunt. It is also somewhat resistant to the hessian fly. It was extensively grown in 1946, but its tendency to shatter, susceptibility to loose smut, and the greater injury suffered by it during the late 1946 spring freeze may retard its increase. Newthatch resembles Thatcher, except that it has more resistance to leaf rust. Henry is resistant to stem rust and is more resistant to leaf rust than other commercial varieties. It is recommended for growing only in Wisconsin, because its milling characteristics differ in some respects from other recently developed, high-quality, hard red spring wheats. Cadet is an excellent beardless type that compares favorably with the other varieties in resistance to both stem and leaf rusts. It performed well in 1946.

Rescue, a still newer variety, was developed by breeders at the Swift Current Station in Saskatchewan to combat losses from the wheat stem sawfly in sections of Canada and Montana. It has shown promise in tests where the sawfly does damage, but it does not resist leaf rust, bunt, or mildew.

The stem rust susceptible Durum varieties, Kubanka and Mindum, are now being replaced by two new varieties, Carleton and Stewart, both highly resistant to stem rust. They have excellent grain quality and were first distributed in North Dakota in 1943.

The Hard Red Winter Region

Hard red winter wheats in 1944 occupied an estimated 30,600,000 acres, about 47 percent of our total wheat acreage. In the central and southern Great Plains, where most of the hard red winter wheats are grown, stem-rust losses have been heavy in some years, and leaf rust, septoria, stinking smut, loose smut, and the hessian fly also have taken a heavy toll. The goal of plant breeders has been to overcome those plagues and to develop sorts that mature early enough to escape drought.

Tenmarq, the first early variety of satisfactory quality, was developed in the coordinated regional program and distributed from the Kansas Agricultural Experiment Station in 1932. In 1944 it was grown more widely in the United States than any other variety of wheat. In then occupied 8,744,000 acres. Tenmarq is 2 or 3 days earlier than Turkey, the variety that had been grown by most farmers in the region for more than half a century. Its weight per bushel is low, but the milling and baking qualities of Tenmarq are excellent.

Cheyenne and Nebred, distributed in Nebraska in 1933 and 1938, have been popular in western Nebraska and the adjacent sections of Kansas and Colorado. Cheyenne is considered a good combine variety because of its stiff straw and erect heads. Nebred is resistant to stinking smut. Both are high-yielding varieties of satisfactory quality, but mature too late to be grown farther south.

Most hard red winter wheat is milled into flour for bread. Bakers want flour having certain characteristics of quality because they must be able to produce a uniform product month after month. Varieties differ markedly in characteristics that determine quality. During the past few years a considerable acreage of varieties that produce inferior flour for bread has been grown in Kansas, Oklahoma, and Texas. These varieties, Chiefkan, Red Chief, and Early Blackhull, have some desirable characteristics from the farmer's standpoint; their test weights are 1 to 2 pounds heavier, and that often means a higher grade on the market. Bakers, however, have difficulty making satisfactory bread from flour that contains a high percentage of those varieties.

Four new varieties of satisfactory grain quality, Pawnee, Comanche, Wichita, and Westar, released to growers in 1943 and 1944, give promise of replacing the varieties of inferior quality. They are earlier and have higher test weights and stiffer straw than the popular Tenmarq, which is a parent of the first three varieties. Pawnee, Comanche, and Westar are about 3 days and Wichita 6 days earlier than Tenmarq. Pawnee is somewhat resistant to leaf and stem rust, loose smut, and hessian fly. Comanche resists stinking smut. Westar withstands leaf rust. Wichita often escapes damage from the rusts as well as drought because of its early maturity.. Comanche was selected from an Oro × Tenmarq cross, Pawnee from a Kawvale × Tenmarq cross, and Wichita from an Early Black-hull × Tenmarq cross. While none of these varieties was grown on more than a few acres in 1943, it is estimated that Pawnee was grown on 1,500,000 acres, Comanche on 1,000,000 acres, Wichita on 200,000 acres, and Westar on 3,000 acres for the 1946 crop.

The Soft Winter Regions

Wheat is not a major crop in the East, although soft red winter varieties are grown there on some 12 million acres and soft white varieties on a million acres annually. Wheat is needed in the rotation and it serves as a cash crop. Wheat of these classes is used for making cake, pastry, cracker, biscuit, and similar flours, and prepared breakfast cereals, and the desired quality characteristics are entirely different from those for the hard wheats. The major production hazards have been the leaf rust, loose smut, septoria, scab diseases, the hessian fly, and winterkilling. Resistance to lodging and short straw are important because much of the wheat is sown as a companion crop with seedings of legumes and grasses.

Thorne, the leading soft red winter variety, was grown on more than a million and a half acres in 1944, about three-fourths of it in Ohio. Thorne was developed by the Ohio Agricultural Experiment Station and was distributed in 1937. Its high yields, short, stiff straw, and resistance to loose smut make it popular with farmers, even though its weight per bushel is low.

Fairfield, distributed in Indiana in 1942, is winter hardy, resistant to loose smut and lodging, and is moderately resistant to leaf rust. It has soft grain of good quality. Prairie, distributed in Illinois in 1943, is a bearded winter-hardy variety with moderate resistance to leaf rust. It promises to become an important variety in central Illinois, where soft wheat varieties previously available have been subject to winterkilling. Blackhawk, distributed in Wisconsin in 1944, is one of the most winter-hardy soft wheat varieties adapted for commercial growing. It is resistant to stem rust, leaf rust, and stinking smut, but is probably too late in maturity for growing except in Wisconsin and northern Illinois.

Hardired and Sanford, distributed in South Carolina and Georgia, respectively, in 1940, are moderately resistant to leaf rust. Both are becoming popular varieties in the South, where they are replacing Purplestraw, a leading variety for more than a century. The development of leaf-rust-resistant varieties adapted to the Southeast should aid in the shift from soil-depleting row crops, such as cotton and corn, to the soil-protecting legumes, grasses, and small grains.

Austin, which resists stem and leaf rust and loose smut, was released in Texas in 1943 and was grown on an estimated million acres for the 1946 crop. Plant breeders are watching with interest to see whether growing this variety in central and south Texas will have an effect on the development of rust epidemics in wheat-growing areas to the north. We expect that the use of resistant varieties in Texas will eliminate a source of overwintering rust spores that start the northward movement of rust in the spring and, if weather conditions are right, build up into the major epidemics farther north.

Yorkwin, a variety of white winter wheat distributed in New York in 1936, is now the leader in its class in New York and Michigan. The acreage of Cornell 595, a still newer variety of this class, is increasing rapidly. Both varieties are high yielding with stiff straw and resistance to loose smut.

The Western Region

The extremely diverse climatic conditions in the Pacific Northwest permit all classes of wheat except durum to be grown there successfully.

The principal varieties are white, and of both winter and spring habit. A considerable acreage of hard red winter varieties is also grown. Stinking smut, or bunt, was one of the most serious hazards to wheat production in the region as recently as the early 1930's. The development and distribution of resistant varieties reduced the percentage of cars grading smutty at the Pacific Northwest markets from 36.7 percent in 1931 down to 2.8 percent in 1942. A more virulent type of stinking smut, referred to as "dwarf bunt", formerly caused extremely heavy losses in the valleys of Utah, Idaho, and western Montana. In 1935, 39.8 percent of the cars received at the Utah markets graded smutty. However, the introduction of adapted varieties resistant to that type of smut caused the percentage of cars grading smutty to drop to 9 percent in 1943. The figures are on market grade and do not reflect the losses in yield on the farm from smut.

The hard red winter varieties Ridit, Oro, and Rio, and the white club variety Albit, were among the first smut-resistant varieties distributed to growers in the Columbia Basin. They have been largely replaced by even better strains. Rex, a bunt-resistant, high-yielding white winter wheat with medium short stiff straw, was distributed in Oregon in 1933. Its milling qualities are not considered equal to those of the better varieties by the trade. Reduced losses in recent years have made growers indifferent to the smut problems. This fact, together with the poor quality of Rex, has caused the acreage of resistant varieties to decrease in the Columbia Basin during the past few years. This has increased the percentage of cars grading smutty to 8.3 percent in 1945. Hymar, a smut-resistant white club wheat distributed from the Washington station in 1935, has yielded well in the sections of higher rainfall.

Orfed, the newest bunt-resistant variety for the Columbia Basin, was distributed from the Washington station in 1944. This high-yielding, smut-resistant variety has soft white grain of good quality and has stiff straw that will stand for combining. It can be grown from either fall or spring seeding, although it is not so winter-hardy as are some of the strictly winter varieties. It should not be seeded early in the fall.

Alicel and Elgin, two productive club wheats with soft white grain and very short stiff straw, are grown to some extent in Oregon, Washington, and Idaho. They are susceptible to most races of bunt and should always be treated before seeding.

Relief was the first resistant wheat released in the area where the dwarf bunt was causing almost complete losses in some fields. It is a hard red winter variety distributed in Utah in 1934. It is being replaced with Wasatch, a bearded variety, and Cache, a beardless variety in Utah and southern Idaho. These two hard red winter wheats also are replacing the other hard red winter varieties in the Gallatin and Kalispell Valleys of Montana, where dwarf bunt has caused heavy losses. These three varieties, all developed in Utah, are susceptible to some races of tall or ordinary bunt, but they have enabled farmers in areas infested with dwarf bunt to continue wheat production. Dwarf smut cannot be controlled by seed treatment or cultural practices, while ordinary bunt can be largely controlled by these measures. Relaxation in seed treatment programs, increase in races of smut that attack varieties resistant to races formerly present, and the continued growing of completely susceptible varieties are resulting in an increase in the percentage of wheat grading smutty at Utah markets.

Growers on irrigated lands needed a spring variety with short stiff straw for use with new clover seedings. Lemhi, which has soft white grain of excellent pastry quality, was developed for them.

Losses caused by stem rust have been practically eliminated from the wheat fields of California through the distribution of Baart 38 and White Federation 38, which are resistant to stem rust and to bunt. Released by the California Agricultural Experiment Station in 1939, they are grown on more than two-thirds of the acreage in that State. Big Club 43, which resists the hessian fly, a cause of heavy losses in some sections of California, was distributed in 1944. Bunt and stem rust do it little harm.

THE AUTHOR

B. B. Bayles, an agronomist in the Bureau of Plant Industry, Soils, and Agricultural Engineering, has made special studies of cereal crops in Kansas, Oregon, and Montana since 1922. He was coordinator of wheat research, cooperating with experiment stations in Western States from 1930 to 1937 and later in the Eastern States.

Flax Moves West

by ARTHUR C. DILLMAN and L. G. GOAR

BECAUSE of its restless, roving character, flax has been called one of the curiosities of agriculture. All through the nineteenth century it was a migratory crop in the United States, advancing from New York and Pennsylvania to Ohio, Indiana, Illinois, Iowa, Minnesota, the Dakotas, and Montana as new lands were opened to settlement.

It was a crop for the pioneer farmer, always moving a step ahead of the fatal wilt disease that developed in soils frequently cropped to flax.

H. L. Bolley, at the North Dakota Agricultural Experiment Station, found in 1900 that flax wilt was caused by a soil-borne fungus which he described and named *Fusarium lini*. Later, Bolley and others developed varieties that withstood the disease, and flax settled down as a permanent crop in the North Central States.

Flax was destined to make another move—the long hop from Mandan, N. Dak., to the Imperial Valley Experiment Station, near El Centro, Calif. Several stations in California had experimented with flax between 1915 and 1918, with little success. Nevertheless, we decided that flax was worth another trial out there.

Accordingly, on November 14, 1927, seed of 10 varieties were sown in single 3-row plots 50 feet long. These were harvested in April 1928. The average yield was the equivalent of 25 bushels an acre, but one variety made 31.2 bushels. It was Punjab, a kind that C. H. Clark had selected from a sample of flaxseed obtained from Punjab, India, in 1913. Clark had made several selections at Mandan in 1914 and 1915. He retained one of the taller selections, probably a natural hybrid, and grew it several years under the designation Punjab.

The first increase plot of Punjab, grown at the Imperial Valley station, produced 212 pounds. In 1931, 2 acres were harvested. The seed was distributed to a few farmers, who harvested 110 acres in 1932 and 350 acres in 1933. All the seed harvested in 1933 was used for planting 8,000 acres in the Imperial Valley. The crop, harvested in May 1934, produced nearly 242,000 bushels.

Now flax was on its way. The one ounce of flaxseed, planted in November 1927, had established a new industry that was to bring employment and a measure of wealth to thousands of people.

In the 1930's, the Imperial Valley, in common with agriculture elsewhere, suffered from low prices and a surplus of its farm products, chiefly alfalfa, barley, wheat, melons, lettuce, and other vegetable crops. Vegetables are high-cost crops, and losses are great when there is an oversupply. That was the general situation from 1930 to 1934. Then, in 1934, flax came to the rescue. It was not a speculative crop. It found a ready-cash market and it made a modest but sure return to growers. As a result, accumulated taxes were paid up; abandoned farms were bought and paid for with one or two crops of flax; and, above all, with the acreage of grain and vegetable crops adjusted to the market, agriculture in general became more profitable.

War always increases the demand for fats and oils. After Pearl Harbor, imports of vegetable oils were greatly reduced. The United States had to depend on domestic production. The response of farmers to the need was notable, indeed. The production of fats and oils increased to the point where large quantities could be exported to our allies. In 1943 and 1944, total exports were approximately 1,600,000,000 pounds annually. Of this total, exports of linseed oil amounted to 224,466,000 pounds in 1943 and 313,244,000 pounds in 1944. In terms of flaxseed, this represents a total of 28 million bushels for the 2 years.

The increase of flaxseed production in California was remarkable. To the Imperial Valley, flax was as important as corn to Iowa. Forty percent of the farm land in the valley in 1943 was put into flax. The higher production of flaxseed in California and Arizona not only supplied the needs of the Pacific coast area for linseed oil and linseed meal, but saved the overtaxed railroads from shipping flaxseed into the area, as was the practice 10 years earlier.

The acreage harvested in California in 1939–44 averaged 183,000; the production of flaxseed averaged 3,136,000 bushels a year. Arizona farmers, chiefly those in the irrigated valley of the Colorado below Yuma, planted an average of 15,000 acres each of the 6 years, and harvested an average of nearly 340,000 bushels. Allowing for seed used on farms, the total commercial crop in California and Arizona for the 6 years was approximately 20 million bushels, or 20 thousand carloads of 1,000 bushels each. For it, the farmers received more than $50,000,000.

Weeds are a serious problem. Where flax is sown in the fall, as in California and Arizona, farmers have a long period before seeding time when weeds can be destroyed by cultivation. A common practice is to irrigate the land two or three times in early fall and cultivate after each irrigation. The land should be plowed or subsoiled (chiseled), disked, and leveled (floated) before the first irrigation. When weeds appear and the surface soil becomes dry, the field should be cultivated thoroughly, but only 3 or 4 inches deep. A spring-tooth harrow is satisfactory for the purpose. A second irrigation, followed by thorough cultivation and harrowing, will generally be enough to eliminate most weeds, and leave the soil in good condition for planting. Sometimes a third irrigation and cultivation are needed to destroy wild oats, canary grass, and other weeds that do not appear until cooler weather comes on.

Another way is to grow a green-manure crop in summer. Sesbania, commonly used as a summer crop, thrives in hot weather. The frequent and heavy irrigation required for a summer crop kills most weed seeds in the surface soil. The green-manure crop is plowed shallow or, better, disked into the surface when the soil is still moist. With heat and moisture, the green crop rots rapidly.

A third method, growing the flax in cultivated rows, has been used successfully but not widely in the Imperial Valley. For row planting, the ground should be well prepared by irrigation and tillage, as for ordinary seeding. The seed is sown in drill rows 18, 21, or 24 inches apart, the spacing determined by the tread of the tractor and the type of cultivator used. The seed should be sown 24 to 30 pounds an acre so as to obtain a thick stand that will check weeds in the rows.

Shallow cultivation should be given as soon as possible after the first and second irrigations. Two cultivations are usually sufficient to eliminate most weeds until the flax is bolled. Timely harvest will then prevent any late weeds from going to seed. Where flax is grown for sale as certified seed, the few weeds that escape in the rows can be pulled by hand.

The broadleafed annual weeds can be checked or killed by spraying with Sinox or other selective spray material that adheres to the rough hairy surface of many weeds but does not wet the smoother leaves and stems of flax or grasses. Sinox is of no value in the control of wild oats, cheat, darnell, or other grass weeds. For best results, spraying should be done when the weeds are very small and the flax is 4 to 6 inches high. In no case should the spray be applied after the flax plants reach the flower-bud stage; at that stage, serious injury may occur. Sinox is most effective on clear warm days when the temperature is above 65° F.

Fifteen years of experiments at the Imperial Valley station indicate that early November is the best time for seeding. The highest yields and quality have been obtained from seedings made from November 1 to 20. In general, there is a reduction in yield when seeding is delayed until mid-December or early January, apparently because of the shorter growing season of the later planting.

Flax sown at different dates, October to December, ripens at about the same time; that is, in late April or early May, when high temperatures force maturity of the crop. Flax sown early in November has a long blossoming period (30 to 50 days), and a growing season of 150 to 180 days. These conditions permit the maximum setting of seed bolls and full maturity of the crop. In the date-of-seeding tests at El Centro, November plantings have shown, on the average, taller plants, a longer blossoming season, larger seeds, a higher oil content, and a higher iodine number of the oil than obtained from December plantings.

In the Imperial Valley it is a common practice to seed flax following alfalfa, sugar beets, carrots, lettuce, or another vegetable crop. Perhaps the best soil preparation for flax is a green-manure crop of sesbania, guar, cowpeas, or clover. These improve the soil, help maintain the nitrogen, control weeds, and reduce the hazard of diseases that may be carried over in the soil. Two or more crops of flax are often grown in succession. Generally, however, this is not a good practice, because both weeds and flax diseases are apt to increase under continuous cropping.

The use of fertilizers depends to some extent on the previous crop or the rotation system followed. Both phosphorus and nitrogen are usually needed for maximum yields. A safe rule is to apply about 65 units of available phosphate before planting, and 32 units of nitrogen in the first irrigation after the flax is up, or any time before the flower buds appear.

The success of flax in California and Arizona has been due to several factors: The excellent adaptation of the Punjab variety as a winter crop under irrigation in the area; the skill, resourcefulness, and cooperation of the pioneer growers of the crop; and a ready market for the high-quality seed. Perhaps the world record for yield of flaxseed was made by Harrison Emrick, of Yuma County, Ariz., in 1939. His field of 24.7 acres of Punjab flax made the remarkable yield of 61.6 bushels an acre.

THE AUTHORS

Arthur C. Dillman, formerly an associate agronomist, Division of Cereal Crops and Diseases, in the Bureau of Plant Industry, Soils, and Agricultural Engineering, is now an agronomist with the Flax Development Committee, of the Flax Institute of the United States, in Minneapolis.

L. G. Goar is an associate in the Experiment Station (Agronomy), California College of Agriculture, and is Superintendent of the Imperial Valley Experiment Station, El Centro, Calif. He has worked with flax and other oil-bearing crops continuously since 1926.

ALSO, IN THIS BOOK

Corn Hybrids for the South

by MERLE T. JENKINS

PROGRESSIVE farmers in all parts of the South want to know what is being done to develop corn hybrids suited to their soil and climate and whether adapted hybrids can duplicate in their fields the outstanding performance of those in the Corn Belt. Encouraging answers can be given them.

The Department of Agriculture is conducting corn-improvement programs in cooperation with 12 State agricultural experiment stations. Five are in the South—North Carolina, Tennessee, Mississippi, Louisiana, and Georgia. Informal cooperation is maintained with all other southern stations that have corn-improvement experiments.

Because corn hybrids are produced by crossing inbred lines, the general quality of a group of hybrids depends upon the characteristics of the parent lines. Outstanding, or elite, inbred lines are isolated only infrequently, and the numbers and relative superiority of elite lines isolated depends largely upon the total number of lines examined and tested.

The early inbreeding programs in the South, like those in the Corn Belt, were small. The elite lines that founded the present hybrids in the Corn Belt were developed as a result of the greatly expanded inbreeding programs organized in the early 1920's. Similar expansion of the southern corn-breeding programs occurred in the late 1930's and early 1940's, but was relatively less extensive than that in the Midwest. The group of elite lines that is beginning to emerge from the expanded programs promises a marked improvement in hybrids for the South in the next few years.

Another prime factor in developing outstanding Corn Belt corn hybrids was the exchange of breeding materials among the cooperating experiment stations. The Purnell Corn Improvement Conference, which functioned from 1926 to 1932, and its successor, the Corn Improvement

389

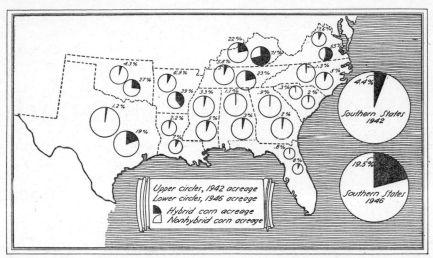

Suitable types of hybrid corn are being developed for the Southeast States. Acreage increased more than fourfold from 1942 to 1946, as shown by this chart.

Conference of the North Central Region, organized in 1937, promoted the exchange. In 1933 a series of uniform tests of hybrids involving a group of elite lines contributed by the different cooperating experiment stations was organized to promote further the wide use of the best of the available breeding material. U. S. Hybrid 13, a direct result of the first of these uniform tests, is the most widely grown hybrid in the country. Many other Corn Belt hybrids involve a relatively small group of elite lines; the uniform tests aided materially in identifying them.

The Southern Corn Improvement Conference was organized in New Orleans, in November 1939, at the instigation of Fred H. Hull of the Florida Agricultural Experiment Station. Uniform tests of crosses among lines grown in the South were organized in 1941 to further the ready interchange of breeding materials; the first tests were made in 1942.

The uniform tests bring to light and permit the selection of parent lines whose hybrids perform satisfactorily over a wide range of growing conditions. Numerous advantages derive from this procedure. Uniform tests in different States give an opportunity to find out how the new kinds perform in different kinds of soil and climate in the same season. We thus get in one season results that are somewhat comparable to those from tests in each of several seasons at a single location. Hybrids involving parent inbred lines whose crosses perform satisfactorily under a wide range of conditions are not likely to perform badly under some peculiar or unusual set of conditions. The identification of these widely adapted parent lines permits simplification of the hybrid corn program as a few widely adapted hybrids can be made to serve a whole region.

Many of the promising new experimental hybrids of the South involve this new crop of elite lines. Outstanding white lines among those of suitable maturity for the area in which Neal Paymaster is adapted are T61 and T13 from Tennessee, and NC34, NC37, and NC45 from North Carolina. T61 probably has more yield factors than any other southern inbred line, but it is subject to root lodging. Outstanding yellow inbred lines of suitable maturity for the same general area are CI.21 and CI.7, developed by the Department, Ky35–7 from Kentucky, NC7 and NC13, developed in North Carolina, and Kys, developed in Kansas.

Experience has amply demonstrated that crosses among lines of widely diverse origin usually have the most vigor. The outstanding hybrids of the Corn Belt usually involve lines originating from more than one State program. In all probability, the same will be found to hold true in the South. The promotion of free interchange of breeding materials sponsored by the Southern Corn Improvement Conference stands directly to benefit every southern corn grower by providing him with better hybrids than he would have otherwise.

Available Hybrids

The first general survey of hybrid corn acreage in the Southern States, made in 1941, gave us the estimate that 1,029,000 acres were planted to hybrids in the South that year; in 1946 the acreage was 5,469,000.

Kentucky, Virginia, Texas, Arkansas, and Oklahoma have been able to utilize some of the later Corn Belt inbred lines and hybrids. But the Southeastern States have not been able to use them, except in a limited way, in the mountains or to grow early feed for livestock. The expansion of hybrid corn in the Southeast, therefore, depends on development of suitable local hybrids. The expanding acreages of hybrid corn in these States are evidence that suitable hybrids are becoming available rapidly.

Among the hybrids adapted to the Southeast, the Tennessee hybrids developed by the Tennessee Agricultural Experiment Station and the Department have had the largest commercial expansion. These hybrids, of which Tennessee Hybrids 10 and 15 are most popular, are combinations among inbred lines out of Neal Paymaster. They resemble Neal Paymaster in general characteristics and fit into the general territory in which that variety has been grown in the past. In 34 comparisons conducted in Tennessee between 1939 and 1945, their average yield exceeded that of Neal Paymaster and Jellicorse by 8 percent, or 5 bushels an acre. Tennessee Hybrids 10 and 15 have performed satisfactorily in most of Tennessee, much of northern Alabama and Mississippi, and in the Piedmont area from North Carolina to Georgia. Their greatest weakness is their tendency to lodge; they are not much better than Neal Paymaster in that respect. A new yellow hybrid that has done well in two seasons of trials was produced commercially on a limited scale in 1946.

The estimated 1945 production of certified hybrid seed corn in Tennessee was 87,098 bushels, or enough to plant about 600,000 acres in 1946.

An estimated 47,000 bushels of seed of North Carolina corn hybrids were produced there in 1946, enough for approximately 325,000 acres in 1947. Somewhat more than 90 percent of that production was of the four yellow hybrids, North Carolina 26, T11, 27, and 1032, developed cooperatively by the North Carolina Agricultural Experiment Station and the Department. North Carolina Hybrid 1032 has extremely strong roots and stalks; in eight tests in the Piedmont area of North Carolina in 1943 and 1945 it outyielded the standard varieties by 21.5 percent. It also exceeded the standard varieties in yield by 18.5 percent in 10 tests in the coastal plain area of that State in 1942, 1943, and 1944. The yield record of North Carolina Hybrid 26 has surpassed that of 1032. North Carolina T11, a top cross, is one of the older North Carolina hybrids and it probably will be replaced soon with a double cross. North Carolina 27 is a relatively new combination of much promise. It is slightly later in maturing than the other three yellow hybrids.

A limited amount of seed of two white hybrids, North Carolina 1111 and T20, also was produced in 1946. They have excellent records in yield, but they probably will not be widely used because they do not stand appreciably better than the open-pollinated varieties. A group of experimental hybrids already tested 2 or 3 years promises to be materially better than those now in commercial production.

Seed of six hybrids developed in cooperation with the Louisiana Agricultural Experiment Station sufficient for planting about 85,000 acres in 1947 was produced in 1946. Two of them, Louisiana Hybrids 468 and 518 are white dent; one, Louisiana Hybrid 731, is a yellow dent; one, Louisiana Hybrid 2909, is a yellow flint similar to Creole Yellow Flint; and two, Louisiana Hybrids 1030 and 1031, have mixed yellow and white kernels. The Louisiana hybrids in commercial production have exceeded the standard Louisiana open-pollinated varieties in yield by about 30 percent. The white dent hybrids have performed satisfactorily in tests in Mississippi and Georgia, as well as in Louisiana. Louisiana Hybrid 2909 is particularly suited to the sugarcane areas of both Louisiana and Florida. The yellow dent hybrid, 731, is a new combination that should be well suited to the central portion of the State. Louisiana Hybrid 1030, the better of the two hybrids with mixed kernel color, has the best record for lodging resistance of any of the Louisiana hybrids and promises to become very popular for that reason. It also has an enviable record for resistance to the corn earworm and to weevils.

Florida Hybrid W–1, a white, prolific hybrid developed by the Florida Agricultural Experiment Station, has established a good record of performance in Florida and the southern coastal plain of Georgia. It has been produced commercially on a limited scale and seed production is gradually expanding. On fertile soils, Florida W–1 is tall, high-eared, and tends to lodge rather badly because of weak roots.

Some of the experimental hybrids developed in cooperation with the Mississippi Agricultural Experiment Station appear promising. One of these made an outstanding record in 1945 and limited quantities of seed of it were produced in 1946. If it continues to perform satisfactorily it probably will enter commercial production within the next few years.

Future of Hybrid Corn in the South

The corn hybrids now available for planting in the South represent only a preliminary effort in the breeding of special types for the area. They are the product of only a fraction of the time, energy, and funds that have been devoted to the development of corn hybrids for the Corn Belt. It is not surprising, therefore, that they answer the requirements of their region less precisely than do the hybrids now available for the Corn Belt. One should remember that the greater hazards of corn production in the South necessarily increase the attributes required in desirable hybrids and, naturally, multiply the difficulties involved in breeding them.

The great numbers of disease and insect pests in the South will require the concentration of many desirable characters in order to obtain the desired levels of resistance. Encouraging progress is being made, evidence of resistance to many insects and diseases is at hand, and definite sources of resistance have been identified in many cases. But much more time will be needed for breeding the generations necessary to transfer, combine, concentrate, purify, and fix the desired characters in the inbred lines that are to become the parents of the outstanding hybrids of the future. Full-season hybrids for most of the South require long, tight-fitting husks to protect them from weevil damage from the time the ears ripen until they are harvested. Many of the Corn Belt hybrids yield well when grown in the South, but they lack the needed husk protection to prevent the grain from being damaged or entirely destroyed in the field before harvest.

The job before us is not easy or quick, but it is worth our best effort, time, and money. Think of the phenomenal expansion and success of corn hybrids in the Corn Belt. From a small beginning in 1933, confined almost entirely to Iowa and Illinois, hybrid corn expanded by leaps and bounds. In 1946 it occupied more than 62 million acres or 67.5 percent of the national corn acreage. This includes 99 percent or more of the acreage in Iowa, Illinois, and Indiana, 90 percent or more of the acreage in Ohio, Minnesota, Wisconsin, and Missouri, and at least 80 percent of the acreage in Nebraska, Michigan, and New Jersey. In 1942, 1943, 1944, and 1945 the national corn production has exceeded 3 billion bushels and the estimated corn production for 1946 also was above 3 billion bushels. These yields are from national acreages appreciably below normal. The greater standability of the hybrids also has resulted in increased economies of production by decreasing the cost of harvesting and thus has resulted in greater profits to growers.

During the three war years of 1917, 1918, and 1919, we produced 8 billion bushels of corn on a total of 311 million acres. During the three war years of 1942, 1943, and 1944, we produced 9⅓ billion bushels on 281 million acres—1,366,201,000 more bushels than in the earlier period, on 30,522,000 fewer acres. This is equivalent to 5 billion pounds more meat a year—38 pounds more per person a year. When you look back to the fact that there were times during the last war when meat rationing got down to as low as 115 pounds a person a year, you can appreciate the importance of this extra production.

The research we are conducting will be a good business investment for Southern States, relatively as good, we hope, as the research of the past. Federal expenditures on corn improvement since the organization of the Department probably total between 4 and 5 million dollars. The increased yield of corn resulting from the planting of hybrid corn in 1945 probably amounted to about 700 million bushels. At a dollar a bushel, the increased income to farmers amounted to 700 million dollars. If only the normal tax of 3 percent were paid back into the United States Treasury on only one-third of this increased income, the extra income tax collected would amount to about 7 million dollars, which exceeds the total Federal expenditures for corn improvement since the Department was organized. These computations omit the extra taxes paid by the producers of hybrid seed corn, a new industry, that amounted to about 70 million dollars in 1945.

THE AUTHOR

Merle T. Jenkins is a principal agronomist in charge of corn investigation in the Bureau of Plant Industry, Soils, and Agricultural Engineering. He organized and had charge of the hybrid corn-breeding program in cooperation with the Iowa Agricultural Experiment Station from 1922 to 1934. Dr. Jenkins is a graduate of Iowa State College.

FOR FURTHER READING

Hayes, H. K., and Immer, F. R.: *Methods of Plant Breeding,* McGraw-Hill Book Company, Inc., New York, New York, 1942.

Richey, Frederick D.: *The What and How of Hybrid Corn,* U. S. D. A. Farmers' Bulletin 1744, 1935.

Wallace, Henry A., and Bressman, Earl N.: *Corn and Corn Growing,* Fourth Edition, John Wiley & Sons, Inc., New York, New York, 1937.

ALSO, IN THIS BOOK

Genetics and Farming, by E. R. Sears, page 245.

Disease-Resistant Oats

by T. R. STANTON

THIS IS the story of a single oat seed and how it revolutionized a large industry. The story goes back to 1929, the year it was found that Victoria oats could withstand crown rust. Crown rust was the scourge of oats; even though three or four varieties were partly resistant, crown rust caused heavy losses every time it became epidemic. Worse, there seemed to be scant prospect of ever breeding oats that could resist it. Two years later, opportunities for constructive breeding were further enhanced by the discovery of the even greater resistance of the variety named Bond. Further, Victoria and Bond were found to be resistant to certain smuts. So they became founders of family trees whose fruits include the amazing Clinton and Benton oats.

The Department of Agriculture had brought Victoria in 1927 from Uruguay, where it had been selected from the so-called "common oat of the country," which probably had been introduced many decades earlier from the Mediterranean region. Bond was originated by the Department of Agriculture of New South Wales from a cross between a sport of the wild red oat (*Avena sterilis*), and Golden Rain, the well-known Swedish variety of common oats (*A. sativa*). It was brought here in 1929.

Victoria is a late, vigorous red oat belonging to the species *A. byzantina*. Bond likewise is a red oat, but of midseason maturity and with a very stiff straw and plump grains. Neither Victoria nor Bond is satisfactory for farm production in this country, but for breeding material they are among the most valuable ever introduced into the United States.

In 1930, at what was then the Department's breeding laboratory in Arlington, Va., Victoria was crossed with Richland. Richland, the pollen or male parent, is a Kherson type with high resistance to stem rust and excellent crop characteristics. It had been grown extensively in the Corn

Belt since 1916. From this pollination only one original crossed, that is, only one so-called "baby hybrid" seed was obtained. But that one seed was enough to change radically the production of oats in the principal producing area of the United States.

The precious seed was planted at Aberdeen, Idaho, in 1930. In 1931 and later, numerous selections from the progeny of this plant were tested for rust and smut resistance at several stations.

From these progenies a group of early short-strawed, Richland-like selections were obtained. They had a combination of resistance to the rusts and smuts, high yield and quality, and a straw that stood up better than that of Richland. From the group, Boone, Control, and Tama were distributed by the Iowa Agricultural Experiment Station. Vicland, Cedar, and Vikota were increased and distributed, respectively, by the experiment stations of Wisconsin, Nebraska, and South Dakota.

These are now dominant varieties of oats in nearly all Corn Belt States. In several States, they are grown almost to the exclusion of other oat varieties. They also have spread rapidly into the Northeastern States. It is estimated that they were grown on approximately 30 million acres in 1946, two-thirds of the oat acreage of the United States that year. They have added many millions of dollars to the agricultural wealth of the country and have placed oats on a much better economic basis. Vicland is the most widely grown of the group. According to agronomists at the Wisconsin station, the 400 million bushels of Vicland oats constituted one-fourth of the 1945 national oat production.

So far, about 30 named varieties have been obtained directly or indirectly from Victoria crosses. Seven named kinds stem from Bond crosses—fewer than from Victoria because of the difficulty in finding lines that are sufficiently uniform.

Bond, however, is an excellent parent. Clinton and Benton are the first varieties developed from Bond crosses to be extensively increased for distribution in the Corn Belt. Three others, Eaton, Bonda, and Mindo, were scheduled for later distribution.

Clinton and Benton originated as selections from a mating between Iowa D69 and Bond made at Ames, Iowa, in 1932. The Iowa D69 parent was the product of earlier cooperative oat-breeding work at the Iowa station. It originated from a cross between Green Russian, one of the pre-Victoria kinds, and Richland, but was not quite good enough to distribute for commercial production.

Numerous productive high-quality strains were selected at Ames from the Iowa D69 × Bond cross. They were highly resistant to the rusts and fairly resistant to the smuts. Because of their excellent performance in Iowa, seed of certain selections was forwarded for testing at the Indiana and Illinois stations in 1939 and 1940. The selection 1335-3 proved to be outstanding for disease-resistance, high yield, quality, and standing ability. It was named Clinton for the Clinton counties in Iowa, Indiana, and Illinois, the three States in which its merits became evident.

A total of 680 progeny rows of Clinton were sown at Ames in 1943 for a purification test. They were checked for resistance to the rusts and smuts and also for uniformity of plant and grain characters. Those that passed inspection were harvested in bulk. Twenty-five pounds of this purified seed was sown at Mesa, Ariz., in the winter of 1943–44, under the direction of A. T. Bartel. The resulting crop of 67 bushels was sown at Aberdeen, Idaho, in the late spring of 1944 under the direction of J. L. Toevs. More than 1,200 bushels of seed were obtained and distributed to farmers in Iowa, Indiana, and Illinois for further increase of the selection in 1945.

About 43,000 bushels of Clinton seed were produced in 1945. This supply was increased again on selected farms in 1946, to nearly two million bushels of seed that were made available to growers in 1947. Clinton has been superior to Tama, Boone, Cedar, and Vicland in Iowa, because of its better resistance to crown rust, stem rust, leaf spot, and lodging and because of its higher yield and test weight. In tests at the Iowa station, the average acre yield of Clinton has been about 16 bushels higher than that of Tama. In 49 and 42 Iowa Standard Community Grain Trials in 1945 and 1946, respectively, Clinton outyielded Tama by about the same margin.

Clinton also has made satisfactory yields in coordinated uniform nursery tests made in cooperation with agricultural experiment stations of the North Central and Northeastern States, but its general performance has not been so promising as in the Iowa tests. Clinton has stiff straw and is well adapted for combine harvesting.

Benton, a sister selection of Clinton, demonstrated its value first at the Purdue University Agricultural Experiment Station in Indiana. There it has been under test, formerly as Selection 1263–1, since 1939. More than 1,300 bushels of Benton were produced by that station in 1945 and distributed to some farmers in Indiana, Iowa, and Illinois for increase in 1946. Thus Benton is being distributed jointly by the experiment stations of the three States.

The chief advantages of Benton and Clinton over Boone, Vicland, and Tama are greater productivity, higher test weight, better resistance to crown and stem rust, and a much stiffer straw. Clinton and Benton are not entirely perfect, however; they are highly susceptible to a hitherto little-known form of crown rust, which was somewhat more prevalent in 1945 than in previous years, and may lessen their future value to some extent. Benton and Clinton are similar in their reaction to the rusts and smuts and also in productiveness, although Clinton may be slightly superior in average yield. In tests in field plots at Lafayette, Ind., Benton, Clinton, and Tama each has averaged around 68 bushels an acre from

1942 to 1945, but in the nursery yield tests at that station, Clinton and Benton averaged about 17 bushels more than Boone.

Benton differs from Clinton primarily in being 4 or 5 inches taller and in having a slightly larger kernel. Benton usually can be distinguished from Clinton in the field by the presence of a collar of short hairs just below the upper stem node. Where a taller variety is desired on the thinner upland soils, Benton may be preferable to Clinton. It also is more uniform than Clinton in certain plant characters.

Eaton resulted from an Iogold-Bond cross made at Ames in 1932. The selection was sent to the Michigan Agricultural Experiment Station at East Lansing in 1940. There it was mass-selected for uniformity of plant height and grain color by E. E. Down and his associates. Eaton is an early to midseason white oat with thin hulls, high test weight, and stiff straw. It also is resistant to crown rust, stem rust, and the oat smuts. In the tests in Michigan, Eaton has been superior in yield and quality to the rust-susceptible, standard variety Huron. Its very stiff straw should make it popular for combine harvesting in Michigan.

Bonda was developed from a Bond-Anthony cross made at the Minnesota Agricultural Experiment Station at St. Paul. It is an early to midseason oat with yellowish-white to white kernels of superior test weight. Its very stiff straw is more resistant to lodging than Tama and Vicland under Minnesota conditions. Bonda is highly resistant to crown rust, stem rust, and smuts. Bonda is fairly uniform in plant and kernel characters and has been a high yielder. It also is especially well adapted for combine harvesting. Seed of Bonda has been increased for distribution to Minnesota farmers in 1947.

Mindo also was developed by the Minnesota station from the cross Bond × [(Minota-White Russian) × Black Mesdag]. It is an early common oat with rather small yellow grains of excellent test weight. The straw is rather short, stiff, and very resistant to lodging. Mindo has the same resistance to the rusts and smuts as Bonda, and is fairly uniform in plant and kernel characters. It also has yielded high and is of promise as a new early oat for Minnesota.

New Oats for the Southwest

Sporadic epidemics of rust, especially of crown or leaf rust, have reduced the yield of oats in the Southwest for many years. The standard rust-susceptible varieties, such as Fulghum (Kanota), Columbia, Fulton, and Red Rustproof, have suffered heavily, with the result that several so-called poor oat years, including 1945, have been experienced by producers of oats.

To meet this crisis, some new, early, highly productive spring red oat varieties with high resistance to the rusts and smuts have been developed from Fulton × Victoria-Richland and Markton-Fulghum × Victoria-Richland crosses. They were made at Aberdeen, Idaho, in 1935. From these crosses, the new varieties Osage and Neosho were released in Kansas; Ventura, a sister selection of Osage, was released in California in 1945. Osage and Ventura resemble Boone and Vicland in many characteristics of plant and kernel, but they mature a little earlier and have an even shorter straw. Neosho is a red oat with a very stiff straw and resistance to the rusts. It also resists certain races of the oat smuts. Osage, Neosho, and Ventura appear to be well adapted to the climate of Kansas and Southwestern States where red oats are grown.

There they should vitalize oat production in the same way that Boone, Tama, Vicland, and Cedar have in the northern oats areas.

Winter Oats for the South

Less important from the national standpoint, but of great value to the South, are several new disease-resistant varieties developed for fall seeding. These were selected from crosses of Victoria and Bond with standard common and red oat varieties such as Lee, Custis, Fulghum, Fulgrain, and Red Rustproof (Nortex).

Some of the most promising new winter varieties have come from a cross between Lee and Victoria. Lee is a hardy productive high-quality oat, but very susceptible to the rusts and smuts. The varieties developed and distributed from this cross are Letoria and Lelina in North Carolina; Stanton (strains 1, 2, 3, and 4) in South Carolina and other Southern States; Lega, Lelate, Levic, and Leroy in Georgia; Florilee in Florida; and DeSoto in Arkansas. These represent a rather distinct new type of common winter oats. They have less hull and better grain characters than are found in many of the more widely grown Red Rustproof strains, a fact not fully appreciated at first by southern oat growers.

Traveler is a promising new variety resistant to crown rust and smut developed from a Victoria-Custis cross at the Arkansas Agricultural Experiment Station. Custis is a sister selection of Lee and of similar type. The cross was made at Fayetteville, Ark., in 1937, where the strain, later named Traveler, was selected. Traveler is a productive, short, fairly stiff-strawed, winter-resistant oat, bred primarily for grazing and clipping purposes. The variety is somewhat variable in certain plant characters and may need further purification.

Varieties of red oats that resist crown rust and smut, originating from crosses of Victoria and Fulghum-type oats, are Quincy Red (Quincy No. 1), and Fultex. Quincy Red was selected from a cross made in 1930 between Fulghum (Kanota) and Victoria. Selections from this cross were first tested at Ames for resistance to crown rust. Then they were grown at Experiment, Ga., and from there, for a more rigid test, they were sent to the North Florida Agricultural Experiment Station at Quincy, where heavy natural epidemics of crown rust occur almost every year. Quincy Red was so outstanding for yield as well as for resistance to crown rust that it was increased and distributed. Quincy Red resembles the Fulghum parent in general appearance. The grain of Quincy Red is plump and reddish in color and tests as much as 38 pounds to the bushel in favorable seasons. It has made oats a safe crop in northern Florida, where practically no oats were grown before crown-rust-resistant varieties became available. Quincy Red also has spread into the adjoining areas of Georgia and Alabama.

Fultex, a short, stiff-strawed kind, resistant to crown rust and moderately resistant to smut, also was developed from a Fulghum-Victoria cross. The selections giving rise to Fultex were subsequently developed at Substation No. 6, Denton, Tex. Although not a top-notcher in grain quality and yield, Fultex is on the increase in north-central Texas and adjacent States, mainly because of its adaptability to combine harvesting.

Some of the most widely grown southern early red oats with resistance to crown rust and smut have been developed by a commercial seed company from crosses of Victoria with the original Fulgrain, which is resistant only to the oat smuts. Fulgrain originated from a cross between Norton 20–93 (Big Boy) and Navarro, made at Hartsville, S. C., in 1925. Fulgrain was crossed with Victoria to obtain resistance to crown rust. This cross produced Fulgrain (strains 4, 5, 6, 7, and 8) and also Victorgrain, a new varietal type; both varieties were resistant to crown rust and smut. Several strains of Victorgrain have been released for commercial production. Fulgrain is the earliest red oat grown extensively in the South. For this reason, it is usually recommended where earliness is of major importance. Both the Fulgrain and Victorgrain strains have contributed substantially to the agricultural wealth of the South.

Red oat varieties with resistance to crown rust and smut have been originated from a cross made at Arlington, Va., in 1930, between Nortex, a typical Red Rustproof oat, and Victoria. These new varieties include Ranger, Rustler, Rangler, and Carolina Red. Ranger and Rustler were selected and proved at College Station, Tex., and Rangler was developed at Denton, Tex. Carolina Red was released in 1943 by a southern commercial seed company. These varieties are rather typical of the Red Rustproof type. Despite their disease resistance, they have not been significantly better in average yield than the Nortex parent in tests. Ranger and Rustler were distributed to farmers by the Texas station after 1940. Ranger is just being increased for possible farm production.

Quincy Gray originated as a selection from a cross of Victoria-Norton × Red Rustproof at Quincy, Fla., where it was released for commercial production in the early 1940's. The cross had been made at the Georgia Agricultural Experiment Station. Quincy Gray is a late-maturing, short, stiff-strawed, grayish-white oat, somewhat intermediate between red and common oats in grain characters but with very little winter resistance. It is also known as Quincy No. 2 and Quincy White. Quincy Gray resists crown rust and smut, but is of much less economic importance than Quincy Red. It is grown only to a limited extent in north Florida and adjoining southern Georgia and Alabama.

Verde was selected from a backcross involving Red Rustproof and Victoria-Richland. The original hybrid material from the cross made at Aberdeen, Idaho, in 1934, was sent to College Station, Tex., in 1935. Verde is resistant to both rusts and smuts. It is rather typical of the Red Rustproof type of oats, but is earlier in maturity. Verde was distributed in the fall of 1944.

Verde is recommended for growing only in southern Texas, because it is not sufficiently hardy to be grown in central Texas. The chief value of Verde oats is for pasture and as the raw material for the manufacture of dried green-grass food and pharmaceutical products. When the oats are to be dried green, the leaves are clipped periodically while they are young.

Camellia is the only named variety of commercial red oats developed for the South from Bond crosses. It originated from a Bond-Alber cross made in 1933, from which numerous selections were tested at Ames, Iowa, for resistance to crown rust and smut. These were later sent to the Louisiana Agricultural Experiment Station for testing. The selection Louisiana 629, which proved to be outstanding for yield and resistance to crown rust, was later named Camellia and distributed to farmers. It is similar to the Bond parent in most plant characters, except that the grains are somewhat larger. Camellia is even more resistant to crown rust than is Bond and also carries resistance to some oat smuts. It is not yet fully uniform in plant characters. Nevertheless, Camellia has made oat production feasible in a region in which very little small grain of any kind had been grown previously.

Thus the offspring of Victoria have markedly improved the economic status of oats as a farm crop. They have given the farmer a larger supply of feed grain at a lower cost and have provided a surplus of grain to sell. Losses from epidemics of crown rust and other diseases have been greatly reduced and, generally, higher yields of oats of superior quality are now being harvested.

Furthermore, the new disease-resistant varieties developed from Bond crosses and now being distributed give promise of making oats a still more satisfactory crop. They are more resistant to the rusts, higher yielding, and of better quality and, above all, have a much stiffer straw. They are exceedingly well adapted for combine harvesting, something farmers have been wanting for a long time.

However, in 1946 the varieties originating as offspring of Victoria suffered somewhat from the attacks of a new *Helminthosporium* blight.

703830°—47——27

Whether this disease will continue to damage these varieties remains to be seen. It has been designated as a new species of *Helminthosporium* and has been found on timothy and certain other grasses. Fortunately, the new varieties developed from Bond crosses are resistant to this disease; hence, they are being increased and distributed as rapidly as possible for commercial production. In 1946, these new varieties from Bond crosses continued to be outstanding for yield, quality, disease resistance, and stiffness of straw in nearly all tests conducted in the northern part of the United States. In brief, they give every indication of eclipsing and replacing the yet relatively new and history-making varieties originating from the Victoria-Richland cross.

Despite these outstanding accomplishments in oat improvement, there is need to do still more breeding, because hitherto unknown or relatively unimportant races of smuts and rusts are becoming more prevalent. Other destructive diseases are appearing that may jeopardize the value and usefulness of these epoch-making varieties. Fortunately, varieties and strains with basic resistance to these new rusts, smuts, and other diseases are available for breeding purposes.

THE AUTHOR

T. R. Stanton is senior agronomist in charge of oat investigations in the Division of Cereal Crops and Diseases, Bureau of Plant Industry, Soils, and Agricultural Engineering. He is the author or co-author of many bulletins and articles on oats. Dr. Stanton is a graduate of the University of Maryland. In recognition of his epochal work in oat improvement, he received the honorary degree of Doctor of Agriculture from Iowa State College in 1945.

ACKNOWLEDGMENTS

The disease-resistant varieties of oats discussed in this article are the result of cooperative research between the State agricultural experiment stations and the United States Department of Agriculture. Many workers have had a part in their development. Credit is due particularly to H. C. Murphy, F. A. Coffman, H. L. Shands, L. C. Burnett, Harland Stevens, G. K. Middleton, R. P. Bledsoe, C. Roy Adair, E. S. McFadden, E. G. Heyne, and C. O. Johnston.

FOR FURTHER READING

Stanton, T. R.: *Maintaining Identity and Pure Seed of Southern Oat Varieties,* U. S. D. A. Circular 562, 1940.

Stanton, T. R., and Coffman, F. A.: *Grow Disease-Resistant Oats,* U. S. D. A. Farmers' Bulletin 1941, 1943.

Stanton, T. R., and Coffman, F. A.: *Disease-Resistant and Hardy Oats for the South,* U. S. D. A. Farmers' Bulletin 1947, 1943.

Stanton, T. R., Coffman, F. A., and Tapke, V. F.: *Field Studies on Resistance of Hybrid Selections of Oats to Covered and Loose Smuts,* U. S. D. A. Technical bulletin 422, 1934.

Improved Varieties of Barley

by G. A. WIEBE

MORE THAN two score varieties of barley have been released in the past decade. They average 3 to 5 bushels more grain to the acre than the ones they replace. Often the new kinds have other advantages, like greater resistance to smut, rust, mildew, scald, spot blotch, stripe, and other diseases, greater winter hardiness, resistance to insect attack, greater tolerance to drought, stronger straw, and smooth awns. Nearly all sections where barley is important have benefited. The improvements are largely the work of plant breeders in cooperating Federal and State research institutions, but the help of farmers has been tremendously important.

In breeding barley it is not often that four varieties stem from a single cross. V. H. Florell made such a one. Working at Davis, Calif., for the Department and in cooperation with the California Agricultural Experiment Station, Florell crossed Atlas, which is rough-awned, with Vaughn, a semismooth kind, in 1927. The parents were well adapted to California and had yielded well. Florell's work was later transferred to Moscow, Idaho, where many selections were made, but all but the 45 most promising ones were discarded. These were distributed to western experiment stations in 1934, and from them four varieties were good enough to be released, Arivat and Beecher in 1940, in Arizona and Colorado, respectively; Glacier, in 1943, in Montana; and Gem, which was scheduled for release in Idaho in 1947. These spring-type varieties are six-rowed and have semismooth awns like Vaughn.

Arivat has yielded 10 percent more grain, in a 9-year test at the Mesa, Ariz., station, than Vaughn. It has a stiff straw and matures early.

Beecher is the earliest maturing variety grown on the Great Plains. At the Akron, Colo., station, its yield has been 8 percent above Club

403

Mariout and about equal to Munsing. Its combination of earliness and drought resistance makes it a promising barley for the Great Plains. Because its straw is stiff and the grain does not shatter, it is suitable for combining. Its most serious defect is its susceptibility to nuda loose smut, which may cause losses up to 10 percent in certain years. Beecher is grown in the area where the borders of Colorado, Kansas, and Nebraska touch.

Glacier is recommended for irrigated and other lands in Montana. It is a six-rowed feed variety, early maturing, and semismooth-awned. In comparison with Trebi, Glacier shows 25 percent less lodging and yields 25 to 35 percent more grain to the acre. It resists covered smut, but is susceptible to nuda loose smut. It is grown in Montana.

In tests at the Idaho Agricultural Experiment Station at Moscow, Gem yielded 21 percent more grain than Trebi. It is recommended as a feed barley for the nonirrigated lands of Idaho. Its straw is a little shorter and stiffer than that of Trebi, and its grain does not shatter, so it is suitable for combining. The semismooth awns give the straw value as a feed.

The keen eye of a North Dakota farmer gave us another spring barley that is grown in Minnesota, North Dakota, and South Dakota. S. T. Lykken, who farms near Kindred, N. Dak., grew a field of barley in 1935, a good kind known as Wisconsin Pedigree 37 and a full sister to the widely grown Wisconsin Barbless. Stem rust was bad that year, and Mr. Lykken decided to plow up his field. On one of the turns across this field he observed a single plant—no small feat, that!—that was different: It had no rust. It had 18 seeds, which he planted in his garden the following year. The next few years the seed was carefully increased; by 1942 its presence as a commercial variety began to be felt. It was named Kindred, after Mr. Lykken's home town; seedsmen also call it "L." Its resistance to stem rust, first observed by Lykken, has been confirmed by others. Kindred resembles Manchuria, and in years when stem rust is absent its yield is the same. But it has a considerable advantage in years when stem rust is bad. Its most serious defect is its weak straw, which often causes lodging and some loss in the amount and quality of grain. It malts well.

Varieties Produced From Composite Crosses

The late Dr. H. V. Harlan, during a third of a century of breeding barley, conceived the idea of improving varieties by combining hybridization and natural selection. These efforts were known as composite crosses, and many parent stocks were used. Hybridization produced the diverse germ plasm upon which natural selection could act. Dr. Harlan had shown earlier that when pure varieties were mixed, natural selection was a powerful force in eliminating poor varieties and preserving well adapted ones, although not always the highest yielding ones.

Composite crosses of both spring and winter types, the two main kinds grown in the United States, were distributed to experiment stations to be grown in bulk plots without selection for a number of years. After 5 to 6 or more years, when nearly all the different types were fixed, and natural selection had played its part, desirable plants were picked from these plots and tested. Several new varieties originated from them. Compana is an example. It was selected and tested cooperatively by the Department and the Montana station and released in Montana in 1941. By 1945 it was sown on 90 percent of the barley acreage in that State.

S. C. Litzenberger, of the Montana station, describes Compana as a spring type that is two-rowed, semismooth-awned, drought resistant, early maturing, and suitable for combining. The seeds are large, plump, and thin-hulled, and 2 to 4 pounds a bushel heavier in test weight than Trebi or Glacier. It is recommended for the nonirrigated lands, where it has yielded up to a third more than Trebi or Horn. On irrigated lands its yield equals that of Trebi, but it is more subject to lodging. It resists nuda loose smut, and grasshoppers hurt it less than other commercial varieties. Compana has a relatively short and weak straw and these characteristics are its two major faults under Montana conditions.

Another barley from a composite cross is called Rojo, meaning red. It was released in 1943. C. A. Suneson of the Department reports that at the experiment station at Davis, Rojo yielded 16 percent more, over 12 years, than Atlas, the commonly grown variety. For California, the difference is 12 percent. It is a spring type, six-rowed, smooth-awned barley, resistant to scald and net blotch. Rojo is desirable for hay because of its smooth awns, relatively disease-free leaves, and stiff straw. The spike is distinctly red, but under some conditions the kernels may develop a less attractive gray color. Some difficulties have been reported in removing the awns from it at harvest. It is now grown only in California.

New varieties of winter barley, which is much less widely grown in the United States than the spring type, also have been produced by selecting from composite crosses. G. K. Middleton, working in North Carolina, I. M. Atkins in Texas, and D. D. Hill and others in Oregon have released kinds developed in the cooperative programs. Davidson is one. It was released in North Carolina in 1939. At the Statesville station, Davidson tops the yield of the older varieties tested, having averaged 44.2 bushels over 14 years. It is said to resist all forms of smut, but is susceptible to mildew. The straw is stiff, the kernels large and plump.

Texan was introduced in Texas in 1941. It is well adapted to the blacklands of central Texas, where it yields about 3 bushels more than Wintex or others. It is six-rowed, smooth-awned, resistant to mildew, and a winter-type variety. Texan lacks strength of straw and tends to lodge on rich land. It is sufficiently winter-hardy for the blacklands and is used for grazing. It is also grown in the Mississippi Delta and Arkansas.

On the Pacific coast, Santiam and Cascade, also winter-type varieties, were released by the Oregon station at Corvallis in 1939 and 1945. Santiam surpassed the varieties grown in western Oregon at the time it was released, but no doubt it will give way in turn to Cascade, a still better kind. The main disadvantage of Santiam is that its straw is so tall and weak that it lodges on rich soil. Cascade is shorter and has a stiffer straw. It is suited to harvesting with combines, as it will stand without shattering after ripening. In 5 years of tests at Corvallis, Cascade produced 14 bushels more an acre than Santiam.

Spring Varieties Produced by Breeding

For spring barley, plant breeders have directed their efforts toward two principal types: Barleys that tolerate humid heat and are adapted for growing in the upper Mississippi Valley and Great Lakes States, and barleys grown in the drier parts of the Pacific coast, Rocky Mountain area, and the Great Plains as far east as the one-hundredth meridian. Three improved varieties of the first group have been distributed.

Bay, a six-rowed, smooth-awned variety, was released by the Michigan station in 1945. J. W. Thayer, Jr., reported that in average or favorable years Bay yields about the same as Wisconsin Barbless; in unfavorable years it will yield a fourth more. It matures a little earlier and has a slightly stiffer straw than Wisconsin Barbless, characteristics that make it a more desirable variety for a companion crop. The heads of Bay do not snap off so easily as do those of Wisconsin Barbless. It has been accepted by the maltsters as a malting barley, being similar in this respect to Wisconsin Barbless. The commercial acreage is confined to Michigan.

Mars was developed at the Minnesota station by LeRoy Powers and the late F. R. Immer, and was released in 1945. It is six-rowed and smooth-awned, matures rather early, and is somewhat shorter than other popular varieties. The straw is stiff. At four Minnesota stations, from 1941 to 1945, it yielded 5 bushels more than Wisconsin Barbless. Its kernels are small; the test weight is high. Mars resists stem rust and stripe, and is moderately resistant to leaf blotch, but it is susceptible to scab, loose smut, and leaf rust. It is considered unsatisfactory for malting, principally because of its low diastatic power and small kernels.

Tregal was produced at the North Dakota station by G. N. Geiszler, L. R. Waldron, and T. E. Stoa, and released to North Dakota farmers in 1943. For several years it has averaged a fifth to a tenth more in yield than Manchuria. Tregal resists nuda loose smut. It is a little shorter and somewhat earlier in maturity than Wisconsin Barbless or Manchuria, but is generally considered unsatisfactory as a malting barley.

In the Rocky Mountain area, Velvon and Velvon 11 were produced by R. W. Woodward in the cooperative work of the Utah station and the

Department. Both are six-rowed, smooth-awned types, and were released in 1935 and 1943. By 1944 Velvon was the leading variety on inter-mountain irrigated lands. Although it is resistant to nuda loose smut and moderately so to covered smut, it has sterile florets or blanks in the spike. Velvon 11 is an improvement in these respects. Both are stiffer strawed than Trebi, the variety formerly grown, and both can be harvested successfully with a combine. The straw is preferred by farmers, who use it for feeding and bedding. Both varieties have outyielded Trebi in most comparisons, except at higher elevations where the percentage of sterile florets tends to increase in the Velvon varieties.

Lico is a six-rowed smooth-awned sort produced by D. W. Robertson of the Colorado station and released in 1937. It yielded 4 to 5 bushels more grain to the acre than Trebi in 10 years of testing under irrigation at the Fort Collins station. Its straw is much stiffer than that of Trebi and, therefore, Lico makes a good companion crop. It is recommended for the irrigated lands in Colorado. Its most serious drawback is its susceptibility to nuda loose smut.

Flynn 37 was introduced in 1941 to farmers in Sherman and Gilman Counties in Oregon by the Moro station. It is the work of H. V. Harlan, D. E. Stephens, and M. M. Oveson of the Department of Agriculture and the Oregon Agricultural Experiment Station. It is superior to older varieties because it yields more, has smooth awns, is suitable for combining, and resists drought. Barley and other cereal grains are used extensively for hay in the Columbia River Basin. Flynn 37, because it has smooth awns, is more likely to replace the hooded types largely used for this purpose, than the rough-awned types grown previously. The straw of Flynn 37 is stiffer than that of Club Mariout, so it is better for combining.

Belford and Rufflyn were produced by the late O. E. Barbee of the Washington station and released in 1943 and 1939. Belford, a hooded kind, outyields Horsford, the commonly grown hooded variety. Rufflyn is bearded and yields 5 percent more grain than Beldi Giant or Blue. Its test weight is somewhat greater, and farmers report it is much easier to thresh. Belford and Rufflyn are grown in Washington.

Flynn 1 meets most of the requirements of farmers in the Great Plains. It was released to Kansas farmers from the Hays station in 1933, H. V. Harlan and A. F. Swanson of the Department being responsible for its production. In tests it yielded 2 to 5 bushels more than the varieties it replaced. Flynn 1 is less open to damage by *Helminthosporium*, grasshoppers, and green bugs than other varieties grown in Kansas, but is more subject to smut. All in all, Flynn 1 is the best spring variety now available for Kansas. It is grown extensively in northwestern Kansas and in eastern Colorado, and to a limited extent in southwestern Nebraska.

Munsing, released from the Akron, Colo., field station in 1944, took plenty of time to grow up. F. A. Coffman, of the Department, commenced working with it in 1920. Later his colleagues, J. J. Curtis and J. F. Brandon, carried on with it. Munsing is a two-rowed variety, like Compana, Spartan, and Vance. At Akron, it yielded slightly less than Beecher, but 15 percent more than Spartan. Munsing has been the leading variety in yield, in 4 years out of 6, in the Uniform Great Plains Nursery; its 6-year average yield being 40.5 bushels an acre, compared to 33.8 for Spartan and 38 for Beecher. It has a high test weight. Munsing has a short straw and the spikes seldom emerge entirely from the boot. The straw is weak, however—its most serious fault. But the straw is soft, and livestock like it. In stooling it beats all others grown on the Plains.

Winter Varieties Produced by Breeding

For winter barley, plant breeders have concentrated on improving yield, winter hardiness, disease resistance, awnless (beardless) and hooded spikes, smooth-awns, and other characters. Winter barley, besides being used for grain, also is used for hay, grazing, as a winter cover crop to control soil erosion, and as a companion crop for small-seeded legumes and grasses.

Improved sorts adapted to the Atlantic Coast States include Wong, Sunrise, Calhoun, Marett Awnless 1, and Smooth Awn 86. Wong was released in New York in 1941. It was bred in China and brought to this country by H. H. Love, of Cornell University. It has a stiff straw, resists mildew, and has nearly awnless spikes. It has yielded 4 to 5 bushels more than other common varieties. It is grown in New York, Pennsylvania, and to a lesser extent in New Jersey, Delaware, Maryland, and Virginia.

Sunrise was produced by J. W. Taylor, of the Department, and introduced by the North Carolina station in 1942. It is awnless and resistant to mildew, but quite susceptible to loose smut and rust. It has a stiff straw that is inclined to be short. At the Statesville, N. C., station, in an 8-year test, it led all other named varieties in yield. Ordinarily it stands well and the combine can be used on it. Sunrise is grown extensively in North Carolina and Alabama and to a limited extent in Virginia, Maryland, South Carolina, and Georgia.

Calhoun also was produced by Taylor and released in South Carolina in 1945. It is similar to Sunrise in type, has stiff straw, and is resistant to mildew, stripe, and nigra loose smut.

Marett Awnless 1, released in South Carolina in 1940, is a true awnless kind especially adapted for grazing because of its semiprostrate and abundant early growth. It is generally grown from fall seeding but it also does well when sown somewhat later. It is resistant to mildew and stripe. Marett Awnless 1 is not adapted to the Coastal Plains section; it is grown in western South Carolina, and to a limited extent in adjacent North Carolina and Georgia.

Smooth Awn 86 is a six-rowed, smooth-awned variety, another of Taylor's handiwork. Released in Virginia in 1939, Smooth Awn 86 is moderately winter hardy and has a medium stiff straw. It resisted green bugs at Denton, Tex., in 1942, when green bugs destroyed nearly all varieties tested, except Smooth Awn 86 and several others obtained from China and Chosen. It is moderately resistant to mildew, covered smut, and nigra loose smut and has given satisfactory yields of grain. It is grown in Virginia.

Jackson and Jackson 1 were released by the Tennessee Agricultural Experiment Station in 1941 and 1944, respectively. These two varieties, sister strains from the same hybrid, were produced by N. I. Hancock of the Tennessee station. Jackson 1 has produced more grain than any other variety tested in Tennessee. The yield of Jackson has been equal to Tennessee Winter 52, the commonly grown variety, except on soils of medium fertility where Jackson outyields this variety. Jackson 1 stools abundantly and is used for winter pasture in combination with crimson clover. Jackson 1 threshes more easily than Jackson and for this reason the grain has a higher test weight. Both varieties are smooth awned and are sufficiently hardy for Tennessee conditions. Jackson is reported to be resistant to scald and nigra loose smut and moderately resistant to stripe. The present acreage is in Tennessee and adjacent Kentucky and Virginia.

Tenkow was released by the Oklahoma station in 1941. It is an example of a variety which finally found its place after a long and devious journey. The cross from which it came was made in 1905 by H. A. Miller, of the Department, who then was conducting cooperative barley experiments at the Maryland station. H. B. Derr, also of the Department, made the selection from the cross that came to be called Tenkow. The Oklahoma station received the variety in 1926, and tests at that station in subsequent years showed it to be superior. It is six-rowed, rough-awned, and has a semiwinter habit of growth. At Stillwater, Okla., Tenkow has yielded 3 bushels more than Ward in a 6-year test, and its test weight has been 2 pounds heavier. It is grown in Oklahoma and northern Texas.

Fayette is a high-yielding, semiwinter barley released by the Arkansas station in 1945. Its moderate resistance ot mildew and leaf rust and its semierect habit of growth make it good for winter grazing when sown early.

Nature Aids the Breeder

A fruitful method of getting improved varieties is to make selections from old varieties long grown in this country. The method has been used to advantage with winter barley, and is especially effective if natural selection has played a major role in first shaping the type of the old variety. Much of the barley first grown in the United States was a mixture of an indefinite number of strains, a condition than can be found even today.

For example, take the old Tennessee Winter variety, which has been grown for many years. Gradually the acreage spread from its beginnings in Virginia and the Carolinas to the Mississippi and beyond. In these fields natural selection gradually shaped the type to fit a particular set of conditions. In this way, the winter-hardy types of Kansas, Oklahoma, and Kentucky and the less hardy types of the Atlantic seaboard and Texas evolved. It remained, therefore, for the plant breeder to select from these surviving populations the superior types adapted to local conditions.

Reno and Ward are two hardy kinds developed by selection from old varieties. Reno was distributed from the Kansas Agricultural Experiment Station in 1939. It was selected from a field on J. A. Johnson's farm at Hutchinson, Kans., who had grown winter barley for many years. Reno can stand cold better than most varieties and, for that reason, has made winter barley a safer crop to grow in Kansas and adjacent States. It matures early and therefore furnishes grain in the early summer when the supply of other grains is often depleted. It is grown extensively in Kansas, Missouri, and, to a lesser extent, in Oklahoma, Arkansas, Texas, and southern Nebraska.

Ward resembles Reno in type and hardiness. Like Reno, it was selected from a farmer's field. Ward was released in 1936 from the Southern Great Plains Field Station at Woodward, Okla., by V. C. Hubbard of the Department. It is adapted to the colder parts of Oklahoma, Kansas, and the Texas Panhandle.

Woodwin is like Michigan Winter, Reno, and Ward, but is not so hardy. It was released in 1942 from Woodward. In a 9-year test at that station it yielded an average of 1 bushel more than Michigan Winter, the variety commonly grown in Oklahoma. It is not so hardy as Reno and Ward and is recommended for areas south and east of Woodward.

Along the Atlantic coast, selections from farmers' fields have resulted in two new varieties. Brier was selected by the West Virginia station from an unnamed variety of winter barley grown by Eugene Tuckwiller, a farmer in Greenbrier County. Brier was released by the West Virginia station in 1941. It yielded 8 percent more grain than several others in tests and for West Virginia as a whole its yield has been 2.5 percent greater. It is resistant to smut and mildew, but susceptible to leaf rust.

Randolph, a six-rowed rough-awned variety, was selected from a locally grown barley by G. K. Middleton of the North Carolina station. It was released to farmers in 1939. It is not tall, but because it makes a heavy fall growth if seeded early, it is valuable for fall grazing. It yields more than the hooded varieties but not so much as do other rough-awned sorts. Randolph matures early and is well suited as a companion crop to lespedeza. It is moderately resistant to covered smut and nigra loose smut but is susceptible to nuda loose smut. It is grown in North Carolina.

Wintex is a less winter-hardy kind selected from progeny of original seed brought to this country. It is a six-rowed, rough-awned variety, first distributed to Texas farmers in 1939. I. M. Atkins, of the Department, selected it from a field of barley on Will Smith's farm near Denton, Tex. It was grown on 50,000 acres in Texas in 1944, despite the fact that it had suffered severe damage by green bugs in 1942 and considerable damage from winterkilling in 1943. Wintex yields 9 to 10 bushels an acre more than Tennessee Winter. It is less winter hardy than Tennessee Winter, but sufficiently hardy in most years for the area in which it is recommended. It is used for grazing because of its broad leaves, abundant tillering, and more upright growth. It is suited to combine harvesting. Its principal faults are its susceptibility to diseases, especially mildew and *Helminthosporium*. Wintex is grown extensively in Texas, in the Delta area of the Mississippi, and to a less extent in Arkansas.

New Mexico Winter 1 was selected to fill a specific need. It is grown on the irrigated lands of southern New Mexico, where winter oats, spring oats, or spring barley are not quite hardy enough when fall sown, or do not yield sufficient grain.

Hooded winter barleys, although not suited for combine harvesting, are commonly grown in the mid-South. This is a preferred type of barley where the crop is to be used for hay. Rough-awned varieties are especially undesirable for this use as the awns cause sores in the mouths of the stock. Hooded varieties tend to shatter more than awned types, but losses from this cause are less in the mid-South than anywhere else in the United States. It is believed that the low ash content of varieties grown here and the relative greater humidity at harvesttime are largely responsible for this difference. Three hooded varieties have been produced as the result of selection.

In 1930 G. K. Middleton of the North Carolina station made a number of selections from a field of Tennessee Beardless 6 on W. B. Crawford's farm near Statesville, N. C. The two most promising selections were named Iredell and North Carolina Hooded 26, and were released in 1940 and 1942. At Statesville they have outyielded Tennessee Beardless 6 by 3 and 4 bushels an acre. They resist certain smuts but are subject to mildew and rust. North Carolina Hooded 26 is somewhat shorter than Iredell and is 5 to 6 days earlier. Because of this earliness it is especially useful as a companion crop with lespedeza. It also has a broader leaf and more abundant early growth and therefore is valuable for grazing. It is grown mostly in North Carolina.

Tucker is a product of the West Virginia station and was released there in 1941. The variety is moderately resistant to smut, leaf rust, and mildew. Its yield and winter hardiness compare favorably with other hooded varieties. It is grown on a limited acreage in West Virginia.

In the early history of barley production in the United States it was common to introduce varieties from Europe and Asia. Until the plant breeder came on the scene, this was nearly the only source of new varieties. The Manchuria variety widely grown in the Upper Mississippi Valley and the Coast variety in California are typical introductions of this kind. These exotic varieties served a very useful purpose during this period, but this means of adding new varieties to our agriculture is now largely supplanted by varieties produced by plant breeders. There are, however, three foreign varieties that possess certain special characteristics.

From among a number of foreign varieties E. S. McFadden of the Department selected a variety named Tunis, which is specially suited to southern Texas. It was tested and distributed in the cooperative work of the Texas Agricultural Experiment Station and the United States Department of Agriculture. The distribution of this variety marks the first instance of a pure spring type being grown from fall seeding south of the main winter barley area in the United States. It is quite probable that spring barleys will be well suited to the entire Gulf area. Tunis is recommended only for southern Texas and in that area has been superior in yield. It is resistant to leaf rust and mildew and is used for winter grazing as well as for grain. It makes a vigorous early winter growth and when grown for grain is suitable for combining. It is not so stiff-strawed as some other varieties and may lodge in wet years when grown on rich soil. It was released in 1943.

Olympia, a winter-type variety, was introduced into this country by E. F. Gaines, of the Washington station, who obtained seed of it from Germany. The Washington station released it in 1937. Olympia matures earlier than Winter Club, the standard variety in the Palouse area, and for this reason is a good variety to grow in the transitional zone between the Palouse and the dry-land area. Under these conditions it yields more grain of higher quality than Winter Club.

Poland, another winter variety, was first grown in this country by John Baron, a farmer near Auburn, N. Y. He obtained the seed from Poland between 1930 and 1932. There is a small acreage in New York, but it is being replaced by Wong. Poland is fairly winter hardy and moderately resistant to mildew and scald, but has a weak straw. On occasions, the variety has shown exceptional vigor during the early growth stage.

THE AUTHOR

G. A. Wiebe is in charge of barley investigations in the Bureau of Plant Industry, Soils, and Agricultural Engineering. He has had 24 years of practical experience in barley-breeding and production research. Dr. Wiebe is a graduate of the University of California.

Tailor-Made Sorghums

by JOHN H. MARTIN

THE FIRST grain sorghums that reached the United States from Africa more than two generations ago could not be harvested and threshed without a lot of hand labor. They grew 4 to 6 feet tall; some had bent heads, and they were not suited to the combine. Engineers and plant breeders joined forces to solve the difficulty. They improved the combined harvester-thresher. It was made lighter and mounted on rubber tires; it could be transported easily, so that operators from the Wheat Belt could move westward into the grain-sorghum region for the autumn harvest. The breeders produced tailor-made new varieties that could be combined. Together the improvements saved seven-eighths of the man-hours needed to harvest the grain by hand and thresh it later. Consequently, during the War, when labor was scarce, many farmers were able to grow eight times more sorghum than if they would have had to depend on hand labor. The extra grain contributed materially to the supply of feed and industrial alcohol. Besides, harvesting with combines saved about two dollars an acre in harvesting costs—a total saving of some 12 million dollars a year.

Even more impressive is the story of six varieties, distributed since 1940, that were grown on 7 million acres by 1944—Martin, Plainsman, Westland, Midland, Caprock, and Bonita. They comprise 80 percent of the sorghum harvested for grain in the United States. They have erect heads and usually grow to only 2 to 3 feet, so that harvesting is easy. Altogether, these developments of a generation have given the Great Plains a crop that is as important to that area as corn is to the more humid Corn Belt.

Combines were not used for harvesting any crop in the Southern Great Plains until about 1918. In 1920, J. B. Sieglinger selected some dwarf, erect-headed plants from the progenies of a cross between milo and kafir that grew at the United States Southern Great Plains Field Station at Woodward, Okla. Nobody had bothered much about such plants before. They were nondescript, unprepossessing hybrids no taller than wheat plants, although both parents stood 4 to 6 feet, and the milo parent had crooknecked heads. But from his selections Sieglinger bred Beaver and Wheatland, which were distributed to growers in 1928 and 1931. The value of Wheatland for Kansas was quickly recognized after small fields of several new varieties were harvested with a combine.

Two quick-maturing combine-type varieties, Colby and Day, originated at Woodward, were distributed later in Kansas and Nebraska after tests of numerous similar strains. The new varieties, especially Wheatland, soon were grown extensively, but they had some serious faults. All were susceptible to milo disease, or pythium root rot, which was first observed in 1925. Also, like their milo parent, they were subject to chinch bug injury. There was a need also for kinds that matured earlier than Wheatland and Beaver, but later than Colby and Day.

The Agricultural Experiment Stations of Kansas, Texas, Oklahoma, Nebraska, Colorado, and New Mexico, cooperating with the Department, set out to breed better kinds. Pythium-resistant offspring of Wheatland were tested extensively. One, named Westland, was distributed in Kansas in 1942 and grown on a million acres by 1944.

A Texas farmer, W. P. Martin, found a promising plant in his field of Wheatland in 1936. When tested in a nursery, it was found to resist pythium root rot. It was increased, given the name of Martin, and distributed in 1941. By 1943 it was grown on 3 million acres, and has been the leader since then. Like Westland, it matures earlier than Wheatland. Martin has reddish-yellow grains somewhat smaller and harder than those of milo. The heads are upstanding and open enough to dry quickly, so that combine operators can even start harvesting it soon after it has been dampened by dew or rain. Martin's early maturity permits it to be grown as far north as South Dakota, yet it is the leading grain sorghum in southern Texas (where the crop is harvested in early summer), other parts of Texas, and Oklahoma.

The breeding work at the Texas Agricultural Experiment Station, at Lubbock and Chillicothe, produced three varieties that were released between 1941 and 1943. Plainsman and Caprock were devolped from milo kafir crosses by R. E. Karper and D. L. Jones. The third, Bonita, was selected from a Chiltex-hegari cross by J. R. Quinby. Plainsman and Caprock mature later and yield better than Martin and Westland when everything is favorable, but are not so well suited to dry conditions or short seasons. Bonita has found an important place in north-central Texas, where chinch bugs may work havoc with other improved kinds.

Meanwhile, a new disease, charcoal rot, appeared. It can cut the yield of all the new kinds and cause their stalks to fall down after they ripen but before the grain is dry enough for combining. Martin is particularly susceptible. A condition called weakneck also causes ripe stalks to fall over and be lost at harvest.

A. F. Swanson selected a stiff-stalked plant from his plots of kalo at the Fort Hays Branch Experiment Station in Kansas. This variety, named Midland, was distributed to Kansas farmers in 1944. In 1945, Midland was planted on 300,000 acres from known supplies of pure seed; probably 200,000 acres more were planted from commercial grain supplies. Midland matures early enough for growing in most parts of Nebraska and western Kansas. Its stiff stalks and resistance to stalk diseases make it good for combining.

Midland produces bronze-yellow grains smaller than typical milo kernels. The stalks are taller and the heads shorter than those of the other combine types. It is as early as Martin, maybe a little earlier. Midland ranks next to Westland in Kansas, and is the leading variety in Nebraska.

Plainsman and Caprock are somewhat alike, except that Caprock ripens later and has larger heads. Both produce large reddish-yellow grains in rather compact, kafir-like heads. Their short, thick stalks resist lodging, but the thick heads, standing barely out of the boot, dry out rather slowly after a rain. Plainsman and Caprock are adapted to places having favorable moisture conditions and a fairly long growing season. Under such conditions, they produce larger yields than do the quicker-maturing sorts.

Westland has large yellow grains. The somewhat open heads extend well above the boot and leaves. Thus, Westland resembles Martin, except in being a little later in maturing. The grains are larger and softer than those of Martin. Westland leads in Kansas.

Bonita is rather unusual because of its numerous tiller stalks and small heads. Each row appears as a wide band of heads. The production of late branch heads often interferes with combining, because the green material adds moisture to the grain. The grains are small, soft, and chalky-white, rather like those of its hegari parent. Bonita is grown mostly in Texas.

Much of the grain sorghum grown under irrigation in California and Arizona since 1938 consists of a variety called Double Dwarf milo 38, a productive, pythium-resistant variety developed by the California Agricultural Experiment Station. It is combined readily when planted thickly on rich irrigated land. In the thinner planting necessary for the Great Plains, it produces recurved heads that make harvesting harder.

A variety called combine kafir is grown on 100,000-odd acres in western Texas and other localities. It was developed at Woodward and resembles the familiar Blackhull kafir, but it has shorter heads and stalks.

Other new kinds, although somewhat taller than the special combine types, also are stocky enough for successful combining. Among these is waxy-seeded Cody, grown for its starch, which makes a tapioca-like dessert. It usually grows 3 to 4 feet tall. It was developed in cooperation with the Kansas Agricultural Experiment Station. Coes, a quick-maturing, white-seeded kind grown in the higher altitudes of the western Great Plains, also is usually combined. Coes grows as high as 4 feet. It was developed in cooperation with the Colorado Agricultural Experiment Station.

All the new disease-resistant types have given the farmer a new crop that he can grow by mechanized methods, an economical and more stable supply of feed grain, and an alternative cash crop for the cotton and wheat regions. Grain sorghum stubble and the crop residue left after combining afford fair protection against soil blowing. The combine varieties stand long enough after maturity for the grain to be gathered by livestock. Sorghum thus can supplement wheat pasture for the range livestock that are fed in the Great Plains region before going East to the packing plants. The "sheeping off" of combine grain sorghums opens a new opportunity in livestock feeding. Breeders and farmers are well satisfied with the improved sorghums, but even better types are on the way.

THE AUTHOR

John H. Martin is an agronomist in the Bureau of Plant Industry, Soils, and Agricultural Engineering. His work includes research on the culture, utilization, adaptation, genetics, economics, and the improvement of sorghum throughout the United States.

FOR FURTHER READING

Leukel, R. W.: Chemical Seed Treatments for the Control of Certain Diseases of Sorghum, U. S. D. A. Technical Bulletin 849, 1943.

Leukel, R. W., Martin, John H., and Lefebvre, C. L.: Sorghum Diseases and Their Control, U. S. D. A. Farmers' Bulletin 1959, 1944.

Martin, J. H.: Sorghum Improvement, U. S. D. A. Yearbook, pages 523–560, 1936.

Martin, J. H.: Breeding Sorghum for Social Objectives, Journal of Heredity, volume 36, No. 4, pages 99–106, 1945.

Martin, J. H., and Stephens, J. C.: The Culture and Use of Sorghums for Forage, U. S. D. A. Farmers' Bulletin 1844, 1940.

ALSO, IN THIS BOOK

Genetics and Farming, by E. R. Sears, page 245.
G-Men of Plant Diseases, by Paul R. Miller, page 443.

Grasses for Hay and Pasture

by M. A. HEIN

THERE ARE about six thousand different species of grass. They are, in the words of Judge Ingalls, the benediction of nature. They are also, as 20 years of drought, insect plagues, and war have demonstrated, of unmeasured value to agriculture and the Nation's economic life.

Grass has gained this new importance and versatility from programs of breeding, introduction, and adaptation that a number of men and institutions have carried on. In 1928 the Department of Agriculture started an intensive effort to improve grass and pastures to help control the corn borer. Beginning in 1933, the Soil Conservation Service and the Agricultural Adjustment Administration developed projects to save soil and stabilize farming by planting more land to hay and forage crops. During the years of drought, special attention was given to the search for hardy, drought-resistant plants of all kinds from foreign sources. We also stressed improvement of grasses by breeding the materials at hand.

Through the Division of Plant Exploration and Introduction we have been extremely fortunate in obtaining a large number of grasses to supplement our native and naturally introduced grasses. Conspicuous examples of this are Sudan grass and crested wheatgrass. Their value and widespread use are already well understood. Many others, brought in more recently, are proving their worth. I give a few examples to illustrate the use that can be made of them under our wide variety of soil and climatic conditions.

Pangola grass (*Digitaria decumbens*), introduced from South Africa in 1936, has shown promise in Florida. It was first released to farmers by the Florida Agricultural Experiment Station in 1942. It produces little viable seed and must be propagated vegetatively. It is a rapid-

417

growing perennial, withstands grazing well, and is quite drought-resistant, but it is sensitive to frost and has not proved winter hardy north of Florida. More information, however, is needed on its range of adaptation.

Russian wild-rye (*Elymus junceus*) was first introduced in 1928 from the Soviet Union. It has about the same range of adaptation as crested wheatgrass and can best be compared with it. Failure to produce seed consistently has been its principal weakness and has limited its use to the Northern Great Plains, where it is best adapted.

Intermediate wheatgrass (*Agropyron intermedium*), another introduction from Russia, has shown considerable promise in the Northern Great Plains and the Intermountain region. The original introduction was a mixture of two species, *A. intermedium* and *A. trichophorum*. As a result, it has shown considerable variation. It is less drought-resistant than crested wheatgrass and more drought-resistant than bromegrass. The South Dakota Agricultural Experiment Station has increased it under the name of Ree wheatgrass.

Turkestan bluestem (*Andropogon ischaemum*) and Caucasian bluestem (*A. intermedius caucasius*), also introductions from Russia, show promise in the Southern Great Plains. They are vigorous, high-producing plants with fair production of seed. Both are finer stemmed and of better texture than our native bluestems.

Three lovegrasses, weeping lovegrass (*Eragrostis curvula*), Lehmann's lovegrass (*E. lehmanniana*), and Boer lovegrass (*E. chloromelas*), all introductions from Africa, have proved to be valuable. Weeping lovegrass, well adapted to the Southern Great Plains, has been widely distributed, and is the most winter-hardy of the three. Lehmann and Boer lovegrass are promising in semiarid parts of the Southwest, southern New Mexico, and Arizona.

From these examples of introductions and their development it is apparent that we cannot depend entirely on introductions to meet our changing agricultural needs. Plant breeding is essential in developing species and strains for a grass and pasture program adapted to the conditions where it is to be grown.

Objectives in the improvement program vary within different grasses and regions and include one or more of the following: Resistance to diseases, insects, drought, heat, or cold; seed production; seasonal growth; compatibility; recovery value after grazing or mowing; palatability and nutritive value; aggressiveness; and high yield. It must be recognized that the improved characters desired in any particular grass will depend largely upon the climate of the region in which it is to be grown and the purpose for which it is to be used.

Almost 70 different species of grass are included in some kind of selection, improvement, or breeding program conducted by the Department alone or by the Department in cooperation with States or State experiment stations. This program also includes increasing field-selected material of native and introduced species for conservation and soil-improvement purposes. These lines have not necessarily been selected for type, but rather on the basis of regional adaptation. That is an important factor, because even in field-selected material that has been growing for many years under a particular environment there has been some natural selection by processes of the survival of the fittest.

Some examples of different species adapted to broad climatic regions of the United States will illustrate the advantages of improved varieties.

Northern Grasses

Bromegrass (*Bromus inermis*) was first introduced into the United States in 1884. By 1890 it had become widely distributed and seemed to find a home on dry lands in the Northern Great Plains and to some extent in the extreme western part of the Corn Belt. The drought of 1934–36 and the demand for a tall grass to grow with alfalfa and other vigorous legumes brought it into prominence in the Midwest. Michigan farmers were probably the first east of the Mississippi to use bromegrass widely with alfalfa. In the early years most of the seed in commercial channels was from the northern United States and Canada; it was well adapted to Michigan and the Northern States but not to the central latitudes. Many failures resulted. Meanwhile, however, some seed had been harvested from old fields in northeastern Kansas and southeastern Nebraska. In field tests this southern-grown seed was found to be better adapted to the central latitudes than that grown in the North.

A certified variety of bromegrass, named Lincoln, was developed by plant breeders in the Nebraska Agricultural Experiment Station and the Department. Foundation seed, which gave similar performance in extensive field-plot tests, was obtained from selected old fields of bromegrass. The oldest of these fields were planted in the late 1890's with seed distributed by the Nebraska station. Some evidence indicates that this seed was of Hungarian origin, in contrast to later introductions from Russia, or of northern origin. Our first tests showed that Lincoln may be grown much farther north than the region in which it has become naturalized, but it is particularly adapted to the central Corn Belt States where its seedling vigor, ease in establishment, and aggressive sod formation make it of especial value for plantings to control soil erosion and as a pasture, hay, or seed crop. We cannot say the same for the poorly adapted strains from northern sources, presumably of Russian origin, which frequently exhibit poor seedling vigor, are difficult to establish on critical planting sites, and produce an open-type sod in the Midwest.

Lincoln bromegrass was named in 1942 and has been increased by farmers under the auspices of the Nebraska Crop Improvement Association and the Nebraska station. Approximately 325,000 pounds of seed were produced by 78 growers in 1945. Much of that seed was sold to farmers in States east of Nebraska, and tests were started to see how it would do in other States and abroad. In other States similar strains of bromegrass are being certified: In Kansas, the Achenbach strain; Iowa, the Fischer strain; and in Missouri, the Elsberry strain. Strains being increased from the old fields in the central latitudes might well be considered identical for the purpose of certification. They are similar in regional adaptation, and in preliminary tests it appears that they are quite well adapted in the North.

Field selections and introductions from foreign sources of northern origin are also available. Some of these are similar in habit of growth to those in Kansas and Nebraska. The Martin strain, a field selection from Minnesota, is an example.

Timothy (*Phleum pratense*), is another grass from which a number of varieties have been developed by simple selection. The Ohio Agricultural Experiment Station and the Department have developed two varieties, Marietta and Lorain, whose seed is being increased.

Marietta timothy heads, blooms, and matures several days earlier than ordinary timothy. Its early maturity increases its value for aftermath pasture and makes it better adapted to the southern part of the timothy belt, because it is ready for harvest or use before the hot, dry weather. Marietta is a composite of three early selections.

Lorain timothy originated from a single plant selection, and is 8 to 10 days later than common timothy. It is best adapted to northern Ohio and other States in that latitude. In southern Ohio, however, it is doubtful if it would be better than common timothy. Because the slower early growth of Lorain does not depress the growth of clover, better yields have been obtained when Lorain or late-maturing strains have been grown in a mixture with red clover. Lorain timothy is quite resistant to leaf rust.

Two strains of timothy have been developed by Cornell University. Seed stocks of one are being increased. Cornell 1777 is a medium early, fine-stemmed timothy of medium height. It stays green until maturity. Cornell 4059 is tall and erect in growth and has medium coarse leafage. It is not so resistant to rust as 1777.

Orchard grass (*Dactylis glomerata*) is another introduction that came in with the early settlers. Only in recent years have attempts been made to develop improved strains. Field collections have been made from old fields for selection and hybridization with new improved strains from abroad.

Some of the imported types of orchard grass have been increased or grown for several years in the United States and, no doubt, have lost part of their original characters, either through natural selection or cross pollination with domestic types. An example is S–143, a strain imported from Aberystwyth, Wales. During its few years in the United States, it has developed into a plant that is tall-growing, a good seed producer, and of medium leafiness. A recent introduction of the same strain from Wales is low-growing, a sparse seed producer, and leafy.

Tall fescue (*Festuca elatior* var. *arundinaceae*), a variety of meadow fescue, has been used extensively throughout the United States for a long time. Beginning in 1890, however, meadow fescue came into prominence, and domestic seed production developed in eastern Kansas, western Missouri, and parts of Indiana in particular. Meadow fescue was short-lived and finally fell into disrepute. With increased interest in grassland agriculture, attention was given to these grasses because they were adapted to semiwet land conditions. The first improvement work on them was started in Oregon.

Alta fescue was developed in 1923 by the Oregon Agricultural Experiment Station and the Department, from a 4-year-old stand of tall fescue. It is long-lived, deep rooted, and has numerous coarse basal leaves. In Oregon, it is taller, more robust, higher in forage yield, and longer-lived than the ordinary meadow fescue. It is highly resistant to crown rust, *Helminthosporium* net blotch, and other diseases that seriously attack meadow fescue. Seed is being produced in Oregon and Washington. The first increase was made in 1932 at the Oregon Agricultural Experiment Station, and by 1936 the first commercial growers had it in production. By 1945 the commercial seed production of Alta fescue in Oregon almost equalled the total domestic production of meadow fescue.

Since the selection of Alta fescue, other strains of the tall fescues almost identical to it have been found growing in other parts of the United States, although they are not in commercial production. In Kentucky a similar strain known as K–31 is under test. At the Nebraska Agricultural Experiment Station another strain was identified as tall fescue and proved to be similar in growth type and habit to Alta fescue.

The principal weakness of this grass as a pasture crop is its coarse, tough leaves. Livestock will graze it, however, when it occurs in mixtures, or even in pure stands if other grasses are not available. Because it has many desirable characters, both for forage and turf purposes, Alta fescue is worth efforts to improve it further.

Southern Grasses

Hay and pasture crops merit special attention in the South, in view of the demand for a greater production of livestock and the need to adjust the uses of land.

In the South, Bermuda grass (*Cynodon dactylon*) is the most widely grown grass. Its tendency to spread to cultivated fields has given it a bad name among farmers who grow row crops like cotton and tobacco, but it grows on upland soils of various types and can control erosion.

In 1929 agronomists at the Georgia Coastal Plain Experiment Station at Tifton found a robust plant of Bermuda grass growing in a cotton field near the station. The plant was increased vegetatively and distributed as Tift Bermuda grass. Later, Department workers started an intensive breeding program at Tifton, planting tall-growing strains that had originated from common Bermuda, Tift, and an introduction from South Africa. These were allowed to cross-pollinate naturally. From these parents seed was collected in 1938, and more than 5,000 single plants were grown for careful study one by one. Of them, 147 of the most promising plants were selected. They were tested further, and among them a superior strain was found. It is now being increased and distributed under the name of Coastal Bermuda.

Coastal Bermuda grass has larger stems, stolons, rhizomes, and longer internodes than common Bermuda. It is also leafier, more tolerant to cold, and resistant to leafspot. Because it produces little or no seed in the Coastal Plains region, it must be increased by vegetative plantings.

A 3-acre nursery of Coastal Bermuda, established in 1943 at the station at Tifton, supplied planting material to more than a thousand farmers in 1944. It is being distributed also by the Soil Conservation Service and other experiment stations in the South. Georgia organized a crop improvement association in 1945, and its members are increasing certified plant material of Coastal Bermuda.

Another new and apparently good hybrid has been named Suwanee. It is being distributed in Florida where it has certain advantages over Coastal Bermuda. It will give a larger yield of hay, and it appears to be more productive on poor soils, but will not stand as much cold or close grazing as Coastal Bermuda.

Bahia grass (*Paspalum notatum*), an early introduction from Cuba and Central America, has several good points as a pasture grass in the South. It is perennial, leafy, and deep-rooted, spreads by short stolons, and grows well on sandy soils. When it is properly managed, it produces abundant seed, an important factor because seed of most grasses has been produced outside the Southeast or imported from foreign sources. But because it is not winter-hardy, its use has been limited mainly to Florida and the Gulf Coast area.

Scientists started intensive tests in 1936 on Bahia grass seed collected from different sources in an attempt to find more types good for controlling erosion. Collections were made by State and Federal workers in the field. Other material was obtained by introductions from plant explorers in Central and South America. In the cooperative work at Tifton, at least six types have been found in the material so far studied. This classification is based largely on growth habits, plant and genetic characters, and winter hardiness. The strains have been identified as Common, Paraguay, Pensacola, Wilmington, Wallace, and Tampa.

Common Bahia represents the type imported from Cuba, Central America, and South America. Because it is susceptible to winterkilling, it is at home mostly in Florida and southern Georgia. It has broader and tenderer leaves than the Paraguay, Wilmington, or Pensacola strains. The Paraguay strain is a smaller-growing type than common Bahia. The leaves are thicker, narrower, tougher, and darker green in color. It is more frost-resistant and can withstand lower temperatures than common Bahia. The strain was named Paraguay because it was developed from introductions made in 1937 from Paraguay. Since that time samples of Bahia grass seed, which proved to be the same type as Paraguay, were obtained from a grower near El Campo, Tex.

Pensacola Bahia was probably introduced from ballast dumped on land near the old Perdido Wharf at Pensacola, Fla. This strain differs from other strains in many respects, but, like Paraguay, it makes excellent pasture in the spring and early summer, although it becomes tough in late summer. It is an excellent seed producer, but the seed shatters readily and is difficult to save. Observations at Tifton indicate that Pensacola spreads more rapidly than other Bahias and tolerates frost a little better than Paraguay. The most striking genetic difference is in the number of chromosomes. The Pensacola strain has 20 pairs of chromosomes; other strains that were studied cytologically have 40 pairs.

Of the several strains collected by men in the Nursery Division of the Soil Conservation Service, Wilmington Bahia, collected near Wilmington, N. C., is the most winter-hardy. Other strains, but of less importance at this time, are the Wallace and Tampa Bahia.

Great Plains and Inter-Mountain Region

The largest areas of natural grass and range lands in the United States are in the Great Plains and the Inter-Mountain region, a vast area where the soil is usually productive but rainfall is a limiting factor. The plant breeder finds there a wealth of material that can be used in a program to improve grass. These grasses can be broadly classified as cool-temperature plants, those that make the most growth during spring and fall, and warm-temperature plants, those that grow best during the summer.

Because the number of desirable grasses in this region is large, I can mention only a few examples to illustrate the efforts to improve them.

Native grasses vary widely in their adaptation. Much of the improvement work therefore has been confined to field selections. Because of variations in winter hardiness, forage production, day length, disease resistance, and other factors, the field selections cannot be moved too far north or south from the region of their origin. Until local tests have proved otherwise, strains we now have should not be planted more than 150 or 200 miles north or south from the area of origin.

Intensive work was started on buffalo grass (*Buchloe dactyloides*) in 1935. Plant breeders want to domesticate this highly variable plant by selection and hybridization. Because of the wide variation in almost every known character in buffalo grass, selection has been used most extensively. Improvement work has been under way in North Dakota, Nebraska, Kansas, Oklahoma, and Texas—most intensively at Hays, Kans., and Woodward, Okla.

The Hays strain is the only improved one in which seed is available for limited distribution in 1947. It was developed at the Fort Hays Agricultural Experiment Station at Hays, in cooperation with the Department. At least 5,000 pounds of foundation seed were produced for distribution annually at that station in 1944, 1945, and 1946.

The main aim of the workers who developed the Hays strain was to breed a type that bears abundant seed on stems for easier harvesting. The strain has been superior to common or field buffalo grass in production of seed and forage. It is said to equal common buffalo grass in resistance to disease, and has the ability to produce seed high off the ground. Other selections of buffalo grass made at the Hays station appear to be even more promising than the Hays strain.

The Southern Great Plains Field Station at Woodward started to increase the seed of three strains of buffalo grass that appeared promising in the preliminary stages of development. One of them gave evidence of being a particularly outstanding cross because it has tall, quick spreading plants bearing seed on the stalk 6 to 8 inches above the ground. It is an aggressive strain—sprigs set out at 5-foot intervals completely fill in the space between them in about 3 months.

Blue grama (*Bouteloua gracilis*) is a warm-season, short grass found growing in association with buffalo grass. It forms a good sod, although it is a typical bunchgrass. Many strains of blue grama occur naturally, but southern strains generally lack winter hardiness when they moved north, and northern strains yield less when grown in the South. Seed is hard to get, because blue grama fails to set seed consistently; the development of desirable seed-producing strains is of major importance. So far, it has been impossible to obtain lines either by selection or hybridization that are superior in seed production under irrigation or dry-land conditions. Intensive studies will have to be made to develop strains of this important range grass.

Side-oats grama (*Bouteloua curtipendula*) is another native, perennial, warm-season grass that ranks high in palatability. It is easily established by seed and forms an important part of the mixture recommended for range land reseedings. Strains from the South are subject to winter injury when moved north, and northern strains are low in production when moved southward.

El Reno side-oats grama was developed from field collections made near El Reno, Okla. It has ranked higher than other strains tested in Kansas for leafiness, resistance to leaf disease, and seed production.

Switchgrass (*Panicum virgatum*) is a native long-season grass that grows alongside the bluestems. It resembles other native grasses in growth and adaptation, but it differs from them in that it is a good seed producer, and the seed can be easily harvested, cleaned, and sown.

One strain that is being propagated is known as Blackwell switchgrass in Kansas. It is a field selection from Blackwell, Okla., developed by the Soil Conservation Service at Manhattan, Kans. It has a fine leafy quality and considerable resistance to rust. It matures seed moderately late and yields well. The leaves remain green until frost. In Kansas, and perhaps in nearby States, it is adapted for use in mixtures. It has been accepted for certification by the Kansas Crop Improvement Association. Another field selection, made from Holt County, Nebr., is a small, leafy type that is well adapted to the sandy soils north of the Platte River in Nebraska. It is susceptible to rust when grown farther south.

Mandan wild-rye (*Elymus canadensis*) is an improved variety of Canada wild-rye. It was developed at the Northern Great Plains Field Station by mass selection from plants grown from seed collected on upland near Mandan, N. Dak. Several vital characters make it superior to ordinary Canada wild-rye. It is longer-lived than many strains and will withstand grazing for several years. It is leafier, finer, and the softer-textured leaves are shorter. It has more resistance to rust than other strains that have been tested. It is easy to establish, grows rapidly, and yields well in seed and forage. It can be used to good advantage in mixtures with other grasses that are slower in becoming established. It seems to prefer sandy soils, but it also makes good growth on other soil types. Seed of Mandan wild-rye germinates more slowly than that of crested wheatgrass. It often sprouts a week later than crested wheatgrass. Establishment is relatively rapid, but it may take a year before weeds are crowded out.

Feather bunchgrass (*Stipa viridula*) has given way to green stipagrass, an improved variety that was developed at the Northern Great Plains Field Station from a single plant selection which originated from a bulk seed lot collected near Mandan. We think it is superior to ordinary feather bunchgrass in vigor and size. It excels in yields of forage and seed. In fact, it is one of the highest yielding of the cool-season grasses that have been tested at Mandan since 1942. After defoliation, it makes rapid regrowth and is useful in mixtures for pasture seedings. It is easily established in areas where weed competition is not too great. Hay cut at approximately the time the plants are in full head is nutritious and palatable. It seems to grow well on most soil types and probably can be grown successfully over most of the Northern Great Plains. Green stipagrass begins growth about a week later in the spring than crested wheatgrass. The seed ripens earlier than most species and reaches maturity about 3 weeks ahead of crested wheatgrass. It is of low germination when the seed is new, but if the seed is held in dry storage for 3 years, germination should be satisfactory.

Unfortunately, farmers and commercial seedsmen have not given enough consideration to the production of grass seed, which all too often has been limited to small localities in a few States or has been only a sideline crop, the seed being harvested from old pastures or natural stands.

The value of the 1944 crop of seed, based on the 1930–39 wholesale prices, was estimated to be approximately $20,000,000. Even though the figure is an estimate, it shows that grass seed as a crop is a sizeable business. The bulk of this represents common seed and does not include improved strains. Facilities for production of foundation seed of improved strains are lacking.

Improvement of grasses can be a success only if these new strains reach the farmer in quantity and quality to meet his needs. The plant breeder must cooperate with him and the seed producer to make this possible. The responsibility of testing new strains for regional adaptation and best uses lies with the plant breeder. He must also be certain that the foundation seed is true to type and will maintain the superior qualities of the new strain. Certified seed should be so grown and isolated as to maintain genetic purity. The consumer must know which strain is best adapted to his particular climatic conditions and requirements. The seed producer must grow those seeds in a manner that will assure the consumer of getting the strain and grade he demands. And, finally, the distributor must handle the seed in cleaning, processing, and bagging so as to keep the strains from becoming mixed.

THE AUTHOR

M. A. Hein, an agronomist in the Division of Forage Crops and Diseases, in the Bureau of Plant Industry, Soils, and Agricultural Engineering, joined the Department of Agriculture in 1928, the year he received the degree of master of science in agronomy from the University of Illinois. He is currently engaged in experimental work with native and introduced grasses for hay, pasture, and silage, adaptation studies, breeding for improvement, cultural practices, and other factors relating to grass.

FOR FURTHER READING

Black, W. H., and Clark, V. I.: *Comparison of Native Grasses and Crested Wheatgrass and of Supplements for Beef Cattle in the Northern Great Plains,* U. S. D. A. Circular 705, 1944.

Fracker, S. B., Garber, R. J., Myers, W. M., and others: *Improving Pastures and Grasslands for the Northeastern States,* U. S. D. A. Miscellaneous Publication 590, 1946.

More and Better Clover

by E. A. HOLLOWELL

HIGH COSTS of feed for livestock, lower yields of a later cash crop, and inadequate conservation of the soil are all closely associated with failures or poor stands of clover. Too frequently those conditions are blamed on unfavorable weather. Too infrequently do farmers look for the real causes of the failures.

When they do, it is often found that the seed used was of a variety not adapted to the local climatic conditions and lacking in resistance to the diseases and insect pests prevalent in the region. The purpose of this article is to report the progress that has been made in improving clover in recent years.

The problems involved are complex. First, there are more than 14 species of true clovers (*Trifolium* spp.) and sweetclovers (*Melilotus* spp.) that are important in United States agriculture. To determine proper objectives of an improvement program, thorough studies must be made of the method of reproduction of each species and of the plant diseases and insect pests that attack it. Special breeding techniques must be developed in many cases to obtain the characteristics that go to make a superior variety. After a new variety has been developed by breeding methods, it must be tested adequately to determine its range of adaptation and its cultural requirements. Finally, seed stocks of the improved and tested variety must be increased and maintained in a pure condition before it can be released for farm use.

Besides the usual factors of adaptation, resistance to low and fluctuating winter temperatures, potato leafhopper, and several leaf-spot diseases, northern anthracnose has recently been recognized as a serious disease in the northern and central regions of the main red clover belt. Breeders are searching for strains resistant to the disease. Another problem is one of adaptation to day-length during the growing season. Within certain limits, strains or varieties adapted to northern latitudes are lower yielding when planted farther south. On the other hand, varieties adapted to the lower latitudes give increased yields as they are moved northward until environmental factors, such as winterhardiness and diseases, limit their productivity. A step toward control of these problems has been made by the development of two new red-clover varieties—Midland and Cumberland.

Improved Red Clover

Midland red clover originated as a composite of equal proportions of four old strains, one each from Ohio, Indiana, Illinois, and Iowa. Thirteen years of testing it and increasing seed stocks were involved in developing Midland. Midland is winter hardy, has good growth characteristics, and has some resistance to northern anthracnose. As the name implies, it is adapted to the middle or central part of the Corn Belt States, and to areas with similar climatic conditions in the Eastern States. In the West, its use is recommended particularly for the production of certified seed for the eastern market. Depending on the environmental conditions, yields of one-quarter to three-quarters a ton more to the acre can be expected of Midland over common red clover.

Cumberland is a superior variety adapted to the southern part of the red clover belt. This southern red clover adaptation zone includes most of New Jersey, the southeastern corner of Pennsylvania, and the area generally south of 40° latitude. It originated as a composite of equal proportions of three identified strains, one each from Kentucky, Tennessee, and Virginia. It also is the result of 13 years of testing and increasing seed stocks and was developed cooperatively in State and Federal research and crop improvement programs. Cumberland has good growth characteristics. It is moderately resistant to southern anthracnose (caused by the fungus *Colletotrichum trifolii*), and has some resistance to crown rot as well. When severe, southern anthracnose may kill the seedling or mature plants of common varieties of red clover, besides lowering the quality of the hay. Cumberland frequently yields a ton per acre more than unadapted red clover in the southern red clover belt.

But varieties even more resistant to diseases than Midland and Cumberland are in the making. A new kind highly resistant to the powdery mildew disease and more resistant to northern anthracnose than Midland is being increased and tested to determine its range of adaptation. Likewise, another new variety highly resistant to southern anthracnose is in the final testing stages. In preliminary tests at a few locations it has lived over into the third year, or second harvest year. If subsequent tests confirm the early results, this fact is of considerable significance. This evidence that by breeding to eliminate the hazards of the environment, there are possibilities of developing superior varieties of red clover that are perennial in length of life. If more extensive tests substantiate the earlier ones, these new varieties will be named and increased as rapidly as facilities permit.

Improved Sweetclover

There are several new varieties of sweetclover, some of which warrant more extensive farm use.

Evergreen, a superior variety of biennial white sweetclover, was developed by the Ohio Agricultural Experiment Station. It is tall, rank growing, and late maturing. It is recommended for use in the Corn Belt, and the eastern edge of the Great Plains States for pasture and for plowing under for green manure. Evergreen yields from ½ ton to 1 ton an acre more than many other common white sweetclovers. It has particular value for pasture purposes because it gives an extra 3 or 4 weeks of grazing during the summer of the second year. Frequently, under humid conditions, Evergreen does not produce an abundance of seed. It has a long flowering period, but considerable seed shatters before and with harvesting operations.

Madrid is a new variety of biennial yellow sweetclover. It is superior to common varieties in that it matures slightly later and yields more. Besides, it has early seedling vigor and resists fall frost in the seedling year. Seed production is heavy and early enough to escape the hazard of drought common during the summer in the Great Plains. It is recommended for the Great Plains and Corn Belt States.

Spanish, a new variety of biennial white sweetclover, is recommended for the Corn Belt, Great Plains, and sections of the Intermountain region. It is midseason in maturity, higher yielding than most kinds of common biennial white sweetclover, and a heavy producer of seed.

Willamette, another biennial white sweetclover, was developed at the Oregon Agricultural Experiment Station. It is midseason in maturity and a higher yielder. Of particular importance is its resistance to stem rot, a disease that frequently kills stands during the winter and early spring months in the Pacific Northwest.

Sangamon is a late-maturing variety of common biennial white sweetclover developed by the Illinois Agricultural Experiment Station. It produces high yields and has the same advantages as Evergreen, except that it matures earlier.

Besides those, there are other less important varieties of sweetclovers. New superior ones that are resistant to Phytophthora root rot and black stem disease complex, common in the Corn Belt, are being increased and tested. A more leafy, fine-stemmed variety, more desirable for hay in the Great Plains than present varieties, is being increased for testing purposes. These varieties will be named and released when their value has been proved.

Improved Crimson and Sub Clovers

Dixie Crimson clover, a new hard-seeded variety, gives promise of eliminating a serious hazard in growing common crimson clover. The seed of common crimson has the undesirable characteristic of immediate germination. This may occur throughout the summer after seed is mature or after seeding in the fall. Light rains frequently provide sufficient moisture for germination, but fail to provide enough moisture to establish the seedling plants. For this reason, stands of common crimson clover are frequently lost. Dixie Crimson was developed by men in the Department in cooperation with the Georgia Coastal Plain Experiment Station and the Georgia and North Carolina Agricultural Experiment Stations. It is a composite of three identified strains of similar growth habits and has the characteristic of hard seeds which delays germination. Dixie Crimson volunteers in the fall from shattered seed, either when used in rotations or in pastures in association with such grasses as Bermuda.

Sub clover, formerly called subterranean clover, presents an outstanding example of the value of a superior variety in the successful introduction of a new species. For the past 30 years, common sub clover seed has been widely tested in the Southeast and Pacific Northwest. The results from these tests were not encouraging, and it appeared that the species had little value in this country. In 1934 seed of a series of sub clover varieties were obtained from Australia and were extensively tested. Among them were the varieties Tallarook, which is late maturing, and Mount Barker, which matures in midseason. Tallarook and Mount Barker have grown so well in the Pacific Northwest that the acreage of sub clover is being increased rapidly. In the Southern States they are also the most promising varieties of sub clover.

Improved White Clover

Ladino white clover, a mammoth or giant variety, is now widely known. It seems appropriate, however, in a survey of improved varieties to mention its rapid spread in farm use. The results of early, extensive tests on Ladino between 1912 and 1930 indicated that it was well adapted in many irrigated sections of the Western States, but not in the humid Eastern States.

After growers recognized that Ladino needed larger quantities of mineral plant nutrients than were formerly used and that continued close grazing had to be avoided for best returns, Ladino proved its value in the Northeast. It is now the symbol of large yields of high-quality feed. More recently, experimental and farm trials in several Lake and Corn Belt States, as well as in the upper sections of the Southeast, have indicated that Ladino has much to offer farmers interested in the production of quality feed.

The leaves, flower heads, and stems of Ladino are from three to five times larger than common white clover, but the seed is the same size and indistinguishable. Well-established seedling plants spread rapidly by large fleshy creeping stems.

Mixtures of Ladino with orchard grass, bromegrass, or timothy have given good results. Frequently Ladino is seeded with other legumes, such as red clover and alfalfa. Since Ladino seed is small in size, 2 pounds an acre with a grass is adequate for a good stand. When seeded with other legumes, and a grass, a half pound to the acre has been sufficient. For seed production most farmers plant Ladino alone, using from 3 to 5 pounds of seed per acre. Remember, however, that a compact seedbed with plenty of phosphate and potash fertilizer where needed is essential for good stands and high yields.

Value of Improved Clovers

The value of superior varieties of clovers has been difficult for some farmers to appreciate. The farm scale of measuring yields of clover in terms of loads of hay is too indefinite. Yields of hybrid corn and improved varieties of small grains are more accurately measured in bushels per acre from known acreages. The difference in yields between superior clover varieties and common kinds, however, is just as great, or even greater, than differences in yields between superior varieties of corn and small grains over common kinds. Too frequently farmers are price buyers. They purchase the lower-priced common seed instead of paying a few more cents a pound for certified seed of adapted superior varieties. The increase in yield more than pays for the extra seed cost. For example, look at red clover. The usual rate of seeding of red clover is 10 pounds an acre. Certified red clover seed of superior varieties costs 6 cents a pound more than common red clover seed. That means that it would cost 60 cents an acre more to use seed of superior varieties instead of common seed. Superior varieties, however, will produce a half a ton or more hay per acre than common red clover. Is not the investment of 60 cents per acre for an additional half a ton of hay profitable?

Unfortunately, the grower cannot distinguish the seed of these superior varieties from common kinds. Since the seed cannot be differentiated by appearance and since many varieties are grown in one region to produce planting stock for other regions, it is imperative that the seed be certified to insure the distributor and consumer that it is true to name. Producers of certified seed are required by regulation to plant seed of approved parentage, in fields free from volunteer seed and isolated to prevent contamination by cross pollination with common clover. Roguing of weeds and off-type plants may be necessary as the crop develops. Careful harvesting of the seed must be done to prevent contamination. The harvested seed must be cleaned and free from noxious weed seed. It must be of high germination, and marketed in sealed bags. These procedures require inspections by agents of the State Crop Improvement Associations. These regulations and procedures protect the varietal purity at a cost of a few additional cents a pound.

THE AUTHOR

E. A. Hollowell, an agronomist in the Bureau of Plant Industry, Soils, and Agricultural Engineering, is in charge of the Bureau's clover investigations; since 1924 he has carried on research pertaining to the cultural phases of clover production and the development of improved varieties. New superior varieties have been developed and their farm use expanded as a result of Dr. Hollowell's work.

FOR FURTHER READING

Hollowell, E. A.: *Ladino White Clover for the Northeastern States,* U. S. D. A. Farmers' Bulletin 1910, 1942.

Hollowell, E. A.: *Persian Clover,* U. S. D. A. Farmers' Bulletin 1929, 1942.

Hollowell, E. A.: *Registration of Varieties and Strains of Red Clover,* Journal of the American Society of Agronomy, volume 35, pages 830–833, September 1943.

Hollowell, E. A.: *Registration of Varieties and Strains of Sweet Clover,* Journal of the American Society of Agronomy, volume 35, pages 825–829, September 1943.

Rampton, H. H.: *Growing Subclover in Oregon,* Oregon State System of Education, Agricultural Experiment Station, Oregon State College, and Bureau of Plant Industry, Soils, and Agricultural Engineering Cooperating, Oregon Station Bulletin 432, October 1945.

Breeding Better Alfalfa

by H. M. TYSDAL

THE BACTERIAL wilt disease of alfalfa forcefully brought to the attention of alfalfa growers the need for improved, disease-resistant varieties of alfalfa. This serious disease, first identified in 1925, is caused by the bacterium *Corynebacterium insidiosum*. It can be classed with winterkilling and drought as among the most serious enemies of alfalfa. Although it was first noticed in the river valleys of Nebraska and Kansas and in some of the Corn Belt States, it is now found in every major alfalfa-producing State. It kills out stands in 2 to 3 years, and even before killing greatly reduces yields.

The Department of Agriculture and several State agricultural experiment stations undertook the problem of combating bacterial wilt by whatever method seemed feasible. Various control methods were tried, including rotation of crops, soil amendments, and breeding for disease resistance. The trials indicated that the selection of resistant varieties was the only practical method of solving the problem. Because domestic varieties were not resistant, the Department sent explorers over much of the world searching for wilt-resistant alfalfas. Through the efforts of H. L. Westover, resistant strains were found in Turkistan.

By intercrossing, plant breeders combined the resistance in the Turkistan varieties with desired characters of domestic strains. Within the past few years two new varieties have been produced and increased that are resistant to bacterial wilt. They have been named Ranger and Buffalo. In areas where bacterial wilt is present, they maintain a good stand after 3 or 4 or more years, while the old varieties, such as Grimm or Common, have been completely killed.

Ranger, produced by Department plant breeders in cooperation with the Nebraska Agricultural Experiment Station, originates from selection within Turkistan, Cossack, and Ladak. In regions where bacterial wilt is not a factor, Ranger is about equal to Grimm in productivity of forage and seed and cold resistance. One disadvantage, particularly in the Eastern States, is that Ranger is slightly more susceptible to leaf-spot diseases and leafhopper yellowing than Grimm or Hardigan. Ranger, however, is recommended for the northern regions of the United States wherever bacterial wilt is serious. It was released for commercial production in 1940, and now several thousand acres are producing seed.

Buffalo, produced by plant breeders of the Department and the Kansas Agricultural Experiment Station, originates from selections made from an old Kansas Common field. Buffalo compares favorably with Kansas Common in yield and adaptation. It surpasses Kansas Common in resistance to the bacterial wilt disease. Buffalo, like Kansas Common, is best adapted in the general latitude of Kansas, and south and east from that State, but its range of adaptation probably will be farther north than that of Kansas Common because of its greater cold resistance. It is recommended for use anywhere within this range where bacterial wilt is a problem.

Ranger and Buffalo have been tested by many experiment stations. At the Iowa station, for example, Buffalo produced 3.60 and Ranger 3.55 tons to the acre in their third year of production. In the same replicated test, the better standard varieties, such as Grimm and Baltic, produced only 2.5 and 1.5 tons an acre, respectively. Similar results were had in Idaho, Ohio, Minnesota, and elsewhere—in fact, wherever the bacterial wilt disease is present. In areas where the disease is unimportant, Ranger and Buffalo yield about the same as an ordinary variety.

Strains resistant to bacterial wilt are not the only new alfalfas introduced to alfalfa growers during the war years. Two other newcomers were released for commercial production: Atlantic, produced by plant breeders of the New Jersey Agricultural Experiment Station; and Nemastan, an introduction from Turkistan.

Atlantic is a vigorous-growing, high-yielding variety and is adapted to the Eastern States. It originates from selections within many varieties, including Hardigan, Grimm, and Baltic. Although it does not withstand the bacterial wilt disease, it is somewhat more tolerant of that disease than standard varieties such as Hardigan or Grimm.

Nemastan, one of the many introductions brought in by Mr. Westover, has been found by research men in the Utah and Nevada Agricultural Experiment Stations and the Department to resist stem nematode. Efforts were started to increase its seed stocks for use in localities in Nevada and Utah and neighboring States where the stem nematode is a serious limiting factor. It is also resistant to the bacterial wilt disease. Nemastan is not recommended for use anywhere in the Eastern States, however, because of its susceptibility to leaf spots. Progress is being made in improving its seed and forage yield and its resistance to other diseases. It is now serving an extremely useful purpose in areas where alfalfa cannot be grown because of the stem nematode.

Plant breeders can use ordinary selection methods to produce good strains of improved alfalfa, but the best strains with maximum improvement can be produced only by making use of hybrid vigor.

Using Hybrid Vigor

In corn, hybrid vigor is obtained in first-generation crosses by detasseling one of the parents to prevent any self-pollination from occurring. In alfalfa it is not practical to prevent self-pollination artificially. About 15 percent of the alfalfa plants, however, are self-sterile. In these self-sterile plants, pollen from a given plant will not fertilize flowers on the same plant but may be fully fertile on another plant. Hence it is possible to obtain practically 100-percent crossing by planting two such plants in an isolated block. The pollen of each plant readily fertilizes the flowers of the other plant, but not its own.

One might raise the question that two such plants would not produce enough seed for a very large hay acreage. Here is where another characteristic of alfalfa comes into use. Alfalfa can be very readily propagated by vegetative cuttings, much in the manner of making geranium slips; a single desirable plant can be increased to any number of plants. Because alfalfa is a perennial, moreover, these plants will live many years and frequent replantings will not be necessary.

Plants selected for hybrid-seed production must be relatively self-sterile. They must also be resistant to diseases, cold, and insect pests. They must combine well with each other. This combining ability is a rather abstract thing. The plant breeder cannot say by looking at a plant whether it will combine well (or "nick" well, as livestock breeders say) with another plant or not. Combining ability depends upon how the genes, or inheritance carriers, of one plant complement those in the other plant. The only way to determine this point definitely is to make the cross. However, a procedure called the polycross method has been developed that helps to pick out the best combiners just as the top-cross in corn helps corn breeders choose the best inbred lines in corn.

In the polycross method, stocks used in the polycross nursery are highly selected, desirable plants. They are selected either from the better varieties of nursery-bred alfalfa or from old fields that have had natural elimination. Highly self-fertile, or autogamous, plants are not selected, because self-fertilization reduces progeny yields. It is not necessary to use selfed lines, as corn breeders do. The plant breeder chooses self-sterile plants and they are propagated vegetatively. These plants are subjected to various diseases to test their resistance. Those that resist diseases and, as far as possible, insect pests, and have the other desirable characteristics are selected. They are increased vegetatively and planted in the clonal polycross nursery. In this nursery each clone (that is, each vegetatively propagated plant) is pollinated by natural methods. Pollen from the same clone or other clones in the nursery is carried to the flowers by insects. Because these plants are relatively self-sterile, it has been found that most of the seed so produced is out-crossed. Thus the seed from one clone or female parent derives its pollen or male parentage from many different clones. The progenies resulting from seed produced in this manner are known as polycrosses.

Tests comparing the combining ability of clones by the polycross method with the performance of the same clones in single crosses, or with their performance in a top cross, have shown that the polycross performance gives a reliable indication of their combining ability. It is much easier and cheaper to produce the polycross seed than to make all possible single crosses or to use a separate isolation block for each top-cross. By vegetative propagation, the original plants can be increased as much as is necessary to produce enough seed for thorough testing under various conditions in different parts of the country. The Eastern States depend largely upon the West and Midwest for their seed supply. It is, therefore, of prime importance to select plants whose progenies are adapted to relatively wide regional areas.

Besides showing the combining ability of clones, the polycross method makes it possible to obtain new superior combinations by natural crosses between selected clones in the polycross nursery. The term cumulative improvement is used to designate this phase of the program. In cumulative improvement it has been found that second-cycle material (that is, plants selected from the polycross progenies) is often better than the original parents. It should be remembered, however, that in cumulative improvement, precautions should be taken to prevent the basic stocks from becoming inter-related. This can be done by separating the various types in different polycross nurseries. It is also advisable to introduce new, unrelated selections into the program as often as possible.

When seed from the clonal polycross nursery is thoroughly tested, the original clones that show the best polycross performance in disease resistance, yield, et cetera, are increased vegetatively and paired in all combinations to produce single crosses. Single crosses are made by planting the two relatively self-sterile clones in alternate rows in an isolated field where they can be naturally pollinated without being contaminated with pollen from other sources. Very little alfalfa seed is produced without the tripping of the flowers by pollinating insects. During this process the pollen is carried by the insects from one clone to another. Thus, with relatively self-sterile clones, usually over 95 percent crossing is obtained.

The possibility of commercial production of hybrid alfalfa was first proposed in November 1941. Since then a number of experimental hybrids have been produced in natural field crossing blocks. These have been tested in both forage and seed yield studies in comparison with the best standard varieties. In a 2-year test conducted at the Nebraska Agricultural Experiment Station, the better hybrids and polycrosses yielded from 4.16 to 4.34 tons an acre. In the same test, Grimm yielded 3.43 tons of cured hay to the acre. The hybrids showed a superiority of from 20 to 27 percent over Grimm. In a seed production test at the Utah Agricultural Experiment Station some of the hybrids yielded 660 pounds of seed to the acre, while Grimm produced 450 pounds an acre.

As I have said, many of these hybrids are resistant to bacterial wilt. Some also show resistance to attacks by the potato leaf hopper (*Empoasca fabae*). It has been found that alfalfa subjected to leaf hopper attacks (alfalfa yellows) is greatly reduced in carotene content. Carotene content is directly related to the vitamin A value of alfalfa hay. Tests under leaf hopper infestation have shown that more resistant hybrids have twice as much carotene (and thus vitamin A) as standard varieties. There is promise of producing hybrids more resistant to the leaf spot diseases. This would be important from the standpoint of increased quality of forage because the leaves of alfalfa contain approximately 66 percent of the protein and 75 percent of the carotene content of the plant. Leaf diseases destroy the leaves, and cause great losses in feeding value. Besides the usual hay types, the possibility of producing rhizomatous hybrids for grazing, for hay, and for erosion control is promising.

It may be possible to produce a double-cross hybrid alfalfa by planting seed of two high-combining single crosses in alternate rows for natural crossing. In that case the result would not be a 100-percent first-generation, or F_1, cross because of some pollination within each single cross. Nevertheless, by using two single crosses that would produce an exceptionally good hybrid between them, the resulting progenies would prove high yielding and certainly much better than present standard varieties. As a matter of fact, yield tests have shown that as much as 25-percent selfed seed planted with the hybrid reduces the yield of the mixture very little below that of the pure hybrid. No doubt this is because in any field planting there are a large number of young plants that die from competition with more vigorous plants. In that event, the strong hybrids would crowd out the plants from selfed seed. In addition to the production of hybrid alfalfa in the above manner, the possible use of male sterility (sterile pollen) should be investigated as a means of producing hybrid alfalfa.

The same procedure outlined for the selection of high-combining clones for use in producing hybrids would be used for the development of superior synthetic varieties. A synthetic variety may be defined as a variety that is developed by crossing, compositing, or planting together two or more unrelated strains or clones, the bulk seed being harvested and re-planted in successive generations. By natural intercrossing the unrelated strains or clones are "synthesized" into a new variety. A synthetic variety can be increased through successive seed generations so long as the de-sired characteristics of the variety are retained. Some synthetic combina-tions have been tested in a preliminary way and have demonstrated their superiority over standard varieties. Thus if hybrids do not show a suf-ficient superiority to merit the extra labor involved, the same clones can be utilized in the production of synthetic varieties. The original clones would be maintained or increased vegetatively to form a source of pure foundation seed. The optimum number of clones to be used to produce a synthetic variety is being investigated.

Field tests have shown clearly that hybrid alfalfa has a definite place in alfalfa improvement. For the production of either hybrid or superior synthetic alfalfas one of the essential features is the use of foundation ma-terials that have high-combining value and therefore maximum hybrid vigor. This must be taken into consideration if maximum improvement in alfalfa is to be obtained.

The production of hybrid and synthetic alfalfas is still in the experi-mental stages, but their utilization promises more certain production of higher quality forage and pasture. Since legumes might well be the key-stone of a permanent and profitable agriculture, improved varieties of alfalfa, an important legume crop, would be of tremendous value for the needed expansion in acreage, for protection against soil erosion, and for furthering the livestock industries at lower production costs.

THE AUTHOR

H. M. Tysdal is an agronomist in the Bureau of Plant Industry, Soils, and Agri-cultural Engineering. He is a graduate of the University of Saskatchewan, Kansas State College, and the University of Minnesota. Dr. Tysdal, as a fellow of the American Scandinavian Foundation, studied plant breeding and plant physiology in Sweden and on the continent in 1927–28; he has also taught at the University of Minnesota, Michigan State College, and the University of Nebraska. He has written numerous papers on the culture and improvement of alfalfa. In an address before the American Society of Agronomy in 1941, he was the first to suggest the possibility of producing hybrid alfalfa commercially.

FOR FURTHER READING

Grandfield, C. O., and Throckmorton, R. I.: *Alfalfa in Kansas*, Kansas Agricultural Experiment Station Bulletin 328, 1945.

Symposium on *Alfalfa Seed Setting*. Journal, American Society of Agronomy, volume 38, pages 461–535, June 1946.

Tysdal, H. M., Kiesselbach, T. A., and Westover, H. L.: *Alfalfa Breeding*, Nebraska Research Bulletin 124, 1942.

Tysdal, H. M., and Kiesselbach, T. A.: *Hybrid Alfalfa*, Journal, American Society of Agronomy, volume 36, pages 649–667, August 1944.

New Legumes for the South

by ROLAND McKEE

IT IS JUST as big an accomplishment to introduce a new and suitable legume into any area as it is to build a highway or perfect a new kind of airplane. The same degree, if not type, of knowledge and skill is needed—basic information about weather and soil, the uses to which the project is to be put, fundamental natural and physical laws and sciences, and adaptation. Adaptation means suitability; in the case of plants, it means suitability to the usual farm operations of a locality, its rainfall, fertility, length of season, temperatures, incidence of diseases, topography, and market requirements. It would not do to plant a crimson clover adapted to Carroll County, Iowa, in Carroll County, Ga., and expect it to do equally well in both places.

In recent years several new legumes have been added to southern agriculture. They fit into places and uses for which other legumes were not available. Some of them are new varieties of familiar crops—lespedeza, field peas, crimson clover, vetch, crotalaria, and lupines. Others, hairy indigo and big trefoil, are new to southern farmers. Lespedeza is perhaps the most important.

Korean lespedeza now covers millions of acres in the United States, but it was unknown to agriculture only 25 years ago. But despite its newness, selection of improved strains has been possible, and two varieties of special value have been perfected. One, known as Early Korean, is recognized as superior for northern parts of the lespedeza area, and has extended the use of the crop farther north. It was first selected 15 years ago, but its increase and extension of use are a current development. The other, even more recent, is a high-yielding, late-maturing strain that has been named Climax. Climax was released in 1946 after experimental tests so the amount of seed could be increased. It is adapted to southern sections and will help extend the use of Korean lespedeza in the South. Furthermore, the habit Climax has of maturing late will extend the grazing season and give larger hay yields.

Both strains have outyielded unselected commercial lespedeza in the region of their adaptation. The Early Korean variety not only yields well, but can be grown farther north than commercial Korean. It also makes earlier growth and thus affords earlier grazing. Climax, on the other hand, produces heavy hay yields, makes late growth, and affords later pasturing than other Korean varieties.

Austrian Winter fieldpeas are used extensively for soil improvement, but diseases have greatly reduced their value. After several years of breeding work and study of these diseases, investigators have evolved varieties with partial resistance to disease. Seed of them is now being increased for more general use. Unfortunately, fieldpeas do not develop seed well in the South, and it is necessary to depend on other regions for seed. In developing disease-resistant strains, hybrid seed selected in the South is sent to other areas for increase and commercial production.

With any legume, old or new, it is desirable or essential that seed be available at low cost. If a crop must be seeded every year, the cost of seed and preparation of land must be given consideration. If a crop can be volunteered from seed produced on the land by a preceding crop, the cost of seeding is cut way down—an especially desirable factor in the case of soil-improving crops. Spotted bur-clover, crotalaria, and roughpea are three such crops that can be handled in this way. Spotted bur-clover has been grown a number of years, but the use of crotalaria and roughpea is recent. Of interest in this connection is a variety of crimson clover that has recently been developed, Dixie crimson clover.

Another winter legume that produces seed well in the South and can be readily volunteered is big-flower vetch. It has proved its worth in experimental tests, and growers have made commercial plantings of it. When once established, it persists without further cost for seed, and because it makes good winter growth it is a promising winter cover crop for soil improvement. Like most commercial vetches, it is of European origin. When the plant is ripe the seed shatters easily—a deterrent to seed increase. High cost of seed, however, is of minor importance when one considers that when vetch is once established it will last 5 years or more.

Although crotalaria has been grown widely since 1930, it is a comparatively new crop. It is of special interest for soil improvement because it makes good growth on poor, sandy soils and does not harbor nematodes.

For that reason, crotalaria helps rid the land of this pest, and can be used to advantage in rotation with crops susceptible to nematode damage. Crotalaria also keeps down weed plants that are hosts to nematodes. In orchards, susceptible trees can be protected from infection by keeping a covering of crotalaria on the land during the season when weeds or other susceptible plants might be growing. The full value of crotalaria for use in reducing nematode damage has not been fully appreciated, but with extended use its value for the purpose will be further demonstrated. The most widely used species is *Crotalaria spectabilis*. It has been favored for improving soil, but it is poisonous to livestock. The seed particularly contain a deadly poison and cause death even when taken in comparatively small amounts. Plant breeders, therefore, have worked to develop species that are not poisonous and that are just as good for soil improvement. Newer species that have shown their value in experimental plantings are *C. intermedia, C. juncea,* and *C. lanceolata.* They are on the way to displacing *C. spectabilis.* Most used for that purpose is *C. intermedia,* a variety that is a good soil improver and can be used for forage. Another species, which surpasses *C. intermedia* in some ways, has been used in experimental plantings for some time and deserves attention for general use. It is *C. lanceolata.* It does not grow quite so tall as *C. intermedia,* but yields about the same tonnage of forage and produces a good crop of seed. In experimental plantings it has volunteered more consistently than others.

Of the recently introduced southern crops, none has developed more rapidly than blue lupine. Its introduction is the result of an experimental program started in 1931 by the Department in cooperation with several Southern States. By 1935, results were sufficiently encouraging to justify small demonstrations and plantings to get more seed. In subsequent years, plantings were further increased, and by 1941 large plantings were being made by commercial growers.

Blue lupine is used primarily as a winter green-manure or cover crop. In the sections to which it is adapted, it is superior for this purpose. Because blue lupine produces an abundance of easily harvested seed, local seed supplies are assured, an important factor because home-grown seed reduces the cost of seeding and assures seed in season. Seed of the common blue lupine cannot be used for feed, nor can the crop be used as forage because of poisonous alkaloids contained in both the seed and plant. Nonpoisonous strains, however, have been developed recently and give promise of producing a late spring feed crop; if these nonalkaloid strains give satisfactory returns, a local seed feed crop also will be had.

Another species of lupine, known as yellow lupine, has given good results in experimental plantings. In some places it has been superior to the blue type. It seems to be more resistant to some of the diseases that have attacked the blue lupine and in very sandy soils it has made better growth. Nonalkaloid or nonpoisonous strains have been developed in this species, as in the blue lupine, that have possibilities of making yellow lupines a forage crop as well as a soil-improving crop. Both lupines make large winter growth, and, therefore, supply greater amounts of organic matter for soil improvement than other winter cover crops. Besides being the largest growing winter cover crops, lupines are the only winter legumes adapted to the South that give promise of producing a seed crop that can be used for livestock feed.

Hairy indigo, a native of Asia, Australia, and Africa, is proving adapted to the lower South for forage and soil improvement. It will grow on moderately poor sandy soil and needs comparatively little lime. The plants are coarse when grown singly, but in thick stands they make good forage. Tests showed it to be a long-season plant. Its seed matures late, however, so that harvesting of seed is difficult. Recently, an earlier strain was obtained that matured early enough to produce seed without difficulty. The Florida Agricultural Experiment Station, in cooperation with the Department, has taken the lead in developing this plant, which, according to information we now have, can best be used in Florida and other areas touching the Gulf of Mexico. Commercial plantings were made in 1945 and seed was harvested in considerable quantity.

Big trefoil, a legume that has been in experimental plantings in the South for several years, gives promise of being adapted to wet, low-land pastures. It is a perennial, leafy, fine-stemmed plant somewhat similar to alfalfa. It is a native of Europe, but it is grown in many parts of the world. In the United States, commercial plantings are confined to the coastal area of western Oregon and Washington. Since wet areas are especially suited to big trefoil, it is under such conditions that it may have a place in the South. It has survived and made good growth for a number of years in low, wet pasture land at the Georgia Coastal Plain Experiment Station at Tifton, Ga., and more recent plantings have survived and done well under somewhat similar conditions in Florida and North Carolina. A good legume for such situations in the South is needed, and big trefoil may serve this purpose. Where big trefoil is being grown commercially it is recognized as having good forage quality. It can be cut for hay and used for pasturage. The plants have underground rootstocks, by means of which it spreads. It is not in any way a weed. The seed habits of big trefoil are poor for commercial harvesting. The seed is extremely small and the pods burst open and scatter the seed when it is ripe.

THE AUTHOR

Roland McKee, a senior agronomist, has been wth the Department since 1905. As director of investigations on miscellaneous legumes, he has seen the now well-known cover crops like Austrian Winter peas, Willamette vetch, purple vetch, Hungarian vetch, monantha vetch, blue lupine, Crotalaria spectabilis, C. intermedia, C. straita, and alyceclover come into use. He has also instigated the development of nonpoisonous strains of lupines in both the blue- and yellow-flowered species, and the development of high-yielding late strains of annual lespedezas, particularly the variety Climax. Mr. McKee's latest major interest has been the establishment of lupines as a crop. The work was begun in 1931, and in 1946 more than 17 million pounds of seed were produced.

G-Men of Plant Diseases

by PAUL R. MILLER

FOOD CROPS are attacked by many enemies even in ordinary times. They are especially vulnerable in time of total war. An epidemic in a mainstay crop in wartime could have disastrous results. There are virulent kinds of deadly organisms that could quickly destroy whole crops if distributed when weather conditions are right.

The freedom with which persons move about in this country and the possibility in wartime of distributing disease-causing material by aircraft favored deliberate attempts at such distribution. Strains on transportation facilities enhanced the opportunity for introduction, by friend or foe, of new pathogens. Imports, which normally come to a few ports, were coming to various points along the east coast and made the job of the Plant Quarantine Service that much harder. Also, the activities of submarines were a constant source of danger, because torpedoed cargoes were washed ashore, with an attendant possibility of escape of disease-producing organisms.

On that reasoning, the Plant Disease Survey established the emergency plant disease prevention project in 1943, with the approval of the Secretary of War and support from the President's emergency funds. Broadly stated, the purpose was to help protect the country's supplies of food, feed, fiber, and oil by insuring immediate detection of enemy attempts at crop destruction through the use of plant diseases, and informing production specialists and extension workers promptly regarding outbreaks of plant diseases, whether introduced inadvertently or by design.

The field work was conducted by 24 pathologists, assigned to territories all over the United States. Special attention was given areas of concentrated food production. The field workers were already familiar with the geography and cropping practice of the region in which they worked, and had the help of experiment station officials, county agents, State workers, and others. Laboratories were established at Beltsville and at Stillwater, Okla., with consulting diagnosticians in charge, to whom puzzling cases of plant diseases were sent for verification.

Attention was focused primarily on important food crops, but an effort was made not to overlook disease developments among other plants. The G-men of plant diseases, who were well versed in field diagnosis, spent most of their time in the field, gathering and recording information. They made weekly reports to officials of the State where the observations were made and to Beltsville for publication and action.

For reasons of national security, it was not prudent during the war to discuss malicious activity, and even now certain important phases of this work must remain untold: The residual effect of the Japanese balloon missions is still to be determined, and biological warfare, although less spectacular, may have a tremendous potentiality for devastation of life, both plant and animal.

Our more obvious findings concern the geographic distribution of disease. During the survey, many diseases affecting various crops were observed that were either new to science, had not been known in this country before, had not been known to attack the particular crop before, or were found for the first time in a particular area.

Of the 150-odd diseases on about 60 crops reported as having been found for the first time in States where they had not previously been known to occur, I mention a few examples.

Phloem necrosis, a destructive virus disease, has killed tens of thousands of elm trees in the Ohio River Valley from West Virginia and Ohio to Illinois and Kentucky during the past few years, but west of the Mississippi River it had been observed only in southeastern Missouri. During the survey, the disease was found for the first time in localities in Kansas, Arkansas, Oklahoma, and the southern two-thirds of Missouri, from the Mississippi River to the Kansas border.

On corn, the fungus *Cercospora zeae-maydis* was found to be the predominant cause of leaf spotting in Kentucky and Tennessee. Previously it had been known only in Illinois.

The yellow-spot disease (*Helminthosporium tritici-vulgaris*) of wheat was found in Virginia, West Virginia, Kansas, and Nebraska. The first known occurrences in this country had been reported from New York and Maryland a few years before. The disease is considered serious in Japan, but has not seemed to be bad in the United States.

Another wheat malady, the virus disease mosaic, was observed for the first time in Missouri, where it was found to be rather prevalent.

White rust (*Albugo occidentalis*) was determined to be one of several diseases causing heavy loss in a commercial spinach area in Oklahoma; previously it had been known in Texas only.

A virus disease of lettuce known as virus necrosis, or brown blight, was found on greenhouse lettuce in Illinois, besides Indiana, where it was first observed.

On onions, smut (*Urocystis cepulae*) was found in Colorado and downy mildew (*Peronospora destructor*) in Texas. A minor infection of the latter was noted in one locality in Idaho. Both diseases are rather widespread, smut in most northern onion-growing areas, and downy mildew more or less throughout the country.

The disease of soybean known as top necrosis, streak, or bud blight, caused by a virus resembling the tobacco ring spot virus, had been recognized in Indiana, Ohio, and Iowa before 1943. During our survey, it was found to be generally distributed in the Central States from Ohio west to Kansas and South Dakota.

The charcoal rot, or ashy stem blight, organism (*Macrophomina phaseoli*), was found in Oregon; in one place it was causing a severe root rot of pumpkin and squash. That disclosed a considerable jump in the known occurrence of the fungus, which has been rather widely reported on many different kinds of plants in the southern two-thirds of the country, especially west of the Mississippi, but had never been encountered in Oregon before, on any host.

Some diseases were observed to be more widely distributed than previously realized in States where they were already present. Among these, to mention only two, alfalfa bacterial wilt (*Corynebacterium insidiosum*) was found for the first time in the main alfalfa seed-producing areas in Minnesota, its known range in Wisconsin also was extended northward, and in some other States it was found to be more prevalent and widespread than had been suspected. The onion bulb nematode (*Ditylenchus dipsaci*), which has been known for some time on a few farms in two locations in New York, was found in another district in a small portion of one field.

The detection of new and potentially important sources of damage was only one aspect of the assistance given by the emergency program to crop production. In many activities it supplemented the work of Federal and State agencies in such matters as the factors that influence infection and spread, the identity and cause of obscure diseases, the determination of distribution and importance of specific diseases, the prediction of the development of a disease during the season, the determination of subjects on which research was needed, and the places where insecticides and fungicides were urgently needed by farmers.

The following crop disease developments, not necessarily new, but nonetheless important, are selected from several hundred cases to illustrate the contributions of another part of the emergency program.

The potato rot nematode (*Ditylenchus destructor*) is a bothersome nematode pest on potatoes in northern Europe. As a result of our work, in cooperation with State officials, the first definite knowledge of its presence on potatoes in the United States was made known. In 1943 infected potatoes were found on three farms in Idaho. Immediate action by officials of the Idaho Department of Agriculture prevented the growing of potatoes on one of the farms, and on the others they stipulated that potatoes could be grown only in designated fields other than those in which the pest occurred in 1943. The agency also prohibited the moving and use of manure from a feed lot, where infected cull tubers were fed, until tests could demonstrate whether the organism could be spread in that way. In 1944, all farms in the vicinity were resurveyed. Nematodes were present in tubers from two farms and from two other nearby farms.

In 1943, the crop of one commercial rutabaga section of Virginia suffered a loss estimated at 10 percent. The trouble was observed and the cause was determined by a field worker as due to a deficiency of boron, which had not previously been suspected in the area. The growers lost more than $20,000 that year, but the information as to the occurrence and cause of the loss, placed in the hands of the State extension pathologist, permitted the application of known control measures the following year.

I cite the epidemic of late blight (*Phytophthora infestans*) on potatoes and tomatoes in the lower Rio Grande Valley of Texas as an example of the application of current crop-disease information to the forecasting of future developments.

Late blight was found widely distributed on the fall crops of both hosts in late 1943 and early 1944, the first time in several years that the disease had occurred on tomatoes in the valley. The significant feature of the prevalence of late blight on the relatively small fall crop was the threat that this abundant source of infection would carry to the important spring crops, which were just being planted at that time and which overlapped the fall crops during the early stages of growth. The danger was so serious that growers were warned in time to undertake preventive measures, and extra supplies of fungicides and insecticides were ordered. The weather remained favorable the next 3 months, and by March the disease had increased to epidemic proportions. In most undusted potato fields all of the foliage had been killed, and the stems were dying by the middle of March, with a total loss of the crop of affected plants, since most were just approaching the flowering stage. The effectiveness of dusting was strikingly evident, but only half of the 10,000 acres of potatoes were dusted. After March, the weather became less favorable and the disease was checked.

An example of the importance of correlating information from State to State, which was one of our functions, is the epidemic of the potato late blight in Southern States during the winter and spring of 1943–44, of which the Texas outbreak was a part. An epidemic of late blight depends on a combination of two factors, the presence of inoculum, that is, a source of infection, and weather that favors its spread—in this case, a great deal of rain and rather low temperatures. Several circumstances combined to produce a considerable amount of late blight in seed planted in the South. The 1943 crop in northern seed potato areas had suffered a widespread late blight attack with heavy tuber infection, and shortage of seed stocks resulted in the use of a great deal of inferior seed. Ordinarily, southern potato areas are too warm for late blight development regardless of seed infection, but the combination of infected seed and weather—plus, in many sections, lack of control equipment and experience with the disease—was bound to result in an outbreak. The observations on the prevalence and importance of late blight in Florida and Texas served as an indication as to what might be expected to develop in other southern areas, given favorable weather, and put pathologists and growers on their guard.

The disease was epidemic in every Gulf State from Texas to Florida, and north to South Carolina, causing losses ranging from a quarter to half or more of the expected yield. In some of the areas it had rarely occurred before.

Disease-producing organisms carried on the seed are responsible annually for great losses in small grain crops through seedling diseases and root rots. A new approach to the control of these diseases was instituted by the emergency work in Minnesota and the Dakotas. Seed of barley, oats, wheat, and flax, originating in widely separated regions of those States, were cultured to determine which organisms were present and to what extent, so that extension workers could know whether to advise farmers to treat the seed. The basis of their advice was whether the particular organisms present could be controlled and whether they were present in such concentration as to call for seed treatment. This project is one of more than merely immediate benefits: It can save the expense of seed treatment to farmers in regions where it is not likely to be beneficial, it can prevent controllable losses in regions where seed treatment is advisable, and it is likely to result in a progressive eradication of some of the sources of loss.

Virus diseases were shown to be more widely distributed and more common in Utah stone fruit orchards than had been realized, and a reliable method was established for diagnosing infection by rusty mottle of sweet cherry in the absence of the typical symptoms.

Much progress was made toward determining the cause and the factors associated with the spread of decline in citrus and avocado groves in California.

Results of the nematode survey in Florida and other Southern States showed that besides the root knot nematode (*Heterodera marioni*) many other plant parasitic forms about which very little is known are widespread and probably of considerable importance.

A survey in Virginia showed that the meadow nematode (*Pratylenchus pratensis*) was very widely distributed and that it was constantly associated with winter browning of boxwood, and probably was involved in much of the so-called winter injury of many plants.

Bad infestations of both the root knot and the meadow nematodes were found on celery in Oregon.

Surveys of diseases of peanuts in the Carolinas, Georgia, and Alabama added a great deal to the available information on distribution of the diseases, the reaction of different varieties to them, the fungi associated with peg rot and with nut rot in the field and in storage, and methods of harvesting and storing to reduce losses from nut deterioration.

The aster yellows virus disease was found in almost·all parts of the country except the southeastern area. Some of the important hosts affected most frequently and severely were potato (on this host the disease is called purple-top wilt), carrots, lettuce, celery, spinach, and onion. In the Winter Garden vegetable growing region of Texas, a severe epidemic affected carrots, an important crop there. A careful watch was kept on the course of its development, including the age when plants became infected, effect on the roots, amount of loss from specific degrees of infection, and abundance of the insect carrier.

In Idaho, on potatoes in field and storage, either a new disease or a new serious aspect of a disease was found. The term "water rot" was applied to the condition, and repeated isolations from typical samples yield a fungus identified at the Stillwater laboratory as *Phytophthora erythroseptica*. In some fields at digging time as many as 50 percent of the tubers showed the trouble, and the rot increased in storage.

I believe the few examples given show the importance of this type of plant disease reconnaissance, whether during time of war or peace. The work provided probably the most comprehensive and constructive picture of plant diseases any country has ever obtained. It seems doubtful that any important plant enemy could have invaded our country during this time without early detection, apprehension, and control. In the past, unfortunately, this has not always been true. As W. A. McCubbin says, the introduction of plant diseases is not a mere theoretical possibility, but a tragic reality. Think of the chestnut-blight fungus that came in, probably from Japan, about 1900, and has since killed practically all of the American chestnut trees; the Dutch elm disease fungus, which arrived about 1930 from Europe, and is still taking its toll of American elm trees; the potato bacterial ring rot organism that came from Europe and has spread throughout the United States; the golden nematode parasite, which has long been a serious pest of potatoes in northern Europe and was found in the United States in 1941.

New diseases, either newly discovered diseases,* or found in the United States for the first time,** or found on the particular crop for the first time***

Crop	Disease and cause	Where found	Remarks
Artichoke.....	Dwarfing and mottling (Virus)*	California........	
Asparagus.....	Charcoal rot (Macrophomina phaseoli)***	Texas............	Organism attacks many hosts.
Bean, lima....	Witches'-broom (Cause undetermined)	Arizona..........	Possibly caused by some virus.
	Leaf spot (Ascochyta boltshauseri)***	North Carolina ...	
Eggplant......	Root rot (Aphanomyces sp.)*	New Jersey.......	Reported on seedlings on one farm.
Lettuce.......	Root rot (Aphanomyces sp.)*	.....do	On seedlings in coldframes on one farm where it caused loss.
Pepper.......	Root rot (Aphanomyces sp.)*	.....do	On seedlings in greenhouse was heavy.
Potato........	Nematode (Ditylenchus destructor)**.	Idaho...........	On a few farms in one potato section.
	Ring spot (tomato ring-spot virus)***.	Colorado, Wyoming.	Potato apparently a new host.
Spinach	Root rot (Phytophthora megasperma)***.	California, North Carolina.	In California the fungus causes root rot on various other hosts.
Cowpea	Stem blight (Diaporthe sojae)***.	Virginia.........	Fungus common as the cause of stem and pod blight of soybean.
	Target spot (Helminthosporium vignae)*.	Louisiana, North Carolina, South Carolina.	Causes severe spotting of leaves and stems.
	Leaf spot (Myrothecium roridum)***.	Louisiana........	One location; fungus consistently isolated from a particular type of leaf spotting.
Peanut.......	Anthracnose (Colletotrichum sp.)*.	Oklahoma........	Isolated from stem lesions.
	Stem blight (Diaporthe sojae)***.	Virginia.........	Common on soybean.
Soybean......	Target spot (Helminthosporium vignae)*.	Florida. (See also cowpea.)	Causes light spotting on soybean leaves.
	Powdery mildew (Microsphaera sp.)**.	North Carolina ...	
	Leaf spot (Myrothecium roridum)***.	Louisiana........	One location; see cowpea.
Soybean......	Yeast spot of seed (Nematospora coryli).***	Oklahoma, North Carolina, South Carolina, Virginia.	Cultures of seed from various sources indicate disease is widespread.
	Seedling blight (Penicillium sp.).*	Ohio............	Found on soybeans being tested for germination; strongly pathogenic in infection experiments.
	Leaf spot (Phyllosticta sojaecola).**	Maryland, New Jersey.	Severe in many instances.
	Bacterial wildfire or halo blight (Pseudomonas tabaci).***	Widespread in soybean areas.	The organism causes tobacco wildfire, but natural infection had not been encountered on soybean before.

Crop	Disease and cause	Where found	Remarks
Corn.........	Bacterial leaf spot and top rot* (Undetermined bacterium).	Kansas, Nebraska.	Potentially important under favorable conditions.
	Leaf striping* (Undetermined virus).	Texas...........	Widely scattered in lower Rio Grande Valley; more common on sweet and popcorn than on field corn.
Oats.........	"Mosaic-chlorosis"* (Virus).	North Carolina, South Carolina.	Rather generally distributed in both States.
Sorghum......	Leaf spot (Microdiplodia sp.)*.	Louisiana........	In one experimental planting.
Apple and pear.	Leaf and fruit spot (Elsinoë piri)**.	Washington, Oregon.	

Of course, plant disease surveys and quarantines cannot absolutely prevent new pests from entering the country and establishing themselves. Furthermore, the ultimate result of the introduction of a new parasite cannot be predicted accurately, where such complex factors as environment, crop resistance and susceptibility, and presence or absence of a carrier of the disease organism, are concerned.

But consider the amount of damage to American crops caused by new diseases from abroad, and the billions of dollars spent on their eradication once they are established; does it not seem to be good insurance to take all possible steps, first to prevent their introduction, and second to discover their presence before eradication has become too difficult? Truly, an ounce of prevention is worth a pound of control.

THE AUTHOR

Paul R. Miller, a pathologist in charge of the Plant Disease Survey, Bureau of Plant Industry, Soils, and Agricultural Engineering, has spent 15 years developing survey techniques and conducting field studies of diseases that occur on major economic crops, including peanuts, tobacco, cotton, and truck crops. Dr. Miller shared with Dr. H. A. Edson (now retired) the administrative responsibility of the War Emergency Project discussed in this article and in this capacity traveled throughout the 48 States consulting with agricultural experiment station officials and supervising the work of the field staff.

FOR FURTHER READING

McCubbin, W. A.: *Preventing Plant Disease Introduction,* Botanical Review, Lancaster, Penn., volume 12, pages 101–139, 1946.

United States Department of Agriculture, Bureau of Plant Industry, Soils, and Agricultural Engineering: *The Plant Disease Reporter,* volume 27, number 15, 1943, through volume 29, 1945.

Spot Anthracnoses

by ANNA E. JENKINS

SPOT ANTHRACNOSES form an important frontier in present-day studies of plant diseases. A decade ago about 30 of the maladies had been recognized, a tenfold increase from 1925, when identification of citrus scab, now called "sour orange scab," drew attention to others of this class of diseases. Collectively they can be referred to as spot anthracnoses, although individually they are frequently called anthracnose, or scab, of the particular plant or plant group affected.

The continued investigation of the diseases has been of an exploratory nature, with dependence upon historical research. Many colleagues in various parts of the world have collaborated in the work that led to the present recognition of approximately 175 different spot anthracnoses. One of them, A. A. Bitancourt, director of research in plant biology, Biological Institute, São Paulo, Brazil, has discovered more spot anthracnoses and isolated in pure culture more of their pathogens than any other investigator. Fully 100 of these fungi have now been described.

But regardless of where one lives, one helps to pay the bills caused by losses from spot anthracnoses. Moreover, one may discover a new spot anthracnose lurking somewhere, perhaps not yet spread about. The range of plants affected extends from the ferns to the composites, usually considered the highest of the flowering plant families. Young tissues of leaf, stem, or fruit are attacked, and then only under damp conditions. Effects may be exhibited in various ways: Spotting of susceptible foliage or fruits, including failure of the fruit to develop, or its early fall (grape anthracnose, sour orange scab, lima bean scab, and so forth), defoliation to a greater or less degree (snowberry anthracnose, and pecan anthracnose in nurseries, for example).

Fortunately, lesions are usually small. Unfortunately, they may be

451

exceedingly numerous. A safeguard for many hosts is their inate tendency to heal by formation of callus. This accounts for the somewhat wartlike leaf spots, limited more or less definitely to one side of the blade, as in citrus scab. Rose anthracnose furnishes a good example of a simpler type of leaf spot (necrotic) with complete killing of tissue. Stem cankers on some woody growth may be comparatively harmless and inconspicuous. Among small fruits, however, grape canes are particularly vulnerable to serious attack. Those of brambles (raspberry, blackberry) also suffer greatly. A capital advantage for the well-being of most plants is that the spot anthracnoses are notably restricted each to its own suscept (any plant or animal capable of being infected by another organism) or related suscept group—that is, the parasites are specific. For instance, the pathogen of avocado scab will not go to citrus, nor will that of sour orange scab attack avocado.

Research since 1925 has revealed that citrus trees suffer not from the attack of one scab alone, but from three; moreover, one of them affects sweet orange, formerly thought to be practically immune from scab. Among these kinds of citrus scab, sour orange scab, Australian citrus scab, and sweet orange fruit scab, only sour orange scab is known in the United States. Different strains within pathogens of these diseases have been proved by experiment with regard to culture characteristic and, in one instance, by R. E. D. Baker, of Trinidad, British West Indies, with regard to host selectivity.

Despite the ability of plants to ward off spot anthracnose attacks, we have only to read accounts of these diseases to realize that almost invariably they gain a place among the most important maladies of the crop concerned. For example, investigating sour orange scab in Florida, J. R. Winston of the Department reported in 1923 that citrus scab (sour orange scab) was "largely responsible for the failure of the lemon industry in Florida, which prior to the introduction of citrus scab gave promise of becoming a profitable undertaking."

For nearly seven decades plant pathologists in this country have recounted more or less extreme losses from bramble anthracnose. The long-accepted basis for assuming that this disease is of European origin is erroneous, as C. L. Shear and I have recently shown. The earliest records of grape anthracnose, however, are clearly traceable to that continent and almost certainly to early Greece and Rome.

Spot anthracnoses are caused by fungi. These micro-organisms in the conidial stage are of the so-called form genus *Sphaceloma A*. In their ascus or perfect stage, where this is known, these pathogens belong to the genus *Elsinoë* of the Myriangiales.

In 1943 Dr. Bitancourt and I reported mango scab as a disease new to science. The known distribution of this disease is Florida, Cuba, Puerto Rico, and the Canal Zone. The pathogen we have now described as

Elsinoë mangiferae. A similar, although apparently not identical, disease has been discovered on mango in Brazil (the States of Amazonas and São Paulo). It appears that one hindrance to the earlier recognition of the scab was that it was not distinguished from the colletotrichum disease of mango. On the fruit, for example, the *Elsinoë* is superficial in its attack, producing small scabs or larger russeted areas. Instead of causing a more or less deep fruit decay, as is common, colletotrichum may produce superficial blemishes also in the form of russeting. Mango scab is said to be of minor importance in commercial groves in Florida, but is a serious disease in mango nurseries.

Stem and foliage scab of sweetpotato discovered in Formosa and the Amani Islands by Japanese plant pathologists has now been found in Guam and Brazil, as A. P. Viégas and I have reported.

Cinchona scab owes its discovery to United States Government botanists who were searching in Central and South America for cinchona, a strategic war material. It was particularly the curved distorted capsules that brought the disease to F. R. Fosberg's attention in Colombia in February 1943. On a subsequent exploratory excursion in November 1943 he was accompanied by W. H. Davis, plant pathologist. It was on the basis of Davis' specimens collected on that occasion that I made the original identification of what we now know as scab of cinchona. The published account describes in some detail the small raised, brown spots characterizing the disease, which are often produced in untold numbers on young leaves, stems, and capsules. In its present known distribution the disease affects *Cinchona pubescens* and *C. officinalis* in Colombia and *C. delessertiana* in Peru. A much wider distribution is certain to be demonstrated, particularly because of the geographical range of cinchona.

Under intensive culture in the Orient, scab, if present, should have been detected and reported long ago; possibly the pathogen (*Elsinoë cinchonae*) has not yet been carried there. The economic threat of such a disease-producing organism is difficult to evaluate; only the future will reveal when and where it can become a serious menace. Certain it is that its capabilities are apparent under natural conditions in the native home of the quinine plant.

The 23 spot anthracnoses known in the United States, Puerto Rico, Hawaii, and Guam in 1942 are listed here with their pathogens.

Disease	Pathogen	Disease	Pathogen
Pecan anthracnose	E. randii	Poinsettia scab	S. poinsettiae
Iresine scab	E. amazonica	Grape anthracnose	E. ampelinum
Avocado scab	S. perseae	Virginia creeper anthracnose.	E. parthenocissi
Bramble anthracnose	E. veneta		
Rose anthracnose	S. rosarum	Violet scab	S. violae
Lima bean scab	E. phaseoli	Hercules club scab	S. araliae
Milk pea anthracnose	S. floridensis	Sweetpotato stem and	E. batatas
Citrus scab	E. fawcetti	foliage scab.	

Disease	Pathogen	Disease	Pathogen
Ledum anthracnose___	E. ledi	Randia scab_____	S. puertoricensis
Lippia anthracnose___	S. lippiae	Plantain (Plantago)	S. plantaginis
Mint anthracnose____	S. menthae	scab.	
Cordia scab_____	E. mayaguensis	Snowberry anthrac-	S. symphoricarpi
Indian mulberry an-	S. morindae	nose.	
thracnose.		Goldenrod scab_____	E. solidaginis

To bring the list up to 1947 would practically double its length. Besides gray scab of willow (*S. murrayae* Jenkins and Grodsinsky), named in 1943, known to occur on five species of Salix and found in Rhode Island, Virginia, New York, California, and Washington, I shall name another spot anthracnose recorded in this country since 1942. This one may be called pome fruit spot anthracnose, or anthracnose of apple and pear. In June 1946 M. J. Forsell, L. W. Boyle, and I reported the discovery of this disease, caused by *Elsinoë piri,* in western Washington and Oregon in 1943–45. There were numerous findings of the disease on apple fruit and leaves and on pear leaves, and one on quince, that at Olga, San Juan County, Wash. In all cases only the conidial stage of the fungus (*Sphaceloma pirinum*) was present. The fact that this exotic malady has been present for a greater or less length of time in our Pacific Northwest without previous detection points to the significance of adequate surveys, together with accurate identification.

THE AUTHOR

Anna E. Jenkins is a mycologist in the Bureau of Plant Industry, Soils, and Agricultural Engineering. Her contributions deal particularly with new or little-known plant diseases and their pathogens. Among these are rose diseases of various etiology, blights of North American maples caused by *Taphrina,* and spot anthracnoses of various plants of economic importance. Dr. Jenkins holds three degrees from Cornell University.

FOR FURTHER READING

Grodsinsky, L., and Jenkins, A. E.: *Sphaceloma Murrayae en Diversas Species de Salix,* Revista Argentina de Agronomía, volume 10, pages 55–58, 1943.

Jenkins, A. E.: *Scab of Cinchona in South America Caused by Elsinoë,* Journal of Washington Academy of Science, volume 35, pages 344–352, 1945.

Jenkins, A. E., Forsell, M. J., and Boyle, L. W.: *Identity and Known Distribution of Elsinoë piri in Washington and Oregon,* Phytopathology, volume 36, pages 458–461, 1946.

Jenkins, A. E., and Shear, C. L.: *Gloeosporium venetum and G. necator: Two Distinct Species on Rubus,* Phytopathology, volume 36, pages 1043–1048, 1946.

Jenkins, A. E., and Viégas, A. P.: *Stem and Foliage Scab of Sweetpotato,* Journal of Washington Academy of Science, volume 33, pages 244–249, 1943.

Better Timber From Farms

by BENSON H. PAUL

STRONGER timber grows in farm woods when the farmer applies the rules of good forestry. Accessibility to all portions of the woods allows scattered cutting throughout the area as needed. Removal of poor and diseased trees or thinning in crowded places favors the better trees and hastens their growth much as weeding a garden promotes the growth of better vegetables.

Among hardwoods like ash, hickory, and oak a rapid and continuous growth of the trees in diameter will develop wood of high strength and toughness. On the other hand, some uses require soft wood that works, carves, and shapes easily. Low shrinkage and freedom from warping are qualities that give a high preference to certain woods, among them yellow poplar, basswood, and black walnut.

The unit weight of wood, or its specific gravity when completely dry or at a known degree of dryness, may be used as a yardstick of certain qualities. Its specific gravity is the ratio of the weight of a given volume of oven-dry wood to the weight of an equal volume of water. A great many tests at the Forest Products Laboratory in Madison, Wis., show how specific gravity affects the quality of wood in different ways. Woods with high specific gravity are generally strong, hard, difficult to work, and have high shrinkage. Woods with low specific gravity are generally soft, weak, easily worked, and have low shrinkage. It follows that woods of uniform specific gravity will have a high degree of uniformity in these other qualities. There will also be less waste in manufacture, fewer rejections by the purchaser, more profit for the producer, and better satisfaction to the consumer.

Unformity in wood is a good watchword—uniformity of growth, of weight (whether heavy or light), and of shrinkage or swelling with

455

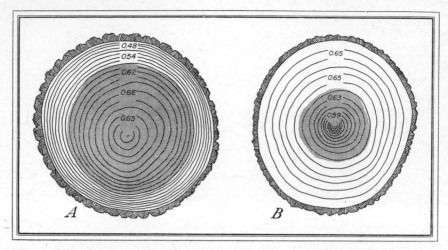

These cross sections of logs show range of specific gravity and rate of growth:
A gives proof of rapid growth when the tree was young and of slow growth in later
years caused by the crowding of an unthinned stand.   *B* shows how a tree will grow
in a properly thinned stand. Numbers are specific gravity values.

changes in weather. Uniformity of growth, which the farmer can control,
will promote uniformity in the other desired qualities and result in a
more satisfactory product.

In investigations of hardwoods, including white ash, the true hick-
ories, rock elm, sugar maple, yellow poplar, and several kinds of oak,
we found that uniformly maintained or uniformly accelerated growth
in diameter produced heavy and strong wood suitable for uses where
great strength is desired. Such wood is used for axe handles made of
ash and hickory; bearing blocks, bowling pins, and flooring made of
sugar maple; and bending stock of rock elm and oak.

Studies made by the Forest Products Laboratory in farm woodlands
show how growth conditions affect wood quality. A farmer in Ohio
owned a woods in which there was a good stand of white ash trees approximately 60 years old. The farmer placed a high value on the trees for
future income and was adverse to cutting any of them, even for experimental study. It was evident that in some places the stand was over-
crowded and growth of the trees in diameter was retarded accordingly.

We made cross sections of trees in the stand and found a reduction
of more than 25 percent in the specific gravity of the wood from the inner
portion of the sections outward for some trees, and an average reduction
of 18 percent for the entire stand. In another crowded stand of white
ash the specific gravity averaged 11 percent lower for the last 15 to 30
years than for the first 30 years of the life of the trees.

To prove whether the reduction in specific gravity of the wood accompanying retardation of growth resulted from crowding, we studied other

white ash trees in a stand where heavy cutting had taken place 30 years earlier. In that stand the ash trees of pole size had responded to the improved growth conditions that resulted from the cutting by producing more wood per tree than trees of the same age in the crowded stands. Also, the wood in cross section of the trees where cutting was practiced was uniformly high in specific gravity and of better quality for handle stock than most of the wood in the ash trees of the crowded wood lots.

Hickory responded to changes in growth conditions in the same way. It had the highest shock resistance when cut from trees with well sustained growth in diameter. Second-growth hickory has better strength than old-growth hickory because second-growth trees have had less competition and grow more rapidly. Old-growth hickory that grew more and more slowly in dense forests had a good deal of light, brash wood. In such old trees the sapwood, or white-hickory portion, was the weakest part of the whole tree. For a long time hickory buyers avoided certain areas of old-growth forests in their search for stock of high strength and toughness. More recently, as good hickory has become more difficult to find, many buyers have learned to select hickory on a basis of its growth rate, from either old growth or second growth, and thus have obtained considerable amounts of strong hickory from the more rapidly grown trees of both.

Hickory trees can be sold when they are 8 or 10 inches in diameter for use in handles, or picker sticks for textile looms. Rapidly grown trees contain much sapwood (white hickory) which, although no stronger than heartwood (red hickory) of equal weight, is liked better by buyers because of its appearance.

A search among hardwoods of high specific gravity and hardness to augment the waning supply of dogwood for shuttles was rewarded by finding that open-grown sugar maple trees contained in their short trunks wood of the required weight, hardness, and other essential attributes for shuttles, including the qualities of high shearing strength and smoothness of wear. The open-grown sugar maple trees had increased rapidly in diameter and averaged only 7 growth rings to the inch, compared to 22 for old-growth sugar maple in Pennsylvania. The wide-ringed open-grown trees produced wood averaging 0.77 in specific gravity. Other sugar maple stands averaged 0.68 in specific gravity. A comparable specific gravity value for dogwood is 0.78.

Sugar maple must be hard when it is used for flooring, furniture, and agricultural implements. But for bearing blocks, bowling pins, printers' type, cogs, shoe lasts, and butchers' blocks, it must be still harder. Purchasers of sugar maple lumber frequently specify sapwood because of its uniform light color. Wide sapwood also is expected to yield a wood superior in hardness. Trees in farm woodlands produce wide sapwood when given growing space enough to maintain rapid growth in diameter.

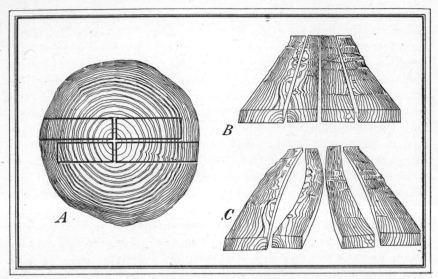

Here's what happens when a nonuniform growth of Southern yellow pine is cut into lumber: *A* is a cross section of the yellow pine log, showing where planks are cut from it; *B* shows the planks immediately after being sawed from the log; and *C* shows what happens because of high longitudinal shrinkage of the edge nearest the pith.

With other hardwoods, including the oaks and yellow poplar, the relationship between specific gravity and growth rate, such as that shown by ash, hickory, and sugar maple, has been found to follow the same general trends with respect to changes in width of growth rings during the development of a tree or stand. This led to a rule based on a record of the historical environment and development of a tree, as follows:

Wood of fairly uniform weight and strength is produced in broad-leaved trees (hardwoods) that have maintained or increased their growth rate from the center outward. A slowing of growth rate at any period in the life of the trees is accompanied by the production of wood of lower specific gravity. These facts make it possible from an examination of the growth rate throughout the life of a tree to determine whether the wood contained in a tree is all of high specific gravity, or whether with later years a declining growth rate produced wood of lower specific gravity and strength.

To improve the growth of cone-bearing trees, or softwoods, such as southern yellow pine and Douglas fir, some modifications of forestry practices are necessary from those required for growing wood of high specific gravity in hardwood species. This applies especially to the growth in diameter in young trees.

High specific gravity and strength in southern yellow pine was found in wood containing a high percentage of summerwood, which is the darker portion of the annual growth ring. The summerwood portion of the growth ring was found to be about twice as strong as the springwood.

Uneven distribution of young trees over an area was one of the prevailing causes of great variation in the specific gravity of wood in second-growth southern yellow pine stands. Young pine trees that had a large amount of growing space had larger, more wide-spreading crowns than trees that grew in closely stocked portions of a stand. Such trees grew in diameter at a rapid rate at first, but since a high proportion of the annual growth ring was springwood the resulting wood was of low specific gravity. Young trees with smaller crowns in more densely stocked portions of the same forest had a slower rate of growth and contained heavier and stronger wood with proportionately much less springwood.

The development of the tree crowns at different ages in the life of a southern yellow pine stand may be regulated by controlling the number of trees to the acre and their distribution over the area. To bring this about, young southern yellow pine stands should be fully stocked from the beginning. Afterwards, the number of trees and the spacing can be regulated as desired by making thinnings. Thus, within certain limits, it was found that the specific gravity of the wood from the pine trees could be controlled. In farm woodlands the thinnings can be used for materials needed on the farm or for sale as posts or pulpwood.

Although a certain amount of crowding or crown restriction increased the specific gravity of the wood in southern yellow pine, overcrowding had an opposite effect, because with very keen competition among the trees the summerwood portion of the growth ring was reduced. Wood resulting under such conditions was of slow growth and low specific gravity. Such wood is found principally in the outer portion of very old pine trees in virgin forests. It is soft, easy to work, has low shrinkage, and is preferred for many uses where high strength is not required. It was not found in second-growth forests.

Wood of southern yellow pine may be grouped into three principal types, depending upon the condition of growth: First, wood of light weight from rapidly growing young trees having large, wide-spreading crowns; second, heavy, dense wood of a medium growth rate from trees in fairly close stands where the crown development has been somewhat restricted; and third, wood of light weight and extremely slow growth from the outer portion of old trees in virgin-growth stands. It is not unusual to find the three types of wood in the same old-growth tree. The first type, however, is more common in second-growth stands; the second type may be found in either second-growth or old-growth; and the third type only in old-growth stands.

Sometimes growth rings of wood of the first type are as much as an inch in width. Because this wood is of low specific gravity and strength, it is not favored for uses where high mechanical strength is required. As the trees increase in size and the forests become more fully stocked, the growth in diameter takes place more slowly. The slowing of the diameter growth of trees results in formation of wood of the second type, so that two quite distinct kinds of wood occur in the cross section of a tree. The first is wide-ringed and light in weight, and the second has narrower rings and is usually considerably heavier. When trees containing these two kinds of wood are sawed into lumber, many boards or timbers may contain one type of wood on one edge and the other type on another edge. The wide-ringed type of wood has been found to shrink much more in length while drying than the wood of less rapid growth, as shown on page 458.

Unfortunately, there are many areas in the South and elsewhere where such partial and uneven stocking has resulted in the growth of low-quality timber. Average differences in the specific gravity of wood from adjacent understocked and fully stocked stands may amount to as much as 22 percent in southern yellow pine.

A well-stocked stand of southern yellow pine will be productive over a long period and supply high-quality timber of uniform growth rate and relatively high strength for poles, piling, and structural timbers. The production of these better products also allows intermittent revenue from the stand during the time that these products are growing. Periodic thinnings, the yield of which may be considerable, are needed to maintain uniform growth. A gradual removal of the mature trees will provide an opportunity for a new crop to become established by natural seeding.

In existing understocked stands of young trees without sufficient seed trees to fill in the openings, improvement of quality in the growing timber can be made by interplanting to provide the desired density of stocking and by pruning lateral branches to prevent the growth of large limbs low down on the trees, thus providing at least one high-quality log 16 feet in length from each tree.

THE AUTHOR

Benson H. Paul is a silviculturist at the Forest Products Laboratory, maintained at Madison, Wis., by the U. S. Forest Service in cooperation with the University of Wisconsin. Before his present position he served as a forester in the New York State Department of Conservation in charge of reforestation; he supervised the planting of some 50 million seedlings during that time. At the Forest Products Laboratory Mr. Paul investigates the effects on wood properties of such forestry practices as pruning, thinning of tree stands, special growth-control measures, importance of soil moisture to growth, and relation of growing space to lumber quality.

FOR FURTHER READING

Paul, Benson H.: *The Application of Silviculture in Controlling the Specific Gravity of Wood*, U. S. D. A. Technical Bulletin 168, 1930.

Paul, Benson H.: *Knots in Second-Growth Pine and the Desirability of Pruning*, U. S. D. A. Miscellaneous Publication 307, 1938.

Timber—A Modern Crop

by R. R. REYNOLDS

TIMBER can be as much an annual farm crop as corn, cotton, or potatoes. Stands of trees are easier to establish than some other farm crops. In reasonably well-stocked and managed stands the production of cellulose to the acre is much greater than that of cotton. And, contrary to the opinion generally held, the crop can be harvested on an annual basis. It is the only one that can be harvested at the convenience of the owner. It can provide profitable off-season employment in winter.

How much timber and value will a farm woodland yield? How much time must a farmer spend in managing and harvesting the timber crop? How does he establish, then manage and tend, and finally harvest the tree crop? These problems and many more are being answered by Forest Service foresters on the Crossett Experimental Forest in Arkansas.

The forest, located in the shortleaf-loblolly pine-hardwood belt of southeastern Arkansas, contains some 1,680 acres of typical second-growth stands. It was given the Government by the Crossett Lumber Co. in 1937 as a timber research center. Most of the area had always been in timber, but some places, which now contain old field stands of pine of pulpwood and sawlog sizes, grew corn and cotton 35 to 60 years ago.

The virgin timber, 12 inches in diameter and larger at the stump, was cut in 1915 and 1916. Since the lumber companies at that time had no thought of growing timber and no idea of ever coming back for a second cut of forest products, no effort was made to care for the young trees in the stands, and, consequently, many were broken or badly injured in the logging. Furthermore, many of the remaining trees were killed by the fires that burned over the area frequently between 1915 and 1934.

The stands present in 1937 varied considerably. A few were well stocked, with volumes running up to 8,000 feet of sawlogs to the acre.

461

Others had less than 1,000 feet an acre. All stands contained large numbers of defective and limby low-grade hardwoods that occupied nearly half of the effective growing space. Because of the repeated fires, some spots had no trees of any kind. Others that had escaped fire bore dense stands in which the trees were growing very little because of overcrowding.

Such conditions are typical of a large part of the farm woodland and the timberland of the larger lumber, pulp, and other wood-using industries in the region. They are a challenge to workers in forest research to find the methods and means of rehabilitation.

The first step in this program of rehabilitation of the Crossett Experimental Forest was complete protection from uncontrolled fires. Where pine seed trees were present, this protection resulted in a dense stand of pine seedlings in the open spots within 3 years after protection was started. Nine years later many of these seedling stands were nearly of pulpwood size and ready for the first thinning. Additional thinnings will be necessary at short intervals; with proper management these stands will produce a cut of products at intervals of 3 or 5 years for 50 years or more without reseeding or establishing a new crop.

Next, the low-grade hardwoods were cut. The stands were further placed in good growing condition by the removal of the mature, crooked, limby, and defective pine. Where the trees were too thick some of the poorest were removed. Five to 9 years after this improvement cutting, 500 or more valuable pines of pulpwood size grow on many acres where originally stood only low-grade hardwoods. Furthermore, the reserved larger trees in the whole forest have responded remarkably to the improvement cutting. The growth rate on the small trees has increased by 30 percent and on trees of sawtimber size by nearly 70 percent over what it was before management was started. Where the growth was originally 200 board feet an acre a year, it is now 340, and still is increasing.

A study of the place that forestry should have on the farm was undertaken in 1937. In it, we used a well-stocked but otherwise natural pine-hardwood second-growth stand of 40 acres. The well-stocked area was selected in order to demonstrate returns that could be expected once the volume per acre of the present understocked average farm forest was built up to desirable levels. The present volume of the growing stock and the total amount of growth produced during the year were first determined by an inventory and growth study. Based on this information, a number of the larger or less valuable trees, having a volume equivalent to the volume of growth during the year, were marked for cutting. From these marked trees a volume of firewood equal to the annual requirements of the average farm was produced first. Next, a number of fence posts needed to repair the farm fences were cut. The rest of the marked trees were then cut into one or more cash crops, such as logs, poles, piling, pulpwood, or veneer blocks.

The products removed in 1945, which were equivalent to the growth during 1945, were: Logs, 13,144 board feet (Doyle scale); pulpwood, 15.33 standard cords; fuelwood, 11.97 standard cords; posts, 42. These products had a stumpage value in the standing trees of $197, or $4.91 an acre. The value of the products, cut and delivered at the mill or market, was $604, or $15.09 an acre.

Of equal importance is the winter or off-season employment that such farm woodlands can provide. In 1945 this 40-acre woodland provided 52 man-days, or approximately 3 man-months, of gainful employment in cutting and delivering the forest products to the mills and markets. For the labor expended in producing this annual cut of forest products, the owner-producer received approximately 60 cents an hour. In addition, he would receive all out-of-pocket costs for use of team and equipment, money for taxes, $40 as interest on his investment in land and timber, plus $197 for the value of the timber removed.

Eight annual cuts of forest products similar to the 1945 cut have been made from this 40-acre tract to date. Yet the volume now is almost identical to that present when the study was started in 1937. Moreover, since the low-quality trees were removed in the first years of the study, the quality of the current stand is much better than when we started.

These annual cuts from this 40-acre farm woodland have produced 99,000 board feet of logs, 249 standard cords of pulpwood, 146 cords of fuelwood, and 252 posts. The material had a value, in the standing tree, of $1,277 and a market value of $4,655. The figures represent a stumpage return of $31.92 an acre and a market value of $116.38 an acre for 8 years, or $3.99 and $14.55, respectively, an acre a year.

The results of the study indicate that timber properly managed is truly an annual crop. Furthermore, because approximately 1,000 pounds of cellulose can be obtained from one standard cord of wood, the farm woodland is producing approximately 27,900 pounds of pure cellulose a year—equal to 1.4 bales of 500 pounds an acre.

To provide the requirements of high-grade forest products to the mills and factories and to make possible a good yearly financial return to the owner of timberland, the selection system of management is being intensively applied and studied on the forest. Under this system, individual trees are removed as they become mature or too crowded, and the adjacent smaller or better trees are reserved to grow to larger sizes and higher values. Areas are being cut at 1-year, 3-year, 6-year, and 9-year intervals in order to determine which is most profitable. Unless the stands are fully stocked to good trees, the volume of timber removed at any one cutting period is always less than the volume that has grown during the interval between cuts. Consequently, the volume of the growing stock as well as the quality is constantly improved.

The results of this type of management have been striking. The logs that have been removed have been large, of high quality, and top value. The stands are building up and producing more volume each year and the income, although good, also goes up each year.

Of equal importance to the private owner of timberland and to the whole country are the possibilities for employment demonstrated on the intensively managed forest at Crossett. Based on records of the Experimental Forest for the past 7 years, year-round employment in the woods can be provided to one man for every 150 acres of timberland. The work includes timber marking, cutting, skidding, loading, hauling of the products, and overhead, but not technical research. But the figure does not indicate the full possibilities, because the stands of timber involved are only partly stocked and are, therefore, not producing at the maximum rate. When the stands are built up to full productivity, we estimate that 125 acres of woodland will provide year-round employment for one man; if work in the woods is added to the work in the sawmills, pulp mills, and other plants that use the products of the forest, 60 acres will provide full time employment for one man.

Our work at Crossett indicates that good forest management has a definite place on the farm. Low production timber stands can be made into good producers in a very short time. Returns per acre and per man-hour of labor expended are excellent. Well-managed forest stands will produce more cellulose per acre than the better cotton stands. Timber is about the only farm crop that can be harvested at the convenience of the grower. If markets are not good one year or labor is not available the timber crop can be left standing and will continue to increase in volume and value until harvested. It is also about the only crop that once established will continue to yield repeated crops of products without artificial replanting. Most people think of timber production as a long-time or lifetime crop. We demonstrated otherwise at Crossett.

THE AUTHOR

R. R. Reynolds is in charge of the Crossett branch of the Southern Forest Experiment Station. For the past 10 years he has been conducting forest management research at Crossett, Ark. He is the author of numerous technical and popular articles on timber growing and forest practice.

FOR FURTHER READING

Mattoon, Wilbur R., and Barrows, William B.: *Measuring and Marketing Farm Timber,* U. S. D. A. Farmers' Bulletin 1210, 1940.

Preston, John F.: *Woodlands in the Farm Plan,* U. S. D. A. Farmers' Bulletin 1940, 1943.

Reynolds, R. R., Bond, W. E., and Kirkland, Burt P.: *Financial Aspects of Selective Cutting in the Management of Second-Growth Pine-Hardwoods Forests West of the Mississippi River,* U. S. D. A. Technical Bulletin 861, 1944.

NEW WORK IN FORESTRY AND USES OF WOOD

e example of progress in forest research is discovery that hybrid vigor applies to trees much the same way as it does to animals and d crops such as corn and wheat. The pine es shown above are all 3 years old and were wn in the same seedbed under identical conions. At left is an average seedling of West-white pine; at right an average Eastern white pine. The two in the middle are typical of seedlings that result from crossing Western and Eastern pines. The young tree shown at the left, below, is a Jeffrey pine; at the right is a Coulter pine. The one in the center is a back-cross hybrid of the two. All three, under test at the Institute of Forest Genetics, Placerville, Calif., are 4 years old.

Besides developing faster-growing trees, machines for planting them faster are being used successfully in some areas. In the Lake States, for example, heavy, middle-buster plows like the one shown above are used to clear off brush and weed trees. A tree-planting mach (below) developed by the U. S. Forest S ice, with a three-man crew, can set ab 1,000 seedling trees an hour. It was used shelter belt planting in the Great Pla

s explained by R. R. Reynolds on page 461,
mber can produce annual returns the same as
rn, cotton, or potatoes. From 40 acres of wood-
nd like that shown above, 10,115 board feet of
ne, 2,260 feet of hardwood, 17 cords of pulp-
ood, and 8 cords of fuelwood were produced
1 year. Total value at mill was $313. On
another 40 acres of intensively managed woodland in Arkansas, the timber (below) from
a year's growth returned $604 to the owner.
A good feature of farm forestry is that if the
market is not good one year, the timber crop
can be left standing to increase in volume for
harvest later at the convenience of the grower.

Of the various different factors that are known to be forest-fire hazards, wind velocity, the amount of moisture in forest fuels, and the condition of vegetation are the most important. Improved scientific methods are used to prevent destruction of our forests by fire. Above, left, are several devices that measure fire danger: Anemometer on top of shelter box; mois- ture-indicator sticks in foreground; scales, shelter, for measuring moisture in the stick and a rain gage at right. A standard alidad (above, right) is used by Forest Guard Guy Er let to determine and report exact location of fire. Below, District Ranger R. E. Harlan ope ates a field radio set to send and receive dire tions for fire control by organized force

siderable progress has been made to find ...ervatives for wood structures that are ex- ...d to weather. The two pine sapwood joints ...wn above were exposed for 4 years to south- ...Mississippi weather. The one at left was ...eated; the other, still in very good condi- tion, was given a 30-minute cold soak in a 5-percent mixture of pentachlorophenol. Moisture condensation on joists (below) of houses without basements can be prevented by covering the soil with ordinary roll roofing. The cost is approximately 3 cents a square foot.

More durable and faster-drying paints are being studied at the Department's laboratory at Peoria, Ill. In the picture above, left, A. J. Lewis prepares panels for outdoor exposure. The pan- els (at right, above) face south and are se 45° and 90° angles. Below, Mr. Lewis comp durability of regular and improved soyb oil paints that have been exposed 7 mor

REGULAR SOYBEAN OIL PAINT, AFTER OUTDOOR EXPOSURE OF 7 MONTHS AT PEORIA.

IMPROVED SOYBEA OIL PAINT. AFTER OUTDOOR EXPOSURE OF 7 MONTHS AT PEORIA.

the U. S. Forest Products Laboratory, Madison, Wis., new uses of wood for both farm and industry are constantly being found. Plywood grain storage houses (above, left), and portable plywood brooder houses (above, right) are among the newer developments. Below, the forestry laboratory's corrugating machine runs off a strip of corrugated boxboard.

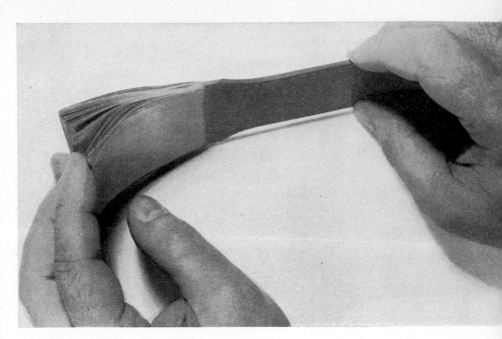

A product called papreg (above) is made by compressing many sheets of resinized paper together under heat and pressure. Some examples of how new wood products will have peacetime uses are shown below. From left to right: A staypak shuttle for looms that wears better than untreated wood shuttles; a comp[...] nut and bolt used in switchboards and ot[...] electrical panels where good insulation is i[...] portant; and a tongued and grooved square[...] flooring with a compreg face, untreated p[...] wood core, and an impreg base. (See page 72[...])

Hybrid Forest Trees

by PALMER STOCKWELL and F. I. RIGHTER

SOON THERE will be hybrid forest trees that may grow to harvesting size in one-half or one-third the time required for a good, nonhybrid timber tree to reach the same size. Our forests and farm wood lots, where planting is practiced, might then be made to produce twice or three times the volume of timber that would be produced by planting standard stock or letting natural growth populate the site.

Already we have a hybrid pine, that at 3 years is more than twice as high and three times as heavy as the better of its two parents. So, a new era is beginning in reforestation and, although the hybridizing of forest trees seems to be at about the same stage that hybridization of corn had reached in the mid-1920's and failures and disappointments are to be expected along the way, we confidently predict that in another 20 years the forester will be using and discussing hybrid tree strains as casually as Midwest farmers now discuss their hybrid corn.

This exciting new development did not come overnight.

In the last decade, it has become increasingly apparent that the forests of the world are not producing timber as fast as the world needs it—particularly timber suitable for construction, packaging, paper making, and kindred uses. So, the tree breeder is at work in many countries, developing new strains to increase lumber production. Most countries are now interested in the improvement of forest trees, but intensive breeding work is carried on in relatively few of them.

Australia and New Zealand, which, like much of the Southern Hemisphere, lack softwood timber, have been leaders in introducing and acclimatizing foreign species. Not having the source materials needed for extensive hybridizing, Australian and New Zealand scientists have concentrated on selection and propagation.

703830°—47——31

The Russians have made contributions particularly with their research on hybrid oaks and poplars. The British are among the leaders in the development and analysis of ideas pertaining to the breeding of trees. The interest of Swedish breeders centered on the production of superior varieties of aspen for paper pulp production and conifers for construction lumber, the result being that several valuable new varieties are being used in forest planting. They have taken advantage of naturally occurring giant forms of aspen and have encouraged the introduction of hybrid poplars from America. Even during the war a few German research workers continued their quest for faster-growing trees. As in Sweden and Russia, the poplars have received most intensive attention in Germany, although the long-sustained German interest in the conifers continues. Denmark has made great strides in the work; indoor techniques for dwarfing trees, forcing early flowering, grafting imported scions on potted rootstocks, and other ingenious devices have reached a high stage of development.

The Union of South Africa established a tree-breeding program in 1943. Its first efforts are directed toward improving the native wattles and the introduced pines. South Americans are aware of the possibilities of tree breeding. Outstanding work has been done on quinine and rubber in the Amazon Valley of Brazil by commercial operators. Other Brazilian scientists are interested in various other species. In Argentina, Peru, Colombia, and other South American countries there is a growing interest, but they have established no specific tree-breeding program as yet. The Canadian tree-breeding program represents the combined action of the Biology Division of the National Research Council with the Dominion Forest Service and the Department of Agriculture of the Dominion. In 1940 the poplar work alone resulted in the production of 10,000 hybrids. The work was largely discontinued during the war but has gained impetus since then. The poplar for paper pulp and match stock production and conifers for paper pulp and construction lumber remain the centers of interest.

Between 1935 and 1945 most of the forest-tree breeding projects in the United States were reduced or discontinued, primarily because of the improved techniques for making paper of other woods than poplar, reduced budgets of Government-sponsored breeding work, and the war. The programs of the Oxford Paper Co. and the Tennessee Valley Authority were practically discontinued; those of the New York Botanical Garden, Harvard University, and the Northeastern Forest Experiment Station suffered almost as much. Only the Institute of Forest Genetics was able to continue its program—and its work was reduced by more than half during the war.

Several fundamental differences between the breeding of agricultural plants and forest trees should be kept in mind.

In the breeding of agricultural plants, genetic uniformity is a necessity. For example, the varicolored corn of the Southwestern Indians cannot compete on the open market with uniform standard varieties. Lack of uniformity in a farm crop would spell financial ruin for the modern farmer. He enhances the natural uniformity of his crops still further by careful grading for size, color, and other qualities—a profitable practice.

But forest trees are genetically quite diverse, although they may appear to be uniform to the casual observer. Natural species owe their existence and perpetuation to variability, which enables some to survive attack by insects or disease and others to invade new environments or withstand changed conditions. Furthermore, the timberman is accustomed to using trees from forests of natural origin and variability does not disturb him as it would the farmer.

Breeding Forest Trees

To make certain of the uniformity and adaptability of new farm crops, long, carefully conducted field trials by the breeder are necessary. The average farmer cannot afford to risk the loss of his land and labor for a year to try out a new strain of unknown value. It may take as long as 20 years to produce and test a new form of an annual crop such as wheat before it can be safely recommended for use. In this respect the forester planter has a distinct advantage over the farmer.

By interplanting a hybrid or other new form with the standard strain or stock that would have been used throughout if the new form were not available, promising new trees may be put to use as soon as they are developed or discovered, without subjecting the forest owner to too much risk. The new trees can be planted at suitable intervals among a natural stand of young trees, or in every fifth row, or other selected interval, where an entire area is to be planted. Several advantages accrue. The new trees can be made to cover a greater acreage by interplanting, thus reducing the cost of using a new and relatively expensive form. If it proves to be superior, it will occupy the site at maturity, crowding out most of the slower-growing natural stand or standard strain.

A common practice is to plant 1,200 trees to the acre where from 100 to 200 trees are desired in the final stand of mature trees. This great excess of planting stock over expected mature trees represents another way in which forestry differs from agriculture. If, on the other hand, the new strain proves to be inferior to the natural stand or the planted standard strain, it will be suppressed and crowded out before the trees reach harvesting size. There would be no reduction of yield because the new form was a failure.

An objection, frequently voiced, to the use of hybrid trees is that, although the hybrids themselves may be superior to standard strain trees, their offspring, the second generation hybrids, will be worthless, and in consequence the entire area would have to be replanted; whereas, if the standard strain were used, the area would be reseeded naturally from these trees and no subsequent replanting would be necessary.

This line of reasoning is applicable to some farm crop plants but it does not apply to forest trees. For example, *Pinus attenuradiata* is a hybrid between the Monterey and knobcone pines, produced at the Institute of Forest Genetics. The first generation hybrids, or F_1 plants, are reasonably uniform in growth rate and other characters. Seedlings from these trees representing the second generation of hybrids, or F_2 plants, show great variability. However, a considerable number of the trees (approaching 50 percent) are as good as the F_1 hybrid, and a few are even better. In a stand composed of this F_2 hybrid population there would be enough good trees of the second generation to repopulate the area and crowd out inferior trees before the stand reaches maturity. Another point is that although many hybrids of crop plants are sterile or practically so, pines are not; in fact, no sterile pine hybrid has yet been reported by anyone.

Besides an acceptable theoretical background for a hybridizing program, numerous techniques to assure the success of the program must be worked out. They will vary with the location of the breeding station, the kinds of trees used, and the individuals doing the work. Because it is impossible to cover all the new methods and techniques in use by tree breeders, a few typical examples based on experience at the Institute are selected.

Techniques that assure control of pollination are essential in plant-breeding work. Most of the genera of timber trees are wind-pollinated, and wind-borne pollen is usually a fine, dry, powdery dust that penetrates all but the most closely-woven fabrics. To find a material for pollination bags, many fabrics were sprinkled with pine pollen and examined under the microscope. A 10-ounce cotton duck was finally chosen because it is light, keeps out foreign pollen, and yet permits a slow circulation of air through the fabric, thus preventing condensation of water inside. The bags are fastened over the cone-bearing branch tips some time before pollen is shed from neighboring trees. The pollen to be used is collected before it starts to shed from the catkins. It is then extracted in the laboratory under conditions that prevent contamination by undesired pollen. At the time the cones are receptive, pollen is injected into the bags with a syringe.

Another serious problem arises when two species that are to be crossed flower or are ready for pollination at different times—sometimes several weeks apart. Usually, pollen is collected from the early form and used to pollinate the late form. At times, however, it is desirable to reverse the procedure, i. e., make the reciprocal cross. It has been necessary, therefore, to work out methods for storing pollen from the late-flowering trees until the following year, when it can be applied to the early forms.

If pine trees are to be hybridized, the worker must have access to both pollen-bearing catkins and young seed-bearing cones. The poplars and certain other species will continue to develop flowers and mature the seeds when the branches are cut and placed in water; thus it is possible to carry out a hybridizing program indoors. That is not possible with the pines. It is necessary in pine breeding to climb the trees repeatedly. To avoid injuring the bark, a rope is thrown over the lowest branch and the geneticist climbs the rope. This strenuous but direct and effective method has been adopted because of the difficulty of transporting ladders or other heavy equipment on the forested mountainsides where the program of the Institute is carried out.

In experimental work time is of the essence, and research workers are always seeking short cuts. Increased growth rate being a most important objective of forest tree breeding, it is of major interest to learn as soon as possible the growth rate of a new hybrid. Recent work by John T. Buchholz of the University of Illinois gives promise that a pine hybrid of superior growth rate may be recognized by examination of some of the embryos even before the seeds mature. This would enable the breeder to evaluate the growth rate of a hybrid within 15 months, instead of waiting 3 to 5 years for the usual nursery trials to indicate its value before large-scale production is started.

At one time field trials of 10 to 20 years were deemed necessary to determine the growth rate of a tree. It is now known that seed size and time of germination affect the early growth rate of a tree but are not related to inherent vigor or ultimate size. In nursery tests, weighing the seeds and comparing trees from seeds of like weights eliminates the variation that would be introduced by using ungraded seeds. All seeds are stratified or packed in moist sand and moss at 40° F. for 60 days or longer. This treatment causes the seeds to germinate more or less simultaneously, eliminating effects due to difference in time of germination. If such factors are controlled, the growth rate of 2- to 3-year-old nursery-grown trees is a reliable guide to the inherent growth rate of the new form.

The Use of Hybrids

The use of hybrids offers exceptional opportunities for increasing crop production, and timber trees may here be considered simply as a forest crop. Tree strains that cross readily do not occur mixed together in the forest, else they would eventually "blend" into one form by hybridizing. We therefore find, except in a small number of specialized cases, that crossable species, varieties, or other categories of plants occupy different localities. Because hybrid trees are usually intermediate between the parents in growth rate and other quantitative characters, the hybrid can be used to advantage in the region where the slower growing parent occurs.

A good example of this type of hybrid is that produced by using the pollen of a hybrid (Jeffrey pine × Coulter pine) on one of the parent forms (Jeffrey pine), the resultant hybrid being known as a backcross. Seeds of the backcross hybrid and of wind-pollinated Jeffrey pine were collected from the same parent tree and planted together in the seedbed. At 3 years of age the hybrid was 184 percent taller than the pure Jeffrey pine. Seeds from the pollen parent were not available, but pure Coulter pine seedlings grow at about the same rate as the backcross hybrid. The hybrid, therefore, will be planted in the range of the slower growing parent, the Jeffrey pine.

Another intermediate type of hybrid is that obtained by crossing the poorly formed, and not very desirable jack pine of the Lake States with the straight-growing lodgepole pine of the Sierra Nevada. At 3 years of age the hybrid trees approximate or slightly exceed the height of pure jack pines and are 179 percent of the height of lodgepole pine. The logical locality in which to use this hybrid in forest planting is where jack pine is now planted, because the hybrid has the straight, erect growth habit of the lodgepole pine.

While the intermediate type of hybrid has a definite field of usefulness, there is another type of hybrid with even greater potential value. This is the type that shows hybrid vigor or, to the geneticist, heterosis. This phenomenon, although not yet fully understood, is of tremendous value to the agricultural world. It is hybrid vigor that makes some of the poplar and pine hybrids grow at twice or more the rate of the parental forms. This means that a timber tree adaptable to the location and having hybrid vigor may grow to harvesting size in one-half or one-third the time required for a good, nonhybrid forest tree to reach the same size.

The hybrid between the eastern and the western white pines, as an example, shows greater growth capacity than either parent. At Placerville the two parent forms grow at approximately the same rate, but the average hybrid at 3 years of age was 232 percent of the height of the seed parent, the western white pine. The difference in volume, or weight, was even greater. At 4½ years the cut-off top of the largest eastern white pine seedling weighed 64 grams, that of the largest western white pine 72 grams, and that of a large (but not the largest) hybrid seedling 232 grams, or 322 percent of the weight of the better parent. This hybrid warrants trial wherever white pines are planted for timber production. It is being tested for resistance to blister rust by Dr. Willis Wagner, of the Department of Agriculture.

With hybrid trees, as with other new things, costs and quantity production must be considered. A record has been made of the cost, in man-days, of hybrid seeds and of the quantity of seeds it is possible to produce. In pine hybridizing, bags are placed over the young conelets that are to be pollinated. This precaution prevents contamination by air-borne pollen of the forest. Because this technique is always used, the bag is a convenient unit of measurement of effort. What is termed a 1,000-bag program carried out by skilled and experienced workers on large trees in the forest would require from 30 to 45 man-days. (The requirements and yields of the 1,000-bag program are estimates based on the use of only a few dozen bags, as manpower shortage has prevented carrying out a 1,000-bag program for any single cross.) The yield per 1,000 bags has varied from 6,500 hybrid seeds for the poorest to a maximum of 432,000 hybrid seeds for the best yield.

By applying the interplanting method, that is, using hybrid seeds for every sixth row, for example, at a spacing of 6 feet by 6 feet, and deducting 40 percent from total seed number for possible losses, the acreage that could be planted per 1,000-bag breeding program would range from a minimum of 19.5 acres to a maximum of 1,296 acres. As more experience is gained, costs no doubt can be reduced.

In some genera of trees hybrid vigor is rare. In others, such as the poplars and the pines, hybrid vigor is more frequent. To date, there is no predicting which crosses will exhibit hybrid vigor and which will not. Of the 12 hybrids between pine species produced at the Institute since 1940, 4 show definite hybrid vigor at 3 years and 1 or 2 others, as yet too young to evaluate, look promising. The remainder are intermediate. Trees that show hybrid vigor will probably become the most used planting stock of the future. Standard strains or intermediate hybrids will have little appeal for the forest planter, except in special cases where resistance to insects, disease, or drought may influence the decision.

Thus far, few hybrid trees have been used in forest planting. R. H. Richens of Great Britain, in the most complete review to date of the literature of tree breeding, lists 405 forest-tree hybrids. Of these, only 54 are coniferous trees, which yield the greater part of the world's construction lumber, while 351 are hybrids of nonconiferous species that are used for paper pulp, cabinet work, match stock, et cetera. The world, facing a rapidly shrinking supply of timber, is looking for some means of relieving the situation. There is a rapidly increasing pressure to try out hybrid trees in forest planting. The indication that fast-growing hybrids can be produced in abundance, together with the possibility that financial risk can be reduced during the necessary trial period by interplanting the hybrids with known varieties, tends to increase interest.

This trend is international in scope. There is hardly a week that does not bring inquiries from foreign lands to the Institute of Forest Genetics. Some of these inquirers wish to send young men for training in hybrid-seed production. Others want information on methods of hybrid production and still others wish to have hybrid seed sent to them.

As for plans in this country—there will be a large increase by many agencies in hybrid planting, both of the hardwoods, such as poplar and chestnut, and the coniferous species, such as the pines. As many hybrids are being produced at the Institute of Forest Genetics as the available manpower permits. Two or three of the most promising new hybrids are being used in this effort. The California Region of the United States Forest Service has started to use the hybrids in forest plantings throughout the State, giving them an actual field test under a wide variety of conditions.

THE AUTHORS

Palmer Stockwell is a geneticist in charge of the Institute of Forest Genetics, a branch of the California Forest and Range Experiment Station, maintained by the Forest Service in cooperation with the University of California at Berkeley, Calif. He has served with the Boyce Thompson Southwestern Arboretum in Arizona, the Carnegie Institute of Washington at Palo Alto, Calif., and the Soil Conservation Service in New Mexico. He is a graduate of the University of Arizona and holds the doctor's degree from Stanford University.

F. I. Righter, geneticist, was with the Eddy Tree Breeding Station before it became the Institute of Forest Genetics. A graduate of Cornell University, where he subsequently taught forest management, he worked on cane plantations in Cuba and Hawaii, and for the Forest Service in the Southern States.

FOR FURTHER READING

Buchholz, John T.: *Embryological Aspects of Hybrid Vigor in Pines,* Science, volume 102, No. 2641, pages 135–142, 1945.

Mackenzie, C. J.: *Twenty-eighth Annual Report of National Research Council of Canada,* page 15, 1944–45.

Ness, H.: *Possibilities of Hybrid Oaks, etc.,* Journal of Heredity, volume 18, pages 381–386, 1927.

Richens, R. H.: *Forest Tree Breeding and Genetics,* Imperial Agricultural Bureaux Joint Publication, No. 8, 1945.

Righter, F. I.: *New Perspectives in Forest Tree Breeding,* Science, volume 104, No. 2688, pages 1–3, 1946.

Stockwell, Palmer, and Righter, F. I.: *Pinus: The Fertile Species Hybrid Between Knobcone and Monterey Pines,* Madrono, volume 8, No. 5, pages 157–160, 1946.

Syrach, Larsen C.: *De enkelte arters anvendelse, Proveniens og foraedling,* Svenska Skogavardsforeningens Tidskrift, volume 41, pages 182–199, 1943. (Plant Breeding Abstracts, volume 14, page 999, 1943.)

Wettstein, W. von.: *Possibilities of Breeding New Ecotypes after Hybridization,* Der Zuchter; Zeitschrift fur Theoretische and Angewandte Genetik, volume 14, pages 282–285, 1942.

Forests for Old Fields

by JOHN T. AUTEN

THE 10 million acres of abandoned fields in the Central States, reforested with the right kind of trees, could produce enough lumber to build 150,000 new 6-room houses each year.

What is the right kind of tree to plant on an old field? The answer is not easy, but I shall tell you what we foresters in the Department of Agriculture have learned about trees and soil. We do not know it all, but we can help your planting average.

Anybody who wants to plant the right tree in the right place has to know something about the soil. He finds that the original stand that might serve as a guide is gone; often much of the surface soil is eroded away, and the old field is covered with briars, brush, and weeds. Many of the natural clues to the original forest have been lost.

Fortunately, we were able to follow a few remaining clues through several years of study and observation to some helpful conclusions. One of the most significant of our findings is that subsoil (the soilsman calls it the B horizon) and topography hold the final answer to the kind of tree that should be planted.

We began this study of soil and trees in the Central States about 15 years ago. At that time the best way to find out what happens to soil under cultivation seemed to be a comparison of virgin wood and nearby field soil. Accordingly, we located and examined 22 remnants of virgin hardwood forests and adjacent fields. One of the most interesting differences that appeared between woods and field soil lay in their ability to absorb water. Sometimes the virgin-wood soil absorbed water as fast as it could be poured and measured, but the field soil absorbed water very slowly. Furthermore, even though high, dry sites exposed to wind absorbed a great deal of water, they produced scrubby hardwoods; and

1. How subsoil affects black locust. The data are based on studies of 135 black locust plantations for soil and growth differences

Soil group No.	Drainage (internal)	Plasticity (wet)	Compactness (dry)	Color	Site index
1	Very slow	Very highly plastic; practically impossible to knead into a ball in hands.	Very compact; breaks into lumps; very difficult or impossible to pulverize in hands.	Blue or drab-mottled below 8 inches.	50
2	Slow	Highly plastic; kneads into a ball with difficulty, very fatiguing to hands.	Moderately compact, reduced only by considerable pressure to coarse granules which are pulverized only by considerable pressure.	Yellowish gray, mottled gray to rusty brown below 14 inches.	60
3	Fair	Moderately plastic; kneads stiffly.	Friable. Pulverizes with moderate pressure to mass of moderately resistant granules.	Grayish yellow to yellow, mottled gray to yellow below 14 to 24 inches.	70
4	Moderate	Slightly plastic; kneads into a ball easily; can be rolled into a wire between palms.	Mellow; pulverizes to mass of fine soft granules.	Grayish brown to yellow and mottled below 36 inches.	80
5	Good to fast [1]	Very slightly plastic; soil wire barely formable between palms without crumbling.	Slightly coherent; pulverizes completely with slight pressure.	Yellow to yellow brown with little or no mottling.	90
6	Good to very fast [1]	Nonplastic; crumbles and cannot be rolled into a wire.	Noncoherent, loose............	Yellowish brown to reddish brown; no B horizon, no mottling.	100

[1] Excessively drained soils, shallow soils over bedrock, and soils eroded down to tight subsoil fall into dry-site group of table 3.

if the soil was coarse and excessively drained also, they produced pines. Moist-cove and north-slope sites were occupied by thrifty stands of red oak, white oak, white ash, walnut, and yellow poplar.

These discoveries brought out two important facts: First, litter-protected, porous woods soil absorbed much more rainfall than bare, compacted field soil; and second, some trees required more water than others. Putting these two facts together, we concluded that cultivation of woods soil makes the site a drier site and temporarily shifts the possible tree cover from high-moisture-requiring desirable hardwoods toward less desirable dry-site species or pines.

But notwithstanding the great differences in rate of water absorption of woods and field soil, the virgin-wood soil and adjoining field soil were alike beneath the surface. Their subsoils had the same color and the same degree of compactness and stickiness—in fact, only the surfaces were different.

Now the question arose: Why were some subsoils drab-colored and others brown? Why were some subsoils mottled and others not, some compact and others loose? More important than any: Why were some kinds of trees growing on drab, tight soils and others on brown, loose soils? Only further research could answer such questions and the best place to find the answers seemed to be where planted trees had succeeded and failed on many different kinds of soil. Accordingly, we studied 135 black locust plantations for soil and growth differences. We examined the subsoil of each plantation for plasticity (stickiness), compactness, and color. We looked the plantation over for general lay of the land and nearness to streams; then we estimated how rapidly we thought the land would drain.

You will probably find the subsoil of your field pretty well described by some one horizontal row in table 1. For instance, if the subsoil is very sticky, it will be very compact when dry. If it is drab or light gray, it probably will be mottled not far below the surface. If you make a bad guess on drainage, pay more attention to the other tests as you go to the right in each column of table 1.

The quality of drainage and aeration indicated in the first table by the various degrees of stickiness, compactness, and color grew in importance as our plantation study progressed. We found very striking examples of the effect of subsoil on trees.

An example is a stand of yellow poplar in the Waterloo Forest, Ohio. At 19 years of age it had grown little more than 2 inches in diameter and 10 feet in height. The site was a lower slope along a stream, sheltered and cool. It should have been an excellent site; the trees should have been 8 to 10 inches in diameter and 40 feet high. They would have been except for one soil condition—a tight plastic clay subsoil. In contrast, a yellow poplar stand in a deep, cool cove in Wolfe County, Ky., was only 33 years old; yet it averaged 104 feet in height. The reason: A very deep, well-aerated soil with no tight subsoil.

Any one of the subsoil properties of the first table may serve to describe a soil, but the other three make the site estimate more reliable. We found out all these facts about soil as we went along. But that was only half of the story. The next step was to learn how fast the trees grew on the different soils.

The height of dominant trees, the ones that grow without crowding or shading, at any given age is really the best measure of site quality. We used 50 years as the standard age, and estimated from growth curves the height of any stand where age was less or more than 50 years. This actual or estimated height at 50 years is known as site index. A stand, for instance, whose current height and age indicated a probable height of 75 feet at 50 years was assigned a site index of 75.

Obviously, comparison of tree heights of two stands, say 10 and 40 years old, would not be a fair comparison of the richness of two soils; but if the height of the 10-year-old stand were calculated from the curve to what it would be in 40 more years, and the height of the 40-year-old stand were calculated to what it would be in 10 more years, the two heights could be compared on a fair basis. This we did by assigning a site index to each stand.

When we placed the site index of each stand in one of the six positions according to its soil, the group site index averages fell into regular order roughly by steps of 10 from 50 to 100. Black locust stands on sites whose subsoil was slowly drained, sticky, compact, and bluish-colored or drab-mottled below 8 inches averaged only 50 in site index—much too low for profitable black locust growth. Stands on sites with good to fast drainage, with crumbly, loose, reddish-brown subsoil, averaged roughly 100 in site index. This arrangement of soil and tree growth brought an order to soil facts that showed how tree growth responds to soil.

The differences in thrift of black locust stands were pronounced. We found knotty, straggly, tight-barked, runty stands; and straight, tall, fluted stems with bulging roundness that seemed to split the bark. All these differences stood out more and more clearly as we measured trees and looked at the soil. The soil was different, too.

A slow-growing stand in Ripley County, Ind., near Osgood, was on a ridge top where the drying winds swept the moisture right out of the soil. To make the site still worse, only a shallow soil lay over bedrock—not much chance for good timber here; only 32 feet high at 25 years. A fast-growing grove in a little valley churchyard near Paris Crossing, Jennings County, Ind., had a deep, mellow silt loam soil (Cincinnati silt loam). Its subsoil was well aerated; its color was a golden brown. The site was sheltered from excessive wind; its soil was moist—small wonder that the trees were 13 inches in diameter and 90 feet high at 40 years.

We began to use simple relations of soil stickiness, compactness, and color to drainage and aeration to explain tree differences.

These simple relations have great value to forestry, but they were not found in a hurry. As early as the late 1920's, Tom Bushnell, chief of the Indiana Soil Survey, was arranging soils by drainage groups.

Richard Bradfield, working at Cornell University, found that roots of apple trees penetrated the soil only so far as it was well oxidized. If the ratio of oxidation to reduction (measured electrically) was high, the roots penetrated deeply and the trees were thrifty. If the ratio of oxidation to reduction was low, the roots died at a slight depth and the trees were slow growing and unthrifty. Dr. Bradfield, of course, knew about the relation of drainage to aeration; he wanted a quick test for apple soil.

His work adds another link to the chain of site evidence. A well-drained soil is a well-aerated soil, and a well-aerated soil is a well-oxidized soil. But the iron oxides in a well-oxidized soil are red and brown, whereas the iron oxides in a reduced soil are blue or green. Therefore the subsoil of a well-drained, well-aerated, well-oxidized soil is red or brown, and the subsoil of a poorly drained, slowly aerated, reduced soil is bluish or drab. The degree of drainage and aeration accordingly are indicated by subsoil color.

Milne, a South African soil scientist, in 1936 gave the name "catena" (Latin for "chain") to groups of soils varying systematically in drainage. Soil surveyors have worked painstakingly and long, mapping and describing soils, and their work continues. Even now they do not fully agree on what a catena really means; its application is new. Some say it is a hydrologic sequence—a high-sounding expression meaning arrangement by degree of soil moistness; some say it is an order of drainage; but whatever they finally decide, black locust growth defines it as a range of usable soil water.

The arithmetic of soil water is simple. Total rainfall less runoff water less evaporation water equals ground water. Obviously, useful water in soil does not depend alone on how much rain falls, or altogether on how much runs off the surface, or even on how much runs into the soil; but it depends also and importantly on how much is evaporated.

A very little observation soon convinces one that a south slope loses more water by evaporation than a north slope because it gets more direct sunlight, and that a wind-swept upper slope or ridge loses more water by evaporation than a lower slope or cove because more moisture-absorbing air passes over it. But evaporation varies so much that a way of evaluating it by sites had to be found for hilly land. At this stage of the search for an answer to site prediction on abandoned fields, we had attempted to find it by measuring the subsoil. The application of topography, with its three parts—aspect, exposure, and position—in making site predictions remained to be studied.

2. Here are the site-index points to subtract from 100 for aspect, exposure, and position in hilly and steep terrain, as shown by studies of 77 yellow poplar stands

Site	Aspect	Exposure	Position	Negative index points
Cove............	....	Sheltered.........	....	0
Do.........	....	Open.............	....	3
Slope...........	Cool.........	Sheltered.........	Lower..........	6
Do..........	.....do......	Open.............	.....do.........	9
Do..........	.....do......	Sheltered.........	Upper..........	12
Do..........	.....do......	Open.............	.....do.........	15
Do.........	Hot..........	Sheltered.........	Lower..........	18
Do.........	.....do......	Open.............	.....do.........	21
Do..........	.....do......	Sheltered.........	Upper.........	24
Do..........	.....do......	Open.............	.....do.........	27
Ridge...........	....	Sheltered.........	....	30
Do.........	....	Open...... :	....	33

How could the effect of topography on tree growth be measured? That is the question we asked ourselves. Trees themselves answer that question. After all, what instrument will take rainfall, temperature, evaporation, and soil data in all their variations, throw them into an equation, and come out with a perfect answer? Trees do it. So to find out how topography affects growth of yellow poplar we examined 77 second-growth and old-field stands in the hilly area of the Central States.

We separated the site indexes of the 77 stands that occurred on slopes into hot and cool groups. (Hot slopes were defined as S., SW., SE., and W. slopes; cool slopes were defined as N., NW., NE., and E. slopes.) The difference between the average hot and cool slope in terms of site quality was 10 site-index points.

But this 10-point difference represented the combined influence of the three elements of topography: Aspect, exposure, and position. Accordingly, we divided the 10 points roughly into 3 parts, attributing 3 site-index points to each—aspect, exposure, and position.

Furthermore, the extreme site-index range between the average exposed ridge and the average sheltered cove was 33 points. Accordingly, we distributed this total difference of 33 points by steps of 3 as in table 2.

This table enabled us to assign a site index to any topographic effect in hilly terrain from cove to ridge. The figures therefore should be subtracted from 100 to give the actual site index attributable to topography.

On the very dry sites it may be necessary to plant pines to add a moisture-conserving litter cover to the soil. Hardwoods then replace the pines naturally if seed trees are near.

The trees to plant on an abandoned field soil that is drier than normal depends on depth of the surface soil or depth to subsoil. Depth to subsoil for black locust of average or better than average site index was found to be 14 inches or more; for black walnut, 16 inches or more; and for yellow poplar, 24 inches or more.

3. This table shows the species of trees that are recommended for various sites

Site character		Original species	Site-index range	Recommended species
Dry sites......	More dry.	Virginia pine.. Blackjack oak. Pitch pine.... Shortleaf pine. Scarlet oak... Rock oak..... Chestnut..... Black oak..... Post oak...... White oak....	40–60. (Based on and too dry for black locust and yellow poplar.)	*Northern portion of region* White pine, red pine, Norway spruce. *Southern portion of region* Shortleaf pine, pitch·pine, Virginia pine. Loblolly pine in extreme southern part.
	Less dry.	Shagbark hickory.		
Moist normal sites.	Less moist.	Pignut hickory Shagbark hickory.	60............	Pines on hot aspects. Black locusts on cool aspects.
		Black gum.... Rock elm..... Black oak..... Scarlet oak...	70............	Black locust or pines. Reserve locust for the deeper soils.
		Chestnut oak.. White oak.... Red elm......	80............	Red oak, black locust.
		Beech........ Red oak...... Black walnut.. White ash.... Yellow poplar. Hard maple...	90............	White oak, red oak. Black walnut. Red oak. White oak.
	More moist.	....	100..........	Yellow poplar.
Wet sites......	Less wet.	Bur oak...... Rock elm..... Red gum..... Beech........ Big shellbark hickory. Swamp white oak. Pin oak...... Cottonwood... Sycamore.....	40–60. (Based on and too wet for black locust and yellow poplar.)	Cottonwood for soils of high water table or first bottom soils frequently flooded. White ash and maple for better drained bottom soils. Red gum for upland flats and first bottoms in southern part of region. White and red oaks for better drained portions of upland flats.
	More wet.	River birch... Willow.......		

Tree growth depends largely on the degree of site dryness or wetness. When the site indexes of the species studied were arranged in order from lowest to highest, three bands of site condition stood out: Dry sites, normal sites, and wet sites. Abandoned fields fell into the normal site group and into normal sites temporarily dry because of loss of litter and surface soil. Yellow poplar stands were found almost altogether in the sites of normal moisture. Black locust stands had a much wider range; a few of them persisted with poor thrift in both dry and wet sites.

Next, let us decide whether your field is a dry, wet, or normal site.

1. It is a dry site if its soil is coarse, deep sand, loose shale, or rock, in any position other than a flat where the water stands near the surface.

It is a dry site if bedrock is nearer than 24 inches to the surface or if erosion has removed the surface soil down to less than 4 inches from a tight subsoil.

2. It is a wet site if it is seasonally waterlogged.

3. It is a normal site if it is neither dry nor wet.

We can dispose of the dry and wet sites at once by turning to table 3. There you will find data on the original species that grew on dry and wet sites and the species that we recommend for them.

If your site is neither dry nor wet it falls into either the flat to gently rolling class or the hilly class. If it is in the flat to gently rolling class we need not worry about topographic effect. And by gently rolling I mean slopes of less than 25 percent and hills not over 50 to 75 feet high. Now look the site over and estimate the rate of drainage according to the first table. Give it a number from 1 to 6, expressing how fast you think rainfall will run through the soil.

In any case if it is a normal site, take your spade, a soil auger, or, better still, a post-hole digger, and dig a hole about 3 feet deep. Examine the subsoil—incidentally, the subsoil here is the tight layer usually 1 to 3 feet below the surface—and classify it according to one of the horizontal columns of the first table. At the right you find the site index.

If your field is a normal site in the hills you must estimate its negative points by placing it according to the second table. Suppose the site index that you get from the first table is 90; and further suppose your field is a lower north slope sheltered from excessive wind. In the second table you will find your field described by the third line (slope—cool—sheltered—lower—6). Simply subtract the 6 from the 90 and get 84, the site index. This figure indicates that on a scale of 100-foot height growth in 50 years, you can expect your stand to be 84 feet high.

Finally when you have the site figure, turn to the third table and there find the species that grew on the original site and the species we recommend for planting.

THE AUTHOR

John T. Auten, a silviculturist with the Research Branch of the Forest Service, has been engaged in forest soil investigations since 1929. He has been a soil analyst for the Iowa soil survey and professor of chemistry and soils at the Pennsylvania State Forest School. Dr. Auten is a graduate of the University of Illinois and Iowa State College.

Canker Stain of Planetrees

by JAMES M. WALTER

SINCE its introduction from England about 1900, the London planetree has become one of the most important shade trees of the United States. It has been planted by thousands in the East and Midwest, in a region that includes New York City, Pittsburgh, St. Louis, and Washington, D. C. By 1939 Philadelphia had planted 153,000 of the trees, valued at about 6 million dollars, and Pittsburgh 75,000, valued at 3 million dollars. The London plane (*Platanus acerifolia* Willd.) is a hybrid between American sycamore (*P. occidentalis* L.) and Oriental plane (*P. orientalis* L.). It grows rapidly, is easily propagated, adapts itself to a wide variety of soils, resists smoke and fumes, and withstands the anthracnose disease that often makes the native planetree unsightly. Those virtues explain its meteoric rise to popularity.

But its utility came in question in 1933 when arborists and shade-tree enthusiasts of the western suburbs of Philadelphia recognized that their trees were dying by the score despite good care. Early pathological studies by Dr. L. W. R. Jackson disclosed that the trees were being killed by a previously unknown fungus of the genus *Endoconidiophora*. Recently we have learned that the fungus occurs occasionally on the native planetree, or sycamore, in remote stands in the Appalachians. It seems likely that the organism is native to North America, although it was not recognized until it became a pest among planted trees. Indications are that London plane is more susceptible than American sycamore, but the disease has caused great losses in some plantings of the latter species.

The disease is characterized by blackened, elongate cankers having rather irregular annual zones ½ inch to 2 inches wide. The cankers occur most commonly on trunks, less frequently on branches, and occasionally on major roots. The most distinctive symptom, however, is the bluish-black or reddish-brown discoloration distributed in the wood in radial patterns beneath the cankers. The distinctiveness of these symptoms allows relatively early diagnosis of the disease and favors its control.

By 1939, an estimated 8,000 of the London planes in Philadelphia had succumbed to the disease; losses were known to be proportionately higher in some of the suburbs; more and more were dying in Baltimore and Washington, and the disease was being reported from new localities with alarming frequency. Congress appropriated $10,000 for an investigation, and organized studies were begun at the Forest Pathology Field Laboratory in Morristown, N. J.

Investigations made during the ensuing 5 years showed that canker stain can be brought under control by simple, inexpensive, and practicable measures. That statement may sound mild enough to the layman, but to the biologist it must smack of dogmatism, and to the student of tree diseases it must be astounding.

Canker stain is unique in that its spread is almost entirely accountable to man, the causal fungus hardly being able to cross a street without the aid of man—or his boys. An inkling of this truth came from early observations on the distribution of cases of the disease. It was noted, for example, that the disease had claimed every tree in the row along a street where the trees had received the best possible care, including regular pruning, while in a row a few feet away, but inside a good fence, the trees had received no attention and none had developed the disease. The problem was tested in every way that we could devise and the answer was always the same—the disease was of no consequence among trees left undisturbed by man. Moreover, tests of dissemination of the fungus by wind and wind-driven rain, common carriers of many disease-producing fungi, resulted in no cases of infection more than 25 feet from the source.

The fungus is spread readily in pruning operations and by other mechanical means. Pruning tools are exceeded in efficiency as transmitters, however, by the commonly used forms of asphalt wound dressing. Wound dressing, besides being a carrier, evidently protects the fungus against weathering, its use in winter resulting in infections at wounds, made with contaminated tools, that would not otherwise become infected.

One of the most important facts concerning the disease is that the fungus is noninfectious in the latitudes of New York and Philadelphia for about three winter months. Between December 1 and February 15, approximately, it is safe to prune, provided the wounds are left bare.

Cooperative tests of local control by sanitary practices were begun in 1940 in two park areas and in two plantings along streets in residential districts. Tree wardens also were encouraged to take precautions against spread of the pest in pruning and to remove dead and dying trees. New information from laboratory and nursery experiments was reported to the tree wardens as it became available, and was taken into account in the tests of local control. Although this work was hampered by changes due to the war, the application of sanitary practices and precautions against further transmission of the fungus quickly checked the losses caused by canker stain in several municipalities.

Measures necessary to control canker stain in localities where it is already established (with brief explanations of important points not emphasized in the foregoing paragraphs) are:

Avoid all unnecessary mutilation of planetrees.

The causal fungus does not enter through undamaged bark, but with enough moisture it enters through the slightest injury.

Remove all diseased trees or parts of trees to eliminate sources from which the pathogen may be transmitted to healthy trees.

Once the infection has developed in the trunk, the tree is doomed; but it usually takes 3 years or longer for the tree to die. Early recognition and prompt removal of infected trees from city streets is important, because the fungus is so readily transmitted by mechanical means. Boys using their knives and hand axes have accounted for many cases of spread. Lawn mowers that were allowed to injure buttress roots have accounted for infections in rows of fine, large trees. Moving vans that scraped trunks and lower branches have accounted for several known cases and are no doubt a hazard for spreading the fungus from city to city.

Some trees having infections definitely limited to branches may be saved by careful pruning. A clearance of 3 feet between the pruning cut and the end of a branch canker nearest the trunk is usually necessary for success in removal of all infected wood, and the surgery must be carefully done to avoid inoculation of the tree at other points.

Disinfect pruning tools, and all other equipment that might have come in contact with an infected tree, before using them in a healthy planetree between February 15 and December 1.

Saws, other cutting tools, soles of climber's shoes, and ladder parts that must make contact with the tree can be disinfected easily by dipping or thoroughly swabbing them in denatured alcohol of the type commonly used as antifreeze.

It is desirable to avoid the contamination of climbing ropes as far as possible. Ropes may be disinfected by exposing them to vapor from commercial formaldehyde for 3 hours. Effective fumigation of rope is attained with one-fourth pound of formaldehyde spread over about 100 square inches below a false bottom in a tightly capped 10-gallon container. *Formaldehyde is poisonous and must be handled with caution.*

If wound dressing is necessary, use a gilsonite varnish (type covered by Federal Specification TT–V–51) in which phenylmercury nitrate has been mixed in a 0.2-percent concentration.

When fortified with this powerful germicide, the paint cannot carry the fungus. The commonly used forms of asphalt paints undoubtedly

YEARBOOK OF AGRICULTURE

have been the most damaging and insidious means of transmitting the fungus. The paint container, as handled by the arborist, collects sawdust and fragments of bark and wood, much of it carried in by adhesion to the brush. Paint contaminated with such matter from diseased planetrees is highly infectious for a long period, and has regularly given infection at 25 to 50 percent of experimental wounds treated during the winter period when there is no danger of infection at wounds left without paint.

Phenylmercury nitrate is not recommended for use with paints based on petroleum-residue asphalt, because that combination may be too injurious to the cambium. Further, use of paint fortified with phenylmercury nitrate will not eliminate the need to disinfect pruning equipment, the tests showing that, despite prompt and careful application, it is not thoroughly effective in preventing infection at wounds made with contaminated tools.

Phenylmercury nitrate is a highly toxic chemical and must be handled with caution. However, a careful workman can safely mix it with the asphalt varnish by first mulling the fine powder in a little linseed oil and then thoroughly stirring it into the varnish. Some people are sensitive to mercurials carried in oils; therefore, anyone using paint fortified with phenylmercury nitrate in this concentration should handle it cautiously and should immediately remove paint spots from his skin.

Restrict pruning of planetrees, as far as possible, to the period from December 1 to February 15.

As previously explained, in the northern half of the range of the disease the chances of spreading it by pruning in midwinter are negligible if no paint is used. All tests on this question have been conducted in the northern part of the involved area, and it is not assured that the results will apply in the South. If paint is used, it is necessary that the pruning tools be disinfected and that the paint be free of contamination or be fortified with phenylmercury nitrate.

Measures necessary to prevent the introduction of canker stain into localities where it is not yet established are:

Require all equipment to be disinfected thoroughly before work is begun on planetrees.

Require that any wound dressing used on planetrees be fortified with phenylmercury nitrate or be from an unopened container and used with new equipment.

THE AUTHOR

James M. Walter served as pathologist in the Bureau of Plant Industry, Soils, and Agricultural Engineering in the Forest Pathology Field Office at Morristown, N. J. He joined the Department in 1933 and resigned in 1946. His research has included the relations of the corn smut fungus to its host, Dutch elm disease and what causes it, and canker stain of planetrees.

Better Soils, Better Food

by KENNETH C. BEESON

NUTRITION begins with the soil. The truth of that statement has been investigated only recently, but it has long been a factor in the thinking of men. Charles A. Browne in his recent book, *A Source Book of Agricultural Chemistry,* has organized in an interesting way the evolution of the concept from the time of Democritus (about 360 B. C.) to Liebig (1803–73).

Democritus, for example, suggested a cycle of indestructible elements from the soil to the plant and to the animal and back again to the soil. Aristotle (384–322 B. C.) taught that plants absorbed through their roots the necessary material for their growth. In turn, bones, blood, milk, hair, and other parts of animals were derived from constituents of the plants. But long before these speculative ideas began to take form in the minds of men, the practical farmer had observed that his animals responded differently to forages from different localities. Through experience he had learned not only what localities were best suited to his needs but he had learned that some were definitely undesirable.

The nutritional problems of animals in relation to soil conditions, however, did not become acute nor were they the subject of scientific inquiry until nearly the middle of the nineteenth century, when their importance was emphasized as the increase in world population was pushing man out into new lands. Many of the new lands were found to be incapable of supporting animal life, particularly when the animals were not permitted to graze large areas and select their food. The need for new lands has continued to create problems of this nature that must be solved. There are still vast areas in the world, and in the United States in particular, that will be suitable for many agricultural purposes when it is learned how to correct their natural shortcomings.

485

Troubles in grazing animals, related to deficiencies or to toxic quantities of mineral elements in soils, have been recognized in the United States for more than 50 years. Many of the ailments have been investigated extensively. A deficiency of phosphorus in soils and forage was among the first to be recognized and described.

More recently an appreciation of the role of the trace elements or micronutrient elements, such as cobalt and copper, has developed. They occur in soils in minute quantities. An acre of topsoil, 1 foot deep, for example, ordinarily contains less than 20 pounds of any micronutrient element. A ton of hay normally contains about 2 grains, or one four-thousandth of an ounce, of cobalt. Where such small quantities are involved, an understanding of their importance was not realized until the refinement of laboratory methods made such studies possible.

It is evident that a deficiency of phosphorus, next to iodine, is the most widespread of any mineral nutritional trouble in grazing animals. Recent work has emphasized that phosphorus may generally be deficient in virgin soils throughout the Atlantic and Gulf Coastal Plains, a fact that becomes apparent as more and more of those undeveloped lands are used for profitable grazing. John Foster, of the North Carolina Agricultural Experiment Station, for example, has stated that the raising of beef cattle is rapidly assuming an important place in the agriculture of the Coastal Plain, where the available forages appear adequate for the protein and energy requirement of the animals, but that limiting factors seem to be deficiencies of phosphorus and possibly some micronutrient elements, such as cobalt.

Deficiencies of phosphorus were observed many years ago in the Coastal Plain regions by investigators in Florida, Alabama, and Texas. The work of W. H. Black, J. M. Jones, and their co-workers in southeastern Texas is one of the more recent contributions to the solution of the problem. According to them, an abundance of vegetation is available in that area. Consequently, there are greater numbers of cattle there per section than in any other range area of the State. The fact that a nutritional deficiency does exist is evident from the small size of the animals, reproduction failures, and malformed bones that are easily broken, and a persistent craving by many cattle for bones, dirt, wood, and other materials.

In Tennessee there is a recognized relationship between the supply of phosphorus in the soil and the health and production of animals and the economic status and well-being of the people. In few parts of the country are the contrasts between good and poor soils more striking. The reason lies in the fact that in Tennessee some of the best agricultural soils of the East are closely associated with much less productive and often actually deficient soils.

Conditions in Minnesota and Montana are probably fairly typical of the Northwest. In Minnesota much has been done in locating deficient areas, and experiments designed to correct the troubles are now under way. The work in Minnesota has emphasized the study of the effect of superphosphate over a large part of the State. Much more work is required to demonstrate the practicability of this on the more extensive range areas farther west.

Since 1937 the importance of cobalt in animal nutrition has been repeatedly demonstrated throughout the world. Several areas in the United States are now believed to have soils deficient in it. One of the most extensive is in the Northeast, where the problem is being studied by men at the New Hampshire Agricultural Experiment Station.

In troubles of this kind it is hard to establish a definite relationship from the soil to the animal, but it has been demonstrated in New Hampshire that ailing animals respond to administrations of cobalt, that the largest proportion of the farms involved occurs on soils developed on materials derived principally from granite, and that there are definite and significant differences in the cobalt content of the forage from good and poor areas. In some cases, however, the cobalt content of poor hay is not acutely low, as measured by the rather uncertain standards that we have.

Troubles in grazing animals due to a lack of cobalt have been known to the scientists in Florida for some time. The situation there (where the first research of this kind in the United States was done) emphasizes that multiple deficiencies may often be encountered. Thus, cobalt and phosphorus, cobalt and copper, or copper and iron have been noted as being simultaneously deficient in forages in those areas. Recognition of this possibility may be helpful in explaining discrepancies in the known facts associated with other trouble areas of the country.

Deficiencies of cobalt have been reported from Michigan and Wisconsin; possible deficiencies have been reported from eastern Pennsylvania, Cape Cod, and northeastern New York. Most of these areas have not yet been studied in sufficient detail to permit generalizations as to the soil, plant, and animal relationships.

Correcting Deficiencies in Plants Through Fertilizers

Fertilizers are used mostly to increase yields; their use over the years has proved to be a satisfactory and economically sound practice. We are confronted now with the problem of whether fertilizing our soils to improve the nutritive quality of the crops, as well as the yield, is a matter of practical importance. The problem has two aspects: The modification of the mineral content of the plant and the modification of the organic constituents, including the proteins, carbohydrates, fats, vitamins, hormones, and other (probably unknown) constituents in the plant. Any attempt to improve the plant with respect to one group of these factors may, of course, modify those in the other group, at least with respect to their relative proportions. For the purpose of this discussion the two groups will be treated separately, although their interrelationships are obvious.

Applications of phosphates to a soil may increase the phosphorus content of a mixed forage in two ways: Through an increase in the phosphorus content of individual plant species, and through an increase in the proportion of grasses and legumes that are normally high in phosphorus in the mixture. The latter way—that is, the change in the botanical composition of the forage—is the one commonly experienced. This principle is, of course, the basis for most of the pasture-improvement programs throughout the country.

Agronomists and others generally assume that an application of fertilizers containing a particular element should result in an increase in the content of that element in the plant. The assumption is probably correct with respect to phosphorus, but there are definite limitations to any generalizations that may be made. A survey of recent findings on the subject suggests that relatively small increases in the phosphorus content of plants often are obtained particularly where the unfertilized plant contains a quantity of phosphorus well below the level required by animals. Experience indicates that frequently even very large and uneconomical applications of phosphate on some soils will fail to build up phosphorus in the plant equal to that normally found in plants from other soils.

Unfortunately, a relatively low phosphorus content in plants may often prove to be the most difficult one to increase by programs of fertilization. That is, the increases that have been obtained are often too small to be of much practical importance to the grazing animal. On the other hand, it has been a common experience of investigators that a plant containing more nearly normal or even relatively high quantities of phosphorus may increase its phosphorus content very appreciably following application of phosphates or other amendments to the soil. A further consideration of this relationship will be discussed in connection with the general problem of nutrient absorption.

The question naturally arises as to whether the application of phosphates to range lands is always profitable. W. H. Black, from his work in eastern Texas, believes that under conditions there it may prove to be so. Under other conditions, phosphates are best supplied directly to the animals as mineral supplements. In South Africa, scientists suggested that the grains as rich as possible in phosphorus could supply the necessary phosphorus to animals that grazed phosphorus-deficient range.

The application of any element, such as nitrogen, to the soil produces so many effects that it is difficult to generalize with respect to its effect on plant composition. The use of nitrogen as a fertilizer has not been associated with any definite trend in the phosphorus content of the plant. Where potassium has been supplied as a fertilizer, there seems to be general agreement that the phosphorus content of the plant is either unchanged or lowered. The differences in phosphorus where there is a change are often small and of little practical importance. The application of lime alone to the soil has likewise had little effect on the phosphorus concentration in plants in most of the experiments reported, although occasionally a reduction of phosphorus is noted. If the limestone is added with superphosphate, however, a greater increase in the phosphorus concentration in the plant has often been obtained than with either material alone. But this trend is not consistent; sometimes no change in phosphorus is reported, even from very carefully controlled experiments.

Deficiencies of calcium have seldom been reported in cattle and sheep. A study of available data indicates that most legumes will always supply sufficient calcium for animals. L. A. Maynard, director of the Cornell School of Nutrition in Ithaca, has stated, however, that, "Generalizations regarding the adequacy of grass hay in calcium content for animal nutrition are unsafe because of the very large variations that can occur." It is, therefore, of interest to examine the effects of fertilization on the concentration of calcium in plants.

It is recognized that liming acid soils tends to encourage the growth of forage plants relatively high in calcium in both pastures and hay crops. The growth of many of the legumes, such as white clover, soybean, sweetclover, alfalfa, and red clover, is favored markedly by limestone, and they are able to displace the nutritionally less desirable grasses and other plants. Since those legumes are higher in calcium than the species in the original pasture or hay mixture, the calcium concentration in the forage as a whole will be increased without regard to the composition of the individual species. There is, in fact, very little evidence that any fertility program will result in an important increase in the calcium concentration of individual forages. The addition of lime to certain soils has increased the calcium concentration of some plants under certain conditions, but the changes are not always of great practical importance. This is in marked contrast to the large differences that have been found in the calcium content of the same species of plants grown in different localities.

The calcium concentration in plants used for human foods is of more interest than the phosphorus content because of the greater possibility of deficiencies of calcium in the diet. Consequently, increasing the calcium concentration in such crops has been considered by several investigators. For example, the workers in some experiment stations in the Southeast organized a broad cooperative project to study the relationships between soils and the composition of certain vegetables, particularly the leafy vegetables used for greens. They noted some interesting effects of calcium and nitrogen fertilizers on the calcium content of turnip greens. For example, very small increases (0.06 percent of calcium) in turnip greens resulted from applications of gypsum to the soil. On the other hand, nitrogen applied to the soil brought a relatively large decrease in calcium (0.36 percent of calcium). Thus, more than six times as much calcium was lost as a result of fertilization of the crop with nitrogen than was gained through fertilization with gypsum. Also, in the experiments, it was shown that soil type had a greater effect on calcium and phosphorus than did minerals applied as fertilizers.

The application of nitrogenous manures has generally been associated with a reduced calcium concentration in the plant. There is some evidence that ammonium sulfate as a nitrogen carrier may be more effective in this respect than sodium nitrate. Effects of nitrogen on the calcium concentration in mixed forages and pasture herbage may be associated with changes in botanical composition, as well as with changes in the chemical composition of individual species. This is due to the effect of heavy applications of nitrogen in encouraging growth of grasses at the expense of legumes. Potassium or magnesium applied as a fertilizer may also be associated with a reduction of the calcium concentration in plants. The effect of magnesium may be small and is ordinarily of little practical importance except in the case of a plant, such as timothy, that normally has a low level of calcium.

Applications of most of the micronutrient elements to soils even in very small quantities will be followed by an increased absorption of the element by the plant. One exception may be iron, and reported changes in copper concentration in the plant have been rather small. Relatively large increases in cobalt and manganese concentration in plants can be obtained by adding these elements to the soil. In New Zealand and elsewhere, cobalt deficiency is often corrected by the use of cobaltized superphosphate, limestone high in cobalt, or simply crude cobalt salts.

Interest has grown in the effect of certain micronutrient elements like boron, on the absorption of other elements, particularly calcium and nitrogen. It appears from work published by R. Q. Parks, C. B. Lyon, and S. L. Hood of the United States Plant, Soil, and Nutrition Laboratory in Ithaca, N. Y., that boron exerts a profound effect on the absorption of nearly every other plant nutrient. At normal levels of boron supply, an increase in the boron content of the nutrient solution caused an increased concentration of boron, organic nitrogen, magnesium, manganese, calcium, iron, cobalt, and sulfur in tomato plants grown in a greenhouse. The concentration of molybdenum, phosphorus, zinc, copper, and potassium decreased in the same plants. The work has not as yet had practical application, but it is of considerable fundamental importance in studies of ion absorption by plants.

Overliming is a common experience on a soil with a low buffer capacity. The troubles arising from too much limestone are often due to its effect on some of the micronutrient elements like boron and manganese in the soil. Symptoms characteristic of deficiencies of these elements appear in the plant as a result either of chemical reactions that make the compounds of these elements unavailable to plants or through adverse ratios of calcium to these elements in the soil or the plant. These visual symptoms appear only in cases of acute deficiency. In less serious deficiencies, retarded growth in various degrees may be the only symptoms. Under subacute conditions only the amount of the micronutrient element absorbed by the plant may be limited. It is the latter condition that may be of greatest importance to the nutritionist. We have no clear evidence yet as to the lowest level that elements such as iron, manganese, and copper can reach in the plant before deficiency symptoms appear. It is certain that the content of iron and manganese can vary tremendously and that copper can vary within a limited range before their absence becomes evident. Apparently cobalt can be entirely absent without any visual physiological disorder being produced in the plant.

The addition of liming materials, consequently, is a practice that farmers and technicians should study carefully, particularly in areas that are subject to overliming troubles. Evidence is at hand that liming will reduce materially the manganese content of forage without reducing yields. It has long been known that the iron content can be lowered, and it is reasonable to assume that cobalt would be lowered under some conditions. The evidence with respect to cobalt is still incomplete.

The micronutrient element content of plants (especially manganese and cobalt) may also be lowered through the excessive use of nitrogenous fertilizers. That is to be expected because of the effects of nitrogen in producing more rapid and greater vegetative growth. If such growth occurs in soils containing minimum quantities of an element, such as cobalt, that is not essential to the growth of the plant, a low concentration of the element in the plant will result.

The Effects of Fertilization on the Quality of Forages

A sound program of fertilization, then, can increase the nutritive value of a mixed forage in two ways—by the introduction of highly nutritious forage plants, such as the legumes and the elimination of less desirable plants, and by an increase in the individual plant of such mineral nutrients as calcium, phosphorus, cobalt, and other of the micronutrient elements.

We can assume that many other constituents, some that are unknown and consequently not subject to laboratory measurements, may be modified by fertilization. These factors, both known and unknown, all contribute to the nutritive quality of forages. Therefore, many workers in an attempt to evaluate the nutritive quality of one forage against another have fed the two forages to animals. The growth response has then been used as an over-all measure of nutritive value.

This over-all measure, which has been termed a bio-assay of soil fertility, is subject, however, to many limitations. A successful or positive result from such an experiment might actually be considered fortuitous.

Two situations that would result in negative conclusions when positive ones would have been justified will be discussed. Many other combinations of circumstances could be considered.

If a forage (assume a pure species) is produced at different fertility levels of the soil, it is assumed on the basis of the foregoing discussion that there may be some measurable difference in their nutritive quality. It may be that these differences are due to constituents unknown with respect at least to their ability to influence animal growth or health, or it may be that some constituent such as protein is the variable. Suppose that a particular fertility level of the soil is associated with a forage containing 20 percent of protein as compared to 15 percent in a forage from a lower fertility level. The two forages are fed to lambs and the growth response is taken as the criterion of the nutritive values of the two forages. But the difference in protein levels would probably not be reflected in a difference in growth of the two groups of lambs, because the optimum protein requirement for this animal is about 10 percent, and both forage samples exceed this. Thus, a negative result would be obtained from the experiment, although there was an actual difference in the composition of the forages.

A second set of circumstances that might give rise to negative results is based on suboptimum, rather than superoptimum, concentrations of a nutritive constituent. Assume that each forage in this case contains 6 percent protein but that there exists a difference in the phosphorus content, one forage containing less than the minimum required for growth of sheep. The difference in phosphorus levels in this case would probably not be detected because of the limiting factor in both forages, the low protein content.

Both these circumstances could be repeated in the relationship between any two or more constituents of a plant that are required in some minimum quantity by animals. It is obvious that the possible combinations resulting in negative conclusions are manifold. The examples illustrate furthermore a basic requirement of such bio-assays, that the nutrients, known or unknown, be fed at suboptimum levels if differences are to be detected and also that nutrients other than those under test be fed in adequate amounts.

Requirements of this kind imply that specific nutrients be under consideration rather than all of them at one time. It is probable that future effort in the field of evaluation of the nutritive quality of plants will be directed largely toward this kind of an approach, which will necessarily be predicated largely on preliminary laboratory examination of the composition of the plant.

E. W. Crampton, D. A. Finlayson, and their co-workers at Macdonald

College in Quebec have contributed materially to our knowldege in this sphere through their numerous publications. They conclude that some factor or factors other than quantitative differences in total protein, energy value, fiber, or minerals (calcium and phosphorus) of mixed forages are responsible for observed differences in nutritive value. In the experiments upon which their conclusions are based, however, the fertilized forage contained nearly four times more white clover than the unfertilized forage did. A corresponding reduction in weeds and undesirable grasses occurred in the fertilized forage. Hence it is not possible to differentiate between the effect of fertilizers on the botanical composition of the mixed herbage and on the chemical composition of individual species. In other words, one cannot conclude from these experiments that the nutritive value of individual forage species has been altered by fertilizing the soil.

W. A. Albrecht and his associates at the Missouri Agricultural Experiment Station have also attempted to measure this improvement in the biological factors in forage plants that follow the use of fertilizers, particularly liming materials and superphosphate. Their general approach, like Dr. Crampton's, has been to use animal growth as an index of the changes in crop quality in response to soil treatment. They assume that the animal should respond to changes in the composition of the forage even though some of the changes cannot be detected even by ordinary chemical analyses.

The greatest danger in work of this kind is the tendency to generalize and oversimplify the situation. For example, in three carefully controlled feeding experiments carried out at the Plant, Soil, and Nutrition Laboratory, S. E. Smith found that in only one was there any indication of an advantage in favor of the fertilized forage.

The work at Missouri has also indicated a variability in results. Thus, in one of the experiments there, the difference in the average weight of sheep that were fed hay from fertilized soils and those fed hay from unfertilized soils was very slight. The daily average gain in the two was 0.1408 and 0.1644 pound per head. Data are not presented to show that this small difference is significant. In fact, allowing for a reasonable variability in the response of the animals, it can be shown that the greater gains could just as well have been made by either group of the sheep if both had been fed identical hays. In view of the additional fact that 50 percent of the hay from unlimed soils and 46 percent of the treated hay was refused by the animals in this experiment, it is manifestly impossible to conclude that the fertilization or liming program had materially altered the nutritive quality of the forage plant. These instances are cited to show how difficult it is to carry out and interpret these over-all bio-assays of nutritional quality of plants.

It has become obvious lately that soils do not tell the whole story with respect to the nutritive quality of food.

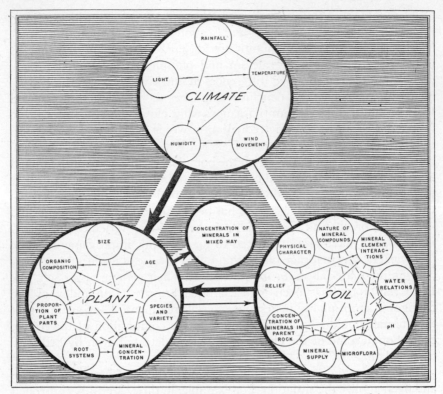

The various factors affecting the mineral content of a mixed hay.

There is the question of sunlight, for instance. Today we know that sunlight is an important factor in the elaboration of vitamins in both plant and animal bodies. The variations in ascorbic acid (vitamin C) in a food, such as the tomato, are amazing. Studies of the causes of such variations have been made by Karl C. Hamner and his associates at the Ithaca laboratory. They concluded that the causes are not so much associated with soil conditions or cultural practices as they are with location. They found that tomatoes of the same variety grown in some parts of the country have three times more ascorbic acid than those grown in another part. Drastic soil treatment failed to modify the vitamin content of tomatoes grown under similar climatic conditions. An explanation for a large part of the variations was found in the amount of light received by the plant. In fact, the effect of variation in the amount of light on a plant is so pronounced that any effect of soil fertility or of fertilizer treatment may be completely obscured. Failure to recognize this point has led to several questionable interpretations in the recent literature of the relationship between fertilization and the vitamin content of foods.

Even the actual amount of sunlight received by the entire plant may not be the deciding factor in determining the vitamin C content of the portion used for food. For example, later and more refined experiments by George F. Somers and Hamner have shown that the vitamin C content of the tomato itself is apparently related to the amount of sunshine that strikes directly on the fruit, for sunshine on the vines apparently has little or no influence on the fruit. Consequently, it is clear that shading of the fruit by an abundant foliage will have an important effect in limiting the vitamin C content. Furthermore, fruit taken from the shady side of the tree or vine or fruit subjected to any other interference from sunlight may be lower in vitamin C than the fruit obtaining direct sunlight. Thus, the total amount of illumination on a field of tomatoes may not necessarily be related to the vitamin content of the fruit from that field because of other factors that are also operating.

Important Problems for Future Study

Since the amount of sunshine, and not soil fertility, seems to be so important a factor in determining the vitamin content of plants, one may be led to conclude that there is little that can be done to bring about an increase of these important nutritional factors. Experimental work carried out at many stations, both State and Federal, shows that there is at least one other way open for improvement, e. g., through plant breeding. For example, there are wide, and fairly consistent, differences in the vitamin C content of various tomato varieties grown commercially at the present time. Some varieties produce fruits that contain much less vitamin C than others. Even the best varieties in use at the present time do not contain the maximum amount of vitamin C that should be obtainable through breeding. Thus, some species of tomatoes, not marketable because their fruits are too small, contain 3 or 4 times as much vitamin C as the existing commercial varieties. By suitable breeding programs, it appears possible to incorporate the tendency to be rich in vitamin C into tomatoes which are commercially acceptable. The results promise to be of much greater importance than could be obtained through any reasonable modification of the mineral supply of the soil.

It is apparent that the studies of the effect of fertilization and soils on the nutritional quality of plants have not yet produced sufficient data obtained under a variety of conditions to permit many conclusions to be drawn. Thus, most of the recognized factors, such as soils, climate, and plant species that modify the influence of fertilizers have been studied in little detail.

The diagram (top page 494) summarizes some factors that would affect the mineral composition of a mixed hay—climate, the properties of soils, and the character of the plants. It is evident that within any one group one must deal with a highly complex and relatively little understood. system. The water relationships in soils, for example, are known to affect

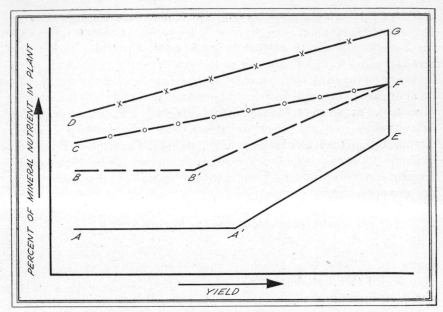

The relationship between the yield and mineral content of plants.

profoundly the mineral supply to the plant, but the magnitude and nature of these effects are probably greatly modified by the other factors, such as the physical character of the soil and the nature of the mineral compounds present. The chart is intended to stress both the direct and indirect effects of climate on the mineral composition of the plant. The direct effect is assumed to be much greater than the indirect effect that reaches the plant through the soil. In the same way the plant has an important effect on the nature of the soil, and this effect will be reflected again in the plant.

Several scientists have observed that a plant may differ to a greater extent in relation to the soil and environment in which it is growing than in relation to any fertilizer treatment on each soil. When the cause of the striking variability of the composition of plants grown in different soils is understood, an important step toward better fertilization programs will have been taken. When one considers the complexity of the biological system under which we produce our food crops, he will recognize as natural the variable results obtained by the superimposition of a fertilizer on a set of soil conditions. The problem is one that requires detailed study of each of these factors and its effect on the others as well as on determinations of the over-all or net effects as found in each soil as a unit.

Paul Macy, during work at Cornell University, has discussed in an instructive way the relationship between the sufficiency of a nutrient and its percentage content in the plant. His concept can be employed to support the observation, for example, that fertilization often does not change materially the mineral content of a plant. This is presented in a chart. When the yield under any set of conditions lies between A and A^1, the application of fertilizers should, theoretically, result only in an increase in the yield. Beyond the point A^1, the addition of fertilizers should result in both an increase in yield and an increase in the concentration of the mineral elements of the fertilizer in the plant. At the point E no additional yield is obtained as a result of fertilization, but the increase in the concentration of minerals in the plant continues. It is recognized, of course, that on a different soil another level such as $B-B^1$ will prevail. Likewise, it is conceivable that other relationships as C–F or even D–G would be found to hold for some soils. The important point is the recognition that any response to fertilization will be a function of the soil characteristics as well as the fertilizer itself.

This concept is of great importance to the animal nutritionist, although it was first considered with respect to problems in plant physiology. It means that the problem of yields is closely related to composition. For example, it is often borne out by experience that the phosphorus concentration of a plant will remain at a low level until growth requirements for the phosphorus are met.

It is evident, of course, that the limiting effects of other fertilizer elements than the one under consideration must also be taken into account. The effect of a deficiency of potassium associated with a high phosphorus content of the plant is an example. The potassium deficiency may limit the growth of the plant causing it to enter the region of "luxury consumption" of phosphorus (E–G, in the figure). A clarification of these factors is of utmost importance in solving the problem of improving the nutritional quality of plants grown for food.

More information is needed concerning the use of fertilizers in widening the choice of crops to be grown. Even if no practical means of altering the composition of a particular plant is found, it is of great practical importance to be able to improve the over-all nutritive quality of a forage crop through introduction of different plant species.

Such a solution may be practical in many of our cobalt-deficient regions. Thus, investigations carried on in the Plant, Soil, and Nutrition Laboratory have shown that different grasses vary greatly in their ability to absorb cobalt from the soil. Likewise, the legumes seem to have a much higher content of cobalt, even in deficient regions, than do the grasses or other forage plants such as reeds.

A knowledge of the relationship between the fertility level of the soil and the character of the botanical population will result in two very important practical things: It will indicate to us the advantage, nutritionally, or fertilizing and liming in order to grow crops that are naturally higher in nutritive factors; we will be able more readily to indicate the characteristics of soil types as they influence the nutritive adequacy of plants.

The need for standardizing the nutritive value of plants in terms of animal health is obvious. Certainly any limited number of laboratory determinations is inadequate with our present fund of information. An adequate evaluation of known factors simply cannot be made by laboratory methods. In undertaking planned animal experiments, however, it must be realized that animal performance is subject to as many variables as is soil fertility. Furthermore, there are differences in the nutritive value of rations which are not measurable in terms of growth performance but which require refined physical, biochemical, and histological techniques. There is before us a real opportunity to contribute to human welfare through the combined experience in the field, the laboratory, and with the experimental animal.

THE AUTHOR

Kenneth C. Beeson, senior chemist at the United States Plant, Soil, and Nutrition Laboratory of the Agricultural Research Administration, Ithaca, N. Y., has been with the Department since 1930. He has published papers on fertilizer technology, particularly on the problem of chemical reactions occurring in mixed fertilizers, and is now undertaking studies of the relationship of soils to the occurrence of nutritional troubles in animals. Mr. Beeson is a graduate of the University of Iowa.

ACKNOWLEDGMENT

George F. Somers of the United States Plant, Soil, and Nutrition Laboratory contributed material for the section on soil fertility and the vitamin content of plants, which was invaluable in the preparation of this article.

FOR FURTHER READING

Browne, Charles A.: *A Source Book of Agricultural Chemistry,* Chronica Botanica, volume 8, No. 1, 1944.

Hartman, A. M.: *Deficient and Excess Minerals in Forage in the United States,* Yearbook of Agriculture, pages 1027–1044, 1939.

McMurtrey, J. E., Jr., and Robinson, W. O.: *Neglected Soil Constituents That Affect Plant and Animal Development,* Yearbook of Agriculture, pages 807–829, 1938.

Russell, F. C.: *Minerals in Pasture—Deficiencies and Excesses in Relation to Animal Health,* Imperial Bureau of Animal Nutrition, Technical Communication No. 15, May 1944.

Organic Matter in Soils

by A. G. NORMAN

SOIL ORGANIC matter is a product of its environment. Climate more than anything else determines the amount present. Climate, temperature, and rainfall together affect the rate of growth of the vegetation and consequently the amount of residues entering the soil. They affect also the activities of the micro-organisms that utilize the vegetation in the soil, and consequently the rate at which decomposition of the residues proceeds.

Some years ago H. Jenny, working at the Missouri Agricultural Experiment Station, showed that there is a clear relationship between mean annual temperature and the amount of organic nitrogen in the grassland soils of the Mississippi Valley or of the Great Plains. The lower the mean annual temperature, the higher the nitrogen and organic matter content of the soil and the wider the ratio between nitrogen and carbon. Similarly, when soils of similar origin along an annual isotherm are examined, the organic matter and total nitrogen content are found to rise with increasing rainfall and humidity.

R. H. Fuller and L. C. Wheeting more recently examined the factor of rainfall in certain prairie soils in western Washington that are relatively uniform in all climatic features except precipitation. Samples were taken from areas on which the annual rainfall varied from 16 to 120 inches. While there was generally a direct relationship between precipitation and organic matter content, there was also clear indication of a narrowing of the carbon-nitrogen ratio with a decrease in mean annual rainfall. In other words, the nitrogen content of the organic matter is low under high rainfall and increases with less rain.

Because of the operation of climate on the renewal and decomposition of organic matter, there is for every soil a stable equilibrium value under

499

virgin conditions that becomes unstable as soon as the land is brought under cultivation.

Ordinarily, cultivation lowers the content of organic matter by speeding up microbial processes and reducing the amount of residues of vegetation that enter the soil. Rarely is the new level higher than the old. For each land use the new equilibrium value will be slowly attained, but, by his choice of rotations and management practices, a farmer can influence the new level at which a balance is reached between the annual additions from the vegetation on the land and that used by the soil micro-organisms. That equilibrium is generally much lower than that attained under virgin conditions. The decline is not abrupt. It is not necessarily a matter for great concern. It must be accepted as inevitably accompanying the use of the land.

There are indications that in the Northern States at least the establishment of a new equilibrium level may take 70 to 100 years; it is probably true, therefore, that much of our farm land is only now approaching stability in content of organic matter. East of the Alleghenies, where the soils have been longer cultivated, and in the South, where both temperature and humidity are such that the rate of microbial utilization of the organic matter is higher, it is likely that the new equilibrium has already been attained.

Information on the effects of cropping practices on the changing level of organic matter in the soil is slowly accumulating. In Missouri, for instance, Dr. Jenny found a reduction in organic matter and nitrogen content of about one-third in 60 years of cultivation. In Pennsylvania, J. W. White and others compared the organic matter in plots that had been in a 4-year rotation of corn, oats, wheat, and mixed hay for 72 years with the organic matter in adjacent plots that had been continuously in grass for 72 years. The whole area previously had been farmed for at least 30 years. The differential that developed in the 72 years was substantial. The unfertilized grassland was found to have a content of organic matter 61 percent above that of the unfertilized cropped plots. Applications of complete commercial fertilizer or manure and lime to the grass caused only a slightly higher equilibrium level to be reached. Similar treatments applied to the cropped plots, however, did reduce the differential to 41 and 23 percent, respectively. The carbon-nitrogen ratios of the cultivated plots and the grass plots were quite similar; where any difference occurred those of the cultivated plots were wider.

The cropping system affects not only the final equilibrium value but also the rate of decline to this value. Under conditions at Manhattan, Kans., a 16-year rotation (including alfalfa for 4 years), a 3-year rotation (corn, soybeans, wheat), and continuous wheat were accompanied by similar losses of nitrogen and carbon. The average annual losses of carbon from the soil under those rotations were respectively 0.59, 0.68, and 0.56 percent. Continuous alfalfa, on the other hand, increased the supply of soil nitrogen and organic matter at the rate of 0.71 and 0.43 percent per year, respectively. The depletion during the corn years in the rotations was at a rate two to three times as great as under continuous wheat. In a 30-year period the loss in organic matter on Webster and Clarion soils in Iowa was greater under continuous corn or a corn-oats rotation than in longer rotations. The decreases in organic matter and nitrogen where manure had been applied consistently were much less, even than where all crop residues were returned.

Under more arid conditions microbial activities may sometimes be impeded. Comparisons were made of the changes in organic matter within a 22-year period at several places in Kansas. The losses were relatively low (about 0.5 percent a year), under systems of continuous grain, or alternate grain and fallow, but were appreciably larger when row crops were grown, or row crops and fallow were alternated.

Again the experience was that manure offset in part the depletion of soil carbon and nitrogen. Twelve tons an acre every third year cut losses by 50 percent or more, without concurrently increasing crop yields.

Irrigation adds another factor, in that the moisture status of the soil is completely changed. This might be expected to speed up microbial processes. Studies in Utah over 20 years revealed great differences in the changes in organic matter in response to cropping systems. Where alfalfa or beets were grown continuously, the latter with a manure application equal to 30 tons an acre annually, organic matter increased about 0.7 ton an acre yearly. At the other extreme, under continuous fallow or continuous oats, the annual loss was 1.6–1.7 tons of organic matter, which was halved in an alternate oats-fallow system. Sugar beets without manure caused an annual loss of 0.5 ton, but the application of 10 tons of manure annually reduced the loss only to 0.2 ton a year.

The Chemistry of Soil Organic Matter

The progress made in the elucidation of the chemical nature of the organic matter of the soil is distressingly slow.

It is now generally accepted that the organic matter of the soil has its origin in the vegetation on the land. It consists only partly of residues of plant constituents that are less available or are modified by the soil microflora. A part originates in cell-substance synthesized by the micro-organisms, or residues therefrom. Indeed, this microbially derived fraction forms a substantial portion of the soil organic matter. Attempts have been made to distinguish between decomposing plant residues, the chemistry of which can easily be related to that of the parent plant material, and fully decomposed residues, or humus, the chemistry of which is obscure.

Studies of the changes undergone by plant materials in decomposition have indicated that lignin, a constituent of the mature cell walls of plants, is relatively resistant to attack, and tends to accumulate, although somewhat modified by loss of methoxyl groups. There is, therefore, a lignin-derived fraction of soil organic matter. Certain of the reactions of soil organic matter, such as its behavior with chlorine, are in accordance with this view.

The changes that the lignin undergoes in decomposition are such that some of the characteristic chemical reactions that normal lignin undergoes do not take place. S. Gottlieb and S. B. Hendricks at Beltsville have shown that these changes must be substantial. They subjected a muck soil and soil extracts that presumably contained a lignin-derived fraction to certain rather vigorous chemical treatments that when applied to native plant lignin gave easily recognizable products. It is a well-established procedure in organic chemistry to attempt to break up an unknown compound into smaller pieces that are simpler and can be identified. They did not obtain from the muck soil or the extracts the products that they expected to find had lignin been present, and they were forced to conclude therefore that "the material derived from plant lignin in the soil is drastically altered in the kind and position of the peripheral groupings on the aromatic rings."

There may be interactions between the inorganic and organic components of soil that result in modification of the properties of both. Various European and Russian soil scientists believe that extremely stable inorganic-organic complexes are formed, particularly in chernozem soils, and that it is combination with the inorganic colloid that confers on the organic fraction its peculiar stability. The extreme in this viewpoint is probably represented by F. Yu Gel'tser, who defines as humus only that fraction of the organic colloid that is capable of forming a stable complex with inorganic colloids. The stable organic-inorganic complexes are said to play an important role in determining soil structure. Furthermore, the organic fraction concerned is not believed to be of plant origin, but to be formed by and from the micro-organisms accomplishing decomposition of the plant residues.

German workers have attempted to distinguish both chemically and functionally between "nutrient humus" (Nährhumus) and "stable humus" (Dauerhumus). Although the former is held to be the substrate upon which the soil microflora develops, and from which some plant nutrients are freed, the latter is regarded as being agriculturally the most vital fraction of the soil organic matter because of its influence on the physiochemical properties of the soil. Paradoxically enough, accumulation of "stable humus" is held to occur primarily under conditions of high biological activity and in the presence of calcium and montmorillonitic clays. Chemically the distinction is based on resistance to treatment with acetyl bromide or a mixture of acetic anhydride, acetic acid, and sulphuric acid. These various theories indicate that there is much yet to be done to clarify the problems of the nature of soil organic matter. Their solution should permit the scientific management of soil organic matter to achieve the maintenance of fertility and conservation of soil.

Special Properties of Organic Residues

Perhaps because the nature of soil organic matter is incompletely understood, exaggerated claims are sometimes made of its role. The use of composts derived from plant materials, with or without the addition of special amendments, with properties that verge on the magical, has been strongly advocated as a means of restoring the depleted supplies of organic matter in the soil.

It has even been asserted that crops grown in soil in which composts have been incorporated are more nutritious and less susceptible to disease. Such advocacy is usually coupled with an attack on commercial fertilizers, which are said to have been responsible for soil depletion, erosion, deficiencies of minor elements or vitamins, and most other agricultural ills. No sound scientific evidence is marshalled in support of such claims. Largely they amount to a criticism of the practice of supplying a portion of the nutrient needs of the crop by application of mineral—that is, commercial—fertilizers that do not at the same time have a beneficial effect on the physical condition of the soil. It is reasonable to inquire, however, whether there is evidence of the presence in composts or decomposing plant materials of any substances that directly affect the growth of plants other than by meeting the nutrient needs or providing a beneficient physico-chemical environment.

Traces of auxins (substances that affect the rate of growth of some plant tissues) have been found in soil. These probably come from applications of barnyard manure, originating apparently in the urine. Thiamine also has been found in both manure and soil, but it has not been established whether it is present as free thiamine or is in the microbial soil population. Plant-growth regulating substances have been found in animal products such as dried blood, bonemeal, or meat. Some persons have strongly advocated that animal products or animal residues always be added to composts, but there is no good evidence that they have value beyond the nitrogen and other nutrients that they contain.

In any event growth substances of the class of the auxins or heteroauxins have not been shown to exert any over-all growth stimulation of plants or to increase their yield or fruitfulness. They may, however, stimulate root growth of cuttings.

It cannot yet be said, then, that there is good evidence that composts or decomposed residues are characteristically endowed with substances that cause exceptionally good crop growth or quality.

It has often been noted that the incorporation of crop residues into soil is accompanied by an improvement in soil structure and an increase in the number and size of the stable soil aggregates. The duration of such improvement may be quite limited. Sod crops appear to be especially valuable in causing the development of an improved physical condition. The grass-derived prairie and chernozem soils developed a notably granular structure that for a period remains stable under cultivation, but that deteriorates slowly in intertilled crops.

There are probably several reasons why clay particles may be caused to stick together to form small aggregates that exhibit some stability when wet or when in water, but it is now certain that directly or indirectly one form of aggregation results from the activities of the soil organisms. To obtain this effect it is necessary that decomposible material be added to the soil. Crop residues affect soil aggregation only as they are decomposed. Soluble energy sources, such as glucose or aqueous plant extracts, have no direct effect on aggregation, but when they decompose they cause as marked an improvement in soil structure as may follow the incorporation of whole plant materials.

The implication of this fact is that it is not any residual fraction of the plant material that is responsible for the effects observed. It is now presumed that the micro-organic cell substance itself or products derived therefrom are largely responsible. The presence of ramifying fungal threads may temporarily serve to bind particles together, but such a mechanical effect might be expected to be of relatively short duration. The rate of formation of stable aggregates has been shown to be highest during the period when microbial activity is greatest, shortly after incorporation of food material. The effect of the organisms is due to products formed by and from them. Many soil bacteria, and particularly some of the aerobic cellulose-decomposers, produce gummy substances, which, it is suggested, may have a cementing action. Such substances would not necessarily be unavailable to other organisms; hence their effect might also be of short duration. There is, of course, the possibility that such gummy products might form some complex with the inorganic colloid that would be more stable.

An alternative opinion is that the cementing substances are the breakdown products of bacteria that develop on and utilize the fungal mycelium that usually appears soon after plant residues are added to soil.

A grass sod has long been recognized as particularly effective in causing the formation of a granular soil structure. This is claimed to be due to the activity of bacteria in the rhizosphere (the zone immediately surrounding the roots and rootlets), utilizing root excretions or sloughed off cellular material. Species of *Pseudomonas* have been said to be particularly numerous, and products of break-down of certain of these species have been shown to exercise strong cementing action. The activity of rhizosphere bacteria on the fibrous ramifying root system of grasses is, accordingly, held to be responsible for the steady increase in soil aggregation that takes place when land is put in sod. Through the constant death and renewal of rootlets, such a crop also supplies energy material other than in the form of root excretions. Upon subsequent plowing there may be additional aggregation at the expense of the fungal tissues that then develop on the grass residues. The great difference between grass and other crops in extent of aggregation caused is, therefore, accounted for by the much denser and more extensive root system of the former and the fact that under sod excessively aerobic conditions do not prevail.

The Soil Population

Other studies have been made of the microbial population of the soil near the roots and the rhizosphere, with somewhat different objectives. The flora of the rhizosphere is much larger numerically, and more active physiologically, than that of the adjacent soil in the same horizon. The presence of the rhizosphere flora must surely affect the development of the plant; conversely, the nature of the plant influences the character of the microflora. Especially may this be true in the case of perennial plants. The incorporation of organic residues may produce substantial changes in the micropopulation of the general soil mass, but may have little effect on the microflora associated with crop roots.

Studies of the nutrient requirements of organisms isolated from the root region have shown that more types dependent on growth factors or amino-acid nitrogen are to be found therein than in soil away from roots. The view that microbial activity in the rhizosphere is maintained chiefly on sloughed off root cells is inadequate. Direct evidence has been obtained of the excretion from roots of soluble substances that are utilized in the rhizosphere and are responsible for the activity of the flora therein. This may be a mechanism that affects the attack on plants by root pathogens. Resistant and susceptible varieties of a crop may differ in the nature of the root excretions. M. I. Timonin in Canada has studied particularly wilt-susceptible and wilt-resistant varieties of flax in this connection, and has adduced evidence of the excretion of minute quantities of hydrocyanic acid by roots of the latter.

Virgin genetic soil types have characteristic and distinctive microbial populations that reflect the influence of the factors involved in their development. When these soils are brought under cultivation, modifications may be impressed upon the flora. The changes that result are sometimes great if the environment is much altered by the new land use, as, for example, when poorly drained peat soils are drained, or forest podzols cleared and plowed to a depth that mixes the shallow upper horizons. The responses that follow different management practices subsequently applied may be much smaller and more difficult to detect. As a measure of these, little reliance is placed upon bacterial and fungal counts because it is appreciated that only a small fraction of the population is represented on agar plates, and, moreover, that the slow-growing forms, which probably constitute the basal autochthonous (native) flora, will not be included.

However, quantitative procedures have been much improved by the studies of N. James and M. L. Sutherland, of Winnipeg, Manitoba, who have examined statistically the reproducibility of the results and have made recommendations for modifications that increase the accuracy of plate counts. In field studies in Manitoba they demonstrated an apparent relationship between numbers of bacteria and soil moisture content. Evidence pointing to a similar conclusion had previously been obtained in counts of organisms in grassland soil, and, inasmuch as the moisture films between soil particles are the actual loci of the active bacteria, it is not surprising that such a relationship should be found.

Each horizon in the soil profile develops a characteristic microflora. Organisms from one horizon introduced into another do not necessarily establish themselves in the new environment. Each population may be likened to a team of compatible organisms, the activities of which fit together so precisely that the available energy is utilized most efficiently. A certain measure of population stability comes from the presence of inhibitory or antibiotic substances produced by some of the established microbial inhabitants. Introduced organisms would be likely to maintain themselves only if they accomplish as well or better some step in the sequence of transformations by which energy material is utilized and are unaffected by any inhibitory substances that may be present. This has implications when serious erosion has occurred since the newly exposed surface soil does not have, and may not readily acquire, a micropopulation similar to that of the uneroded surface soil.

Nitrogen Transformations

The nitrogen cycle in soil, although well known in all its general aspects, still is incomplete in many details. It is predominantly, if not entirely, a biological cycle, but the populations or organisms responsible for the various steps differ greatly in degrees of specialization. The application of physiochemical methods to the study of the biochemistry of some of the chief transformations has been quite productive. The availability of the stable isotope of nitrogen, N^{15}, is now permitting a greater refinement of such studies. The latter has so far been applied mainly to questions relating to nitrogen fixation by *Rhizobium* (bacteria which cause nodules to form on the roots of legumes and which fix nitrogen only when inside the nodules) and *Azotobacter* (bacteria which are free living in the soil and independent of plants). The technique will be of equal usefulness in attacking problems relating to immobilization or release of nitrogen in decomposition. Absolute values can now be obtained for recovery of nitrogen by a crop from some previous crop residues incorporated in the soil.

Study of the behavior of a large number of plant residues in soil in Australia has led to the conclusion that it is highly improbable that any material with a total nitrogen content of less than 1.5 percent will give a positive return of nitrogen in one season, and that only when the nitrogen exceeds 2.5 percent is a large early release secured coincident with the demand of a crop planted shortly after incorporation. In terms of the carbon-nitrogen ratios, these limits may be expressed approximately as 27–1 and 16–1, respectively.

Nitrate is the form of nitrogen ordinarily used by plants. The decomposition processes in soil result in the liberation of nitrogen as ammonia, and therefore the final step of conversion of this ammonia to nitrate, which is known as nitrification, is an important process. This change has been little studied in the last decade except in India where a number of purely chemical reactions said to be able to bring this change about have been under investigation. The activity of microbial nitrifying systems has, however, not been disproved, and there is no good reason for abandoning the long-established theories about the part played by this group of bacteria in soil. It must be admitted that the conditions under which the appearance of nitrate in soils occurs cannot be entirely reconciled with those under which the classical nitrifying bacteria carry out the oxidation of ammonia in pure culture in the laboratory.

Nitrogen has recently been supplied to irrigated crops by dissolving ammonia gas in the irrigation water. The subsequent oxidation of the ammonia to nitrate has been found to proceed only to the nitrite stage in certain alkaline desert soils in Arizona. The ammonia in solution is not toxic to the bacteria that should complete the oxidation even at a concentration as high as 300 parts per million; but if the soil is more alkaline than pH-7.7 the nitrite is not transformed to nitrate, and the crop cannot benefit properly from this unusual nitrogen fertilization.

The subject of nitrogen fixation has continued to attract many investigations with diverse interests and objectives. Some of the most refined techniques that have been devised for studying the physiology of bacteria have been applied to this problem, which is a challenging one because nitrogen-fixing organisms can accomplish readily what the chemist can accomplish only under extremely high pressures and temperatures. It is easier to work with *Azotobacter* than with the rhizobia, which fix nitrogen only when this bacteria is in the nodules of a living leguminous plant. The first step in the process is believed to be the combining of nitrogen from the atmosphere with some component of an enzyme system, called the azotase system, in the organism. Very fundamental investigations on the characteristics of this system have resulted in a unification of the subject of nitrogen fixation that did not appear probable a few years ago. They make it highly likely that the biochemical mechanism of fixation is identical in *Azotobacter* and in nodulated legumes.

Attempts have also been made to find out the nature of the chemical steps involved in the fixation process and a plausible theory, partly supported by experimental evidence, has been proposed by A. I. Virtanen of Finland. He identified some organic compounds which under certain circumstances pass out or are excreted from the roots of leguminous plants into the soil or sand in which they are growing. As a result he suggested that hydroxylamine was first formed and that this then combined with oxalacetic acid produced by the plant. This next is converted to aspartic acid, an amino acid that could be used in protein building. Others have maintained that ammonia is a key intermediate. Experiments by P. W. Wilson and others at Madison, Wis., in which *Azotobacter* was grown in the presence of various nitrogen compounds in a nitrogen atmosphere enriched with the heavy isotope, N^{15}, showed that ammonia or compounds readily converted to ammonia are used by the bacteria to the exclusion of the nitrogen of the atmosphere.

Further studies of the distribution of species of *Azotobacter* in soils have indicated that this organism is found in all parts of the world but that its local distribution is erratic and limited primarily by the pH of the soil. *Azotobacter* rarely are found in soils, the pH of which is <6.0. The acid-tolerant species *A. indicum*, originally isolated from certain Indian soils, does not occur generally in acid soils. That an environment of pH 6.0 is apparently limiting in distribution is strong presumptive evidence for the view that *Azotobacter* in soil are dependent on the fixation process, because this same pH value has been proved to be the limit below which fixation does not occur. When supplied with combined nitrogen, these organisms can develop under considerably more acid conditions.

Excretion of nitrogenous compounds from the nodules of leguminous plants, if it is of general occurrence, would be important in farming practice. It has many times been demonstrated that nonlegumes growing together with legumes in such a manner that their root systems are intertwined seem to derive benefit from the association. The growth of the nonlegume is increased and sometimes also its protein content is higher, just as would be the case if additional nitrogen had been made available to it. This effect of associated growth may not be solely or even usually due to excretion of nitrogen from the nodules because the latter has not been proved to be a general occurrence. A. I. Virtanen in Finland, under the environmental conditions there, obtained evidence that led him to think the phenomenon a common one, but workers in places as diverse as Scotland, Australia, Washington, D. C., Wisconsin, and Kentucky have only in a few instances obtained any evidence of excretion. In these instances the amounts concerned have invariably been small, and the experiments have not been reproducible.

The explanation of the beneficial effects of associated growth on the nonlegume may lie instead in loss of nodules from the legume, a process that is apparently normal but which is accentuated by clipping the tops of the legume as would occur in grazing or mowing of pastures. Nodule tissue is exceptionally high in nitrogen (about 6–10 percent), and would decompose rapidly with the liberation of available inorganic nitrogen that might be used by the nonlegume.

Strains of the various species of *Rhizobium* that differ in effectiveness have long been recognized. Some are almost wholly ineffective in benefiting the host legume. One of the features of "ineffective" strains now established is that the nodules they produce are smaller and, therefore, contain less active bacterial tissue. Another is that they remain on the roots for a shorter period before deterioration and degeneration occur. They may be no less efficient in fixation per unit mass of nodular tissue, but the shorter size and shorter duration of attachment together account for the smaller contribution made to the nitrogen economy of the legume.

In choosing commercial cultures for inoculation of leguminous crops it is common practice now to select and mix several effective strains isolated from widely planted varieties of the crops in question. There is a tendency, however, to imply that effectiveness or ineffectiveness is wholly a property of the organism. In the efficient operation of the fixation process the plant has its part, and there is some evidence to indicate that ability to be nodulated and to participate in this unique relationship may also be a plant genetic character.

The concept of "cross inoculation" groups of plants that can be nodulated by one species of *Rhizobium* is not now interpreted as rigidly as at one time was the case. Many individual exceptions in which plants of one group have been nodulated by an organism isolated from a plant in another group have been observed at various times, but the practical convenience of the grouping in the preparation of cultures for use by farmers is not impaired. It may, however, be desirable to introduce additional requirements into the selection of strains of rhizobia for incorporation into commercial legume cultures if the newly recognized factor of competition between strains is to be taken into account. It has been shown that effectiveness in nitrogen fixation and dominance in competition between strains are independent. Where two strains are present together in the zone surrounding the root of the legume the strain having the higher initial growth rate may suppress the development of the weaker strain and, therefore, be responsible for almost all the nodules. The object, therefore, will be to select for commercial cultures strains that are effective in fixation in the desired varieties of the crop in question and that are also vigorous in competition with other strains capable of nodulating the same plant.

Commercial legume inoculants are now quite generally dependable. The most common form consists of a heavy suspension of organisms absorbed by peat, packaged in such a manner that moisture losses subsequently are minimized. There is a possibility, however, that lyophilized cultures (dried under vacuum at low temperature), that maintain viability for long periods and that would be less bulky, may be developed to the state of practicability. Some changes in procedure followed in seed inoculation may be desirable when seed disinfectants are used. Certain of these compounds are not compatible with rhizobia; others do not reduce nodulation if a heavier rate of inoculation is practiced and if the seed is planted shortly after treatment. An alternative which has been found effective when planting treated pea seed in Washington is to use bulk inoculant which is placed in the furrow through the fertilizer attachment of the grain drill.

Claims have been made at various times by Russian workers that very substantial yield increases in a variety of crops have followed inoculation of the soil with *Azotobacter* species, and such inoculants have apparently been prepared and used in a large scale. Trials of a similar character in this country in greenhouses and on small plots, where adequately replicated, have yielded predominantly negative results, although in one or two isolated cases significant and otherwise unaccountable yield increases have been obtained.

THE AUTHOR

A. G. Norman was professor of soils at the Iowa State College until the fall of 1946, when he began research work for the Chemical Corps of the Army. He has interested himself particularly in studies of the decomposition of plant materials, and the chemistry of soil organic matter. Before 1937 he was biochemist at the Rothamsted Experimental Station, England.

FOR FURTHER READING

McCalla, T. M.: *Influence of Micro-Organisms and Some Organic Substances on Soil Structure*, Soil Science, volume 59, pages 287–297, 1945.

Nicol, H., and Thornton, H. G.: *Competition Between Related Strains of Nodule Bacteria and Its Influence on Infection of the Host Legume*, Royal Society of London, Proceedings, Series B, volume 130, pages 32–59, 1941.

Soil Organisms and Disease

by SELMAN A. WAKSMAN

FEW OF THE bacteria and other micro-organisms that cause human and animal diseases survive long in the soil. Once introduced, they are inhibited or killed by antagonistic organisms, which produce active chemical substances known as antibiotics.

This purifying effect of the soil has been recognized since the early days of modern bacteriology, that is, since about the latter part of the nineteenth century. But because antibiotics vary greatly in chemical nature, selective antibacterial properties, toxicity to animals, and activity, it is only in recent years that a systematic attempt has been made to use them to control infections in man and animals. The most promising antibiotics now known are penicillin, tyrothricin, and streptomycin.

Only comparatively few groups of soil organisms have so far been examined for their antibacterial potentialities. Nothing is known yet of the ability of soil organisms to combat viruses and other infectious agents for which no adequate methods of control are now available. The field for further investigation is broad, therefore, and offers promise of potential practical developments.

Pasteur was the first to observe, in 1877, that the presence of certain "common bacteria" in the culture of an anthrax organism brought about considerable modification of the pathogenic properties of the latter. He suggested, therefore, the possibility of utilizing "common bacteria" for therapeutic purposes. When soon afterward, in 1881, the gelatin-plate method for counting and isolating bacteria was introduced by Koch, the attention of the medical bacteriologist was focused upon the soil as a habitat of disease-producing bacteria and as a possible source of infections and epidemics. The soil was analyzed for the total number of bacteria and for the presence of organisms capable of causing infections and epidemics.

511

The results obtained were, however, entirely negative; they did not justify the fear that human pathogens may multiply or even remain in a viable state for any length of time in the soil. On the contrary, it soon became established that the great majority of bacteria causing the common infections, such as diphtheria, anthrax, typhoid, cholera, dysentery, undulant fever, various staphylococci, and even the tuberculosis organism rapidly disappears from the soil.

More detailed and more recent investigations of the problems of soil pollution by intestinal infections revealed that the rate of destruction of typhoid, dysentery, and colon bacteria in the soil depends upon a number of factors. Chief among them are the moisture content of the soil and its reaction, and the nature and abundance of its microbiological population.

In most soils, a large proportion of such disease-producing bacteria was found to die out within 10 days. It was also found that various other pathogenic organisms that cause some of the most deadly human and animal scourges, namely, leprosy, pneumonia, bubonic plague, influenza, cattle mastitis, cattle abortion, and many human and animal virus infections, that constantly find their way into the soil in large numbers, also disappear there sooner or later.

As a result of these and numerous other studies, no one now ever raises the question concerning the role of the soil as a carrier of the great majority of disease-producing organisms or as the cause of severe or even of minor epidemics and infections. One must, of course, exclude from consideration certain spore-forming bacteria, responsible for such infections as tetanus, gas gangrene, and anthrax, or capable of producing toxic substances when they find their way into improperly sterilized foods, such as botulinus. These organisms are of only minor importance and are readily subject to control.

It was quite logical, therefore, that the question should have been raised as to what becomes of all the bacteria excreted by infected individuals. This was expressed by the writer and H. B. Woodruff in 1940 as follows: "If one considers the period for which animals and plants have existed on this planet and the great numbers of disease-producing microbes that must have thus gained entrance into the soil, one can only wonder that the soil harbors so few bacteria capable of causing infectious diseases in man and in animals. One hardly thinks of the soil as a source of epidemics."

Several theories have been proposed in order to explain the rapid disappearance from the soil of disease-producing bacteria and other micro-organisms. The theories can be grouped into six categories:

The soil offers an unfavorable environment for the growth of disease-producing micro-organisms.

The soil is lacking in a sufficient or in a proper food supply for the growth of such micro-organisms.

The disease-producing bacteria are destroyed in the soil by various predaceous agents, such as protozoa and other animals.

The bacteria are destroyed in the soil by specific bacteriophages.

The soil-inhabiting micro-organisms acting as antagonists are responsible for the destruction of the pathogenic bacteria and other organisms that find their way into the soil.

These antagonists form specific toxic or antibiotic substances which destroy the pathogenic bacteria, the viruses, and the other disease-producing agents.

It has gradually become recognized that the effectiveness of the soil as a purifier depends upon its nature, to a considerable extent. Actually, the soil exerts a double action upon the contaminating bacteria. In the first place, it removes them by physical adsorption. Heavy loams or clay soils, incidentally, are far more efficient in removing the bacteria from sewage or from contaminated soils than light, sandy, porous soils. Secondly, soil removes bacteria by biological destruction. Different soils show differences in abundance of antagonistic micro-organisms. As a result of early studies on the survival of the cholera organism, some soils are now recognized as "cholera-immune" or "cholera-destroying" soils.

The fate of some of the intestinal organisms, notably *Eberthella typhosa* and *Escherichia coli,* received special consideration. The typhoid bacillus was found to be able to survive only a short time in unsterilized soil, but much longer in sterile soil. Such bacteria are able to survive and even to multiply in sterile soil; however, when added to a well-moistened and cultivated soil they are rapidly destroyed. Similar results were obtained when typhoid bacteria were added to a culture of a soil organism in a nutrient medium. The logical conclusion was, therefore, reached that the typhoid bacillus is destroyed in the soil, and that the products of decomposition taking place there are largely responsible for this destruction. Such effects of soil-inhabiting micro-organisms upon disease-producing bacteria were believed to exist in some soils but not in others.

W. D. Frost made an exhaustive study of the destruction of the typhoid organism by antagonistic micro-organisms. He observed that when typhoid bacteria are added to the soil they are rapidly destroyed: 98 percent of the cells were killed in 6 days; in the course of a few more days all the cells tended to disappear entirely. When conditions were not very favorable to the development of the antagonistic organisms, the bacteria survived not only for many days, but even for months.

He visualized clearly the antagonistic effects of micro-organisms: "Bacteria in nature occur almost invariably in mixed cultures. Their association may be without effect on the various species, or it may effect them in various ways. They may offer mutual or one-sided aid, and thus live in a symbiotic relation. They may, on the other hand, offer mutual or one-sided injury, i. e., they may exert an antagonism on one another."

This antagonism results not only in the inhibition of growth of the pathogenic organisms, but in their actual destruction. The effect of the saprophytic micro-organisms—those that feed on decaying organic material—upon the pathogenic bacteria was found to be due not to the exhaustion of the food supply, to the action of proteolytic enzymes, or to a change in reaction, but to the production of specific agents, designated as "antagonistic substances" which are thermostable in nature.

Dr. Frost also suggested that there was no evidence that would lead one to believe that the antagonistic substances exist as such in the soil, but rather that the antagonistic organism produces substances which are responsible for the destruction of the pathogens. The rapidity of the death-rate of *E. typhosa* as the result of the presence in the soil of an antagonist was found to depend on the period of preliminary cultivation of the antagonist, which Frost designated as an "antibiont."

It thus became definitely established that the survival of *Eberthella typhosa* in manure and in soil depends upon the development of saprophytic micro-organisms; these produce specific substances that are antagonists to the pathogenic bacteria and bring about their rapid destruction.

Similar observations were made for the survival of *Escherichia coli.* This organism is rapidly crowded out by other microbes in manure piles; the addition of 9 million *Escherichia coli* and 13 million *Aerobacter aerogenes* cells to a soil resulted in reductions to 6,000 and 25,000 cells, respectively, in 106 days; in 248 days, both organisms had completely disappeared from the soil. Gradually evidence began to accumulate that tended to indicate that the occurrence of coliform bacteria in the soil depends entirely on the degree of pollution; soils relatively free from pollution contain none or only a small number of coliform bacteria.

The organism that causes malta fever, *Brucella melitensis,* is closely related to that responsible for brucellosis and contagious abortion in cattle. It survived in sterile tap water 42 days and in unsterile water only 7 days; it survived 69 days in dry sterile soil and only 20 days in unsterile manured soil. The cholera and diphtheria organisms, as well as other disease-producing bacteria, were found to disappear rapidly in the soil. The same was true of the bacillus causing tuberculosis.

The great importance of soil micro-organisms in the destruction of disease-producing bacteria has thus become definitely established. The nature of this process aroused considerable speculation. In the early days of microbiology, when the antagonistic relations of micro-organisms were first observed, the terms "antibiosis" and "struggle for existence" were used as virtual synonyms. Such interpretations would have been jusified when applied to micro-organisms only in those cases when one organism secretes enzymes that actually destroy the other organism. The production by one microbe of a substance that interferes with the life of another microbe, without necessarily benefiting its producer by such an effect, could hardly be thus interpreted.

The numerous interrelations among micro-organisms in natural environments include: (a) Favorable effects, which range from the consumption of oxygen by an aerobe, thereby making conditions favorable to an anaerobe, to the production by an organism of growth-promoting substances necessary for the growth of another; (b) strict symbiosis, which benefits both participants; (c) unfavorable effects, which include the undesirable effect of an acid produced by one organism upon the growth of another, specific nutrient competition, and the phenomenon of antagonism or antibiosis when one organism produces substances exerting an unfavorable effect upon the growth of another. The phenomena of metabiosis, or the living together of two organisms without any apparent effect of one upon the other, fall in a separate category.

G. Papacostas and J. Gaté suggested that the application of the Darwinian concept to the interactions among micro-organisms be completely abandoned. However, in an attempt to clarify or simplify inhibitive phenomena, they applied the term "antibiosis" to mixed cultures (in vitro) and "antagonism" to mixed infections (in vivo); such designations tended to suggest that the interactions among micro-organisms in the test tube are distinctly different from those in the animal body.

Recent evidence in the field of antibiotics does not bear out this distinction. In differentiating between these two terms, the suggestion that the term "antagonism" be applied to the complex unfavorable effects of one living system upon another, when the mechanism involved is not yet clearly understood; and that the term "antibiosis" be used to describe the phenomena of specific selective activities of chemical substances, or antibiotic agents, produced by one organism upon another, appears to have greater justification.

Gradually there evolved the concept of antibiotics, or those agents that are produced by micro-organisms and that have the capacity of inhibiting the growth and destroying bacteria and other micro-organisms. More important yet is the practical application of some of these antibiotics in the control of human and animal infections. The action of antibiotics against bacteria and other micro-organisms, as distinct from the common antiseptics and disinfectants, is selective in nature, that is, the antibiotics act upon some bacteria and not at all, or to only a limited extent, upon other bacteria. Some act readily upon fungi and others do not. Some are readily soluble in water and others are not. Antibiotics also vary greatly in their toxicity to animals. Because of these characteristics, certain antibiotics have remarkable chemotherapeutic properties and can be used for the control of various bacterial diseases in man and in animals.

The most important property of antibiotics is their selective action upon bacteria and other cells of lower and higher forms of life. Because of this, they may be active upon bacteria, without affecting the host cells. Although some 100 antibiotics have now been isolated, only 3 have so far found definite practical application. This small percentage of agents having chemotherapeutic potentialities is due to several factors: Some substances are too toxic to animal tissues; some leave undesirable after-effects in the animal body; some are inactivated by blood or tissue constituents of the body; some are not very active and are inferior to others that possess greater activity.

The organisms that produce the three important antibiotics, tyrothricin, penicillin, and streptomycin, represent typical soil forms, namely, *Bacillus brevis, Penicillium notatum-chrysogenum,* and *Streptomyces griseus,* respectively. Although these organisms may also be found in other substrates, the soil may be considered as their natural habitat.

Tyrothricin is produced by a group of aerobic spore-forming bacteria belonging to the *B. brevis* group. Although many other soil bacteria, notably strains of the spore formers *B. mycoides, B. subtilis* and *B. mesentericus,* as well as various non-spore-formers (*Pseudomonas aeruginosa*), are also capable of producing antibacterial substances, these differ greatly in their chemical composition, antibacterial action, and in vivo activity. A number of antibiotics have now been isolated from soil bacteria, in addition to tyrothricin. It is sufficient to mention subtilin, simplexin, bacillin, pyocyanase, and pyocyanin. Tyrothricin is the best known. It is a polypeptide, or rather a group of polypeptides, several of which have been crystallized, notably gramicidin, tyrocidine, and gramicidin S. Tyrothricin is not soluble in water, but is soluble in alcohol. It acts largely against gram-positive bacteria, but since it is hemolytic, it can be used only for topical and not for parenteral administration. It is utilized for the treatment of a variety of infections caused by gram-positive bacteria, such as various streptococci and staphylococci, that cause carbuncles and other skin eruptions, sinus infections, and cattle mastitis.

Penicillin is produced by a large number of fungi belonging to the genera *Aspergillus* and *Penicillium.* For manufacturing purposes, however, only certain strains of *P. notatum* and *P. chrysogenum* are used. The ability to form penicillin is characteristic of both of these species, although different strains vary greatly as regards the quantitative production and the chemical nature of the penicillin type. These fungi are widely distributed in the soil. In 1916, for example, strains of *P. notatum* and *P. chrysogenum* were isolated from a variety of soils collected from New Jersey, Louisiana, Colorado, North Dakota, and Puerto Rico. Penicillin is active only against certain bacteria. The soil contains many organisms capable of destroying penicillin, and it is produced on artificial media only under special conditions of culture. It is highly improbable therefore that penicillin is formed in a natural soil and, even if traces of it are produced, that it is of any significance in the survival of the fungi producing it.

The utilization of specific strains of fungi for the production of penicillin became the high mark of chemotherapy during the Second World War. Many infections caused by various gram-positive and certain gram-negative bacteria were brought under control. It is sufficient to mention the various staphylococcal and streptococcal diseases, the pneumococcal, meningococcal, gonococcal, and clostridial infections; as well as syphilis, anthrax, actinomycosis, and a variety of others. Penicillin is nontoxic and can be used liberally in the treatment of these and other infections.

Streptomycin is produced by certain strains of an organism known as *Streptomyces griseus,* belonging to the actinomycetes. As opposed to that of penicillin production, the property of forming streptomycin is characteristic not of the genus *Streptomyces,* nor of the species of *S. griseus,* but only of certain strains of this organism. Other species of the genus *Streptomyces* are also capable of producing antibiotics, but these are markedly different from streptomycin in their physical and chemical properties, antibacterial action, and in vivo activity. The closest antibiotic to streptomycin is streptothricin, produced by *S. lavendulae,* another soil species. This substance is much more toxic to animals than is streptomycin.

Streptomycin is active against a variety of gram-negative and gram-positive bacteria not affected by penicillin, including *Mycobacterium tuberculosis.* It is not very toxic to animals and can be administered parenterally for the treatment of a number of infections, including those of the urinary tract, tularemia, pertussis, typhoid, and tuberculosis. It can also be used orally for the elimination of certain bacteria in the digestive system. It is not active against viruses and fungi and has only a limited effect on anaerobic bacteria.

THE AUTHOR

Selman A. Waksman is a microbiologist at the New Jersey Agricultural Experiment Station, New Brunswick, N. J.

FOR FURTHER READING

Herrell, W. S.: *Penicillin and Other Antibiotic Agents,* W. B. Saunders, Philadelphia and London, 1945.

Hotchkiss, R. D.: *Gramicidin, Tyrocidine, and Tyrothricin,* Advances in Enzyomology, Interscience Publications, New York, volume 4, pages 153–199, 1944.

Waksman, S. A., and Schatz, A.: *Streptomycin, Origin, Nature, and Properties,* American Pharmaceutical Association, Journal, volume 34, pages 273–291, 1945.

Waksman, S. A., and Woodruff, H. B.: *The Occurrence of Bacteriostatic and Bactericidal Substances in the Soil,* Soil Science, volume 53, pages 233–239, 1942.

Waksman, S. A., and Woodruff, H. B.: *Survival of Bacteria Added to Soil and the Resultant Modification of Soil Population,* Soil Science, volume 50, pages 421–427, 1940.

Ways to Till the Soil

by F. L. DULEY and O. R. MATHEWS

FOR CENTURIES the plow has been the basic tool and symbol of farming. Men in all ages have worked hard to develop it and ways of using it to kill weeds and prepare the ground for planting. The ancients used a crooked stick and primitive peoples in some parts of the world still use a wooden implement, which does considerable breaking and loosening of the soil without burying deeply the organic material on the surface. In more recent times the modern steel moldboard plow has been evolved, and now there is a sharp questioning of the value of plowing too well—perhaps the ancients had a point, after all.

For centuries people have observed that clean-tilled land, free of vegetation, loses more soil by erosion than stubble land or land covered by growing vegetation. But the wisdom of using the moldboard plow and other implements that leave the land bare went almost unchallenged until the second decade of this century. Experiments at the Missouri Agricultural Experiment Station then showed that more runoff takes place and much greater erosion occurs on bare cultivated land than on land protected by a growing crop, particularly grass.

Various tillage methods have been used in an attempt to reduce water erosion on clean-tilled land by reducing runoff. Plowing, especially listing, and seeding on the contour, have been of some help. Constructing small dams in lister furrows by means of a damming attachment was tried as a means of holding more of the water on the land and avoiding the necessity for contour cultivation. The method has not been widely accepted because the dams may not hold unless the work is done on an approximate contour. If done on the contour it has little advantage over ordinary listing and is more expensive.

Another way to impound water on the soil is to use various types of

518

pitting implements that leave shallow holes or pockets on the surface; the pockets reduce runoff, but when they are filled with water or washed-in soil, their effectiveness is destroyed. The difficulty of obtaining weed control while maintaining pockets on the surface is another reason why the practice has not been more widely adopted.

Clean tillage is a major cause of wind erosion. This is especially so in the Great Plains, where the highest average wind velocities occur in the late winter and early spring when the soil is most likely to move. Tillage that brings clods to the surface or that roughens the surface can protect the soil for a temporary—but only a temporary—period. In dry-land areas soil must be cultivated when no crop is growing in order to destroy weeds and conserve moisture for the following crop.

Effect of Residue on Runoff and Erosion

.Research in Nebraska has shown that tilled land that has the dead residue from the previous crop remaining on the surface has a higher rate of infiltration and retains it longer than bare tilled soil or soil where the residue has been partly buried by disking or one-waying. When raindrops strike bare soil, the structure particles are broken and the surface is sealed over; this compact layer, often less than an eighth of an inch thick, may become slick on the surface. It then reduces the rate of infiltration and increases runoff. Residue over the surface prevents the raindrops from striking the bare soil and allows the water to trickle down gently through the mulch. The surface structure remains intact and a high rate of infiltration is maintained. The stability of the soil structure may affect the time during which water may seep down through it before the infiltration rate is greatly lowered. If the soil becomes fully saturated and has heavy layers in the subsoil, the rate of infiltration may be limited by soil conditions below the surface, and then the intake is not so greatly affected by surface residue.

Along with the reduction of runoff there is a consequent reduction of water erosion. In fact, a stubble mulch is relatively more effective in reducing erosion than in reducing runoff. A considerable quantity of water can run over a mulched surface without carrying much soil.

Leaving crop residue on the surface also has had a marked effect in reducing wind erosion. Undecayed straw or other residue that is well distributed over the surface will reduce the wind velocity at the surface, so that particles of soil are less likely to start to move. If they do start to move, the residue provides places where the particles may lodge. Moving particles may also strike residue material and have no abrasive effect.

The effect of crop residues on soil blowing has long been recognized. As early as 1915 the Department, in a bulletin discussing tillage in eastern Colorado, directed attention to the fact that a smooth, well-harrowed surface was subject to soil blowing and that stubble left on the field might help to catch snow and prevent the soil from blowing.

The adoption of fallowing as a farm practice in the Great Plains was greatly hampered by the wind-erosion hazard that it created. Efforts to control wind erosion by tillage that kept the surface in a cloddy or roughened condition were reasonably successful on some soils, but not on others. Plowless fallow experiments, where the land was cultivated with implements like the duckfoot or field cultivator that left much of the residue on the surface, were started in the early 1920's. They demonstrated that residues were valuable in preventing or reducing wind erosion, and that the expensive operation of plowing was not essential in fallowing operations. That plowing was not needed regularly in the production of small grains in that area had already been demonstrated. In the Columbia River Basin, where fallowing has been an established practice for many years, soil blowing on the lighter soils led to the adoption of such implements as the plow without a moldboard for controlling erosion. This implement stirs the ground deeply without completely turning it.

Tillage implements differ in the depth to which they stir the soil, their effectiveness in killing weeds, the position in which they leave the crop residue, and in their cost of operation. The advantage of one tillage method over another may not be so much the depth or extent to which it stirs the soil as the position in which it leaves the crop residue.

So far, four methods have been used in the disposition of crop residues: Removed from field or burned, completely turned under by plowing, partly buried by disking or some similar operation, and left entirely on the surface by some method of subsurface cultivation. The first three are well known to most farmers; the fourth is newer.

Stubble-Mulch Farming

The process of leaving the residue on the surface while the land is being farmed is generally called stubble-mulch farming, or stubble mulching. It involves tillage beneath the residues for soil pulverization and weed control, final preparation of a suitable seedbed without unduly destroying the residue, planting through the mulch, and performing subsequent tillage or cultivation under the mulch. It also involves the use of such crops in the rotation as to supply an adequate amount of residue to protect the land if properly used.

Equipment has been devised for running beneath the surface of the soil and tilling the land thoroughly without inverting the soil or burying the residue. This type of work is called subsurface tillage. Some types of implements performing this kind of tillage are called subsurface tillers, or the name may be shortened to subtiller.

Three main types of equipment have been used for subsurface tillage.

One of the first to be used was the V-shaped sweep. The duckfoot or field cultivator with shovels up to 14 inches in width has long been used in the Great Plains, but it is not satisfactory with heavy residues because of clogging and has not been called a subsurface tiller. Later developments have been along the line of wider sweeps with stronger shanks. The use of longer and fewer shanks results in less clogging in heavy stubble, and the wider sweeps cause less disturbance of the surface cover. These sweeps have differed greatly in width, varying from about 22 inches to as much as 7 feet. Most of those used so far have ranged from 22 to 31 inches, although wider sweeps are being used to some extent.

The sweeps are drawn beneath the surface of the soil at depths varying from 2 to 6 inches. As the blade moves forward, the soil over it is first crumpled and elevated, and then dropped as the blade passes. This rise and fall loosens and breaks up the soil thoroughly if it has the proper moisture content. A rolling coulter in front of the sweep cuts through the residue and prevents it from collecting on the shank. If the soil is too wet when subtilled, it tends to hang together rather than break up into small lumps. Cultivation of wet soil does not kill weeds so readily as when the soil is relatively dry. Of course, it is bad practice to plow land when it is too wet, but it seems that land can be plowed effectively with a somewhat higher moisture content than it can be subtilled, because, in plowing, weeds are turned completely under.

If land must be subsurface-tilled to check weed growth when it is too moist for effective work, it should be followed by some implement that further breaks up the soil.

Other types of equipment used for subsurface tillage include the straight-blade tiller and the modified rod weeder. The action on the soil of these implements is similar in principle to that of the V-sweep. The soil is broken as it is raised up onto the blade or rod and again as it falls off behind. The straight blade, when it has considerable rise on the forward side, lifts the soil higher than does the V-sweep and causes more crushing and breaking when the soil is lifted. The slightly greater fall gives more breaking to the rear of the blade. There is a tendency, when the soil is compact or weedy, for the soil to break off in long slabs at the back of a straight blade. Consequently, the tiller must be followed by some other implement to break up the soil further and kill weeds.

The rod weeder can be fitted with a subsurface attachment, which consists of a bar beneath the revolving rod. On this bar are mounted small points or shovels. These enable it to penetrate rather compact soil. The points on the attachment help break up the soil, and the revolving rod tends to keep the bar free of trash. The rod weeder is an efficient implement for killing weeds. When used without the attachment it is best adapted for use on land that has been cultivated previously with some blade or sweep implement or with a one-way. Besides killing weeds, it brings clods and partly buried residues to the surface. It is frequently used for the last cultural operation before seeding. When operated at a shallow depth, it has a packing effect on the soil below the rod and helps prepare a firm seedbed.

In some localities, farmers have modified the moldboard plow into an implement used for subsurface tillage. The moldboards are removed, and the shares are used without moldboards. Straps of steel about 3 inches wide and the full length of the shares may be bolted above them. These raise the soil more and make the implement more effective for killing weeds and volunteer grain. The modified moldboard plow is most often used for the first cultivation of stubble land. It breaks the soil into large clods and at the same time keeps most of the residue on the surface.

The one-way disk, while not a subsurface tillage implement, fits in with a system of subsurface tillage if used with discretion. It is most useful where the residue is very heavy or where there is volunteer grain to be killed. It can operate through heavy residue without clogging. It breaks down the stubble and cuts it up enough so that later use of other implements is made easier. If it is operated at the proper angle and speed, much of the residue is left on the surface. If later operations are performed with sweeps and rod weeders, enough surface residue for erosion control can be maintained from a normal combine stubble. In heavy stubble, more than one cultivation with a one-way may be desirable. The one-way is the most effective implement available for quickly and completely destroying a crop of weeds, and can be used on land too dry and hard for other implements to penetrate readily. However, it pulverizes the surface soil, and in the absence of crop residues its use may lead to serious wind erosion.

Among other tools that might be mentioned is one type of mulcher that rakes combine straw or other loose residue from the side of a strip of land that is being plowed, packed, and seeded in one operation, and spreads the straw behind the seeder. This new implement is being tried on certain soils in parts of the spring-grain area where seeding must be done at the earliest possible time. Under such conditions there is no opportunity to kill a crop of weeds in advance of seeding, and turning under the weed seed on the surface is desirable for weed control. The soils on which it is being tried are principally those that are likely to blow after spring plowing.

Another development, often confused with subsurface tillage and widely discussed in recent years, is keeping the soil organic matter in the surface layer by repeated cultivations with a disk. Disking, because it is a cheaper operation than plowing, was tried out under dry-land conditions many years ago but has lost favor. Where the period of land preparation before seeding is a long one, the disk has all the disadvantages, and not all the advantages, of a one-way. The soil where considerable organic matter is disked in is somewhat more resistant to water erosion than soil where residue is plowed under. Disking residue into the soil, however, does not control erosion so effectively as leaving it on the surface.

The final goal regarding the type of seedbed and the amount of residue desired at planting time must be kept in mind throughout the time of preparing the land. If the residue is so heavy that more than is wanted might remain on the surface at planting time, some of it should be disposed of. Usually that can be done by tillage well in advance of seeding that mixes some of the residue with the surface soil. Except during very dry periods, residues that are in contact with the soil or mixed into the surface decay more rapidly than those on the surface. In other cases it may be necessary to remove some residue from the field. If the residue is scanty, care should be taken to see that it is not unduly destroyed by the tillage operations, and thus expose the land to erosion.

When the soil under a residue mulch that has been pulverized with a subtiller is too loose and open for a good seedbed, supplementary working is necessary. The implements used for preparing a seedbed on plowed land are not satisfactory, as a disk may bury too much of the residue and a harrow may drag it into bunches that interfere with planting or with later cultivation. In the winter wheat area, a shallow rodweeding as the last tillage operation before seeding generally leaves a weed-free seedbed where the wheat may be planted in firm soil. The rod weeder does not destroy the surface cover. To prepare a satisfactory seedbed under a stubble mulch, another implement has been devised that packs and pulverizes the soil in a single operation. It is called a treader and has been used with considerable success. It consists of a certain type of rotary hoe on which the pronged wheels have been reversed. The reversed prongs have more packing and less cultivating effect than when run in the normal position.

The treader can be run over heavy residue without clogging, and it does not bury the residue. It breaks clods and increases the pulverization of the furrow slice. It also acts as a packer in that the prongs go down into the soil and fill open spaces and firm the soil. Some of the residue is pressed into the soil and anchored so that it cannot be blown away. The treader leaves the surface of subtilled soil in good condition for drilling.

Small grains and grasses or legumes require a firm seedbed, and the treader leaves the soil thoroughly tilled but firm. Where an especially firm seedbed is required, a second time over with the treader is helpful. The need for a second operation arises when stands of grasses or legumes like clover or alfalfa are being established on sloping land. For those crops it is important that the soil be very firm but protected by a residue cover while the crop is being started. The cover may prevent the formation of small rills or gullies while the crop plants are making enough growth to protect the soil. If such erosion gets a start in alfalfa fields, it is difficult to control. Residue on the surface at seeding time may be all that is needed to protect the soil through that critical period.

Row crops require less firmness in the seedbed than small grains or grasses, and use of the treader to pack the soil is not always needed. It is often used behind a subtiller, however, when the soil tends to break up cloddy or slabby, in order to kill weeds.

Planting and Cultivating on Stubble-Mulch Land

When small grain is being seeded on land with considerable residue cover, it is desirable that the drill make a clean furrow in which to plant the seed. When this is done, as with a hoe or disk drill, the residue is partly covered, but enough remains on the surface and mixed with the surface soil between the rows to protect the soil against blowing, increase the infiltration capacity, and reduce danger of water erosion.

Seeding alfalfa, clover, or grasses on stubble-mulch land does not require that all the mulch be pushed aside. The shallow seeding makes this impracticable. Drills should be operated so that they will barely cover the seed. It has also been found practical to seed those crops with a seeder attachment on the treader.

Planting row crops through a stubble-mulch requires that the seed be placed in a clean furrow to obtain a better stand and to make future weed control easier. The use of some form of furrow opener on the planter is the best means of doing this. Any germinating weeds and much of the weed seed, as well as the residues, are thrown out of the furrow and between the rows. A treader used ahead of or in tandem with the row-crop planter smooths the ground and facilitates later cultivation.

Much of the residue can be kept on the surface during the early growth of row crops if sweeps, rather than regular shovels, are used for cultivation. A residue cover that affords considerable protection can be maintained on row-crop land usually throughout the period of cultivation, but as the season passes decay renders it less effective. By this time, however, the crop will be large enough to give some protection to the soil.

Tillage that retains residues on the surface can be done at a cost comparable to most other methods of farming, and probably at a lower cost than a system that involves plowing. It usually takes a year or two to get a field into a good subsurface tillage system. After a field is subtilled a few times, it tends to become somewhat more uniform on the surface. Any depressions become filled and high spots are leveled. This makes it possible to subtill at more shallow and more uniform depths. It is thus easier to control weeds, since they are most easily killed if undercut at a very shallow depth. It is therefore important that subsurface tillage work be very carefully done. The method requires the right kind of equipment, in proper adjustment. It also requires timeliness of operation. Tillage under proper moisture content and dry weather conditions will be far more effective in eradicating weeds than if the work is done under wetter conditions.

There appears to be no one implement that is more satisfactory than others for subsurface tillage work under all conditions. Best results often require an interchange of implements. The logical tillage program is one that controls weeds and keeps the proper amount of residue on the surface to maintain the capacity of the soil to absorb water and to provide the erosion protection needed. These things can all be done while the soil is given proper tillage for good seedbed preparation.

Application of Results

The fact that stubble-mulching is mechanically feasible and is desirable for erosion control would appear to make it widely adapted. But like all other tillage practices it has limitations that tend to limit the area to which it can be applied. Among those that might be mentioned are greater difficulty under some conditions in weed control, greater incidence of certain insect pests, and reduced formation of nitrates. Under some conditions, however, subsurface tillage is being used as a means of control of certain insects.

The practice of stubble mulching has been given a wider trial and appears to be better adapted to the Great Plains and to the drier parts of the Columbia River Basin than to more humid sections. The factors that reduce yields operate less frequently in those areas, and the need for wind erosion protection is greater. Average yields of small grain resulting from its use are as high as from other methods of tillage. Corn production has not been so widely tested, but results to date indicate that yields tend to be lower under stubble-mulch tillage. Under practical operating conditions, the quantity of residue on the surface should be controlled and so adjusted as to achieve proper weed control and satisfactory operation of tillage and seeding implements.

The effect of stubble-mulch methods on yields of crops under all conditions has not yet been definitely determined. Many comparisons have been made; in some cases yields have been higher and in some lower than with conventional methods. There appears to be a rather definite tendency for stubble mulching to show to advantage under conditions of low rainfall or during dry years. When rainfall is higher or in more humid regions, subsurface tillage has usually given somewhat lower yields than plowing. Under such conditions, factors other than moisture may limit yields. The advantage of stubble mulching in saving water would therefore not be important under these wetter conditions. However, under these same wet conditions, the advantage of the mulch in reducing erosion on rolling land may be very evident, and this must be taken into account in the final evaluation of the method.

Much evidence is available to indicate that care needs to be exercised in conducting stubble-mulch farming properly. Slipshod methods will not suffice and the farmer who would be most successful with it must think much of the timeliness of tillage operations. If the work is properly done, there is undoubtedly a great area in this country where yields can be maintained and runoff and soil blowing more effectively controlled than where land is tilled by methods that leave the surface bare a considerable part of the time.

The value of surface residue for increasing intake of water and for erosion protection is generally recognized. Continued efforts should be made to improve field methods and the mechanical equipment needed to effect the degree of erosion control required. Efforts should also be made to increase the area to which stubble-mulch tillage may be adapted, in order to obtain its advantages in soil and moisture conservation over a wider territory.

THE AUTHORS

F. L. Duley, a soil conservationist in the Division of Research, Soil Conservation Service, is in charge of Soil Conservation Service research in Nebraska. In 1923, with M. F. Miller, he published one of the first reports on soil-erosion measurements. He was one of the first group of regional directors of Soil Conservation Service when it was started in 1933. He has published numerous bulletins and journal articles on soil conservation, soil fertility, and soil management. Dr. Duley holds degrees from the University of Missouri and the University of Wisconsin.

O. R. Mathews, an agronomist in the Division of Soils, Fertilizers, and Irrigation of the Bureau of Plant Industry, Soils, and Agricultural Engineering, has been engaged in experimental work in tillage and crop rotation in the Great Plains for more than 30 years. He is the author of many bulletins on crop production, livestock pasturing and feeding, and soil moisture accumulation and use under dry-land conditions. In 1936, with A. L. Hallsted, he published a report on the relation between the depth to which the soil was wet at seeding and yields of winter wheat. The findings reported have been widely used as a planting guide by individual farmers, and as a guide to recommendations by State and Federal agencies. Mr. Mathews holds two degrees from South Dakota State College.

ACKNOWLEDGMENT

In much of the work reported in this paper the senior author has had the collaboration of J. C. Russel, a soil conservationist in the Soil Conservation Service and professor of agronomy in the University of Nebraska. Professor Russel has contributed also to the preparation of this paper.

Rotations in Conservation

by R. E. UHLAND

GOOD CROP rotations provide for systematic cropping of land in a way that will maintain or improve soil fertility, yields, and the nutrient value of the crops. The type of rotation that should be used on any given piece of farm land depends on the characteristics of the land. If the land is very steep, only sod crops can protect it against serious erosion. If it is gently rolling, rotations that provide a sod cover 1 or 2 years out of every 3 to 5 will keep it from deteriorating. Some level lands can safely be tilled almost every year. Any cropping system, to be fully effective, should be supplemented with conservation practices such as contouring, terracing, application of needed plant foods, soil amendments, return of crop residues and manures, and strip cropping, according to the needs of the particular field or farm.

A glance back at some recent experiences will show the importance of rotations in our future farming.

Although our land has suffered a great deal because of erosion and deterioration, it still possesses enormous unexhausted soil productivity, as demonstrated by the 30-percent increase in wartime food production. That production was something to be proud of, but it involved a speed-up in exploitation of our soil resources, which was not counterbalanced by soil-conserving practices. Many farmers, in fact, dropped legumes from their rotations during the emergency, with the result that much soil organic matter and nitrogen were lost.

The tremendous part that unexploited soil productivity played in supplying food during the war years 1942 and 1943 is illustrated by the relative production during those years of the lands that were more recently brought into use for crop production. In those 2 years the North Central Crop Reporting Division, which includes Ohio, Indiana,

527

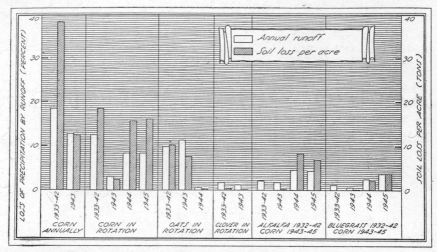

Here is shown the amount of runoff and soil loss from plots of 9-percent slope under various cropping systems on Marshall silt loam at Clarinda, Iowa, from 1933 to 1945. The average rainfall from 1932 to 1942 was 28.33 inches; 31.1 inches in 1943; 39.24 in 1944; and 34.78 in 1945. The corn plots were listed on the contour in 1943 and surface planted up and down the slope in the other years.

Illinois, Minnesota, Nebraska, Kansas, North Dakota, and South Dakota, produced these large percentages of the Nation's total of principal food and feed crops: Corn, 76.7; soybeans harvested for grain, 92.8; wheat, 59.5; oats, 82.3; tame hay, 49.9; alfalfa, 37.8; cattle and calves, 54.1; sheep and lambs, 35.9; and hogs, 74.7.

In 1935–39, intertilled crops were grown on 46 percent of all the land used for crops in the five Corn Belt States—Ohio, Indiana, Illinois, Iowa, and Missouri. In 1943–44, the corresponding percentage was 52.1. In Iowa, the percentages of all cropland on which intertilled crops were grown in the two periods were 45.7 and 52.5; in Illinois, they were 50 and 56.9; in Ohio, 38.2 and 45.5. With such proportions of all cropland under tillage in 1943–44, the best possible sequence of crops would not have prevented excessive exploitation of soil resources.

A productivity balance—that is, the net result of the processes contributing to soil productivity and those tending to exhaust it—has been computed for the soils of Ohio farm lands for each of the years from 1929 to 1945 according to a system devised at the Ohio Agricultural Experiment Station. The results indicate that deterioration of the soils slackened during the first decade of that period; the productivity balance changed from a 0.65-percent loss in 1929 to a 0.5-percent loss in 1939. Under the pressure of war, the trend was reversed; the loss increased from 0.61 percent in 1942 to 0.78 in 1945.

If the same system of measuring the soil-productivity balance were applied for all Iowa and Illinois, the calculated wartime losses would be greater than those for Ohio; in those States, much larger percentages of cropland were used to grow intertilled crops and the practice of growing such crops year after year on the same land was much more common. These figures point to an inescapable conclusion of the highest importance to every farmer and every other citizen: During the next few years agriculture in the Corn Belt and in the entire United States must be directed toward attaining a positive balance in soil productivity through appropriate crop rotations and supporting practices.

Crop Rotations Control Runoff and Erosion

Experiments conducted by a number of State agricultural experiment stations and the Soil Conservation Service have shown that type of crop and type of cultivation have a marked influence upon runoff and erosion. I give a few examples.

At Bethany, Mo., a Shelby loam area cropped annually to corn for 10 years lost 27.2 percent of the rainfall as runoff and, on an average, lost annually 50.9 tons of soil per acre, equivalent to more than one-third inch. Adjacent land that was cropped to a 3-year rotation of corn-wheat-hay lost only 16.5 percent of the rainfall as runoff and lost only 7.51 tons of soil per acre annually. Continuous covers of alfalfa and bluegrass permitted only 6.7 and 8.1 percent runoff, respectively, with only a trace (0.15 ton an acre) of soil loss.

At Temple, Tex., a plot of Houston clay soil with a 2-percent slope cropped annually to corn for 11 years lost 8.8 percent of the precipitation and 22.72 tons of soil an acre a year. Adjacent land in Bermuda grass lost only a trace of water and soil. When oats followed the corn, 13.4 percent of the precipitation ran off and annual soil loss per acre averaged 2.06 tons.

The runoff and erosion from a 7.7-percent slope of virgin Stephensonville fine sandy loam cropped to a rotation of cotton-wheat-sweetclover at Guthrie, Okla., were compared with those from adjacent plots where cotton was grown annually. The water losses were 9.29 percent and 11.35 percent, respectively. The annual soil losses from the land in cotton averaged 4.4 times as great as those from the land in rotation. Percentages of water lost from areas in cotton, wheat, and sweetclover averaged 10.07, 11.55, and 6.25; annual soil losses averaged 9.04, 1.69, and 0.52 tons an acre. Soil loss from cotton in rotation was only a little more than half that from annual cotton. Here again the results clearly show the value of wheat and legumes in a rotation in retarding loss of soil.

Near Zanesville, Ohio, in 1934–42, the runoff from land in a 4-year rotation was only half that from land cropped continuously to corn, and the soil loss was less than one-seventh as great.

Similar results were obtained on Marshall silt loam near Clarinda,

Iowa. In the 10 years 1933–42, land cropped annually to corn lost 2.3 times as much of the precipitation and 5.32 times as much soil as land in a 3-year rotation of corn-oats-clover. Low runoff and only a trace of soil loss were recorded for plots in alfalfa and bluegrass. A marked cumulative influence of these two crops in reducing erosion became evident when the land was plowed and planted to corn.

Investigations on many farms in different sections of the Corn Belt have yielded evidence as to how type of cropping and farm cultural practices affect depth of topsoil and, consequently, yield of corn. Loss of topsoil through erosion from fields under different cropping systems and from different locations within a field was clearly reflected in crop yields. Yields of corn in relation to depth of topsoil for 18 fields near Fowler, Ind., in 1940 were found to be:

Depth of topsoil (inches)	Corn yield per acre (bushels)	Depth of topsoil (inches)	Corn yield per acre (bushels)
0	19. 8	7–8	53. 1
1–2	30. 0	9–10	56. 8
3–4	39. 2	11–12	62. 4
5–6	47. 0	12+	69. 5

You will note that where practically all the topsoil was gone the yield of corn to the acre averaged much less than half of what it was where 7 to 8 inches of topsoil remained and less than a third of what it was where the topsoil was 11 to 12 inches deep. Similar results were obtained in other studies near Fowler, at Coshocton, Ohio, at Bethany, Mo., and at Shenandoah and Greenfield, Iowa.

Soil Aggregation Improved by Rotating Crops

Much of the benefit from growing sod crops is due to the influence they have upon aggregation, or the binding together, of soil particles. A high degree of aggregation permits rapid movement of water and air within the soil and consequently prevents excessive runoff.

Marshall silt loam plots on which alfalfa and bluegrass had been grown were found to have 50 and 58 percent greater soil aggregation, respectively, than plots on which corn had been grown annually. The improvement in aggregation on the plots formerly in alfalfa and bluegrass was still evident when these plots had been cropped to corn for 3 years. The losses of water and soil from the plots for the 3 years they were in corn, 1943–45, were markedly less than those from plots where a single crop of corn followed one of clover. In other words, land should be kept in a hay crop two or more years at a time in order to improve aggregation and stabilize the soil.

To find what effects different cropping systems had had on the stability of aggregates in soil at Bethany, Mo., we made counts of the drops of water, falling 30 centimeters, required to disperse an aggregate about the size of a BB shot and wash it through a 20-mesh screen. Tests were made on 180 aggregates taken from the surface inch of soil on each plot. Aggregates of soil on which corn had been grown and of soil that had lain fallow were collected in early spring when oats had been seeded and had grown to a height of about an inch. The results:

Cropping system	Average number of drops required to disperse aggregate	Cropping system	Average number of drops required to disperse aggregate
Corn annually	6.2	Alfalfa 13 years	40.2
First-year meadow	37.7	Bluegrass 13 years	31.2
Corn after meadow	10.1	Clean fallow 13 years	7.5
Second-year meadow	41.2		

All over the country one can observe the superior physical condition of soils under sods. Where sod has been turned under for corn, more rapid infiltration and less runoff and erosion occur. Also, microbial activity and aeration are greater than where corn has been grown annually.

Rotations Increase Soil Organic Matter and Yields

On nine experimental plots having an 8-percent slope at Bethany, the organic-matter content of the soil at plow depth (the top 7 inches) was 3.25 percent in 1930. For the next 13 years the plots were variously cropped or permitted to lie fallow, and plots 6 and 7 were treated with lime and phosphate. In 1943 a second test was made to determine soil organic-matter content. The result was:

Plot No.	Cropping system	Organic matter Percent
2	Corn annually	2.23
3	Rotation corn-wheat-clover	3.23
4	Rotation corn-wheat-clover	3.23
5	Rotation corn-wheat-clover	3.15
6	Rotation corn-wheat-clover	3.38
7	Alfalfa, continuous	3.93
8	Bluegrass, continuous	3.61
9	Topsoil, clean fallow	1.93
10	Subsoil, clean fallow	1.41

The depletion of nitrogen in soils that had been farmed poorly for 50 to 75 years was disclosed in tests by the Ohio Agricultural Experiment Station of seven such soils and comparable virgin soils of adjacent areas. The nitrogen content of the top 7 inches of these cropped Ohio soils had been reduced by from 17 to 48 percent.

After 60 years of cropping to corn and oats the soil organic matter at plow depth of a Shelby loam area in northern Harrison County, Mo., averaged 1.83 percent. On an adjacent area that had remained in grass during the period, the corresponding percentage was 5.91. Similar Harrison County land cropped to a good rotation for nearly 60 years still retained 4.11 percent organic matter in the plow depth. Land under

This table shows the average annual yields of individual crops and of digestible nutrients produced under different cropping systems in tests made on Wooster silt loam by the Ohio Agricultural Experiment Station in 1921–35. It also shows the nitrogen content of the cropped soil at the end of the test period.

Item	Corn annually	2-year rotation	3-year rotation	4-year rotation	5-year rotation
Corn.....................bushels..	27. 0	64. 0	77. 2	70. 6	82. 1
Oats........................do....					62. 9
Wheat......................do....		32. 4	38. 3	38. 4	
Alfalfa:					
First-year...............tons....			2. 74	3. 17	2. 63
Second-year..............do....				4. 10	3. 59
Third-year...............do....					3. 92
Total digestible proteins [1]...pounds..	108	237	382	520	533
Total digestible nutrients [1]....do....	1, 215	2, 250	2, 710	3, 092	3, 055
Total nitrogen..............do....	1, 425	2, 075	2, 263	2, 450	2, 487

[1] Calculated on the basis of harvested grain and hay.

rotation cropping during this 60-year period lost about 30 percent of its original supply of organic matter; without rotation, the loss averaged 69 percent, or 2.3 times as much.

Crop rotations with varying proportions of corn were tested on Wooster silt loam by the Ohio station in 1921–35. Rotations of 4 and 5 years with only one crop of corn each produced larger amounts of digestible proteins and digestible nutrients annually than shorter rotations or continual cropping to corn. They produced five times as great an amount of digestible protein and twice as great an amount of digestible nutrients as continuous cropping to corn. Where a 5-year rotation had been practiced, the nitrogen in the plow depth of soil was 2,487 pounds an acre, compared with 1,425 pounds where corn had been grown annually.

Corn yields on Marshall silt loam at Clarinda, Iowa, were found to be affected markedly by previous cropping. For the 3 years 1943–45, plots cropped to a 3-year rotation of corn-oats-meadow yielded, on an average, 88.6 bushels an acre, or 3.87 times as much as nearby plots that had been cropped to corn annually since 1932. The lower yield on the annual-corn plots was attributed to damage by the northern rootworm, nitrogen deficiency, and the poor physical condition of the soil. Great damage was done by the northern rootworm where two or more crops of corn were grown in succession. Such damage was rather common in southwestern Iowa.

Similar insect injury to crops is associated with continuous cropping in many sections. High yields of corn are common after crops like alfalfa and bluegrass, which have a fine network of roots that permeate the soil. Each year, many of the roots die and supply organic material to the soil. The action of roots in binding soil particles together, plus alternation of

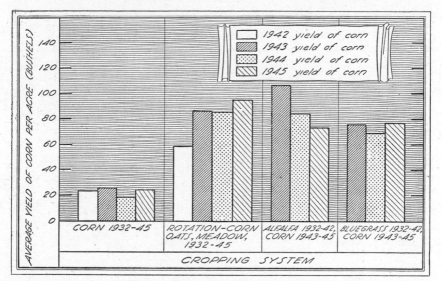

The average annual yields of corn on variously cropped plots of Marshall silt loam at Clarinda, Iowa, from 1942 to 1945.

wetting and drying and of freezing and thawing, brings about a granular condition characteristic of soil under sod. When land in grass or meadow is turned for corn, the rotting of the roots and stubble makes much plant food available for the corn.

On the Fry farm, near Wooster, Ohio, injury from drought to corn that was grown in a rotation was much less where corn occupied the land only a small part of the time than where two or more crops of corn were grown in sequence. Where a 5-year rotation included 3 years of alfalfa and 1 year each of corn and wheat, corn yielded 40 bushels an acre in the drought year 1944, in contrast with only 15 bushels where the rotation included 3 years of corn. Where the 5-year rotation was supported by applying manure or leaving crop residues, the yield in 1944 was 45 bushels an acre. The corn yield for the 3-year rotation of corn–wheat–sweetclover was markedly lower in both 1943 and 1944 than that for the longer rotations.

Rotations for Improving Eroded Land

Much of the cropland in different sections of the United States has lost a large part of its topsoil. The productive capacity of severely eroded lands can be increased, although it cannot be fully restored. The Ohio experiment station initiated a study in 1937 to determine the relative crop production of topsoil and subsoil. Measurements were made of yields of hay in 1940 and corn in 1941 on topsoil and subsoil under differ-

A crop rotation of corn-wheat-alfalfa-alfalfa, plus lime, fertilizer, and manure, resulted in best yields of hay and corn in tests begun at the Ohio experiment station in 1937. Yields from subsoil were less than those from topsoil.

Soil management system,[1] including rotation	Hay yield per acre, 1940		Corn yield per acre, 1941	
	Topsoil	Subsoil	Topsoil	Subsoil
	Tons	Tons	Bushels	Bushels
C–O–W–Rdcl	2.8	1.4	67	32
C–O–W–Rdcl, L	3.1	1.3	64	28
C–O–W–Rdcl, L+F	3.1	2.2	83	44
C–O–W–Rdcl, L+F+M	3.6	2.7	108	64
C–W–A–A, L+F	3.7	3.4	121	76
C–W–A–A, L+F+M	4.1	3.6	125	86

[1] C=corn, O=oats, W=wheat, Rdcl=red clover, L=lime, F=fertilizer, M=manure, A=alfalfa.

ent systems of cropping and management. Higher yields of hay and corn on both topsoil and subsoil were obtained through combined soil treatments. Yields on subsoil remained substantially lower than those on topsoil, a fact that emphasizes the desirability of initiating good rotations and whatever other conservation practices are needed before serious erosion or soil deterioration takes place.

In preliminary studies at McCredie, Mo., rotations including deep-rooting legumes proved effective in deepening the feeding zone for crops in Putnam silt loam. Placing lime and fertilizer deep in this soil facilitated deepening of the root zone. When lime and fertilizer had been placed at a depth of 9 to 18 inches in the shattered claypan soil, sweetclover roots penetrated to a depth of 20 inches, compared with 6 or 8 inches where only the topsoil was treated. Corn following sweetclover on this specially treated soil in 1945 yielded 6 to 9 bushels more to the acre than corn following sweetclover on adjacent plots where subsurface treatment had not been given.

The part played by crop rotations and soil management in rebuilding eroded soils is further illustrated by the results of an experiment carried out at Bethany, Mo., in 1932–42 to find how rapidly the organic-matter content of exposed subsoil of Shelby loam and crop yields from this soil might be increased. Seven plots were subjected to four cropping systems, with and without soil treatments. The topsoil of the experimental area had been eroded to about half its original depth. Except on plot 1, the remaining topsoil was removed artificially. Plots 3–7 were treated with lime and with superphosphate, which was applied on oats at the rate of 200 pounds per acre. Manure was applied on plot 6 before corn, at the rate of 8 tons per acre. Rainfall during the experimental period was scanty. In 1942 corn was grown on all the plots, to find how corn yields might be affected by past cropping and management. The cropping system and the 1942 corn yields were as follows:

Plot No.	Cropping system	Yield of corn per acre (bushels)
1	Corn-oats-red clover and timothy-timothy	43. 0
2	Corn-oats-red clover and timothy-timothy	20. 5
3	Corn-oats-red clover and timothy-timothy	34. 6
4	Corn-oats-red clover and timothy	32. 2
5	Corn-oats-sweetclover (sweetclover turned under)	44. 0
6	Corn-oats-sweetclover (sweetclover turned under)	64. 6
7	Grass-legume mixture, not harvested	44. 2

The 1942 corn yield of plot 2, untreated subsoil, was 48 percent of that of plot 1, untreated topsoil. Plot 3, exposed subsoil that was limed and fertilized, yielded 80 percent as much corn as the untreated topsoil. Plot 5, with a 3-year rotation including sweetclover which was turned under in the spring before corn was planted, yielded 102 percent as much corn as plot 1. (Fields with topsoil comparable to that of plot 1 that were treated with lime and superphosphate yielded about 80 bushels of corn an acre, or almost twice as much as plot 1.) Where manure was applied before sweetclover grown on exposed subsoil was turned under for corn, the corn yield was 150 percent of the yield from the comparable plot where manure was not applied. On plot 7, which was limed and fertilized and seeded to a grass-legume mixture that occupied the land for 10 years, the 1942 corn yield was 102 percent of the yield of untreated topsoil and 215 percent of that of untreated subsoil.

In this Missouri experiment runoff and soil loss averaged markedly lower for the higher-yielding subsoil plots. For example, for plot 2 the water loss was 1.63 times as great as for plot 3 and the soil loss was 2.3 times as great. These results emphasize the desirability of using needed soil amendments to rebuild eroded soils. The highest gains in soil organic matter were recorded for plot 6, on which sweetclover was turned under and manure was applied, and plot 7, where a good grass-legume cover was maintained for 10 years without being harvested.

On many eroded areas, crop rotations cannot satisfactorily be used until large quantities of lime have been applied, along with needed mineral fertilizers. Figures compiled in 1945 by C. E. Carter, of the Production and Marketing Administration, indicate that cropland in the United States needs 36,618,000 tons of limestone a year and pasture land needs 14,762,000 tons. In the North Central States alone, the limestone needed annually for cropland and pasture land together was estimated at more than 25 million tons.

A farmer who grows only a single crop, such as corn, cotton, or wheat, not only exposes his soil to serious erosion and robs it of its stored plant nutrients but fails to provide steady employment for himself and his help throughout the year. A good rotation usually provides for cash crops, feed crops, and pasture. For this reason and because it improves the quantity and quality of crop yields, a good rotation makes possible the fullest and best use, all year, not only of soil, livestock, and equipment but also of labor, one of the largest items of cost in producing crops. Well-planned crop rotations, supported by other soil conservation practices and supplemented by the growing of livestock of the types that will best utilize the feed crops, provide steady employment and insure a more dependable farm income.

THE AUTHOR

R. E. Uhland is research specialist in agronomy in the Soil Conservation Service. He was reared on a Missouri farm and educated at the University of Missouri, where he later carried on research for 7 years. For several years he was the superintendent of the soil-erosion experiment station at Bethany, Mo., and regional conservator in charge of Soil Conservation Service work in Missouri, Iowa, Illinois, Wisconsin, and Minnesota.

ACKNOWLEDGMENT

Acknowledgment is made of the cooperation of R. E. Yoder, chief, Department of Agronomy, Ohio Agricultural Experiment Station, in supplying statistics compiled by that station.

FOR FURTHER READING

Bartholomew, R. P., Carter, Deane G., Hulburt, W. C., and Kapp, L. C.: *Influence of Rainfall, Cropping, and Cultural Methods on Soil and Water Losses,* Arkansas Agricultural Experiment Station Bulletin 380, 1939.

Leighty, Clyde E.: *Crop Rotation,* U. S. D. A. Yearbook, pages 406–430, 1938.

Reports on 10-year studies in erosion control and reclamation of eroded land, published by the U. S. Department of Agriculture in cooperation with State experiment stations, include the following, prepared by the soil conservation stations named: (1) The Conservation Experiment Station, Bethany, Mo., Technical Bulletin 883, April 1945; (2) The Central Piedmont Conservation Experiment Station, Statesville, N. C., Technical Bulletin 873, August 1944; (3) The Northwest Appalachian Conservation Experiment Station, Zanesville, Ohio, Technical Bulletin 888, May 1945; (4) The Red Plains Conservation Experiment Station, Guthrie, Okla., Technical Bulletin 837, January 1943; (5) The Blackland Conservation Experiment Station, Temple, Tex., Technical Bulletin 859, January 1944; (6) The Palouse Conservation Experiment Station, Pullman, Wash., Technical Bulletin 860, April 1944.

Managing Surface Runoff

by D. B. KRIMGOLD

RAIN OR SNOW WATER that runs off the surface of farm land instead of sinking into the soil may serve a useful purpose if it is properly managed, but it may cause great damage if it is not controlled. Many farmers and ranchers in the United States have no springs, no wells, and no streams on their land, and must depend on impounded runoff water for livestock and other purposes at all times. On the other hand, water flowing over unprotected land loosens and carries away topsoil; further damage results when this soil is deposited in stream channels and reservoirs and on valley floors and when fertile bottom land is flooded.

Our studies have shown that more of the rainfall runs off where soils are tight, shallow, and wet, vegetation is poor and thin, and rainfall is heavy and intense; and that the larger the amount of runoff water and the faster it moves, the greater is its cutting power and the greater is the load of sediment and debris it can carry. The speed with which surface water runs off a small agricultural area depends on its amount, the slope along which it flows, whether its course is straight, the size and shape of the drainage area, the number of watercourses, and whether its path is obstructed.

We have learned to reduce the amount of surface runoff by rotating crops and protecting the soil with trees and grasses and with crop residues, and by practicing contour cultivation, strip cropping, terracing, pasture furrowing, and basin listing. To limit the speed of flow and protect the soil against erosion, we use drainage terraces, diversion ditches, spillways, gulley plugs, culverts, and channels lined with vegetation and with masonry. The size and cost of such structures, the space they require, and the extent to which they interfere with farming operations vary according to the quantities of water expected.

To control and make use of surface runoff from agricultural areas we must find out how much water flows off, in terms of gallons, acre-feet, or cubic feet, and how fast it flows, in terms of gallons per minute or cubic feet per second. A great part of this task has been to develop suitable instruments and procedures. Through laboratory experiments, weirs and flumes have now been developed with which we can accurately measure flows ranging from less than one-half gallon a minute to 800,000 gallons a minute. These devices can be used for measuring all flows except those carrying exceptionally heavy loads of debris.

Rates of runoff and total amount of water running off an area within a given time are calculated from the depth of water flowing over a weir or through a flume. Rate of surface runoff from a small area changes rapidly and irregularly. Therefore, to determine amounts of surface runoff from such an area we must have a record of the depth of flow for each 10-, 5-, 2-, or even 1-minute interval. A new type of water level recorder has been devised that gives a continuous record of the depth of flow to the nearest 0.01 foot for every minute. In this recorder a chart is mounted on a cylinder, which is rotated by a fast moving clockwork. A pen moved by a float rests on the chart with the result that a continuous record of depth of flow appears on the chart.

Since the development of adequate devices for measuring runoff from small areas, studies of runoff have been undertaken in some of the major agricultural areas of the United States, on small drainage basins of various sizes that are typical as to soils, vegetation, and other factors. Altogether, more than 100 experimental watersheds have been used.

The runoff from small areas is extremely variable. A question therefore arises as to what sorts of flow should be provided for in designing control structures. When we build terraces, diversion ditches, and other structures for control of runoff, should we make them large enough to carry the greatest flows expected at any time?—or should we make them only large enough to carry flows that, on an average, are expected once in 10, in 15, in 25, or in 50 years? On a small agricultural area, the farmer must ask himself which would in the long run be more economical—a smaller structure that might overtop or even fail at long intervals, or a larger one that might cost a good deal more, might occupy more land, and might interfere more with farming operations. Soil conservation structures on the farm are usually made large enough to carry flows expected once in 10 or 25 years. Occasionally, one is made large enough for the flow expected once in 50 years.

Early results of the runoff studies already mentioned showed that rainfall of a certain intensity on a certain area does not always result in the same rate of runoff; that, for instance, the most intense rainfall in 15 years on a certain area does not necessarily produce the heaviest runoff in 15 years from that area. Accordingly, in designing measures for control of runoff we use runoff records rather than rainfall records. Any reliable estimate as to how heavy a runoff should be expected from a certain area once in 10 or 25 years, for example, must be based on records of runoff over a long period. The longer the record, the more reliably can such things be estimated.

Where runoff water is used for livestock and other farm purposes, it is usually stored in ponds or reservoirs. We estimate that in 1943 there were more than a million farm and ranch ponds in the United States. A great deal of work should be done to improve those existing ponds, and many more are needed. Reports of the postwar planning boards of 12 States called for a total of more than 250,000 new ponds and reservoirs. The need for farm ponds and reservoirs is by no means limited to the arid and semiarid parts of the country; the postwar planning board of Georgia, for example, estimates that 34,000 are needed in that State.

In planning a farm pond, we need to assure ourselves that the water supply will be sufficient for the intended purpose after evaporation and seepage take their toll. We cannot do much to control evaporation, and very seldom can we entirely eliminate seepage. To estimate properly how much usable water we can expect to obtain from the pond, we must set up a sort of bookkeeping, based on records of past rainfall, runoff, and evaporation, and on characteristics of the proposed pond site. Our ledger must show, for any given period, how much water would flow into the proposed pond and how much rain and snow would fall on it, how much water would go over the spillway, how much would evaporate from the pond surface, and how much would be lost by seepage through the bottom and through the dam or dyke. If the balance is too small for the intended purpose, and we cannot make up the deficit by building a higher dam, we shall need to increase either the drainage area or the quantity of runoff. One way to increase the drainage area is to locate the pond farther downstream; another is to divert water from an adjoining drainage basin by means of terraces or ditches. The amount of runoff can sometimes be increased by putting a larger portion of the drainage area in cultivated crops. Care must be taken to protect the pond from silting. This is done by following conservation practices on the cultivated land within the drainage area and by providing a protective strip of grass around the pond.

The bookkeeping suggested cannot safely be done on the basis of average conditions. Rainfall, runoff, and evaporation at any place vary greatly from time to time; and when rainfall and runoff are least, evaporation and the quantity of water needed for farm purposes may be greatest. Obviously, the balance may be favorable in 1 year and unfavorable in another. How often the balance must meet farm needs if the pond is to be worth what it cost depends on how badly the water is needed, whether the pond will be the only source of water on the farm, the losses that would result from lack of water, and the cost of providing water from other sources. With these practical considerations in mind, the farmer can decide whether the proposed pond must provide this balance in 4 out of 5, 9 out of 10, 14 out of 15, or 24 out of 25 years.

Records of runoff and of evaporation are still meager and far too short. However, with the understanding of surface runoff and of related factors gained through research, these limited records are being put to good use.

Technical reports giving information needed in planning farm ponds in the claypan prairies of Missouri, Oklahoma, Iowa, Kansas, Illinois, and Indiana have been issued by the Soil Conservation Service in cooperation with State agricultural experiment stations.

Because the information we now have to guide us in controlling and utilizing runoff water is so limited, we have to play safe and use structures and practices that often turn out to be more expensive than necessary. However, if adequate records of surface runoff and information on evaporation and seepage are obtained, in all parts of the country, we can look forward to managing runoff better and more cheaply as time goes on.

THE AUTHOR

D. B. Krimgold, a soil conservationist, joined the Soil Conservation Service shortly after its establishment. He helped set up the Hydrologic Division and with C. E. Ramser wrote the working plan for the experimental watersheds. He directed the selection of the watersheds in Ohio, Texas, and Nebraska, and the technical phases of the runoff studies in some 22 States.

FOR FURTHER READING

Harrold, L. L., and Krimgold, D. B.: *Devices for Measuring Rates and Amounts of Runoff Employed in Soil Conservation Research,* Soil Conservation Service Technical Bulletin 51, 1944.

Krimgold, D. B.: *Runoff from Small Drainage Basins,* Agricultural Engineering, volume 19, pages 439–446, October 1938.

Krimgold, D. B.: *What is There to Know About Farm Ponds,* Agricultural Engineering, volume 26, pages 283–284, July 1945.

Krimgold, D. B., and Minshall, H. E.: *Hydrologic Design of Farm Ponds and Rates of Runoff for Design of Conservation Structures in the Claypan Prairies,* Soil Conservation Service Technical Bulletin 56, 1945.

Ramser, C. E.: *Runoff from Small Agricultural Areas,* Journal of Agricultural Research, volume 34, pages 797–823, September 1927.

Grass in Farm Waterways

by C. E. RAMSER

A DENSE cover of grass or other close-growing plants is nearly always the best and cheapest protection for farm waterways— the draws and other channels through which excess surface water flows off farm lands into streams. Unless these channels are well protected against erosion, the action of flowing water can turn them into gullies.

Any farmer who has vegetation-lined natural waterways on his land will find it profitable to maintain the vegetation within them and keep them from being damaged by farm implements, livestock, or rodents. Whenever necessary, the waterways should be fertilized and reseeded. It is much cheaper to improve and maintain natural waterways than to build and maintain artificial ones.

Artificial waterways should be established on farm land only where adequate natural waterways are not available. If a farmer lays out terraces that cannot drain into a natural waterway on his own land, he may be able to extend them to one on the land of a neighbor.

To be safe from erosion, a waterway must have vegetative or mechanical protection, or both. Also, it must be large enough not to be flooded by the greatest flow of water that usually comes off the land draining into it. The most commonly used mechanical device for protecting a waterway is the check dam—a small dam of concrete, stone, wood, or other material. A series of check dams in time transforms the slope of a waterway into a succession of steps with low risers and long, almost flat treads. At times of storm flow, water falls abruptly over each dam but flows much less rapidly than it would have if dams had not been used. Thus the danger of soil erosion is reduced.

Although for many years farm terraces have commonly drained into vegetation-lined natural waterways, until rather recently a farmer who established an artificial terrace outlet or other waterway usually depended on check dams alone to control erosion within it. Research in the use of vegetation for lining artificial waterways began with the establishment in 1929, at Guthrie, Okla., of the first of 10 soil-erosion experiment stations. In a terrace outlet with a 2½-percent slope, concrete check dams 6 inches high were used and Bermuda grass was planted. At the station at Bethany, Mo., an outlet with a 6-percent slope was protected by burying 2- by 12-inch planks on edge at vertical intervals of 2½ feet and sowing seed of lespedeza, White Dutch clover, Kentucky bluegrass, and redtop.

Both methods proved effective. Later results at Guthrie indicated that in the gently sloping outlet a good growth of Bermuda grass, once it had become established, would have controlled erosion satisfactorily even without the concrete check dams, which served mainly to prevent erosion during the period required for the establishment of an adequate growth of vegetation. Also, it has since been found generally possible on moderate slopes in most localities to dispense with plank checks such as were used in the waterway at Bethany. One way of doing this is to prepare the vegetation-lined outlet before constructing the terraces. Another is to divert the flow from the terrace outlet until vegetation has become well established.

When these waterways were built we did not know much about how fast water could flow through waterways lined with various kinds of vegetation without injuring the vegetation and scouring the soil. In 1935 the Soil Conservation Service established an outdoor hydraulic laboratory near Spartanburg, S. C., primarily for study of the flow of water in vegetation-lined channels. Such study was begun later at Mc-Credie, Mo. At each of these places, test channels were prepared and different plants common in the locality were grown in them and exposed to flows of different velocities. Thus we have found out a good deal about the rates of flow to which different kinds of vegetative channel linings can be exposed without damage. A farmer who is planning to establish a waterway can now learn from a Department technician what sort of vegetative lining he should use, and whether he should use check dams or other mechanical protection. The needs are determined by the slope and size of the waterway, the character of the soil, and other local conditions.

For vegetation-lined channels in which water flows only part of the time, permissible velocities of flow (that is, the highest rates of flow found to be safe) are greater than for those in which water flows constantly. Where flow is intermittent some scour can be permitted; usually any part of the surface that becomes slightly eroded heals over quickly or the damage can be repaired between rains. The velocities listed here as permissible, therefore, include some that may cause slight scour.

For waterways lined with most kinds of vegetation, higher velocities are permissible when the plants are green and uncut than when they are dormant or dead, or have been cut short. Dense, tall vegetation retards water flow, and thus reduces the capacity of the waterway.

At the Spartanburg laboratory, comprehensive waterway experiments were made on Cecil sandy clay loam with Bermuda grass, common lespedeza, sericea lespedeza, kudzu, and a mixture of redtop, orchard grass, common lespedeza, and Italian ryegrass. A few tests were run on centipede grass, Sudan grass, and a mixture of Dallis grass and crabgrass. Seeding of Dallis grass in one of the channels resulted in a poor stand, so that crabgrass came in thickly. The experiment was continued because the same thing is likely to occur in field practice.

Bermuda grass, an important pasture plant in the South, proved highly satisfactory as a lining for waterways, particularly because of its vigor and persistence. Velocities of flow that were found to be safe for channels lined with Bermuda grass in various conditions are:

Condition:	Land slope (percent)	Permissible velocity (feet per second)
Green long	Less than 10	8
Green long	10 to 20	7
Green short, kept cut	Less than 10	9
Green short, cut just before test	Less than 10	6½
Dormant long	Less than 10	8
Dormant long	10 to 20	6
Dormant short	Less than 10	6

Bermuda grass offers almost as much resistance to injury by flowing water when dormant as when green. Bermuda grass was injured less easily by the flowing water if it had been cut frequently during the season than if it had recently been cut for the first time.

Common lespedeza, an annual legume that is very widely useful for forage in the South and grows satisfactorily as far north as southern Pennsylvania, was tested in these four conditions: Uncut green vegetation, cut stubble, fall dead stubble, and spring dead stubble. The uncut green lining was found to protect a waterway fairly well, permitting a velocity of about 5½ feet a second. When the green vegetation had been cut, a flow of more than 7 feet a second caused very little damage. In the fall, the dead stubble endured a flow of about 4½ feet a second. By spring, however, the dead plants had rotted at the base and were very easily broken off by flowing water, so that any flow of more than about a foot a second caused damage. The low protective value of the dead stubble in the spring makes common lespedeza unsuitable to be used alone for lining waterways. When seeded together with grasses such as orchard grass, Italian ryegrass, and redtop, this plant does help protect waterways.

Sericea lespedeza, a perennial legume, has been used extensively as a lining for natural waterways in combination with mixed grasses. Sericea lespedeza exposed to flows of moderate velocity tends to permit considerable scour if it is green and woody and somewhat greater scour if it is dormant and uncut. Safe velocities of flow for channels lined with sericea lespedeza in various conditions, according to the results, are:

Condition:	Land slope (percent)	Permissible velocity (feet per second)
Dormant uncut_____	6	2½
Green uncut, woody_____	6	3
Green uncut, not woody_____	3	5½
Dormant long or short_____	3	3
Green short_____	3	3½

Mixed grasses are good for linings that are to be grazed, because they provide variety in the forage. The tests made with the mixture of redtop, orchard grass, common lespedeza, and Italian ryegrass showed that this mixture offers excellent protection. For channels lined with this mixture, the permissible velocity is believed to be about 6½ feet a second in the summer and after cutting in the fall, and 5 feet a second in early spring.

The plants in this mixture give better all-year protection because they have different periods of flush growth and dormancy. In early spring, when the redtop and orchard grass were dormant and the new lespedeza seedlings had not yet appeared, the Italian ryegrass was green and offered good protection.

Moreover, orchard grass and redtop grow in clumps. If either of these grasses were grown alone in a waterway, flows would tend to be rather irregular. The other plants, growing among the clumps, made the lining more uniform, with the result that it had a more satisfactory influence on flow. When flows are deep enough to submerge the plants entirely, the effect of any unevenness of the channel lining largely disappears.

It is believed that under northern conditions equally satisfactory protection would be given to waterways by the Cornell utility mixture, that is, timothy, redtop, Kentucky bluegrass, Canada bluegrass, Mammoth red clover, Alsike clover, and Ladino clover.

Kudzu, a prolific perennial vine that produces dense foliage, was found to have much less protective value than any other kind of vegetation tested. On a 3-percent slope, the permissible velocities for the various conditions tested were:

Condition:	Permissible velocity (feet per second)
Live, heavy growth:	
Uncut _____	4
Cut_____	3
Dormant, heavy growth, uncut_____	2½

The test channels were free from sharp changes in grade, alinement, and cross section, and had dense, uniform linings of kudzu. Under less favorable conditions, these velocities would be too high. When kudzu was dormant, the loose mulch of dead leaves, stems, and vines gave very little protection.

Kudzu is suitable for use in large natural waterways or gullies where reduction of cross section by its heavy growth is not objectionable.

Centipede grass, a heavy sod-forming grass adapted to the Southeast, competes successfully with other vegetation but can be killed easily by plowing. Therefore it offers promise as a channel lining to be used by farmers who object to the vigorous spreading characteristics of Bermuda grass. No tests were made on cut centipede grass, because this grass does not grow tall and is seldom cut. The permissible velocity of flow for channels lined with centipede grass and having slopes of less than 10 percent was 9 feet a second when the grass was green and 8 feet a second when it was dormant. Centipede grass cannot be grown successfully farther north than South Carolina.

Sudan grass, a fast-growing annual, was tested as a temporary cover for waterways from which flow cannot be diverted while perennial plants are becoming established. For a Sudan grass-lined waterway having a 3-percent slope the permissible velocity of flow is about 4 feet a second when the grass is full grown and green and about 3 feet a second when the grass is dead.

An objection to using Sudan grass as a channel lining is that during dry years it crowds out any permanent vegetation seeded with it, so that the channel has very little protection after the grass dries or is harvested, and it is difficult to establish permanent vegetation before the following spring.

Sudan grass is grown successfully as far north as the northern boundary of South Dakota.

Dallis grass and crabgrass offered rather poor protection in comparison with other grass mixtures. For a channel lined with these grasses and having a 6-percent slope, permissible velocity of flow is about 3½ feet a second. Dallis grass is adapted to southern conditions only.

At McCredie, Mo., tests have been made on two kinds of channel lining, Kentucky bluegrass and a mixture of timothy and redtop, in channels in Putnam silt loam.

Kentucky bluegrass occurs throughout the northern half of the United States, except where the climate is too dry. The results of the tests showed that the permissible velocity of flow for a channel of 4-percent slope lined with a poor 1-year-old stand of Kentucky bluegrass was only 3 feet a second. After another year, however, permissible velocity for this channel had increased to 7 feet a second. In any locality, the permissible velocity for a channel lined with Kentucky bluegrass is governed by the density of the stand of grass that the soil can produce and maintain. It may be as low as 1 foot a second or as high as 8 feet a second. Kentucky bluegrass that is thick and long enough to shingle the channel surface completely can withstand velocities much higher than 8 feet a second, but the possibility that such a stand will deteriorate makes it unjustifiable to use this grass where velocity will be high.

Timothy and redtop make a good grass mixture for our purpose in northern climates. A channel lining of timothy and redtop withstood a velocity of 7 feet a second at the end of a year and about the same velocity after 2 and 3 years. Only moderate scour resulted when this lining was exposed to a flow of 8 feet a second.

For waterways on soils that are sandier and more easily erodible than the Cecil sandy clay loam at Spartanburg or the Putnam silt loam at McCredie, permissible velocities of flow are lower, of course. Channel vegetation must be carefully maintained if it is to be dense, uniform, and free from weeds. Any damage such as may be caused by rodents, livestock, or farm implements should be repaired immediately. Long-continued heat or drought often reduces the density of vegetation in waterways, with the result that parts of the soil surface are left thinly covered or entirely bare, and thus are likely to be eroded even when velocities of flow are less than those classed here as permissible.

In considering the recommendations I have made, the farmer should bear in mind that the test channels were carefully constructed and were free from irregularities and that nearly all the linings were in uniformly good condition. For waterways of irregular cross section or waterways in which the vegetative lining is expected to become less dense as it grows older, the permissible velocities are lower.

THE AUTHOR

C. E. Ramser, research specialist in hydrology of the Soil Conservation Service, grew up on an Illinois farm, was graduated from the University of Illinois, and has devoted the past 33 years to engineering research in the Department of Agriculture. His contributions to agriculture won him the 1944 award of the John Deere medal of the American Society of Agricultural Engineers.

FOR FURTHER READING

Cox, Maurice B.: *Tests on Vegetated Waterways,* Oklahoma Agricultural Experiment Station Technical Bulletin T–15, 1942.

Palmer, Vernon J.: *A Method for Designing Vegetated Waterways,* Agricultural Engineering, volume 26, pages 516–520, 1945.

Smith, Dwight D.: *Bluegrass Terrace Outlet Channels,* Agricultural Engineering, volume 24, pages 333–336, 1943.

Smith, Dwight D.: *Bluegrass Terrace Outlet Channel Design,* Agricultural Engineering, volume 27, pages 125–130, 1946.

The Control of Salinity

by H. E. HAYWARD

IN REGIONS where rainfall is sufficient for agriculture, an excess of soluble salts does not ordinarily accumulate in the soil. Rain water is essentially free from salts, and soluble material is leached from the root zone and is carried away in the drainage water. But where there is too little rain for successful farming and land must be irrigated, special care must be taken, or salinity may spoil the productivity of the land, because all irrigation water contains soluble salts.

Of approximately 30 million acres of irrigable land in the 17 Western States, more than two-thirds is under irrigation. Reclamation projects will materially increase the acreage: The Columbia Basin Reclamation Project alone will add an estimated million acres more to the present irrigated total. On much of the area now irrigated in the West, crop yields are reduced by salinity, and economic losses consequently are serious. If irrigation agriculture should fail, dry farming, stock raising, forestry, mining, and manufacturing also would suffer, and the economic stability of the West would be jeopardized.

All soils contain some salt, although the amount present in agricultural soils of the East is low. The successful growing of crops depends upon the availability of the essential nutrients in the soil or soil solution, but plant growth is retarded when salts accumulate in large amounts. If the concentration of salt is too high, seed germination is reduced and the seedling plants may die. In severe cases of salinity, symptoms of injury may be evident, such as burning of leaves and dieback of branches. Under less severe conditions no specific symptoms are detectable, but the plants may be stunted and produce low yields.

Basically, the two major phases of the salt problem are too much total salt in the soil and soil solution, and the presence of too much sodium.

547

Although no absolute rating of water quality is possible, the standards given here, which are approximate upper and lower limits, can be used as a general guide

| Water-class | Conductivity (k×10⁵ at 25° C.) | Salt content | | Sodium | Boron |
		Total	Per acre-foot		
		Parts per million	*Tons*	*Percent*	*Parts per million*
Class 1 [1]...........	0–100	0–700	1	60	0. 0–0. 5
Class 2 [2]...........	100–300	700–2, 000	1–3	60–75	. 5–2. 0
Class 3 [3]...........	over 300	over 2, 000	3	75	over 2. 0

[1] Excellent to good, suitable for most plants under most conditions.
[2] Good to injurious, probably harmful to the more sensitive crops.
[3] Injurious to unsatisfactory, probably harmful to most crops and unsatisfactory for all but the most tolerant. Any class 3 water should be considered unsuitable under most conditions. Should the salts present be largely sulfates, the values for salt content in each class can be raised 50 percent. Because soil, crop, climate, drainage, and soil management all influence the suitability of water for irrigation, no simple classification scheme will hold for all cases.

The soil may be saline because of its origin and formation, or soils that are slightly salty may become highly saline because the input of salt exceeds the output. An unfavorable salt balance can result from the use of irrigation water with high salt content, inadequate irrigation, or poor drainage.

To study the problems of salinity in irrigation farming over a wide area, the Regional Salinity Laboratory was established in Riverside, Calif., in 1937. Its work is done in close cooperation with the agricultural experiment stations of 11 Western States and Hawaii and with other agencies of the Government. Its chief functions are to study the relationships of the salinity of irrigation waters and soils to plant growth, investigate the factors that relate to a permanently successful irrigated agriculture, and develop practical applications of the laboratory findings so that field conditions are known and can be controlled. The program involves research in irrigation, drainage, soil chemistry, soil physics, and plant physiology.

The control of salinity requires accurate information on the degree and type of salinity in an area. If reclamation projects are initiated without prior knowledge of saline conditions, serious economic losses may result. To help eliminate this possibility, field methods and procedures are being developed to survey such areas. These include methods for estimating total salts present, the amount and degree of saturation of sodium on the exchange complex, permeability, and other soil-water relationships. The object of a salinity survey is to get an evaluation of the over-all conditions within a given area, including a salinity map, so that recommendations can be made for the improvement or control of saline and alkali soil conditions. Important in a survey are field observations, including the character of the native vegetation, topography and characteristics of the soil profile, drainage conditions, and sources of salinity; soil and water analyses, and soil permeability and the effect on permeability of the quality of the irrigation water that is to be used.

The reclamation of an area that is high in soluble salts and the maintenance of the productivity of potentially saline areas involve the same basic principle. The removal of salts from the root zone of the soil must exceed the quantity of salts deposited by the irrigation water. That can be accomplished by good drainage and proper control of irrigation unless the amount of sodium in the soil or the irrigation water is high.

Good drainage is essential. That means that the water table should be at least 5 to 6 feet below the surface. In order to observe variations in the water table throughout the year, an efficient observation well was developed that consists of lengths of ⅜-inch pipe terminating at different depths in the soil and a device for measuring the distance to water. With it, the pressure and direction of movement of ground water and information regarding soil permeability can be determined. The drainage engineer can use the information in selecting the most practical methods of drainage, improving drainage design, and evaluating the effectiveness of drainage systems already in operation.

Where artificial drainage is necessary, three methods are used—tile systems, open drains, and pumped wells.

In many irrigation projects, deep open drains are installed and tile drains are frequently used as an adjunct to them. If the surface soil is permeable and is underlain with gravel deposits, wells of satisfactory capacity can be developed, and pumping from them may be the most feasible and cheapest method of controlling the water table. The water collected by these methods is usually removed by large outlet drains, which discharge into the river system. In many places drainage water pumped from wells is mixed with irrigation water and used over. Proper management of irrigation water is as important as good drainage.

Assuming that water of satisfactory quality is available, the amount of water applied in irrigation is a primary consideration in saline or potentially saline areas. The total amount of water required under non-saline conditions is the quantity of water, expressed in acre-feet per cropped acre per year, used by the crop in the formation of plant tissue or transpired through the leaves, plus the water that evaporates from the soil surface. To this requirement, sometimes called consumptive use, must be added irrigation losses during water conveyance (seepage, leakage, wasteways, and evaporation) and losses during application (surface runoff and deep percolation).

In saline areas, besides the requirements just noted, sufficient water must be supplied to leach the soil and carry excess salts down below the root zone. Both underirrigation and overirrigation must be avoided. Salts will accumulate if a salty soil is underirrigated, and all the water applied is used by the plant or evaporated. For example, Colorado River water (a class 2 water) contains 1.1 tons of salt per acre-foot. Continued use of water of that degree of salinity in amounts insufficient to cause leaching and drainage will eventually make the soil too saline for use. Overirrigation is also dangerous, especially where drainage is poor, since the excess water passing into the subsoil may cause a rise in the water table and bring about an increased accumulation of salts in the root zone.

Alkali Soil

The soil may be only moderately salty but may be high in sodium. A saline soil with that characteristic is commonly known as black alkali. The particles of clay and organic matter in soils have the property of adsorbing upon their surfaces salt constituents (cations) such as sodium, calcium, and magnesium. In nonsaline soils, the surfaces of the soil particles are largely saturated with calcium and magnesium, the calcium usually predominating. If a nonsaline soil comes in contact with saline irrigation or drainage water that contains a high proportion of sodium salts, an exchange reaction occurs between the sodium in the water and the calcium held by the soil particles. Some of the sodium is adsorbed and an equivalent amount of calcium is released to the solution. Conversely, adsorbed sodium in soils can be replaced by the addition of a calcium or magnesium salt solution. Such a reaction involving the exchange of cations (sodium, calcium, or magnesium) is termed cation exchange. It is described here because of its importance in the reclamation of alkali soils.

The physical properties of soils are greatly influenced by the degree to which the clay and organic matter are saturated with sodium. Soils saturated with calcium and magnesium are usually flocculated and have a good granular structure. Soils containing appreciable amounts of adsorbed or exchangeable sodium ordinarily have poor structure. Studies of saline soils have shown that when sodium makes up 10 percent or more of the total exchangeable cations (calcium, magnesium, potassium, and sodium) the soil tends to become dispersed. The aggregates of the resulting alkali soil are relatively less stable, and there usually is a change from the granular condition in which the particles are aggregated to a dispersed phase. The soil structure deteriorates, the soil becomes tight or impermeable to water and air, infiltration of irrigation water is retarded, and drainage is difficult. If the irrigation water that is applied to the soil is high in sodium, these unfavorable changes in the physical condition of the soil may take place. No absolute value can be given for the percentage of sodium in irrigation water that will be injurious, but 60 to 75 percent is an approximate value. Other factors that determine the severity of the condition are the texture of the soil, its salt status and content of organic matter, the mineralogical composition of the clay, drainage, and the way soil is managed and cropped.

Use of Soil Amendments

When high-sodium conditions exist, the essential consideration is to remove the excess sodium. Leaching alone may not do this; it may even aggravate the soil condition. The application of soil amendments to replace the sodium with calcium is a generally recognized practice to improve impermeable alkali soils. The basic principles involved have been worked out by W. P. Kelley, W. T. McGeorge, and others, but more study is needed to determine the most economical methods and means of reclamation.

Gypsum, sulfur, lime, or calcium chloride may be used to supply a source of soluble calcium or to make more soluble the calcium already present in the soil in the form of lime. For example, sulfur is oxidized in the soil to sulfuric acid, which reacts with calcium carbonate to form the more soluble gypsum, a calcium compound. The process requires time, and the sulfur should be worked into the soil and permitted to oxidize for several months before leaching. The selection of a soil amendment may be determined by its availability from local sources and the expense involved.

The use of manure may be effective in improving soil aggregation and permeability. It is thought that the decomposition of the added organic matter liberates carbonic acid, which in turn increases the solubility of the calcium carbonate in the soil. Green-manure crops accomplish the same purpose; in addition, the action of the roots of growing crops improves the soil structure. If the soil has become dispersed or puddled in the process of reclamation, drying is beneficial.

In areas where it is uneconomic to attempt complete reclamation by the application of soil amendments, it is sometimes possible to effect partial reclamation to an extent sufficient to permit the establishment of some vegetative cover. If given time, a good stand of native vegetation or even weeds will bring about a gradual improvement of soil structure and permeability. With careful management and a program of limited application of amendments, such an area may be reclaimed to a point where it is suitable for agricultural use. Thus, successful reclamation may involve a combination of leaching, soil amendments, and good soil and crop management.

Seed germination is often reduced in saline soils, and plants are more sensitive to salt in the seedling stage than when they are more mature.

Seedlings of relatively salt-tolerant plants, like alfalfa, sugar beets, and cotton, may be retarded in growth or die if the soil is moderately saline. It is important that the seedbed be carefully prepared and the soil leached before seeding. Where a raised-bed method and furrow irrigation are used, as with lettuce and some other truck crops, soluble salts tend to accumulate toward the peak of the convex beds. If the seed is planted on the shoulders of the bed the danger of salt injury is lessened. The soil should be sufficiently moist to germinate the seed; it should not be allowed to become dry during the seedling stage because salts may accumulate in the row. The use of small furrows along the seed row to keep the soil leached and moist during the early stages of growth has been practiced with some success.

Plant-Water Relations in Saline Soils

Recent research has clarified considerably the problem of availability of water to plants in saline soil. In nonsaline soil, plants stop growing when the supply of available water is exhausted, that is, when the soil moisture approaches the wilting point.

The condition of the soil moisture or the tenacity with which soil holds moisture can be expressed in terms of the moisture stress, or soil-moisture tension. That property of the soil water can now be measured over the whole range of soil moisture that will permit the growth of plants, and progress has been made in relating the growth of plants to it. In saline soils, an additional stress is set up at the plant roots because of the osmotic effect of salts in the soil solution. Preliminary results of the research indicate that, when expressed in atmospheres, the effects of soil-moisture tension and osmotic pressure are additive in inhibiting the growth of plants.

If further work substantiates this principle, it will represent an important step in understanding and overcoming problems of salinity. It will establish a quantitative basis for expressing salt tolerance and will help in selecting methods and measurements for surveying unreclaimed saline areas and in appraising damage due to salinity. The studies already made indicate that for good plant growth the soil must be kept wetter when salts are present.

If soil salinity can be reduced to moderate levels, the land can be farmed successfully under proper management. It is important to select crops that are well suited to the prevailing climatic conditions and that are sufficiently salt-tolerant. Crops do not behave alike in their response to the combined effect of climate and salt. In general, a species of plant will tolerate more salt when grown under the climatic conditions best suited to it than when it is poorly adapted to its environment.

If a plant is climatically adapted to its environment, the factors that are important in determining its salt tolerance are the total concentration of salts in the soil solution and the toxic effect of specific salts or ions. When there are large amounts of soluble salts in the soil solution, the osmotic concentration will be high and the intake of water by the plant will be reduced. The kind of salt present in the soil solution must also be considered. In general, chloride salts are more toxic than sulfate salts when considered on the basis of chemical equivalents. Magnesium toxicity has been reported for wheat, beans, and guayule.

Several crops have been tentatively classified on the basis of salt tolerance. Sugar beets, milo, Bermuda grass, and Rhodes grass are strongly salt tolerant. Alfalfa, cotton, tomatoes, sorgo, and several rye grasses are regarded as having good tolerance. Onions, squash, rice, barley, wheat, and flax are moderately salt tolerant. Wax beans, navy beans, field peas, and Elberta peaches exhibit weak tolerance.

Within a given species, certain varieties or strains may be more salt-tolerant than others. Trials are being conducted with varieties of alfalfa and cotton; by careful testing, it is believed that selections can be made that are better adapted to saline conditions than those now in use. As additional information is obtained, recommendations on crop tolerance will be made available to the farmer.

THE AUTHOR

H. E. Hayward is director of the U. S. Regional Salinity Laboratory, Riverside, Calif. He has published a number of papers on the anatomical and physiological responses of agricultural crops to saline conditions, among them flax, tomatoes, peaches, and oranges. He is the author of *The Structure of Economic Plants*. Dr. Hayward is a graduate of the University of Minnesota and received his doctorate from the University of Chicago, where, before joining the staff of the Salinity Laboratory, he was professor of botany.

FOR FURTHER READING

Fireman, Milton, and Magistad, O. C.: *Permeability of Five Western Soils as Affected by the Percentage of Sodium of the Irrigation Water,* Transactions of American Geophysical Union, volume 26, pages 91–94, 1945.

Gardner, Robert: *Some Soil Properties Related to the Sodium Salt Problem in Irrigated Soils,* U. S. D. A. Technical Bulletin 902, 1945.

Hayward, H. E., and Magistad, O. C.: *The Salt Problem in Irrigation Agriculture,* U. S. D. A. Miscellaneous Publication 607, 1946.

Hayward, H. E., and Spurr, Winifred B.: *The Tolerance of Flax to Saline Conditions,* American Society of Agronomy, Journal, volume 36, pages 287–300, 1944.

Magistad, O. C., and Christiansen, J. E.: *Saline Soils, Their Nature and Management,* U. S. D. A. Circular 707, 1944.

Richards, L. A., and Weaver, L. R.: *Moisture Retention by Some Irrigated Soils as Related to Soil Moisture Tension,* Journal of Agricultural Research, volume 69, pages 215–235, 1944.

Wadleigh, C. H., and Ayers, A. D.: *Growth and Biochemical Composition of Bean Plants as Conditioned by Soil Moisture Tension and Salt Concentration,* Plant Physiology, volume 20, pages 106–132, 1945.

Phosphate Fertilizers

by W. H. PIERRE

ONLY A LITTLE more than a century ago Sir John Lawes of England first produced soluble phosphate fertilizers by treating ground bones with sulfuric acid. About 25 years later his process was applied in the United States to phosphate rock, deposits of which had been found in South Carolina. Little was known then about the use of phosphate fertilizers, but information on the phosphate needs of American soils gradually accumulated, and the phosphate fertilizer industry soon became well established. Today, nearly 4 million tons of phosphate rock are mined annually for the production of superphosphate fertilizers and for direct application to the soil. American farmers spend about 200 million dollars annually for phosphorus, the important plant food element that is added to soils through the use of phosphate fertilizers.

Of the total amount of phosphorus found in soils, only a small percentage is in a form readily available for use by plants. Most of it is found in compounds from which plants cannot obtain sufficient amounts for rapid growth and maximum yields.

Cropping results in a continuous removal of the most available soil phosphorus. Furthermore, as H. T. Rogers in Virginia and O. R. Neal in New Jersey have shown, it is this small but most valuable portion of the total soil phosphorus that is most readily lost by erosion.

But the problem of phosphate fertilization is not simply one of adding to soils an amount of phosphorus equal to that removed by crops or lost by erosion. Soils differ greatly in the kinds of phosphorus compounds they contain and in their ability to pass along to the plant the phosphate added in fertilizers. Moreover, crops vary in their ability to use the phosphorus compounds of the soil and in their response to phosphate fertilizers. The kinds of phosphate fertilizers used and the way in which

554

they are applied are other factors that affect the returns obtained. Only through a better understanding of such factors can farmers bring about the most efficient use of phosphate fertilizers and insure adequate consumption for soil improvement and conservation.

The amount of phosphate as well as other fertilizers used on American farms reached an all-time peak in 1946, largely because of the great war-born demand for agricultural products and the relatively high level of farm income. Despite variations through the years, associated with changes in farm income, the trend in the use of phosphate fertilizers has been definitely upward.

As with other fertilizers, the use of phosphate fertilizers varies in the different States. Even in the East, where rainfall is not the limiting factor in crop production, large differences exist; in 1943, seven Southeastern States used 224,609 tons of phosphorus in fertilizers, or more than 40 percent of the total used in the United States.

The use of phosphate fertilizers in the various States is in sharp contrast to the calculated amounts of phosphorus removed in harvested crops. Five Corn Belt States—Ohio, Indiana, Illinois, Iowa, and Missouri—for example, removed in harvested crops in 1943 more than 30 percent of the 740,000 tons of phosphorus removed in the entire country, according to calculations made by J. H. Stallings. And even though half of the phosphorus contained in crops may be returned to the soil in manures, cropping results in a much heavier drain of phosphorus from the soils of the Corn Belt and other North Central States than from those of the Eastern States. Eastern farmers use relatively large amounts of phosphate fertilizers because their soils are inherently less productive and have been farmed longer than the soils to the west and because of the kinds of crops they grow and their type of farming. Potatoes and truck crops usually give a high net return from fertilizers because of their high acre value, and ordinarily receive at least a ton of fertilizer to the acre. Tobacco and cotton get much more than are usually applied to grain and hay crops.

Most of the phosphate fertilizer used in the United States consists of ordinary superphosphate, containing 16 to 22 percent P_2O_5, and concentrated superphosphate, containing 40 to 45 percent P_2O_5. Both materials contain monocalcium phosphate, a form readily available to crops. Finely ground phosphate rock also is used for direct application to the soil. It is less readily available to crops than is superphosphate, but when used with legumes in the cropping system it has proved effective in building up the productive level of acid, phosphorus-deficient soils.

Since about 1934, extensive investigations have been in progress to determine the value of several new phosphate materials prepared by the Tennessee Valley Authority for use as fertilizers. Most of the experimental work was done with concentrated or triple superphosphate and with two new products, calcium metaphosphate and fused tricalcium phosphate.

Calcium metaphosphate is produced when the elementary phosphorus issuing from a phosphate-reduction furnace is burned to P_2O_5 and is allowed to react with phosphate rock heated to 1,200° C. Because it contains about 65 percent P_2O_5, it is a concentrated phosphate, as compared with ordinary superphosphate. A summary prepared by the Tennessee Valley Authority of 758 experiments conducted in the seven Tennessee Valley States with cotton, corn, small grains, and hay shows that the yields with calcium metaphosphate averaged 99 percent as high as with ordinary superphosphate. On calcareous soils and on certain acid soils where it is not well incorporated into the soil, calcium metaphosphate has been found inferior to superphosphate.

Fused tricalcium phosphate is produced by heating phosphate rock to 1,500°–1,600° C. in the presence of water vapor. The process causes a disruption of the apatite structure of the phosphate rock and the loss of fluorine, so that a tricalcium phosphate that contains about 30 percent P_2O_5 is formed. The degree to which fluorine is removed and the fineness of grinding influence the cost and the availability to crops. Experiments conducted since 1941, and summarized by the Tennessee Valley Authority, have resulted in the establishment of tentative maximum limits of 0.4 percent fluorine and 40-mesh size as standards that insure relatively high availability to crops along with economy of production. In general, the availability of fused tricalcium phosphate on acid soils has been found to be slightly less than that of superphosphate. Like calcium metaphosphate it has been found to be inferior to superphosphate on calcareous soils and when applied as a top dressing.

The main advantage of these newer forms of phosphate, as well as of concentrated superphosphate that contains about 45 percent P_2O_5, is the economy in cost of transportation and handling. If further work shows that they can be produced as economically as superphosphate they should find greatly increased use. Because concentrated phosphates do not contain sulfur, that element would need to be added separately to sulfur-deficient soils if concentrated phosphates come into general use.

Soil Requirements and Efficient Use

Some of the most significant field and laboratory investigations relating to the use of phosphate fertilizers have been concerned with the determination of the phosphorus requirement of different soil types under various farming systems, and with more efficient methods of use. The results have given farmers a sounder basis for determining the need for phosphorus and estimating the amount required.

That the efficiency in use of phosphate fertilizers depends also on other soil conditions and on crop requirements is illustrated by some recent investigations in Mississippi and Iowa. In the South, oats and corn often have not shown profitable responses from phosphate fertilizers despite the low amounts of soluble phosphates in the soils and low average yields. The recent work of Russell Coleman in Mississippi shows, however, that this lack of response to phosphate may be due largely to inadequate amounts of nitrogren. Where no nitrogen was applied in fertilizers, an application of 200 pounds of superphosphate (16-percent P_2O_5) an acre did not increase the yields; but where 48 pounds of nitrogen was used, the phosphate increased the yield of oats by 17.3 bushels and that of cotton by 215 pounds of seed cotton an acre.

Similar results were obtained by L. B. Nelson, Kirk Lawton, and C. A. Black in Iowa. In 22 experiments with oats conducted in different parts of the State in 1945 they found that the use of superphosphate (20-percent P_2O_5) at the rate of 200 pounds an acre increased the yields by only 3.1 bushels an acre where no nitrogen had been applied, but by 7.8 bushels an acre where 40 pounds of nitrogen was used.

Studies have also been continued on better methods of applying phosphate fertilizers. In general, band placements have been found to be most satisfactory, but the best methods vary considerably with the kind of soil, the crop, and the kind and amount of fertilizer used. On soils that combine strongly with the phosphate to make it relatively unavailable to crops, the application of soluble phosphates in bands rather than broadcast has been found to be particularly advantageous. With relatively insoluble forms of phosphate, however, mixing of the fertilizer with the soil appears desirable.

Investigations on the deep placement of fertilizers have been stimulated by the desire to increase the rate of fertilization in order to obtain maximum production. This is particularly true of nitrogen fertilization. In experiments of W. H. Metzger and Floyd Davison in Kansas, the placement of phosphate fertilizer in the row at a depth of 6 inches resulted in considerably greater yields of sorghum than did more shallow placement. Experiments with corn in several Midwestern States, however, have shown no such advantage. It remains to be established, therefore, whether deep placement of phosphate is desirable, especially where only small amounts are applied and where the plants are likely to suffer from phosphorus deficiency before the root system contacts the deep placement zone. The greatest advantage of deep placement would seem to be in the case of nitrogen fertilizers and in areas of limited summer rainfall.

Residual Value of Phosphate Fertilizers

Phosphate fertilizers have long been used along with barnyard manure, because of the fact that manure is low in phosphorus as compared with nitrogen and potassium. Investigations by Alvin R. Midgley and David E. Dunklee in Vermont have re-emphasized the value of the practice.

They found that greater increases in crop yields result from applying the manure and phosphate together than when applied separately.

When soluble phosphate fertilizers are added to soils they form new compounds that are largely insoluble in water and only partly available to plants. For that reason usually not more than 10 to 20 percent of the phosphorus in fertilizers is used by the crop to which it is applied. The remainder accumulates in the soil although much may be lost by erosion. A major problem in the efficient use of phosphate fertilizer in areas of intensive use, therefore, is to know the amount of phosphorus that accumulates, how it may be kept in forms most available to plants, and to what extent fertilizers may be needed by succeeding crops. There is some evidence to show that on soils used largely for such crops as citrus, potatoes, tobacco, and vegetables, a large accumulation of phosphorus has taken place.

Early in 1944 soil scientists at Beltsville initiated a cooperative study with a number of State agricultural experiment stations for a comprehensive study of the problem. Samples of soil collected from 425 fields in the important potato-producing areas of Alabama, Maine, Maryland, North Carolina, New Jersey, New York, and Virginia were analyzed for total and readily soluble phosphorus. Field experiments are also being conducted on selected farms for determining to what extent present changes in phosphate fertilization practices might be warranted. The results obtained thus far show that the plowed layer of soil in many of the older potato fields has accumulated as much as 800 pounds of phosphorus. There has also been a marked increase in readily soluble phosphorus, the amount depending on the chemical characteristics of the soil and on the farm management practices followed. The longer the soil has been farmed under intensive fertilization the greater has been the accumulation of phosphorus.

Other evidence that the needs for phosphate fertilizers may be materially affected by past fertilization is shown by the results of a 15-year experiment conducted at the Alabama Agricultural Experiment Station under the direction of Garth W. Volk and L. E. Ensminger. Where the superphosphate (20-percent P_2O_5) application of 300 pounds an acre annually was reduced one-half after 5 years, the yield of cotton remained fairly stable at about 95 percent of the yield obtained where the 300-pound annual application was continued. Where the applications of phosphate were omitted after the first 5 years, the yields dropped to about 85 percent within 3 years and to 65 percent within 8 to 10 years. Even after 8 years, however, the yields were still about twice as high as where no phosphate had been applied during the entire 15-year period.

The amounts of superphosphate used in this experiment were, of course, much higher than those usually applied in a legume-livestock or grain system of farming. Not only is the amount of residual phosphorus less where the rates of fertilization are lower, but the availability of the residual phosphorus is also lower. Moreover, the very fine sandy loam soil on which the experiment was conducted was relatively low in clay. Soils high in clay, especially those high in reactive iron and aluminum compounds, usually show low residual effects from applied phosphate.

Needs and Potential Use

Although our farmers have used phosphate fertilizers for more than 75 years, the amounts now used are still inadequate from the standpoint of both efficient production and soil conservation. That conclusion was reached in 1944 by the State Production Adjustment Committees of the State agricultural experiment stations working in cooperation with Department statisticians. Their estimates of the amount of fertilizers that could be used profitably under generally prosperous economic conditions are that for the whole country nearly four times more phosphate fertilizer is needed than was used before the war (1935–39) and more than twice as much as was used in 1944. The suggested increase over 1944 ranges from 25 percent in the Northeastern States to approximately 250 percent in the Corn Belt and Lake States.

Although 8 Corn Belt and Lake States account for 47 percent of the total suggested increase (compared to only 34 percent for the 20 States of the Southeast, Appalachian, and Northeast regions), the increased needs in the latter States should not be minimized. Those States have large acreages of rolling and eroded soils that should be in permanent pasture or are now producing only scant and poor vegetation. Many field experiments have shown that phosphate and lime are the primary essentials in the establishment of a good vegetative cover of high quality legumes and grasses.

Although in many of the States several times more phosphorus is added in fertilizers than is removed in crops, much of the consumption is concentrated in areas growing cash crops of high value per acre. In areas of concentrated use, phosphorus accumulation will no doubt lead to reduction in acre applications, but on large acreages of poor crop and pasture land increases in use are essential to good land use and conservation. Millions of acres of pastures in the Central States also need improvement through the use of phosphates. According to Donald B. Ibach of the Department, less than 6 percent of the permanent pasture in the humid region was fertilized in 1943.

The need for improving the phosphate status of many soils is also emphasized by the advances made in the development of better adapted and higher yielding crop varieties. It is evident that improved crop varieties make a greater demand on the soil for phosphorus and other elements than do lower yielding varieties, and that a higher phosphate level is necessary if full advantage is to be realized from crop improvement programs aimed at higher acre yields and greater efficiency in production.

Moreover, it is a well-established fact that poor crop quality and lower feeding value are more often associated with phosphorus deficiencies in soils than with deficiencies of any other mineral element. This is particularly true of pastures where phosphates increase not only the phosphorus content of the forage, but also the proportion of the more desirable and nutritious plant species.

Like other practices aimed at soil improvement and conservation and at greater efficiency in production, the practice of phosphate fertilization must be considered a part of a unified program of good soil management. Its place in this program varies with the soil, with the crop grown, and with the system of farming. It is a practice, therefore, that must be adapted to the individual farm.

THE AUTHOR

W. H. Pierre is professor of soils and head of the Department of Agronomy, Iowa State College, Ames, Iowa.

ACKNOWLEDGMENT

Dr. Charles A. Black, associate professor of soils, Iowa State College, assisted in the preparation of this article.

FOR FURTHER READING

Alway, F. J., and Nesom, G. H.: *Effectiveness of Calcium Metaphosphate and Fused Rock Phosphate on Alfalfa,* Journal, American Society of Agronomy, volume 36, pages 73–88, 1944.

DeTurk, E. E.: *The Problem of Phosphate Fertilizers,* Illinois Agricultural Experiment Station Bulletin 484, 1942.

MacIntire, W. H., Winterberg, S. H., Hatcher, B. W., and Palmer, George: *Fused Tricalcium Phosphate: Relation of Degree of Defluorination to Fertilizer Value of Quenched Fusions of Rock Phosphate,* Soil Science, volume 57, pages 425–442, 1944.

Mehring, A. L.: *Fertilizer Expenditures in Relation to Farm Income,* Better Crops with Plant Food, volume 28, No. 8, pages 10–16, 47–48, 1944.

Midgley, Alvin R., and Dunklee, David E.: *The Availability to Plants of Phosphates Applied with Cattle Manure,* Vermont Agricultural Experiment Station Bulletin 525, 1945.

Neal, O. R.: *Removal of Nutrients from the Soil by Crops and Erosion,* Journal, American Society of Agronomy, volume 36, pages 601–607, 1944.

Rogers, H. T.: *Plant Nutrient Losses by Erosion from a Corn, Wheat, Clover Rotation on Dunmore Silt Loam,* Soil Science Society of America, Proceedings, (1941), volume 6, pages 263–271, 1942.

Smalley, H. R.: *The Phosphate Problem is Complicated by Many Factors,* Fertilizer Review, volume 19, No. 3, pages 8–12, 14, 1944.

ARMERS in the 17 Western States look hope-
lly to snow-capped mountains like these for
their next year's supply of irrigation water.
How deep this snow is, so shall the harvest be.

WATER FROM MOUNTAIN SNOW

ow was first measured for its water content
this country by Charles A. Mixer in Maine
out 1900. He proved that snow—a frozen
ass of air and water—varies too widely in
nsity for its depth alone to show how much
ater it will make. In 1908 Dr. J. E. Church
the University of Nevada developed the
t. Rose sampler, a forerunner of the Federal
mpler currently used. With it, a snow
mple can be taken and weighed and the
snow readily converted into water inches.
Now, a thousand or more snow surveyors face
sudden storms, snowslides, and exposure to
measure each year the snowfall in the Western
States where irrigation farming is the backbone of cropland agriculture. The surveys
usually start in December; measurements are
taken on or about the first of each month until
the spring thaws set in. The Soil Conservation
Service is responsible for compiling the data.

Water that flows from this white, frozen mass is all-important, not only to farmers, but to hydro-electric power companies, flood contr agencies, and many others in the valleys belo

Natural lakes and specially constructed reservoirs hold the melted snow so that controlled and equitable distribution can be made of according to the amount nature has provide

PROPERLY USED, THIS WATER
SPELLS PROFIT OR LOSS

Nearly all of the water for irrigating some 24 million acres of flat and fertile cropland of the West comes from snow laid down on mountain watersheds during the winter months.

To find out what the snow water supply will be, hardy snow surveyors, traveling in pairs for safety, trek high into the mountain watersheds to measure the water content of the snow pack.

This is one type of motorized equipment now used in a few areas of the country to make at least a part of the long trip to the carefully selected courses where snow samples are taken.

Shelter cabins that have been built and maintained for the surveyors are sometimes buried under 20 feet of snow. Here the surveyor enters through a so-called Santa Claus chimney.

Out on the course a snow sample is taken by thrusting the Federal sampler—a 1¾-inch hollow, aluminum-alloy tube—down through many feet of snow to the ground beneath.

The sample is immediately weighed on special hand scales with markings that show the inches of water in the snow. Measurements are noted and carefully recorded for future compilation.

the end of a day's work these weather-worthy bins, supplied with food by pack train during the summer, are lifesavers to the snow surveyors who often travel 25 miles or more a day.

ack in their shelter cabin, Surveyors R. A. ork and Max Wilson do some preliminary checking and compiling of their data before starting down the mountains to headquarters.

Snow survey data thus obtained are sent to central offices by air mail, telegraph, telephone, or short-wave radio and are immediately compiled and relayed to waiting water users.

At the end of winter, water experts representing local, State, and Federal agencies get together and, with the use of snow survey and other data, forecast the stream flow and total amount of reservoir storage water that will be available for the forthcoming irrigation season.

ERE ARE RAINDROPS driving into unpro-
ted soil at 14 miles an hour. On the re-
und the splashes may carry as much as 40
rcent soil, making a muddy mixture that
ore rain can and usually does wash away.

To determine the destructive effect of rain
hitting unprotected soil, this relatively simple
machine was built (below). It can imitate
rain of high or low intensity, large or
small drops, and rain at controlled velocity.

The soil sample at left, with coins to simulate protected surface, was photographed after 45 seconds of rainfall. The white splash board, 6 inches away, is already flecked with mud. T[other sample was snapped 1¼ hours later ar shows what rain splash will do to open so

Here, in an open field, is proof that beating raindrops, as well as surface flow, will gradually carve away the good earth. Each pedestal of soil is shaped to the rock or crust on top. Only 1 inch of driving rain on erodible soil (b low) can splash and move as much as 170 to an acre, mostly downhill. Soon—tco soon the light-colored, unproductive soil shows u

ut not all this splashed soil moves downhill.
he finest and richest part can even be floated
it of contour furrows, leaving only the coarser,
ss fertile soil behind. Good cover crops
ill help prevent destructive splash erosion.

The farmer who owned this land (below) was
surprised to find a rail fence under about
4 feet of soil at the base of a long field
slope. Good cover crops would have prevented this; contouring also would have helped.

Other damage frequently caused by raindrop splash is that it seals the surface of the land so that water goes off—not into—the soi This puddled soil is practically waterproo

W. D. Ellison of the Soil Conservation Service shows samples, left to right, of the splash col- lected from a bare field, a field with som cover, and one that had good protective cove

field of young corn (left) is a wide-open
·get to splash erosion. Even when corn has
·own to more than knee height (right) many
·indrops can get through to bombard the soil.

From an eye-high level the young oats crop
(below) would look like a tight cover—but
looking straight down at it we can readily
see how the driving rains might raise havoc.

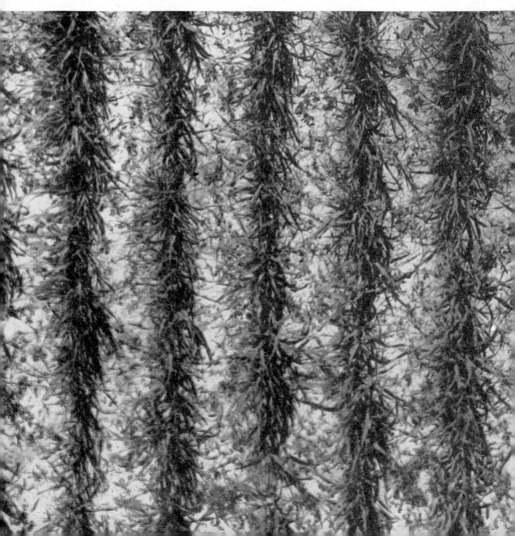

Beating rain has little chance of getting through good vegetative cover like this combination of clover and timothy. The splash process is prevented, the soil remains stable, and the water soaks into it. Of course, all land can not be kept covered all the time. But by usin what we know about protecting the land t rate of soil loss can definitely be retarde

THE CONTROL OF WATER is vital in the ~~ e of the land. On one Iowa farm (above, ~~ t) heavy rains washed tons of soil across a ~~ nfield. On another Iowa farm (above, right) contour furrows prevent downgrade washing and promote good conservation farming. Below, left, erosion is ruining a pasture; right, vegetation-lined waterways help protect fields.

Sedimentation between eroding farm fields and the oceans is costing us dearly. An example is deep gully erosion in Wisconsin (above, left) from which a vast amount of sterile sand was washed over nearby bottomland cornfields (right). Silting of reservoirs, like this one South Carolina (below, left), is an outstand example of sedimentation. It can be stop in various ways: By gully-control structu (right), dams, and revetments to halt eros

led land on which dead residues from pre-
ous crops are left resists erosion better than
re soil. A photographer removed residues
m a small area (above, left) in a field to
w how surface structure remained intact after rain. Subsurface tillers (right), treaders (below, left), and a two-row seeder behind a treader are implements for stubble mulching. An article on Ways to Till the Soil, by F. L. Duley and O. R. Mathews, begins on page 518.

Soil maps help farmers put their land to its best permanent use. A soil surveyor (above, left) maps slopes, a factor in good land use. Right, men in the Department's Soil Survey Division put data on maps that show soil types and production possibilities of each farm. [low, a Vermont farmer and county agent stu[their county maps; later, a farmer plans what plant and how to improve his land. Nea[a third of our farm land is now mapp[

Use of Nitrogen Fertilizers

by F. W. PARKER

WAR LIVES on nitrogen. All explosives except the atomic bomb are nitrogen compounds. War increases the need for nitrogen fertilizers for growing more food and fiber. To meet increased wartime needs, the United States more than doubled its capacity to produce fixed nitrogen compounds, by building 10 new synthetic nitrogen plants. As a result, our Army and Navy had plenty of ammunition, and American farmers used more fertilizer nitrogen than they had ever used before—in fact, 10 times the 62 thousand tons they used in 1900. But even this record supply was not all they wanted or could well have used.

Nitrogen for fertilizers comes from natural organic materials like dried blood, tankage, and cottonseed meal, or from chemical compounds like ammonium sulfate, sodium nitrate, ammonia solutions, and ammonium nitrate. A sharp cut in the price of chemical nitrogen between 1925 and 1935 followed the development of synthetic nitrogen processes, stimulated the use of nitrogen, and caused a trend away from the higher priced natural organics.

Farmers in some States use a great deal of nitrogen. Others use very little. In Maine, Florida, and Ohio mixed fertilizers supply most of the nitrogen. In California, Mississippi, and South Carolina most of the nitrogen is used as nitrogen fertilizer materials unmixed with phosphate and potash. Seven States along the South Atlantic and Gulf coasts use 53 percent of the fertilizer nitrogen; Iowa and Minnesota and the great wheat-producing States use little nitrogen. Why?

Several factors are involved, among them the nitrogen content of the soil, rainfall, cropping or farming system, and the value of the crop per acre. In the Southeast, where rainfall and mean annual temperature are relatively high, the soils are low in nitrogen and farmers use a large

The use of nitrogen fertilizers by American farmers has increased tenfold since 1900. As consumption increased, the proportion of nitrogen in the form of ammonium sulfate, sodium nitrate, cyanamide, ammonia solutions, and ammonium nitrate has increased. Much of the change from natural organics has been due to price changes in favor of chemical nitrogen, prices of which dropped sharply from 1925 to 1935 because of improved synthetic processes for making it. Here are significant facts

Year	Nitrogen consumption	Percentage of fertilizer investment chargeable to nitrogen	Part supplied as chemical nitrogen	Average wholesale price of 20 pounds of nitrogen as—		Percentage of total plant food supplied as nitrogen
				Natural organics	Chemical nitrogen	
	Tons	Percent	Percent	Dollars	Dollars	Percent
1900.........	62, 000	35	12	2. 57	2. 42	15. 7
1910.........	145, 900	41	46	3. 63	2. 76	16. 1
1920.........	227, 800	40	66	8. 71	4. 26	19. 9
1930.........	376, 600	45	84	4. 50	2. 14	24. 7
1940.........	419, 100	43	88	3. 55	1. 42	23. 7
1944.........	626, 200	40	94	4. 82	1. 40	24. 9

quantity of fertilizers. In the Corn Belt the soils are higher in nitrogen, and less is applied as fertilizer.

Difference in rainfall is an important factor. Generally speaking, rainfall in the States west of Minnesota, Iowa, Missouri, and Arkansas is so low that water, rather than nitrogen, limits crop yields except on irrigated land. There is some evidence that nitrogen fertilizers may be profitably used for the production of grass seed and wheat under certain conditions in parts of the West, but for the most part the use of nitrogen is limited to irrigated crops.

A third factor is the farming system. In a good livestock system legumes are grown and much of the nitrogen is returned to the land in farm manure. In a cash crop system a higher proportion of the nitrogen is sold. In eight Southeastern States, 75 to 85 percent of the farm income is from the sale of crops. In the Corn Belt States only 20 to 40 percent of the farm income is from the sale of crops, whereas 60 to 80 percent is from livestock. Differences in farming systems as well as differences in soils and rainfall are important.

The value of the crop being grown also is a factor. High-value crops, such as citrus, tobacco, potatoes, and vegetables, usually are heavily fertilized. Cotton, one of the higher valued field crops, receives moderate fertilization. Lower valued crops generally are fertilized at lower rates.

Large quantities of nitrogen are required for high yields of most crops. A 60-bushel corn crop contains about 95 pounds of nitrogen, 57 pounds in the grain and 38 pounds in the stover. This nitrogen must come from the soil, legumes that have been turned under, manure, or fertilizers.

The time when the crop needs nitrogen corresponds with its rate of growth. Little nitrogen is needed in the seedling stage, but that little is highly essential. The demand is greater when growth is quite rapid. Usually this is in midsummer for spring-planted crops. Corn planted on

May 22 in Ohio needed only 12 pounds of nitrogen before July 1. Between July 10 and August 10 the crop absorbed 81 pounds of nitrogen—almost 60 percent of the nitrogen required for the 117-bushel crop. These figures indicate the corn crop needs most of its nitrogen during the 1 month of maximum growth.

The nitrogen may be supplied in a mixed fertilizer, one containing nitrogen, phosphoric acid, and potash, or as a fertilizer containing only nitrogen. One point is important. The crop should be well fertilized with phosphate and potash if they are needed. Nitrogen fertilization will not give good results if there is a deficiency of other nutrients, insufficient water, or other factors unfavorable to growth. Ordinarily when other nutrients are needed, all or part of the nitrogen required is included with them in the application of a mixed fertilizer. This is an efficient and convenient method under many conditions.

Where large quantities of nitrogen are to be applied or in regions of high rainfall and light soils, a common practice is to apply a part of the nitrogen in mixed fertilizer at planting and the rest as a side dressing along the row. This is the general practice with cotton and corn in the South. On some soils nitrogen is the only fertilizer that gives profitable returns. Examples are the soils of the Mississippi Delta and certain soils in California.

Row crops are usually fertilized somewhat as has been indicated for corn; namely, all or a part of the nitrogen is applied in a mixed fertilizer at planting. Supplementary nitrogen may be applied as a side-dressing shortly after the crop is well established and is making good growth.

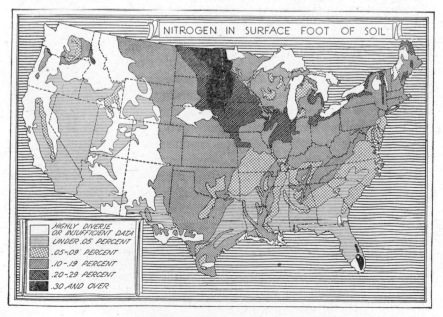

NITROGEN IN SURFACE FOOT OF SOIL

HIGHLY DIVERSE
OR INSUFFICIENT DATA
UNDER .05 PERCENT
.05-.09 PERCENT
.10-.19 PERCENT
.20-.29 PERCENT
.30 AND OVER

This table, taken from the March 1940 issue of Better Crops With Plant Food, shows the nitrogen content of some common nonlegume crops. Potatoes rank very high

Crop	Yield per acre	Nitrogen content	Crop	Yield per acre	Nitrogen content
		Pounds			Pounds
Cotton......	1 bale..........	65	Potatoes.....	300 bushels.....	125
Tobacco....	1,500 pounds....	80	Tomatoes....	10 tons.........	100
Corn.......	60 bushels......	95	Cabbage....	15 tons.........	100
Wheat.......	30 bushels......	50	Apples.......	400 bushels.....	30
Oats.......	50 bushels......	50	Peaches.....	500 bushels.....	85
Timothy....	1.5 tons........	40	Oranges.....	600 boxes.......	90

Wheat in the Midwest is usually fertilized at planting in the fall with a complete fertilizer containing 2 to 4 percent nitrogen. Additional nitrogen may be applied as a top dressing in the spring, but that is not a well established practice. In the South, a spring top dressing of nitrogen fertilizer on small grains is a general practice.

Details of fertilization vary so much with soil, crop, and climatic conditions that it is advisable for farmers to consult local and State authorities for specific recommendations.

The selection of a satisfactory nitrogen fertilizer is not difficult. All of the nitrogen fertilizers on the market give good results when used properly. In general, there are no great differences in their efficiency.

A few facts should be understood regarding differences in the properties of various forms of nitrogen:

Both ammonium and nitrate nitrogen are readily absorbed by plants in the early as well as later stages of growth. Nitrate nitrogen moves with the soil water and may be leached from the soil by heavy rainfall. Ammonium and related forms of nitrogen are not readily leached from the soil.

Sodium nitrate and cyanamide are slightly basic in residual reaction. Their continued use tends to reduce slightly the soil acidity.

Ammonium sulfate is quite acid in its action on the soil. It requires about 1 pound of limestone to correct the acidity from 1 pound of ammonium sulfate. Ammonium nitrate and uramon produce only one-third as much acid as an equivalent amount of ammonium sulfate.

The physical properties of nitrogenous fertilizers, found in the market, range from fair to excellent. Granular materials free of dust are easier to handle and are generally preferred by farmers.

Since equivalent amounts of the different nitrogen fertilizers give substantially the same results for most crops, their relative cost is an important consideration. They should be purchased on the basis of cost per unit of nitrogen, with small allowances for differences in some of the properties indicated, if those properties are important considerations under the conditions of use. Comparative unit costs are calculated by dividing the ton price by the percentage of nitrogen (N) in the fertilizer. At any given location and time the price relationships shown in the table

This table shows the relative retail price of nitrogen in different fertilizers. Prices are based on the average OPA ceiling for March 1946 for three regions

Fertilizer	Nitrogen content	Relative retail price of nitrogen (ammonium sulfate = 100)		
		Southeast	Midwest	New England
	Percent			
Ammonium sulfate.	20. 5	100	100	100
Sodium nitrate.	16. 0	133	144	128
Ammonium nitrate.	32. 5	98	85	84
Cyanamide.	21. 0	128	124	119
Cal-nitro.	20. 5	107	119	111
Uramon.	42. 0	86	88	79

above may not hold. Buyers, therefore, should calculate unit costs from the guaranteed analysis and price data furnished by the dealer or salesman.

The final selection of a nitrogen fertilizer can therefore be made on the basis of cost per unit of nitrogen, physical properties, and their influence on the chemical and physical properties of the soil.

The crop returns from the use of nitrogen fertilizer depend on many factors other than the kind of fertilizer selected and how it is used. Nitrogen fertilizers give best results when their use is combined with other good soil and crop management practices. The soil should be limed when needed, have a good supply of available phosphate and potash, be in good tilth, and have a satisfactory supply of moisture. The crop should be an improved variety with date of planting, rate of seeding, and cultural methods best adapted for local conditions. What returns can be expected from nitrogen fertilizers when a farmer does all this?

Extensive field experiments, many of them in cooperation with farmers, indicate that the approximate increase from the use of 10 pounds of nitrogen on crops will be about as follows:

Cotton, 100 to 140 pounds of seed cotton; corn, 3 to 5 bushels; wheat (Ohio, Indiana), 2 to 3 bushels; oats (South), 6 to 8 bushels; timothy or Sudan grass hay, 300 to 400 pounds; potatoes (Eastern States), 6 to 8 bushels; apples, 30 to 90 bushels; peaches, 20 to 60 bushels.

The data are representative of returns obtained in States east of the Mississippi River at normal to good rates of fertilization—30 to 60 pounds of nitrogen to the acre in most cases. They show that where nitrogen fertilization is needed it gives good returns.

THE AUTHOR

F. W. Parker is an assistant chief in the Bureau of Plant Industry, Soils, and Agricultural Engineering and is in charge of soil and fertilizer research in that Bureau. Before joining the Department in 1942 Dr. Parker was an agronomist in the ammonia department of E. I. du Pont de Nemours Co.

The Liming of Soils

by EMIL TRUOG

ABOUT three-fourths of the cultivated land in our humid regions needs lime. What would happen if farmers stopped applying it? Just this: Yields on lands where more than half of our agricultural crops are now produced would start to go down. For a few years we would not notice the decline very much. In a decade it would become quite pronounced. In 30 years or so the yields might be cut in half; in 50 years the result would certainly be hunger and disaster. And not only would harvests drop; control of soil erosion would become increasingly difficult.

In recent years American farmers have become well aware of the need for liming: In 1944 they used nearly 25 million tons of agricultural lime, four times the amount applied just 8 years earlier and seven times more than in 1929. Calculations by C. E. Carter of the Department indicate that about 40 million tons of lime annually should be used for the next decade on our arable and pasture lands. That a usage approaching that figure may be attained in the near future seems quite probable.

Extensive educational work on liming by the State and Federal agencies, including hundreds of thousands of tests for acidity and numerous field demonstrations of results, has brought about a general and thorough realization among farmers of the widespread need for lime and its benefits. Because liming of acid soils has been shown to have a favorable effect as regards fertility on the physical, chemical, and biological properties of soils, farmers now appreciate, as never before, why liming of land is often referred to as the backbone of profitable and permanent agriculture in humid regions.

Occasionally the application of lime has reduced crop yields, and some farmers naturally doubted its value. Now we know why: For the most part, it turns out to be a lowered availability of boron and man-

566

ganese. Sometimes the application of too much lime, especially to sandy soils that are low in active organic matter, makes the boron and manganese in the soil less available. In this country, James A. Naftel, of Alabama, was the first to demonstrate the relationship of overliming to a deficiency of available boron. His early investigations, made with a number of crops, notably cotton grown on Norfolk loamy sand, emphasize the great importance of carefully regulating the amount of lime added in accordance with needs as indicated by soil tests.

Boron is a nutrient element required in small amounts—a ton of alfalfa hay may contain about an ounce—by all crops for normal growth. The amount present in fertile soils in available form (that is, extractable with hot water) is usually not more than 1 to 5 pounds per acre plow layer. In some soils, particularly those that are low in organic matter and have been severely leached and exhaustively cropped, as is the case with many sandy soils of the South and Southeast, the content of available boron is so low that a slight reduction in availability, such as may be effected by liming, greatly reduces crop yields. The application of 25 to 50 pounds of borax to the acre remedies the condition, so that the lime needed to grow satisfactory crops of alfalfa, clover, and other crops may be added.

The relation of the availability of manganese to liming is much like that of boron. It has been known for 20 years or more that high pH (alkalinity) or heavy liming sometimes induces a deficiency of available manganese, but not until recent years was the frequency of the occurrence established by means of controlled experiments. Plants need but little manganese—a ton of alfalfa hay usually contains about 1 pound—but that amount is greater relatively than the requirement of boron.

The supply of available manganese in sands and loams that are low in organic matter and in certain peats that have little manganese-containing minerals is frequently too small for crop needs when their pH rises above 7 and—more important—when they are calcareous. The explanation for this is now quite clear. As long as the soil is acid (that is, the pH is below 7), a considerable part of the manganese tends to be in the divalent (reduced or manganous) form. In that form it acts like calcium or magnesium, particularly as an exchangeable cation, and is readily available because it is brought into solution as a bicarbonate through the action of the ever-present carbonic acid. As the pH rises to 7 and higher, there is a greater tendency toward the oxidation of divalent manganese to the tetravalent form by the oxygen dissolved in the soil solution, in accordance with the following reaction: $2Mn(OH)_2 + O_2 = 2MnO_2 + 2H_2O$. Tetravalent manganese in the form of manganese dioxide (MnO_2) is insoluble in carbonic acid, and is, therefore, not readily available for crop use.

Because oxygen is required in the reaction for the formation of the highly insoluble manganese dioxide, we would expect that the excessive aeration of the soil would also favor the formation. That is the case. Thus, a combination of high pH and excessive aeration is the condition under which a lack of available manganese most frequently occurs. Because sands and loams that are low in organic matter and water-holding capacity are often over-aerated, it is these kinds of soils that are most subject to a lack of available manganese when the pH is high. Some peaty and very sandy soils are so low in total manganese and so severely leached that even when they are strongly acid they lack an adequate supply of this element in available form.

On the other hand, the heavier soils and those containing considerable organic matter hold much more water and do not easily become over-aerated; in fact, a lack of aeration often occurs in the heavier soils, especially during periods of heavy rainfall. Such soils are usually also better supplied with organic matter, which, on decomposition, releases its manganese in available form and favors the transformation of manganese minerals to the available type. A lack of available manganese at high pH, therefore, occurs much less frequently in the heavier soils than in the lighter ones. In either case the lack is usually remedied by an application of 25 to 100 pounds of manganese sulfate to the acre.

The discovery of the relationship between liming and the availability of boron and manganese and the remedy is one of the reasons for the recent rapid increase in the use of lime in some sections of the South and Southeast where the soils are generally very acid. This greater use of lime is a great boon there; it makes possible the production of good crops of the more valuable legumes, which, in turn, add badly needed nitrogen and organic matter to the soils.

It is of interest to note what Edmund Ruffin wrote about reduced yields that occasionally follow the application of lime (marl) in excessive amounts to acid soils: "There are many practices universally admitted to be beneficial—yet there are none, which are not found sometimes useless, or hurtful, on account of some other attendant circumstance, which was not expected, and perhaps not discovered. Every application of calcareous earth to soil is a chemical operation on a great scale; decompositions and new combinations are produced, and in a manner generally conforming to the operators' expectations. But other and unknown agents may sometimes have a share in the process, and thus cause unlooked-for results. Such differences between practice and theory have sometimes occurred in my use of calcareous manures (as may be observed in some of the reported experiments) but they have neither been frequent, uniform, nor important."

Possibly the reduced yields of which Ruffin wrote more than a hundred years ago were caused by a lack of available boron or manganese, or both; prophetically, his words carry the inference that the cause of the reduced yields would some day be elucidated so that proper remedial measures could be taken. He found that sandiness and paucity of organic matter accentuate the overliming injury, that clover was less affected than other crops, and that its growth with attendant addition of organic matter would in time overcome the unfavorable condition for other crops. These observations are in accord with ours today. Possibly the reason that legumes that persist for more than one season, like red clover and alfalfa, are less affected by overliming than certain annuals is because by the second year their well-established root system are feeding to advantage for nutrients, such as manganese, below the limed layer. Also, by feeding throughout the growing season, they are able to take advantage of more favorable periods when there is abundant moisture.

Liming and the Availability of Plant Nutrients

The influence of reaction and accompanying conditions on the availability of the plant nutrients obtained from the soil proper is shown diagrammatically on page 570, which is simpler in form but more complete in several respects than that published by N. A. Pettinger. Reaction is expressed in terms of the pH scale. The reader is reminded that on this scale, a pH value of 7.0 (the middle vertical line in the diagram) represents the neutral point, while values to the left and progressively less than 7 express increasing acidity, and values to the right and progressively greater than 7 express increasing alkalinity. Also, a change in pH of one unit expresses a tenfold change in reaction; thus, pH 5 expresses acidity which is 10 times as intense as that at pH 6; likewise, at pH 9 the alkalinity is 10 times as intense as at pH 8. This change in intensity of acidity and alkalinity is shown in the diagram by the change in width of the heavily cross-hatched area between the curved lines.

In the drawing the influence of reaction and accompanying conditions on the availability of each nutrient element is expressed by the width of the band (the wider the band the more favorable the influence) carrying the name of the respective element. Thus, for the maintenance of a satisfactory supply of available nitrogen, a reaction or pH range of 6.0 to 8.0 is the most favorable. This does not mean that if the reaction of a soil falls in this range that a satisfactory supply of available nitrogen is assured. All it means is that as far as reaction is concerned, the conditions are favorable for a satisfactory supply of available nitrogen. Also, the narrowed band for nitrogen at pH 5 does not necessarily mean that a deficiency of this element will prevail at that pH; it means that as far as reaction is concerned, the conditions are not favorable for an abundant supply of available nitrogen; other factors than reaction and the usual accompanying conditions may even promote the presence of an abundant supply; moreover, certain crops having a low requirement may be fully satisfied with a low supply. What I have said about nitrogen holds also for the other nutrient elements.

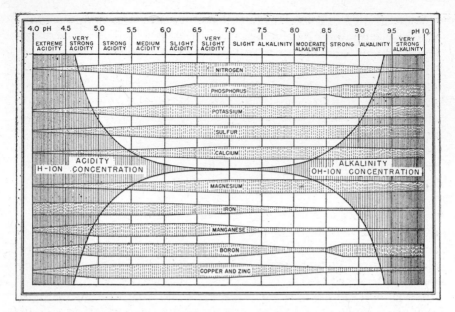

This chart illustrates the general trend of the relation of reaction (pH) and accompanying conditions to the availability of plant-nutrient elements.

At both strong acidity and strong alkalinity, the conditions as regards the fixation of nitrogen by legumes and the transformation of organic nitrogen to forms available to plants become increasingly less favorable.

In the case of phosphorus, you will note that in the pH range of 6.5 to 7.5 conditions are most favorable for high availability. Below pH 6.5 the influence as regards availability rapidly become less favorable. That is an important reason why acid soils should be limed to pH 6.5. In fact, if lime produced no other benefit than its favorable influence on phosphate availability, it would usually pay to use it. At pH 6.5, lime is sufficiently abundant and available to keep a considerable portion of the phosphorus in the form of calcium phosphate, which is soluble in carbonic acid and hence is readily available to crops. This holds for both the phosphorus naturally present in soils and that applied as manures and fertilizers.

When lime is present or added in amounts so as to raise the pH beyond 7.5, the influence on phosphate availability gradually becomes less favorable, although this is usually not serious until the pH goes beyond 8 and there is present 2 to 3 percent and more of free calcium carbonate. The reason for this is explained by-these reactions:

$$CaCO_3 + H_2CO_3 = Ca(HCO_3)_2$$
$$Ca_3(PO_4)_2 + 2H_2CO_3 = Ca_2H_2(PO_4)_2 + Ca(HCO_3)_2$$

The action of carbonic acid on calcium carbonate is expressed by the first reaction, and on calcium phosphate by the second reaction. The solubility of all the products is low, but adequate for plant nutrition.

You will note that calcium bicarbonate is formed in both reactions. Now, if a great abundance of calcium carbonate is present in a soil, the action of carbonic acid on it will keep the soil solution saturated with calcium bicarbonate, and this will greatly retard or even stop the second reaction, because it also involves the formation in solution of calcium bicarbonate. In other words, when the soil solution is once saturated with a certain product, such as calcium bicarbonate, all reactions involving the formation of this product are brought to a standstill until some of the product is removed by leaching or plant feeding. The explanation coincides with the principle of chemistry usually referred to as the law of mass action. Our observations indicate that usually a soil must contain several parts per hundred of calcium carbonate—that is, enough to permeate all the minute areas of a soil—in order to retard seriously the availability of phosphate. Of course, since 1 percent of calcium carbonate in a soil represents 10 tons of lime to the acre, a condition of this kind is seldom, if ever, produced by liming.

It is to be noted that when the pH of soils goes higher than 8.5, the availability of their phosphorus tends to increase again. This is because in this higher pH range the soil solution contains small amounts of sodium hydroxide which reacts with insoluble soil phosphates and forms small amounts of the highly soluble and available sodium phosphate. Since little or no leaching usually accompanies this high alkalinity, most if not all of the sodium phosphate thus formed is available for use by such crops as will grow at this high alkalinity.

It will be noted in the chart that conditions associated with acidity, especially of a pronounced degree, are unfavorable as regards the availability of sulfur, potassium, calcium, and magnesium. At strong acidity, the conditions for both the accumulation of sulfur in organic matter and its subsequent transformation to sulfate for plant use are not favorable. With increasing acidity, the amounts of the other three elements in exchangeable or readily available form usually decrease because of the attendant severe leaching; furthermore, the elements are held more tightly by the excess of insoluble acids against solution and plant feeding.

The availability of the other nutrient elements, iron, manganese, boron, copper, and zinc (often referred to as the minor nutrient elements), is influenced greatly by reaction. The influence on boron and manganese has been discussed. It should be noted that beyond pH 8.5, the influence of reaction is again in the direction of making boron more available; that is due to the presence of sodium hydroxide in the soil solution, which forms soluble salts of boron that are available for plant use.

The influence of reaction on the availability of iron is similar in nature to that of manganese, but due to the great abundance of iron in soils compared to manganese, deficiency of the former in available form does not occur nearly so often as of the latter. Below pH 6.5, small amounts of iron tend to exist in the ferrous state. In that form the iron is soluble in carbonic acid, and so is readily available. In fact, at extreme acidity and restricted aeration, toxic concentrations of ferrous iron sometimes exist. Also, at strong acidity, the ferric oxide, which is always present, dissolves in sufficient amounts to supply crop needs. As the pH rises above 6.5, soluble ferrous iron tends to become oxidized to ferric oxide, which is so insoluble under neutral and alkaline conditions that a deficiency for crop growth sometimes occurs under such conditions. As is the case with manganese, a good supply of active organic matter tends to overcome a lack of available iron at high pH because it not only carries and furnishes available iron, but also produces local reducing areas where iron is kept in the readily available ferrous state.

Crops need only minute amounts of copper and zinc. But, even so, deficiencies sometimes occur, particularly under calcareous and highly alkaline conditions, which greatly lower the solubility and availability of the two elements. Also, in strongly acid soils the amount present in readily available forms may be too low for crop needs because of depletion by leaching during the development of the acidity and strong retention by the soil acids of the other portions which exist as exchangeable bases.

A most important point to note is that pH 6.5 is a very favorable reaction as regards the availability of all of the elements listed and obtained by plants from the soil proper. That is why for general farming it is usually recommended that acid soils be limed to pH 6.5. Of course, for the control of potato scab and the culture of certain ornamental plants that need a lower pH, that condition may not be feasible or advisable. I also emphasize that the chart is a generalized diagram. Because adequate and precise data relating to certain aspects of the subject are still lacking, I had to make some assumptions in its preparation and so there are undoubtedly some inaccuracies in it. There will be cases that do not conform to the diagram because of the inaccuracies, or special and peculiar conditions that are involved, e. g., conditions that are associated with orchard crops. But in the main, especially in the reaction range of pH 5.5 to 8.5, I believe the diagram presents a fairly reliable picture. It should be added that where rather pure calcium lime is used, a deficiency of available magnesium may be created at pH 6.5 or any other pH value.

Loss of Lime by Leaching and Cropping

Fortunately, scientists are discovering that the rate of loss of lime by leaching is much less than was formerly believed to be the case; some of us used to assume that the annual loss was 500 to 1,000 pounds an acre. Recent data obtained by R. S. Stauffer in Illinois and Victor J. Kilmer, Orville E. Hays, and Robert J. Muckenhirn in Wisconsin show that when silt loams in their area are kept in crops, very little soil water percolates beyond a depth of 4 feet and that very little leaching of lime beyond the root zone can therefore occur. Their data were obtained with lysimeters that allowed natural surface drainage.

In some of the older lysimeter experiments, surface drainage was not provided, and all the rainfall was forced to enter the soil. Under such conditions, the amount of drainage water causing loss of lime may be multiplied several times, because it is that excess of water beyond a certain amount that the soil can hold or is used by crops that eventually drains out and causes leaching. With an annual rainfall of about 30 to 35 inches, the excess or percolation under cropping of the better soils when surface runoff is allowed may amount to only 2 or 3 inches annually; without runoff, it may amount to 8 to 10 inches.

That lime is not lost by leaching as rapidly as we once believed is substantiated by a consideration of the amount found present in many virgin soils. In eastern Wisconsin, for example, there exists a red clay loam soil which either contains lime carbonate throughout the soil profile, or is, at the most, only slightly acid in the surface layer. Geologists estimate that the parent material of this soil (lacustrine clay with some calcium carbonate) was laid down by glacial action about 25,000 years ago. If the annual loss of lime over that period had averaged 500 pounds an acre, the total loss for the whole time would amount to about 3 feet of powdered limestone. Obviously, nothing like that has taken place, otherwise the soil to a considerable depth would now be decidedly acid. Undoubtedly the native vegetation, a mixture of hardwoods and conifers, markedly retarded the net loss of lime by providing annual returns from the deeper layers to the surface in the form of deposits of tree leaves. I think that under these conditions the annual loss of lime carbonate by leaching was not more than a hundred pounds to the acre.

Investigations by J. W. White and F. J. Holben, carried on in connection with the old soil fertility test plots on Hagerstown clay loam at the Pennsylvania Agricultural Experiment Station, give information bearing directly on the leaching of lime under cropping. From a plot which had received lime (CaO) at the rate of 35,200 pounds an acre in 40 years, they calculated from their soil analyses that 4,353 pounds of CaO were leached out of the surface soil layer (0–7 inches) during the period. On an annual basis, that amounts to 109 pounds of CaO, or 195 pounds of $CaCO_3$. Because the loss occurred in a soil that was kept very heavily limed (maintained at a pH well above 7), it is higher than would be the case under most farming conditions (soil at pH 6.5 or less) in a similar climate. Moreover, some of the lime that was removed from the surface soil layer was retained by the soil below and so was not lost for soil improvement and crop use.

For the northern States of the humid region, an average annual removal by leaching and cropping of 200 pounds of calcium and magnesium carbonates an acre would seem to be a conservative estimate. In farming, as usually carried on, much of the lime removed by cropping can be returned and should be returned in the form of manure and crop residues. If that is done, the annual net removal would be less than 200 pounds in many cases. Even with an annual net removal of 200 pounds an acre, an application of a ton of lime to the acre will resupply what is removed in 10 years.

As one goes from north to south in the humid region of this country, the rainfall, temperature, and character of soil in many places become much more conducive to loss by leaching. Possibly the average net loss by cropping and leaching in the Southern States may be 25 to 50 percent higher than that estimated for the Northern States. A ton of lime an acre should, on the average, put back at least what is lost in the Southern States in a period of 7 or 8 years. It may be considerably longer in certain cases, depending on type of soil and cropping system.

The Cost of Maintaining the Lime Supply

What does it cost to provide and maintain a proper supply of lime in the soil?

Obviously the cost varies with conditions. I give one computation. In the North Central States, where about two-thirds of the country's agricultural lime is used, lime delivered at the farm frequently costs about $3 a ton. If 3 tons an acre are needed to bring the soil to a pH of 6.5, a capital investment of $9 is required; at 4-percent interest that represents an annual carrying charge of 36 cents. If the annual net loss or depletion of lime is 200 pounds an acre, it will take 30 cents annually to cover this. Thus, under these conditions, the total annual cost per acre of providing and maintaining a satisfactory supply of lime in a soil that needs 3 tons of lime an acre to start with is only 66 cents. The annual returns, as revealed by numerous field tests, from this investment in terms of increased yields of crops of higher quality, and soil improvement and conservation may easily amount to 10 or 20 times the annual cost. In fact, in time, it may mean the difference between complete crop failure with soil ruination, and bumper crops with permanent soil fertility and conservation. In these considerations it is understood, of course, that the lime would be supplemented with fertilizers as needed.

Because liming is so important in the humid regions, it is fortunate indeed that an inexhaustible supply of lime exists in most of the areas that need it. Calculations based on analyses of the earth's crust show that enough limestone exists for an application of approximately a half million tons to every acre of the earth's land surface, or close to 10 million tons for every acre of arable land. Moreover, the lime that leaches out of the land forms new deposits, pound for pound. Thus, the use of lime need never be curtailed because of an inadequate or dwindling supply.

We need more information particularly on two points: The loss of lime by leaching and cropping, and the fineness of grinding of limestone. Recommendations on the second point vary greatly. Authorities in several States favor rather coarsely ground material; others prefer finer grinding and have had laws passed that set up standards of purity and fineness.

A product that allows at least 50 percent to pass through a 60-mesh sieve is of high grade and economical as regards fineness for large-scale general use. Very fine material, most or all of which passes a 100-mesh sieve, is on the market; it costs more, but is well adapted for small-scale use, such as gardens, intensive cropping, and special cases where only a small amount of quick-acting material is permissible, as in potato culture.

Differences in recommendations as regards fineness of grinding have probably arisen in some cases because of marked differences in the character of the stone being used. It is well known that the dolomitic stone is much less soluble than the calcium stone, and so probably requires finer grinding if equal activity is desired. But, all in all, the solubility or availability of agricultural lime as influenced by composition and fineness, its subsequent movement, use by crops, and loss by leaching, all deserve much additional investigation.

And Finally

It should be understood that the acids that cause soil acidity are not in themselves undesirable substances to have in a soil. In fact, without them soils would be unreactive and unretentive of the elements of fertility. The acids act as a great reservoir where calcium, magnesium, potassium, and other bases may be stored in a readily available form for crop use and regulation of soil conditions. An acid condition is simply a positive signal that the supply of these bases needs to be replenished. This replenishment is done for the most part by the use of lime, and the more acid the condition the greater the need of the replenishment.

One of the most telling arguments for the liming of soils is an exposition of the relation of liming to the utilization of atmospheric nitrogen. In the atmosphere over every acre of land there are, in round numbers, 35,000 tons of nitrogen, which, if transformed to a fixed (nongaseous) form like ammonium nitrate, would have a commercial value as fertilizer of more than 5 million dollars. It is ironical, then, that many yields are greatly reduced because of a lack of nitrogen in usable form. How can the farmer draw upon this tremendous and inexhaustible supply of nitrogen? He can do so by growing legumes, which, when properly inoculated and grown on land well supplied with lime and mineral nutrients, have the power of fixing atmospheric nitrogen that they can then use for the synthesis of their own proteins, and pass on for use by other plants, as well as animals. Nonlegumes, regardless of how grown, cannot utilize atmospheric nitrogen. They depend for nitrogen on that fixed by the legumes, or supplied in manure and commercial fertilizers.

Now, it so happens that the legumes best in quality of forage and soil building, such as alfalfa and the clovers, like lime; that is, they grow satisfactorily and fix nitrogen efficiently only when the soil is well supplied with lime. A season's growth of alfalfa on an acre under favorable conditions may fix atmospheric nitrogen worth $10 or $20—more than enough to pay the cost of an ordinary application of lime, which usually produces benefits for a decade or more. Yes, the cost of liming land is only a small fraction of the total value of all of the benefits lime produces.

THE AUTHOR

Emil Truog is professor of soils and chairman of the Department of Soils at the University of Wisconsin. His principal contributions pertain to soil testing for lime and fertilizer needs, methods of fertilizer application, availability of plant nutrients, and the training of soil scientists.

FOR FURTHER READING

Berger, K. C., and Truog, E.: *Boron Determination in Soils and Plants,* Industrial and Engineering Chemistry, Washington, D. C., volume 11, pages 540–545, 1939.

Kilmer, Victor J., Hays, Orville E., and Muckenhirn, Robert J.: *Plant Nutrient and Water Losses from Fayette Silt Loam as Measured by Monolith Lysimeters,* American Society of Agronomy, Journal, Geneva, New York, volume 36, pages 249–263, 1944.

Naftel, James A.: *Soil Liming Investigations: V. The Relation of Boron Deficiency to Over-Liming Injury,* American Society of Agronomy, Journal, Geneva, New York, volume 29, pages 761–771, 1937.

Pettinger, N. A.: *Useful Chart for Teaching the Relation of Soil Reaction to the Availability of Plant Nutrients to Crops,* Virginia Agricultural Experiment Station Bulletin 136, pages 1–19, 1935.

Ruffin, Edmund: *An Essay on Calcareous Manures,* Edition 2, page 53, Shellbanks, Va., 1835.

Stauffer, R. S.: *Runoff, Percolate, and Leaching Losses from Some Illinois Soils,* American Society of Agronomy, Journal, Geneva, New York, volume 34, pages 830–835, 1942.

White, J. W., and Holben, F. J.: *Residual Effects of Forty Years Continuous Manurial Treatment: III. Ultimate Fate and Some Physical and Chemical Effects of Applied Lime,* Soil Science, Baltimore, volume 22, pages 61–74, 1926.

ALSO, IN THIS BOOK

The Use of Minor Elements

by MATTHEW DROSDOFF

SOIL SCIENTISTS use names like "minor elements," "trace elements," and "secondary elements" for boron, copper, zinc, manganese, and iron. The substances are secondary in name and quantity only; they are highly essential to plant growth although they are generally needed in very small amounts. Many a story is told of how a minute bit of iron or copper or zinc that has washed off a bucket carelessly left outside has saved a tree.

Scientists began investigating the practical problems of plant nutrition more than a hundred years ago, but only in the past two decades has proper attention been paid the minor elements. Now, in the past few years, their use in fertilizer practice has rapidly expanded, and all but a few States have reported soils deficient in one or more of the minor elements to the extent that without their use in fertilizers plants of good quality cannot be grown on these soils.

Considerable study is in progress on the need of other elements, especially molybdenum, and before another decade passes some may have to receive consideration in crop production. Other investigations have been directed toward the practical aspects of the problem, rather than—as at first—determining the need of plants for the minor elements.

Several important recent developments have helped considerably to speed progress in the application of the research. One is the symptom diagnosis, that is, the recognition of certain abnormalities of the foliage, fruit, or other plant parts as being associated with certain minor-element deficiencies. Another development is the widespread use of foliar diagnosis, or chemical analysis of leaves as a guide to the mineral-element nutrition of the plant. If a particular element is not supplied by the soil in quantities sufficient for normal plant growth or the elements are out

703830°—47——38

577

of balance, the condition can be detected before any plant symptoms develop by a chemical analysis of the leaves.

A third factor is the increasing awareness that such mixed materials as soils cannot always supply enough minor elements for normal plant growth. As might be expected, the highly leached sands of the Coastal Plain, especially in Florida, were among the first to show deficiencies of the minor elements under field conditions. Somewhat more unexpected was the discovery that the organic soils of the Florida Everglades required the addition of such elements as copper for the satisfactory production of vegetables.

These developments led to the investigation and ultimate discovery of minor-element needs on similar soils elsewhere. Meanwhile, other types of soils were found that required one or more of the elements for the successful production of certain crops. For example, some soils were so high in lime that the minor elements present were relatively unavailable to certain crop plants. Much evidence has been accumulated on the harmful effects of over-liming in limiting the availability of certain of the elements. Some soils that formerly had an adequate supply of minor elements have become so depleted by heavy cropping through the years that it has become necessary to replenish the supply of these elements through fertilization.

Scientists have found that certain minor elements may be present in amounts sufficient to produce a good crop but not enough for a high-quality product. A notable example is the external or internal cork of apples due to boron deficiency. Although certain elements like cobalt and iodine have not been shown to be necessary for normal plant growth, they are needed by animals and humans. The quality of a feed crop, therefore, is dependent on the presence in adequate amounts of these elements. An instance of great economic importance is the salt sickness of some Florida cattle that feed on forage low in cobalt.

The trend away from organic fertilizers and manures and toward the use of more concentrated materials has accentuated the need for supplemental elements. Manure and compost usually contain a balanced amount of minor elements, and farmers who still use large amounts of those materials are less likely to encounter deficiencies of minor elements.

Many of the practical problems concerned with the use of minor elements are in a sense parts of the one major problem, that is, how to supply the elements to the plant in the most efficient and economical manner. This involves the fundamental consideration of the requirements of the plant, the nature of the soil and the soil-fertilizer interaction, and the relationships between the different elements. Though a number of crops on many soils require supplements of the minor elements, many do not. Only certain soils and often only specific crops on these soils require minor-element fertilizers.

soil at any one time as determined by the chemical soil test is a good indication that potash fertilization is not likely to give a profitable return.

On the other hand, different soils with a low available potassium content do not give equally good responses to applications of potash. Although the available potassium supply in the soil at any one time, as determined by the chemical test, may be relatively low, many investigators have found that the amount of available potassium in certain soils remains remarkably constant, even upon intensive cropping. This would indicate that as the plant removes the available potassium from the soil, some of the difficultly soluble forms of potassium are converted into the available form. Thus when the supply of available potassium in the soil is replenished from the difficultly soluble forms rapidly enough to keep pace with the removal of potassium by the crop, the potassium-supplying power of the soil may be considered adequate even though the amount of available potassium at any one time, as revealed by the chemical test, may be low.

Similar conditions apply to the test for determining available phosphorus.

Many mineral soils having a total phosphorus content of more than 1,000 pounds to the acre in the surface layer respond well to as little as 50 pounds of phosphorus an acre applied in the form of superphosphate, especially if no phosphatic fertilizer has been previously used. This apparent discrepancy is due to the fact that most of the native soil phosphorus is tied up in the form that is not available to plant roots. Even the applied phosphorus is tied up so strongly by some soils that, unless a sufficient amount is added to satisfy at least partly the phosphorus-fixing capacity of the soil, little or no crop response can be observed even though the soil is deficient in phosphorus.

Soil chemists have been searching for a chemical phosphorus test that would be sufficiently specific to differentiate the available forms of phosphorus from the difficultly available forms and that would thus predict accurately responses of different crops to phosphorus fertilization on different soils. Such an ideal phosphorus test is yet to be found. Some of the chemical soil tests for phosphorus in current use, however, give fairly reliable results when properly correlated with crop responses on different soil types.

The tests for some of the constituents may be considered quite satisfactory. The soil acidity test, for example, which can be readily made even in the field, is now extensively employed as a basis for lime recommendations. But, here again, the translation of the results of the soil acidity test (pH of the soil) into the amount of lime that needs to be applied to grow a certain crop requires some knowledge of soil characteristics and plant requirements.

Despite these limitations, the chemical soil tests have been shown to be of great value as a guide to fertilizer recommendations, especially in detecting extreme deficiencies and toxicities of plant nutrient elements in the soil.

The chemical soil tests, for example, can show that continuous, heavy fertilization over a period of years may result in accumulation of one or another plant nutrient element in sufficient amount to warrant the reduction or even omission of that constituent in the fertilizer without sacrifice of yield or quality of the crop. The soil problems in commercial greenhouses are often associated with accumulation of excessive and injurious amounts of fertilizer salts. Such a condition can be readily detected by chemical soil tests.

Chemical soil tests are also useful as an aid to diagnosing crop failures. Admittedly, crop failures may be due to many different factors other than lack of adequate supply of plant nutrients. Poor drainage, lack of moisture, and insect or plant-disease damage may be the cause of the trouble. Diagnosis from the results of chemical soil tests is often difficult, but some clues as to possible causes of the trouble may be obtained largely by the process of elimination.

These tests are now used extensively by many State agricultural experiment stations, principally in the central-western area, Corn Belt sections, and eastern Atlantic region, as an aid in furnishing advice to farmers and growers regarding fertilizer use and soil management. Many States render this service free of charge to resident farmers, growers, and public agencies of the State. Special soil containers with detailed instructions for collecting the soil sample printed on the container are provided for this purpose by some State soil-testing laboratories. It is imperative, of course, that the soil sample be properly taken in the field. When submitting the soil samples for testing, the farmer is also requested to fill out special blank forms, giving pertinent information regarding the field and the soil problem. This is necessary for proper interpretation of the results of the tests and for making the final recommendations.

Plant-Tissue Tests

Because of the limitations of soil tests as a guide to fertilizer recommendations, some investigators prefer to use the chemical composition of the plant itself. This procedure makes allowance for the variations in different crops in their nutritional requirements and in their ability to utilize the nutrients in the soil. Plant composition also reflects changes in the nutritional status of a crop as a result of varying climatic conditions. For instance, deficiencies of nitrogen and magnesium occur more frequently in seasons of high rainfall than in dry years. Boron and manganese deficiencies, on the other hand, occur more often in dry seasons than in wet seasons. Obviously, these complicating factors should be eliminated if the diagnosis of nutritional deficiencies is based on the composition of the plant itself as it grows under natural conditions in the field.

To ascertain nutrient-element deficiencies at an early stage of growth, chemical analyses of the entire plant or of certain parts of the plant have been used. The principle involved is the same as that of the well-known Neubauer test except that the tests are made for each specific crop under field conditions.

This procedure is based on the following assumptions: Nutrient deficiencies in the soil must be reflected accurately by the correspondingly low concentrations in the plant at an early stage of growth; differences in composition of deficient and normal plants must be large enough to be easily measured; critical concentrations—the minimum concentration of the different elements in the plant tissue below which growth is retarded—must be reasonably constant under different soil and climatic conditions to serve as a basis for comparison.

Unfortunately, little work has been done to verify the correctness of the assumptions. Many investigators have demonstrated that deficiencies of nitrogen and potassium are reflected in correspondingly low concentrations of the elements in the plant. But it has not been shown conclusively that analysis of tissues reveals these deficiencies at an earlier stage of growth than can be recognized by visual symptoms of the foliage. Also, a deficiency of phosphorus in the soil may effect a definite reduction in yield of the crop without causing an appreciable lowering of the phosphorus content of the plant tissue.

The determination of the fertilizer needs by chemical plant-tissue tests has been most successful with fruit trees and crops that require more than a single season to mature, such as sugarcane and pineapples. It is more difficult, if not impossible, to establish definite critical concentrations for short-season crops, especially where such crops are grown under widely different climatic conditions.

The chemical methods of plant analysis vary from simple plant-tissue tests carried out in the field to careful laboratory analysis of the ashed plant material. Field tests are little better than qualitative tests and they are useful only for ascertaining extreme deficiency or abundancy.

The tests for nitrates by means of diphenylamine is perhaps the most useful of the field tests. Failure to develop a deep blue color when this reagent is added to the split lower petiole of many crop plants is a good indication of nitrogen deficiency. On the other hand, a positive test is no proof that the plant contains sufficient nitrogen for maximum growth when applied to such crops as potatoes or tomatoes, which normally have a high concentration of nitrate in the tissue.

Tissue tests are now made on a purely experimental basis. Again, as in soil tests, there is a complete lack of standardization with respect to sampling procedure, extraction methods, and analytical methods used. A great deal more fundamental work is needed to furnish the answer to questions such as these: What part of the plant should be sampled for analysis; does the soluble fraction of the nutrient element constitute a better index of the nutritional status of the plant than the total quantity of the element present; are differences in composition as a result of nutrient deficiencies large enough to overcome sampling errors; and, finally, is it possible to state the absolute, critical concentration for each nutrient and for each crop under different climatic conditions?

Not until we have answers to these questions can we finally appraise plant-tissue testing.

Deficiency Symptoms

The simplest and in many respects the most satisfactory method for ascertaining the need for certain nutrients is to recognize deficiency symptoms by the color of the foliage, the size of the plants, and their growth habit.

A light-green or yellowish color of corn plants indicates to every farmer the lack of nitrogen in the plant. Symptoms of nitrogen deficiency may be temporary on cold, wet soils and may disappear in early summer under more favorable soil conditions. Color charts are now being used by growers to measure the color of the leaves of apple trees. It serves as a fairly dependable method for ascertaining the nitrogen requirements of apple trees. No doubt this procedure could be used to advantage with many other crops.

Symptoms of deficiencies of other nutrients, like potash, magnesium, manganese, and boron, are now well established. Phosphorus deficiency remains one of the most difficult to recognize. Excellent descriptions of commonly occurring deficiency symptoms in the important crops have been published in *Hunger Signs in Crops*. It should be pointed out, however, that an accurate diagnosis by means of deficiency symptoms requires considerable experience and close observation. Faulty diagnosis is not at all uncommon. For instance, the chlorotic leaf margins of alfalfa caused by leaf hopper injury are easily mistaken for boron deficiency. It also is difficult to distinguish between the symptoms of magnesium and manganese deficiency. Nevertheless, when used by an experienced observer, diagnosis by means of deficiency symptoms is one of the most useful methods of determining the fertilizer needs of crops.

Thus soil tests, plant-tissue tests, and deficiency symptoms are useful for identifying nutritional disorders in crops. Each technique has its limitations, it is true; but when properly used, especially in conjunction with each other, they can be of help as guides to fertilizer recommendations and for finding out why crops fail.

THE AUTHORS

Michael Peech is professor of soil science at Cornell University, Ithaca, N. Y. A native of Canada, he was graduated from the University of Saskatchewan in 1930 and completed his graduate studies in soil chemistry at Ohio State University. Since 1933 he has been doing research in and teaching soil chemistry at several colleges and State agricultural experiment stations. Dr. Peech has made extensive investigations of the chemical properties of soils in relation to their inherent fertility and response to fertilizers, particularly in an effort to develop rapid chemical soil tests for determining the fertilizer needs of soils.

Hans Platenius is associate professor of vegetable crops at Cornell University, Ithaca, N. Y. He had his early training in agricultural chemistry in Germany and later continued his graduate work in plant sciences and biochemistry at the University of Nebraska and at Cornell. As a member of the research staff in the department of vegetable crops at Cornell University, Dr. Platenius has spent much time in recent years making a systematic study of the value of chemical analysis of plants for diagnosing deficiencies of nutrient elements in vegetable crops.

FOR FURTHER READING

Bray, Roger H.: *Soil-Plant Relations: I. The Quantitative Relations of Exchangeable Potassium to Crop Yields and to Crop Response to Potash Additions,* Soil Science, volume 58, pages 305–324, 1944.

Bray, Roger H., and Kurtz, L. T.: *Determination of Total, Organic, and Available Forms of Phosphorus in Soils,* Soil Science, volume 59, pages 39–45, 1945.

Carolus, R. L.: *The Use of Rapid Chemical Plant Nutrient Tests in Fertilizer Deficiency Diagnoses and Vegetable Crops Research,* Virginia Truck Experiment Station, Bulletin 98, pages 1530–1556, 1938.

Chandler, Robert F., Peech, Michael, and Bradfield, Richard: *A Study of Techniques for Predicting Potassium and Boron Requirements of Alfalfa. I. The Influence of Muriate of Potash and Borax on Yield, Deficiency Symptoms, and Potassium Content of the Plant and Soil,* Soil Science Society of America, Proceedings, volume 10, pages 141–146, 1945.

Colwell, W. E., and Lincoln, Charles: *A Comparison of Boron Deficiency Symptoms and Potato Leafhopper Injury on Alfalfa,* American Society of Agronomy, Journal, volume 34, pages 495–498, 1942.

Emmert, E. M.: *Plant-Tissue Tests as a Guide to Fertilizer Treatment of Tomatoes,* Kentucky Agricultural Experiment Station Bulletin 430, 1942.

Hambidge, Gove, Editor: *Hunger Signs in Crops,* The American Society of Agronomy and the National Fertilizer Association, Washington, D. C., 1941.

Merkle, F. G: *Soil Testing, Operation, Interpretation, and Application,* Pennsylvania Agricultural Experiment Station Bulletin 398, 1940.

Morgan, M. F.: *Chemical Soil Diagnosis by the Universal Soil Testing System,* Connecticut Agricultural Experiment Station Bulletin 450, 1941.

Peech, Michael, and English, Leah: *Rapid Microchemical Soil Tests,* Soil Science, volume 57, pages 167–195, 1944.

Scarseth, George D.: *Plant Tissue Testing in Diagnosis of the Nutritional Status of Growing Plants,* Soil Science, volume 55, pages 113–120, 1943.

Spurway, C. H.: *Soil Fertility Control for Greenhouses,* Michigan Agricultural Experiment Station Special Bulletin 325, 1943.

Ulrich, Albert: *Plant Analysis as a Diagnostic Procedure,* Soil Science, volume 55, pages 101–112, 1943.

Wolf, Benjamin: *Rapid Soil Tests Furnish one of the Implements for Increasing Crop Yields,* Better Crops with Plant Food, volume 29, pages 14–20, 47–49, 1945.

Nutrient-Element Balance

by C. B. SHEAR and H. L. CRANE

BALANCE is a fundamental part of nature's law. But man's activities have a way of upsetting nature's balance and usually it takes a serious unbalance to make us see the situation and try to correct it.

Our increased concern over our own diets exemplifies an unbalance. The variety of foods that comprise the average normal diet should provide enough of the essential minerals and vitamins to meet our normal requirements. But not so. Many of the soils on which food crops are grown do not supply the plants with sufficient minerals to meet our needs or to enable the plants to synthesize vitamins in quantities to meet our demands. Further, and worse, we are not satisfied to use many plant products, particularly the cereals, in the form in which nature gives them to us, but demand that they be processed and "purified." These purifying processes remove some of the nutrients, and unless we know which and how much of the nutrients are removed, and supply them in our diets from other sources, we do not get enough of them.

Much the same situation exists with respect to the nutrition of our crops. The soils upon which plants depend for their food materials developed from minerals, which originally contained a fairly well-balanced supply of the essential mineral nutrients for the plants that became native to each soil. Plants with different nutrient requirements developed on soils having different powers to supply nutrients. Many soils, in their virgin state, do not furnish a balanced nutrient supply for agricultural crops. Man, however, has not restricted his cultivation to the soils best suited to the crops he wants to grow, nor has he been careful to protect the soil from erosion and leaching. Furthermore, he has continued to crop the soil year after year and has failed to return to the soil all of the nutrients removed in the crops produced. The

592

organic matter of the soil, one function of which is to act as a reservoir of slowly available nutrients, has also been allowed to be depleted.

When America was a predominantly agricultural country, a high proportion of the products of the land was returned to the soil in the form of manure, thus helping to maintain the original soil fertility. As the country became more industrialized and the farm mechanized, less and less of the material produced on the land was returned to the soil. The farmer came to depend more and more on chemical fertilizers to maintain crop production.

The so-called complete chemical fertilizers that he used generally contained only three "plant food" elements, nitrogen, phosphorus, and potassium. Even they were not supplied in the quantities or proportions in which they were removed in the crops. In the early days of commercial fertilizers, the materials used in making them were of low grade, and contained substantial quantities of other elements of value in crop production. When fertilizers of high analysis were developed, it became necessary to use purified materials in compounding them, with the result that they contain few or no impurities. Calcium, in the form of lime, was applied in some localities as a means of correcting soil acidity, but it was not generally considered a plant nutrient, but rather a soil amendment.

The other chemical elements that the plant physiologist has determined in the laboratory to be essential for normal plant growth were thought to be required in such small quantities that they would never be of practical concern to the farmer. It has been only within the last two decades that deficiencies of such elements as magnesium, manganese, zinc, boron, and copper have been observed and diagnosed on plants growing on our principal agricultural soils, even by experienced horticulturists and agronomists. Only more recently have we recognized that the prevailing practice of returning to the soil only nitrogen, phosphorus, potassium, sulfur, and sometimes calcium was hastening the depletion of the other plant nutrients through increased crop production.

The explanation of this depleting effect of the so-called "complete fertilization" now seems quite simple. Continued application of only part of the necessary plant food materials maintained crop yields at the level that the available supply of the other nutrients in the soil would permit. As each succeeding crop was removed from the land, the supply of these other essential nutrients became less and less. The effect of their diminishing supply was reflected in reduced plant growth and yields long before their effect was evident in definite symptoms of malnutrition. It was not until these advanced symptoms appeared and their causes determined that the failure of the "complete fertilizer" to maintain the original producing power of the soil was recognized. Man, by his lack of knowledge regarding nature's complex balance, had now brought about a condition that made it necessary for him to determine the balance required for his crops and find means of obtaining and maintaining that balance. This was no simple task.

The first method of attacking the problem was to try to determine the quantities of the many essential elements in the soil. The method produced valuable information about the chemical composition of the soil, but it soon became evident that the amounts of the elements extracted from the soil by the various solvents employed in the laboratory did not necessarily represent the amounts of those elements available to a plant growing in that soil. Evidently the plant had its own way of obtaining its nutrients from the soil.

Perhaps the answer lay in "asking" the plant what it needed and what it was able to get from the soil. The only means of "asking" the plant was through chemical analysis of the plant, or some part of it.

The idea of making chemical analyses of plants or plant parts was not new. Thousands of analyses for certain elements in many plants had been made. Much needed to be learned, however, regarding the relationships between plant composition and plant growth and also the factors that influence the absorption of nutrients from the soil and their accumulation in the plant. Only with such information could the results of plant analyses be interpreted in terms of nutritional requirements. Our information in this field is still meager. Nevertheless, for certain crops enough of the principles have been determined to permit surprisingly accurate diagnoses of the causes of nutritional disturbances to be made by means of leaf analyses.

Let us see what some of these principles are and how they can be applied to the diagnoses and correction of nutritional disorders.

First of all, we must select carefully the part of the plant to be sampled for analysis. The leaves are the factories in which are manufactured the food that is used by the plant to build tissue and as the source of energy to carry on its life processes. It is here, in the presence of chlorophyll (the green coloring matter), that the energy of sunlight is utilized to combine the raw materials obtained from the soil and the air into food (carbohydrates, proteins, and fats). The exact part that each essential mineral element plays in the complex chemical processes involved in the manufacture of these foods and in their utilization by the plant in growth are not all understood. It is known, however, that unless carbon, hydrogen, and oxygen, which are obtained from air and water, and nitrogen, phosphorus, potassium, calcium, magnesium, iron, manganese, zinc, copper, and boron, and perhaps other elements, which are obtained from the soil, are all available to the plant, it cannot grow. If maximum growth and yield are to be obtained, all these elements must be present in the leaves in the proper quantities and proportions.

Because of these facts, and because sufficient leaf tissue for chemical analysis can be removed from the plant without causing permanent damage, leaves are the ideal part of the plant to use for analysis.

The stage in the development of the plant at which the leave are sampled and the position of the leaves are important. The quantity and proportion of the different mineral elements in the leaves vary greatly during the course of the growing season. They also vary according to the position of the leaf on the shoot and, in trees, the position of the shoot on the tree. It is therefore necessary to take the leaves to be analyzed from comparable locations on the plant and shoot, preferably from the median portion. Furthermore, they should be taken when the plants are in the same physiological condition, as for example, soon after all terminal growth of the shoot has ceased or at the time of fruit maturity. Without such a carefully standardized sampling procedure the results of leaf analysis would be of little value in diagnosing the nutritional condition of the plant.

Many carefully controlled experiments in which analyses were made of leaves from thousands of plants grown under hundreds of different conditions of nutrient supply were necessary to gain the knowledge required to diagnose the nutritional condition of field-grown plants on the basis of their leaf composition.

The idea has prevailed a long time that for each crop there was a definite minimum leaf content for each essential element: If the content of a given element in the leaves fell below the minimum for that element, a deficiency, evidenced by leaf symptoms, would result. A plant was not usually recognized as being deficient in a given element until symptoms characteristic of a deficiency of that element appeared on the plant.

The results of recent work in plant nutrition show that these beliefs do not agree with the facts. Some of these results have even made it necessary for us to revise our conception of what constitutes a deficiency.

The first and only infallible symptom of the deficiency of any element is evidenced by a reduced rate of growth and, unless a more severe nutritional unbalance develops later, that will be the only symptom expressed. Because of the innumerable possible nutritional conditions that might be responsible for reduced growth, it would be impossible to determine its cause by merely examining the plant externally. On the other hand, to wait until the nutritional unbalance had become so severe as to produce symptoms would result in serious economic loss through reduced yields. Because of the great similarity between the symptoms of deficiencies of different elements, and because it is now recognized that symptoms once thought to be typical of the deficiency of a certain element may result from a number of different conditions of unbalanced nutrition, the most dependable means of diagnosis, even in advanced stages, is by leaf analysis.

We now know that when the available supply and the consequent

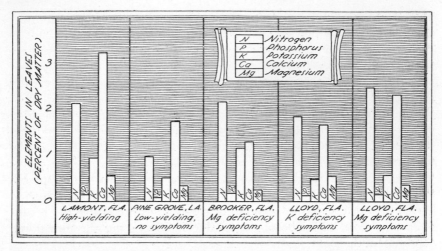

This chart, based on experiments with tung trees in five different areas, shows the resulting balance of leaf elements under various conditions of soil fertility.

accumulation of one nutrient element is reduced, the plant responds by accumulating an increased quantity of some other element or elements. Conversely, when an increased accumulation of one element is brought about by an increase in its available supply, the plant responds by accumulating a smaller quantity of some other element or elements. Thus it becomes obvious that we cannot consider the effects of the altered supply of one element in terms of that element alone, but must consider its effects in terms of the altered accumulation of all of the elements that are affected. The situation is further complicated by the fact that the magnitude of the effects an altered accumulation of one element will have on the accumulation of others is influenced not only by the chemical nature of the altered element but also by the available concentration of all the other elements. This phenomenon has been variously termed antagonism, compensating effect, or competition.

Perhaps the outstanding competitive effects of the nutrient elements are illustrated by the interactions among the three principal bases occurring in plants—potassium, calcium, and magnesium.

Potassium is the most active, chemically, of the three and, therefore, exerts a more pronounced effect on the accumulation of calcium and magnesium than do either of the latter on potassium or on one another. Magnesium is second and calcium third in this respect. When the potassium content of the leaf of a plant is increased through increasing the available potassium supply without at the same time increasing the available supply of calcium and magnesium, the accumulation of these latter two will be decreased, the decrease of calcium being of a greater magnitude than that of magnesium. If magnesium accumulation is increased, both potassium and calcium will decrease, calcium generally being more affected than potassium, while an increase in calcium usually results in a greater decrease in magnesium than in potassium.

Only within the past few years have we recognized that symptoms of the deficiency of one element can be brought about by an excessive accumulation of one or more of the other elements. Several workers have recently demonstrated on a number of crops the occurrence of magnesium deficiency caused by the excessive accumulation of potassium. They have been able experimentally to induce symptoms of magnesium deficiency by applying excessive amounts of calcium or induce signs of calcium or potassium deficiency by causing the excessive accumulation of either or both of the other two bases.

We have had to change our idea of what constitutes a deficiency because of new data obtained from analyses of leaves from plants exhibiting deficiency symptoms caused by excessive accumulations of other elements. The results of leaf analyses have demonstrated that it is not necessary for the percentage—or absolute amount—of an element in the leaf to drop below a definite level in order for a deficiency to exist. The controlling factor in the occurrence of a deficiency is the relationship or balance between the level of the critical element and the levels of all of the other elements in the leaf.

That a low level of an element in the leaves of a plant results in characteristic symptoms of a deficiency only when some other element or elements are unproportionately high can be well illustrated by comparing the analyses of leaves from tung trees grown under different conditions of soil fertility. The accompanying chart shows the percentage of five elements in the leaves of tung trees under various conditions of fertility.

The orchard at Lamont, Fla., is one of the highest yielding tung orchards in the United States. Although the concentrations of the mineral nutrients in the leaves from trees in this orchard may not indicate the best possible balance, they do represent a high level of nutritional intensity and balance. The leaf analyses from the trees at Pine Grove, La., represent extreme contrasts with those from Lamont. The level of each element is only about one-half of that found for the same element in the leaves from the Lamont orchard, yet the elements occur in very nearly the same proportions in the leaves from both orchards. Because of the low level of all of the elements in the leaves from Pine Grove, these trees made little growth and yielded poorly. However, because a proper balance between the elements was maintained in the leaves, no symptons of malnutrition other than reduced growth and yield appeared.

If we look at the results of some of the other leaf analyses shown in the chart, we can see the effects of increasing the leaf content of only part of the mineral nutrients. The data from the orchard at Brooker,

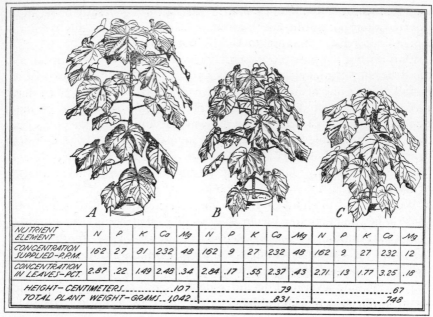

NUTRIENT ELEMENT	N	P	K	Ca	Mg	N	P	K	Ca	Mg	N	P	K	Ca	Mg
CONCENTRATION SUPPLIED—P.P.M.	162	27	81	232	48	162	9	27	232	48	162	9	27	232	12
CONCENTRATION IN LEAVES—PCT.	2.87	.22	1.49	2.48	.34	2.84	.17	.55	2.37	.43	2.71	.13	1.77	3.25	.18
HEIGHT—CENTIMETERS	107					79					67				
TOTAL PLANT WEIGHT—GRAMS	1,042					831					748				

Here are three 8-month-old seedling tung trees grown in sand cultures. All received solutions containing the same concentrations of the essential elements other than those listed under each seedling. Seedling A made good growth indicating a good balance of nutrients; seedling B received insufficient potassium in proportion to the other nutrients. Note from data under seedling B the increased accumulation of magnesium in the leaves along with the decreased potassium accumulation. Less growth is the only evidence of nutritional unbalance; seedling C did not get enough magnesium. The increased accumulation of both potassium and calcium, accompanied by decreased magnesium accumulation, adversely affected growth.

Fla., show what could be expected were trees in the condition of those at Pine Grove given a "complete fertilizer" consisting of only nitrogen, phosphorus, and potassium. The levels of these three elements in the leaves from the trees at Brooker are even higher than those found in the good orchard at Lamont. The levels of calcium and magnesium, however, are even lower than those in the leaves from Pine Grove. This extreme unbalance resulted in severe symptoms of magnesium deficiency and greatly reduced growth and yield.

The data for the leaf analysis from one of the orchards at Lloyd, Fla., indicate what might be expected should an orchard in the condition of that at Pine Grove be fertilized with only nitrogen, phosphorus, and magnesium. Here, the leaf content of these three elements is very nearly that of the leaves from the Lamont orchard, while the contents of potassium and calcium are almost identical to those from Pine Grove. This unbalance resulted in the appearance of potassium-deficiency symptoms, poor growth, and low yield. The analysis of leaves from the other orchard at Lloyd illustrates still another unbalanced condition due to improper fertilization. In this case, nitrogen, phosphorus, and calcium have been maintained at high levels, while potassium and particularly magnesium have remained low. The result has been the occurrence of magnesium-deficiency symptoms.

The accompanying drawing shows some of the relationship between leaf composition and growth, certain of the competitive effects among the three major bases, and decreased growth as the only sign of nutrient unbalance. Compare the leaf analysis data given at the bottom of the illustration and those given in the chart and you will see the similarity in the concentrations of the mineral elements found in leaves from trees grown in properly conducted sand-culture experiments and those found in the leaves of field-grown trees. This similarity makes possible the interpretation of leaf analyses from field-grown trees on the basis of data obtained from sand-culture experiments.

Samuel Merrill, Jr., formerly of the United States Laboratory for Tung Investigations, Bogalusa, La., and S. R. Greer, of the Mississippi Agricultural Experiment Station, Poplarville, Miss., have obtained leaf analyses and growth measurements on tung trees that show that, when the concentration of all the essential elements with the exception of nitrogen and phosphorus are high, it is necessary to increase the accumulation of both elements in order to increase growth. The application of either of these elements alone did not result in increased growth, even though the leaf content of the applied element increased.

The necessity for maintaining a proper balance among the elements in the leaf is not restricted to the five elements so far discussed. The so-called minor elements—iron, manganese, zinc, copper, and boron—must be accumulated in the proper proportions to one another and to the other elements if satisfactory crop production is to be maintained. Also, just as is the case with the other nutrient elements, the accumulation of the minor element in the leaves is not dependent alone on their available concentration, but is influenced by the available concentrations of all of the other elements.

Experiments with the tung tree have shown that the appearance of symptoms associated with manganese deficiency may result from a high accumulation of any one of the three major bases, and that these symptoms are the most severe when all three of the bases are high in proportion to manganese. It has also been demonstrated that the three major bases exert the same influence on iron, zinc, copper, and boron. Thus, conditions promoting increased accumulations of calcium, magnesium, and potassium work in two ways to bring about deficiencies of one or more of the minor elements: First, by depressing their accumulation, and second, by increasing the concentrations required in the leaf to create a proper balance with the other elements.

Because the accumulation of each of the minor elements is affected to a different degree by the accumulation of each of the major bases, an unbalanced accumulation of potassium, calcium, and magnesium may also result in an unbalanced relationship between two or more of the minor elements. In experiments with tung trees, for example, too low a level of potassium in proportion to calcium and magnesium has resulted in an unfavorably high ratio of manganese to copper in the leaves. Other examples of similar phenomena have been observed on a number of different crop plants. For instance, boron toxicity may occur when the level of one or more of the three major bases is unduly low, yet at high levels of the bases the plant may become boron deficient. This deficiency is not the result of depressing the boron content of the leaves below a critical level, but is caused by an unfavorable balance between boron and one or more of the bases.

It has been long known, and demonstrated on numerous crop plants, that an excess of iron in proportion to manganese may induce manganese deficiency and that an excess of manganese in proportion to iron may induce iron deficiency.

S. G. Gilbert and M. Drosdoff, of the United States Laboratory for Tung Investigations, Gainesville, Fla., and H. M. Sell, of the Michigan Agricultural Experiment Station, have demonstrated that increasing the nitrogen content of tung leaves already low in copper will result in severe copper-deficiency symptoms. This was found to be true even though the copper content of the leaves in the fall when the copper-deficiency symptoms were most severe was higher than that of the leaves early in the growing season when the copper deficiency was much less pronounced.

Only a few of the more important relationships between the essential elements have been discussed here. Many other relationships and other instances of decreased growth or other symptoms of malnutrition resulting from improper nutritional balance within the plant have been demonstrated on a number of crop plants. The relationships between the elements and the examples of unbalance which have been given should indicate to the reader that the problem of plant nutrition is by no means a simple one. It should also be evident that the use of deficiency symptoms to diagnose nutritional difficulties is like waiting until the horse is stolen before locking the stable. In order to reap the maximum returns from the land our crop plants must be maintained in a well-balanced nutritional condition. This cannot be accomplished through hit-or-miss fertilization but must result from the integration and application of all of our available knowledge concerning the nutrient requirements of each crop, the nutrient-supplying power of our soils, and the effects of the rate of supply of each element on the accumulation and function of all the other elements in the plant.

It is unfortunate that our present knowledge in these respects is too inadequate for most crops to permit the determination of their fertilizer requirements by means of leaf analysis. It is hoped that such knowledge will be accumulated in the near future. When such knowledge is available, it should be possible for properly trained soil scientists and plant physiologists to make accurate fertilizer recommendations on the basis of complete leaf analyses.

THE AUTHORS

C. B. Shear, a physiologist in the Bureau of Plant Industry, Soils, and Agricultural Engineering, has been working on the nutritional requirements of the tung tree since 1939. He has made special studies of the nutrient-element balance and the determination of the nutrient requirements of plants through leaf analysis. He is a graduate of the University of Maryland.

H. L. Crane, horticulturist, Bureau of Plant Industry, Soils, and Agricultural Engineering, has been in charge of the Bureau's investigations on nut crops since 1935. He is largely responsible for the research required for the successful development of the pecan and tung industries. In 1946 he visited China as tung specialist on the China-United States Agricultural Mission. Dr. Crane is a graduate of Cornell.

FOR FURTHER READING

Boynton, Damon, and Burrell, A. B.: *Potassium Induced Magnesium Deficiency in the McIntosh Apple Tree,* Soil Science, Baltimore, volume 58, pages 441–454, 1944.

Merrill, Samuel, Jr., and Greer, S. R.: *Three Years' Results in Fertilization of Tung Seedlings in the Nursery,* American Society for Horticultural Science, Proceedings, volume 47, 1946.

Shear, C. B., Crane, H. L., and Myers, A. T.: *Nutrient-element Balance: A Fundamental Concept in Plant Nutrition,* American Society for Horticultural Science, Proceedings, volume 47, 1946.

Wallace, T.: *Magnesium Deficiency of Fruit Trees,* Journal of Pomology and Horticultural Science, London, volume 17, pages 150–166, 1939.

Walsh, Thomas, and O'Donohoe, T. F.: *Magnesium Deficiency in Some Crop Plants in Relation to the Level of Potassium Nutrition,* Journal of Agricultural Science, volume 35, pages 254–263, 1945.

ALSO, IN THIS BOOK

Irrigation in the West

by GEORGE D. CLYDE

MORE THAN 20 million acres of land west of the ninety-seventh meridian can be used successfully for farming and livestock production only because it is irrigated. Private enterprise irrigates about four-fifths of this total, the Federal Government about one-fifth.

In planning and operating irrigation systems, one has to know how much water the crops will need and how much more will be lost, through evaporation and seepage, in conveying and applying the needed amount. The need of applying just the right amount is recognized by courts and engineers responsible for allocating limited water supplies and by farmers among whom the supplies are divided. Irrigation should be planned so as to give the crops enough moisture but not more than enough. If more water is applied at any time than the soil of the root zone can hold, the excess will percolate out of the root zone and go to waste or the soil will become waterlogged.

Farm crops differ in the amounts of water they require. Any one crop needs different amounts in different soils, at different stages of growth, and in different kinds of weather. Plants use more water in warm weather than when it is cool. Winds, especially warm winds, increase the transpiration of plants and the evaporation from soils. For best growth, soil moisture should be easily available to plants from the time the seed is deposited in the soil until the crop matures. The quantity of irrigation water required depends chiefly on the rate at which the crop uses the water and the length of the growing season of the crop.

Water for irrigation comes chiefly from surface streams. A little is pumped from natural reservoirs under the ground.

Over the great part of the West, precipitation during the wet season occurs chiefly as snowfall. Snow accumulates on high mountains; in

602

melting it feeds the surface streams. The streams fed by snow melt reach their highest stages in the spring—not in the season when irrigation water is most needed. Part of their flow, therefore, must be stored artificially, in surface or subsurface reservoirs. Frequently it is possible to divert a stream over a spreading ground so that its waters will percolate into an underground water basin, and thus to increase the supply of water available for pumping.

A farmer or stockman who depends on irrigation needs to know at the beginning of the season about how much irrigation water will be available to him, so that he can adjust his plans to his water resources. In 12 Western States having mountainous areas on which snow accumulates, Federal and State investigators have developed methods of surveying snow and forecasting streamflow that are now widely used in this country and in Canada.

The value of water-supply forecasts is illustrated by one of our experiences with drought in Utah. In 1934, snow surveys on April 1 indicated that the Utah supply of irrigation water for that year would be only about 35 percent of normal. Governor Blood called a meeting of all users of water. Two emergency programs were put into operation—one to develop supplemental irrigation supplies before the crops needed them and one to conserve water drastically so as to save perennial plantings.

Under the first program, 400,000 acre-feet of water was added to the available supply in 6 weeks by pumping from wells, lowering outlets of reservoirs, draining lakes, and developing springs. Under the second program irrigation streams were united, acreages to be irrigated were reduced, and long, small irrigation ditches were abandoned. Strict water-conserving practices were put into effect among the water users. The result was that more than $5,000,000 worth of crops matured that might otherwise have been lost.

Out of 125,000 miles of irrigation canals and laterals in use in 17 Western States in 1939, all but about 5,000 miles, or 4 percent, were unlined, untreated earth channels. Such channels are the cheapest to construct, but they are expensive to maintain, and they permit seepage losses often amounting to 70 percent or more.

A lining of clay 4 inches thick, we have found, effectively reduces seepage losses from earth canals, and if such a lining is covered with a blanket of gravel it becomes highly resistant to erosion. It is, however, subject to weed growth. Bentonite with and without a mixture of soil has been used experimentally as a canal lining. Straight bentonite has a permeability of only about 0.001 foot per year, and if even as little as 2 to 10 percent of bentonite is mixed with soil, the mixture is apparently just as impermeable.

Treating channel surfaces with light oil reduces seepage, stabilizes the channel, and eliminates weed growth. The procedure is to spray 16- or

22-gravity oil under high pressure on the sides of the channel and sluice additional oil on the bottom. Three applications are needed, with enough time between them to let the oil sink in. The oil should penetrate to a depth of 8 to 10 inches. This treatment takes 1½ gallons of oil to the square yard of surface.

A simple and effective device—the Parshall flume, which may be constructed of wood, metal, or concrete—has been developed to measure streams of water ranging in volume from a few gallons per minute to 2,000 cubic feet per second. Thousands of the flumes have been installed on irrigation canals, laterals, and farm ditches throughout the irrigated areas of the West.

In many parts of the West, particularly the Southwest, irrigation is made difficult by the large quantities of sand and gravel moved along the beds of flowing streams and irrigation canals. Such materials, both when in motion and when deposited, present one of the greatest maintenance problems in irrigation projects. Sand deposited in one Colorado canal in a single day reduced its capacity from 800 to less than 500 cubic feet per second. Such deposits are expensive to remove, and the water loss they cause during the critical crop-growing season is many times the cost of removal. Four practical sand-trap devices have been developed— the vortex tube, the riffle deflector, the vane deflector, and the under-sluice. The vortex tube seems to be the best for moderately high velocities, narrow channels, and coarse materials. The other types seem preferable for moderate velocities, wide channels, and fine sediment. Sand traps installed on irrigation canals have effectively removed the bed load of sand and gravel. These sand traps save many thousands of dollars in maintenance costs each year.

The primary concern of the farmer in irrigating is to apply uniformly, at each irrigation, the full amount of water that can be held by the soil within the plant root zone until it can be consumed. Water applied to the soil is classed as consumed if it is either used by the plants or evaporated from the soil surface.

The efficiency of application of irrigation water on a farm is the ratio of the amount of irrigation water that is stored in the soil root zone to the total amount delivered to the farm. For high irrigation efficiency, the water must be applied to the land surface in such a way that it will percolate into the soil at a fairly uniform rate. To bring this about, the farmer should know the water-holding capacity and other characteristics of his soil and the depth of the plant root zone, measure the water he applies at each irrigation, and limit it to the storage capacity of the soil within the root zone.

Tests made on Utah farms over a 5-year period indicated that water-application efficiencies averaged 34 percent for valley-land farms, 38 percent for foothill farms, and 44 percent for benchland farms. Studies made in 1940 in the Pecos Valley of New Mexico showed efficiencies of 22 to 76 percent for corn, cotton, orchards, and alfalfa. Studies on potatoes in eastern Idaho in 1945 showed a variation in efficiency from 25 to 44 percent.

Land preparation, including leveling, is the first requirement for efficient irrigation. An adequate distribution system with suitable control structures is important. On relatively few farms are both requirements met. High irrigation efficiencies mean saving of water, reduced costs of water application, greater profits to the farmer, and conservation of soil and water resources.

In order to prepare his land adequately for irrigation, the farmer needs good maps indicating topography, soil classifications, and soil profiles. Such maps enable him to decide on the sizes and slopes of fields and to plan the necessary land leveling and the lay-out of laterals and field ditches for best methods of applying water.

Size of stream and length of run should be adapted to slope of land and permeability of soil. On soils of high permeability, the water should be applied quickly. This requires large streams and short runs. For soils of low permeability, small streams and longer runs may be used. Care should be taken to avoid excessive surface runoff and deep-percolation losses. The degree of slope that permits safe irrigation and the desirable size of stream depend on erosion characteristics of the soil.

Studies made in Utah indicate that, on areas of loose silty loam and sandy loam soils, irrigation furrow slopes of 2 percent and higher are excessive and that harmful erosion results when irrigation streams of 10 gallons per minute, or more, are run into each furrow. Furthermore, doubling the furrow slope more than doubles the erosion of loose silty loam and sandy loam soils by the same sized streams.

Close-growing crops like hay, small grain, and pasture on land that is rolling to steep may be irrigated by spreading water from contour ditches. Usually the contour ditches are small and are laid out on a flat grade. The distance between ditches depends on the slope, the size of stream available, and the permeability of the soil. To control the flow and obtain uniform distribution, a furrow should be plowed parallel to and immediately below the contour ditch, the soil being thrown uphill. Water may be diverted into the furrow from the contour ditch through a small wooden "tube outlet box" with a slide-gate control. From the furrow the water spreads in a thin sheet over the land surface.

On even, gentle slopes, border dikes may be used for irrigation. The water is confined between low earthen dikes spaced 20 to 100 feet apart according to slope, size of stream, and length of run. The longitudinal slope of the border strip is kept low, and its cross slope is usually zero. The border method permits quick application and uniform distribution of water.

Row crops, such as corn, beets, and potatoes, are usually irrigated by the furrow method. In furrow irrigation the water flows to the field through one or more head ditches and is conducted to the rows through any one of several types of delivery structures. The head ditch is provided with checks—small metal or canvas dams—to raise the water level. From the head ditch the flow is carried to a regulation bay, or secondary ditch. From the regulation bay, water is supplied to each row by means of a spile. Raising or lowering the water in the regulation bay will control the flow to the rows so as to get uniform distribution and good penetration without erosion.

The use of plastic siphon tubes in place of lath boxes or other spiles has been perfected by the Nebraska Agricultural Experiment Station. The siphon tube has many advantages over the common type of spile. It can be placed over the ditch bank without disturbing the bank and can be used without a regulation bay. The tubes are light, strong, and durable. They are 1 to 2 inches in diameter and 30 to 40 inches long. A popular size is the 1½-inch diameter, which will discharge 13 gallons a minute with a head of 2 inches. By raising or lowering the discharge end of the tube the rate of flow can be controlled. The use of siphon tubes is saving farmers money in labor and reducing soil losses and water cost through better control.

On steep or uneven ground, portable pipes serve as a convenient means of irrigation. Sprinkler systems, stationary or portable, are recommended for irrigation use where the land is too rough for surface irrigation and cannot be leveled because the soil is too shallow; where the soil is too porous to hold sufficient quantities of water from surface irrigation in the root zone; where the stream of irrigation water is too small for reasonably rapid application by surface methods; where land slopes steeply and soils are either highly erodible or relatively impermeable; and where water is expensive or labor scarce.

Wherever irrigation is practiced, drainage problems are likely to arise. As the higher lands in a valley are irrigated, the lower lands become wet and sometimes alkaline. Both ancient and modern history offer examples of the abandonment of once fertile, productive areas because of waterlogging or the accumulation of alkali. Research has shown how these conditions can be avoided or controlled by applying irrigation water properly and by removing excess water and alkali.

Methods of locating the source of water that is causing a drainage problem and charting its flow pattern have been improved greatly in the past few years.

Among various types of hydraulic probe, available for charting lines of flow in the field, is the piezometer, developed through cooperative research in the Imperial Valley of California and in Delta, Utah. This device is a ¼- or ⅜-inch galvanized iron pipe, which is quickly and easily driven with a jackhammer into the ground to depths as great as 300 feet. After being flushed out and primed, it forms an observation well that reflects accurately the hydrostatic pressure within the soil at its termination point. When a series of piezometers are set in the field so as to terminate above, below, and out from either side of a tile line, they reflect a pattern of hydrostatic pressure around the tile line from which streamlines can be drawn. From such drawings it is possible to trace the source and direction of seepage from canals and to chart the effectiveness of tile systems, open drains, and interception lines; to determine the presence of artesian wells; and, with supplementary information on soil permeability, to predict the effect of pumping from relief wells.

THE AUTHOR

George D. Clyde is chief of the Division of Irrigation, Soil Conservation Service. He started learning about irrigation during his boyhood on his father's farm in Utah. He was graduated in agricultural engineering from the Utah State Agricultural College, and taught civil engineering there after graduate studies at the University of California. In 1945, after 22 years of work at the Utah State College, Mr. Clyde resigned as dean of the school of engineering and director of research work in the engineering experiment station to join the Soil Conservation Service.

FOR FURTHER READING

Christiansen, J. E.: *Ground Water Studies in Relation to Drainage,* Agricultural Engineering, volume 24, pages 339–342, 1943.

Donnan, W. W., and Christiansen, J. E.: *Piezometers for Ground Water Investigations,* Western Construction News, volume 19, 1944.

Harris, Karl, and Hawkins, R. S.: *Irrigation Requirements of Cotton on Clay Loam Soils in Salt River Valley,* Arizona Agricultural Experiment Station Bulletin 181, 1942.

Israelsen, O. W., Clyde, George D., and Lauritzen, C. W.: *Soil Erosion in Small Irrigation Furrows,* Utah Agricultural Experiment Station Bulletin 320, 1946.

Israelsen, O. W., Criddle, Wayne D., Fuhriman, Dean K., and Hansen, Vaughn E.: *Water-Application Efficiencies in Irrigation,* Utah Agricultural Experiment Station Bulletin 311, 1944.

Parshall, R. L.: *The Parshall Measuring Flume,* Colorado Agricultural Experiment Station Bulletin 448, 1945.

Pillsbury, Arthur F.: *Observations of Use of Irrigation Water in Coachella Valley,* California Agricultural Experiment Station Bulletin 649, 1946.

Rohwer, Carl: *Putting Down and Developing Wells for Irrigation,* U. S. D. A. Circular 546, Revised, 1941.

Rohwer, Carl: *Design and Operation of Small Irrigation Pumping Plants,* U. S. D. A. Circular 678, 1943.

Making More of Irrigation

by B. T. SHAW and O. J. KELLEY

WE HAVE a long way to go before we reach a ceiling on crop yields. Just lately we have realized how great are the returns obtained from the use of several good practices in combination—how a farmer can put two and two together and get more than four.

An example is given by L. M. Ware of the Alabama Agricultural Experiment Station. Sweet corn failed completely in a field at Auburn, when no commercial fertilizer was used, he reported in 1945; the plant food in the soil was inadequate to support corn production. But when a commercial fertilizer was added, a yield of corn valued at $153 an acre was obtained. When a commercial fertilizer was added and the corn irrigated, a crop was produced that had a value of $253 an acre. When a commercial fertilizer and manure were added, the crop was valued at $439.50 an acre. When a commercial fertilizer and manure were added and the corn was irrigated, a crop was produced that had a value of $553 an acre. When a commercial fertilizer and manure were added, a crop of vetch was turned, and the corn was irrigated, a yield was produced that had a value of $699.50. Each fertility factor artificially supplied helped to provide more nearly the optimum conditions for corn production. The effect on the yield of corn was cumulative. When all factors were supplied, a yield of 13,845 pounds of marketable green corn was produced.

Another illustration of our thesis comes from B. A. Krantz of the North Carolina Agricultural Experiment Station. In 1944, yields of corn of more than 100 bushels an acre were reported in a section of the country where corn normally yields from 10 to 20 bushels an acre. Under ordinary conditions of spacing (about 4,000 to 5,000 plants on an acre), fertilization (0 to 30 pounds of nitrogen to the acre), and cul-.

tivation (too deep and too close to the plant so that roots are pruned), and with ordinary open-pollinated varieties, 20 bushels would have been normal. With shallow cultivation and ordinary spacing and fertilization, adapted hybrids yielded up to 54 bushels an acre. North Carolina hybrid 1028 gave a yield of 84 bushels when the nitrogen fertilization was boosted to 120 pounds. Then, by increasing the number of plants per acre to 8,000, a yield of 100 bushels was obtained.

During the war, research was initiated to see what could be done to speed up rubber production with guayule under irrigation. The standard practice for growing guayule then was to transplant nursery-grown plants 20 inches apart in rows that were 28 inches apart. The plants were irrigated until they were established and then were left to depend on normal rainfall. The yield of shrub in 19 months was 0.86 ton an acre. At this moisture level, increasing the number of plants on an acre raised the yield to 1.20 tons because of the more efficient utilization of water. Nitrogen fertilization was without effect. Increasing the supply of water but keeping plant spacing the same, increased the yield to 1.38 tons without nitrogen and to 1.61 tons with it. Increasing the number of plants at this higher moisture level by cutting the distance between plants in the row to $6\frac{2}{3}$ inches boosted the yield to 2.21 tons without nitrogen and 2.59 tons with it. This yield of 2.59 tons is three times that obtained by standard practice.

Great as the responses in the examples were, one wonders if they might not have been much higher. How high would the return have gone in the Alabama experiment if spacing and variable moisture had entered the experiment as in the guayule study, and different hybrids as in the North Carolina test? What would have been the effect of supplemental water on the North Carolina results? How high would the yield of guayule have been if a strain of guayule bred for high levels of nutrition and water had been used? How would controlling insect damage have affected all results? These are unanswered questions, of course, but, to repeat, it seems that we have a long way to go before we reach a ceiling on crop yields.

So much for research results. How can the farmer use them?

It is not necessary to tell anyone who has herded a stream of water over a farm that irrigation farming is different. The irrigator is beset with most of the hazards that plague ordinary farming: Weeds, insect pests, and plant diseases; the problem of selecting the best crop, variety, or hybrid; growing the selected crops in the best sequence; the uncertainty of continued soil fertility and the problems of maintaining it. Besides, farmers under irrigation face problems of salt accumulation in soil, the best use of available irrigation water, and erosion due to irrigation. Also, under irrigation, a greater proportion of the costs of production are in the form of fixed charges that must be met regard-

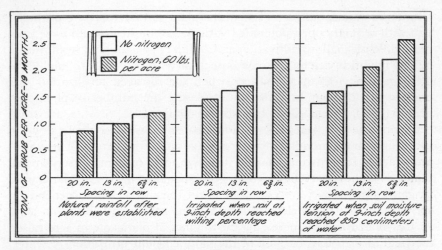

Research started during the war to speed up guayule rubber production by irrigation resulted in yields three times as high as under the old standard methods.

less of the yield of the crop, or even if there is a total crop failure. Thus, while the possibilities of getting larger returns are greater where the hazards of drought have been eliminated, the financial risks are correspondingly increased unless superior yields are assured.

Most irrigation farmers know and practice many features of good soil management. They realize that all irrigation waters contain salts, and that it is necessary, therefore, to leach the soil occasionally or salts will accumulate. They know the value of maintaining a high organic matter content in soil, which usually can be accomplished through good crop rotations and liberal use of manure. Irrigation farmers who have sloping lands realize that often it is necessary to plant on the contour to reduce erosion to a minimum. While these and other good practices for irrigation are well known and, if used, usually will result in relatively high yields, the yields without a doubt are not the highest economic yields obtainable.

The irrigation farmer should not be content with using water to eliminate the hazard of drought, even though this results in an annual yield of alfalfa of 8 tons an acre, as compared to annual yields of 3 to 4 tons in the humid regions. He should ask himself, why not 12 tons? He cannot afford to use row widths and spacings of plants in the row that were found to be satisfactory in the humid region where water limited yields. He cannot assume that since his yields are higher than those of humid-region farmers he cannot make profitable use of fertilizers. He must not be content with superior strains of plants developed in the humid region, but must select plants adapted to the favorable environment he can create. In short, the irrigation farmer should ask himself: "Now that I have eliminated the hazard of drought, how should I modify my other farming practices to take full advantage of my opportunities?"

One modification on many irrigation farms that would result in higher returns is an increased use of commercial fertilizers. For a long time western farmers boasted of their fertile soils and too many still believe that it is a reflection on their farming if they have to use fertilizers to maintain yields. This prejudice is gradually breaking down, as evidenced by the rapid increases in fertilizer consumption during recent years. The country as a whole used 7.4 percent more plant food in 1944 than in 1943, but in the West the increase was 30.6 percent. When compared with the 5-year (1935–39) average, usage in 1944 was 243 percent of prewar in the western region. This is marked progress, but even so, western farmers have only begun to exploit the possibilities of using fertilizers in crop production under irrigation.

Some irrigators have tried using fertilizers and have concluded that the yield responses obtained were not sufficient to be economic. Others have reaped large increases through fertilization. One important fact in this connection is that intelligent use of fertilizers will require that other management practices be adjusted in keeping with the increase in plant nutrients. With higher levels of fertility we will want more plants per acre and we will use more water than was used in growing half of the potential crop.

Consider again the guayule experiment. It is readily seen that plants that received the amount of water under the standard practice did not respond to nitrogen. This was true regardless of the spacing at which the plants were grown. Had this been the only moisture treatment used in the experiment, it would have been concluded, certainly, that there was ample nitrogen in the soil for guayule and that added nitrogen would not increase yield. But when we consider all the data, it is quite evident that under the conditions of that moisture treatment, water was the factor limiting plant growth, and that regardless of the fertilizer added, there was not enough moisture to produce yields potentially possible with the natural soil fertility. We begin to see evidence that when a sufficient number of plants was supplied with sufficient water they produced enough growth to cause nitrogen to be a limiting factor in growth. All plants that received even more moisture benefited from added nitrogen. The thicker the plants, the more benefit obtained.

This experiment points up the need for studying in combination the various important factors affecting plant growth. It also shows how extremely important it is for farmers to have the right combination of practices if they are to obtain potential maximum production.

On any farm, at whatever level of soil fertility, maximum plant growth cannot be obtained if moisture is a limiting factor. Where moisture and plant nutrients are supplied in adequate amounts, the highest production will be obtained only when there are enough plants to utilize fully the space available for growth. It is only when the best combination of the various practices is obtained that the farmer may expect a maximum yield.

THE AUTHORS

B. T. Shaw became assistant administrator of the Agricultural Research Administration in 1947, after 4 years as agronomist in the Bureau of Plant Industry, Soils, and Agricultural Engineering. He grew up on irrigated farms in Utah and Idaho. His undergraduate training was completed at Utah State Agricultural College and his postgraduate studies at the Ohio State University.

O. J. Kelley is a soil scientist, Division of Soils, Fertilizers, and Irrigation, Bureau of Plant Industry, Soils, and Agricultural Engineering. He also is a westerner. He did his undergraduate work at Colorado State College and received his postgraduate training at Ohio State University.

FOR FURTHER READING

Kelley, O. J. Haise, H. R., Markham, L. C., and Hunter, A. S.: *Increased Rubber Production From Thickly Seeded Guayule,* Journal of American Society of Agronomy, July 1946.

Krantz, B. A.: *Corn Fertilization Studies in 1944,* Agronomy Information Circular 139, North Carolina Agricultural Experiment Station, January 1945.

National Resources Planning Board: *The Pecos River Joint Investigation: Reports of the Participating Agencies: Consumptive Use of Water,* part 3, section 3, 1942.

Taylor, C. A., and Furr, J. R.: *Use of Soil Moisture and Fruit-Growth Records for Checking Irrigation Practices in Citrus Orchards,* U. S. D. A. Circular 426, 1937.

Ware, L. M.: *Supplying Optimum Conditions for Truck Corps in the South,* Market Growers Journal, February 1945.

Young, Arthur A.: *Irrigation Requirements of California Crops,* State of California Bulletin 51, 1946.

The Tax We Pay to Insects

by F. C. BISHOPP

MAN IS engaged in a constant battle against insects. Doubts about the outcome have been expressed many times. Maurice Maeterlinck said insects are our rivals here on earth—and perhaps our successors. W. J. Holland prophesied that the last living thing on the globe will be some active insect sitting on a dead lichen, which will represent the last of plant life. During the years of severe insect visitations from Biblical times down to this very day the destruction wrought gives point to such dismal expressions. But, on the other hand, the results forthcoming from research lend hope that man will overcome his insect foes and reduce the extent to which he provides food for the insect hordes.

We must not forget, however, that the battle is still on and that insects have the advantage because they can multiply with incredible speed and adapt themselves to almost any condition and an endless variety of foods. Furthermore, the number of distinct kinds of insects on earth probably exceeds a million, and the number of individual insects is so great that it is impossible for us to set down the figure.

In 1931, L. O. Howard, that venerable scientist who, as chief of the unit that is now the Bureau of Entomology and Plant Quarantine, led the insect fighters of the Department of Agriculture for half a century, vividly brought to attention in his *Insect Menace* the bitterness of this struggle and the need for man to sharpen his wits and weapons if he is to survive.

The previous year Dr. Howard pointed out to a group of Maryland scientists that many forms of life have been tried, have been found wanting, and have disappeared in the course of the ages, but the insect has persisted: "The human type may be one of nature's experiments that will fail," he said. "It has not been in existence long enough to have been

613

thoroughly tried out. Prophets of evil tell us that human overpopulation of the world is approaching, and approaching rapidly; that mass starvation is sure to come . . . if greater production of plant food cannot be stimulated or if new foods cannot be invented. There is a third way of postponing the coming of the starvation era, and that is by the stopping of all waste. Probably the greatest of these wastes is the tremendous but unnecessary tribute that we pay to insects. In the United States alone, the labor of one million men each year is lost through their damage to crops and to our other vital interests."

The loss occasioned by some of the more important mites, ticks, and insects in the United States was estimated by J. A. Hyslop in 1938 to be more than $1,600,000,000 annually. Although our insect enemies assess this burdensome tax on our people, on the other side of the ledger we have a number of insects that contribute millions to our food resources through the pollination of our seed and fruit crops. Confronted with this situation, there is every reason for the entomologists to put forth Herculean efforts to control our insect enemies and to protect our insect friends. There is also every reason for our people to become familiar with these foes and friends and with the weapons scientists are developing to combat the former and means they are evolving to husband the latter.

Some of these discoveries and developments were war-born, others had their inception before the war, and still others were hastened because of war needs, partly because of opportunities for testing them on a large scale in many parts of the world. The simple and effective ways developed to combat lice on humans kept our armies free from the scourge of typhus and avoided heavy loss of life among civil populations.

Typhus was kept from our own country by the disinfesting of prisoners and others before they entered the United States. Methyl bromide fumigation for ridding clothing and equipment of vermin plus the MYL and DDT powders developed by the Bureau of Entomology and Plant Quarantine were largely responsible for these results.

The contribution of the Department entomologists who devised means of combating mosquito carriers of malaria, dengue fever, and filariasis, scrub typhus mites, and dysentery-carrying flies was of great value in our military operations. Their research gave rise to such notable contributions as the aerosol bomb, mosquito repellents, dimethyl phthalate as a typhus mite killer, a benzyl benzoate-DDT formula for the control of lice and scabies, and DDT as a killer of mosquito wrigglers and adults.

Although rapid advancement was made through research in the insecticide field during the war period, sight should not be lost of the sound information gathered through preceding years upon which such advances must be based. The full answers to complete biological problems come slowly, and in the case of DDT and other insecticides developed during the war much still remains to be learned.

Insecticides are only one phase of our armament in the war against insects. True, their use is the most direct and spectacular. Their promiscuous and improper use, however, may lead to other serious problems. There is especial danger of destroying the beneficial forms of life, including insect predators, fish, frogs, or even birds by the use of a material such as DDT. The killing of honeybees and other insect pollinators by insecticides must be prevented if we are to produce abundant yields of legume seed and of many fruits and other crops. There is also danger of plant injury from the use of insecticides, either directly from improperly compounded or diluted material or through soil contamination. Research has not only found some effective insect killers but it has indicated the precautions that must be taken in their use to safeguard the crops, wildlife, and health of our domestic animals and ourselves.

A successful campaign against the multitude of insect species with their diverse and often subtle methods of attack requires every type of weapon and carefully planned strategy. Modification of agricultural and other practices is of great importance in combating insects. These include time and method of planting and cultivation, choice of varieties, fertilization, methods of harvesting, disposal of waste, rotation of crops, water-table control, use of traps, methods o f constructing buildings, silvicultural practices, breeding of insect-resistant varieties, use of natural enemies, and proper wrapping, packing, and storing of commodities.

All these problems have received attention from our research workers and some of the interesting and important discoveries and developments are set forth in the articles that follow.

THE AUTHOR

F. C. Bishopp is assistant chief in charge of research in the Bureau of Entomology and Plant Quarantine. He has been engaged in research on various entomological problems for some 40 years. In his early work he dealt with insects affecting cotton and later for many years studied the relation of insects to man and animals and how these pests can be controlled. Dr. Bishopp was born and reared on a ranch in Colorado and educated at Colorado State College and Ohio State University.

ALSO, IN THIS BOOK

The Chemistry of DDT

by H. L. HALLER and RUTH L. BUSBEY

OLD PEOPLE in Germany used to say that moths would not attack woolens dyed green. The saying was untrue, but it influenced the investigations that led to the discovery of DDT as an insecticide. Born thus of a fiction, the almost miraculous killer of disease-carrying insects is still the center of a good deal of fiction.

In a few years it has excited the imagination of scientists and laymen alike—and rightly, for it is effective against a wider variety of agricultural pests than any other synthetic insecticide heretofore tested; it gives control of those history-old scourges, the body louse, the mosquito, and the fly; and, wonderful to relate, its effect lasts, sometimes as long as a year. Evidence of the tremendous interest in DDT is that more than 2,000 articles have appeared in scientific, trade, and general magazines and newspapers about it, almost all of them acclaiming its merits. A colleague of ours, R. C. Roark, in 1944 compiled a 12-page list of publications that had appeared on the subject since 1874; in the next few months, so great was the flood of writing on it, he had to revise and expand the list twice.

This tremendous interest in one compound created one near-fiction involving DDT, the impression in some minds that few studies have been made to find chemicals effective for the control of injurious insects. Actually, the use of chemicals to control insect pests has been going on for centuries. The earliest insecticides were arsenicals and sulfur. Systematic attempts to control insects were first made about 1865 when, in this country, paris green, which was available as a paint pigment, was used to destroy the Colorado potato beetle. Paris green was so effective that for many years it was the most widely used agricultural insecticide; even today our farmers and gardeners use about 4 million pounds of it a year.

In 1892 lead arsenate was developed for use against the larva of the gypsy moth, a serious foe of shade and forest trees. Lead arsenate was found to be effective against many insect pests; its use has continued to increase, and about 80 million pounds of it were used in 1945.

Actually, also, the modern era of the development of new insecticides began about 1910. Investigators here and abroad became interested in how insecticides kill and emphasized the importance of physical characteristics, such as wetting and spreading of sprays on foliage and insects. At that time some of the more important insecticides and fungicides, the arsenicals, nicotine, pyrethrum, derris, lonchocarpus, lime-sulfur, and bordeaux mixture, had been known a long time and some of them had been in use. Much of the effort since then has been devoted to the study of these and related products in order to discover their range of usefulness; to increase their efficiency; and to find more powerful substitutes, safer to man, domestic animals, and plants.

The studies leading to the discovery of DDT as an insecticide can in a measure be traced back to some research initiated about 30 years ago. In 1915 the Bayer dyestuffs company in Leverkusen, Germany, undertook an intensive investigation of chemicals that might be suitable for mothproofing wool. The early investigations were influenced by the saying that woolens dyed green are not attacked by the clothes moth. Investigations proved the saying to be erroneous. Further investigation showed that the early green dyestuffs had a bluish shade, and in order to produce better greens it was the practice to add a yellow dye. For this purpose, Martius Yellow, 2,4-dinitro-1-naphthol, was commonly used. Tests showed the compound to be effective against the clothes moth. For practical use, however, it had faults, primarily color and lack of fastness. The findings were followed by the testing of many synthetic organic compounds against the clothes moth and led to the development of several products; one group was named "Eulans."

The "Eulans" achieved some commercial success and stimulated interest in mothproofing agents by other chemical manufacturers. Soon after the "Eulans" were made commercially available, J. R. Geigy, S. A., in Switzerland started a research on mothproofing agents. After an extensive series of investigations, the Geigy firm developed and marketed a class of mothproofing agents known as "Mitins." The studies in the Geigy organization on mothproofing agents were expanded to the testing of compounds against other insects and led to the discovery of DDT.

Probably the most accurate account of the introduction of DDT into this country is given by Victor Froelicher, an official of the Geigy company in this country. In an article in Soap and Sanitary Chemicals, he wrote:

"In August 1942, we received from Switzerland 100 pounds each of 'Gesarol' spray, containing 5 percent active ingredient, and 'Gesarol' dust, containing 3 percent active ingredient. At about the same time, we received news that Maj. A. R. W. De Jonge, American Military Attaché at Berne, Switzerland, had shown great interest in our new lousicidal composition called 'Neocid,' which contained the same active ingredient as the 'Gesarol' products. It was indicated that 'Neocid' had great significance in controlling the typhus-carrying body louse.

"On October 16, 1942, we contacted Dr. R. C. Roark at Washington, and handed him a Swiss report giving the results of tests which had been made with 'Gesarol' on a great variety of insects, some of which, like the Colorado potato beetle, are familiar to us in the United States.

"Dr. R. Wiesmann, Assistant Chief of the Swiss Agricultural Station, was responsible for these reports, which, incidentally, seemed altogether too good to be true. These reports indicated that 'Gesarol' was not only a contact, but a stomach poison as well. Entomologists were at first reluctant to accept the statements which were made, and frankly, we felt the same skepticism, for, of over 3,000 products which had been tested by the United States Department of Agriculture, a rare one or two could claim both contact and stomach insecticidal properties. . .

"Up to that time nothing was known of the chemical constitution of the product, as little factual information could be obtained because of the difficulties of communication. Dr. H. L. Haller at Beltsville had extracted the active ingredient in 'Gesarol,' and analyzed and synthesized some of the active ingredient in his laboratory, simultaneous with which there arrived . . . the information of its chemical composition."

The symbol DDT is a contraction for dichloro-diphenyl-trichloro-ethane, the generic name of the active insecticidal principle. Theoretically, there are 45 possible dichloro-diphenyl-trichloroethanes, excluding stereoisomeric forms. However, the term DDT has been confined to the product obtained on condensation of chloral (or its alcoholate or hydrate) with chlorobenzene in the presence of sulfuric acid. The product thus obtained is termed technical DDT. It is a white to cream-colored powder, possessing a fruitlike odor. Its major constituent is 1-trichloro-2,2-bis(p-chlorophenyl)ethane, which has the formula $(ClC_6H_4)_2 CHCCl_3$ and is called p,p'-DDT.

This compound may be obtained pure by recrystallization of technical DDT from 95-percent ethanol. The pure compound melts at 108.5° to 109° C. It was first described in 1874 by Zeidler, who prepared it while working on his doctor's thesis at the University of Strasbourg.

The preparation of DDT is relatively simple. It requires no elaborate equipment, and all the starting materials—ethanol, chlorine, benzene, and sulfuric acid—are readily available. The basis of the commercial process is the original procedure of the first chemist to make the compound—that is, the condensation of monochlorobenzene with chloral in the presence of sulfuric acid. A considerable amount of research has been carried out in this country, as well as in Great Britain and Canada, on the optimum conditions for the condensation, such as temperature and concentration of reactants, and for preparing the starting materials.

As its name implies, technical DDT is a commercial grade. Since it melts over a range of several degrees, the solidification point rather than the melting point is used to give an indication of its purity.

Intensive studies, involving fractional crystallization, chromatographic adsorption, distillation in high vacuum, and cryoscopic analysis showed the presence of 14 different compounds in the early samples of technical DDT. The p,p'-DDT varied in the samples of different manufacturers from 65 to 75 percent. The major impurity was found to be 1-trichloro-2-(o-chlorophenyl)-2-(p-chlorophenyl)ethane (which is called o,p'-DDT) which was present to the extent of 19 to 21 percent. This compound is considerably less toxic than p,p'-DDT to insects. The other impurities were isolated in amounts ranging from 0.007 to 4.0 percent. The impurity present to the extent of 4.0 percent was identified as 1,1-dichloro-2,2-bis-(p-chlorophenyl)ethane (TDE). It is formed from dichloroacetaldehyde, an impurity in chloral, and chlorobenzene. TDE is also an effective insecticide but the other minor components are relatively nontoxic to insects.

DDT is practically insoluble in water, but is soluble in a wide variety of organic solvents, such as acetone, benzene, xylene, chloroform, carbon tetrachloride, vegetable oils, petroleum oils, and many others. Crude or unrefined kerosene can be used to prepare solutions containing 5 percent of DDT, but refined kerosenes require the addition of 10 to 20 percent of an auxiliary solvent. For this purpose xylene, cyclohexanone, and alkylated naphthalenes have been used.

When pure, p,p'-DDT is a reasonably stable compound. It can be heated at 115° to 120° C. for several hours without decomposition. Irradiation of the solid material, spread in a thin layer, for 35 hours with a mercury-vapor lamp caused only a slight depression in melting point and an alcoholic solution showed no change after exposure to sunlight for over a year. Under certain conditions (temperatures above 95°–100° C. or in some organic solvents) it has been shown that a number of materials, even in very small quantities, cause decomposition of DDT with the formation of products that are of little or no value as insecticides.

DDT Formulations

In its undiluted form DDT is not suitable for use as an insecticide. It would be uneconomical for most purposes to use so potent an agent without diluting it greatly and the physical properties of DDT make it unsuited for direct application. DDT is practically insoluble in water and by itself will not form a satisfactory suspension in water. Its crystals are so soft that they lump or cake easily, and they cannot be ground alone to make a satisfactory dust. When DDT is mixed with talcs, clays, pyrophyllite, or various other diluents, however, it can be ground to a fine powder, which can be applied as an insecticide dust or—after treatment with a wetting agent—can be suspended in water for use as a spray. DDT can be dissolved in various petroleum oils, xylene, or other organic solvents for making spray solutions or water emulsions. It has been incorporated also in insecticidal aerosols.

Dust mixtures of DDT usually are prepared by grinding technical DDT with talc, clay, pyrophyllite, sulfur, or another diluent. Because technical DDT softens at a temperature somewhat below 89° C., care must be exercised during grinding to avoid overheating the mill. In this way dusts that contain a wide range of DDT concentrations can be obtained readily. By grinding DDT with a conditioning agent, such as certain grades of silica gel, preparations containing up to 90 percent of DDT can be made that are fine and free flowing and can be diluted with any of the diluents mentioned. For most purposes the final concentration of DDT used in dusts ranges from 1 to 10 percent. By the addition of a wetting agent to the dusts, they also can be dispersed or suspended in water for use as sprays. When certain types of clays are used as the diluent, water-dispersible powders containing as much as 50 percent of DDT can be prepared without the addition of any wetting agent. The concentration of DDT in sprays prepared from water-dispersible powders is 0.1 to 5 percent.

Dusts also have been prepared by the impregnation of the diluent with a solution of DDT in a volatile solvent such as acetone or benzene. The solution may be mixed with the dust diluent, the solvent allowed to evaporate, and the mixture then ground, or the solution may be gradually sprayed into the diluent during the grinding process. Solutions of DDT in nonvolatile solvents such as certain alkylated naphthalenes from petroleum may be incorporated in the diluent provided that the amount of solvent required is not so great as to impair the dusting qualities of the mixture.

Solutions of DDT in various petroleum oils, such as kerosene, have been used for spraying or painting walls, furniture, screens in buildings, and the like. A solution containing 5 percent of DDT is most commonly used. The solubility of DDT varies greatly with the type of oil used. In the case of kerosenes the solubility is higher in those of naphthenic base than in those of paraffinic base. If the purified, deodorized type of kerosene generally used in household insect sprays is used as the solvent, it is desirable to add about 15 percent of an auxiliary solvent (for example, certain petroleum products rich in alkylated naphthalenes) to increase the solubility of the DDT, especially if the product is to be stored at low temperature. More volatile solvents, such as acetone, xylene, and dry-cleaning solvents, have been used for the preparation of DDT solutions to impregnate clothing and other fabrics.

Aqueous emulsions prepared from solutions of DDT in solvents that are substantially insoluble in water have proved very useful. Water-miscible solvents should not be used for the purpose. Two types of emulsions have been used—those in which the DDT is dissolved in a volatile solvent, such as xylene, which evaporates after spraying to leave a deposit of DDT crystals, and those in which the DDT is dissolved in a relatively nonvolatile solvent, such as a petroleum oil, which leaves the sprayed surface coated with a solution of DDT in oil after evaporation of the water. A great variety of emulsifying agents is available for the preparation of DDT emulsions. The use of excessive amounts of emulsifier should be avoided in order to prevent excessive runoff of the spray and to avoid coating of the DDT deposit by the emulsifier after evaporation of the water and solvent. A convenient type of preparation for many purposes is an emulsion concentrate, consisting of a xylene solution of DDT containing an aralkyl polyether alcohol as emulsifier, from which emulsions ranging from 0.1 to 10 percent in DDT content can be prepared by mixing with water.

DDT has been incorporated in the pyrethrum-Freon aerosol, which has been widely used by the armed services and is now on the civilian market. Because of the low solubility of DDT in Freon–12 it is necessary to add an auxiliary solvent to the formula. Cyclohexanone and certain aromatic hydrocarbons derived from petroleum have been used for the purpose.

Insecticidal preparations containing DDT have a longer lasting residual effectiveness than other commonly employed insecticides, but the length of the effective residual periods varies considerably. In field tests on agricultural crops, the residual effect is relatively short. Under certain conditions (indoors or protected from sunlight and wind) where the physical environment is more uniform than under agricultural conditions, much longer periods of effectiveness have been reported. The type of surface is important, as would be expected in a contact poison. When DDT is applied to screens, its action lasts longer on copper screening than on iron. Iron has been shown to decompose DDT.

Whenever a new chemical is produced for large-scale use as an insecticide it becomes necessary to develop analytical procedures for it. DDT has five chlorine atoms in its molecular structure. They constitute 50 percent of the compound by weight. One of the chlorine atoms is readily removed as hydrogen chloride and is termed labile or hydrolyzable chlorine.

Methods for the determination of total chlorine or of hydrolyzable chlorine content are generally used for the analysis of DDT residues or preparations containing DDT. Neither of these methods is specific for

DDT, since other compounds containing chlorine interfere. Considerable discretion must be used in interpreting results obtained with either of these methods especially when minute amounts of chlorine, such as are found in spray or dust residues, are determined.

Several methods that are specific for the determination of DDT have also been developed. One of these, which has found considerable use, is based on the fact that when DDT is treated with a mixture of concentrated nitric acid and sulfuric acid, a tetranitro derivative is formed. This product when treated with sodium methylate yields a blue color with pure p,p'-DDT and a wine-red color with o,p'-DDT. Intermediate colors are obtained when technical DDT is determined.

The methods so far developed have proved useful, but further work is needed in this field.

THE AUTHORS

H. L. Haller, a chemist in the Bureau of Entomology and Plant Quarantine, is a native of Cincinnati, Ohio. He has been with the Department since his discharge from the Army during the First World War, with the exception of a few years when he was with the Rockefeller Institute for Medical Research as an associate in chemistry. In his present position he is project leader of the researches on plant insecticides and synthetic organic insecticides. In collaboration with his colleagues he has published about 125 papers on naturally occurring and synthetic organic insecticides. For their studies on the determination of the structure of rotenone, Dr. Haller and Dr. F. B. LaForge in 1933 received the Hillebrand prize, given annually by the Washington Chemical Society.

Ruth L. Busbey, a chemist in the Division of Insecticide Investigations, Bureau of Entomology and Plant Quarantine, has been engaged in research on insecticides since 1930. She has conducted synthetic and analytical studies on organic insecticides and chemical investigations on fumigants, especially hydrocyanic acid fumigation to control California red scale on citrus trees.

FOR FURTHER READING

Carter, R. H., and Hubanks, P. E.: *The Determination of DDT Deposits on Fruits, Vegetables, and Vegetation,* Association of Official Agricultural Chemists, Journal, volume 29, No. 1, pages 112–114, 1946.

Fleck, E. E., and Haller, H. L.: *Solubility of DDT in Kerosene,* Industrial and Engineering Chemistry, volume 38, No. 2, pages 177–178, 1946.

Haller, H. L., Bartlett, P. D., Drake, N. L., and others: *The Chemical Composition of Technical DDT,* American Chemical Society, Journal, volume 67, pages 1591–1602, 1945.

Mosher, H. S., Cannon, M. R. Conroy, E. A., and others: *Preparation of Technical DDT,* Industrial and Engineering Chemistry, volume 38, No. 9, pages 916–923, 1946.

Rueggeberg, W. H. C., and Torrans, D. J.: *Production of DDT,* Industrial and Engineering Chemistry, volume 38, No. 2, pages 211–214, 1946.

Schechter, M. S., Soloway, S. B., Hayes, R. A., and Haller, H. L.: *Colorimetric Determination of DDT,* Industrial and Engineering Chemistry, Analytical Edition, volume 17, No. 11, pages 704–709, 1945.

Aerosols for Insects

by RANDALL LATTA and L. D. GOODHUE

INSECTICIDES in aerosol form have become, since 1940, an important means of controlling insects. Aerosols had just emerged from the laboratory and were undergoing practical testing when the United States entered the Second World War. They were immediately adopted by the military forces to combat disease-carrying insects, such as the malaria and yellow-fever mosquitoes. Because of accelerated research and widespread use during the war period, the aerosol today is a household word and item.

The modern insecticidal aerosol is simply a very fine spray, so fine that the individual particles will stay suspended in air for some time. By staying suspended, the minute particles of insecticide have greater opportunity to touch an insect than larger particles, such as those in an ordinary fly spray, which rapidly fall to the floor or ground. Like-wise, the ability of an aerosol to remain airborne makes it possible to drift an aerosol cloud for long distances under the proper meteorological conditions. When the particles of an aerosol are liquid, a fog is formed, whereas solid particles form a smoke. At present the most efficient aerosols are composed of liquid particles and are true fogs, not smokes.

Aerosols are efficient when properly used because of the minimum of wastage. For example, enough aerosol to contain only 5 milligrams (one small drop) of pyrethrins will kill all yellow-fever mosquitoes in a thousand cubic feet of space.

The particles in an aerosol range anywhere from 0.5 to 35 or 40 microns in diameter. (One micron is 1/25,000 of an inch.) Above this size, particles tend to be airborne for shorter and shorter periods as their weight increases.

Particles of an aerosol come in contact with an insect by settling on it through gravitational fall or by striking it through motion of the particles or the insect. When aerosols are used in confined spaces, such as a room, the contact is partly by the first method, and the time necessary for enough particles to accumulate on a resting insect to cause its death is related to the rate at which the particles settle.

It would be necessary, for instance, to expose an insect 85 times as long to an aerosol composed of particles 1 micron in diameter as to an aerosol composed of particles 10 microns in diameter. On the other hand, too large particles fall too rapidly, are not diffused as well by convection currents, and reduce the number of chances of coming in contact with an insect. For example, one 40-micron particle will make 64 10-micron particles. By biological testing, an average size of 10 to 20 microns was found most effective for aerosols under confined conditions.

Outdoors, aerosols drifting parallel to the ground strike objects in their paths according to the weight and velocity of the particles and the shape of the object. Biological tests have shown that below a certain range of size the ability to strike decreases rapidly, so there would have to be a corresponding increase in the amount of insecticide. Above that range practically all particles are deposited on insects in their paths; therefore greater size would be of no benefit. The range was determined to be in the neighborhood of a diameter of 10 microns.

Because of the small dosages necessary in confined spaces, and the airborne characteristics in outdoor applications, aerosols generally leave minute deposits and are considered an unsatisfactory means of applying insecticides where a residual effect is desired, although overdosing or repeated applications may leave an effective insecticidal deposit.

Aerosols are made by several methods. It is believed that the method by which they are generated has little effect on their action upon insects, provided that they are composed of the same elements and are of the same particle size. They can be generated (1) by incomplete combustion of materials containing insecticides; (2) by spraying solutions of insecticides in oil on a hot surface, thus vaporizing the liquid which immediately condenses into a fog when the vapor is cooled by contact with air; (3) by dissolving insecticides in a liquefied gas, such as dichlorodifluoromethane, and forcing the solution through a small orifice by the pressure of the gas, where it is broken into a fine spray, which is further reduced in particle size by the immediate evaporation of the liquefied gas; (4) by heating a mixture of water and an oil solution of the insecticide until the water is converted into superheated steam, and passing this mixture of oil and steam through nozzles where it is broken up into aerosol-sized droplets; and (5) by mechanical means, such as atomizing nozzles.

The original experiments with foglike aerosols were made by spraying solutions of insecticides in oil onto a hot plate. This new method was found to be highly effective in comparison with other methods of dispersing insecticides known at that time. It was soon supplanted by the liquefied-gas method. Later the method was reconsidered in attempts to create large aerosol clouds for outdoor applications. It was determined that the particle size produced was too small for high efficiency against insects under such conditions.

Liquefied-gas aerosols are composed of a liquefied gas, such as dichlorodifluoromethane; from 7 to 20 percent of nonvolatile materials, such as sesame oil, lubricating oil, and solvents; and an insecticide, which may be pyrethrum, DDT, thiocyanate, nicotine, rotenone and derris resin, phenothiazine, and so on. The aerosol solution is held under pressure (approximately 80 pounds per square inch for dichlorodifluoromethane) in a metal cylinder. When released by a simple valve, the gas pressure forces the clear solution through the nozzle orifice to create an aerosol. The particle size is regulated by varying the content of nonvolatile material in the formula, and the size of aperture in the nozzle.

Hand dispensers vary in size. The widely used military and civilian model contains 1 pound of aerosol and is popularly called the aerosol bomb because it resembles a small bomb. Others hold from $\frac{1}{2}$ ounce to 5 pounds. Industrial dispenser systems that are supplied from a large cylinder of aerosol solution have also been developed, as well as agricultural equipment with multiple outlets fed by a single supply cylinder.

Liquefied-gas aerosols are best adapted to controlling insects in confined or restricted spaces. The military forces used a pyrethrum-sesame oil aerosol, and later a pyrethrum-DDT aerosol, to destroy disease-carrying mosquitoes in airplanes to prevent their dissemination from one area to another along air routes. The same aerosols were used to control insects in foxholes, tents, barracks, rooms, mess halls, and such. More than 40 million 1-pound dispensers or "bombs" were supplied to the military forces. The British Army used several million one-shot $\frac{1}{2}$-ounce dispensers. A large war plant with 27,000,000 cubic feet under one roof, located in a mosquito-breeding zone, increased worker efficiency enormously by frequent application of aerosols from a portable dispensing apparatus.

Liquefied-gas aerosols can control a variety of household insects, such as mosquitoes, flies, sand flies, fleas, and adult moths. An aerosol can kill only the insects that it touches and consequently it is relatively ineffective against those that are protected, such as clothes moth larvae, carpet beetles, and bedbugs.

Aerosols have been widely used by international air lines since 1941 to destroy disease-carrying insects accidentally introduced into plane cabins. They have also been used during the war and since to prevent the spread of agricultural insects of importance.

Aerosols have been used to control a number of insects in greenhouses. Nicotine in an aerosol is twice as effective as when applied as a burning mixture. Lorol thiocyanate aerosols controlled cyclamen mite on snapdragons. DDT aerosols were effective on thrips, whiteflies, aphids, sowbugs, ants, and crickets. Pyrethrum aerosols gave good control of flies in mushroom houses.

Liquefied-gas aerosols were found to be of practical use for control of some pests of agricultural crops. When retained briefly over pea vines by means of a small canopy, small dosages gave good control of the pea aphid. The aerosols were applied by a multiple dispenser composed of a supply tank of the aerosol mixture with several outlets, mounted on a light, hand-drawn or jeep-drawn carriage. Various insects on truck crops were controlled by aerosols applied in the same way. These aerosols contained a larger proportion of nonvolatile material than those usually prepared for indoor use, in order to increase particle size.

Numerous other uses have been found for liquefied-gas aerosols. Seedless tomatoes have been produced by applying plant hormones as aerosols. Germicides can be applied by this method. A patent has been issued to Department workers for a combined germicidal-insecticidal aerosol. Certain soluble fungicides also work well in aerosol form.

Thermal-generated aerosols are very efficiently formed by heating a mixture of water and oil-insecticide solution. A 50–50 mixture of water and the oil solution is pumped through a coil suspended in a furnace, where enough heat is applied to convert the water to superheated steam. The pressure generated by the steam forces the mixture of steam and oil through a nozzle where it is broken up into aerosol-sized particles. The range of particle size can be regulated by varying the viscosity of the oil used, or the temperature to which it is subjected. Generators are now available which have capacities as high as 40 gallons of oil an hour, which may contain 30 percent or more of DDT. A relatively nonvolatile oil should be used or the aerosol particles will shrink by evaporation during application.

Thermal-generated aerosols are strictly for large-scale use. They are applied to outdoor areas by drifting the aerosol cloud across a desired area. Usually the generator is mounted in a truck and moved back and forth across a front at right angles to the direction of air movement. The cloud must be applied under meteorological conditions which will hold it close to the ground. Inversion conditions (a layer of colder air next to the ground) are the most favorable and usually occur during the periods near dawn and dusk. A wind movement of from 1 to 3 or 4 miles an hour is desirable.

The concentration of aerosols, and therefore their effectiveness, is greatest nearest the generator and diminishes with the distance. In order to obtain a high degree of control at a given distance, it is necessary to overdose the intervening area. For this reason it is more economical to treat in narrow strips than in deep areas. Mosquito adults and larvae were controlled downwind from the point of generation for distances ranging from 1,200 feet in heavily wooded areas to nearly a mile in open terrain. Gypsy moth larvae in naturally infested forests were apparently completely wiped out for distances up to 900 feet. Furthermore, enough residue remained to be repellent to migrating larvae, which prevented reinfestation in all except the marginal areas.

In recent tests by H. A. Jaynes and his associates, adult onion thrips on young cabbage plants were effectively reduced for a distance of 200 feet but the nymphs were not controlled; cabbageworms on cauliflower were reduced 85 percent at this distance; species of *Empoasca* were controlled for 150 feet in parsnips, in a weed field for 600 feet, and on alfalfa for 250 feet; beet armyworms were reduced over 90 percent in a weed field for 500 feet, completely killed for 100 feet in broccoli, and over 70 percent for 200 feet in tomatoes; *Lygus* bugs were reduced 90 percent for 250 feet in alfalfa. Unsatisfactory results were obtained against insects on very low growing plants or with low dense foliage, such as red spiders on celery or aphids on potatoes.

Thermal-generated aerosols were found to be very toxic to adult horn flies on cattle. Herds can be quickly treated and enough residue remains to prevent reinfestation for several days.

Aerosols have been created by various types of mechanical dispersion, particularly by various methods of atomization. In one method, an oil solution of insecticide is sprayed into a stream of high-velocity exhaust gases, where it is broken up into aerosol-sized particles. A simple venturi arrangement is attached to the exhaust pipe of an airplane or vehicular motor for this purpose. One type of a proprietary generator utilizes this principle also by burning gasoline or fuel oil in a forced draft of air, thus producing a high velocity-gas stream which is used in the same manner to break up an oil solution into an aerosol. Other kinds of atomizing nozzles and also whirling disks are being investigated.

THE AUTHORS

Randall Latta is an entomologist in the Bureau of Entomology and Plant Quarantine. Since 1942, in addition to other duties, he has been in charge of the development of new methods and equipment for applying insecticides. He made the initial tests with army screening smoke equipment in an attempt to convert it to make insecticidal aerosols, and later supervised a study of the use of heat-generated aerosols for outdoor control of insects. As a part of these studies, the Department carried on cooperative work with the National Defense Research Committee on the fundamental characteristics of aerosols in relation to particle size and speed of motion.

L. D. Goodhue was a chemist in the same Bureau until he resigned December 28, 1945. He also is a native of Iowa. Dr. Goodhue was a cooperator in the original studies on insecticidal aerosols; he was a coinventor of the liquefied-gas aerosol and has been a leader in the development of these aerosols since their origination. He played an important part in the military adaptation of aerosols, through his chemical studies on formulations.

New Insect Repellents

by BERNARD V. TRAVIS

THE OLD MIXTURES of citronella and pennyroyal that had been used for generations to ward off mosquitoes and punkies and blackflies had little value on Bougainville and Guadalcanal. They gave inadequate protection; they had an objectionable oiliness; they did not last long enough, especially on wet and sweating men. In fact, scientists who undertook to discover new and better repellents for the Army found 500 organic chemicals, of the 7,000 they tested for insect repellency, that are superior to the older repellents containing the aromatic oils. More than comfort was involved for the soldiers.

Early in the war it was recognized that men in the outer perimeter of the combat zones would have to rely on repellents for personal protection from the bites of mosquitoes and other insects; at that time control procedures were not known that would quickly eliminate the disease-carrying insects from the active-combat zones, and repellents offered an important means of protection for isolated troops.

Civilians also need good preparations to keep insects away. In certain areas permanent control measures for mosquitoes, sand flies, punkies, and chiggers may be impossible because of unfavorable terrain. In other places control is possible, but the low value of the land or sparse population make it unwise to levy sufficient taxes for the installation and maintenance of permanent control. Large sections of our finest recreational land are unusable because of the extreme annoyance from biting insects during vacation seasons; besides parks and other playground areas, there are sections that remain undeveloped where insects seriously interfere with agriculture or commerce during at least part of each year. For those areas, where control of the pests is either impossible or impractical, good insect repellents and miticides can give satisfactory protection.

In an effort to find improved repellents and to supply the armed forces with information, a project was initiated by the Bureau of Entomology and Plant Quarantine at Orlando, Fla., under the sponsorship of the Office of Scientific Research and Development. In this project chemicals were tested in the customary manner as a skin application and also as a clothing treatment.

In 1944 A. H. Madden, A. W. Lindquist, and E. F. Knipling reported that when the new organic insect repellents were applied to their clothing they received almost complete protection from chigger or red bug bites. Before that protection from chiggers was obtained largely by dusting sulfur on clothing. The sulfur method gives only partial protection and is objectionable to many persons. The Australians later showed that the repellent materials acted on chiggers largely as toxicants rather than as repellents; therefore, in discussing chiggers, the term "miticide" is used here instead of repellent. Between 1942 and 1946, F. M. Snyder and others of the Orlando laboratory tested about 7,000 materials on cloth in their search for better miticides. Many materials were found to be effective as fresh treatments, but only about 300 were outstanding in their resistance to removal by water.

In the investigations we encountered a number of important problems for which we do not yet have answers. Because most of our work was to test the effectiveness of chemicals as repellents, we had little time to get fundamental information as to how the chemicals repel insects. As basic information is accumulated on the repellent mechanism, it may be possible to develop superior repellents.

Another problem is the variation in effectiveness of individual chemicals when tested against different insects. Certain materials that are satisfactory against some species may fail to repel others. Dimethyl phthalate, for instance, is a good repellent for the common malaria vector in the United States, *Anopheles quadrimaculatus* Say, but it is almost worthless for one of the South Pacific malaria vectors, *Anopheles farauti* Laveran. Also, during certain periods, an insect species may bite immediately on skin that has been freshly treated, but at other times it may be repelled completely for several hours.

There is considerable variation in the effectiveness of repellents when used on different individuals. The same material may protect one person for several hours, but on another it may be effective for only a few minutes. The insects will bite readily on any spot either on exposed skin or through clothing where no repellent has been applied or where it has been rubbed off. All repellents are washed from the skin easily with water or excessive perspiration.

Repellents have some rather undesirable characteristics, and efforts are being made to discover new materials that do not have these properties. All of the better liquid repellents now in use are rather viscous and feel oily on the skin. Most of the repellents are plastic solvents and will damage paints, varnishes, and many other plastic materials and synthetic cloth, but they can be applied safely to cotton or wool. Care must be taken in their use, as they cause temporary smarting of tender skin or mucous membranes.

Of all the thousands of chemicals tested, fewer than 10 percent showed sufficient promise to be of service as insect repellents, and only about 15 percent as miticides. After the toxicologists eliminated those that were too toxic or irritating for frequent use, only a very few were left that can be recommended for use on man.

Because of the extreme variation in effectiveness of individual chemicals as repellents, it is impossible now to name even one that will be effective against all species. For instance, Indalone (*n*-butyl mesityl oxide oxalate) has been found to be one of the most effective repellents against the stablefly, *Stomoxys calcitrans* (L.), dimethyl phthalate is the best for our malaria mosquito, *Anopheles quadrimaculatus* Say, and such materials as dimethyl carbate and Rutgers 612 (2-ethyl-1,3-hex-anediol) are excellent repellents for various pest mosquitoes of the *Aedes* group. Selected mixtures of repellents are effective against a wider range of species than any one of the individual chemicals. The most satisfactory mixtures now known are composed of 60 percent dimethyl phthalate and 20 percent Indalone; the other 20 percent may be any of the chemicals that are particularly effective against *Aedes* mosquitoes. The famous 6-2-2 insect repellent developed during the war is composed of 6 parts dimethyl phthalate, 2 parts Rutgers 612, and 2 parts Indalone. Mixtures containing only two repellents have proved better than single chemicals, but they are generally not so effective as the mixtures containing three selected chemicals.

Any of the repellents I have named may be used for protection from chigger bites if used as a clothing treatment. Dimethyl phthalate is the preferred repellent to use because of its effectiveness, availability, and low cost. Its chief weakness is that it is quickly removed by washing. Benzyl benzoate is much superior to dimethyl phthalate because it is quite resistant to water. However, it is a poor mosquito and fly repellent, and the cost is rather high. If a person wishes protection from chiggers for only short periods and does not expect to get wet, dimethyl phthalate or any of the other repellents may be used with excellent results. If it is desired to use a chemical that is resistant to water and that will remain effective even after the clothes are laundered, benzyl benzoate is by far the most effective available chemical.

Simple water emulsions can be made with either dimethyl phthalate or benzyl benzoate by using emulsifiers such as Stearate 60-C-2280, Tween 60, Tween 80, or a polymerized glycol monostearate. These emulsions are useful for impregnating clothing with miticides or repellents.

Insect repellents must be applied in a thin, uniform film to hands, faces, arms, or other places where insects bite. They must be reapplied as often as needed. This may be every few minutes or every few hours, depending on the species of insects and the conditions of use. Usually the repellent is applied to the skin by pouring a few drops into the palms of the hands and rubbing the hands where a film of the repellent is desired. The repellents should be applied with caution to tender places, such as eyelids and lips, because they will cause a temporary smarting. This reaction is more pronounced on sweaty skin. The same procedure may be used for applying the repellents to clothing, such as socks, shirts, or trousers, where bites occur. Care should be taken not to apply the repellents to clothing that may be damaged by the chemical, such as synthetic cloth. If the numbers of insects are unusually high, it may be desirable to spray the repellent on the clothing or use the water emulsion method described in the next paragraph, although the dilution of the repellent-emulsion mixture with water should be less—1 quart of the mixture to 1 gallon of water.

The principal use of miticides is on clothing, because the chemicals are not so long lasting as skin applications. The materials may be applied by rubbing the chemicals on the clothing by hand or with a sprayer. If these methods are used, special attention should be given to apply the chemical heavily along the openings to the clothing and on the socks both above and below the shoe tops. When complete protection from chiggers is desired, and the exposure to their bites is severe, clothing may be treated with water emulsions of the miticides. The most practical way to use the emulsions is to dissolve 10 parts of the emulsifier in 90 parts of the dimethyl phthalate or benzyl benzoate by weight. Use one-half pint of this mixture to 1 gallon of water. It is best to agitate vigorously 1 part of the concentrate in 2 or 3 parts of water to form a creamy emulsion and then dilute with the remainder of the water. Agitate the emulsion while using to assure a uniform emulsion. Repellents applied to the suit, or shirt and trousers, will greatly reduce the bites from ticks and fleas.

THE AUTHOR

Bernard V. Travis is an entomologist in the Division of Insects Affecting Man and Animals, Bureau of Entomology and Plant Quarantine. He has conducted research in wildlife parasites with special reference to fire ants; screwworm biology; salt-mrash mosquito biology and control; and repellents and insecticides for the armed forces, as a member of the Department and in the Navy.

ACKNOWLEDGMENTS

Cooperating in the work reported in this paper are members of the staff of the laboratory in Orlando; acknowledgment is made particularly of the help of Fred A. Morton, E. F. Knipling, and F. M. Snyder.

Pests That Attack Man

by E. F. KNIPLING

EXPERIENCE during the war demonstrated that we must concern ourselves with insect problems throughout the world, especially the control of insects that affect man.

Hundreds of species of insects, ticks, and mites annoy man. But of far greater importance is that they transmit dangerous diseases. During the war, when our men and women were stationed all over the world, we had to fight lice, which carry louse-borne typhus and relapsing fever; mosquitoes, vectors of malaria, filariasis, dengue fever, yellow fever, and encephalitis; flies, transmitters of typhoid, dysentery, and cholera; fleas, which spread plague and murine typhus; mites, carriers of a disease known as tsutsugamushi or scrub typhus; and ticks, which carry tularemia and spotted and relapsing fevers. There are other important disease carriers among the insects and arachnids (ticks and mites), but the ones mentioned are all of vital importance throughout the world, particularly in this age of fast and complicated transportation. All of them occur in this country. Fortunately, most of the diseases I listed are not present here, although malaria, encephalitis, relapsing fever, spotted fever, tularemia and murine typhus, and certain fly-borne diseases are a problem in the United States.

As a result of the research by entomologists, chemists, and engineers, new insecticides and more effective control methods were developed for every important pest that affects man's health. The Army, Navy, United States Public Health Service, Tennessee Valley Authority, Rockefeller Foundation, National Defense Research Committee, and various other agencies and industrial concerns have made valuable contributions. The advances that have resulted will make this country and other parts of the world healthier and more pleasant places in which to live. They will also be a tremendous factor in the economic development of many areas that are now handicapped because of insects and insect-borne diseases.

Among the thousands of chemicals tested by the entomologists, one material, DDT, proved outstanding. Most of my discussion is devoted to DDT, but other materials have been found useful for certain purposes, and studies on a number of promising insecticides are under way in efforts to determine their full potentialities.

The body louse (*Pediculus humanus corporis* Deg.) carries the dreaded typhus disease; often it is found in the clothing of destitute peoples, hidden in the seams and folds. Although a common and important parasite of man through the ages, control methods until recently were generally ineffective or unsatisfactory.

A colony of body lice was maintained under the direction of G. H. Culpepper in the Bureau of Entomology and Plant Quarantine Laboratory at Orlando, Fla. Human subjects, serving as guinea pigs, fed the lice and allowed themselves to be infested in order to test new insecticides. R. C. Bushland, Gaines W. Eddy, and associates in the same laboratory found that DDT was many times more effective than the best of the other materials known at that time. One ounce of a powder containing 10 percent of DDT, dusted on the inside of the underwear, killed all lice present at the time of treatment and killed any lice that hatched from eggs or that crawled on the person as long as a month after treatment.

Even though DDT in powder form was very good, research was continued in an effort to find even more effective ways to use the material. When clothing was dipped into a dry-cleaning solution (Stoddard solvent) containing from 1 to 2 percent of DDT, and all excess liquid wrung from the garments, Howard A. Jones, chemist, found that the treatment would prevent lice from living in the clothes for many months and it even continued to kill lice after four to six washings. A water-emulsion preparation containing 1 to 2 percent of DDT was also developed. This was made from a concentrate consisting of 25 percent of DDT, 65 percent of xylene, and 10 percent of Triton X–100.

After the value of DDT for louse control was fully established, the chemical was recommended for use by the armed services. The Army then developed simple methods of treating large numbers of people by using ordinary dust guns. The chemical has since been used in many parts of the world. The Army in Naples and the Rockefeller Foundation in Mexico demonstrated that typhus epidemics can be stopped almost immediately after the people are deloused. As a result, louse-borne typhus is now one of the diseases of man that can be easily and quickly brought under control; now we can hope that this disease, which has killed more people than all wars, will eventually be eradicated from the earth.

The head louse (*Pediculus humanus humanus* L.) is closely related to the body louse. Its habits are different, however, in that the head louse lives in the hair of the head instead of in the clothing. It is common throughout the world and is a problem of considerable importance in this country, especially among school children. ·

DDT powder dusted in the hair is effective in controlling the insects, but a powder is somewhat objectionable. Consequently, several liquid preparations containing DDT were developed by Dr. Eddy. The formula most widely used by the Army, which was known as the NBIN concentrate, consisted of 68 percent of benzyl benzoate, 6 percent of DDT, 12 percent of benzocaine (ethyl p-aminobenzoate), and 14 percent of a suitable wetting agent that makes the solution mix with water. One part of the concentrate must be diluted with 5 parts of water before it is applied. The resulting solution, which then contains 1 percent of DDT, kills the lice and prevents infestations for at least 2 weeks. The eggs of the lice are not affected by DDT but are killed by the benzocaine present in the formula. The benzyl benzoate, which I shall mention again later, is used because it will control the human itch mite and is a solvent for DDT and benzocaine.

The crab louse (*Phthirus pubis* (L.)) is not a disease carrier, but is one of the annoying parasites that must be dealt with. It can also be readily brought under control with either the 10-percent DDT powder or with the NBIN solution. The powder must be dusted thoroughly on all hairy portions of the body, and on individuals having much body hair it should be dusted over the entire body. Because DDT will not kill the eggs or nits, a second treatment must be given from 7 to 10 days after the first.   The NBIN concentrate must be diluted with 5 parts of water, as described for use against the head louse, before it is applied. The liquid formula, well applied, will control crab lice in one treatment.

The development of DDT for the control of mosquitoes is one of the most important of all advances in the field of medical entomology. The insecticide is effective against larvae and adults of both the *Anopheles* (malaria carriers) and culicines (pest mosquitoes and transmitters of other diseases).

In carrying out the extensive investigations that were necessary to study the various aspects of mosquito control, a large colony of a malaria mosquito (*Anopheles quadrimaculatus* Say) was reared under laboratory conditions in order that insects would be available for test purposes. Several thousand new materials and special preparations of promising chemicals have been tried against the larvae and adults in the laboratory, and the more effective compounds and formulas were tested in natural breeding places.

Paris green and oil (kerosene, Diesel, and fuel oils) were widely used before DDT became available for controlling larvae of the malaria mosquitoes. Oil was also the standard method of controlling the various

Culex, Aedes, Psorophora, and related mosquitoes. One to 2 pounds of paris green per acre of water surface was generally needed for adequate anopheline larvae control. C. C. Deonier and assistants of the Orlando laboratory demonstrated that DDT in dust form (using 1 to 2 percent of DDT in talc) was more effective when applied at the rate of 1 pound to 20 acres. For routine treatment, however, DDT in dust form is recommended at the rate of 1 pound to 10 acres.

Furthermore, when dissolved in kerosene or fuel oil and properly applied, 1 quart of oil containing 5 percent of DDT was shown to be equally as effective as 20 to 25 gallons of oil that did not contain DDT. The great savings in cost of materials, transportation, and labor for the DDT treatments are therefore readily apparent. For routine control operations against various kinds of mosquitoes 5 quarts of a 1-percent DDT solution of fuel oil applied as a fine mist is recommended for each acre of breeding area. Ordinary garden-type pressure sprayers and even hand pressure sprayers have been found satisfactory for the small breeding areas. Where large areas involving hundreds of acres are to be treated, and if the DDT is not applied by means of airplanes, power units may be employed.

DDT may be used in ways other than dusts or oil solutions. The DDT emulsion concentrate already mentioned in connection with the control of lice was found useful in mosquito control. This concentrate (or several modifications of this formula) when diluted with water so that the finished spray will contain 1 percent or less of DDT was found to be a very effective and satisfactory treatment. The recommended dosage of 0.1 pound of DDT per acre meant that less than one-half pint of material had to be transported for each acre of larval breeding area.

Airplanes, formerly used extensively for applying paris green dusts, are very useful for applying DDT sprays. Good control of the *Anopheles* and most of the other kinds of mosquito larvae can be obtained with 1 to 2 quarts of fuel oil containing 5 percent DDT per acre applied with special spray equipment.

Studies by the Tennessee Valley Authority, the armed services, and the Bureau of Entomology and Plant Quarantine have shown that excellent control of *Anopheles* mosquito larvae can also be obtained with fine mist sprays by applying as little as one-half pint per acre when a 20-percent DDT solution is employed. This means that an airplane that can carry 1,000 pounds can treat 2,000 acres with one load.

DDT has provided new and strikingly effective means of controlling adult mosquitoes. There are three general methods of attack on adult mosquitoes with DDT. The methods were first investigated by A. W. Lindquist, J. B. Gahan, B. V. Travis, and others of the Orlando laboratory. First, and perhaps the most important, is the use of this insecticide as a residual or surface spray. Never before has an insecticide been em-

ployed in this way for controlling adult mosquitoes, although R. Wiesmann of Switzerland had shown that flies could be controlled thus. The
spraying of the inside of buildings, under bridges, inside hollow logs, or
even the vegetation itself with DDT leaves a deposit of DDT that will
kill mosquitoes which rest in such places for weeks or even months later.

Many laboratory tests were run in 1943 with many types of DDT
sprays. Different rates of application were used on various surfaces. The
tests showed that some differences existed in regard to the effectiveness
of the DDT on different kinds of surfaces, but in general a single treatment at the rate of 1 gallon of 5-percent spray for each 1,000 square
feet remained effective for many months. After the laboratory tests, field
experiments were run in Arkansas in 1943 and 1944. The inside walls
of barns, toilets, chicken houses, bridges, and other places where
Anopheles mosquitoes rest were treated with 5-percent DDT solutions.
Kerosene or the water emulsion already mentioned were tested. As long
as 5 months after one treatment there was a reduction of about 99 percent in the number of mosquitoes resting in the buildings.

A mosquito cannot transmit malaria until about 2 weeks after it has
fed on a person having the disease. If the houses and other resting places
of mosquitoes in the vicinity of human habitations are treated, the mosquitoes will be killed sometime during the 2-week period. This break in
the chain is the key to the success of DDT in the control of malaria and
other diseases transmitted by mosquitoes. It is sometimes difficult to
realize how important this one development is to people everywhere, but
the fact is that malaria and other important mosquito-borne diseases
cause more than 100 million cases of illness and many deaths each year.

Another new method of utilizing DDT involves spraying large areas
to kill the adult mosquitoes as well as the larvae. Airplane equipment
was used, and it was shown that adult mosquitoes as well as the larvae
could be controlled. When epidemics of mosquito-borne diseases occur,
this method permits immediate control of the disease by killing the
already infected mosquitoes in the area; the destruction of the larvae
prevents a rapid increase in the mosquito population.

Adult mosquitoes can also be controlled with equipment that can be
used on the ground. In fact, in the first tests with DDT for killing adult
mosquitoes outdoors, hand dusters and sprayers were used. Because of
the success of those early tests, investigations of various types of equipment to disperse DDT fogs and sprays for mosquito control were undertaken. V. K. LaMer of the National Defense Research Committee, working with Randall Latta, developed special fog machines, which are
proving effective and practical for controlling mosquitoes, sand flies,
gnats, and various other annoying insects.

A third way to use DDT against adult mosquitoes consists of sprays
and aerosols for use inside houses and other confined space to give im-

mediate but temporary control of the insects present. Pyrethrum has been widely used in household sprays. DDT added to such a spray was found to increase its killing power for flies and mosquitoes. Ordinary refined kerosene containing DDT and pyrethrum makes an effective space spray for mosquitoes and for general household use. The method is not to be confused with residual or surface application.

DDT was found useful in the pyrethrum aerosol bomb, which was developed by L. D. Goodhue and W. N. Sullivan. In order to add the 3-percent DDT to the Freon aerosol, the amount needed for general use, the formula had to be modified. After testing many preparations, the Orlando scientists and those at Beltsville developed formulas.

The common housefly carries filth and disease. Sanitary practices and the use of screens, sprays, and other methods give a fair degree of control against the insect. Too often, however, available control measures are not judiciously followed. Army and Navy personnel realized the danger of flies. Dysentery, a disease spread by flies, was a major problem in certain war theaters, and the presence of many flies lowered morale.

Fortunately DDT is a powerful weapon. Early in 1943, even before we had heard that Wiesmann of Switzerland had previously employed DDT residual treatments for fly control, Mr. Lindquist had shown DDT treatments to be effective for several months when tested under laboratory conditions. Practical tests at dairies and military establishments in Florida showed that a 5-percent DDT-kerosene spray, thoroughly applied at the rate of 1 gallon for each 1,000 square feet of surface, would reduce flies by more than 95 percent as long as 4 months after treatment. Since that time DDT has been widely employed in oil solutions, emulsions, wettable powders, and dusts. The amount of DDT to apply varies with the length of the fly season, climate, and the type of surface to be treated, but it is generally recommended that $\frac{1}{2}$ to 3 ounces for each 1,000 square feet of surface be used in solutions containing from 1 to 5 percent of DDT.

The treatment may be applied with garden-type pressure sprayers or with power equipment. The surfaces where flies concentrate (such as garbage cans, animal houses, and so on) should be thoroughly covered. The spray should also be applied on the inside of the establishment that is to be protected. It is preferable to paint the doors and window screens, because spraying them would be wasteful. Although DDT is an excellent control for flies, it is recommended that sanitary practices, such as the elimination of breeding places, the disposal of garbage, and screening, be continued. DDT is slow in its action, and several hours' exposure is frequently required to kill flies. So, if the fly population is high, a reduction as high as 95 percent may leave enough flies to create a problem.

The use of DDT in conjunction with pyrethrum in sprays and the aerosol bomb has already been discussed. The pyrethrum is included mainly to increase the speed of knock-down, but the DDT is the principal killing agent.

Fleas are usually considered an occasional or accidental pest of man. In this country this is largely true, but in many parts of the world many houses are infested with the human flea (*Pulex irritans* L.), and they are found in the clothing and on the body of man much as they occur on our pets. Bubonic plague and endemic typhus are caused by fleas.

Our researchers found that DDT is highly effective for controlling fleas both on the person and in buildings. As a spray it may be employed as a residual treatment (in a manner similar to that already described for flies and mosquitoes), but dusts containing 10-percent DDT are also recommended. The DDT dust or spray should be thoroughly applied to the floor and furnishings or to the infested soil. If possible, the source of the infestation should be determined and eliminated. If pets cause the trouble, as they generally do, they and their bedding should be treated with a suitable flea powder. DDT can be used safely on dogs, but it should not be used on cats. When infestations occur on the person, the clothing should be thoroughly dusted the same as for body lice.

DDT destroys fleas on rats. Early work on this problem was undertaken by the Bureau of Entomology and Plant Quarantine station at Savannah, Ga., and by the Menard, Tex., station in cooperation with the Texas State Board of Health. The United States Public Health Service has also studied the problem extensively. The studies indicate that it may be possible to control murine typhus, which is transmitted by the rat flea (*Xenopsylla cheopis* (Rothsch.)).

Bedbugs fortunately do not carry disease but they are common and widespread pests. They are easily and effectively controlled with DDT.

After the usual preliminary laboratory tests procedures, A. H. Madden of the Orlando laboratory treated the bedstead, springs, and heavily infested mattress of a bed with about 3 ounces of a 5-percent DDT spray. For a year after the treatment he tried to reinfest the bed with bugs from the laboratory colony, but the efforts were unsuccessful—all the bugs died within 48 hours. While such experiments were still in progress, thousands of beds in military establishments at Orlando were treated by the Army as an experiment. For at least 6 months after the treatment, not a single bedbug was found alive in the beds.

The small insects called sand flies in the United States include the *Culicoides*. They are commonly referred to as punkies or, because of their small size, no-see-ums. The true sand flies (*Phlebotomus*) are of little importance in this country, but in many parts of the world they are major pests, mainly because of certain diseases that they transmit.

DDT can be employed as a residual treatment applied to the inside of buildings, stone fences, screens, and other favorite resting places for controlling the true sand flies. The method of treatment is essentially the same as for mosquitoes. The number of sand flies and punkies in this country can be reduced by the use of airplane sprays, fog machines, and by treating the screens and the inside of houses.

Pyrethrum is not a new insecticide, but some new uses for it have been found, and its toxicity to insects has been increased by combining it with materials that by themselves are not toxic—an action that is termed activation or synergism. In 1940 C. W. Eagleson, of the Dallas, Tex., laboratory of this Bureau demonstrated that sesame oil used in pyrethrum fly sprays greatly increased the activity of this insecticide.

Other materials have been developed for use in fly sprays and for other types of insecticide materials that contain pyrethrum. Among these is N-isobutylundecylenamide, which, when tested in combination with pyrethrum, was found to increase the effectiveness of the insecticides from 10 to 100 times. This development was the basis for the first louse powder recommended for use by the armed services. The powder, known as MYL formula, contained 0.2 percent of pyrethrins (the active principle of pyrethrum extract), 2 percent of N-isobutylundecylenamide, 2 percent of 2,4-dinitroanisole (for killing louse eggs), 0.25 percent of Phenol S (a pyrethrum stabilizer or antioxidant) in pyrophyllite dust.

The MYL powder, the most effective treatment known at the time, was widely used by the armed services for the control of lice attacking man, and as a general-purpose insecticide. Although it was replaced by DDT, the research leading to the development of the pyrethrum-synergist combination insect powder was important and further emphasizes the potential value of synergists for pyrethrum. A number of other promising synergists have been tested for possible use in fly sprays and other treatments involving the use of pyrethrum. Among these, two of the most effective are piperonyl cyclohexenone, and piperonyl butoxide.

Experiments with pyrethrum, even before DDT was available, had shown that this insecticide has good residual killing properties. Excellent control of bedbugs for several weeks after treatment was demonstrated by making residual treatments of pyrethrum sprays. The use of N-isobutylundecylenamide increased the activity of the residual treatment against this insect. Investigations also showed that pyrethrum applied as a residual treatment is effective against other insects including adult mosquitoes, houseflies, and cockroaches; and certain synergists greatly increase the effectiveness and lasting properties of such treatments.

Benzene Hexachloride

This material, investigated by the French and British before it was tested in this country, is equal to DDT in many respects. Research at Orlando in 1943 and 1944 showed that the crude product containing 12 percent of the gamma isomer (the gamma isomer is the most toxic form of this material) was about as effective as DDT on body lice when used at a concentration of 10 percent in pyrophyllite. When applied as a residual spray against flies and mosquitoes, its properties resembled that of DDT, but it generally was more rapid in its action. It was also found to be quite effective as a mosquito larvicide but less so than DDT. E. R. McGovran, in work at Beltsville, found that the gamma isomer is actually about eight times more toxic than DDT to flies when used as a space spray.

The insecticide is effective against chiggers when dusted or sprayed on infested soil or vegetation. As little as 5 pounds to the acre of the crude material will give practically complete control of the mites for several weeks after treatment. Sulfur, which was formerly recommended for this purpose, requires at least 100 pounds an acre to produce the same results. DDT was found to be relatively ineffective.

Benzene hexachloride is also effective against fly maggots, for which DDT is generally unsatisfactory. When prepared as a benzene emulsion containing 0.1 to 0.25 percent of benzene hexachloride and sprayed on animal carcasses, it completely destroyed the maggots present.

These brief accounts of results with benzene hexachloride show that it is a potent insecticide. It has, however, an undesirable and persistent odor, a serious draw-back in controlling insect pests of man.

Benzyl Benzoate and Other Mite Killers

Among the most annoying pests of man in the United States are small mites (*Eutrombicula* and related genera), commonly known as chiggers or red bugs. The first or larval stage will attach itself to man in a manner somewhat similar to a tick and cause extreme local irritation and, sometimes, secondary infections. In certain parts of the world, especially in Burma and some of the Pacific islands, similar mites transmit a serious disease called tsutsugamushi disease.

Early in 1942 A. H. Madden, of the Orlando laboratory, investigated materials and methods of protecting individuals from chiggers. He found that dimethyl phthalate, one of the insect repellents, applied as a barrier about 1 inch wide to all openings in the clothing, was an effective treatment. The chemical was utilized effectively by our military personnel through further research by the United States of America Typhus Commission, United States Army. The only objection to dimethyl phthalate was its lack of persistence when treated clothing got wet. Dibutyl phthalate, first tested by the Australians, was also a good mite treatment, but results with this were somewhat erratic against the chiggers in this country.

Consequently, further research was undertaken at the request of the Typhus Commission of the Army to find more persistent materials.

F. M. Snyder, another colleague, tested more than 5,000 materials; among them he found a number of effective miticides. One of the most practical was a commercially available product, benzyl benzoate. Clothing dipped into a 5-percent water emulsion of benzyl benzoate gave complete protection when freshly treated and was effective even after two or three launderings. The treatment became standard.

A skin disease known as scabies and sometimes as 7-year itch is caused by the human itch mite (*Scarcoptes scabiei* Deg.). It is a common ailment, especially among school children; but under wartime conditions, when people are often closely crowded, epidemics may break out among adults. Various forms of sulfur have been used for it, without much success.

Benzyl benzoate was known to be a good treatment for scabies and was rather widely used in Europe even before the war. In the development of louse control preparations, as previously discussed, benzyl benzoate was included. The preparation, when diluted at the rate of one part of concentrate to five parts of water and thoroughly applied (1 to 3 ounces) to the entire body, has given complete control of the itch mite infestation in a single treatment. The treatment is indicated to be more effective than other types of preparations containing 10-percent benzyl benzoate possibly because the benzocaine aids in destroying the mites and eggs.

Ticks cause severe local irritation, and transmit certain diseases, among them relapsing fever and spotted fever. Methods of protecting the individual from ticks are not entirely satisfactory, but some progress has been made on this problem. H. O. Schroeder of the Orlando laboratory and C. N. Smith of the Savannah, Ga., laboratory found that clothing sprayed with dimethyl phthalate, Indalone, Rutgers 612, or benzyl benzoate at the rate of about 6 to 7 ounces per suit would provide almost complete protection from the "seed" ticks—the first stage. Against the nymphal stage, the control was about 90 percent, but only about 60 percent reduction in attachment was obtained against grown ticks.

Other Promising Insecticides

After the potentialities of DDT as an insecticide were fully recognized, chemists began to make related materials in an effort to find more effective insecticides. Although DDT is still outstanding, certain close relatives show some promise. TDE (1,1-dichloro-2,2-bis(*p*-chlorophenyl)ethane) was found to equal or perhaps slightly excel DDT against *Anopheles* larvae. It is less effective, however, against lice, flies, and mosquitoes.

Chemical 1068 is a recent material known only as 1068 (mixed isomers of $C_{10}H_6Cl_8$), which was developed by the Velsicol Corporation and first reported upon by W. C. Kearns and associates of the University of. Illinois. In preliminary tests it proved more toxic than DDT to the body louse, *Anopheles* larvae, houseflies, adult mosquitoes, and certain household pests. This chemical shows great promise, but further practical tests under a variety of conditions must first be made and information as to its toxicological effects on man and animals must be obtained before its value can be fully established.

A chlorinated camphene (3956), developed by the Hercules Powder Co., warrants further consideration, because preliminary tests show it to equal DDT in effectiveness against the body louse; it approaches DDT in its toxicity to mosquito larvae and adults and to the housefly. It also shows promise for use against ticks and mites.

Sabadilla is an old insecticide and a plant product that is said to be used by natives in South America to control lice on man. It has recently been investigated by T. C. Allen of the University of Wisconsin, and methods of handling the product have been developed that increase its effectiveness. It is a powerful toxicant for flies and mosquitoes, according to tests made by Allen and by E. R. McGovran at Beltsville. It is also one of the more effective materials that have been tested against the body louse.

Chloromethyl-*p*-chlorophenylsulfone, known as Lauseto Neu, was one of the most effective insecticides used by the Germans. It was tested against several pests after the war. It was found to be a good insecticide, but less effective against lice, flies, and mosquitoes than DDT. It is, however, one of the best chemicals tested against louse eggs.

Hydroxypentamethylflavan, developed by E. I. du Pont de Nemours & Co., Inc., was found by W. G. Bruce and C. N. Smith of the Savannah laboratory to be an excellent chemical for controlling chiggers in the ground. In comparative tests it proved more effective than benzene hexachloride. Since it does not possess the disagreeable odor of the latter compound, it will no doubt be the preferred treatment.

THE AUTHOR

E. F. Knipling is in charge of the Division of Insects Affecting Man and Animals in the Bureau of Entomology and Plant Quarantine. He has been with the Bureau since 1931, during which time his work has been almost entirely in the field of medical and veterinary entomology. During the war he was in charge of the Bureau's laboratory in Orlando, Fla., where he helped develop the methods used at home and abroad by the armed services for the control of disease-carrying insects. Mr. Knipling was awarded the United States of America Typhus Commission medal for his part in these developments.

FOR FURTHER READING

Laboratory of the Bureau of Entomology and Plant Quarantine, Orlando, Fla.: *DDT and Other Insecticides and Repellents Developed for the Armed Forces,* U. S. D. A. Miscellaneous Publication 606, 1946.

DDT in the Home

by L. S. HENDERSON

EVER SINCE man began to live under a shelter, insects have followed him into that shelter. Whether he has lived in a cave, a grass hut, a tent, a log cabin, a frame house, or a palatial mansion, insect pests have been present. They may be only annoying, or they may be injurious. Insects in man's home may bite him, spread disease, contaminate or destroy his food, damage his clothing, ruin his household furnishings and possessions, or even attack the structure of the dwelling.

From the time man was first troubled by these pests in his home, he has spent a great deal of time and effort in attempting to develop new and better ways of getting rid of them. Early methods were often crude and ineffective. Modern advances in biology have revealed information that helps us to know when and where we can best apply control measures. Physics and engineering developments have helped us devise new equipment and new ways of applying insecticides. The chemists have found or made up new compounds that are more effective for controlling insects.

One such compound is DDT. Its discovery has opened the way to new and better methods for controlling insects in the household. Chemists are developing other similar or closely related compounds, and already some have been found that may prove even more useful than DDT.

The older sprays available for the control of household insects had to be used so the insects were hit directly with the spray. Such sprays were useful in obtaining an immediate reduction in the number of insects present, but the effect of the spray lasted for a few minutes and then more insects would begin to come in again. Often it was impossible to hit all the insects and many of them escaped or were unharmed in protected places. Repeated applications of spray had to be made in an attempt to control such pests as roaches, bedbugs, carpet beetles, silverfish, fleas, brown dog ticks, flies, and mosquitoes.

Investigators found that DDT sprays had an unusual property not possessed by the common household sprays. They found that when DDT insecticides were sprayed on surfaces, insects crawling over the remaining residual deposit of DDT were killed. This residue continued to be effective for several months, and sometimes for a year or more. In practical tests in homes where repeated applications of an ordinary household spray would have been required to eliminate insect infestations, a single DDT residual treatment did the job. Insects in protected places not hit by the spray have to crawl over a DDT deposit when they come out into a treated room in search of food and water, and are killed. Not only is the existing infestation eliminated but for some time after that any insects that happen to find their way into the treated area are killed before they can establish a new infestation.

Insects are not killed immediately upon contact with a DDT residue. As they crawl over it, however, the DDT is absorbed into the body through the feet and body wall. Exceedingly small amounts in the insect body begin to affect the nervous system. The first symptom is a restlessness or excitement which may cause the insect to crawl or fly away. Later the insect is seized with tremors and convulsions, loses its ability to make coordinated movements of flight or crawling, and eventually rolls over on its back. Kicking and twitching of the legs continues for some time, but gradually the insect grows weaker, and death follows.

Death may occur a few minutes or several hours after contact with DDT, depending upon the resistance of the insect and the condition of the deposit. Death may not occur for several days in the case of some of the more resistant insects that touch only small amounts of residue.

DDT has no fumigating effect and insects will not be killed simply by being in the same room where DDT has been used. They do not have to eat the material to be killed, but they must actually come in contact with it, although continuous contact is not necessary. During the first brief contact with a DDT residue a fatal amount of DDT is absorbed by the insect, and it will die, even if it moves off to an untreated area. During the period of excitement some insects may fly or crawl for a considerable distance before they become inactive. In some cases very few dead insects may be found immediately in a treated area. This does not mean that the DDT is not effective. You should look for its results in the absence of live insects, not in the presence of dead ones.

Although the DDT residue is slower in killing insects than are some other insecticides and although it is not effective against all kinds of insects, it does have advantages that other insecticides do not have. One is its long-lasting effect. Another is that DDT is effective against more different kinds of insects than most other insecticides, and its use provides the most effective and simplest method of control yet discovered for some household insects. As is true of the best of insecticides, however, DDT must be used properly in order to give satisfactory results.

Another advantage is its adaptability to use under different conditions and by different methods. It can be formulated into a number of different kinds of sprays and dusts, although it is not a good insecticide in its original form. Preparation of most DDT formulations requires special equipment or technical knowledge and skill and cannot be done satisfactorily in the home.

There are several DDT sprays that may be used in the home for the application of a DDT residual deposit. The most suitable one is a 5-percent solution of DDT in deodorized kerosene. An emulsion containing 5 percent of DDT can be prepared from commercially available concentrates. If the concentrate contains 25 percent of DDT, mix one part of concentrate with four parts of water to form a 5-percent spray. Wettable powders are also available for the preparation of DDT suspensions. These powders have been specially prepared so they can be mixed with water, and usually contain 50 percent of DDT. Follow the directions on the container label for preparing the spray mixture.

Many of the household fly sprays now on the market have from 1/2 to 3 percent of DDT added to the toxic ingredients already present in the spray. Such sprays will give a quick kill of crawling insects that can be hit directly with the spray. Their best use is as a space spray, where the air is filled with a fine floating mist of spray, to obtain quick, temporary relief by killing the flying insects in your home. You should not use preparations containing more than 3 percent of DDT as space sprays. Although there may be some slight residual effect from these weak DDT solutions, you should not depend on them for applying an effective DDT residual deposit.

The gas-propelled aerosols now available commercially are a war development and are another form of space spray. Most of them contain DDT and pyrethrins and they are excellent for obtaining a quick kill of flying insects in a closed room. When used at many times the normal rate of application they may be helpful in the control of crawling insects. At these high concentrations they may be irritating, and they have no lasting effect. For permanent results repeated applications are required.

DDT can be ground and diluted with inert carriers such as talc or clay, and in this form it is a good insecticidal preparation for applying a residual deposit, especially against some of the crawling insects. Some DDT dusts for agricultural purposes contain only 1 to 3 percent of DDT, but for use as a household insecticide a dust should contain 10 percent of DDT.

In order to obtain the greatest benefit from the use of DDT, you should take advantage of its long-lasting effect and apply it to surfaces as a residual treatment. The important thing to remember is that you should treat surfaces where the insects to be controlled will come in contact with the DDT deposit. It is evident that the treatment will have to be applied in different places for the control of different household pests, because of their varying habits. A rather complete coverage of all surfaces can be made for general insect control. It is not often necessary to make such a general application to control any one insect problem. The usual procedure will be to treat only selected areas to control certain insects.

A 5-percent solution of DDT in refined kerosene is most suitable for the control of flying insects such as flies, mosquitoes, and wasps. It is important to treat screens on windows and doors. In localities where insects are not abundant this may be sufficient. Even where insects are abundant it is not necessary to spray the entire interior. For the control of flies, spray such favored resting places as hanging light fixtures and drop cords; projections or uneven places on walls and ceiling; and edges of beams, arches, and door and window frames. Pay particular attention to treating the kitchen and dining room, where flies may be attracted by food odors. It will be helpful to spray outside the house on the porch, around doors, and around garbage cans. If this is done, many flies will be killed before they get a chance to enter the house. For controlling mosquitoes spray in dark corners or secluded spots, and under beds or other furniture where they may hide during the day.

A paint brush may be used for applying the DDT solution to screens. Any good sprayer that produces a moderately coarse spray can be used to apply the solution in other places. Most ordinary household sprayers will do. Put on just enough spray to moisten surfaces thoroughly. One quart of solution will cover 250 to 500 square feet, depending upon how absorbent the surface is.

For the control of crawling insects such as roaches, silverfish, clothes moths, carpet beetles, ants, bedbugs, fleas, and brown dog ticks, the solution may have to be sprayed on floors, lower parts of walls, around baseboards or moldings, around door and window frames, in corners, in cracks or crevices, on beds, behind or underneath objects, or within cabinets, cupboards, drawer spaces, closets, or storage spaces. Remember the habits of the insect to be controlled so a DDT residue will be left in places where they develop, feed, seek shelter, or will crawl over the deposit in the course of their normal activities.

The 10-percent DDT dust is useful against many crawling insects. It should be applied with a small hand duster of the bellows, bulb, or plunger type, using the nozzle to blow the powder into cracks or crevices, and behind or underneath objects where it would be difficult to reach with a spray. The spray should be applied in exposed places where the appearance of the white powder would be objectionable, and to vertical or underneath surfaces where a powder would not adhere. Although most infestations can be controlled with either the liquid or powder, the combined use of the two, each in the places to which it is most suited, will often give more rapid or more satisfactory control.

Precautions

Although DDT is a poison, it is not so dangerous as sodium fluoride or arsenicals, which are commonly used. It is perfectly safe to use if a few simple precautions are observed.

Do not contaminate food or utensils when using DDT. Do not store DDT containers where they might be mistaken for food packages, or where children can reach them. Food in packages can be stored safely in sprayed places after the spray has dried.

Do not spray an oil solution near open fires. Avoid excessive or prolonged contact of the skin with an oil solution of DDT. Wash with soap and water when you are through spraying. Do not breathe large amounts of spray mist.

Caged birds and goldfish should be removed from rooms being treated with DDT insecticides. Any oil spray is likely to injure house plants.

THE AUTHOR

L. S. Henderson is an assistant chief of the Division of Insects Affecting Man and Animals in the Bureau of Entomology and Plant Quarantine. A graduate of the University of Kansas, Dr. Henderson joined the Department in 1938. After 4 years in Alabama, where he tested insecticides against the white-fringed beetle, he transferred to the Agricultural Research Center at Beltsville. He did the preliminary work on a method of testing and evaluating liquid roach insecticides and was in charge of the household insect project before he was brought into the divisional office in Washington in his present capacity.

FOR FURTHER READING

Laboratory of the Bureau of Entomology and Plant Quarantine, Orlando, Fla.: *DDT and Other Insecticides and Repellents Developed for the Armed Forces,* U. S. D. A. Miscellaneous Publication 606, 1946.

ALSO, IN THIS BOOK

The Chemistry of DDT, by H. L. Haller and Ruth L. Busbey, page 616.
Pests That Attack Man, by E. F. Knipling, page 632.
Air War Against Insects, by H. H. Stage and Frank Irons, page 835.
Blowers for Insecticides, by W. L. Popham, page 839.
Pests in Stored Products, by R. T. Cotton, page 874.

Crops That Resist Insects

by C. M. PACKARD, B. B. BAYLES, and O. S. AAMODT

MANY A FARMER has seen the prospect of an abundant crop ruined by the onslaught of an insect pest that he was powerless to prevent. To make matters worse, nobody was able to tell him how to avoid like losses in the future. For years farmers, entomologists, and agronomists have wished and looked for crops or varieties that could be planted with assurance of freedom from destruction by one or another insect. It is, therefore, a pleasure to report material progress in the discovery and development of varieties of several different crops that have a high degree of resistance to certain insects.

Probably the most effective results to date have been achieved in the breeding of winter wheats resistant to the hessian fly.

Kawvale and Pawnee wheats were developed cooperatively by State and Department workers at the Kansas and Nebraska State Agricultural Experiment Stations. Both wheats carry a considerable degree of fly resistance and are in commercial use. The increase in acreage of Pawnee has been particularly rapid. Poso 42 and Big Club 43, two fly-resistant, soft white club wheats recently released in California, have given excellent performance in field plantings. Big Club 43 carries resistance to stem rust, bunt, and root rot, and a high degree of fly resistance.

Other promising fly-resistant varieties of hard red winter wheats for the West Central States and of soft red winter wheats for the East Central and Eastern States have been developed. They are highly resistant to the hessian fly and to several of the most serious fungus diseases. The best of the strains are being tested for yield and quality, but are not yet commercially available.

Wheats resistant to the wheat stem sawfly have been developed. One, named Rescue and developed by Canadian workers, has been increased

648

for distribution in sections of Canada and Montana, where the insect has caused heavy losses. Wheat varieties showing considerable resistance to the chinch bug have also been discovered by research workers.

Intensive work is in progress on the production of lines of corn resistant to the earworm, European corn borer, chinch bug, and stored-grain insects. Although the degree of resistance still found in corn to any of these insects has not been so great as that found in wheat to the hessian fly, results so far are promising. The commercial hybrid sweet corns Ioana and Golden Hybrid No. 10, for example, carry considerable resistance to the earworm. Several experimental lines of dent and sweet corn not yet commercially available are even more highly resistant. They suffer only a tenth to a quarter as much injury by the earworm as the most susceptible lines and when crossed with lines having other desirable characters they can transmit earworm resistance to their progeny.

Studies have shown that earworm resistance is not all due to anatomical characters such as long, tight husks and flinty kernels. For some reason not yet understood the silks and kernels of certain strains do not appear to fill the dietary needs of the young worms and few of them become established. It is possible that much of the loss in corn yields caused by the earworm can be prevented through the use of earworm-resistant inbreds—which are still in the experimental stage—in the production of commercial hybrids. Earworm-resistant corn would be particularly valuable in the Southern States, where the insect is an important factor in growing field and sweet corn successfully.

Resistance in corn to the European corn borer appears to be of three types—unattractiveness to the egg-laying adult moths, inability of the young worms to survive, and ability of the corn to stand up and yield well despite infestation. Through the testing of hundreds of pedigreed lines, a few that have one or more of these qualities have been found.

Survival of first-generation borers in dent lines R4 and L317, for instance, is less than half of that in ordinarily susceptible lines. R4 and L317 have been used to some extent in the production of commercial hybrids. Another line, P8, has almost as good resistance to survival of first-generation borers and also stands up and yields well under the second-generation borers that attack corn late in the growing season. This line has just been released for commercial use. About 30 lines of borer-resistant sweet corn, among which Yellow Bantam, Country Gentleman, and Evergreen types are represented, have also been found. A few of them, such as Iowa 45 and Iowa 1445, are used in the production of commercial hybrids. The comprehensive corn breeding program now in progress seeks to find and produce commercially desirable lines of corn more completely resistant to the European corn borer and there is a fair prospect of eventually attaining this goal.

Work on insect resistance in other crops has been much less extensive than on corn and wheat. Nevertheless, striking results have already been obtained. Sorghum resistant to the chinch bug, barleys resistant to the green bug, alfalfa resistant to pea aphid and potato leafhopper, sugar beets resistant to the beet leafhopper, sugarcane resistant to the sugarcane borer, sunflower resistant to seed weevils, and even locust trees resistant to the locust borer are prominent examples. R. O. Snelling pointed out that the available literature includes records of resistance in nearly 100 plant species involving more than 100 insect species.

In almost none of the crops mentioned has it yet been possible to determine with certainty the particular characteristics responsible for the resistance. Thus, in the course of the breeding process, the only way yet found of selecting the resistant plants is to subject them to heavy infestation, usually by artificial means, since natural infestations cannot be depended upon to develop on all the plants. Testing and selection for insect resistance, in addition to all the other essential characters, further complicates the already difficult procedure of improving crop plants by controlled breeding.

Even with crops that can be put through one or more generations a year, the production of insect-resistant and otherwise satisfactory varieties is a long and slow process. Varieties that have the desired insect resistance must first be found by preliminary exploration. After that, many years of breeding may be necessary in order to transfer the resistance into varieties having the other characteristics, such as high yield, quality, and resistance to disease, that are essential to profitable commercial use. Despite these difficulties and others, accomplishments to date indicate that resistant varieties of crops offer one of the most promising means of solving many of the insect problems for which we have heretofore had no satisfactory solution.

THE AUTHORS

C. M. Packard is an entomologist in charge of the Division of Cereal and Forage Insect Investigations in the Bureau of Entomology and Plant Quarantine.

B. B. Bayles is an agronomist in the Bureau of Plant Industry, Soils, and Agricultural Engineering. Dr. Bayles is a graduate of the University of Wisconsin.

O. S. Aamodt is an agronomist in the Bureau of Plant Industry, Soils, and Agricultural Engineering, in charge of the Division of Forage Crops and Diseases.

FOR FURTHER READING

Snelling, Ralph O.: *Resistance of Plants to Insect Attack,* Botanical Review, volume 7, No. 10, pages 543–586, October 1941.

ALSO, IN THIS BOOK

Corn Hybrids for the South, by Merle T. Jenkins, page 389.
New Varieties of Wheat, by B. B. Bayles, page 379.
Improved Varieties of Barley, by G. A. Wiebe, page 403.
More and Better Clover, by E. A. Hollowell, page 427.

Control of Forage Pests

by W. A. BAKER

IN THE ever-present battle to control insects attacking cereal and forage crops in the field, the use of insecticides has been restricted. One limitation was the generally low per-acre value of the crops compared to the costs of the insecticides that have been available. That limitation is being overcome by recent discoveries of new insecticides and more efficient ways to apply them.

But it must always be stressed that the application of poisonous materials on crops to be eaten by man or animals is complicated by the hazards of residues remaining on the crops. There is constant need for precautions or adaptations in their use. Up to now our experience with the new insecticides has been too limited to permit a thorough evaluation of the problems of residues, and our recommendations for their use on cereal and forage crops must be qualified accordingly. Several of the insecticides have given satisfactory control of various insects against which they have been tested, and we hope further work will reveal entirely safe ways to use them.

The first of the newer materials to come to our attention was DDT. Late in 1942 we included DDT in laboratory tests against the European corn borer (*Pyrausta nubilalis* (Hbn.)). Its performance was outstanding. In subsequent field tests we found it highly effective against the corn borer and several other insect pests of cereals and forage crops.

An outstanding exception was the sugarcane borer (*Diatraea saccharalis* (F.)), a serious pest of sugarcane. Populations of this insect actually were higher in some DDT-treated plots than in plots receiving no treatment, probably the result of the adverse effect of the insecticide on parasites and predators that otherwise help keep the borer population down.

With grasshoppers, various dust and spray formulations of DDT were effective, but the dosages required to obtain the results were so heavy

651

that we cannot now recommend its use to control grasshoppers: The cost is high, but, more important, there are possible hazards of poisonous residues if livestock graze in treated fields or are fed hay or other forage harvested therefrom.

We have had promising experimental results from DDT against the European corn borer; the corn earworm (*Heliothis armigera* (Hbn.)); the white-fringed beetle (*Pantomorus leucoloma* (Boh.)); and the chinch bug (*Blissus leucopterus* (Say)). Both spray and dust preparations have been effective against the corn borer infesting market sweet corn; treatments with dilute sprays applied with ground equipment at a dosage of about three-fourths pound of DDT per acre provided the maximum protection. Good results also were obtained with dust mixtures containing 6 percent of DDT in pyrophyllite applied at a rate of 40 pounds of mixed dust, or 2.4 pounds of DDT per acre application. Airplane applications of the dust at the same rate, or of a concentrated spray containing DDT in an oil carrier (the latter applied at a rate of 2.75 gallons containing about 2 pounds of DDT per acre application), also gave promising results in preliminary experiments.

Most of our tests with DDT for corn borer control have included four applications of each treatment at approximately 5-day intervals, beginning with the first hatching of borer eggs. Results obtained in a number of experiments, however, indicate that a satisfactory degree of control can be had with fewer applications. The cost would then be lower, and there is the possibility of extending the method to sweet corn grown for canning and to field corn in localities where the borer causes losses.

We got much better control of the corn earworm in sweet corn and dent seed corn with injections of mineral-oil solutions or emulsions of DDT into the developing corn ears at about the time the silks were beginning to turn brown, than with preparations containing pyrethrum or styrene dibromide. The injection of DDT preparations into ears of sweet corn that are to be used for food is not considered safe, however. Very satisfactory protection from earworm attack has also been obtained in preliminary tests by atomizing DDT in oil solutions or emulsions onto the ears and silks of sweet corn. With further development of formulations and application equipment, this method promises to reduce greatly the cost and inconvenience of controlling this insect on corn.

DDT is the most potent insecticide we have tested against adults of the white-fringed beetle, a destructive pest of many crops in the South. Both sprays and dusts are effective as stomach and contact poisons. As a stomach poison, DDT in dust form was 69 to 74 times more toxic than sodium fluoaluminate, and a spray containing one-eighth pound of DDT per 100 gallons of water was about as effective as one containing 8 pounds of synthetic cryolite (85.4 percent sodium fluoaluminate). As a contact poison, DDT in dust form was effective when applied directly to the beetles or on the soil surface, or when mixed with soil, DDT is also highly toxic to white-fringed beetle larvae; dosages of 2½ pounds of DDT or more per acre, mixed in the upper 3 inches of soil, killed all newly hatched larvae. Somewhat higher dosages are necessary to give complete kill of mature larvae. Solutions of 0.5 to 5 pounds of DDT in 7.5 gallons of kerosene have given net mortalities of white-fringed beetle eggs in excess of 99 percent when the eggs were dipped for an instant in the liquid, and were equally as effective as 1 pound of 2, 4-dinitrocyclohexylphenol in 7.5 gallons of kerosene.

Although DDT has been found effective as a contact poison against chinch bug adults and nymphs, the dosages required to get satisfactory kills have been too great to be of practical value with formulations we have tested thus far. But when used as a barrier line on the ground against migrating bugs, dust mixtures of 5 percent or less of DDT in pyrophyllite compared favorably with dust mixtures containing 4 percent of dinitro-o-cresol in halting the bugs; a mixture containing 3 percent of DDT gave almost perfect protection from the young nymphs.

Other promising results obtained with DDT are:

In bait preparations for control of the armyworm (*Cirphis unipuncta* (Haw.)) infesting small grains and the fall armyworm (*Laphygma frugiperda* (A. & S.)) attacking field corn.

In dusts and sprays for control of the tobacco thrips (*Frankliniella fusca* (Hinds)) on seedling peanuts, the potato leafhopper *Empoasca fabae* (Harr.)) on alfalfa and peanuts, and the velvetbean caterpillar (*Anticarsia gemmatilis* (Hbn.)) on peanuts and velvetbeans.

In dust mixtures against the rice stinkbug (*Solubea pugnax* (F.)), the lespedeza webworm (*Tetralopha scortealis* (Led.)), and a grassworm (*Pachyzancla phaeopteralis* (Guen.)) on lawns.

In sprays for control of the corn flea beetle (*Chaetocnema pulicaria* (Melsh)) on sweet corn. Further experimentation is needed to develop effective formulations, dosages, and methods of application that will not leave dangerous residues, before DDT can be recommended for control of any of these insect pests.

Besides DDT, a number of other synthetic organic compounds have been tested in preliminary experiments against insects attacking cereal and forage crops in the field with varying results.

Benzene hexachloride, the most promising of these, has been found to be highly effective against grasshoppers, the white-fringed beetle, the sugarcane borer, and the rice stinkbug, and somewhat less effective against the European corn borer.

A DDT analog, di(p-methoxyphenyl)trichloroethane, was found to be comparatively ineffective against the European corn borer, fairly effective against the white-fringed beetle, and much more effective against grasshoppers than DDT.

Piperonyl cyclohexenone in a spray suspension was very effective against the European corn borer, but alone or in combination with pyrethrins in spray and dust preparations it had little value as a contact insecticide against the chinch bug.

TDE, or 1,1-dichloro-2,2-bis (p-chlorophenyl)ethane, in emulsion form was found to compare favorably with DDT when atomized onto the silks and husks of sweet corn for control of the corn earworm.

Among the plant materials that have recently received increased consideration as insecticides, ground sabadilla seeds and ground stems of *Ryania speciosa* have been of particular interest. Both sprays and dusts containing *Ryania* have been effective against the European corn borer in sweet corn. They have given better control than recommended rotenone preparations and practically as good as preparations containing DDT. *Ryania* has also been found to be highly toxic when used as a contact insecticide against the chinch bug, although heavy dosages were required to produce a high rate of mortality under field conditions. Used as a dust mixture applied to 3- or 4-day-old sweet corn silks, however, *Ryania* gave no control of the corn earworm.

As with *Ryania,* good control of chinch bugs in small grain and corn has been obtained with heavy single applications of dust containing 5 to 20 percent of sabadilla. Minimum effective dosages of this material against the chinch bug have not been determined in our experiments.

Observations on the effects of the various materials I have discussed have shown that, with only a few exceptions, none of them has affected plant growth adversely, whether applied as sprays or dusts, or as foliage or soil treatments against cereal and forage crops in the field. None caused any plant injuries when applied to foliage, but DDT has been observed to injure rye and tomatoes planted in sandy soil that had been treated with 10 pounds or more of technical DDT per acre mixed with the top 3 inches of soil. Also, plant injury has been observed in rice, cowpeas, and oats growing in light soil containing 10 pounds or more of the gamma isomer of benzene hexachloride to the acre, mixed thoroughly with the top 3 inches of soil.

THE AUTHOR

W. A. Baker, an entomologist in the Bureau of Entomololgy and Plant Quarantine, was appointed assistant leader of the Division of Cereal and Forage Insect Investigations in 1943. Before that he investigated insects and their control in the field, particularly cereal and forage insects in the Southwest, the European corn borer, and the utilization of parasites in the control of the gypsy and brown-tail moths and the European corn borer in New England and the Midwest.

Insecticides for Cotton

by R. W. HARNED

COTTON, an important crop since before the dawn of history and one that has been grown in North America since the earliest colonial days, has always had serious insect enemies. Against them, most of the materials known to control insects attacking plants in the United States have been tried. The boll weevil, bollworm, cotton leafworm, cotton aphid, cotton flea hopper, and other pests continue, however, to reduce yields and destroy cotton crops.

The first potent weapon was paris green, the use of which was recommended in 1872 by Prof. C. V. Riley, then the State Entomologist of Missouri, to control the cotton leafworm. Its use spread rapidly, especially in the Gulf Coast States, and during the next 40 years thousands of tons were used against the cotton leafworm and the bollworm.

Next came the discovery in 1916 by workers in the Department of Agriculture that calcium arsenate dust of certain specifications was effective and practical for the control of the boll weevil. Later investigations showed it to be useful against the bollworm, and in mixtures with sulfur to be of great practical value in the control of the cotton flea hopper, tarnished plant bug, and other plant bugs and stinkbugs that attack cotton. Because of its wide use for boll weevil control and its lower cost, it largely replaced paris green for the control of the cotton leafworm and bollworm.

For the control of cotton insects about 50 million pounds of this arsenical insecticide are now used each year. The need for applying calcium arsenate to large acreages of cotton stimulated improvement of dusting machines, but no ground machines could be satisfactory for use when the soils were saturated with water. In 1922 airplanes were first used for the application of calcium arsenate to cotton. This method was so satisfactory that within a few years there were several dozen companies operating hundreds of airplanes used largely for dusting cotton.

During the decade 1920–30 two other materials, sulfur dust and nicotine, were first used extensively for the control of cotton insects. Sulfur had long been known as an insecticide, but was not used on cotton until it was found to be helpful in reducing losses caused by the red spider and the cotton flea hopper. Sulfur later was found to be useful in reducing infestations of the tarnished plant bug and rapid plant bug and its use helped to check the reduction in quality of cotton in fields where injurious stinkbugs were abundant. Mixtures of sulfur and arsenicals, such as calcium arsenate and paris green, were found to be more effective against the cotton flea hopper and the other plant bugs and stinkbugs that attack cotton, and in recent years millions of pounds of these mixtures have been dusted on cotton in Texas, Arizona, New Mexico, and California. The cotton aphid had always been a minor pest of cotton until the extensive use of calcium arsenate for boll weevil control, about 1920, caused it to become a major problem. The heavy aphid infestations develop because calcium arsenate decreases the acidity of the plant juices and there is some evidence that this favors the rapid development and reproduction of the aphids. The arsenical dust also kills the beneficial parasitic and predaceous insects that normally destroy the aphids and prevent serious infestations. Nicotine was found to be fairly satisfactory for the control of the cotton aphid and its use for this purpose has steadily increased during the past 25 years. The method of application generally used is to mix nicotine sulfate with calcium arsenate or with lime for dusting cotton. During recent years the supply of nicotine available for use on cotton has not been sufficient to meet the demand.

During the 1930's the insecticides recommended and widely used for the control of cotton insects were calcium arsenate, sulfur, lead arsenate, paris green, nicotine sulfate, and mixtures of them.

Recent research has developed several materials that may be as effective as the insecticides developed in the years since paris green was first used in the cotton fields, or even more effective. Experiments have shown that mixtures of basic copper arsenate and sulfur have good dusting qualities and when applied at the rate of 12 to 15 pounds an acre are more effective than calcium arsenate for the control of the bollworm. They are more effective than sulfur or mixtures of sulfur and calcium arsenate for the control of the cotton flea hopper, nearly equal to calcium arsenate against the boll weevil and less likely to cause injurious aphid infestations, and better than calcium arsenate and equal to lead arsenate against the cotton leafworm because they adhere to the foliage and are effective for weeks after application. Their chief disadvantage is that they cost more than calcium arsenate or mixtures of calcium arsenate and sulfur.

Cryolite applied at the rate of 8 to 10 pounds an acre is more effective against the bollworm than calcium arsenate, but is much less effective against the boll weevil and cotton leafworm. Research had shown that rotenone has possibilities against the cotton aphid, but the war interfered with investigations with this material and it was not available for use on cotton. Additional research may disclose that it may be useful against aphids and possibly other insects on cotton.

Sabadilla is another material that shows promise against the stinkbugs and plant bugs.

Another period in the development of insecticides for the control of cotton insects occurred during and immediately following the war, when many synthetic organic chemical compounds were tested to determine their toxicity to insects.

In 1943, preliminary tests indicated that DDT was effective against such cotton pests as the bollworm, the tarnished plant bug, and other plant bugs, the Say stinkbug, the brown stinkbug, the conchuela, the onion thrips, and the tobacco thrips, but was comparatively ineffective against the boll weevil, the cotton leafworm, and the cotton aphid.

During 1944 extensive tests conducted with DDT against cotton insects confirmed the results obtained in 1943. In addition, it was found to be effective against six other cotton pests, the pink bollworm, the cotton flea hopper, the red-shouldered plant bug or stinkbug, the superb plant bug, the small darkling beetle, and the beet armyworm, and not effective against the red spider mite. In fact, the use of DDT dust on cotton sometimes causes an increase in the red spider and cotton aphid populations, probably because it destroys their natural enemies.

Many experiments in 1945 indicated that in DDT an insecticide had been discovered that is of practical value for the control of the pink bollworm; that is more effective for use against the bollworm than cryolite, basic copper arsenate, lead arsenate, and calcium arsenate, the materials that previously had given the best results against this insect; and that in Arizona gave notable increases in yields of cotton when used for the control of sucking bugs. As a result, during 1946 many thousands of acres of cotton, especially in Texas and Arizona, were dusted by farmers with mixtures containing DDT for the control of the cotton flea hopper, bollworm, and other insects, and the Governments of Mexico and the United States cooperated in applying thousands of pounds of 10-percent DDT dust by airplane for the control of the pink bollworm to hundreds of acres of cotton on dozens of farms on both sides of the river in the lower Rio Grande Valley.

Another organic chemical, benzene hexachloride, which was first made by Michael Faraday in 1825, was shown to be a promising insecticide in England in 1942. Preliminary tests with this material against cotton insects in 1945 indicated that it might be more effective against the boll weevil, cotton leafworm, cotton aphid, and certain stinkbugs than any insecticide that had previously been used.

Experiments with benzene hexachloride in 1946 indicate that it may be the most potent insecticide thus far discovered for use against the boll weevil, cotton aphid, and cotton leafworm. It may be equal to DDT in effectiveness against thrips, the cotton flea hopper, tarnished plant bug, and some of the other cotton insects, but is less effective against the bollworm, pink bollworm, and beet armyworm.

Experiments conducted by the Department in cooperation with the State agricultural experiment stations in South Carolina, Mississippi, Louisiana, Texas, and Arizona in 1946 indicate that the proper use of DDT or benzene hexachloride or mixtures of these materials may greatly increase the yields and improve the quality of cotton in all areas where insects are seriously injurious to this crop. At Waco, Tex., a mixture of DDT and benzene hexachloride gave remarkable results in increasing the yields of cotton by controlling heavy combined infestations of the boll weevil, cotton aphid, bollworm, and cotton leafworm.

Another new organic compound tested at Waco in small plots and large-scale field experiments showed very promising results against heavy infestations of boll weevils, cotton aphids, bollworms, and leafworms. Laboratory and cage tests also indicated it would control the cotton flea hopper, stinkbugs, loopers, and garden webworms. This material is a chlorinated camphene known as Hercules 3956. It does not have some of the objectionable features connected with benzene hexachloride.

Other less promising organic compounds are hexaethyl tetraphosphate and another chlorinated hydrocarbon known as Velsicol 1068.

THE AUTHOR

R. W. Harned, entomologist in charge of the Division of Cotton Insects of the Bureau of Entomology and Plant Quarantine, has been associated with cotton insect investigations since 1907, when he joined the staff of the Mississippi Agricultural Experiment Station. From 1908 until 1931 he was in charge of entomological activities in Mississippi. He organized the State Plant Board of Mississippi in 1918 and was in charge of the regulatory work until he assumed his present position in 1931.

FOR FURTHER READING

Folsom, J. W., *Insect Enemies of the Cotton Plant.* U. S. D. A. Farmers' Bulletin 1688, 1932.

Control of Cotton Insects. U. S. Bureau of Entomology and Plant Quarantine E–569, 1942. (Processed.)

Loftin, U. C., *Results of Tests with DDT Against Cotton Insects in 1944.* U. S. Bureau of Entomology and Plant Quarantine E–657, 1945. (Processed.)

Orchard Insecticides

by B. A. PORTER

RAPID PROGRESS is being made in the effective and economical control of the important orchard pests. Government agencies
and chemical companies are developing a growing number of new and
effective insecticides. The situation is quite different from that of the
first 25 years of the century, when fruit growers had a limited and
rather rigid list of insecticides. By that time lead arsenate had largely
replaced other arsenicals for the control of the codling moth, plum curculio, and other chewing insects. Lime-sulfur and mineral-oil sprays were
used during the winter for scale insects. Kerosene emulsion, nicotine sulfate, or soap was used to check aphids and other soft-bodied insects. Citrus
growers used sulfur, mineral-oil sprays, and hydrocyanic acid fumigation
under tents. Paradichlorobenzene was effective in controlling the peach-
tree borer. Those insecticides were almost the entire list of materials
available for general use in the orchard.

The second 25 years of the century is witnessing the introduction of
many new insecticides for use in orchards. From 1925 to 1935 perhaps
the chief addition was cryolite, several million pounds of which are now
used annually in the Northwest for codling moth control. In 1925, growers began to use the highly refined "white" or "summer" oils for spraying
fruit trees in foliage. These oils are less injurious to plant tissue than oils
of less refinement. They are used as contact sprays for scale and certain
other insects, and as stickers or deposit builders for lead arsenate and
other stomach poisons.

Many of the new materials that are now appearing are the reward
of long and extensive efforts to find a suitable material to replace lead
arsenate to control the codling moth. Lead arsenate is still standard in
most areas but it does not always give adequate control. It often injures

the trees, and results in excessive undesirable accumulations in the soil. In many localities a full schedule of lead arsenate applications leaves excessive spray residues on fruit at harvesttime.

Literally thousands of materials have been tested as possible replacements for lead arsenate, but few have survived initial tests.

New ways of using nicotine have been devised. Originally employed chiefly as a contact insecticide against soft-bodied sucking insects, nicotine was used in such a form that it volatilized readily, and was washed off quickly by rains. Several compounds of nicotine have now been developed that remain effective on the fruit or foliage over periods of days or weeks. The leading mixture of this type is nicotine bentonite, which has been used effectively in thousands of acres of apple orchards in Indiana, Illinois, and elsewhere.

Phenothiazine, first tested in 1934, is very poisonous to the codling moth, but has given uncertain results. Much of this irregularity was overcome in the drier parts of the Northwest by the use of a very finely divided material. Elsewhere the finely divided material is still not entirely dependable. Unfortunately phenothiazine causes certain susceptible individuals to suffer a serious skin condition similar to severe sunburn. Spray men, pickers, and others who work in sprayed trees may suffer from it. Phenothiazine causes some interference with proper sizing and coloring of fruit; it is also rather expensive. Despite these difficulties, a few growers use phenothiazine, usually mixed with lead arsenate.

Xanthone also has shown promise for control of the codling moth, especially in the Northwest, but the results have been irregular and its acceptance by growers has been limited. Xanthone exhibits one unexpected quality: Its continued use seems to prevent outbreaks of orchard mites and the woolly apple aphid. On this account there is now some interest in the use of xanthone with DDT.

Tartar emetic, formerly used chiefly as a poison in ant baits, came into use for the control of the citrus thrips in California about 1939. Within a few years, however, it seemed to have much less value for the purpose in certain areas. Apparently the susceptible thrips had been killed off, leaving a more resistant race of them to carry on.

The outstanding new material is DDT. From the very first laboratory tests, it has given marked control of the codling moth. In many cases a spray containing one-half pound of DDT, in a water-dispersible powder, per 100 gallons, has given much better control than 3 pounds of lead arsenate. The use of DDT at reduced strengths (4 to 6 ounces per 100 gallons), with about half the usual strength of lead arsenate or nicotine bentonite in all apple sections and with cryolite or xanthone in the Northwest, has also given good control. Besides the usual small-scale experiments, tests have also been carried on in large blocks in commercial plantings, in cooperation with growers, with similar outstanding results.

DDT has also shown promise in limited tests against many other fruit insects, among them the tarnished plant bug, which causes distortion of peach fruit, the oriental fruit moth, the rose chafer, the pear thrips, several species of leafhoppers, and the Japanese beetle and its grubs. Tests against the grape berry moth, the apple maggot, the cherry fruitflies, the peach-tree borer, and some other insects affecting fruit trees have given inconclusive or conflicting results.

DDT seems to have little or no practical value against such important orchard insects as the plum curculio, the San Jose scale, other scale insects, the pear psylla, and several species of orchard mites.

DDT seems to be safe enough for use on fruit trees. Some injury has resulted from the application of mixtures with oil emulsion, but the part played by DDT in this injury has not been entirely clear.

One factor that is important with such a powerful insecticide as DDT is its unfavorable effect on beneficial insects that normally keep many of our insect pests within bounds. Probably the most serious problem of this kind has been the tremendous increase in the populations of mites of various species that has often followed the use of DDT. At ordinary strengths, DDT has little effect on the mites, but it does kill off many of the ladybird beetles and other enemies of the mites. If the use of DDT in orchards becomes general, mite control is certain to become a major problem, even in orchards in which growers have never previously realized that mites were present.

Another problem is that of spray residues. On the basis of studies made thus far, the Food and Drug Administration has announced that no action would be taken on apples or pears containing residues of DDT not in excess of 7 parts per million (about 0.05 grain per pound).

Remarkable as DDT seems, it may prove to be only a stepping stone to even better insecticides. Certain compounds closely related to DDT are being tested; some material in this group may be found that has the effectiveness of DDT without its disadvantages. Many other complex organic compounds are also receiving attention. Prominent among them is benzene hexachloride. Benzene hexachloride has given promising results against the plum curculio and several other insects not affected by DDT, without stimulating increases in mite populations. Unfortunately, benzene hexachloride has an offensive, musty odor that could be imparted to sprayed or dusted fruit.

Several new insecticides are available for spraying when the trees are dormant. Neither lime-sulfur nor the petroleum oils, used during the first 25 years of the century, had much value in the control of aphids, which pass the winter as tiny black eggs on the twigs and smaller branches. Several materials have recently become available for use against aphid eggs during the dormant period.

For a number of years tar-distillate oils, byproducts from the manufacture of gas, have been used effectively for the control of aphids in the winter egg stage. More recently there have been introduced several materials referred to as dinitro compounds. Two of the more common of these are dinitro-*o*-cyclohexylphenol and dinitro-*o*-cresol. These compounds are effective against the eggs of aphids and may be used with oil sprays for the combined control of aphids, European red mites (in the egg stage), and the San Jose and other scale insects. So, instead of one or two materials for dormant spraying, the grower now has a choice of a half dozen.

The control of the plum curculio in southern peach orchards has been approached from a new angle in the chemical treatment of the ground late in the spring. Two compounds, dichloroethyl ether and dichloroethyl formal, have been successfully used for this purpose on an experimental basis. If the soil treatment is found feasible, it will reduce or eliminate the need for lead arsenate, which causes serious damage to peach foliage and is only partially effective in curculio control.

New materials have been found for the control of the peach-tree borer, to replace paradichlorobenzene, which sometimes injures young peach trees and has other disadvantages. Emulsions of ethylene dichloride have been found effective over a wider range of conditions than paradichlorobenzene, and, when properly used, are less likely to cause injury to the trees. More recently propylene dichloride has been found even more effective in borer control than ethylene dichloride.

Many of the new insecticide materials have been tested over too short a period to permit any evaluation of their probable ultimate place in the orchard insect control program. Despite the increasing complexity of the list of available insecticides and the problems occasioned by their use, rapid progress is being made.

THE AUTHOR

B. A. Porter is in charge of the Division of Fruit Insect Investigations in the Bureau of Entomology and Plant Quarantine. He joined the Department in 1917, and for many years conducted field investigations of various orchard-insect problems in Connecticut, Indiana, and elsewhere.

Insecticides for Vegetables

by W. H. WHITE

THE perfect insecticide for vegetables must meet several definite specifications. It must leave no residue or deposit on the fruit or edible leaves of the plant to endanger the health of the consumer—a point that is especially important in controlling insects on leafy vegetables like cabbage, broccoli, kale, lettuce, celery, and asparagus, and almost as important in the case of vegetables that bear edible pods or fruits. The residues on leafy vegetables are not readily removed by washing. The insecticide for vegetables must be poisonous to a number of different kinds of insects and have no effect upon plant growth, whatever the climate. Temperature and humidity should not affect its toxicity to the insect or its physical qualities. It should be compatible with fungicides.

A material or combination that meets fully all these specifications has not yet been discovered, although many hundreds have been tested. But insecticides containing pyrethrins and rotenone as the principal toxic agents, developed during the past 15 years, have given satisfactory control of some important insect pests and have practically eliminated the hazard of residues.

The ground flowers of the plant *Pyrethrum cinerariaefolium* is the principal raw product from which pyrethrum insecticides are prepared. Before the war, Japan was the principal source of the raw product, but during the war supplies were obtained largely from Kenya Colony, Africa. The two toxic ingredients of the flower buds are known chemically as pyrethrins I and II. The raw product from Kenya Colony contains, on an average, 1.3 percent of total pyrethrins.

Rotenone insecticides are prepared from the ground roots of two kinds of plants, *Derris elliptica* (derris) from the Malay States and Dutch East Indies, and *Lonchocarpus* species (cube, timbo, barbasco) from South

America. The ground roots of these plants contain, besides rotenone, other ingredients toxic to insects, but rotenone is considered the most important, and is used as a basis for the preparation of rotenone insecticides.

In the late 1920's and early 1930's the condemnation by food officials of vegetable products, such as celery and cabbage, because of undesirable insecticide residues emphasized the necessity of developing insecticides less hazardous to man than the arsenical compounds and of providing schedules for applying insecticides that would reduce or eliminate the spray-residue problem for certain types of vegetables.

In general, the problem was approached from two angles: To study the growth of the plant to determine the latest period in its development that an arsenical insecticide could be applied without involving a risk of contaminating the part of the plant that is used as food; to develop the use of pyrethrum and rotenone products and extend the use of nicotine insecticides for leaf-feeding insects.

The problem of residues was particularly acute in areas where arsenicals were used for the control of cabbage caterpillars, especially where the cabbage is marketed with several loose leaves around the head. Therefore, the investigations initiated in 1932 were concentrated on the control of insects affecting cabbage and related cole crops. Plant-growth studies on the Wakefield variety of cabbage grown near Charleston, S. C., which is marketed with four outer loose leaves, revealed that objectionable residues will follow the use of arsenicals applied 30 days before harvesttime, or after the head begins to form. On cauliflower similar residues remained if the application was made after the curd or head had begun to form.

Pyrethrum and Rotenone

The investigations on rotenone and pyrethrum insecticides showed that either or both of the materials could be used to protect the crop from green caterpillar damage after it became unsafe to apply arsenicals or similar poisons. Since the insecticidal value of both pyrethrum and rotenone varies with the species of insect involved, the determination of which material to use depends upon the species of worms that are predominant in the infestation. For example, pyrethrum insecticides are more effective than rotenone against the cabbage looper; rotenone is more effective for the control of the larva of the diamondback moth and the imported cabbageworm. Therefore, when the predominating caterpillars are the imported cabbageworm and the larvae of the diamondback moth, a dust containing 1 percent of rotenone is recommended. If the cabbage looper is the most abundant species, a dust containing 0.3 percent of pyrethrins will yield more satisfactory results.

Studies were also conducted to find means of increasing the efficacy of the simple dust mixtures containing these insecticides, especially rotenone.

For this purpose various wetting agents and oils were added, and different types of diluents or carriers were tried. Both mineral and vegetable oils were found to increase the effectiveness of rotenone dust mixtures against some insects, but were of little or no value against others. For example, 2 percent of mineral oil increased the toxicity of rotenone to the pea aphid and cabbageworms, but for Mexican bean beetle control rotenone dusts containing oil showed little superiority over simple dust mixtures. Experiments with the various carriers or diluents, such as clays, talc, sulfur, bentonite, and lime, for the rotenone-containing root powders showed talc and particularly pyrophyllite to be the most satisfactory.

Liquid extracts of pyrethrum flowers and of rotenone-containing roots, as well as powders impregnated with pyrethrum extracts, have also been prepared and used successfully.

The work on pyrethrum and rotenone conducted during the past 10 years by Federal, State, and commercial workers has shown that rotenone has a greater over-all usefulness on vegetables than pyrethrum and that the use of either product does not involve a residue hazard. The raw materials of both can be imported into this country and processed, and the products can be prepared and distributed at a reasonable cost.

As previously stated, these insecticides are selective in their action. Rotenone insecticides are outstanding for the control of the Mexican bean beetle on the green bean crop, the pea weevil, and the asparagus beetle, and they are useful for the control of the green cabbage caterpillars on cabbage and other cole crops, loopers on lettuce, several kinds of flea beetles and aphids, the Colorado potato beetle, and the striped cucumber beetle. However, they are of little or no value against the tomato fruitworm, the tomato pinworm, webworms, the cabbage aphid, the pepper weevil, the celery leaf tier, leafhoppers, the garden flea hopper, or plant bugs. The term "plant bug" is applied to a group of insects that obtain their food by sucking the juices from the plants. Common among these are the squash bug, the harlequin bug, and the tarnished plant bug.

Pyrethrum insecticides, on the other hand, are outstanding for their usefulness against the celery leaf tier, webworms, the cabbage looper, and the bean or potato leafhopper. They are useful for the control of the imported cabbageworm, the garden flea hopper, and some species of plant bugs. Careful and frequent applications of pyrethrum dusts will control the Mexican bean beetle and the immature forms of the squash bug and the striped cucumber beetle. As is the case with rotenone, pyrethrum insecticides are of little or no value against the tomato fruitworm, the tomato pinworm, the pepper weevil, or the cabbage aphid.

Rotenone insecticides for vegetables are currently manufactured in three general types:

1. Rotenone dust mixtures containing from 0.75 to 1 percent of rote-

none, designed for applying in the dry form without any further dilution.

An examination of the label on a package of a dust containing 0.75 percent of rotenone should show the following:

Active ingredients:	Percent
Rotenone	0. 75
Other cube or derris resins	2. 25
Inert ingredients	97. 00

Dust mixtures of this kind should be used at the rate of 20 to 30 pounds to the acre.

2. Undiluted ground-root powder containing 4 to 5 percent of rotenone, designed for mixing with water and applying as a spray.

The label on such a package should read about as follows:

Active ingredients:	Percent
Rotenone	5. 00
Other cube (derris) resins	15. 00
Inert ingredients	80. 00

Root powders are mixed with water at the rate of 2½ to 3 pounds to 100 gallons of water and applied at the rate of 120 to 150 gallons per acre for Mexican bean beetle control.

3. Extracts containing 1.5 to 2 percent of rotenone, designed for dilution with water and application as a spray.

Pyrethrum insecticides are also prepared in three general forms: Pyrethrum flowers mixed with a diluent such as talc or sulfur; dust mixtures prepared by incorporating a pyrethrum extract with a powder such as pyrophyllite; and pyrethrum extracts. All these preparations are made up to contain at least 0.3 percent of total pyrethrins. The first and second are applied in the dust form at the rate of 20 to 30 pounds to the acre, and the third is diluted with water and applied as a spray.

The toxic ingredients of extracts of both pyrethrum and rotenone when applied to plants in the liquid form dissipate more rapidly and therefore lose their effectiveness faster than they do in the dust mixture or powders mixed with water and applied as sprays. However, rotenone dust mixtures remain effective not longer than 4 days, and pyrethrum for even a shorter period.

The far-reaching results of this work with rotenone and pyrethrum were brought into focus during the war, when the War Food Administration set up controls as to their use on essential food crops.

Cryolite

During the course of investigations during the war period to develop insecticides from new materials, several hundred chemicals and combinations of chemicals were tested. This work was accentuated because of the shortage of pyrethrum, rotenone, and the arsenicals. Fluorine compounds were in good supply. One of these, cryolite or sodium fluoaluminate, recognized for many years as having possibilities as an insecticide, was experimented with extensively. Emphasis was placed on the improvement of its dusting qualities and on the determination of the most effective strength and dosage per acre to use against various vegetable pests. As a substitute for calcium arsenate it was found that, under conditions in southern California, a cryolite dust mixture containing 70 percent of sodium fluoaluminate with talc as the diluent gave satisfactory control of the tomato pinworm and the tomato fruitworm. In the same area a mixture containing equal parts of sodium fluoaluminate and talc yielded good control of the pepper weevil. It was necessary, however, to establish a special washing device to remove the cryolite residues from the peppers.

In the Yakima Valley of Washington, where a cryolite dust mixture containing 55 percent of sodium fluoaluminate with pyrophyllite was used, 95 percent of the potato tubers were not damaged by the tuber flea beetle larva.

In eastern Virginia a satisfactory control of the corn earworm on late beans was obtained with two applications of a cryolite mixture containing 70 percent of sodium fluoaluminate with sulfur.

It was also found that sodium fluosilicate, a close relative of cryolite, in a wheat-bran bait was more effective than calcium arsenate against the Puerto Rican mole cricket and would also poison the southern mole cricket, a species not affected by a bait containing calcium arsenate. An effective bait against both species consisted of 8 pounds of sodium fluosilicate to 100 pounds of dry wheat bran, applied once at the rate of 20 pounds to the acre.

DDT as an Insecticide for Vegetables

Investigations on the use of DDT as an insecticide for vegetables from the fall of 1942 to the spring of 1946 have led to the following conclusions: This chemical in its various formulations, including dust mixtures, emulsions, wettable powders, and aerosols, is toxic to a wide variety of insects. However, the range of usefulness of DDT is limited because of the residue factor. Its performance against several pests of potatoes, such as the potato leafhopper, the Colorado potato beetle, potato flea beetles, aphids, and psyllids, has been outstanding. It can be used with bordeaux mixture and the other so-called basic coppers. From the present knowledge it should not be used with copper-lime dusts, that is, mixtures of dehydrated copper sulfate and lime.

As an insecticide for tomatoes in southern California, DDT has proved to be more effective than either cryolite or calcium arsenate against the tomato fruitworm, and it is compatible with sulfur. Therefore, mixtures of DDT and sulfur can be used for the control of both the tomato fruitworm and the russet mite.

Its usefulness on beans is limited, as it will not control the Mexican bean beetle, although it is effective against the bean leafhopper and the corn earworm. The earworm attacks the tender shoots, flowers, and pods of snap and lima beans in some sections of the country.

On cabbage it has given a high degree of control of the various caterpillars, including the cabbage webworm and some kinds of cutworms, which attack cabbage in the South and oftentimes are destructive to the cabbage crop. However, because of the residue factor, the precaution must be followed that is necessary with arsenicals; that is, the crop should not be treated when there is foliage on the plant that will remain on the product prepared for market.

On peas the control of the pea weevil with DDT has been equal, if not superior, to that obtained with rotenone. In the dust, emulsion, and aerosol forms it has yielded more satisfactory control of the pea aphid than any material tested heretofore. However, the use of DDT on the pea crop both for pea weevil and pea aphid control is recommended with the reservation that pea vines be withheld from livestock until more is known about the residue hazard.

On onions DDT has given a slightly higher degree of onion thrips control than either nicotine or tartar emetic-sugar mixture.

Against the pepper weevil dust mixtures containing from 2 to 5 percent of DDT have given excellent control and have also controlled the green peach aphid, which often causes damage in pepper fields following the use of either calcium arsenate or cryolite.

As an insecticide for cucurbits (squash, pumpkins, cantaloupes, watermelons, and cucumbers) the indications are that the usefulness of DDT will be limited, because it is injurious to some of these crops, particularly certain varieties of squash.

DDT has been tested on a wide variety of vegetable plants for plant tolerance and, with the exception of the cucurbits, it appears that in most sections of the United States the insecticide can be used without injury to the crop. However, injury to peas and tomatoes has been reported from New Jersey.

DDT in aerosol form has been tested extensively in Maryland against the pea aphid, and this method of applying DDT to the pea crop appears to have a decided advantage over other methods because of the lightness of the load. However, analyses of residues on pea vines indicate that there is a greater residue from the aerosol treatment than from the use of dusts or emulsions, which may prohibit the use of DDT in the aerosol form on peas where the vines are to be used as cattle feed.

DDT as a soil insecticide has been tested against wireworms, and while it is slow acting against these pests, the indications are that it may be useful as a means of keeping wireworm infestations to a minimum.

Sabadilla and Soil Fumigants

Sabadilla was introduced into the vegetable-insecticide field during the war by T. C. Allen, of the University of Wisconsin. Sabadilla insecticides are prepared from the ground seed of a tropical lily or lilies. The active principle of the seeds is a complex mixture of alkaloids called veratrine. This material appears to have its greatest usefulness in the control of the squash bug, harlequin bug, and the potato or bean leafhopper.

Following the successful use of a mixture of dichloropropane and dichloropropene, known commercially as D-D, for nematode control in pineapple plantings in Hawaii, by Walter Carter, of the Pineapple Growers Association, this material was tested in California and Washington against wireworms. The results were promising. Another product having for its toxic agent ethylene dibromide gave equally good, if not superior, results against the sugar-beet wireworm. Success in the use of a soil fumigant is dependent on the method of application, and within the last 2 years machines for effectively applying soil fumigants have been developed. This, together with more effective soil fumigants, should aid materially in reducing wireworm infestations in lands devoted to vegetables where the returns per acre will justify a comparatively large output of funds.

––––––––––

THE AUTHOR

W. H. White is in charge of the Division of Truck Crop and Garden Insect Investigations in the Bureau of Entomology and Plant Quarantine.

FOR FURTHER READING

Reid, W. J., Jr., Smith, C. E., Reed, L. B., and Bare, C. O.: *Studies on the Control of Cabbage Caterpillars with Derris in the South,* U. S. D. A. Circular 615, 1942.

Reid, W. J., Jr., Smith, C. E., Reed, L. B., and Thomas, W. A.: *Field Studies of Insecticides Used to Control Cabbage Caterpillars in the South,* U. S. D. A. Technical Bulletin 782, 1941.

Smith, C. E., Reid, W. J., Jr., Harrison, P. K., and Bare, C. O.: *A Study of Arsenical Dusting of Cabbage in Relation to Poison Residues,* U. S. D. A. Circular 411, 1937.

Controlling Pests of Stock

by E. W. LAAKE and W. G. BRUCE

OUR SEARCH for improved insecticides and research to make better those already in use have brought developments that promise far-reaching effects on the control of serious pests of livestock. There are many such pests—cattle grubs, lice, horn flies, stableflies, mosquitoes, ticks, mites, and other external parasites of domestic animals—and every livestock raiser knows how seriously they can cut his profit.

The outstanding development was the discovery of DDT. When experiments showed its effectiveness against insect pests of man, experimental work was begun with it on the various insect pests of livestock.

Our early work with DDT demonstrated its superiority against many pests over insecticides formerly used. Although its initial action is relatively slow, compared to pyrethrum, its continued action for weeks or months after a single application puts it in a class by itself. The duration of effective residual toxicity of the old insecticides when applied to livestock was usually not more than 3 days for cattle lice and at best approximately 1 or 2 days for the horn fly. Daily treatment was required therefore to control horn flies and at least two treatments at a certain interval were necessary to eradicate cattle lice, because the louse eggs were not affected by the materials formerly used and the effective residual toxicity ceased long before all the eggs hatched.

In contrast, rather low concentrations of DDT kill all horn flies on the animals at the time they are treated, and the residue remaining on the animal continues to kill this species for 2 to 3 weeks. Because that period is longer than the life cycle of the fly from egg to adult, the entire population on a farm may be wiped out with one treatment. Reinfestation will result, however, after the effective residual toxicity

670

ceases if horn flies are introduced on untreated animals or if the treated animals are exposed to infested premises nearby. Therefore, the duration of control would vary with the size of the area treated and would be proportionately longer as the size of the treated area is increased. This advantage no doubt will encourage communities to undertake treatment of a large area with DDT for the control of the horn fly.

The remarkable results to be had in controlling the horn fly with DDT were well established in a series of tests in 1945. They showed that treated cows and calves gained 42.2 to 51 pounds and 46.9 to 70 pounds, respectively, more per animal than comparable untreated cows and calves in approximately 3 months. The gains were obtained at an expenditure of less than 10 cents a head for DDT. On the basis of the results of the tests (which were made on rather small, scattered ranches that required three or four treatments during the season of horn fly abundance), each pound of technical DDT spent yielded a gain of from 1,202 to 2,306 pounds of beef on treated over untreated animals. The formula used contained only 0.2 percent DDT in suspension, applied at the rate of one-half gallon per animal.

Greater concentrations of DDT in suspension have given longer protection and have an advantage where animals cannot be corralled for treatment as often as desired. The results reported from different areas in the United States with DDT for the control of the horn fly apparently differ considerably. They indicate that the low concentrations that give excellent results in some areas are not so effective in other areas and are relatively ineffective in still others.

The amount of rainfall and the intensity of sunshine seem to be the main factors that bear on the effectiveness of DDT. The application to animals of DDT in the form of an aerosol fog has promise of being a desirable method for treating large herds quickly. Dipping animals in suspensions of DDT to control horn flies and lice has given results fully as effective as those obtained with sprays. Where neither spraying nor dipping is feasible, DDT may be dusted on cattle and other domestic animals. Good hand dusters for small herds or a power duster for larger herds are satisfactory. The effectiveness of DDT against the various livestock insects depends upon the concentration used, rather than on the method of application.

For controlling the stablefly, DDT has not given satisfactory results when applied to animals, but excellent control is obtained when it is applied as a spray in concentrations of from 2.5 to 5 percent to barns, fences, and other objects about the barnyard upon which these flies rest. When the interiors of barns and sheds are sprayed, the DDT residue on the treated surface continues to kill stableflies, houseflies, mosquitoes, and other insects for a long time after treatment.

For lice on livestock, DDT is excellent. The motile or crawling stages of all species of lice are easily killed with low concentrations of DDT applied as a dip, spray, or dust; but because the eggs of lice are not affected by DDT, somewhat higher concentrations are needed in order to obtain sufficient duration of residual toxicity to kill all the young lice that hatch after treatment.

No satisfactory control of horseflies and deer flies has yet been obtained with DDT. Because those species usually do not enter barns or other buildings, they cannot be controlled by spraying buildings, and because DDT is so poisonous to fish, its use in streams and ponds, where the horseflies and deer flies spend their immature stages, is not feasible.

For the control of the sheep tick or ked, DDT is apparently at least as effective as any of the old insecticides. But for the true ticks and mites attacking livestock, DDT has not given satisfactory results, except possibly for the brown dog tick, which seems to be less resistant to it than other species of ticks and mites. For the control of the cattle grub, DDT has shown little or no merit even when applied in high concentration. The rotenone-bearing powders—derris and cube—are still the only effective materials for control of cattle grubs.

Benzene Hexachloride

Benzene hexachloride, a synthetic compound that was discovered in England during the war, has also shown good possibilities for the control of some livestock parasites. It has not been available in the United States long enough or in sufficient quantity to permit more than preliminary tests. In the first tests it seemed superior to DDT for the control of cattle lice. It has also shown considerable promise for the control of cattle grubs, ticks, and mites. Tests in foreign countries, particularly in Australia, where more than 3,000,000 sheep have been treated with this material, have resulted in excellent control of the ked or sheep tick. This pest was eradicated with one treatment, and the residue remaining in the wool prevented reinfestation for a month or longer.

In contrast to DDT, which is ineffective for destroying insect eggs, benzene hexachloride appears to be a promising ovicide. Therefore, if further investigations confirm earlier results, it is possible that lice of cattle and other livestock can be eradicated with one treatment. This has not been possible with the older insecticides and only with higher concentrations of DDT, which are somewhat expensive. Where two or more treatments were necessary for eradicating an insect, as was the case with the older insecticides for cattle lice, the treatments had to be spaced at definite intervals based on the developmental period of the insect. That is often impossible because of unavoidable delays (in bad weather, for example) in applying the second treatment, and then eradication is not accomplished except by additional treatment.

Another promising insecticide developed during the war is benzyl benzoate. It was used effectively by the Army in the South Pacific for the protection of our troops against mites attacking man. It is likely, therefore, that benzyl benzoate may become an important insecticide for the control of mites attacking livestock.

Other new insecticides, especially some of the newest chlorinated compounds, have shown excellent results for controlling certain insects upon which they have been tested. Also new synergists, or activators, for some of our older insecticides have promise of being greatly superior to those formerly used.

THE AUTHORS

E. W. Laake, an entomologist in charge of the Kerrville, Tex., laboratory, has been with the Bureau of Entomology and Plant Quarantine since 1913. His work has concerned mainly insects affecting the health of man and domestic animals. Dr. Laake was president of the Texas Entomological Society from 1932 to 1934 and president of the Cotton States Branch of the American Association of Economic Entomologists in 1944.

W. G. Bruce is an entomologist in charge of the Savannah, Ga., Laboratory of the Division of Insects Affecting Man and Animals, Bureau of Entomology and Plant Quarantine. His first assignment with the Bureau was to study the ecology of the cattle grub in the Red River Valley. Since that time Mr. Bruce has conducted research on insects affecting animals in all sections of the United States. During the Second World War he was liaison officer between the Division of Insects Affecting Man and Animals and the various defense agencies in problems of insect control in military establishments.

FOR FURTHER READING

Laboratory of the Bureau of Entomology and Plant Quarantine, Orlando, Fla.: *DDT and Other Insecticides and Repellents Developed for the Armed Forces*, U. S. D. A. Miscellaneous Publication 606, 1946.

ALSO, IN THIS BOOK

The Chemistry of DDT, by H. L. Haller and Ruth L. Busbey, page 616.
Pests that Attack Man, by E. F. Knipling, page 632.
DDT in the Home, by L. S. Henderson, page 643.

News About Bee Diseases

by A. P. STURTEVANT

AMERICAN foulbrood is the most destructive and widespread disease of honeybees in the United States. For many years apiarists generally believed that once a colony became infected it was doomed to die if left alone. Various methods of treatment have been tried with incomplete success. Even attempts to eradicate the disease by destroying all infected colonies have not eliminated this threat to beekeeping.

Because of the emphasis previously placed on treatment or regulatory control measures, the few early recognized cases of apparent recovery from American foulbrood were more or less overlooked. The increasing frequency of such cases reported by beekeepers eventually brought to the attention of investigators the possibility of the discovery and development of strains of bees that might be resistant, if not actually immune, to American foulbrood.

Early work on this problem by investigators in Iowa demonstrated that a certain resistance to American foulbrood does exist in honeybees. It was demonstrated also that resistance could be inherited from one generation to another through the queen bees—an indication that, through continued selection and breeding of queens from colonies of bees showing resistance to the disease, strains of bees might be developed that would be highly resistant and of value in combating the ravages of American foulbrood.

Extensive investigations concerned with the development of strains of bees resistant to American foulbrood have been carried on during the past decade by the Bureau of Entomology and Plant Quarantine in cooperation with several State agricultural experiment stations. The results have shown encouraging progress.

The methods used, in general, are as follows: Colonies of bees located

674

in isolated apiaries to prevent accidental spread of the disease, and headed by queens selected for testing, are inoculated artificially in one way or another with American foulbrood material containing spores of *Bacillus larvae,* the cause of the disease. The colonies are examined regularly thereafter for manifestations of disease. Disease may occur in some colonies, which may then either show recovery or may develop disease beyond hope of recovery. Still other colonies may remain healthy, the bees never permitting disease to develop, at least so that it can be seen by the investigators. These "negative colonies" are considered to be the most highly resistant to the disease and are the ones from which queens are selected for further intensive breeding and subsequent testing the next year. During most of the time succeeding generations of test queens have been reared in isolated locations by natural mating methods, the parentage being controlled as much as possible under natural conditions.

Three strains of honeybees have been developed by this method. During the several years that these strains have been under observation and test, we have noted a definite improvement in resistance in two of the strains and a much slighter improvement in the third strain.

Improvement was rapid at first, but later the curve of improvement tended to flatten out at different levels somewhat below complete resistance. Recently some cross-breedings by natural matings between two of the resistant strains have shown an increased resistance, with a possible development of hybrid vigor, as indicated by increased resistance and honey production.

Since 1943 the studies have been accelerated by the use of artificial insemination for queen bees. By this method of breeding, the parentage of the test queens can be completely controlled, either through intensive line-breeding or by known cross-breeding. A notably significant improvement in the level of resistance has been observed in all three of the line-bred resistant lines since use of the artificially bred queens was begun. The majority of such queens show as good colony performance as queens reared under natural conditions. Some of the intensively inbred queens produce brood of poor quality. These do not develop strong colonies. However, with most of the colonies headed by artificially inseminated queens, particularly those crossbred between two of the lines showing the highest resistance to disease, the results have been outstanding. This has been true not only as regards resistance but also as regards production of brood of high quality and increased production of honey. This again would indicate the development of hybrid vigor through cross-breeding.

A limited number of queens of strains bred for resistance to American foulbrood have been distributed throughout the United States. On the whole, favorable reports have been received concerning their use, largely in prevention rather than eradication of disease. Such strains have not yet been stabilized, however, and are not completely desirable for commercial beekeeping purposes. The greatest effort has been concentrated on improving their resistance to American foulbrood. Some of the experimental strains are inclined to be hot-tempered and not all of them are outstanding in honey production.

Unfortunately, the development of resistance to one disease does not confer protection against other diseases. With continued inbreeding of the naturally mated as well as the artificially inseminated queens, it has been noted that certain strains of bees resistant to American foulbrood are showing an undesirable susceptibility to European foulbrood. Therefore it will be necessary to continue more intensive breeding and selection work before completely desirable strains of bees can be developed that are resistant to both American and European foulbrood and have other desirable characteristics.

Our studies regarding the behavior of bees toward American foulbrood have given new information concerning factors associated with the development of the disease and the nature of resistance.

The behavior of bees toward diseased brood was observed by placing combs from experimental colonies in a cell-locating frame, noting the exact location of individual diseased cells, describing them, and examining the same cells at regular intervals.

We discovered that bees of all colonies removed some or all of the diseased brood remains. The time required for removing the material and the chances of recovery by its complete removal were found to be closely related to the number of cells of diseased brood present in the colonies. Light infections sometimes were overcome whereas heavy infections were not. No close relationship was found between colony populations, queen vigor, or strain of bees and the rapidity of cleaning the cells, or the spread of disease within the colonies. The diseased material usually was removed without disturbing the comb.

Many cells in which diseased brood was found were used again for brood and for storage of honey or pollen after the bees had removed all visible diseased material from them. The bees seemed able to clean out all infectious material efficiently. Only in the heavily diseased colonies did any of the new brood reared in such cleaned-out cells become infected. It appears that honey in most cases would not become contaminated when stored in such cells. This does not preclude the eventual spread of the disease organisms to stored honey or to other healthy larvae by the bees engaged in the cleaning process.

Brood from resistant and nonresistant colonies was found to be equally susceptible to American foulbrood infection when reared under controlled conditions in the center of heavily infected brood nests of diseased colonies. This fact suggests that colony resistance to American foulbrood depends on behavior factors, like the housecleaning abilities of the bees, rather than on actual physiological resistance in the larvae. No evidence of physiological resistance to the disease in honeybee larvae was found, other than the decrease in susceptibility associated with their age. Brood susceptibility was found to be greatest during the first day of larval life. It decreased thereafter to the extent that larvae more than 2 days and 5 hours old did not become infected. This period corresponds closely to the period of mass feeding of the larvae. The failure of some brood to develop disease when reared under infectious conditions may be the result of the short time in larval life when inoculation must occur to produce infection, and to the type of feeding at that time.

We obtained conclusive information that substantiated these observations as the result of the development of new method for the controlled inoculation of individual honeybee larvae of known age without causing general contamination of the colony. This method also has been applied as an additional test for determining a high level of resistance in colonies. It consists of adding, by means of a special microsyringe, known numbers of spores of *Bacillus larvae* in a small drop of water suspension to the food of the larvae within 1 day after they hatch from the egg. The exact locations and disposition of the inoculated larvae are determined for further observations on the development of disease with the aid of the same cell-locating frame used in previous studies. The comb of inoculated larvae is then returned to the colony for feeding and sealing of the brood.

Disease was produced by this method of inoculation in the brood of resistant colonies as readily as in that from susceptible ones. All diseased brood was removed by the bees of the most highly resistant colonies before any symptoms of the disease were apparent. It was found that *Bacillus larvae* in the vegetative rod stage is noninfective. In the resistant colonies the bees allowed no diseased brood to remain long enough to permit the organisms again to reach the infective spore stage, but in a susceptible colony infected larvae were allowed to remain long enough for spore formation to occur.

The conclusions to be drawn from the results of these various investigations are that resistance to American foulbrood in the honeybee colonies of resistant strains consists in the ability of the worker bees to detect and remove diseased brood before the causative organism, *Bacillus larvae*, reaches the infectious spore stage in the diseased larvae. That is what occurs in the so-called "negative colonies" considered most highly resistant in the apiary investigations of the development of resistance to American foulbrood. This is a purely behavior character that is developed and transmitted to succeeding generations through intensive breeding.

Up until the past few years, beekeepers in the United States attached relatively little importance to the disease of adult bees known as Nosema disease, caused by a protozoan parasite, *Nosema apis*. Like sacbrood, it has been accepted as a troublesome disease of minor importance, to be more or less controlled by good beekeeping practices. Recent investigations have shown that the disease is much more widespread through most of the country than beekeepers had supposed. Furthermore, we learned that Nosema disease is responsible for many cases of winter dysentery, weakening of overwintered colonies, and spring dwindling. There is considerable evidence to show that many queen bees are superseded and lost because they are infected. Package-bee colonies tend to show the effect of Nosema disease on brood rearing more than normal colonies and they are more likely to lose their queens because of the disease.

Recent laboratory studies with bees in cages disclosed that temperature materially influences the development of Nosema disease. The causative organism, *Nosema apis,* develops in the intestinal tract most rapidly at temperatures near 88° F., or slightly below the normal temperature of the active brood nest. Development was checked at about 93° or 94° F., which is near normal brood-rearing temperatures, and was completely inhibited above 98° F. Development also was checked by temperatures below the optimum and was completely inhibited at temperatures below 51° F. These temperature relations may explain the slower development of the disease during the broodless period of the winter, increased development of infection with the start of brood rearing in the later winter, and decreased development with the rapid increase of brood rearing and active bee flights in the spring. Thus, increased flight activity, the production of young bees, and higher brood-nest temperatures accompanying the active season may help either to eliminate infection or control its further spread among the bees of strong colonies. In further experiments, infected bees held in cages at 99° F. for 14 days appeared to have recovered completely from the infection. Whether some form of heat treatment for Nosema disease would be practical is not yet known.

The term "paralysis" has long been used to designate various little-understood disorders of adult honeybees that are characterized by trembling, sprawled legs and wings, occasional partial hairlessness, and, in some cases, a black and shiny appearance. The last two symptoms are not always as common as the other symptoms. Often a heavy death rate results, and the disease may affect whole colonies.

Recently in laboratory experiments in which material prepared from bees affected with so-called paralysis was fed to bees in cages under controlled conditions, we established that at least one type of paralysis is caused by a filtrable virus. A virus is an ultramicroscopic organism so small it passes through porcelain filters that hold back ordinary bacteria.

The discovery that a virus causes paralysis of adult bees may lead to finding a preventive or cure. With this more accurate knowledge of symptoms, beekeepers can judge better when it is necessary to requeen or otherwise manipulate infected colonies. The maintenance of strong colonies headed by young, vigorous queens is about the best preventive known at present. Beekeepers should watch primarily for signs of trembling, with sprawled legs and wings, as the most reliable symptoms of the paralysis disease in the hive.

THE AUTHOR

A. P. Sturtevant is an apiculturist in the Bureau of Entomology and Plant Quarantine. After graduation from Clark University, and 2 years of graduate study at Massachusetts Institute of Technology, he started his first research work on bee diseases as assistant in comparative pathology at the Massachusetts Agricultural Experiment Station in 1915. Since 1926 he has been in charge of the Intermountain States Bee Culture Laboratory of the Division of Bee Culture, Bureau of Entomology and Plant Quarantine at Laramie, Wyo., where his principal research interest has been with the various investigations concerning American foulbrood, and American-foulbrood-resistance studies in particular. He received a doctorate from George Washington University in 1923.

FOR FURTHER READING

Burnside, C. E., and Sturtevant, A. P.: *Diagnosing Bee Diseases in the Apiary*, U. S. 85, No. 10, pages 354–355, 363, 1945.

Burnside C. E., and Sturtevant, A. P.: *Diagnosing Bee Diseases in the Apiary*, U. S. D. A. Circular 392, 1936.

Hambleton, Jas. I.: *The Treatment of American Foulbrood*, U. S. D. A. Farmers' Bulletin 1713, 1933.

Park, O. W.: *Results of 1935 Disease Resistance Program*, Iowa State Apiarist's Report for the Year 1935, pages 49–57, 1936.

Park, O. W., Pellett, F. C., and Paddock, F. B.: *Disease Resistance and American Foulbrood, Result of Second Season of Cooperative Experiment*, American Bee Journal, volume 77, No. 1, pages 20–25, 34, 1937.

Woodrow, A. W.: *Susceptibility of Honeybee Larvae to American Foulbrood*, Gleanings in Bee Culture, volume 69, No. 3, pages 148–151, 190, 1941.

Woodrow, A. W.: *Behavior of Honeybees Toward Brood Infected with American Foulbrood*, American Bee Journal, volume 81, No. 8, pages 363–366, 1941.

Woodrow, A. W.: *Susceptibility of Honeybee Larvae to Individual Inoculations with Spores of Bacillus Larvae*, Journal of Economic Entomology, volume 35, No. 6, pages 892–895, 1942.

Woodrow, A. W., and Holst, E. C.: *The Mechanism of Colony Resistance to American Foulbrood*, Journal of Economic Entomology, volume 35, No. 3, pages 327–330, 1942.

Woodrow, A. W., and States, H. J., Jr.: *Removal of Diseased Brood in Colonies Infected with A. F. B.*, American Bee Journal, volume 83, No. 1, pages 22–23, 26, 1943.

More Honey From Bees

by C. L. FARRAR

RECENT RESEARCH on the problems of the management of bees has opened up new opportunities for regulating the development of bee colonies regardless of the weather. Formerly good weather throughout the spring was necessary for the development of a colony— not only so a variety of plants would produce pollen and nectar, but so the bees could gather these foods for use in raising young bees. We now know how to provide the food required for brood rearing, thus making the colony less dependent upon early sources of pollen and nectar. The main honey plants bloom and produce nectar with fair regularity at a time when the weather is more settled. Successful management demands that colonies be developed for the honey flow rather than on the flow.

Probably less than 10 percent of the available nectar supply is gathered by the 5½ million colonies of bees in the United States. Beekeepers have an opportunity and a challenge to contribute more fully in the development of our agricultural resources by supplying the bees needed for pollination and to make honey available to more people. The pollination of fruit and seed crops will be proportional to the increase in honey production, because both depend upon the number of blossoms visited by the bees.

In the United States the average colony yield of 35 to 40 pounds could easily be raised to 75 to 100 pounds. Man has been the honeybees' worst enemy by his failure to provide adequate food reserves for their overwintering or to supply the needed hive space for the developing colony. The more or less indiscriminate use of insecticides has also caused heavy losses. Few branches of agriculture could withstand the losses experienced by the beekeeping industry and survive. The tremendous reproductive powers of the honeybee have made it possible for the beekeeper to replace his losses in bees, but not his loss of the honey crop.

The opportunity for increasing production may be seen by comparing the 57-pound average yield in Wisconsin for the period from 1938 to 1945 with the maximum yields obtained from 2 classes of colonies operated during the same period by the North Central States Bee Culture Laboratory at Madison, Wis. Single-queen colonies built from 2-pound packages and headed by outstanding queens showed a mean maximum yield of 254 pounds, compared with an over-all average of 109 pounds for 1,227 package colonies. Variations in the productivity of lines of stock were largely responsible for this difference between the best colonies and the over-all average yields. Overwintered colonies managed under a two-queen plan showed a mean maximum yield of 434 pounds, compared with an over-all average of 265 pounds for 261 two-queen colonies.

The available nectar supply in the vicinity of Madison was probably similar to that in Wisconsin as a whole. Furthermore, most beekeepers obtain average yields equal to only one-third those produced by the best colonies in their apiaries. We must conclude that the honey crop is limited more by the condition of the colonies than by the available nectar supply.

The Colony as a Productive Unit

The colony consisting of a queen, 10 thousand to 60 thousand workers, and sometimes several thousand drones should be viewed as a unit organism. The individuals making up the colony are as subject to change as the cells within the animal body. Their ability to function apart from the colony is extremely limited. The object of management is to maintain the colony in a maximum state of productivity, even though this means that both the queen and workers will wear out more quickly.

The honey production for any given number of bees increases as the population of the colony increases. For example: While 4 colonies each with 15,000 bees are producing 100 pounds of honey, 1 colony with 60,000 bees will produce more than 150 pounds of honey. A larger proportion of the total population engages in brood rearing in the small colony than in the full-strength colony. The greater gain made by the large colony is due to the larger proportion of field bees available to gather nectar.

The colony population is limited by the queen's capacity to lay eggs, the time of development from egg to the adult, and the duration of life of the bees. A colony's development may be further limited by insufficient food (both pollen and honey), by insufficient space for the rearing of brood, or by disease. Insufficient space or its improper organization may seriously affect the working morale.

The most important recent advance made in colony management came from a study of the pollen requirements. Experiments on wintering bees demonstrated that the survival of overwintering populations was largely proportional to the amount of reserve pollen present in the hive. Surveys of pollen reserves in widely separated geographical areas showed that most colonies did not have enough pollen for the overwintering of highly productive colonies.

Further investigations showed us a way to supplement pollen with soybean flour. No satisfactory complete substitute for pollen has yet been devised, but when 3 pounds of expeller-processed soybean flour is mixed with 1 pound of pollen, approximately 30 thousand bees can be reared, as compared with 4,500 bees from 1 pound of pollen alone. The pollen for supplemental feeding is trapped by forcing the bees to pass through a grid that has 5 openings to the inch. From 1 colony approximately 20 pounds of pollen can be obtained; that is enough to supply the critical needs of 50 colonies when 3 parts of the soybean flour are added.

The supplemented pollen is fed in cake form by mixing 1 part of dry matter (1 part pollen and 3 parts soybean flour) with 2 parts of sugar sirup (2 parts sugar and 1 part water).

Brood rearing, which is the basis for colony development, can be regulated independent of weather conditions by feeding these pollen cakes. Thus, we have a means of timing the development of the colony so that it can reach full strength for any expected honey-flow period.

Because brood rearing increases the consumption of honey by the colony, it is necessary to provide more reserve honey for colonies that are to be developed early through pollen feeding. In most northern locations, a reserve of 90 pounds is desirable to carry the colony from the end of brood rearing in October until the spring honey flow. The problem is not how much a colony consumes but how much it produces over and above consumption. The higher consuming colonies produce the largest surplus.

Supplemental pollen feeding is equally important for the development of new colonies from package bees. Packages installed in April should be provided with all the pollen cakes and reserve honey they will consume to insure uninterrupted brood rearing before the honey flow. In most seasons they will require 25 to 40 pounds of honey and more or less continuous pollen feeding if they are to be built to full productive strength for a June honey flow.

The high-producing colony must be headed by a queen that can lay 1,500 or more eggs a day. The queen's physical development, as well as her genetic constitution, determines her capacity to produce eggs.

The mating habits of bees have made it difficult to improve honeybee stock. Selective breeding has been limited to the queen, because there was no way of choosing the drone or male with which she mates. Progress has been made, however, since production tests have shown some commercial lines of stock to yield two to five times as much honey as other lines. The great variability within both high- and low-producing lines is suggestive of the progress that may be made through careful selection and controlled breeding.

The market demand for queens and the ease with which they can be reared have established standards of quantity rather than quality. Great variation in the physical development of sister queens is evidence that they are subject to environmental influences while they are being reared. The best small queen is never so productive as the best large queen. Before real progress can be expected through selection and controlled breeding, it will be essential to establish standards for rearing that will insure full physical development of the queens.

The Importance of Good Stock

Improvement of stock promises to be an important coming development in beekeeping. A technique for the artificial insemination of queen bees has been available since 1925, but until 1943 very few artificially inseminated queens were capable of laying a sufficient number of fertile eggs to build full-strength colonies. Recent improvements in the technique by Otto Mackensen and William C. Roberts enable us now to mate queens that perform as well as naturally mated queens.

Prolific queens and long-lived workers are essential in a superior strain of bees. Also, large, industrious bees that can carry more nectar may add to the productivity. Some progress has been made through selection and breeding for resistance to American foulbrood. Improvements in resistance to this and other brood or adult diseases may be hoped for. A superior bee must not be nervous or inclined to sting without provocation, or prone to swarm. We have opportunities for breeding a bee for beauty of color or one for fine capping of the combs where fancy section honey is to be produced.

Selection for the desired characteristics among the extremely variable honeybee stock requires intensive inbreeding. Honeybees that have been closely inbred lose vigor rapidly and the viability of the queen's eggs decreases. Preliminary studies on the hybridization of inbred lines are suggestive that a program of breeding not unlike that used in the production of hybrid seed corn may be necessary. Two selected inbred lines may have to be combined to produce a hybrid queen to establish vigor for egg laying. The hybrid queens may be top-crossed with a third male line to produce double-hybrid worker progeny.

In 1945 the highest producing stock used was a double-hybrid line
that averaged 266 pounds of surplus honey, but the bees were intoler-
ably vicious. When sister queens of this line were top-crossed with another line of drone stock, the disposition of the workers was equal to the
gentler strains of bees.

Bee breeding should gain momentum because of the opportunity for
applying genetic principles worked out in other fields. The relatively
short life of the breeding stock is a disadvantage, but it may be offset
by the rapidity with which successive generations can be obtained.

Two-Queen Colonies

A practical way of increasing colony populations is through the use
of two queens. By dividing a strong overwintered colony 5 to 7 weeks
before the honey flow and introducing a young queen to the division,
it is possible nearly to double the yield of honey. The colony is reunited
to a single-queen status about a month before the end of the honey flow.

Between 1935 and 1945, 287 two-queen colonies averaged 270
pounds, with a mean maximum of 434 pounds. The yields obtained over
a period of years indicate there is sufficient nectar available in most
areas now supporting commercial beekeeping to permit first-class two-
queen colonies to produce an average in excess of 400 pounds a year.
This would be more than 10 times the national average yield.

Hive Equipment

The standard beehive of today is essentially like the original movable
comb Langstroth hive developed in 1851. The size of the hive has been
increased by adding more bodies of comb. The increased production
obtained through the use of supplemental pollen feeding and improved
queens or two queens has emphasized a need for hive equipment adaptable to intensive management. In the Intermountain States, where
the work with two-queen colonies was started, satisfactory results were
obtained by using 7-story hives. When the project was transferred to
the Central States, the character of the honey flow in the more humid
atmosphere there made it necessary to increase the hive capacity to
9 and 10 stories. Similar yields were obtained in both areas, but a
need for a hive providing greater capacity nearer to the ground became
a necessity.

Preliminary experiments, started in 1940 with a shallow type of hive,
have demonstrated the opportunity for improving hive equipment. To
be practical, any style of hive must use the same size of frame for both
brood chambers and supers. A shallow-type square hive taking 12 frames
6¼ inches in depth has shown practical advantages. Besides reducing

the height of the hive, it allows greater flexibility of manipulation for proper colony control. The full supers are easier to handle as they weigh 15 to 17 pounds less than the standard-depth supers. These are usually finished 7 to 10 days sooner than the standard-depth supers, so that honey can be extracted and the combs returned for refilling. Most colony manipulations can be made by interchanging the position of hive bodies instead of manipulating frames. The disadvantage of the shallow type of hive is its slightly greater cost because more frames are used. The added cost is offset by better colony control that favors increased production.

THE AUTHOR

C. L. Farrar, an apiculturist in the Bureau of Entomology and Plant Quarantine, is in charge of the North Central States Bee Culture Laboratory, which is maintained in Madison by the Bureau and the University of Wisconsin. He is professor of apiculture in the University of Wisconsin. Dr. Farrar, a graduate of Kansas State College and Massachusetts State College, was associate apiculturist at the Intermountain States Bee Culture Laboratory from 1931 to 1938 and specializes in the behavior, development, and management of the honeybee colony, the causes of queen supersedure, and stock testing for honey production.

FOR FURTHER READING

Farrar, C. L.: *Influence of Pollen Reserves on the Surviving Population of Over-wintered Colonies*, American Bee Journal, volume 76, No. 9, pages 452–454, 1936.

Farrar, C. L.: *The Influence of Colony Populations on Honey Production*, Journal of Agricultural Research, volume 54, No. 12, pages 945–954, 1937.

Farrar, C. L.: *Nosema Disease Contributes to Winter Losses and Queen Supersedure*, Gleanings in Bee Culture, volume 70, No. 11, pages 660–661, 701, 1942.

Farrar, C. L.: *An Interpretation of the Problems of Wintering the Honeybee Colony*, Gleanings in Bee Culture, volume 71, No. 9, pages 513–518, 1943.

Farrar, C. L.: *Nosema Disease*, Gleanings in Bee Culture, volume 72, No. 1, pages 8–9, 35, 1944.

Farrar, C. L.: *Productive Management of Honeybee Colonies in the Northern States*, U. S. D. A. Circular 702, 1944.

Farrar, C. L.: *Two-Queen Colony Management*, Bureau of Entomology and Plant Quarantine Circular E–693. Processed, May 1946.

Roberts, William C.: *The Performance of the Queen Bee*, American Bee Journal, volume 86, No. 5, pages 185–186, 211, 1946.

ALSO, IN THIS BOOK

A Bonus From Foulbrood

by E. C. HOLST

FOR AMERICAN foulbrood, a bacterial disease of honeybee larvae, and by far the most serious plague of beekeeping, no proved cure is known. Reasoning that a treatment or cure may be discovered through an increased knowledge of all the factors involved in the disease, we investigated the physiology of the causal organism, *Bacillus larvae*. As is often the case, this pure research yielded much information concerning an antibiotic that is active against several species of bacteria, as well as certain enzymes produced by the bacillus. The information has had immediate practical value, though the original physiological problem has not been solved.

The nutritional requirements of *B. larvae* were first studied. From findings gained through this work, it was possible to design a superior diagnostic culture medium for this organism that is cheap and easily prepared. With earlier media, an inoculation of at least 50,000 bacterial spores was required before growth occurred, but this one gives growth with only one or two spores. This is of particular advantage in determining whether a honey contains bacteria infectious to bees or is safe for feeding honeybee colonies. *B. larvae* is pathogenic only to bees, fortunately not to man or animals.

The new medium was satisfactory for routine diagnostic work, but it was unsatisfactory as a stock medium and for the production of the enzymes or the antibiotic to be discussed, because the bacillus on the medium does not complete its life cycle with the formation of spores. A water extract of honeybee larvae added to the medium, though, was found to induce spore formation.

Since larvae are difficult to obtain in quantity, and can only be obtained during a limited season, we tried to find a substitute for the extract. We

686

tried all the known vitamins as replacements, but without success. Asparagus pulp, added to the medium, however, was found to stimulate *B. larvae* to sporulate. The chemical nature of the substance is being studied further.

We discovered also that during the spore-formation stage of the life cycle of *B. larvae* an enzyme was produced that rapidly liquefied the casein, or curd, in milk. The enzyme was quite powerful and acted even at 90° C. (194° F.). It was found to be uniformly present in larvae dead of American foulbrood (scales), which contain huge numbers of *B. larvae* spores. When such scales are dropped into a small amount of diluted whole or reconstituted milk at ordinary temperatures, the milk becomes clear and transparent, usually within 15 minutes. Because no field test for American foulbrood existed, the use of the reaction as the basis for such a test was probed. The test proved specific for American foulbrood; no other disease or material found in the hive gave a "false positive." The only exceptions were American foulbrood scales that had been fumigated with formaldehyde or paradichlorobenzene. In such cases the reaction was either slower or completely negative. Sulfa drugs did not interfere.

For many years scientists have examined larvae dead of American foulbrood and have found *B. larvae,* almost without exception, present in pure culture. That is quite unusual, for when animal tissue dies, it is usually attacked at once by a large number and variety of bacteria. The data indicated that *B. larvae* might be suppressing such secondary invaders in the dead-honeybee larvae by producing an antibiotic.

A few preliminary experiments showed that *B. larvae* did indeed produce an antibiotic active against a wide range of bacterial species. Plates of nutrient agar were seeded with a soil suspension or market milk. Scales were placed on the surface on the medium, and the plates were incubated. After 24 hours, zones free from bacterial growth surrounded the scales, while large numbers of colonies had grown outside the zones. An antibiotic had obviously diffused out from the scales, preventing bacterial development. Sporulated laboratory cultures also produce the agent.

The results were so encouraging that similar experiments were made in which pure cultures of bacteria were used. Some of these organisms were harmless, but we observed an effect against bacteria that cause boils, typhoid, undulant fever, abortion in cattle, and human and bovine tuberculosis, but not avian tuberculosis. Such action against disease-producing bacteria in artificial culture does not, of itself, mean that the material can be used in animals affected by the organisms. To determine this requires extensive animal experimentation.

A serial dilution test was used for estimating the potency of solutions prepared from American foulbrood scales. The minimum amount of antibiotic required to inhibit growth of a test organism in one milliliter of nutrient broth is considered as one unit. Since *Bacillus subtilis* proved to be extremely sensitive, it was used as the test organism. By using the serial dilution method, it was shown that different species of bacteria vary greatly in their susceptibility to the antibiotic. In one instance where an aqueous scale extract was used, *B. subtilis* was inhibited by 1 unit per milliliter, *Staphylococcus aureus* by 10 units, but *Escherichia coli* was not inhibited by 100 units. On the other hand, whereas *E. coli* cells are dissolved by a strong scale extract, *S. aureus* cells are not.

As a first step in determining whether the antibiotic could be used therapeutically, water extracts of scales were tested by abdominal injection into mice. Massive doses (400 units per gram of the animal's body weight) proved fatal. Doses of 200 units produced acute toxemia for approximately 48 hours, while doses of 50 units produced symptoms of 2 to 3 hours' duration.

Attempts to purify the agent and reduce its toxicity by the means commonly used in the antibiotic work were unsuccessful, because it is insoluble in the usual organic solvents. Several hundred methods of purification and detoxification have been tried, of which three or four appear promising. After a method has been tried, the product is routinely tested for potency by serial dilution assay, and tested for toxicity by intraperitoneal injections into mice. If the mice show no symptoms, the material is similarly tested in guinea pigs. Frequently lots of material show no symptoms in mice, but prove very toxic to guinea pigs, since the guinea pig is an extremely sensitive animal.

It appears that the antigram positive and antigram negative fractions of the antibiotic may be separate factors. By some of the purification methods, both factors come through, while in others the anticoli factor is destroyed or left behind; it has never been separated by itself.

Because some lots of the antibiotic with encouragingly low toxicity and high potency have been produced, the work is being continued in the hope that toxicity can be further reduced if not completely eliminated. Some of these products have seemed very close to the threshold of therapeutic safety.

THE AUTHOR

E. C. Holst is an associate bacteriologist in the Division of Bee Culture, Bureau of Entomology and Plant Quarantine. A graduate of the University of Wisconsin, Dr. Holst has done extensive research on the southern pine beetle.

The sprays and dusts that are used against insect pests are the products of long research, as these pictures show. Before tests are started of a new material, chemists study its chemical make-up to get a preview of its value. Here R. C. Roark (left), in charge of insecticide investigations at Beltsville, and H. L. Haller examine a model of atoms in a DDT molecule.

TESTING AN INSECTICIDE

In the next step, chemists at the Agricultural Research Center at Beltsville make compounds of the material so that entomologists can test it. Here E. E. Fleck, a chemist, transfers to small bottles a preparation of DDT that he has just purified and mixed with a suitable carrier.

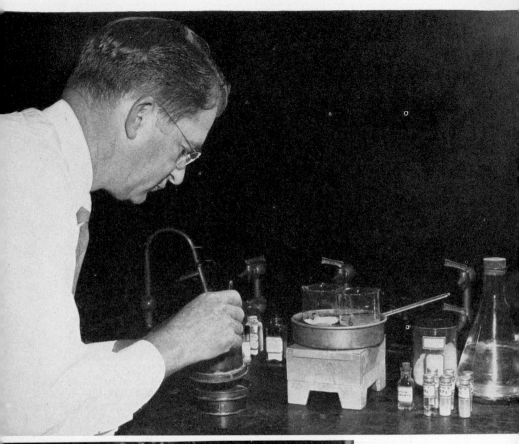

Then small-scale tests revea[l] whether the material merit[s] more tests. E. R. McGov[e-]ran (above) prepares a com[-]pound to be applied to bea[n] leaves that will be infeste[d] with Mexican bean beetle[s.] An assistant, Thelma Clar[k] (left), infests sprayed leave[s] with beetle larvae, reared i[n] the laboratory for such use[s.] It may take years to com[-]plete investigations of som[e] new materials that have pos[-]sibilities as effective insect[i-]cides. Sometimes chemis[ts] engaged in the task must de[-]vise new methods of analy[-]sis. DDT holds the center [of] the stage in the Department['s] research on new insecticide[s]

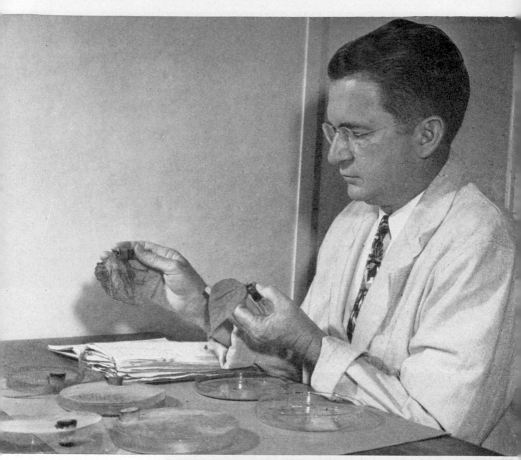

Dr. McGovran (above) finds that the beetles hardly touched a leaf treated with the insecticide under test. An untreated leaf was badly eaten. In another trial, Grace T. Babers removes an apple plug sprayed with a new insecticide and exposed to newly hatched codling moth worms for 1 or 2 days. Besides the trials mentioned here, the chemicals are examined in many other ways and places: DDT in various forms was tried out against sweetpotato weevils at Sunset, La, for example, and sprayed from airplanes in Oregon, where hemlock loopers destroy much timber.

Preparations that pass apple-plug tests in laboratory "orchards" at Beltsville go on to the Vincennes, Ind., station of the Bureau of Entomology and Plant Quarantine for large-scale tests in an orchard under commercial condition. K. W. Lamansky (above), an entomologist Vincennes, uses a new compound on apple tre taking care to reach all parts of the apple tre

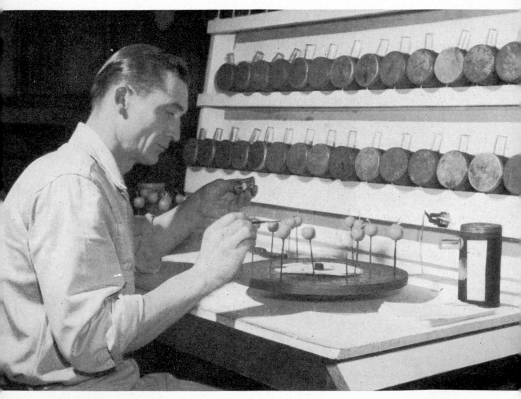

Apples from the sprayed trees are brought into the laboratory and artificially exposed to recently hatched codling moth worms. Lamansky, using a camel's hair brush, here transfers codling moth worms to each of 12 fruits on revolving tray, where they are left 7 to 9 day

Next, the fruits are inspected to determine the effect of the insecticide on the worms. The examination by H. J. McAlister (above) may disclose live worms inside some apples and skin punctures or stings on others. He rates low the insecticides that do not keep worms from entering the fruit. High ratings go to materials that kill worms before damage is done.

Chemists at Vincennes analyze deposits on treated fruit to see whether people eating it would face a spray residue hazard. Chemical analyses, plus data from entomologists, also show how much poison is needed to control codling moth worms and effects of weather on spray deposits. J. E. Fahey here dissolves the deposits from samples before analyzing them.

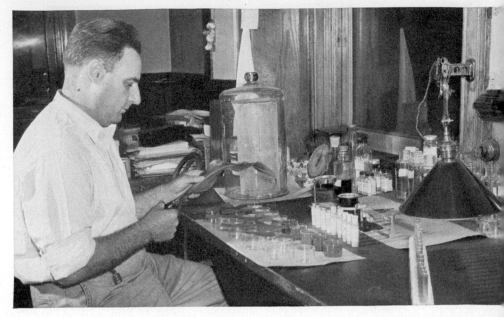

Entomologists at the Toledo, Ohio, station of the Bureau have tested hundreds of preparations offered as effective weapons against the European corn borer. In preliminary laboratory tests, corn leaves treated with the experimenta[l] insecticide are infested with young borers raise[d] for the purpose. Here David Questel prepare[s] to treat a corn leaf with a test preparation[.]

Again, preparations that pass laboratory tests are tried out in a field as sprays or dusts under natural conditions. To be considered good enough for commercial use, an insecticide must protect crops and not cost too much. Here [a] dust preparation is being applied to corn wit[h] a self-propelled power duster developed b[y] engineers of the Department of Agricultur[e]

ests on DDT and other insecticides for use in ontrolling insect pests on sugar beets grown or seed are made at the Bureau's station at hoenix, Ariz. Here the late K. B. McKinney adjusts around a sugar beet seed plant a cage into which he has put 100 tarnished plant bugs. All plants in this test plot are of the same age and have been treated with different insecticides.

t its Whittier, Calif., field station the Bureau Entomology and Plant Quarantine seeks a ew way to control the California red scale, costly citrus pest that resists fumigation with hydrocyanic acid gas, once used to good effect against it. Here two members of the laboratory staff, H. D. Nelson and Ruth L. Busbey, determine the required concentration of gas.

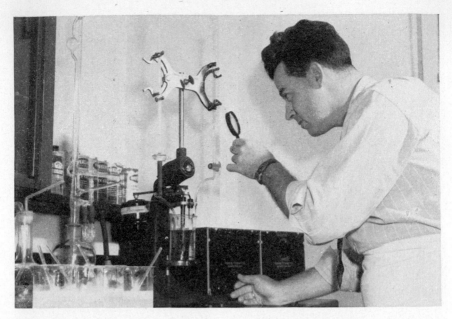

At least two more questions must be answered before the Department can publicly recommend an insecticide. To learn the amount of residue retained, P. E. Hubanks (above) uses electro- metric titration on DDT residue from a plant sample. H. D. Mann, also a chemist at Belts- ville, analyzes (below) milk from cows fed for- age that was sprayed with a new compound

More than ever, industry and the general pub- lic seek the Department's stamp of approval for products offered as insect killers. But first chemists and entomologists must satisfy them- selves on many points. Will the compound kill an insect? Harder and more important: In which stages of an insect's life is it effective— egg, pupal, larval, or adult? How can it best be applied? Does it need special equipment? Will it injure plants? Is it toxic to man and domestic animals? Does it kill beneficial in- sects? Does it leave harmful residues? Does it give uniform results? Can it be produced in practical quantities and at reasonable cost?

RESEARCH ON FOOD AND CLOTHING

DRYING FOOD is an old, cheap, easy, and popular way to preserve it. But much is still to be learned about factors that affect the quality of foods dried at home. Most foods require partial cooking before drying to destroy enzymes that might cause off-flavors, change colors, and lower the vitamin content. Kay Stein (above), measures the vitamin C in raw, precooked, and dehydrated cauliflower. Elsie H. Dawson (below), uses the Munsell color standards to check the color of dried apples that have been pretreated in different chemicals.

Home canning methods must include protection against harmful bacteria. Olive Allen (above) determines thermal death times on spoilage organisms. Howard Reynolds, a bacteriologist (below), inspects cultures of organisms that cause costly spoilage of home-canned foods. This subject is discussed by Edward Toepfer and Reynolds in an article beginning on page 787.

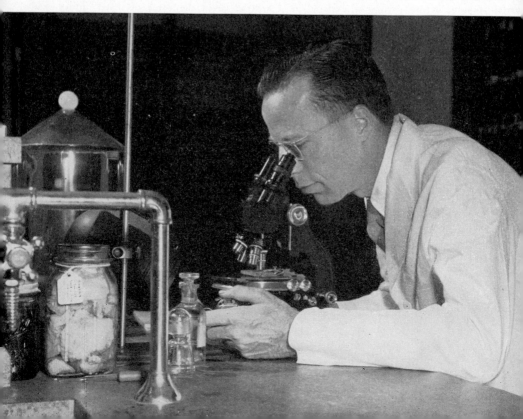

Before making recommendations to American homemakers, research workers test scores of processes and kinds of equipment. To study changes in freezing food at home, Equipment Specialist Dorothy Skinner (right) inserts a thermocouple into a carton of liquid. Below, Physicist Earl C. McCracken connects thermocouples to an automatic recorder of temperature changes and makes notes from it. In an article that begins on page 801, Esther L. Batchelder says: "People want to know what are the most suitable kinds and varieties of foods to freeze; how to select, prepare, and freeze them; how long to store frozen foods; and how to thaw or cook them."

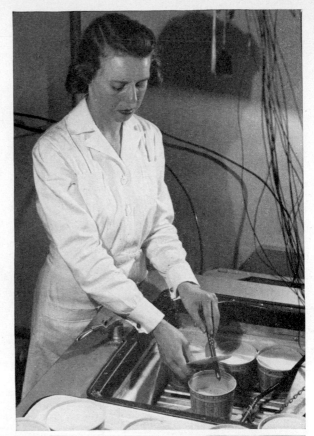

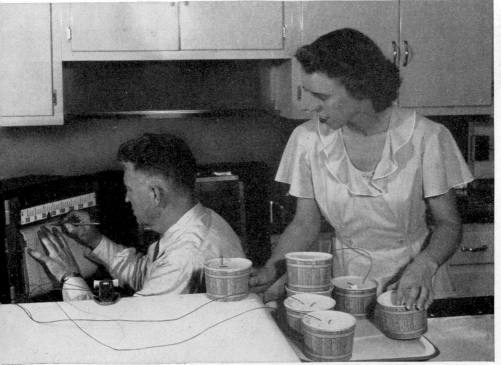

D. Breese Jones, whose article on protein begins on page 761, displays stuffed but valid evidence of the effect of quality of protein on growth. The rats, litter mates, got the same proportions of protein, fat, carbohydrates, minerals, and vitamins, but the big rat had high-quality protein from peanut meal; the small one got poorer protein from ground lentils. Below, Amos Blum runs a test to determine the amount of lysine, an amino acid, in soybean flour.

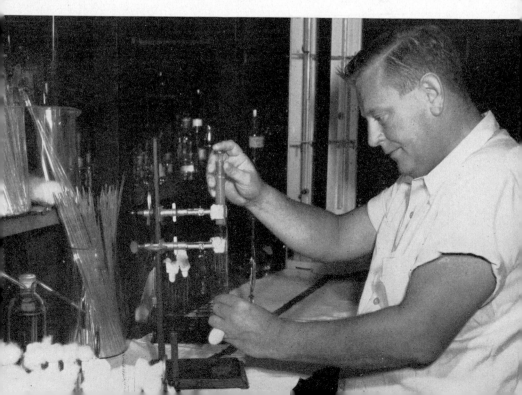

MILK and certain other foods contain an unidentified nutrient, as explained by C. A. Cary and A. M. Hartman on page 779. At right, Dr. Hartman (left), and Dr. Cary display two rats to illustrate the difference in growth of rats in the nutrient tests. The two shown here are brothers; both were fed exactly the same diet except that the one on the right received nutrient X while the other did not. The lower picture shows the authors examining one of the many rats used in the tests. In their article the authors point out that "The war emphasized both our ignorance and the necessity for more complete knowledge of the nutritive value of milk; fundamental work intended to broaden this knowledge is now in progress in many laboratories."

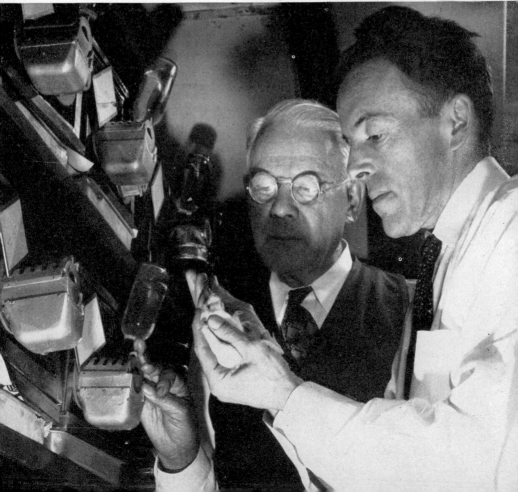

Field suit with detachable sleeves, fitted ankles.

The WORK CLOTHES shown on this and the next page are some of the simple, practical garments designed by Clarice L. Scott and de- scribed by her on pages 807 to 810. They look good and include features that assure a high degree of safety, comfort, and convenience.

Basket apron—useful in the garden.

Tailored work aprons for men or women.

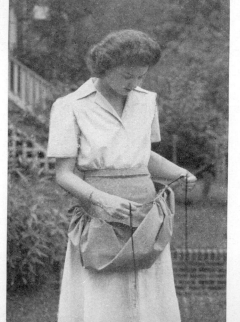

Protect-all for stormy weather around the farm.

Coverette for milking and other farm chores.

For certain kinds of housework, such as scrubbing, this apron gives protection and holds the dress off the floor.

To test the resistance of various chemically treated fabrics to termite attack, a wooded area (above), is prepared. When termites have become active, a sample of fabric is placed under the blocks of wood. After 130 days the cloth is inspected (below). The procedures and results of the test are described by Margaret Furry in Fabrics Without Mildew on page 81

New Uses for Farm Crops

by H. T. HERRICK

CONGRESS in 1938 authorized the establishment of four regional laboratories to work on new scientific, chemical, and technical uses for agricultural raw materials. Commodities in surplus and important to each area were assigned to the laboratories, which, named for the four points of the compass, are located in Peoria, Ill.; Wyndmoor, Pa., adjoining Philadelphia; New Orleans, La.; and Albany, Calif., near San Francisco. The buildings were completed and work was started in 1940 and early in 1941.

In the few years since, the results of research in the laboratories have made a deep impression on the life of the Nation. From them have come a process for the production of penicillin; a way to make sweetening materials from wheat flour; rutin; sweetpotato starch, and many other products and processes that are described elsewhere in this volume. Many other pieces of work are going on or have been finished. They are being fitted into the mosaic of the industrial utilization of agricultural raw materals and into the lives of all citizens.

Northern Regional Research Laboratory

The Northern Regional Research Laboratory in Peoria is assigned the task of finding new uses for corn, wheat, and the less important cereal crops; soybeans and other oilseed crops of the area, and agricultural residues. This last project is more national than regional, because it deals with agricultural residues of all kinds—straws, stalks, corncobs, hulls, and such—wherever found in the United States.

Just as cereal crops are the most important commodities in the laboratory, starch is the most important component of the cereal crops.

689

Focussed on it are many lines of research—fibers, adhesives, industrial fermentations, and chemicals of industrial importance. There is a starch acetate fiber, for instance, that has certain properties all its own, although it resembles the cellulose acetate material that is prepared from cotton linters and other cellulosic raw materials. There is saccharic acid, which may find wide use as a food acid, and there is a family of products that stem from the action of micro-organisms on starch or the corn sugar manufactured from starch. Penicillin is the outstanding product of fermentation. Another part of the work with fermentation is making alcohol from the starch found in the cereal grains of the Midwest. The studies include work on a laboratory and a pilot-plant scale. A pilot plant is an experimental production unit equipped to work with industrial materials and processes on a scale somewhere between laboratory and full industrial size. Much information on the production of alcohol from wheat was made available to industrial users at a time when the properties of wheat as a raw material for alcohol were unfamiliar to many persons.

Two processes were developed for the production of starch from wheat and wheat flour. Conversion of the wheat starch commercially produced by these processes into glucose sirup and dextrose sugar provided millions of pounds of sweeteners. Some day the processes may provide an outlet for surplus wheat.

Besides starch, all cereals contain proteins of various types. When starch is manufactured from corn, these proteins are found in the so-called corn gluten, which is ordinarily used for cattle feed. This gluten is treated industrially with alcohol to extract an alcohol-soluble protein known as zein. Research in the Northern Laboratory has indicated the possibility of using zein in the production of a promising industrial fiber which, in both wet and dry strengths and in other properties, compares favorably with fibers prepared from other protein-materials. Zein has also found wide industrial use in shellac, printing inks, and adhesives.

The growing of soybeans, a more recent crop than corn and wheat in our national economy, has increased rapidly during the past generation. Soybeans contain an oil that lies midway between the more commonly used food oils and the so-called paint oils. There are great possibilities in both directions. Much of the research at the Northern Laboratory on soybeans has been devoted to improving the properties of soybean oil to a point where it can meet the competition of other oils in their own particular fields. For example: Soybean oil in storage may develop unpleasant flavors that make it undesirable for use in cooking fats, salad oils, and other foods. Research workers at the laboratory have studied the problem several years and have made progress in correcting the difficulty. For paint, soybean oil has desirable and undesirable qualities. It is more or less immune to the yellowing that has been objectionable with interior linseed oil finishes, but it does not dry fast and hard enough to be used for the best type of surface coatings. Research has indicated that a new chemical treatment can cut the drying time of the oil without affecting its other properties. The new process has been made available to the industry.

Other materials produced from soybean oil are Norepol and Norelac. (Names of many products of the laboratory contain the first syllable of *Nor*thern and *Re*gional, and another syllable that describes the product.) Norepol, a rubber substitute, filled a gap during the early days of the war before synthetic rubber was in large-scale production. Norelac, a thermoplastic resin, was in industrial pilot-plant production for more than 2 years before it came on the market as a full-fledged commercial product. Norelac is largely used as a heat-sealing and waterproof coating for paper and food packaging.

Tons and tons of cornstalks, corncobs, straw, hulls, and similar materials are wasted or poorly used on United States farms. To put them to good use is a national problem. They can be used unchanged or modified by chemical treatment. One use for some of them is to make a substance that replaces sand for cleaning machine parts, castings, and so on. It is expected that with the increase in the cost of wood, agricultural residues, like straw and stalks, will find a wider use in making paper. Much research has been devoted to this development.

The difficulties are largely economic. The question always is, Will it pay? With the working out of proper procedures that will collect the residues and deliver them to the factory at a reasonable price, there is no reason why these materials may not take their place in the manufacture of paper.

With a new process perfected in the Northern Laboratory, it is possible to produce from agricultural residues furfural, a colorless, oily liquid used in purifying butadiene and making plastics, that has great promise as the basis for a new chemical industry; glucose, from which alcohol can be made cheaply; and lignin, a material that is now used as fuel but has great possibilities for chemical development. All this is done in a continuous, chemical process. Agricultural residues also are used in making Noreseal, a product that may replace cork in seals and tops for bottles, plastics, and building materials.

Southern Regional Research Laboratory

Research at the Southern Regional Research Laboratory deals primarily with cotton.

Lately the production and consumption of synthetic fibers that compete with cotton have expanded markedly. Rayon is the outstanding example. Not long ago nearly all rayon was used for clothing and household fabrics, where appearance is an important consideration, but during the war the production of a new, high-strength type of rayon was greatly expanded, primarily for truck, bus, and airplane tires.

In this connection the claim has been made that rayon is superior to cotton for tire cord, particularly for heavy-duty tires. The statement must be qualified. Tests have shown that present types of commercial cotton cord are entirely adequate for passenger-car tires. Some tests made by the Army have indicated that tires made with rayon cord are better than tires made from ordinary cotton cord for some types of heavy-duty military service. On the other hand, tires made of cord from selected varieties of cotton stood up so well in other tests made by the Army and by the War Production Board that any assertion that rayon is superior for certain types of service may well be questioned. Of course, the strength and other properties of cotton vary considerably with the variety, and some varieties, such as Wilds 13, are better suited for tire cord than others. This is a fair example of the point that industrial markets for cotton and other agricultural commodities may depend on growing specific varieties that possess the characteristics needed for specific end uses.

Research on tire cord is continuing, with the object of developing a still better cotton cord for use in tires for heavy trucks and busses.

Most persons have had occasion to apply a bandage to a cut or sprain and have found it difficult to bind the injury with just the right amount of tension. Too much tension may interfere with circulation and cause throbbing; too little may permit the bandage to loosen and fail to function. By means of a modified mercerization process developed by the Southern Laboratory, standard cotton gauze may be made semi-elastic and used to advantage in bandages for several types of injuries. This new all-cotton material will bend and give with the flexing of a joint, will expand if there is swelling, and is liked by doctors and nurses, particularly for cases where a mild-pressure dressing is required. About 30,000 rolls of the bandage have been produced at the Southern Laboratory and used in clinical trials by Navy, Army, and private hospitals.

Cotton that must be exposed to the action of the elements will mildew and rot, become weak, and finally fail in its function entirely. This applies to tent material, mosquito netting, fish nets, sandbags that come in close contact with the soil, and so on. Sandbags have uses in peace and war, for fortifications, protection of buildings, levees, and so forth. The Southern Laboratory has developed an accelerated rotting test to discover which of the various mildew- and rot-proofing agents are effective in increasing the life of cotton sandbags. The test is made by burying samples of cloth in warm, moist soil and measuring its loss in strength. One especially effective treatment to preserve fabrics against mildew and bacterial rot is the partial acetylation of the cellulose of the cotton fiber, so that it is more practically proof against attack by cellu-lose-destroying organisms. Several bags made of acetylated cotton fabric were filled with sand and placed outdoors with one side in contact with the soil. After 2 years these bags were still intact and serviceable.

Unlined cotton fire hose has been constructed from a specially treated cotton yarn, which, when properly woven into the hose, acts like linen yarn in rapidly absorbing water. It swells enough to close the minute openings in the tightly woven structure, so that the hose carries water without too much leakage. The treatment was intended especially to make cotton serve as a substitute for linen in rubberless hose for use in fighting fires in buildings, ships, and forests during the war. The same principle is being applied to the development of water-resistant military and civilian fabrics.

Large amounts of low-grade cotton fabrics, such as osnaburg, are produced, sold, and used as gray goods, that is, without finishing treat-ment. The improved effect of various finishing agents and processes upon the appearance and utility of these low-grade materials was studied. After extensive tests with several durable-type finishing agents, a modi-fied cellulose compound was selected as the most satisfactory generally as to increased strength and resistance to wear imparted to the fabric and the retention of those properties after repeated launderings. In many cases it was found advantageous to combine a mercerization treatment with the finish. By compacting and rounding the yarns, as well as by increasing luster, mercerization imparts an improved character to cotton cloth. Results of work on a pilot-plant scale indicate that useful and attractive fabrics for household uses and garments may be obtained by further processing of low-grade cotton products.

Because only short cotton fibers, like cotton linters, could be purified with existing commercial equipment and because of the threatened shortage of chemical cellulose during the war, a study was made of cutting machines that would reduce lint cotton to lengths comparable to second-cut linters. A pilot-model machine was designed and con-structed, followed by a larger experimental machine that was tested in a commercial linters purification plant. On the basis of the results of these tests, the War Production Board financed a full-size commercial unit designed for cutting both lint cotton and mill-run linters. Prelim-inary production tests indicated that the machine should be capable of cutting approximately 10 tons of cotton an hour to a length satisfac-tory for purification and nitration. Although this machine was de-veloped to fill a wartime need, it may possibly be used to advantage for mill-run linters or short-staple cotton to relieve shortages of chemical cellulose.

For many years gossypol was the only pigment known to be associ-ated with cottonseed. Research at the Southern Laboratory led to the detection of many other pigments, three of which have been isolated and identified: Gossypurpurin, purple in color, and gossyfulvin, orange in color, both of them from raw cottonseed, and gossycaerulin, blue in color, from cooked cottonseed. Microscopic investigation of the distribution of the predominant pigments in cottonseed tissue has shown that they are concentrated in distinct organs of the seed, that is, in pigmented glands. The glands are mechanically strong, resist the action of many organic liquids, and have a density less than that of other cottonseed tissue. With this knowledge, a process was devised for the mechanical removal of pigments from cottonseed; it consists in floating the largely intact glands on the surface of a mixture of organic liquids that has a density intermediate between that of the glands and that of the other seed tissue. A fractionation unit of prepilot plant scale has been constructed and operated to separate pigment glands from solvent extracted cottonseed flakes. The liquid for the fractionation process is a mixture of tetrachlorethylene and Skellysolve B, adjusted to a specific gravity of 1.378 at 27° C. For the first time, a sufficient quantity of cottonseed pigments is available for a determination of the physical, chemical, and toxicological properties of these coloring matters, and a study of their functions in relation to seed maturity, seed storage, processing conditions and industrial utilization, and toxicological and nutritional factors.

Eastern Regional Research Laboratory

The commodities studied at the Eastern Regional Research Laboratory, near Philadelphia, comprise milk, tobacco, animal fats and oils, vegetables, apples, hides, leather, and tanning materials.

Whey, a byproduct in the production of cheese and casein from milk, contains lactose, or milk sugar, which can be transformed into lactic acid by the action of certain micro-organisms. From lactic acid a material known as methylacrylate can be produced. When this methylacrylate is combined with such materials as butadiene, isoprene, and so forth, it can be converted into a rubberlike material known as Lactoprene. The vulcanizing or curing characteristics of three types of Lactoprenes have been studied extensively. The resulting materials are resistant to oil, oxidation, sunlight, and heat and appear to have possibilities for the manufacture of various kinds of articles for special uses.

The kind of synthetic rubber now being produced in greatest volume results from the combining of butadiene and styrene while they are suspended as minute globules in an emulsion. Much difficulty was experienced with the soaps that were used to prepare the emulsion. Because about 90 million pounds of tallow a year are needed for such soap, the Eastern Laboratory, in cooperation with the Rubber Reserve

Company, undertook an investigation of tallow and tallow soaps in order to determine the effect of minor constituents of the tallows on the polymerization process. The investigators found that the presence of certain minor constituents in the soap was largely responsible for the retarded polymerization of the synthetic rubber. They also learned that a hydrogenation of the tallows before they were used for the preparation of soap would completely eliminate the troublesome variability in the finished soap. As a result of the work, the Rubber Reserve Company specified that all its soap in 1946 be hydrogenated to a precise degree. The requirements can be met by the use of nonedible tallows and greases, instead of edible tallows as formerly used. The research contributed substantially to the synthetic rubber program.

Because of the shortage of hog bristles for paint brushes, a process involving the extrusion of a heated plastic mixture of casein and water into air was developed. One manufacturer put in operation a pilot plant, with the cooperation of the Eastern Laboratory, to test the bristle. There appears to be an excellent market for the material, and it is expected that casein bristles can be produced more cheaply than natural bristles or other artificial products.

A new starch compound was prepared at the Eastern Laboratory. It is allyl starch. It dissolves in many organic solvents to yield a lacquer, or spirit varnish, which polymerizes after drying and becomes very hard and resistant to agents that often damage varnish surfaces. When properly formulated, varnishes containing allyl starch dry and harden to a mar-resistant coating much more rapidly than some oil- and resin-containing furniture varnishes. The resistance of the hardened finish to hot and cold water and to alcohol and other organic solvents is notably superior to that of several commercial furniture finishes.

During the war in the South Pacific it was found that leather goods and equipment used in the tropical atmosphere were in many cases seriously damaged by mold growth. In cooperation with the Office of the Chief of Ordnance, the Eastern Laboratory developed several compounds and treating procedures to meet this difficulty. Of these compounds, three were found to be especially effective when applied to completely fabricated leather equipment, and gave greatly increased resistance to both moisture and mold growth in laboratory tests and service tests in the Pacific and Panama areas. These compounds are composed of salicyl anilide paranitrophenol, and dinitro-ortho-cresol.

As chestnut wood becomes more and more limited because of ravages of blight, this country will become increasingly dependent on foreign and synthetic tannins unless additional domestic sources are developed. The Eastern Laboratory has given careful consideration to the production of domestic tannin from a number of potential tannin sources. Among these are Western hemlock bark; canaigre, a field plant grown in Texas,

New Mexico, and Arizona; scrub oak bark from Florida; and domestic sumacs. The problem in all of these materials is more economic than chemical. A good quality of tannin can be obtained from each of them. The problem to be solved is whether the material can be produced at a price competitive with the imported or synthetic article.

Western Regional Research Laboratory

Fruits, vegetables, alfalfa, poultry, and wheat are the crops assigned to the Western Laboratory. These products, with the exception of alfalfa and wheat, are used almost entirely for human food. For that reason research on food products and processes commands an important place in the work of the Western Laboratory.

During the war, studies on vegetable dehydration were urgently needed to assist industry in meeting military demands for large quantities of dried foods. More than a billion pounds of dehydrated vegetables were produced during the war. Several important discoveries made at the Western Laboratory helped make possible this production. It was shown, for example, that easily controllable factors, such as moisture content and the composition of the package atmosphere, are effective in preventing rancidity and staleness in many kinds of dehydrated vegetables. Improved processing methods, studies on the suitability of raw materials, more precise analytical procedures, and better designs for equipment are among the contributions. A large amount of new information is available in the form of publications on these and other related subjects.

Commercial production of spray-dried whole-egg powder was greatly increased during the early months of the war to such an extent that egg drying became a major wartime industry, with an annual volume of 300 million pounds. As many servicemen can testify, serious trouble developed with the spoilage of stored egg powders. To solve the problem, research for the improvement of the keeping quality of dried eggs was requested by the Army Quartermaster Corps and much work was done on it at the Western Laboratory. Factors such as moisture content, atmosphere in the sealed container, and acidification of the powders were studied. Besides, chemical research yielded important basic information on the components and reactions in dried eggs that cause spoilage.

The control of acidity during the drying and storage of eggs will extend by at least four times the useful "shelf life" of the product. The beating or whipping properties of unacidified-spray dried eggs are poor, while those that have been properly acidified before drying are about equal to fresh eggs. The process consists of adding a small amount of hydrochloric acid to the eggs before drying. After dehydration, enough sodium bicarbonate is mixed with the dried powdered eggs to neutralize the acid. Upon reconstitution of the powder with water, the reaction between the acid and soda forms a small amount of sodium chloride. The salt thus introduced is barely detectable. The results of the studies on dried eggs make them a much better and more useful material and may thus serve to provide additional market opportunities.

Research on frozen foods is an important activity at the laboratory. Although a large and expanding industry now exists, the freezing methods of preserving foods present many problems that require technical attention. Work was done on fruit purees and other contributions have been made in freezing technology.

The pack of frozen apricots in California alone increased from 55,000 pounds in 1940 to 34,800,000 pounds in 1944, and that of peaches from 97,000 to 22,700,000 pounds. Most of these frozen fruits were used in pies. A large share of them was treated with a sodium bisulfite bath to prevent darkening, a procedure developed at the Western Laboratory. Large quantities of fruit were processed in that way which could not be canned because of metal shortages. It was noted that scalding sweet corn on the cob before removing and freezing the kernels gave a better product than when removal from the cob is the first step. Progress has been made in solving the problem of preventing the development of undesirable flavors in frozen peas. Tests to determine the sanitary history of frozen fruits and vegetables have been developed, together with other procedures, and recommendations to assure a continuation of the generally good conditions of sanitation that now prevail in this industry.

It has been found that some wastes from canneries and freezing plants can be employed as culture media to grow useful yeasts, molds, or bacteria. One example is the use of pear cannery waste in the production of a feed yeast rich in proteins and vitamins. Semicommercial-sized batches of yeast products have been made and are being tested for their feed value by cooperation with the Oregon Agricultural Experiment Station.

Another possibility under investigation is the use of the wastes as a culture medium for the production of antibiotic compounds. The juice from waste asparagus butts is especially suitable for this purpose. Among the antibiotics being studied are tyrothricin, citrinin, and subtilin. Subtilin was discovered and named by the Western Laboratory in 1943. A method for its preparation has been found and tests were started in cooperating medical clinics to determine its usefulness. Preliminary indications are that subtilin may be helpful in treating tuberculosis and amoebic dysentery. The use of these and other similar antibiotics also is being investigated for the control of plant diseases. For this purpose it is not necessary to purify the products; hence costs will be much lower than for a material planned for medical use.

Investigations on different phases of fiber production from proteins are under way in all four regional laboratories. At the Western Laboratory the proteins are the keratins (important constituents in feathers, hooves, hair, and horn) and the proteins from wheat, alfalfa, and egg white. Each has been used in the experimental production of fibers, plastics, and adhesives. Most of the work done thus far is quite fundamental in nature, in order to establish a firm scientific basis for the production of useful specialized products. Keratin proteins are of particular significance because they are nonfood proteins and are, for the main part, now wasted or diverted into products of low value.

The use of agricultural products as basic raw materials for industry holds great promise for the country as a whole. Much of our economy is based on the utilization of expendable raw materials drawn from the oil well and the mine. When these materials are gone, and the time is near for some and distant for others, we shall be faced with the necessity of turning to the supply of reproducible raw materials offered by agriculture. At present we are in the position of an individual who is living on his capital. When that capital is gone, there will be none to replace it. Let us live industrially on our agricultural products, our income, and postpone the bankruptcy which will face the country when our stored-up supplies of fuel and other materials are spent.

THE AUTHOR

H. T. Herrick is special assistant to the chief of the Bureau of Agricultural and Industrial Chemistry. After 15 years' experience in industrial work, Mr. Herrick came to the Department in 1926. He has been chief, Industrial Farm Products Research Division; assistant chief, Bureau of Agricultural Chemistry and Engineering; and director, Northern Regional Research Laboratory.

ALSO, IN THIS BOOK

Penicillin

by KENNETH B. RAPER

Penicillin was still a laboratory curiosity in the summer of 1941. It might have remained so had it not been for certain fortuitous events and the urgency of developing new drugs during the war. Today the drug is being manufactured in large quantities. It is the drug of choice for the treatment of many infections and diseases, and it aided immeasurably in reducing the number of war casualties. To produce the drug in the quantities needed in war and peace, it was necessary to develop a new industry with buildings and equipment valued at more than 25 million dollars. New outlets for agricultural products were realized in the development of this industry. The production of lactose, or milk sugar, was almost doubled, and a new and important use was found for corn steep liquor, a byproduct of the wet corn milling industry.

Penicillin was discovered in 1928 at St. Mary's Hospital in London by Alexander Fleming. He noted the presence of a contaminating blue-green *Penicillium* in plate cultures of *Staphylococcus* and observed that adjacent to this mold the colonies of bacteria were apparently being lysed, or dissolved. The phenomenon was investigated. When grown in pure culture, the mold, which was subsequently identified as *Penicillium notatum* Westling, was found to produce a substance that inhibited the growth of *Staphylococcus* and other disease-producing, gram-positive bacteria. Professor Fleming published the results of his investigations in 1929 and to the active substance he applied the name "penicillin," after the generic name of the mold that produced it. He determined that the substance was relatively nontoxic and he pointed out that it might have therapeutic value if it could be produced in quantity.

In the years that followed, penicillin was almost forgotten. It was not until 1940 that real interest in it was revived. Professors Florey, Chain,

Heatley, and their collaborators at Oxford University demonstrated that a crude penicillin in the form of a brown powder (now known to have contained only 2 or 3 percent pure penicillin) possessed curative properties when injected into mice previously infected with *Staphylococcus* and other disease-producing bacteria. A year later they presented clinical data on six patients, who showed a favorable clinical response. The toxicity of the substance was found to be very low.

Because of conditions then prevailing in England, it was not feasible to produce there the amount of penicillin needed for further clinical trials. For that reason, aided by the Rockefeller Foundation, Drs. Florey and Heatley came to the United States. Here they were referred to the National Research Council and to Charles Thom, principal mycologist in the Department of Agriculture in Washington. They were advised to come to the Northern Regional Research Laboratory in Peoria, Ill., where members of the staff of the fermentation division had had experience in mold fermentations and a large collection of molds was maintained. Dr. O. E. May, then director of this laboratory, and Dr. R. D. Coghill, head of the Fermentation Division, realized the tremendous possibilities of the drug, and arrangements were made to begin work on the problem at once.

Research on penicillin at the Peoria laboratory was directed primarily along the following lines: To develop, if possible, a culture medium that would favor the production of a greater amount of penicillin; to investigate the possibility of producing penicillin in submerged culture; and to try to develop strains capable of producing increased yields.

The Lactose-Corn Steep Liquor Medium

Dr. Fleming had employed a nutrient broth as a culture medium, and Florey and his associates produced penicillin in a modified Czapek-Dox solution containing yeast extract and glucose. At the Northern Regional Research Laboratory, the nutrient solution was altered in many ways by A. J. Moyer, microbiologist, and many substances, known to promote the growth of micro-organisms, were investigated for their ability to increase penicillin production. Of such substances, corn-steep liquor, commonly referred to as "steep liquor," was found to be outstanding. At levels below those that actually inhibited mold growth, yields of penicillin were found to increase with the addition of increased amounts of this product. It was recognized that the steep liquor constituted the principal source of nitrogen and apparently contributed other important nutrients necessary for the formation of penicillin.

At the same time various sources of carbon were investigated, including glucose, sucrose, lactose, corn dextrin, and corn starch. Of these different carbon sources, lactose, or milk sugar, was found to be slowly assimilable by the mold and most generally favorable for penicillin production.

The Northern Regional Research Laboratory therefore recommended for the production of penicillin a culture medium whose principal ingredients were corn-steep liquor and lactose. Through Dr. A. N. Richards, chairman of the Committee on Medical Research, Office of Scientific Research and Development, these discoveries were made available to all producers of penicillin in the United States and allied countries. With certain modifications in the proportions of the ingredients used, depending upon the particular mold culture employed and the method of production, this medium has remained in general use.

The pioneer work of Professor Fleming had been done with surface or still cultures, as had also the equally important work of Professor Florey and associates. It was natural, therefore, that the same method should have been followed in our early work, and it was from studies with surface cultures that the lactose-steep liquor medium was developed. Experience with other fermentations, however, indicated that penicillin could, in all probability, be produced at a much lower cost, if a satisfactory tank or submerged fermentation could be developed. Attention was early directed toward this goal. Penicillin-producing molds were inoculated into lactose-steep liquor medium and subjected to continuous and vigorous agitation for several days, during which time the broth was assayed daily for penicillin content. When thus agitated, the mold grows submerged, usually assuming the form of small, rounded pellets.

The original Fleming strain and all substrains derived from it were found to produce disappointingly low yields of penicillin when grown submerged. Different molds in our collection that belonged to the *P. notatum-chrysogenum* group were then investigated. Another culture of *P. notatum,* designated NRRL 832, was found to produce promising yields. The details of the work were communicated to other research laboratories and to the producers of penicillin. Strain NRRL 832 was made available to the penicillin industry and for several months in 1943 and 1944 it was responsible for a large proportion of the penicillin production in this country. More productive strains have since supplanted it.

Culture solutions whose principal ingredients are corn-steep liquor and lactose are most favorable for the production of penicillin in both surface and submerged culture. For submerged production, however, the concentration of these nutrients should be approximately one-half that employed for production in surface culture. When increased amounts of steep liquor are employed, the growth of the mold is excessively heavy and the yield of penicillin is markedly reduced. Standard solutions for surface and submerged production were recommended.

Some modifications in the composition of the culture solution for both surface and submerged cultures can be made without seriously affecting penicillin yields, and such alterations are often desirable when new equipment is employed or a new penicillin-producing mold is investigated.

The two methods of penicillin production worked out in the laboratory have their direct counterparts in industry. Penicillin has been made successfully on a commercial scale by both methods.

In the surface-culture method, the mold is grown upon the surface of a quiescent nutrient solution which is dispensed in flasks, bottles, or trays usually to a depth of $\frac{1}{2}$ to $\frac{3}{4}$ inch. A common practice is to use bottles of approximately 2-quart capacity and to incubate them on their sides to obtain the greatest possible amount of culture surface. This method entails a great deal of hand labor, and manufacturing costs are high. In some industrial plants as many as 30,000 bottles were inoculated each day and the plants were operated on a 6- to 10-day cycle. Maximum penicillin is produced at a temperature of about 24° to 25° C., and large incubating rooms had to be built to accommodate the 200,000 to 300,000 growing cultures.

The surface-culture method has now been supplanted by the submerged process. It was the process first developed on an industrial scale, however, and all the penicillin used in the clinical trials that first established the curative properties of the drug was produced by it.

All penicillin now made in the United States is produced by the submerged, or tank process. Inoculation with the mold may be in the form of spores or growing culture, commonly referred to as preformed inoculum. Fermentation periods vary somewhat, depending upon the mold employed and the equipment used, but commonly range from $2\frac{1}{2}$ to 4 days. Large amounts of sterile air are required and the mold growth must be constantly stirred. The fermentation must be run at a favorable temperature of approximately 24° to 25° C., and measures must be taken to remove or dissipate the heat generated by the vigorously growing mold.

Other methods of producing penicillin have been recommended but have not succeeded in large-scale operations.

Different molds are employed for different methods of production. The strain isolated by Fleming was employed for all of the early studies, and in early tests made at this laboratory it was found to produce higher yields than any other unimproved strain when grown in surface culture. The Fleming strain was observed to be quite unstable in laboratory culture, and substrains possessing different cultural characteristics could be separated from it. Although most of the latter failed to equal the productivity of the parent strain, one of them, designated NRRL 1249.B21, produced yields approximately double those of the parent culture and raised the titre, or penicillin content, from about 75 to 100 units per milliliter to 150 to 200 units per milliliter. It was made available to producers and was thereafter generally employed for the production of penicillin by the surface-culture method.

More spectacular success has been achieved in developing improved cultures for the production of penicillin in submerged culture. As it became apparent that the submerged fermentation was industrially feasible, the need for developing higher-yielding submerged cultures was recognized. Strain NRRL 832, the culture employed for this type of production, was studied intensively. Efforts to obtain from it a natural variant characterized by substantially increased production were unsuccessful. Attention was then directed toward the isolation of new strains from nature. Previous work had shown that almost all members of the *P. notatum-chrysogenum* group produced some penicillin. It seemed probable, therefore, that new strains possessing greater productive capacity than NRRL 832 might be obtained if a large number of isolates were examined. Such a search was undertaken early in 1943.

New cultures were obtained from moldy food products, fruits and vegetables in early stages of spoilage, and from fertile soil collected from various stations in the United States and from many foreign countries.

The most important culture discovered, however, was isolated from a moldy cantaloupe in Peoria. The culture represented a strain of *Penicillium chrysogenum* Thom, a species closely allied to *P. notatum,* and was designated NRRL 1951 in our collection of cultures. When first studied, it produced penicillin in slightly greater yields than NRRL 832, but within a few months a natural variant, which more than doubled the amount, was developed from it. This substrain, designated NRRL 1951.B25, was studied intensively here, and was at the same time made available to the penicillin industry in 1944. It was soon generally adopted for submerged production.

Faced with the demand by the armed forces for ever-increasing amounts of penicillin, the Office of Production Research and Development of the War Production Board early in 1944 set up projects at the University of Wisconsin, Stanford University, and the Carnegie Institution of Washington to discover or develop more productive cultures. Largely because of the work already done at the Northern Regional Research Laboratory, it then seemed probable that cultures capable of producing greatly increased yields of penicillin might be obtained by one or more of the following means: The isolation of new strains from nature; the selection of natural variants from such new stocks; and the production of induced mutations from known good producing strains by X-ray and ultraviolet radiation, or by other artificial means.

At the Carnegie Institution a mutation was produced that possessed outstanding merit. This culture, designated X–1612, was produced by X-ray radiation of spores of NRRL 1951.B25. It was first tested at the University of Minnesota, but its real potentialities were established at the University of Wisconsin in small vat fermenters. The superiority of the strain was subsequently verified at this laboratory. Yields more than twice those produced by NRRL 1951.B25 were obtained from X–1612 and it soon supplanted the parent culture as the principal strain for commercial production. Another great step forward was made by exposing spores of X–1612 to ultraviolet. In this way, the Wisconsin group succeeded in producing a mutation, designated Q–176, which doubled the yield produced by strain X–1612. The development of this outstanding culture for submerged production can·be summarized as follows:

NRRL 1951	*P. chrysogenum,* isolated from a moldy cantaloupe, capable of producing approximately 100 u/ml. of penicillin in submerged culture.
NRRL 1951.B25	A naturally occurring variant from NRRL 1951, capable of producing up to 250 u/ml. of penicillin.
X–1612	An X-ray-induced mutation from NRRL 1951.B25, capable of producing more than 500 u/ml. of penicillin.
Wis. Q–176	An ultraviolet-induced mutation from X–1612, capable of producing more than 900 u/ml. of penicillin.

The importance of the foregoing developments to present penicillin production cannot be overemphasized, because current yields of 750 to 900 units per milliliter are obtained in nutrient solutions of approximately the same composition as those used to produce maximum yields of 75 to 100 units per milliliter with NRRL 832 just a short time ago.

Some difficulties were encountered when these high-yielding strains were first adopted for commercial production, for they were found to produce primarily penicillin K, a type that is rapidly destroyed in the animal body and hence is much less useful clinically. However, if phenylacetic acid or phenylacetamide is added to the production medium, these strains can be made to produce primarily the more useful penicillin G. This procedure has been adopted by industry.

Types of Penicillin and Assay

Although we refer to the drug penicillin as a definite product, it should be noted that molds are known to produce at least six different penicillins. Four of these, commonly referred to in this country as F, G, X, and K, are produced under natural culture conditions by members of the *P. notatum-chrysogenum* group. They represent different chemical compounds and possess different physical and chemical properties. Two or more of these penicillins may be produced in the same culture solution and may, in varying proportions, be contained in the final dried product of commerce. Whereas penicillin F was the first penicillin to be studied and crystallized, experience soon showed that penicillin G was chemically more stable and hence more easily recovered. Furthermore, the culture (NRRL 832) first employed for the submerged production of the drug yielded penicillin mostly of type G. For these reasons, commercial penicillin soon came to represent primarily penicillin of this type.

The several penicillins differ in their inhibitory effect upon susceptible bacteria, some being relatively more effective against particular species than others. Besides, they differ markedly in their behavior within the animal body. These differences render some penicillins more effective than others in combating disease. For example, pure sodium penicillin K when tested *in vitro* against *Staphylococcus aureus* shows an activity of 2200–2300 u/mg. in contrast to pure sodium penicillin G, which contains 1667 u/mg. When tested *in vivo*, however, penicillin K is rapidly destroyed and adequate blood levels are difficult to maintain. It is not a satisfactory drug.

On the other hand, penicillin X, which is chloroform-insoluble, and hence can be obtained free from the other types without great difficulty, has been found to be more effective against streptococci, pneumococci, and gonococci than commercial penicillin containing mostly penicillin G. Believing that the production of penicillin X might be of importance from a clinical point of view, we have successfully developed a mold that produces substantially increased amounts of this type of penicillin. From a culture that produced penicillin X in yields approximating 15 percent of the total, an ultraviolet-induced mutation has been developed that produces penicillin X in 50-percent yields. It remains to be seen whether penicillin X will attain significance as a distinct drug.

Before October 1944, penicillin was measured in terms of the Oxford unit—the amount of penicillin which, when dissolved in 1 cubic centimeter of water, gave the same inhibition as an arbitrary standard, established by Florey and associates, which produced zones of inhibition averaging 24 mm. in diameter. In October 1944 a conference was held in London under the auspices of the Health Organization of the League of Nations for the purpose of establishing an international standard and an international unit of penicillin. Pure sodium penicillin G was adopted as the international standard and the international unit was defined as the specific penicillin activity contained in 0.6 microgram of the international penicillin standard. Pure sodium penicillin G, therefore, by definition contained 1,667 units per milligram. An international standard was subsequently prepared by F. H. Stodola and J. L. Wachtel, chemists at the laboratory, by the recrystallization of pooled samples of sodium penicillin G contributed by manufacturers in the United States and Great Britain. Two strains of *Staphylococcus aureus* were designated as standard test organisms, namely the Food and Drug Administration No. 209P (NRRL B–313) and the strain employed by Heatley (NRRL B–314).

In the assay, or measurement, of penicillin potencies, the so-called cylinder plate method is generally used. Modifications and improvements have been made since 1941 by W. H. Schmidt, in charge of penicillin assays at the laboratory, and others, but the method remains basically the same as that originally developed by Dr. Heatley. A plate containing nutrient agar is warmed to 37° to 40° C., evenly flooded with a suspension of the test bacteria in warm agar (approximately 45° C.), and allowed to solidify. On the surface of this plate are placed a number of hollow cylinders, which make a water-tight seal. Into these are pipetted small amounts of the solutions to be tested. A part of the cylinders in every plate contains a standard of known penicillin content for purposes of comparison.

The plates are then incubated overnight at the optimum temperature for the test bacterial species. The penicillin contained in the cups diffuses into and through the underlying agar, inhibiting the growth of the bacteria in circular zones. The zones of inhibition for all samples are then measured in millimeters, and the potencies of the unknown are determined by comparing their average diameters with those produced by the samples of known penicillin content. The method is reasonably accurate for measuring aqueous solutions containing from 1 to 4 units per milliliter. To attain these levels of concentration, the samples to be tested are diluted with sterile phosphate buffer of pH 6.0.

A modification of the above method, now in common use, involves the use of paper disks of standard dimensions that are dipped into the penicillin solutions to be tested and placed on the surface of seeded agar plates. The plates are then incubated and zones of inhibition measured and evaluated as in the cylinder-cup technique. Two other methods of assay have been successfully used, the serial dilution method and the turbidimetric method.

Recovery

When the fermenters contain maximum titres of penicillin, the mold mycelium is removed by filtration or centrifugation. In current practice the mycelium as well as the exhausted liquid residues are usually discarded. Feeding trials by the Bureau of Animal Industry, however, indicate that the dried mycelium and the culture-liquor residues may be successfully used in poultry feeds. The remaining clear broth is immediately chilled to prevent the development of bacterial contaminants which would otherwise quickly destroy the penicillin. Recovery practices differ, but a common procedure is to set the pH of the broth at pH 2.0 to 3.0 and then extract all of the free penicillin into a solvent such as amyl acetate, butyl alcohol, or chloroform. Penicillin is also subject to rapid decomposition in the presence of strong acids or alkali, and this destruction is tremendously accelerated at elevated temperatures. The extraction step, therefore, should be carried out as rapidly as possible and at a low temperature. The solvent containing the penicillin is then extracted with aqueous sodium bicarbonate to yield a solution of the sodium salt. To concentrate the penicillin further, it can be transferred back and forth between various solvents and buffer solutions of appropriate pH. An alternative procedure is to adsorb the penicillin from the filtered broth on charcoal, then remove it with a solvent, and purify it.

The final concentrated solution of sodium penicillin is then vacuum dried. This may be done in the same containers in which it is subsequently marketed, or the penicillin may be dried in bulk and added to vials in weighed amounts. Generally these are small rubber-stoppered vials of 20 milliliter capacity. To use the penicillin it is only necessary to pierce the stopper with a sterile hypodermic needle and redissolve the penicillin salt in sterile saline or water. As marketed, penicillin is a white to pale yellow powder generally containing about 60 to 90 percent of sodium penicillin and assaying from 1,000 to 1,500 units per milligram. The remaining portion represents salts of organic acids contained in the broth and other nontoxic impurities carried over in the recovery operations. While penicillin is usually recovered and marketed as the sodium salt, other salts such as potassium, calcium, or barium penicillin have been prepared to meet special needs. In recent months a few manufacturers have come out with crystalline products containing essentially pure penicillin. It seems probable that in the near future penicillin will be generally marketed in this form.

Before they are sold, samples of all commercial lots of penicillin are carefully tested by the Food and Drug Administration for toxicity and for the presence of pyrogens, or fever-producing substances.

Chemistry and Production

The chemistry of penicillin has been thoroughly investigated by many workers in university, Government, and industrial laboratories collaborating under the joint supervision of the Committee on Medical Research, Washington, D. C., and the Medical Research Council, London. The intense interest in this chemistry was due in great part to the belief held during the early days of commercial production that the enormous military needs could be met only if chemical synthesis were accomplished. A practical synthesis of penicillin, however, was not realized during the war; fortunately, the production by fermentation proved adequate.

So far, six naturally occurring penicillins have been isolated in the pure state and all have the same empirical chemical formula, $C_9H_{11}O_4SN_2-R$. All of the penicillins show the same qualitative action against microorganisms. The quantitative differences in potency (from 900 to 2,300 units per mg:) between the penicillins depend on the nature of the R-group. Of the different penicillins, penicillin X, first isolated by Stodola, Wachtel, and Coghill of this laboratory, is of unusual interest in that new, highly active penicillins can be produced from it by substitution reactions.

Before January 1943, the commercial production of penicillin was negligible, although much valuable clinical information had been obtained. In the 5-month period ending May 1943, 400 million units were produced, or roughly enough penicillin to treat 400 hospitalized cases. In the following month, 425 million units were produced and since June 1943 production has climbed steadily and rapidly. In the latter part of 1945, monthly production reached a level of approximately 800 billion units; during the 30 months after July 1943 it increased more than a thousandfold. In May 1946 approximately 2,700 billion units were produced, with an estimated value of approximately $15,000,000. There is every reason to anticipate still greater production. During the period from June 1943 to July 1946, the price of penicillin dropped from $20 per 100,000 units (acknowledged to be less than cost) to about 55 cents per 100,000 units. Parallel with the increase in production and the decrease in price there has been a steady improvement in the quality of the drug manufactured. Penicillin, as marketed in 1943, commonly contained about 100 u/per mg. of pure sodium penicillin; now the average is very much higher, with 1,500 u/per mg. of material not uncommon.

Uses of Penicillin

Penicillin is now the drug of choice in the treatment of many types of bacterial infection. It is not a cure-all, however, and it is of little or no value in the treatment of many serious diseases. Generally speaking, its application can be correlated with the identity and character of the pathogen. It is particularly effective against the pyogenic cocci and the gram-positive, spore-forming bacilli, including the anaerobic forms belonging to the genus *Clostridium*.

Penicillin may be administered in a variety of ways, including intramuscular, intravenous, or local injection; by continuous intravenous drip; and by topical application. The intramuscular method is most commonly used. A solution of penicillin of appropriate concentration is made with sterile isotonic saline, or distilled water. The dosage commonly ranges from 10,000 to 30,000 units and is administered every 3 hours, day and night. It is important that the injections be continued until the clinical picture clearly warrants their cessation.

The intravenous method is usually employed for the purpose of obtaining quickly a blood concentration of penicillin adequate to halt or reduce infection. Penicillin may be injected locally into abscesses, joint cavities, and so forth in varying doses, depending upon the extent of the infection. Penicillin may also be administered topically at localized sites of infection, where it is applied in the form of wet compresses or as a powder. As penicillin becomes more generally available it is probable that it will be administered orally on an increasingly greater scale. To obtain the proper blood levels to combat and eliminate infection, it is necessary to give four to five times the amount required if administered parenterally. The patient's gain in comfort would more than compensate for the added cost of the drug.

The total amount of penicillin necessary to clear up an infection depends upon the nature and extent of the infection and the sensitivity of the causative organism. The gonococci are the most sensitive of all pathogens and most cases of gonorrhea can be cured by a series of 3 to 6 intramuscular injections of 30,000 units administered at 3-hour intervals. Cases of bacterial endocarditis, on the other hand, require much greater amounts of penicillin, often running to several million units administered at rates of 200 thousand to 1 million units a day. While specific hospital cases require varying amounts of the drug, an average figure would be approximately a million units administered over a period of 3 to 7 days.

Penicillin is usually marketed in the form of the sodium salt and the methods of administration cited above are based upon the use of solutions of the drug in this form. It may also be embodied in the form of ointments or creams that find their greatest usefulness for the treatment of second- or third-degree burns and localized surface infections. It may be suspended in a suitable vehicle for nebulization and used as a nasal or oral spray to combat infection of the throat and nasal passages. The use of penicillin in the form of troches and dental cones has been recommended to combat oral infections.

Penicillin has played a major role in military medicine. It was employed quite freely in forward areas as a preventative measure to forestall the development of gas gangrene and other serious infections. Behind the lines, it found wide application in the treatment of osteomyelitis and other deep-seated wound infections in addition to the multiple uses for which it is recommended in general practice. New uses for penicillin are constantly being discovered, new modes of administration are being developed, and clinical practice, therefore, is undergoing continual change.

In the field of veterinary medicine, the most successful application of penicillin has been made in the treatment of bovine mastitis in which the causative organisms were *Staphylococcus aureus, Streptococcus agalactiae, Streptococcus dysgalactiae,* and *Streptococcus uberis.* Streptococcic infections responded to smaller doses than those in which the invading organism was *Staphylococcus aureus.* The penicillin solution is administered through the teat canal immediately after a milking period and apparently has no adverse effects on the mammary glands or on the quality of the milk.

Penicillin has been used with positive results in the treatment of strangles of horses caused by *Streptococcus equi,* in hemorrhagic septicemia of cattle, "shipping fever" of horses, swine erysipelas, peritonitis and osteomyelitis in dogs, and canine distemper. The method of administration and the dosage varies with the size of the animal, the nature and severity of the infection, and the identity of the causative organisms.

Additional pathogens causing diseases in animals that are known to be penicillin-sensitive include: *Actinomyces bovis,* causing actinomycosis of cattle; *Bacillus anthracis,* causing anthrax in cattle, sheep, and horses; *Clostridium chauvoei,* causing blackleg in cattle and sheep; *Corynebacterium renale,* causing pyelonephritis in cattle; *C. equi,* causing suppurative pneumonia in foals; *Erysipelothrix rhusiopathiae,* causing erysipelas in swine; *Leptospira canicola,* causing leptospirosis in hogs, dogs, cats, and foxes; *Listerella monocytogenes,* causing encephalitis in sheep, cattle, and swine; *Streptococcus gallinarum,* causing septicemia in chickens; and others.

Some investigations have indicated the possible usefulness of penicillin to combat certain plant diseases. Such studies have been limited in number and would need to be performed on a much more extensive scale before any conclusions can be reached regarding the usefulness of the drug in this field.

The addition of penicillin to milk and other highly perishable food products has been recommended but its usefulness as a food preservative is questioned. Penicillin in low concentrations will inhibit the growth of many bacteria responsible for food spoilage. It is not effective, however, in preventing the growth of other forms often equally responsible. Gram-negative species are usually not affected, and among the gram-positive forms, which are generally penicillin sensitive, a number of spore formers, such as *Bacillus cereus,* produce enzymes, termed penicillinases, which rapidly destroy the drug. While the addition of penicillin may extend somewhat the useful life of a product under certain conditions, the varied microflora normally present precludes its continuing effectiveness.

THE AUTHOR

Kenneth B. Raper is senior microbiologist in charge of the Culture Collection Section, Fermentation Division, Northern Regional Research Laboratory, Peoria, Ill. He has been associated with the Bureau of Agricultural and Industrial Chemistry during most of the past 18 years. Dr. Raper holds degrees from the University of North Carolina, George Washington University, and Harvard University. At the Northern Regional Research Laboratory, Dr. Raper and his co-workers are building a large collection of cultures of fungi, yeasts, and bacteria, many of which are essential in the industrial fermentation processes used in the production of antibiotics and use full organic chemicals. During the period in which penicillin fermentation was being developed, he examined hundreds of cultures obtained from all parts of the world in efforts to discover strains of the *Penicillium notatumchrysogenum* group that would be more satisfactory than existing strains for the production of high yields of penicillin.

Rutin for the Capillaries

by JAMES F. COUCH

THE PRINCIPAL effect of rutin when taken into the body is to restore the strength of the capillary walls when they become weakened. Rutin is a new, cheap, nonpoisonous drug that comes from buckwheat, tobacco, yellow pansies, and at least 35 other plants. Extensive clinical studies of its use in various disease conditions associated with hemorrhage or weak capillaries have demonstrated the value of rutin in medicine.

In 1936 a Hungarian biochemist, A. Szent-Györgyi, announced that he had accidentally discovered a substance that would restore weakened capillaries to normal. The substance, which he called vitamin P, could be obtained from citrus fruits and red peppers. It was distinct from vitamin C, which had previously been thought to have this strengthening action. Szent-Györgyi and his co-workers began a search for the new factor and soon announced that it was a glucoside termed hesperidin, a well-known constitutent of citrus fruits that had been discovered more than a century previously. Further research, however, indicated that the vitamin P activity of hesperidin was due to some other substance, present as an impurity in the original crude crystals. Continuing the search, they prepared a concentrate that contained eriodictin (eriodictyol glucoside), a compound closely related to hesperidin but more soluble in water.

Clinical studies showed this material to be active against increased capillary fragility, but again it was found that the activity was due to some other substance mixed with the crude eriodictin concentrate. Evidence was obtained that a related substance, long known as quercitrin, was present in these extracts. It was subjected to study on guinea pigs and appeared to be inactive. Szent-Györgyi concluded from all his experiments that vitamin C (ascorbic acid) is needed to activate vitamin P and that when vitamin C is given simultaneously, both hesperidin and eriodictin restore weakened capillaries to normal.

Meanwhile, certain adverse reports were published, but favorable results were reported by scientists in Scotland and England. Many other fruits were studied and several gave evidence that they contained the capillary factor. From the contradictory accounts in the scientific journals, it became clear that the content of active material in the natural products is variable and that some samples may even be devoid of activity. Possibly the active factor is more concentrated at certain stages of growth, or the chemical processes used in concentrating the experimental fruit extracts may damage or destroy it.

The search for the missing factor was continued in various places. A. L. Bachrach and his co-workers in England have contributed extensive chemical studies on citrin and related substances. A. J. Lorenz and L. J. Arnold in California have reported a method of analysis for vitamin P. W. P. Wilson, also of California, has developed a colorimetric method for estimating flavonols. R. H. Higby, in the same laboratory, has studied a soluble form of hesperidin, the chalcone, which he thought might be the active form of the vitamin.

From what was known of the chemistry of the active material, it was evident that this elusive factor was most likely to be of a flavonol structure. The chemical structures of the compounds are similar:

Hesperidin
(a flavanone)

Eriodictin
(a flavanone)

Quercitrin
(a flavonol)

The differences between the flavanone and flavonol structures are slight, but important. The flavonols contain an extra double bond and an hydroxl (OH) group, which are absent in the flavanones. Because these structures usually confer greater physiological as well as chemical activity on the compounds that contain them, we can expect that the flavonols would be more potent in the body than the flavanones.

The structure of rutin is the same as that of quercitrin, except that the sugar portion of the molecule is composed of glucose and rhamnose, whereas in quercitrin the glucose is absent and rhamnose alone is present. We reasoned, therefore, that rutin should possess a vitamin P action and might be the long-sought factor. Clinical testing for 4 years has substantiated the conclusion, and rutin is now established as a remedy for weakened capillaries.

Rutin can be prepared in a highly purified condition as a light-yellow, tasteless powder of definite chemical composition. Under the microscope, it appears in characteristic tufts of crystals. It is not toxic. Extensive feedings of large doses to laboratory animals over long periods as well as administration to human patients for many months have shown no deleterious effects.

Thirty-eight species of common plants are known to contain rutin. Among them are buckwheat (*Fagopyrum esculentum*), yellow pansy (*Viola tricolor*), elder (*Sambucus canadensis*), forsythia (*Forsythia splendens* and *fortunei*), hydrangea (*Hydrangea paniculata*), and tobacco (*Nicotiana tabacum*).

At the Eastern Regional Research Laboratory, rutin was first prepared from flue-cured tobacco of high quality. The yield was not large, averaging about 0.4 percent, at a material cost of $135 to $150 a pound for the drug. Other types of tobacco, especially the air-cured varieties, were never found to contain more than minute traces. Because of the expense involved in preparing rutin from tobacco, a search was begun to find a cheaper source. Many plants were examined in the laboratory. Several of these, like elder blossoms and leaves, pansy flowers, and white hydrangea flowers, contained enough rutin to be given consideration as possible though somewhat expensive sources.

When buckwheat plants became available, a sample was collected and brought to our laboratory. Analysis showed that it was the most promising plant examined up to then. Further research, including studies of the rutin content of buckwheat at different stages of growth and under varying conditions of handling and storage, disclosed that buckwheat gave a much higher yield (3 to 5 percent) and was so cheap that the material cost of rutin could be reduced to $1.10 a pound. Ten dollars worth of green buckwheat will furnish as much rutin as $1,000 worth of tobacco. Besides, buckwheat is a quick crop. In 25 to 30 days after sprouting, the plant contains the highest percentage of rutin, but the greatest yield per acre is obtained 10 to 14 days later, advantage being taken of the extra growth of the plant during that period. This short period of about 40 days from planting to harvest makes it possible to obtain three crops a year from one plot of ground, an economic feature of some importance.

Green buckwheat, however, must be processed within 24 hours after harvesting, because it loses its rutin rapidly when cut. It cannot be dried in the field as hay without nearly complete destruction of the rutin. Even moderately fast drying results in considerable loss of the active constituent.

A process for flash drying has been worked out in which, under certain specified conditions of temperature and air flow, the leaves and blossoms may be desiccated in 45 minutes with a minimum loss of rutin. In this process the stems are not dried but are separated from the leaves and blossoms and discarded.

The dried material may be utilized as a source of rutin. Several solvents will extract the substance. A process has been developed at the Eastern Regional Research Laboratory in which boiling water is used to dissolve out the rutin. Another process, also developed at the laboratory, employs 65 percent alcohol for the purpose. Denatured alcohols or isopropanol can also be used.

When drying is not desirable, the buckwheat can be processed green as soon as it is harvested. The whole plant is submerged in alcohol in a vat and allowed to stand until the next day. The alcoholic solution is drawn off and replaced with fresh alcohol, which is allowed to stand for another day and then drawn off. The alcoholic solutions are distilled to remove the solvent, leaving in the still a mixture of rutin and soluble plant constituents partly dissolved in water derived from the green plant. This is drawn off and cooled. Crude rutin separates out and is collected on a filter. This is now refined by removing the impurities with solvents and recrystallizing until pure rutin remains. The purity of the product is rigorously tested. The over-all yields by this process are somewhat larger than in the procedure that involves drying, because little rutin is lost if the plant is covered with alcohol 3 to 4 hours after harvesting.

Among the other constituents of the plant that are removed from the rutin during refining are some interesting byproducts—sugars, lecithin, sitosterol, and others that may find commercial application.

Rutin was on the market in 1947 in somewhat limited quantities and usually druggists dispensed it only on physicians' prescriptions. Several large manufacturing drug companies entered the field, and plentiful supplies of the substance were expected in a short time.

Clinical investigations of the use of rutin in disease were initiated by Dr. J. Q. Griffith, Jr., of the Robinette Foundation, Medical School, University of Pennsylvania, who has studied its medical applications. Rutin for medical study has been furnished to approximately 400 physicians, hospital clinics, and research workers. A summary of their experience follows.

In patients suffering from high blood pressure there often is rupture of weak capillaries, with production of more or less severe hemorrhage. At times these accidents occur in the retina and cause partial or even complete blindness. Several patients suffering from retinal hemorrhage have been treated with rutin. In 83 percent of the cases, no further rupture of the capillaries occurred. Bursting of blood vessels in the brain leads to apoplexy. Rutin cannot cure the apoplexy once it has occurred, but it may help to prevent future attacks. In 3 years no patient receiving rutin has had an apoplectic stroke, although all were suffering from hypertension and in more or less danger of such an accident.

An interesting development occurred in the treatment of hypertension. One of the best remedies for high blood pressure has an unfortunate tendency to weaken the capillaries of some patients. This fact forces the physician to use this powerful remedy with great caution in such cases. However, if the patient is given rutin, the tendency to weakening of the capillaries is counteracted, and the physician may proceed with his treatment. Similar effects have been noted in connection with the therapeutic use of salicylates and arsenicals, which also tend to weaken the capillary walls.

Although rutin itself is not advocated as a cure for hypertension, a drop in the blood pressure has been noted in 36 percent of the cases under observation. In 6 percent, the decrease was marked; in the remainder, it was moderate. There is a possibility that rutin may be of value in the treatment of diabetic retinitis, a condition that frequently occurs in diabetes and involves bleeding in the retina. Patients with unexplained bleeding from the lungs, not due to tuberculosis, have been relieved by rutin.

Rutin acts like a vitamin in that it restores these conditions to normal, but the affliction may return if rutin is discontinued. Persons who have a natural tendency to increased capillary fragility often relapse some weeks after discontinuing the remedy.

THE AUTHOR

James F. Couch, a native of Massachusetts and a graduate of Harvard University, received a doctor's degree from American University in 1926. In the Bureau of Animal Industry, 1917–40, he did research on the chemistry of poisonous plants, locoweeds, larkspur, lupines, milksickness, and cyanide poisoning. Since 1940 he has been a chemist in charge of the tobacco section in the Bureau of Agricultural and Industrial Chemistry.

FOR FURTHER READING

Bachrach, A. I.., Coates, M. E., and Middleton, T. R.: *A Biological Test for Vitamin P Activity,* Biochemical Journal, volume 36, pages 407–412, 1942.

Couch, J. F., Naghski, J., and Krewson, C. F.: *Buckwheat as a Source of Rutin,* Science, volume 103, pages 197–198, 1946.

Griffith, J. Q., Jr., Couch, J. F., and Lindauer, M. A.: *Effect of Rutin on Increased Capillary Fragility in Man,* Society for Experimental Biology and Medicine, Proceedings, volume 55, pages 228–229, 1944.

Shanno, R. L.: *Rutin, a New Drug for the Treatment of Increased Capillary Fragility,* American Journal of the Medical Sciences, volume 211, pages 539–543, 1946.

Scarborough, H.: *Observations on the Nature of Vitamin P and the Vitamin P Potency of Certain Foodstuffs,* Biochemical Journal, volume 39, pages 271–278, 1945.

Dairy Byproducts

by EARLE O. WHITTIER

WHENEVER more milk is produced than is needed to supply the demand there arises the problem of disposal of the surplus. One solution is to increase consumption by urging greater use of milk, a slow method, or reducing prices, not always a feasible method. The problem usually is partly solved by converting the surplus milk into relatively nonperishable products like butter, whole-milk cheese, evaporated and sweetened condensed whole milk, and dried whole milk—products that can be easily stored or transported to places that need them.

The greatest money value of whole milk is in the milk fat, so primary emphasis is put on products containing all or most of the fat. Its value, though, makes it impractical to consider the use of milk fat for nonfood purposes; many cheaper fats are available and suitable for such uses. It is generally true that use in food is the most gainful way to utilize all the components of milk.

The production of butter and cheese from surplus milk leaves, as byproducts, skim milk, buttermilk, and whey, which also are byproducts in the making of cream, butter, ice cream, and cheese from nonsurplus milk. The problem of disposal of surplus milk includes, therefore, not only the primary one relating to the milk fat and foods containing milk fat, but also finding use for the practically fat-free byproducts.

The problems of disposition of surpluses and byproducts of the dairy industry are not new. They were becoming increasingly acute in the years before the war. During the war there were other problems—insufficiency of food and feed—but they are gradually disappearing again, and the utilization of surpluses and byproducts requires increased attention.

A general prejudice against the use of fluid skim milk as food has existed among our people, presumably mostly because so much of it has been fed to animals. In what degree skim milk is less palatable than whole milk is a question each individual must answer for himself. But the nutritive value of skim milk is not a matter of opinion. It is a matter of fact. Skim milk lacks the fat and the accompanying vitamin A of whole milk, but is equally rich in protein, lactose, calcium, phosphorus, and riboflavin. The diets of many individuals lack adequate calcium and riboflavin. Most of the skim milk used as food in the fluid condition is consumed as chocolate milk and cultured buttermilk. This indicates that added or developed flavor is an effective means of making skim milk attractive as a drink and has led to efforts to produce other flavored milks. The canned caramel-flavored milk, developed by the Bureau of Dairy Industry in conjunction with a manufacturer of evaporated milk, is one result of such efforts, but, since the recommended formulas include some fat, it is not strictly a skim-milk product.

The conversion of skim milk into cottage cheese is a convenient means of concentrating the protein for easier distribution and for marketing in a more popular form. Nutritively, cottage cheese lacks most of the riboflavin, lactose, and minerals of skim milk, but it is an excellent source of protein. Improvements in the texture, palatability, and uniformity of cottage cheese in recent years, resulting from work in the Department and several State experiment stations, have increased its popularity.

Skim milk in its concentrated forms is a convenient source of nonfat milk solids in ice cream. The proportion that can be used has been limited by the tendency of the lactose to crystallize in the ice cream. Because the crystallized lactose is hard and slow to dissolve, the ice cream sometimes had an objectionable sandy texture. To solve the problem, a low-lactose skim milk has been developed.

If skim milk is concentrated sufficiently to cause lactose to crystallize, it becomes so viscous that the crystallizing lactose is finely divided and difficult to separate, but if cane sugar is added to the skim milk before evaporation the concentrated skim milk is thin and the lactose crystals are large and can be separated easily by filtering in a centrifuge. Since cane sugar is needed as an ingredient of the ice cream, it can be supplied in the skim milk as suitably as at a later stage. The lactose removed from the skim milk is a valuable product. This procedure has been used profitably in dairy plants that make ice cream.

The use of fluid skim milk in bread and other bakery products is limited, largely because of its perishability and its bulk. Plain and sweetened condensed skim milk are popular sources of milk solids in bakery products, the latter being an especially convenient form when both milk solids and sugar are required. Dried skim milk is the form most generally preferred for incorporation in foods because of its high degree of concentration and its excellent keeping quality. It improves the texture, physical appearance, and flavor of many food products, and increases their nutritive value.

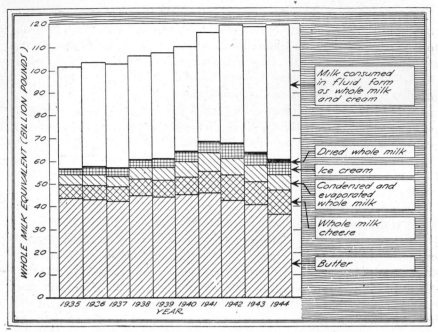

The increasing trend of milk production before the war would seem to indicate that
the yield of 1944 would have resulted without wartime demands.

The largest use of dried skim milk is in bread. Department chemists
showed in 1927 that the heating of skim milk to 85° to 95° C. for a short
period before drying had the effect of improving the baking quality of a
bread dough mix in which the dried skim milk was used. As a result, practically all the skim milk dried for use in breadmaking in this country is
given this heat treatment before drying.

When only the protein of skim milk is required, as in cheesecake, pot
and bakers' cheese are used. In cities in regions of meager milk supply it
has been the practice for some years to make cottage cheese from reconstituted dried skim milk. Recently technicians have demonstrated that
a satisfactory bakers' cheese can be made from dried skim milk. This
makes it possible for bakers in large cities at a distance from milk-producing areas to obtain freshly made bakers' cheese.

One possibility of utilizing both skim milk and surplus potatoes is in
making a wafer containing one-third skim-milk solids and two-thirds
potato solids. Boiled potatoes and skim-milk solids are thoroughly mixed
and seasoned and the mixture is extruded as a ribbon, which is then dried
and toasted to a light brown. These wafers have a cheese-like flavor and
the texture of potato chips. Having no fat, they will keep for a year or
more. This special product has not yet been commercialized, but in the
procedures involved are suggestions for many similar products.

The tendency of skim milk to foam when it is agitated is a trouble-some factor in several dairy processes, but this property has been utilized to advantage in preparing home-made fruit whips. Sugar and fruit pulp are added to dried skim milk that has been reconstituted with one-half the usual quantity of water, and air is whipped in until the volume of the mixture is increased from one and one-half to four and one-half times the original. These whips are perishable and hence of no direct commercial interest, but this property of whipping can be put to use in many ways in home and restaurant kitchens.

Casein

The only industrial products manufactured directly from skim milk are acid-precipitated and rennet-precipitated casein, which are relatively pure chemical products. Purified casein is suitable for food, but it is not necessary or even desirable that casein be purified for food use. Cottage cheese and cheeses of the harder varieties are essentially casein of the acid-precipitated and rennet-precipitated varieties, respectively, that have not been freed from other food substances present in milk. But, for industrial use, it is necessary that casein be refined by removing the non-protein organic nutrients to as great a degree as possible.

The chemical differences between acid-precipitated casein and rennet casein are not well understood, but a mixture of rennet casein with a small proportion of water is characterized by its formation of a plastic mass that is suitable for the manufacture of buttons and many other articles, such a umbrella handles, buckles, and costume jewelry. Plastic casein would have greater use were it not that no satisfactory means have been discovered to prevent the finished products from expanding in humid air and contracting in dry air. Efforts have been made to find plasticizers for casein so that it can be used as a molding powder rather than as an extruded plastic, but these efforts have been only partially successful.

The average quality of the acid-precipitated casein produced in the United States has improved markedly in the past 20 years. The devising of the grain-curd process in the Bureau of Dairy Industry and the development by several manufacturers of continuous processes of manufacture, all requiring careful control of acidities and effective washing, have been the major contributions to the wider production of uniform, high-grade casein. The quality of casein is highly important to the paper-coating industry, which used about three-fourths of the total supply in the prewar years. Quality is of less importance to the casein adhesive and casein paint manufacturers, who used 10 and 5 percent, respectively, of the prewar supply. For the newer uses in fabrication of synthetic rubber and in making casein fiber, it is essential that the casein be of high grade.

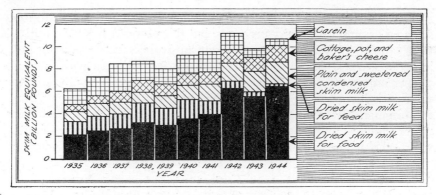

From 1935 to 1944, the amount of dried skim milk used of food has nearly tripled.

The popular and relatively new water-emulsion paints usually contain casein to the extent of about 3 percent of the total solids. Casein is used in these paints principally for its emulsifying action, but it also functions as a binder. The use of the insecticide DDT in water-emulsion paints is expected to increase the market for casein.

Although the quantity of casein used in synthetic rubber is small, this use is important, since no adequate alternative substance has been found. The casein is said to act as an internal lubricant, and thus prevents excessive heating of synthetic rubber articles, such as tires, when they are flexed during use. The quantity of casein required in the future for this purpose depends, obviously, on the extent to which synthetic rubber is used, but there is a probability that casein will be used also in tires made from natural rubber.

A thin, transparent, wrapping material made from casein was in limited commercial use in the early 1930's. Its production was abandoned because it developed a cloudy appearance and brittleness. A recent patent on improvements in the manufacturing process indicates the possibility that it may again be on the market.

Casein has been used in small quantities in the textile industry for years for bonding, loading, finishing, and waterproofing fabrics, but only since 1940 has there been commercial development from casein of an artificial fiber that seems to be finding a definite place among our textile fibers. Application for the first practical patent for making fiber from casein was filed in 1935 in Italy and commercial production was begun there the following year. The first of a series of eight patents resulting from research in the Bureau of Dairy Industry was issued in 1939 and, in the 6 years immediately following, about 40 United States patents were granted to other inventors on phases of this development. Currently, the production of casein fiber in this country, which began only a few years ago, probably approaches 10 million pounds a year.

The conversion of the casein of skim milk into textile fiber is not a process that can be carried out on the farm. The casein must be made by a controlled procedure possible only in a dairy plant or a plant making casein exclusively. The conversion of casein into fiber requires the knowledge and experience of textile engineers and equipment similar to that of plants producing viscose rayon. The casein is dissolved in alkali, various other substances are added, and the solution is extruded through the fine apertures of a spinneret into a bath containing acid and dehydrating and hardening agents. Next, the fiber is chemically treated. It is then cut into staple lengths, after which it it either felted in mixture with hair or wool or spun into yarn, which is woven into fabrics in mixture with cotton, rayon, or wool yarn. Most felt hats sold in the United States contain some casein fiber; garments and fabrics containing casein fiber may be purchased in stores.

Among the characteristics that have established casein fiber in the textile field are its property of felting in mixture with hair and wool whereby it acts as an extender of these more expensive fibers; the soft feel imparted to fabrics that contain it; and the fineness of fiber possible— finer than the finest wool. The fact that casein fiber has somewhat less tensile strength than wool, especially when it is wet, has prevented its being woven into fabrics without admixture of other, stronger fibers. Fibers from soybean protein and from peanut protein resemble casein fiber but do not equal it, and have not yet been commercialized; the synthetic nylon is similar chemically to casein and offers serious competition since it is now being produced as a wool-like fiber.

Buttermilk and Whey

The uses for buttermilk are similar to those for skim milk. It is a desirable component of bakery products and other foods, the condensed and dried forms being the most convenient ones. Fluid and condensed buttermilk are fed to animals and dried buttermilk is fed in mixed feeds. Casein made from buttermilk is different in many respects from skim-milk casein. For most purposes it is less desirable than casein from skim milk, but for casein paints it is especially suitable, provided it is used in paste form without being dried.

Despite the need in our diets for the calcium, phosphorus, and riboflavin readily available in whey, we drink no whey and consume as food practically none of it in its concentrated forms, except as a component of other foods. Feed uses account for the largest proportion of whey, increasing amounts being used in the dried condition, especially for feeding chickens. Dried whey, besides being of high general nutritional value, is of specific use in the chicken industry, since the lactose acts as a preventive of coccidiosis, and riboflavin is essential to hatchability of eggs and optimal growth and aids in preventing curled toe paralysis. The most recent advance in manufacturing dried whey for feeding chickens is the use of bacteria to synthesize riboflavin in the whey before drying. This procedure was commercialized during the war when sufficient equipment was not available to dry enough whey to meet the needs for riboflavin in feed. It is possible to concentrate the riboflavin in whey, either normal or enriched, by absorbing it on lactose. By partly concentrating the whey, some of the lactose is caused to crystallize. On concentrating further, more lactose crystallizes, carrying with it most of the riboflavin of the whey. By careful regulation of the process, a bright yellow sugar can be obtained containing 0.3 milligram riboflavin per gram. Four grams of this lactose—about one-seventh of an ounce—can furnish a person's full daily requirement of riboflavin. This yellow lactose is also suitable for addition to bread and other foods to increase their riboflavin content.

Whey can be used as an ingredient in other foods either as fluid or concentrated whey. Fluid whey may be combined with vegetable juices, such as tomato juice, to produce beverages of improved food value, or with tomatoes, peas, or beans to produce soups. In acid soups, such as tomato, whey has the advantage over skim or whole milk that it does not form lumpy curds on heating, but, instead, gives a fine-textured, smooth body.

Sweetened condensed whey is a new product developed to provide a cheap nonperishable form of whey solids to be used wherever sugar is also needed. It is suitable for use in candies, especially those of the fudge type. It adds nutritive value, gives a smooth body, and aids in keeping the candy soft and fresh. Sweetened condensed whey has been used successfully also in canned puddings, and dried whey in canned brown bread. Formulas for all of these products have been developed in the Bureau of Dairy Industry.

Whey protein, isolated as a byproduct in the manufacture of lactose and lactic acid, finds use in feeds, and efforts have been made to isolate it in a condition suitable for use as food. One method that has been successful on a laboratory scale is to condense whey, remove the lactose that crystallizes, and dialyze it to remove the salts. Another method that shows promise is to stir spray-dried whey with 70 percent alcohol and to filter out the whey protein promptly. Lactose crystallizes slowly from the filtrate and, after its removal, the alcohol may be recovered and the remaining liquid used as a source of riboflavin.

Lactose and Lactic Acid

Lactose has been made from casein whey for many years and used mainly in infant foods. The suddenly increased demand during the war for lactose to use in producing penicillin came at a time when domestic casein production was greatly reduced, but when cheese production was greatly increased. Consequently, cheese whey was much more readily available than casein whey. The Department had accumulated information on the making of lactose from cheese whey which was published as six practical methods, each adapted to some special condition or requirement. These processes differ in cost of operation, in the purity of the lactose produced, and in the solubility of the whey protein obtained as a byproduct. Several companies have been producing lactose from cheese whey and have thus bolstered the supply needed in making penicillin.

Fermentable sugar present in dairy byproducts can be utilized in the production of alcohol and organic acids. One plant in the United States is producing alcohol from whey and converting the alcohol into vinegar. The only organic acid being produced directly from whey by commercial fermentation is lactic acid. The Bureau of Dairy Industry devised a process whereby more than 90 percent of the lactose in whey is converted to lactic acid in 24 hours. This is a continuous process, in which raw whey flows in at one end of a tank and fermented whey flows out at the other. The commercial process is a batch process requiring a 48-hour turn-over. In brief, the whey is fermented by a bacterial culture, the lactic acid being neutralized from time to time by lime in order that the bacterial action may continue. When the sugar is all fermented, the whey is boiled to coagulate the whey protein and the clear liquid is evaporated to cause calcium lactate to crystallize. The calcium lactate is removed on a filter and, after purification, is treated with sulfuric acid to convert it to lactic acid.

If increased quantities of lactic acid are to be made, greater use for it must be found. To this end two bureaus of the Department have developed procedures for converting lactic acid to acrylates. These acrylates, when polymerized, are flexible, glass-like substances that have use as plastics and in waterproofing cloth, and that can be converted into rubber-like materials. But acrylates can be made more cheaply from other starting materials and this has aroused interest in ways of cheapening the present expensive method of refining—which is the largest proportion of the cost of lactic acid. This acid cannot be crystallized or distilled by any method that is commercially practical, but it can be combined with alcohols to give lactates that can be easily distilled and thus purified. Three patents on such procedures have been issued to workers in commercial laboratories. These purified lactates can be shipped in undiluted form and in inexpensive containers, in contrast to dilute lactic acid that must be shipped in expensive, noncorrodible containers. At the point of use the lactates can be converted back to lactic acid of any desired concentration by boiling with water. It is reasonable to expect that some of the needed reduction in cost of lactic acid to the user can be attained by application of these methods of refining and handling.

Another use for lactic acid that is not yet commercialized is in lacquers and protective coatings. When a lactic acid solution is heated, water distills off and the lactic molecules combine with one another to form resinous substances of increasing viscosity and insolubility. Public service patents have been issued to Paul D. Watson of the Bureau of Dairy Industry who has discovered that these resins may be combined with oils or with small percentages of metals to give lacquers. Baked on glass or metal surfaces, these are tough, elastic, and firmly adherent coatings that resist the action of steam, acids, and dilute alkalies, and are affected only by strong alkalies and few organic solvents. These coatings have been tested with satisfactory results on milk cans, pails for cottage cheese, cans for evaporated milk, mechanical pencils, and cigarette lighters.

THE AUTHOR

Earle O. Whittier is a research chemist in the Division of Dairy Research Laboratories of the Bureau of Dairy Industry, where he has worked for 25 years on chemical problems related to milk and its byproducts. He was educated as a chemical engineer at the University of Maine. His published researches on the chemistry of milk won for him the 1943 Borden award of the American Chemical Society.

New Goods From Wood

by ALFRED J. STAMM and G. H. CHIDESTER

P RACTICALLY everything was scarce the first year or two of the war, and we tried to make wood a substitute for steel, aluminum, rubber, and many other materials. Then wood became scarce, so we worked to make wood products as serviceable as possible in the uses to which they were most applicable. Our research in both periods had the same technical objective: The improvement of wood service.

From the search came an array of materials with strange names. Many of them will doubtless find their way into the production lines of the Nation's furniture, farm machinery, building, and other industries. The new products include woods specially treated to fortify them against shrinking, swelling, and the inroads of decay organisms, and other ills that raw wood is heir to; low-cost wood plastics made of the wastes ordinarily burned or otherwise disposed of by sawmills, paper mills, and similar wood-using plants; and paper and wood-pulp materials strengthened and made more durable for exposure to rain, heat, cold, and other rigorous conditions. Many of the materials are adapted to large-scale production methods.

We worked on three principal types of materials. One was the so-called "modified" woods, consisting principally of wood in the form of thin veneer sheets that were given various treatments to decrease their natural tendency to swell, and that were sometimes compressed or molded under heat and pressure to form panels or molded products. From these treatments came impreg, compreg, and staypak.

The second principal type of wood materials extensively developed during the war can be broadly called "plastic" wood-base materials, or "lignin plastics." The basic production process consists of a chemical treatment of hardwood sawdust or wood chips that removes part of the cellulose and leaves a residue of stable cellulose and lignin. When a plasticizer like phenol-formaldehyde is added to the resulting powder or pulp, it can be molded under heat and pressure to form various boards and other articles.

The third general type includes various paper-base laminates and wood-pulp plastic materials that can be molded. Most important among these products during the war was papreg, the basic material of which is a special paper chemically treated so that it can be compressed under heat to form a multilayered sheet suitable for many uses. Thin papreg can also be molded to the faces of plywood to provide a water-resistant surface that hides plywood defects, minimizes checking, and can be painted readily. Among molded pulp materials is a long-fibered pulp preform that can be compressed to various shapes in a mold.

Impreg (from "impregnated") is wood treated with phenolic resin-forming chemicals according to a method developed at the Forest Products Laboratory, in which the chemicals enter and bond to the cell-wall structure, and the resin is dried and cured within the structure. When resin is thus made an integral part of the wood, the tendency of the wood to swell and shrink is permanently reduced. Phenolic resin-forming systems have proved to be the most effective in stabilizing wood dimensionally. It is possible to reduce swelling and shrinking to 30 percent of normal.

The stabilizing of wood by a resin treatment differs from preservative and fire-retardant treatments in that it must be much more complete. The resin must be uniformly distributed throughout the entire cell-wall structure to be fully effective. For this reason the treating of lumber and the treating of freshly felled logs have not met with the success that some investigators have claimed. Veneer of practically any species can be adequately treated. Practically none of the woods can be properly treated in lumber thicknesses and lengths. Even if lumber could be adequately treated, the increase in cost would make the material prohibitively expensive for the majority of proposed uses.

For these reasons, development work on impreg and its commercial production have been confined to the use of resin-treated veneer. These treated plies have proved suitable as facing for solid wood or untreated plywood. The chief advantage of such resin-treated facings is that they practically eliminate face checking and greatly reduce grain raising, even when exposed outdoors without a surface finish. Even the checking of fancy crotch veneer used in furniture can be nearly eliminated.

The treatment also imparts to the panels considerable resistance against decay and attacks by termites and marine-borers. Panels consisting of two resin-treated face plies with a single untreated core ply were inserted in the ground for a year in a field in Mississippi where termite action is severe. The termites tried the faces but found them not to their liking.

Like soldiers who failed in a frontal thrust, they tried a flank attack and, finding the untreated core just what they wanted, proceeded to clean it out. Similar material that has had the edges protected with a preservative treatment and all the plies treated is frequently sound after 5 years.

The resin treatment cuts down the passage of water vapor through the panels to a marked extent and greatly increases the electrical resistance and the resistance to most chemicals, except strong alkalies. Resin treatment has a negligible effect upon fire resistance. Fire-resistant salts, however, when incorporated in the wood with the treating resin, are fixed in the structure and give the wood good fire-retardant properties.

Only a few of the strength properties of wood are significantly increased by a resin treatment. Toughness is lowered, but hardness and compressive strength are increased.

Impreg was manufactured during the war only for military use. The most interesting use was for facing laminated redwood aircraft carrier decking to obtain a wear- and splinter-resistant decking equivalent to teak but lighter than Douglas fir. Service tests on one carrier indicated wearing qualities far superior to Douglas fir. Another wartime application of impreg was as housing for electrical control equipment, in which its superior electrical properties proved especially advantageous. Impreg shows the greatest promise as resin-treated faces for ordinary plywood. Such panels might be used as siding for houses, trailers, and boxcars, flooring, and paneling. It remains to be proved, however, that the improved properties warrant the increased cost of the treatment.

Compreg

Compreg is the name given to a stable form of phenolic resin-treated compressed wood. Its dimensional stability and its resistance to wood-destroying organisms, chemicals, and flow of electricity are practically the same as that of impreg. Most of the strength properties are increased about in proportion to the compression. It is tougher than impreg but not quite so tough as the original wood.

Because of the plasticizing action of the resin-forming chemicals on wood at temperatures used in hot pressing, the treated wood can be appreciably compressed under a pressure that scarcely compresses untreated wood at all. Because of this plasticizing action of the resin-forming chemicals on wood, it is possible to make a combination of resin-treated compressed faces on an untreated and uncompressed core in a single assembly and compression operation.

When compreg is compressed to about one-third to one-half the thickness of normal wood, it assumes a glossy finish. A marred surface can be sanded and buffed to virtually its original glossy finish without the use of applied coatings. This is a feature of compreg that would make it desirable to use in furniture and flooring. Panels with a yellow-poplar compreg face, a yellow-poplar impreg back, and a Douglas-fir plywood core have been made for a flooring service test at our laboratory.

Compreg, largely in the form of thick, highly compressed panels, was manufactured by several companies for war use, chiefly in the manufacture of airplane propellers. Compreg has also been used to some extent for various connector and bearing plates, aerial antenna masts, and tooling jigs. Solid compreg shows promise for use in fan blades, pulley and gear wheels, bearings, and tooling jigs; shuttles, bobbins, and picker sticks for textile looms; high-strength electrical insulators; handles, such as for knives; and various decorative novelties.

Compreg has better strength properties than fabric-reinforced plastics, and it should be appreciably cheaper because veneer is cheaper than fabric, and about half as much resin is used in making compreg as is used in the fabric-reinforced plactics. Compreg may thus replace these plastics in a number of uses.

Impreg and compreg are made with synthetic resins of the phenolic (related to carbolic acid) type. A somewhat similar product can be made with chemicals that, under conditions comparable to those used in manufacturing impreg, form resins of the urea type within the wood. Treatment of wood with these urea-resin chemicals was pioneered by the Forest Products Laboratory, but research was suspended during the war because the phenolic resins appeared more promising. Commercial development of urea treatments was undertaken elsewhere, however, with great fanfare. The laboratory later resumed research with these chemicals to determine whether the properties of wood so treated are as markedly improved as the publicity about the commercial products set forth. This newer research has demonstrated that, on the whole, wood treated with phenolic resins has superior properties to that treated with urea at comparable cost of production.

The chief advantage of urea resins is that they are freer from color and taste than are the phenolic resins. On the other hand, under the most favorable conditions they are only about one-half as effective as phenolic resins in curbing the tendency of wood to shrink and swell with changes in its moisture content. Possible economies resulting from the relative cheapness of urea are in large part nullified by the fact that much more urea resin than phenolic resin is needed to attain even a moderate amount of stability in the dimensions of wood. It is no easier to treat wood with urea than with phenolic resins; assertions that urea can be used to treat dry wood in lumber sizes have not been substantiated by laboratory tests. Such properties as compressive strength and abrasion resistance are no better in wood treated with urea resins than in that treated with the phenolics. Decay, termite, and marine-borer resistance of urea-treated wood appears somewhat inferior to that obtained with phenolic resins.

These findings have led to the conclusion that, while urea treatment may be suitable for a few special applications, its usefulness in its present stage of development appears limited.

Staypak and Staybwood

Resin-treated wood in both the uncompressed and compressed forms is more brittle than the original wood. To meet the demand for a tougher compressed product than compreg, a compressed wood containing no resin was developed at our laboratory. It will not lose its compression under swelling conditions as will ordinary compressed wood. The material, named staypak, is made by modifying the compressing conditions so as to cause the lignin-cementing material between the cellulose fibers to flow sufficiently to eliminate the internal stresses.

Staypak is not so water-resistant as compreg, but it is twice as tough and has higher tensile and flexural properties. The natural finish of staypak is almost as good as that of compreg. Under weathering conditions, however, it is definitely inferior to compreg.

For outdoor use staypak should have a good synthetic-resin varnish or paint finish. Staypak can be used in the same way as compreg where extremely high water resistance is not needed. It shows promise for use in propellers, tool handles, forming dies, and connector plates where high impact strength is required.

The cheapest and simplest method of imparting dimensional stability to wood thus far found is to heat the wood under conditions that just avoid charring. This can be done with a minimum loss in strength properties by our method of heating the wood under molten metal for a few minutes. The wood becomes dark brown in color and loses about one-half of its original toughness, and a moderate amount of other strength properties. Equilibrium swelling and shrinking can be reduced to 60 percent of normal and an appreciable decay resistance is imparted to the wood by this treatment. Staybwood may find some use in places where dimensional stability and moderate decay resistance are more important than strength.

Lignin Plastics

Lignin, which in a sense is nature's cementing material between the cellulose fibers, can be freed from the cellulose by a mild acid hydrolysis and subsequently used as a semiplastic to bond the structure together again.

Besides breaking the cellulose-lignin bond, the mild hydrolysis converts the hemicelluloses to sugars while the stable cellulose remains with the lignin to serve as a plastic reinforcing material. The removed sugars can be either fermented or used for the growing of yeast. The residue is dried and then ground to a powder. Although this hydrolyzed residue does have some plastic properties, it does not make a good plastic when used alone, because of the extremely high temperature necessary to cause the lignin to flow even moderately and the relatively low water resistance of the product. For this reason it is used preferably in conjunction with other plastics, such as phenol-formaldehyde, which improve both the flow and the water resistance.

Under these conditions, a plastic quite similar in appearance, water resistance, and electrical properties to common black phenol-formalde-hyde plastics can be made by using 75 percent of hydrolyzed wood and 25 percent of phenolic resin. This mixture is in contrast with the mixture of 50 percent of wood flour and 50 percent of phenolic resin used in making the phenol-formaldehyde molded products. The strength properties— notably toughness—of the lignin plastic are slightly lower than those of the normal phenol-formaldehyde molded products. Mold flow is also inferior, but the acid resistance of the lignin product is better.

A commercially developed modification of the acid-hydrolysis process, in which the wood is hydrolyzed with an alkaline medium that becomes slightly acid at the end of the cook, gives a similar molding powder with strength properties superior to those of the acid-hydrolyzed product. This material, when used with only 25 percent of phenolic resin, still lacks the rapid and more extensive flow of the ordinary phenol-formaldehyde molding powders. Although the addition of more resin improves the flow, it reduces the price advantage. It is this lack of flow that has held back the commercial use of hydrolyzed-wood plastics. In large objects with limited need for flow, hydrolyzed-wood plastics may be used to advantage, however, because of their lower cost.

Unfortunately, none of the molding compositions shows promise of utilizing very large quantities of wood waste. For example, if all the present phenol-formaldehyde molded products were to be replaced by the hydrolyzed-wood plastics, three moderate-sized lumber mills could furnish all the raw material needed in the country. As board materials show promise of larger volume consumption, we have focussed considerable attention upon such materials.

The hydrolyzed-wood molding powders are not suitable for making board materials with adequate strength properties, notably toughness. The strength properties can be greatly improved by having the cellulose reinforcing material in longer-fibered form. This can be accomplished by using hardwood chips in place of sawdust and abrading the washed hydrolyzed chips while still wet to a pulp rather than grinding them to a powder. This pulp can be made into paper on a paper machine. After 10 to 15 percent of phenolic resin has been added, the sheets can be pressed at high temperatures and a pressure of about 2,000 pounds to the square inch into a high-density board with good strength properties and water resistance. The board cannot be nailed but can be drilled. This fact, together with its high density and molding cost, makes it unsuitable for general housing applications. It appears suitable for electrical paneling and for such purposes as shower-bath walls.

Pulp boards have been made in the laboratory from the hydrolyzed chip fiber by forming thick pulp mats that are pressed wet under a pressure of 100 pounds to the square inch or less without the addition of any phenolic resin. The boards have properties comparable to those of untempered commercial hardboards. They can be nailed. They can be made from softwoods as well as hardwoods, but the strength properties and water resistance of the softwood product are somewhat inferior to those of the hardwood product.

Although these and other similar hardboards show promise for use as a sheathing material for houses and in other ways that wood is used, they are far from being synthetic lumber. Their use in housing should nevertheless expand.

Cooperative research with a paper mill has demonstrated the possibility of using soda-pulp lignin in laminated plastics. Soda-pulp lignin is the simplest to isolate and has the best plastic properties of the various forms of lignin waste. It can be incorporated with the pulp in the beater to form a laminating sheet which requires no auxiliary resin to produce a dense plastic material with good properties. This is potentially one of the cheapest plastic laminates now known and should find considerable use. We have learned that soda-pulp lignin can be used to dilute phenolic resin and the solution can be applied to paper or fabric. It can replace 50 percent of the phenolic resin ordinarily used without significantly affecting the properties of the resulting laminate.

Papreg

Paper laminates treated with phenolic resins have been made for a number of years. They have been used chiefly for electrical insulating panels and for other nonstructural uses that do not require exceptional mechanical properties. The manufacturers, in developing these materials, have approached the problem primarily from the resin standpoint. We felt, therefore, that further development of paper-base laminates, from the standpoint of finding the most suitable paper for the purpose, was a promising field of research. This proved to be the case. Within 6 months after the research was started, a paper-base laminate was developed that possessed several properties having more than double the mechanical values of those of the former laminates. For example, before the war the tensile strength of materials of this type rarely exceeded 14,000 pounds per square inch. Parallel-laminated papreg is now being made with tensile-strength values from 35,000 to 50,000 pounds to the square inch.

Papreg is stronger than fabric-base plastics, and can be molded at considerably lower pressures—75 pounds to the square inch—in contrast to 1,000 to 2,000 pounds to the square inch. It is not equal to the cloth laminate in toughness, however.

Several commercial concerns make papreg. It was extensively used in airplane parts and accessories, such as gunner's seats, gunner's turrets, ammunition boxes, and the surface of a type of cargo aircraft flooring. It was tried to a limited extent for the skin surface of structural airplane parts, such as wing tips. The chief objection to it in this use is that it is more brittle than aluminum and requires special rather than conventional fittings. By modifying the fittings, we were able to fabricate a papreg fin for a trainer airplane that met laboratory tests as well as did the counterpart aluminum fin.

Papreg is not so readily molded to complex shapes as are fabric laminates, but can be made to take considerable double curvature. Normally it has a tan to amber color, but can be made from pigmented paper in a number of the darker colors. When the surface sheets are treated with a melamine rather than a phenolic resin, pastel surface colors are obtainable. Papreg shows considerable promise for use in a number of products.

Plastic Paper-Faced Plywood

During the war, plywood was faced with plastic paper laminates to increase its water resistance, hide plywood defects, minimize grain raising, and to produce a readily paintable surface. The paper surface can be molded directly to plywood under pressures as low as 75 pounds to the square inch without compressing the plywood. When it is desired only to hide plywood defects and avoid grain raising, high-strength grades of paper need not be used.

A considerable amount of paper-faced Douglas-fir plywood was made during the war for military use in storage lockers, table tops, and similar objects. New uses indicated for plastic paper-faced plywood are walls, floors, partitions, cabinets, showers, ramps, bins, sheathing, and concrete forms for buildings; boxcar, passenger car, and truck-trailer lining and siding; hulls, bulkhead, and cabins for small boats; airplane cabin linings; refrigerators; and boxes, trunks, and containers in general.

Low-Density Core Materials and Pulp Preforms

Wartime airplane construction needs produced a growing demand for a light core material to be used between plywood or metal faces to obtain skin surfaces less subject to flexing and buckling, without significantly increasing the weight of the airplane. A material was sought that was as light or lighter than balsa wood but more uniform in properties, readily available, and obtainable in larger sheets. These requirements were met with a light insulating type of board treated with phenolic resin to impart stability to the core. This and related cellular materials may find postwar use in prefabricated house construction, soundproof partitioning for boats, railroad passenger cars, doors, and other uses where lightweight and high rigidity are necessary or desirable.

Wartime research showed that plastics with a high percentage of long-fibered filler possess general strength and impact properties far superior to those obtainable with ordinary molding powders. In many cases, moreover, the double curvatures needed are too great to permit molding preformed flat laminates to the desired shape. For such purposes, the Forest Products Laboratory devised a means of molding special ordnance items by the pulp preform method, which consists of forming a mat of resin-treated pulp in a suction box with screen surfaces having approximately the contour of the final item. After they are dried, these preforms are compressed in a conventional mold. For some articles uncontoured preforms can be used and flowed to shape in the mold.

Shaped preforms would appear to be especially suitable for large contoured objects where exceptional toughness is required. Refrigerator cabinets, theater seats, desk drawers, cafeteria trays, furniture, and motorcar and aircraft parts have been suggested. It might be used also for smaller objects such as ashtrays, hand wheels, instrument cases, and other purposes for which the usual molding-powder plastic is too brittle.

THE AUTHORS

Alfred J. Stamm has been a member of the Forest Products Laboratory staff since 1925 and chief of its Division of Derived Products since 1945. He has been largely responsible for the development of impreg, compreg, and staypak. A native of Los Angeles, Dr. Stamm is a graduate of California Institute of Technology and the University of Wisconsin. His research in the physical chemistry of wood won for him a Rockefeller Foundation fellowship, which enabled him to spend a year at the University of Upsala in Sweden. While there he represented the United States at the International Forestry Convention in Stockholm. Dr. Stamm has also investigated the electrical properties of wood, various aspects of the way moisture is held within wood, and the molecular properties of wood constituents.

G. H. Chidester has spent the past 20 years at the Forest Products Laboratory doing research in pulp and paper manufacture. Since 1942, he has been chief of the Laboratory's Division of Pulp and Paper. He has specialized in the sulfite and semichemical processes of pulping woods, seeking to reduce costs and waste and to adapt the processes to a wider assortment of tree species, especially hardwoods little used for pulping. During the war he directed the laboratory's research in the field of paper plastic materials. A native of Hastings, Mich., Mr. Chidester is a chemical engineering graduate of the University of Michigan and worked for 5 years in pulp mills and on the staff of a paper-trade magazine before joining the laboratory staff.

Corncobs Enter Industry

by ELBERT C. LATHROP

ABOUT 200,000 tons of corncobs were put to interesting and profitable industrial uses during the war. They performed an essential service so well that increasing quantities are destined no doubt to serve more extensively in the days of peace. Other industries have made a market for this agricultural commodity whose previous utility was limited largely to corncob pipes, starting the kitchen fire, and stopping up the hayfield water jug.

Of the tonnage of cobs used industrially during the war, more than half went into the production of furfural, a chemical essential to the new synthetic rubber industry. Many thousands of tons were used in manufacturing ordnance. But perhaps the most interesting new use was one developed by the Northern Regional Research Laboratory at Peoria, Ill., in cooperation with the Navy, a method for cleaning carbon and oil deposits from airplane engines with ground corncobs in an air blast. To supply these industrial needs about 50 grinding plants were established to produce cob products; only one existed before the war.

An expanding industrial utilization of corncobs, however, depends on the processor's ability to obtain them in large quantity without paying too much for collecting and transporting them. Several industrial attempts to use them have failed because those conditions could not be met. Yet the supply of cobs is plentiful and fairly well concentrated. A survey we made in 1943 showed that 16 million tons of cobs are produced yearly; 3 million tons of them came from corn sold off the farm. Illinois and Iowa account for three-fifths of that amount; Minnesota, Nebraska, Indiana, Ohio, and Missouri also produce large quantities.

Cobs that accumulate at country mills or elevators or at hybrid-seed plants are the easiest and cheapest source, particularly if operators grind the cobs. We found more than 100,000 tons of cobs collecting at elevators each year within a radius of about 80 miles of one point in Illinois, and 42,000 tons in an Indiana area 150 miles long and 40 miles wide. Cobs were a nuisance at the plants, and some large elevators built special incinerators to get rid of the cobs. During the war, some operators increased the concentration of cobs at their elevators by paying a slight premium for ear corn. It has been practical also to collect cobs from farms.

Industrial Uses that Depend on Physical Properties

The secret of finding industrial uses for farm wastes lies in capitalizing the unusual or unique properties of each. Cobs have one such property that is outstanding.

A cob is composed of four rather distinct parts: Light chaff; coarse chaff in the form of tough, wood-like flakes; pith; and a woody ring. The ring and the coarse chaff are tough, woody, and resistant to abrasion and granulation. That is their industrially important property. The two parts constitute 94 percent of the entire cob—in processing, therefore, the yield of salable product is high.

The early impetus to the introduction of cobs to industry came from the need by the naval air forces for a method to supersede the use of solvents and hand tools in cleaning carbon and oil deposits from cylinders and pistons when giving airplane engines their usual overhaul after 800 hours of flying. The solution, it appeared, would be found in soft-grit blasting. Work on the problem led to the discovery that corn grits, a form of hominy, if used in a sand-blasting machine under about 90 pounds pressure, did a safer, faster, and less expensive job. But the Navy's plan to use 100,000 bushels of grits a year had one serious drawback— there could be no salvage of the grits for food or the production of alcohol because of the poisonous lead in the cylinder deposits. Thus, in an effort to save this food and improve the process, this laboratory, working with the Norfolk Naval Air Base, developed the use of a mixture of 60 percent ground corncobs and 40 percent unground rice hulls.

With this mixture as the soft-grit in the blasting, the cob particles lasted about 10 times longer than corn grits. Costs were lowered more than 80 percent. The Navy has standardized on those materials, and its specifications call for corncobs ground to pass a 10-mesh screen and to be retained on a 32-mesh screen. Chaff and fine particles must be absent and not more than 13 percent moisture may be present.

Using this process, the Navy found that the cleaning operations were practically foolproof. The hard carbon, oil, and scale were rapidly and completely removed. The cob particles were nonabrasive on the metal, hence no change in the close dimensions of parts occurred. Dirt does not collect on the particles; the particles can be used repeatedly until they finally become powder and are blown out of the blasting booth.

The soft-grit blasting method is being rapidly put into industrial use. For example, one of the major automobile companies is using the method in several of its plants where engines and parts are rebuilt or repaired. A manufacturer of farm equipment has installed it to clean aluminum-foundry core boxes. A logging company is using it for maintenance of tractors and other logging equipment. Several glass companies use it for cleaning molds.

Almost any kind of deposit may be removed from metals by it, except hard mill scale. Automobile paints and lacquers are easily removed. In all cases a smooth, clean, dry surface results. The method can have wide use in garages. It can be used to clean farm machinery. Moreover, numerous tests and demonstrations, made in cooperation with a number of different industries, show there are many purposes for which sand and possibly shot are now used as cleaning agents where soft-grit blasting would do as good a job with greater safety. There are many other jobs for which sand or shot cannot be used, but for which soft-grit is ideal.

Ground corncobs were used to some extent before the war for burnishing metal parts by tumbling in a barrel. The manufacture of ordnance for the Army and Navy greatly increased such use, particularly for burnishing cartridge cases. Specifications by one arms manufacturer called for ground cobs passing a 10-mesh and being retained on a 48-mesh screen.

This laboratory has shown that any of the corncob fractions ground to pass a 100-mesh screen can replace wood flour in the manufacture of certain of the lower-cost phenol-formaldehyde plastics. White cobs are preferred to red. The outlet for cobs in this market, however, is restricted. Freight rates on cobs from the Corn Belt to the eastern seaboard are higher than the rates manufacturers pay on wood flour from Maine and New York. When and if these plastic molding powders are manufactured in the Central States, this use will represent a potential market for corncob fractions.

An increasing market is developing for coarsely ground cobs for use as chicken litter, especially in laying houses. When prepared for this purpose, the cobs are coarsely ground and the fine particles screened out. Trials show that material passing a 2-mesh screen and retained on a 4-mesh screen is considered acceptable, although some poultrymen prefer particles up to 1 inch long. For litter use, cobs have the advantage of being clean and absorbent. There is also the possibility that with the addition of chemicals an ideal litter may be produced.

A number of uses for corncobs which, strictly speaking, are not new uses should be mentioned. A chief use is for pipes. One company in

Missouri is said to have produced 30 million pipes in 1940. The industry depends, however, on a special variety of corn that requires exceptionally fertile soil for development of cobs of suitable size.

During the war, cob particles about the size of sawdust were used for packaging metal parts for shipment. The cob particles kept the parts dry and prevented a certain amount of corrosion.

Finely ground cobs are in use in floor-cleaning and ·sweeping compounds. Cob particles that pass a 20-mesh screen have been used a number of years in cleaning furs.

Uses Depending on Chemical Properties

Furfural is an amber-colored liquid. It has been manufactured for more than 20 years at a plant in Cedar Rapids, Iowa, by treating oat hulls with dilute sulfuric acid and steam. The residue from this treatment is used as fuel or sold as fertilizer filler. Important uses for furfural have been found in making plastics, refining wood rosin, making lubricating oils from petroleum, and in producing other important chemicals derived from it. When it was found that furfural was one of the best chemicals for purifying butadiene used in making synthetic rubber, the production requirements were so great that the Government built a plant at Memphis, Tenn., that produces 12,000 tons of furfural a year and uses 100,000 tons of cottonseed hulls or corncobs as raw material.

Although cottonseed hulls were available to the Memphis plant and oat hulls to the Cedar Rapids plant, the value of these raw materials during the war for augmenting the supply of scarce livestock feeds caused attention to be turned to cobs, since cobs had long been known as a good source of furfural. Vast quantities of cobs, therefore, ground to pass a 1-mesh screen, were bought by both furfural plants.

The prospects are bright for an expanding market for furfural. Many large chemical companies here and in other countries have carried on extensive research to find new uses for it. We, too, have been actively engaged in such research since the founding of the Regional Laboratories. It is now known that many new and important uses are possible. For example, fibers like nylon can be made from chemicals prepared from furfural.

More than 100 years ago chemists learned that when starch or cellulose was treated with sulfuric acid under right conditions glucose, also known as corn sugar, resulted. The sugar, glucose, is the raw material used in the fermentation process for making alcohol. In the present process for making furfural the cellulose of the hulls and cobs is destroyed and appears in the residue. We believed that if the right conditions could be found, it should be possible to produce furfural from corncobs on the one hand and glucose on the other, both from the same material and at the same time. The smaller amount of residue resulting should be just as valuable as the present furfural residue.

Our research confirmed this idea, with the result that this laboratory has been able to develop a process that gives promise of producing both furfural and glucose at lower costs than was possible before. We are now studying this process in a semicommercial plant at the Northern Laboratory, built under a special appropriation by Congress for the production of synthetic liquid fuels from nonpetroleum sources. If our expectations can be realized, a greatly expanded market not only for corncobs but also for other agricultural residues such as peanut shells, rice hulls, cottonseed hulls, flax shives, and the like will exist.

Although thousands of bushels of ear corn are ground whole and fed to cattle with good success, ground cobs have not been considered desirable for addition to mixed feeds. Indeed, many States prohibit such use in commercially prepared feeds. During the time of feed shortage, however, cobs ground to pass a one-eighth screen were moving in carload quantities into this market. Cobs may have some value, also, in feeds of high molasses content, but they contain very little protein and their vitamin content is very low.

Corncob processing will be found to be just like any other business— markets must be established, and sales and managerial ability will be even more important than ability to process the product. Careful investigation should be completed before investments in processing plants are made. Cob prices, it should be realized, can never be high but a small return to the farm per ton will result in a good percentage return on net farm income. A market should be found for all fractions resulting in cob grinding. Furfural plants can use any of the fractions, coarse or fine. With the start made, and with intelligent effort, there should be an industrial market for cobs and hulls, whether we consider the raw material either in its physical or its chemical composition.

THE AUTHOR

Elbert C. Lathrop, chemical engineer in the Bureau of Agricultural and Industrial Chemistry, organized and has directed the research work of the Agricultural Residues Division at the Northern Regional Research Laboratory since 1939. From 1909 to 1918 he did research on soil fertility in the Bureau of Plant Industry, was with E. I. du Pont de Nemours and Co., in the development of the dye industry from 1918 to 1922, and was director of research and later vice president of The Celotex Corporation for some 12 years. He was technical director of the Crown-Zellerbach Corporation from 1934 to 1938. Dr. Lathrop was awarded the Edward Longstreth medal by the Franklin Institute in 1912.

Uses for Vegetable Wastes

by J. J. WILLAMAN and R. K. ESKEW

VEGETABLES are important but wasteful. Twenty-odd kinds of plants are commonly grown for vegetables in the United States. In every State they are grown commercially; the highest concentrations are in California, New York, Texas, and Wisconsin; returns from them to growers approach 300 million dollars a year. But not more than 20 to 30 percent of the crop is eaten.

The waste portions—4 million tons of them—are mostly leaves. Some wastes are left on the ground to be plowed under; some are fed; some are discarded in dumps; some are a plain nuisance; a tiny fraction is artificially dried for feed. The most conspicuous constituent of the wastes is water—about 75 to 90 percent.

One of the tasks assigned to the Eastern Regional Research Laboratory was to find further uses for vegetable crops. We found out soon enough that if any of these widely scattered, widely diverse wastes were to be utilized industrially certain conditions had to be met. The materials must contain some valuable constituents. For most uses they must be dried, partly for preservation, partly to cut down transportation costs. They must occur abundantly in a restricted area, to minimize hauling to the drier or other processing unit. A succession of wastes must be available, in order to keep a drier occupied for as long a season as possible. Two of the requisites—the chemical composition and the preparation of dried material—are technical questions, and we have directed our attention mostly to them. The others are questions of economics and have to be answered mainly by the person who is considering the exact location of a plant to use the wastes.

Because leaves are the manufacturing parts of the plant, we would expect them to be high in valuable constituents. And they are: Meal

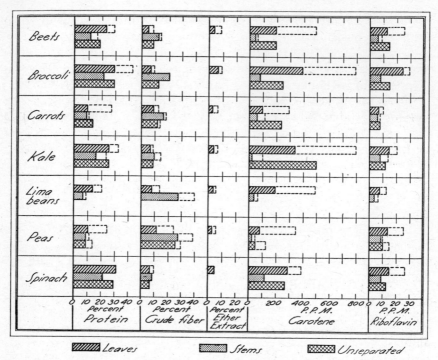

This chart gives a general idea of the composition of various vegetable leaf wastes, on a moisture-free basis. Broccoli and spinach rank high in protein.

from alfalfa leaves is more nutritious than meal from alfalfa stems; grass leaves are highly nutritious. We therefore looked to leafy wastes as the most promising materials for study and were ultimately rewarded by being able to produce leaf meals of good quality, with high protein, high carotene, fairly high fat, and low crude-fiber contents.

At first, the leaf blades, midribs, stems, pods, and other tissues were separated by hand for chemical analysis. When it became obvious that the leaf blades were the important portion, a special drying technique and mechanical separation were devised for recovering them.

The leaf meals commonly have a protein content of 25 percent or more. Broccoli actually has reached 44 percent, which approaches that of oilseed meals. A few scattered analyses of other leaf meals show 30 percent for celery, 27 for collards, 27 for rhubarb, and 32 for rutabagas.

Carotene, a yellow pigment that becomes vitamin A in the body, is abundant in green leaves, but is low in the less green stems. The carotene content of all these vegetable leaf meals compares favorably with that of alfalfa; in fact, considering the nature of the leaf meal and its other nutritive constituents, a carotene content of 830 International units per gram (500 parts per million in the accompanying chart) compares favorably with a fish-liver oil standardized at 4,000 I. U. And a riboflavin content of 20 parts per million is appreciable in comparison with 25 in skim-milk powder, a product used largely as a source of that vitamin.

Considering all three of these nutrients, the vegetable leaf meals show very good analyses for feed value. As one truck grower put it, "I am wondering if we humans aren't eating the wrong parts of the plants."

There is considerable range in the content of a substance in any one kind of vegetable. Most of the data we have are for vegetables grown along the Middle Atlantic seaboard. Samples from other regions might be different. In fact, the highest protein found in carrot leaves was in samples from the Florida Everglades. Dead leaves accompanying the waste reduce the values. We have noticed year-to-year variations. Within the same year, broccoli has shown a peak in protein and in carotene in August.

The proof of the pudding is in the eating. Do feeding trials confirm the chemical analyses of these leaf meals? They do, within the limits of some experiments with poultry at the Delaware Agricultural Experiment Station and at a commercial poultry farm.

A preliminary investigation on the use of dried vegetable wastes was made by substituting dried pea vine, lima bean vine, turnip, broccoli, and carrot leaf meals for the 8-percent alfalfa leaf meal in a practical all-mash broiler ration. None of the wastes had harmful effects on the birds, growth was best with broccoli and carrot diets, and feed efficiency and pigmentation were best with broccoli and turnip. Furthermore, the chicks liked the new leaf meals better than they did alfalfa.

The carotene in 3 percent of broccoli leaf meal gave as much growth as an equivalent amount of vitamin A in fish-liver oil. The broccoli imparted a deep-yellow color to shanks and skin, giving the birds a good market appearance. Although a level of 1 percent supplied sufficient vitamin A, it had to be supplemented with a little riboflavin for maximum growth.

Pea vines are abundant in several sections of the country and are already collected at the viners in great piles. Because of difficulty in obtaining a true leaf meal from them, their analyzed nutrients are lower than in other wastes, and are about equal to those of alfalfa leaf meal. In a feeding trial with chicks, the pea-vine meal was about equal to alfalfa; it was inferior one year and superior the next.

Spinach, rhubarb, and beet leaves contain appreciable amounts of oxalic acid. This acid is usually frowned on, because it may sequester calcium in feed. In actual trials with chicks, however, at levels at 2.5 to 3.8 percent of the normal basic ration, just as good growth was obtained as with 5-percent alfalfa or pea vines.

Kale and lima bean leaf meals have also been used in chick mashes with complete success.

In laying trials involving about 800 birds, 2.5 percent of broccoli leaf meal alone was substituted for the 5 percent of alfalfa leaf meal and 0.5 percent of fish-liver oil in the controls. Slightly higher egg production was obtained with the broccoli mash over a 3-month period. In hatching experiments, nearly equal hatches were obtained when 2.5 percent of broccoli and 0.5 percent of fish-liver oil were substituted for 5 percent of alfalfa and 1 percent of fish-liver oil.

We can conclude, then, that these leaf meals are satisfactory supplements to chicken feed, whether for growing, laying, or hatching. They have not been tried on other poultry or on other farm animals.

The Drying Process

Obviously the first thing to be done in preparing a leaf meal is to dry the leaves. In the method of fractional drying developed at the Eastern Regional Research Laboratory, in Philadelphia, the thin and more valuable leaf-blade portion dries much more rapidly than the thicker and less valuable midribs and stems. To take advantage of these factors, the leaves are dried rapidly to the point where the blades are brittle but the stems and midribs are still tough. The material is immediately fed into a hammer mill having no screen. This breaks the brittle leaves loose from the stems. The two fractions are then separated in a current of air adjusted to blow the leaf fraction away from the heavier stems. The process is about 95 percent efficient. The wet stems can be discarded, or they can be crushed and dried separately to give a less valuable product.

In final pilot-plant studies a triple-belt, continuous drier was used. In it the air is circulated at high velocity downward through each belt individually. It is equipped for control of wet- and dry-bulb temperature, air velocity, and percentage of air recirculated. Experiments showed the following conditions to be best for this type of drier: Inlet air temperature of 240° F., rapid circulation of air through the bed of material at a rate of 175 cubic feet a minute per square foot of bed, a light loading on the first belt and heavier loading on the successive belts, and agitation of the material as it falls from one belt to the next to break up any lumps. The permissible load on the first belt varies with the kind of waste.

The actual size of the drier required would naturally depend on the quantities of waste available and hourly capacities desired, but for the purpose of general discussion and comparison of capacities for different wastes, a drier having a total drying area of 930 square feet has been selected. It would have an hourly production rate of from 300 to 1,200 pounds of dry, separated leaf meal, depending upon the waste being processed. With a belt 8½ feet wide, a three-belt multiple-deck drier with this drying area would be approximately 40 feet long. A hammer mill that could handle approximately 1 ton an hour would take care of the drier output. The material then goes to an air separator consisting of a fan and large diameter pipes so arranged that the leaf fractions are discharged at the top through a cyclone separator and the stems come out at the bottom. The cleaned leaf material is then ground in a hammer mill to produce the final meal.

Waste lettuce, citrus pulp, and tomato skins and seeds are now being artificially dried for feed. In the Everglades section of Florida, where a large variety of vegetable materials are grown over a long season, utilization of waste for feeds is proving practical. Drying equipment is already installed for preparing feeds from sweetpotato vine (sweetpotatoes are grown in large quantities for the production of starch), ramie tops, which are removed before processing the plants for fiber, and a special kind of grass from which lemon oil is distilled. Machine-dried alfalfa is commonplace. Can some of the vegetable wastes we have mentioned join the ranks?

The tonnage of wastes is tremendous. Some are already accumulated in great quantities at viners and packing sheds; others could easily be harvested mechanically, as is now done with sugar-beet leaves. Their seasonal span is favorable (beginning in June with peas, followed by various vegetables throughout the summer, lima beans in September, and broccoli in October and November). A highly nutritious leaf meal can be prepared from a number of them; they are relished and well utilized by poultry, at least. The mechanics of the drying and separating have been worked out. The over-all cost of the final leaf meal will vary with the different materials from $22 to $95 a ton.

The commercial feasibility of the proposition depends largely on two questions: Can exact locations be found where sufficient wastes are readily available for a sufficient number of successive weeks to keep the operating costs to a minimum? And will the consumer pay for the real worth of these meals, considering at least their content of protein, carotene, and riboflavin? We believe the answer to both questions is yes.

THE AUTHORS

J. J. Willaman is head of the biochemical division of the Eastern Regional Research Laboratory, Philadelphia, Pa.

R. K. Eskew is head of the chemical engineering and development division of the Eastern Regional Research Laboratory, Philadelphia.

FOR FURTHER READING

Charley, Vernon L. S., Hopkins, D. P., and Pollard, A.: *The Utilization of Surplus Carrots,* Fruit Products Journal, volume 23, pages 180–183, 1944.

Tomhave, A. E., Hoffman, Edmund, Kelley, Edward G., and others: *A Preliminary Investigation on the Use of Certain Dried Vegetable Wastes as Poultry Feeds,* Delaware Agricultural Experiment Station Bulletin 247, 1944.

Starch From Wheat

by CECIL T. LANGFORD and CARL E. RIST

STARCH is one of the most imporant industrial commodities derived from agricultural crops. Just before the war the annual domestic production was nearly 4 billion pounds. More than 98 percent of it was produced from corn, and only about 1 percent from wheat. The almost complete reliance on corn as a raw material has been due to the normally higher price of wheat as compared with corn. Another factor is the good return of oil as a byproduct from the milling of corn for starch.

Shortly after we entered the war, when large quantities of corn were being diverted to livestock production and industrial alcohol, it became apparent that a starch shortage would ensue. Because of the scarcity of cane and beet sugar, it was also evident that the production of corn sugar and sirup would be inadequate to meet the increasing demand for sweetening agents.

Accordingly, investigations were undertaken at the Northern Regional Research Laboratory in Peoria, Ill., for working out new processes whereby starch could be produced from wheat and wheat flour, both of which were plentiful then. There were two necessary restrictions: The processes should require a minimum of equipment for new installation, and, if possible, they should be adaptable to existing available plants. As a result of the work, two processes were developed for producing wheat starch for conversion into sirup, sugar, or industrial alcohol.

The use of wheat flour as a raw material for the production of starch had several advantages. The ample flour-milling capacity available permitted the use of existing equipment to remove more than 25 percent of the starch-poor constituents in the form of bran and other feed products. This initial purification saved the installation expense of hard-to-get new equipment in starch-processing plants. A rather ample supply of clear grade flour also was available, a byproduct of milling wheat for other products. The two major constituents of wheat flour are starch and gluten. Accepting wheat flour as a raw material, the problem was to develop a process that would give a separation of the two in relatively pure form.

Starch and Gluten From Wheat Flour

A successful process was developed at the Northern Regional Research Laboratory that required no extensive installation of equipment. It was called the batter process because it involved mixing flour and water to give an elastic but free-flowing batter. The basic principle involved is readily understood by anyone who has chewed wheat grain. Slow mastication leaves in the mouth a gummy, chewy mass of gluten—a farm-made chewing gum of years past.

One part of flour and about one and one-fourth parts of warm water (depending on the type of flour and gluten content) are mixed. The batter, after thorough mixing for 10 to 20 minutes, should be quite smooth and free of lumps. Compared with the usual pancake batter, this is a stiff batter because it contains about one-third less water.

In the next step the batter is mechanically broken up in the presence of about 2¾ parts of cold water. The starch is quickly and almost completely washed out of the batter, and the gluten is left suspended in the slurry of starch and water in the form of lumps or curds. The gluten is separated by allowing the whole slurry to be drained or pumped onto a vibrating screen that has 60 to 80 meshes to the inch. The lumps of gluten collect into larger masses on the screen and fall off the end. The starch and the water that contains other flour solubles pass through the screen. The suspension of starch in water is usually called starch milk.

This starch milk, containing some fine fiber, soluble protein, and a small amount of fine gluten particles, may be used directly for fermentation into industrial alcohol. Without further purification, the starch milk may also be converted into glucose sirup or dextrose by being cooked in the presence of hydrochloric acid. The sirup and sugar produced by the use of the starch milk as it comes through the screen will not be of the highest quality. Unless extra-large quantities of decolorizing agents are used, the sirup and sugar will be slightly dark in color. Also, the protein contained in the sirup will cause it to become cloudy on long standing. To make the best refined sirup and sugar, the starch has to be purified by removing the protein and impurities in the starch milk.

Prime-quality starch is obtained by allowing the starch to settle out on starch tables. In large-scale practice, the tables are long troughs about 2 feet wide and 90 to 120 feet long. They are set on an inclined base, dropping about 5 inches from the head to the tail end. The settled starch is flushed off the tables by strong streams of water, collected in tanks, and finally filtered. Besides being used to prepare refined sirup and dextrose sugar, the purified starch may be dried and used for numerous other purposes. Sirup may also be made by the action of malt on either the crude-starch milk or the purified starch. The resulting product is either crude or refined malt sirup, depending on the purity of the raw material.

The crude gluten passing over the end of the mechanical screen contains 72 to 75 percent protein and about 20 percent starch on the dry basis. When this first crude gluten is washed again in fresh water, the protein content is easily raised to about 85 percent, and the starch content is reduced to about 10 percent on a moisture-free basis. Gluten containing up to 95 percent protein can be prepared by repeated washings in water.

When it is dried at a low temperature, the gluten is called "undevitalized," or natural-gum gluten. This dried product, when water is added, reverts to the natural gumlike gluten and is, therefore, suitable for fortifying low-protein flour for bread making or use in other food products. Gluten dried at temperatures substantially higher than 112° F. yields a product that does not become gummy upon the addition of water. Such a product is suitable for raising the protein content of foods in which the properties of an "undevitalized" gluten are not needed or wanted. Devitalized gluten is also useful for making high-protein stock feed and industrial products.

The chief industrial use of wheat gluten now is as a raw material for making monosodium glutamate. Heating the wheat gluten with strong hydrochloric acid breaks down the proteins into amino acids. Glutamic acid is recovered from the mixture of amino acids by crystallization and then converted into the monosodium salt, a product that gives a meatlike flavor to foods.

The batter process can be applied to flours from practically all types of wheat except those whose protein content is less than 7 to 8 percent. Its advantages lie in the speed and simplicity of operation, the fact that no chemicals are required, and the practically complete recovery of the wheat gluten in an undevitalized state. The process is especially valuable for making non-highly-refined glucose sirup because there is no loss of dry substance. Typical yields from 100 pounds of dry wheat flour containing 12 percent protein are 100 to 104 pounds of glucose sirup and 12 pounds of dry gluten having a protein content of 80 to 85 percent.

Many commercial organizations have tested the batter process on a pilot-plant scale; several have installed equipment to produce sweetening agents, industrial alcohol, and wheat gluten. Recent annual-production rates have been: Dextrose sugar and glucose sirup, 150 to 200 million pounds; devitalized wheat gluten, 20 to 30 million pounds; and several million gallons of industrial alcohol. The production varies because some producers depend upon alternate sources of raw material for starch.

The process developed at the laboratory for producing wheat starch from the whole wheat kernel is analogous to that used in the wet milling of corn. Indeed, with only minor alterations in equipment and operating procedure the process can be conducted in corn wet-milling plants. The starch obtained from sound wheat is of excellent quality. It may be converted to sirups and sugar by the same methods used in the conversion of cornstarch. Good starch can be extracted from damaged wheat that otherwise is unsuitable for use as food or feed.

The wheat is steeped in water that contains sulfur dioxide. This steep water, maintained at a temperature of 100° F., is circulated over the wheat for about 15 hours. Corn, on the other hand, is steeped at a temperature of 130° F. for about 40 hours. The lower temperature for wheat is necessary in order to avoid any gelatinization of the starch, but even at the low temperature the grain is softened sufficiently in a much shorter time. At the end of the steeping period the steep water is allowed to drain from the grain. It contains soluble materials that have been extracted from the wheat and is concentrated in a multiple-effect evaporator. The resulting sirup is used later in preparing a byproduct cattle feed.

The steeped wheat is ground in a buhrstone mill with water, which serves as a lubricant. In the pilot plant the slurry from the buhrstone mill is screened over a 26-mesh stainless-steel wire gauze to remove coarse fibers; the material that passes through is screened over No. 17 standard silk bolting cloth to remove the fine fibers. The fiber fractions are washed twice in order to remove additional starch. The washings are combined with the suspension of starch and gluten that passed through the screens, and the combined liquor is known as mill starch. Both fiber fractions are utilized in the preparation of feed. As the process has been conducted in two corn wet-milling plants, the ground wheat has been passed through the regular mill-house equipment for the production of coarse fibers, fine fibers, and mill starch. The coarse fibers are squeezed in a mechanical press to reduce their moisture content to 74 percent, and the slurry of fine fibers is filtered through a filter press to give a cake containing 72 percent water.

The mill starch is a suspension of starch and gluten in water. The starch is heavier than the gluten and to separate them the slurry is allowed to flow over starch tables. The pitch of the table and the rate at which the mill starch flows over it are such that the bulk of the starch settles out and practically all of the gluten is carried over the end of the table in suspension. The starch is flushed from the table with water, and the resulting slurry is screened through No. 17 standard silk bolting cloth to remove small quantities of fiber and foreign material. The slurry is then filtered, and the starch is washed two or three times with fresh water. If the starch is to be marketed as such, it is dried; but this is unnecessary if it is to be converted into sirup or sugar.

The gluten slurry that flows over the end of the table is allowed to settle and the clear supernatant liquid is drawn off. Part of the clear liquor is used in preparing steep water for processing fresh grain, and the remainder is used as process water for washing the fiber fractions. The thick gluten slurry is centrifuged to recover the suspended gluten for use in preparing feed; and the clear liquor is used as process water. The sirup produced by evaporating the steep water is combined with the fiber fractions and the gluten, and the mixture is dried for the production of a byproduct feed of excellent quality.

In this process no attempt is made to recover the wheat germ. In the wet milling of corn the steeped grain is degerminated and the germ is processed for corn oil. Wheat contains less than half as much oil as does corn and a much smaller proportion of the wheat oil is concentrated in the germ. The small size of the wheat germ makes its separation from the ground grain very difficult. For these reasons it does not seem practical to recover the wheat germ. During the milling operations the bulk of the wheat oil stays with the gluten and some of it remains in the fibers, but fortunately it does not contaminate the starch. Except for minor losses, all of the oil appears in the byproduct feed.

The starch produced by this process is of excellent quality; on the average it contains 0.25 percent protein, whereas cornstarch contains 0.35 percent. From a 60-pound bushel of soft winter wheat containing 60 percent starch, the yield of commercial starch, containing 12 percent moisture, amounts to 33 pounds. In the wet milling of corn, the yield of commercial starch averages 34 pounds per 56-pound bushel. In the wet milling of wheat the yield of commercial feed, containing 12 percent moisture, is approximately 22 pounds per 60-pound bushel; that in the commercial wet milling of corn averages 16.7 pounds per 56-pound bushel. This type of feed has sold for about 2 cents a pound.

In the Corn Belt, where the price of wheat exceeds that of corn, the wet milling of wheat has been conducted only during periods of acute shortages of cash corn. In the summer of 1945 a corn wet-milling company processed approximately 2 million bushels of wheat for the production of glucose sirup. Careful study of both processes revealed that only minor changes are required in plant equipment and operating methods in order to utilize wheat in a corn wet-milling plant. The objection to the change arises from the fact that the capacity of the plant is greatly reduced. In order to obtain wheat starch of high quality it is necessary that the density of the mill starch to the tables should not be greater than 6° Baumé. The volumetric rate of feed to a given table is the same in both instances; hence the table capacity in a corn wet-milling plant will be reduced by approximately 50 percent. Because the quantity of wheat that can be processed in such a plant is limited by the tables available, the remaining equipment will not be used to full capacity. If a plant were being designed specifically for the utilization of wheat the condition obviously would not obtain.

Both processes that have been described contributed materially to our war effort, and undoubtedly their use will continue in suitably located plants. The batter process appears to be ideally adaptable as an adjunct to beet-sugar factories. The wet-milling process will probably continue to be used in areas where the price of wheat is normally less than that of corn.

Advantageous use of the batter process can be made in beet-sugar factories and sugar refineries to produce starch for conversion into sweetening agents. At such sites equipment is available for processing the saccharified starch liquor into sirup or sugar. Because beet-sugar factories operate on a seasonal basis, the production of sweetening agents from starch could be carried out during the off season. Such a scheme would keep the plants and labor force occupied throughout the year. Some installations of the process have been made in beet-sugar factories.

In the Pacific Northwest, where the price of soft white wheat is relatively low and, in normal times, is invariably lower than that of corn at Chicago, the wet-milling process appears to be economically feasible. For a small plant with a capacity of 10,000 bushels a day, the total cost of processing is estimated to be 23 cents a bushel. Assuming a price of $1 a bushel for soft wheat, the cost of raw material and processing amounts to $1.23. With no credit for oil, the only byproduct credit is that for feed, amounting to 44 cents a bushel. Thus the net production cost for 33 pounds of marketable starch is 79 cents or an average cost of 2.39 cents a pound. That figure probably exceeds the production cost of cornstarch, but it is much lower than the 1947 market price of wheat starch and is considerably less than the market price of cornstarch.

THE AUTHORS

Cecil T. Langford is head of the Engineering and Development Division of the Northern Regional Research Laboratory, Peoria, Ill., one of the laboratories of the Bureau of Agricultural and Industrial Chemistry. His work is concerned with the development, on a pilot-plant scale, of processes that show industrial possibilities after the fundamental research has been concluded in other divisions of the laboratory. Dr. Langford holds degrees from the University of Oklahoma and the University of California.

Carl E. Rist is acting head of the Starch and Dextrose Division of the Northern Regional Research Laboratory. He joined the Department in 1929 as a member of the Fixed Nitrogen Research Laboratory. His work involves the development of processes for the production of starch and sirups and the development of industrial products derived from starch and dextrose.

Paper From Flax

by ARTHUR C. DILLMAN

TEN YEARS AGO cigarette paper, made chiefly from linen rags, was imported from Europe. Now it is made from American flax straw. On the day that the Second World War broke out, the first commercial roll of cigarette paper made entirely from flax straw came off a machine at Pisgah National Forest in North Carolina. Now it is turned out at the rate of 50 or 60 tons a day, more than enough to make the 250 billion cigarettes smoked each year in the United States. Besides supplying domestic requirements, American cigarette paper is shipped to nearly every tobacco-consuming country in the world.

The successful development of this new industry was almost entirely the work of private industry. For more than 50 years, beginning in the eighteen nineties, experiments had been conducted by Federal, State, and commercial organizations to use the fiber in flax straw. In the experiments, work was done on the production of thread for spinning, sacking cord, binder twine, counter board, boxboard, writing paper, and other products. The research gave valuable information but generally the processes developed were expensive or not adapted to commercial use. Before we started making fine paper from it, the main industrial uses of fiber from flax straw were upholstery tow, insulating board, boxboard, counter board, rugs, and coarse cloth. Probably not more than 25,000 tons of flax tow were used annually for those products—equivalent to about 125,000 tons of flax straw.

L. F. Dixon, of Pisgah forest, estimated that the quantity of processed flax straw converted to industrial use, chiefly for making cigarette paper, was 5,200 tons in 1937; 147,200 tons in 1940; and 360,000 tons in 1945.

The principal types of paper made from the fiber of flax straw include cigarette paper, carbon paper, condenser paper used in electrical con-

750

densers, high-grade letter paper for air-mail correspondence, and thin book paper. For all these uses, a thin, strong paper is required. Flax fiber is reported to be one of the strongest and most durable fibers known. As for durability, consider the linen wrappings of ancient Egyptian mummies. Currency and bank-note paper is made from the better grades of fiber-flax tow; it contains about 80 percent flax fiber and 20 percent cotton.

Flax straw is a variable product. The yield and quality of its fiber appears to depend on seasonal growing conditions, the variety of flax grown, the rate of seeding, the time and method of harvesting, and on the amount of exposure or weathering of the straw after harvest.

The fiber content of flax stems ranges from about 14 to 20 percent in different varieties. Moreover, there is a marked difference in the amount of fiber that can be recovered by mechanical methods from different varieties. This varies also with the weather, or growing conditions of the crop. The dry, overripe straw produced under conditions of drought is of little value for fiber.

The yield of flax straw as usually harvested and threshed on farms in Minnesota is 1,000 to 1,500 pounds an acre. In experimental plots, where flax is pulled and all of the straw is recovered, yields at the rate of 1,200 to 3,000 pounds an acre are obtained. The possible or potential yield of straw from seed flax, therefore, compares rather favorably with that of fiber flax. As usually harvested, one-fourth or more of the straw is left in the field as stubble.

About 80 percent of the flax tow used in the manufacture of cigarette paper is produced in Minnesota, some 10 percent in California, and the remainder in North Dakota, South Dakota, and Iowa. Tow mills are located at Red Lake Falls, Crookston, Marshall, Minneapolis, Le Roy, and Winona, Minn., and at El Centro, Calif. Besides the fiber produced in tow mills, much straw is processed by means of portable decorticating machines which move from farm to farm.

These decorticating machines are in fact tow mills on wheels. The straw is carried between fluted steel rollers under pressure by coil springs. The rollers, meshing like gear teeth, break the inner woody portion of the stems, separating it more or less from the outer bark or fiber tissue. Beaters and other devices help to separate the wood or shives, while controlled air suction removes chaff, leaves, shives, and dirt. This operation reduces the bulk or weight of the original straw about one-half. This effects a considerable saving in the cost of baling, trucking, and freight.

The making of cigarette paper begins in the pulp mill, a huge, spherical, revolving cooker or digester, where steam and chemical reagents separate the usable fiber from the remaining shives or woody material of the tow. The pulp is washed thoroughly to remove the woody material, bleached with chlorine, and then beaten and cut into a finely divided mass of fiber. In the final beating process, powdered chalk is added to control the speed of burning in the final product. In a cigarette the paper must burn at the same rate as the tobacco.

To a novice, the Fourdrinier paper machine, which makes paper in an endless web and was developed in England at the beginning of the nineteenth century, is something strange and wonderful. The liquid pulp material for cigarette paper flows, like milk, from the headbox onto a moving fine-mesh screen. The excess water drips through the screen; the wet paper film is picked up on a roller, passed over heated rolls, then through drying chambers, and finally it comes out as a continuous sheet of paper. In this journey from screen to roll, the paper travels some 100 feet in about 5 minutes. All moving parts of the machine must work with clock-like accuracy or the paper would be either torn or crumpled. The large rolls are finally cut in strips and wound on bobbins.

At present there is a well-established market for flax-straw fiber for the manufacture of special papers. It seems likely that the demand for flax straw will continue as long as suitable straw is available at a price the industry can afford to pay. Since 1939 the price of flax straw on the farm has gone up from about $1 to $2.50 a ton. The cost of baling, trucking, and shipment brings the cost up to $10 to $15 a ton at the tow mill. If the farmer is equipped to bale his straw and truck it to the tow mill or shipping point, he can get this additional income for his labor.

There are still many problems to be solved in the economical production and handling of flax straw as a source of fiber for paper making. The technical problems of paper manufacture have been overcome. The future of the industrial use of flax straw is likely to depend on the supply and quality of the raw material.

THE AUTHOR

Arthur C. Dillman, Minnesota-born, grew up on a farm in South Dakota and took his college work at State College in Brookings, S. Dak. He entered the Department of Agriculture in 1908, and carried on research work in plant physiology and the breeding of drought-resistant forage crops for the northern Great Plains until 1921, when he was transferred to the Division of Cereal Crops and Diseases, in charge of flax investigations. In his work on the improvement of seed flax (linseed) he has worked closely with the several State and Canadian experiment stations and with the linseed industry and the manufacturers of cigarette papers. At the beginning of the cigarette-paper industry, he suggested the use of a portable "flax break" or decorticating machine to process flax straw on the farm, thus effecting savings in the cost of shipping the bulky straw to tow mills. On October 1, 1946, Mr. Dillman took up new work as an agronomist with the Flax Development Committee, of the Flax Institute of the United States, with headquarters in Minneapolis.

FOR FURTHER READING

Emley, Warren E., Compiler: *Flax and Its Products, Production and Utilization,* U. S. National Bureau of Standards, 1942.

Robinson, B. B.: *Flax-Fiber Production,* U. S. D. A. Farmers' Bulletin 1728, 1940.

What We Eat, and Why

by ESTHER F. PHIPARD

WHAT PEOPLE eat at any time depends on three things—what they like, what is available, and what they can afford. The relative importance of these is not always the same. During the war and early postwar years, what was available came first, and likes came last for a substantial part of the world's population. People have had to accept what they could get, whether or not they liked it.

As far back as we can remember, however, we have taken for granted that our town and city markets would have a great variety of foods and that everyone could choose freely among them and buy as much as desired as long as he had the money. The war changed that. Customary foods were not available in the quantities necessary to satisfy demand. Rationing and standing in line and the disappearance of many favorite foods came to determine what people ate. After the early postwar period, likes and ability to pay played a more important role.

Patterns of eating were not always as they are at present, nor are they uniform throughout the country. Food habits are the result of many factors including experience, availability of foods, and purchasing power. A brief backward look helps to illustrate the point and to indicate some of the forces that make for change.

Food habits may be deeply rooted in the nationality, religious customs, and cultural background of forebears. Early settlers lived close to the land and learned fairly soon to adapt their food habits to the foods they could grow or procure locally. Later, large numbers of families from various countries settled in groups in the larger towns and cities. These communities had their own restaurants, bakeries, and grocery stores where they could obtain the customary foods of the old country. Thus food habits of other countries were perpetuated in the United States. In parts of the

How much food is available for each person each year in the United States?
Here are the estimated figures for selected years from 1910 to 1945

Year	Milk, and milk equivalent of cream, cheese	Eggs	Meat, poultry, fish	Fats and oils, including butter, bacon, salt pork	Dry beans, peas, nuts	Potatoes, sweetpotatoes	Citrus fruit, tomatoes	Leafy, green, and yellow vegetables	Other vegetables and fruit	Grain products	Sugars, sirups
	Qt.	*Doz.*	*Lb.*	*Lb.*	*Lb.*	*Lb.*	*Lb.*	*Lb.*	*Lb.*	*Lb.*	*Lb.*
1910	160	25	157	59	12	209	44	74	205	306	89
1915	169	25	143	62	12	194	51	75	224	279	90
1920	187	24	144	57	13	166	54	88	225	249	102
1925	193	26	147	65	16	160	59	82	211	233	118
1930	199	27	137	67	16	146	60	88	216	226	124
1935	198	22	128	60	18	159	77	97	215	195	108
1940	215	26	148	71	19	139	95	103	226	192	107
1945	257	31	157	60	20	142	116	133	237	203	91

country distinct regional food habits also developed. These were related
to the kinds of foods that could be produced in the area, facilities for
storing, preserving, transporting and marketing foods, and the general
level of purchasing power.

Little by little, through the process of mixing and blending, food patterns of different nationality and regional groups have become more alike.
People move around more, meeting new people, eating new foods, and
finding old foods in new dishes.

Food has done more and better traveling, to large cities and smaller
places alike. Refrigerator cars, fast motor freight, and improvements
in processing and marketing have contributed to the amazing variety of
foods offered for sale the year around. Agricultural sciences have played
a part with improved varieties and quality of food. Modern education
in foods and nutrition has had a part in changing demand. Even before
the war people were becoming more conscious of the effect of food on
health; and during the war education about nutrition was extended
widely. School lunches and factory lunchrooms were expanded and
proved, when well planned, to be effective in improving food habits.

What We Have Been Eating

One of the best ways of studying trends in American food consumption
is through figures on food supplies. For many years the Bureau of Agricultural Economics has estimated the quantities of food going to consumers. The estimates take into account production, imports, exports,

stocks on hand, and foods consumed on farms where they are produced. Total quantities of food for domestic consumption in a given year are divided by the total population to give per capita averages. For the war years, only civilian supplies and civilian population figures were used. Estimates of per capita consumption are then adjusted for losses that occur up to the point at which consumers buy their food.

A series of such estimates for the years 1909 through 1945 gives an excellent picture of the changes in over-all food consumption that have occurred in the past 37 years in this country.

As a Nation we have been eating less and less of some kinds of foods and more of others. Consumption of grain products, for example, has fallen markedly throughout the period. In fact, in the years 1941 to 1945, the amount used was about one-third less than during the period 1909 to 1913, a difference of about 100 pounds a person a year.

The consumption of potatoes, too, has declined. The general trend fluctuates from year to year, but it is unmistakable. From 1941 to 1945 civilians ate only about three-fourths as many potatoes as they did from 1909 to 1913.

Grain products and potatoes are important sources of calories, and it is natural to wonder what foods have replaced them. Actually there has been an increased consumption of several types of foods.

One of the most marked and significant changes has been the increase in the use of milk. The general trend has been upward since 1909—the beginning of the series. But since 1934 the increase has been continuous, with an especially rapid rise during the war years. As a result, average consumption of milk and its products (except butter) was 45 percent greater from 1941 to 1945 than from 1909 to 1913. In 1945 we used about 90 quarts a year more than in 1909. At the 1945 level, consumption averaged nearly three cups a day per person. This includes the milk used in bread and other bakery products, in candy and other foods, as well as the milk equivalent (on the basis of protein and mineral content) of cheese and ice cream.

The consumption of tomatoes and citrus fruit, important sources of ascorbic acid, increased gradually since 1909, but in the past 10 years the rise has been spectacular. In 1945 the average civilian consumed 116 pounds, compared to about 45 pounds in 1909.

A large part of this increase has been in citrus fruit, a result of improved market supplies at relatively lower prices than 20 or 30 years ago. There was a time when for many people oranges were a special treat for the Thanksgiving fruit bowl and the toe of the Christmas stocking. Today they are a daily food for millions of Americans during a large part of the year and there are ample supplies of canned citrus juices of good quality at reasonable prices.

Tomatoes have always been a stand-by. They are easy to grow, easy to

Our diet has changed considerably since 1910. Here is the average daily nutrient content of the per capita food supply for selected years from 1910 to 1945

Year	Food energy	Protein	Fat	Calcium	Iron	Vitamin A value	Thiamine	Riboflavin	Niacin	Ascorbic acid
	Calories	Grams	Grams	Grams	Milligrams	I. U.	Milligrams	Milligrams	Milligrams	Milligrams
1910....	3,520	99	124	0.75	15.2	7,500	1.74	1.73	17.6	104
1915....	3,440	95	126	.77	14.4	7,500	1.68	1.73	16.7	105
1920....	3,350	93	125	.84	14.6	8,000	1.63	1.79	16.1	108
1925....	3,460	93	135	.85	14.1	7,100	1.62	1.83	16.3	103
1930....	3,460	91	134	.87	14.0	7,600	1.63	1.83	15.4	101
1935....	3,170	85	125	.87	13.5	8,200	1.47	1.78	14.9	115
1940....	3,350	93	142	.93	13.9	8,200	1.69	1.93	16.4	120
1945....	3,330	100	137	1.09	18.6	9,700	2.19	2.52	21.3	140

can, and rural families have come to rely on them. City people, too, use tomatoes in considerable quantity, because they lend variety to meals and, in cans at least, they have been relatively cheap. Canned tomato juice, which came on the market about 1930, rapidly became a favorite and has contributed to the increase in consumption of tomatoes.

Leafy, green, and yellow vegetables form another group that has gained importance in our national diet. From 1909 to 1913, annual consumption averaged about 74 pounds a person. Twenty years later it had increased to about 90 pounds. From 1941 to 1945 we had 121 pounds for each person, or nearly 65 percent more than the consumption from 1909 to 1913. Of the foods in this group, cabbage is consumed in largest quantity, but the increases that occurred were in the use of other vegetables, especially carrots, lettuce, and other salad greens. The increase in the use of canned products was greater than that of fresh vegetables. Green and yellow vegetables are good sources of vitamin A and as a group contribute important amounts of ascorbic acid. Nutritionists have been urging people to eat more of these foods—perhaps one of the reasons why consumption has increased.

There has been an upward trend in the consumption of dry beans and peas and units, including peanut products. The average quantity used in 1945 was about 20 pounds a person, as compared to 12 pounds in the early years of this series.

Americans like sweets, and use a large amount of sugar in soft drinks, candy, canned fruit, ice cream, ready-baked goods, and in many other ways at home. From 1942 to 1945, sugar consumption was limited by supply, but the lowest figure for any one of these years, 91 pounds in 1945, is about the same as the average for the first 10 years of this series— 1909 through 1918. An increase is expected when supplies are more abundant again.

For other groups of foods no consistent trend in consumption since

1909 is apparent. Consumption of meat tended to go down from 1909 to the late 1930's. It rose sharply, however, during the recent war years, when average incomes were high, evidence that many persons had not been consuming all the meat they wanted. But the consumption of fats and oils (including bacon and salt pork) has risen, at least until wartime shortages limited supplies. The consumption of eggs has fluctuated between 22 and 28 dozen per person a year, except in 1945, when it rose to 31 dozen.

What These Changes Mean for Nutrition

From the nutritional point of view, it is important that figures on food consumption be translated into terms of calories, protein, minerals, and vitamins. The figures indicate the extent to which available food supplies, if equitably distributed, would provide for the nutritional needs of the population. They show how shifts in consumption have altered the nutritive value of the national diet over the years.

Calories.—There has been little change in the calories provided by the per capita food supply between 1909 and 1945, except that during the depression years in the 1930's calorie averages were rather low. The lowest figure, 3,170 calories for each person a day, occurred in 1935. At that time the purchasing power of many families was low and the drought of 1934 brought smaller supplies of some foods. But even this level is higher than the prewar consumption in most countries.

All foods contribute some calories to the diet. Therefore a study of the proportion of the total calories coming from different groups of food is one way of seeing the effect of shifts in consumption over a period of years. The upward trends in consumption of milk, of citrus fruit and tomatoes, and of green and yellow vegetables are reflected in their contribution of calories. Likewise the downward trends in consumption of grain products and of potatoes are clearly apparent.

Protein.—The amount of protein in the per capita food supply declined slightly from 1909 to the middle 1930's, a result of lowered consumption of grain products and meats. Since 1935, the year of the lowest average, the protein content of the diet has increased because of higher consumption of milk, of meat, poultry and fish, and of dry beans, peas, and nuts.

Fat.—The amount of fat, visible plus invisible, in the over-all food supply has been increasing, partly because of larger supplies of fats as such and partly because of increased consumption of milk.

Calcium.—Probably the most striking trend in the nutritive value of the national diet is the increase in calcium that has occurred during the 37 years of this series—1909 to 1945. This trend parallels closely the increase in milk consumption, since from two-thirds to three-fourths of the calcium in the diet has come from milk. For no other food is there so

Of the total calories in the food supply, we now get a larger share than formerly
from milk, eggs, fruits, and vegetables, but less from grain products and potatoes

Year	Milk, cream, cheese	Eggs	Meat, poultry, fish	Fats, oils	Dry beans, peas, nuts	Potatoes, sweetpo- tatoes	Citrus fruit, toma- toes	Leafy, green, and yellow vegetables	Other vegetables and fruit	Grain products	Sugars, sirups
	Per-cent	Per-cent	Per-cent	Per-cent	Per-cent	Per-cent	Per-cent	Per-cent	Per-cent	Per-cent	Per-cent
1910	8. 5	1. 8	11. 0	16. 0	1. 5	5. 6	0. 5	0. 7	3. 6	38. 7	12. 0
1915	9. 3	1. 9	10. 5	17. 4	1. 6	5. 3	. 6	. 7	4. 2	35. 9	12. 4
1920	10. 5	1. 9	10. 7	16. 5	1. 9	4. 8	. 6	. 9	4. 5	32. 9	14. 4
1925	10. 4	1. 9	10. 7	18. 4	2. 1	4. 3	. 7	. 8	4. 0	29. 9	16. 4
1930	10. 6	2. 0	10. 1	18. 9	2. 2	4. 0	. 7	. 9	4. 0	29. 0	17. 3
1935	11. 3	1. 9	9. 9	18. 8	2. 7	4. 8	. 9	1. 0	4. 4	27. 3	16. 4
1940	11. 6	2. 0	11. 2	20. 7	2. 8	3. 9	1. 1	1. 1	4. 3	25. 4	15. 3
1945	14. 1	2. 5	11. 4	17. 7	2. 9	4. 0	1. 5	1. 4	4. 4	26. 9	12. 7

direct a relationship between its consumption and the average quantity
of a single nutrient in our diet.

Iron.—Trends in the iron content of the national diet reflect changes
in consumption of grain products and meats, which together furnish
nearly half of the total iron. Because the consumption of both of these
groups declined between 1909 and 1935, per capita supplies of iron
decreased also. There was little change during the 1930's, but a marked
increase occurred after 1941 when meat consumption went up, and
especially after flour and bread began to be enriched with iron and some
of the vitamins.

Thiamine (Vitamin B₁).—Nearly a third of the thiamine in the food
supply comes from meat. Pork is an especially rich source. Trends in the
thiamine content of the diet follow very closely the trends in meat consumption. Whole-grain cereals are excellent sources of thiamine but most
of the grains used in this country during the period were highly refined.
Therefore, this food group contributed only about a fourth or less of the
total thiamine. The enrichment of flour and bread introduced during the
war had by 1944 brought up the thiamine contribution from grain
products to about a third of the total. As a result of this program the
average thiamine content of the per capita food supply in 1943, 1944,
and 1945 is estimated to be about one-fourth higher than it would have
been without enrichment.

Riboflavin (Vitamin G).—This vitamin is often too low in American
diets. Nearly half of the total quantity in the food supply comes from
milk and from 15 to 20 percent from the meat, poultry, and fish group.
The average amount of riboflavin in the diet showed little change between

1909 and 1939 or 1940 when the gradual increase in milk consumption was partly offset by a decline in meat. Between 1940 and 1945, however, the riboflavin in the diet increased almost one-third following the rapid rise in milk consumption, the enrichment of grain products, and some increase in meat consumption.

Niacin.—The amounts of niacin available for consumption throughout the years of this study have followed the same trend as protein, iron, and thiamine. Since nearly half of the total comes from meat, the average quantities decreased from 1909 to the late 1930's; they increased during the war years because of greater supplies of meat, poultry, and fish and the enrichment of grain products.

Vitamin A value.—The increase in consumption of green and yellow vegetables is one reason for the larger amounts of vitamin A available, especially from 1941 to 1945. More whole milk, also a source of vitamin A, was consumed and victory gardens supplemented market supplies of vegetables.

Ascorbic acid (Vitamin C).—Nearly all the ascorbic acid in the diet comes from vegetables and fruit. Therefore, any changes in consumption of these foods are reflected in ascorbic acid values. From 1909 to the middle 1930's, there was a slow upward trend in vitamin C values. From then on, however, the increase was spectacular. A large part of this increase came from the larger quantities of citrus fruit and tomatoes; part of it came also from green and yellow vegetables.

How Good Is Our Diet? Is It Improving?

These trends in the nutrient content of the food supply from 1909 to 1945 show that the national diet has improved in nutritional quality. In fact, during the war years the levels of nearly all nutrients studied have been higher than at any time during the series. This is partly the result of relatively high purchasing power, together with large supplies of essential foods. Also, the enrichment of flour and bread has made important contributions of iron, thiamine, riboflavin, and niacin.

The quantities of the several nutrients in the wartime food supply were sufficiently high to provide every person in the country a nutritionally good diet if the nutrients had been distributed exactly in accordance with need. Unfortunately this is not the case. Dietary studies have shown that large numbers of people have less than they need of one or more nutrients. Others have liberal margins over and above what are considered adequate allowances. If diets now unsatisfactory could be brought up to recommended nutritional levels, average nutritive values for the country as a whole would need to be even higher than they now are.

The extent to which further nutritional improvement can be expected will depend for one thing on future shifts in consumption. For example, when grain products and potatoes, good sources of several nutrients, are replaced by foods giving chiefly calories (sugars and fats), the nutritional quality of the diet is impaired. If, however, some of the calories are replaced by good nutritional investments such as milk and fruits and vegetables, there may be a net gain in the quality of the diet. Consumer demand for various foods will in turn be affected by such factors as income, relative price levels, education, and further improvements in production and marketing.

Programs for better distribution of food to low-income groups, to children, and others with special food needs offer a means of improving the national diet. Still another possibility lies in improving the nutritional quality of foods themselves, through plant breeding, and through greater conservation of naturally occurring nutrients in the utilization of foods.

————————

THE AUTHOR

Esther F. Phipard, a food economist in the Bureau of Human Nutrition and Home Economics, has for the past 10 years been finding out about American diets—what kinds and quantities of foods are consumed by different groups of families and how good their diets are nutritionally. She is coauthor of four Department bulletins reporting these studies. More recently Dr. Phipard served with a group of nutrition specialists assisting the Food and Agriculture Organization in analyzing food supply data for different countries.

FOR FURTHER READING

Bureau of Human Nutrition and Home Economics: *Family Food Consumption in the United States,* U. S. D. A. Miscellaneous Publication 550, 1944.

Bureau of Human Nutrition and Home Economics: *Tables of Food Composition in Terms of Eleven Nutrients,* U. S. D. A. Miscellaneous Publication 572, 1945.

Clark, Faith, Friend, Berta, and Burk, Marguerite C.: *Nutritive Value of the Per Capita Food Supply, 1909–45,* U. S. D. A. Miscellaneous Publication 616, 1947.

Cochrane, Willard W.: *High-Level Food Consumption in the United States,* U. S. D. A. Miscellaneous Publication 581, 1945.

Stiebeling, Hazel K., and Phipard, Esther F.: *Diets of Families of Employed Wage Earners and Clerical Workers in Cities,* U. S. D. A. Circular 507, 1939.

Stiebeling, Hazel K., Monroe, Day, Coons, Callie M., and others: *Family Food Consumption and Dietary Levels, Five Regions,* Farm Series, U. S. D. A. Miscellanous Publication 405, 1941.

Stiebeling, Hazel K., Monroe, Day, Phipard, Esther F., and others: *Family Food Consumption and Dietary Levels, Five Regions,* Urban and Village Series, U. S. D. A. Miscellaneous Publication 452, 1941.

Protein Is Essential to Life

by D. BREESE JONES

MORE THAN a hundred years ago a Dutch chemist named Mulder was studying the chemical composition of "silk gelatin" and egg white. He observed that they were largely composed of a material that is widely distributed in plant and animal tissues. He concluded that this substance is fundamental to all plant and animal life, and named it "protein," from the Greek word "to take the first place."

Protein is the essential constituent of all living cells. Without it life cannot exist. Most of the tissues of the body are made up largely of protein material. No other substance can take its place. The human body is about 18 percent protein.

Protein is needed to supply material for building body tissues and to furnish particular amino acids that are needed for the construction of many of the hormones and enzymes. These substances are secreted in the body in comparatively small quantities, each one performing a specific task in regulating the many physiological activities upon which life and health depend.

Pepsin, trypsin, and other enzymes that are necessary for the digestion of food protein in the alimentary tract are of a protein nature. Insulin, a hormone secreted by the pancreas gland, controls the level of sugar in the blood. It is composed of nine amino acids. Thyroxine, an amino acid containing iodine, is secreted by the thyroid gland. A deficiency of thyroxine is associated with goiter, and retarded mental and physical development. Adrenaline, a product of the adrenal glands, profoundly affects the blood pressure. Glutathione, composed of cystine, glycine, and glutamic acid, is essential for controlling the body's chemical reactions that depend on oxidation and reduction.

The nitrogenous constituents of foods consist chiefly of protein, combined or associated with other material such as fat and carbohydrate. Protein rarely occurs in a pure or free state. Chemically, protein is one of the most complex of all organic substances. With few exceptions, proteins are composed almost entirely of the elements, carbon, hydrogen, nitrogen, oxygen, and sulfur. Some contain small quantities of phosphorus and other elements. Proteins are characterized primarily by their nitrogen content. Most proteins, particularly those of animal origin, contain about 16 percent of nitrogen, a few as high as 18 percent.

The term "protein," used as a class name to distinguish it from other substances, does not signify an individual compound. In fact, an innumerable number of proteins may contain the same elements in the same percentages and still differ radically in their chemical, physical, and physiological properties. Because of differences in the pattern of their chemical structure, some proteins and protein-like material behave as agents of destruction to health and life itself. They are generally referred to as toxalbumins; among them are ricin (the albumin of the castor-bean), the venom of certain reptiles and insects, and bacterial toxins.

Our interest in proteins increased markedly shortly before we entered the war. All of us knew there would be a much heavier demand for protein foods, particularly those of animal origin—meat, milk, and eggs— and that a lower production in war-devastated lands would probably cause a world shortage. The situation emphasized the need of developing as quickly as possible more information on proteins that would help meet some of the anticipated problems.

Amino Acids

Investigations in Federal and State agencies, educational institutions, and industrial laboratories made many valuable contributions to that end. Our knowledge of the composition and properties of proteins was extended. New methods for determining the quantities of amino acids in foods were perfected; they are a way of evaluating the nutritive value and supplementary relationships of their proteins. We found out much more about the relative nutritive values of plant and animal proteins, and how they best can be used in combinations and help conserve the scarcer and more expensive protein foods. Scientists demonstrated the variations in the requirements of different species of animals for individual amino acids, and proved that too little protein in the diet means lowered resistance to infections. A lack of certain amino acids in the diet of experimental animals was found to lead to specific physiological injury. More information was obtained on the effect of heat, during commercial processing of foods, on the nutritional properties of their proteins.

Proteins can be discussed only in the light of the amino acids of which they are composed. The nutritive value of proteins, their chemical and physical properties, their relation to health and disease, their effective use in therapy, their commercial applications, all depend on the kind and proportions of the amino acids they contain.

We know that most food proteins are made up of 18 different amino acids combined in different order and manner. Eight of these are nutritionally essential for our well-being: Isoleucine, leucine, lysine, methionine, phenylalanine, threonine, tryptophane, and valine.

The other ten are: Alanine, arginine, aspartic acid, cystine, glutamic acid, glycine, histidine, proline, serine, and tyrosine.

Other amino acids present in some proteins are hydroxyproline, norleucine, and thyroxine. Others have been reported, but not confirmed.

During digestion in the alimentary tract, proteins are broken down into their constituent amino acids, which are then assimiliated and recombined to form new proteins needed for the growth of body tissues and for the formation of compounds essential for various body requirements.

The animal body cannot make all the amino acids it needs. It can produce some of them, but the others must be supplied by the proteins in food. Each of the large number of different proteins that enter into the composition of tissue cells requires a different, but a very definite, assortment of amino acids. A lack of any one that is essential for the formation of any particular protein constitutes a missing link in the chain. That protein cannot be synthesized, no matter how great a surplus there may be of the other amino acids.

The amino acids that cannot be manufactured within the body but must be supplied by the food are generally termed "nutritionally essential." This expression, however, does not imply that the other amino acids are of negligible importance. They are also "building blocks" of tissue proteins, and are necessary, whether or not they are supplied in the diet or whether they have to be manufactured within the body.

Experiments first conducted with young rats showed that ten of the amino acids are indispensable constituents of their diet: Arginine, histidine, lysine, leucine, isoleucine, methionine, phenylalanine, threonine, tryptophane, and valine. Nine are necessary for growth and maintenance. The tenth, arginine, is not necessary for satisfactory growth, but is required for maximum increases in weight. These ten were therefore classed as nutritionally essential.

But later we found that the needs for amino acids vary with different species. Adult humans need neither arginine nor histidine for nitrogen equilibrium. Scientists, therefore, now generally believe that only eight amino acids are nutritionally essential for man. Glycine, an amino acid that is not essential for the rat, is indispensable for young chicks, otherwise they are subject to poor growth, weakness, and imperfect feather formation. Further investigations will probably reveal other such variations. Little is known about the requirements of the larger farm animals.

Poor growth is not the only noticeable result of a lack of amino acids in the diet of young animals. A lack of certain ones may lead to very specific consequences. Investigators report that a deficiency of tryptophane causes lesions in the eyes and the development of cataracts.

Recently, two new amino acids have been discovered. Lanthionine, which contains sulfur, was obtained from acid hydrolysates of proteins that had been first subjected to mild alkali treatment. Lanthionine is not believed to be a naturally occurring amino acid constituent of proteins, but is derived from cystine in the protein by action of dilute alkali. It was isolated in two forms, one of which is capable of replacing cystine and methionine in the diet of animals. Another amino acid, containing sulfur and selenium, was isolated as a naturally occurring constitutent of a plant grown on soil containing selenium. Plants and grains grown in certain areas where the soil contains selenium are known to have toxic properties, and have caused great losses to feeders of farm animals.

Great progress has been made in developing new methods for determining the amounts of amino acids in proteins. At first long and complicated processes were used. The protein was broken down into its amino-acid constituents by boiling with strong mineral acids. From the mixture thus obtained, most of the amino acids were separated, crystallized, and finally weighed in pure form. The entire procedure required many weeks; the final values in most cases were far too low; unavoidable losses occurred during their separation and purification. A number of highly accurate and rapid methods are now available.

One of the newest is called the microbiological method. It involves the use of certain bacterial organisms that require culture media containing specific amino acids for their maximum growth. Their rate of growth in media containing definitely known quantities of protein hydrolysates is used as a basis for estimating the amount of the amino acid sought in the protein analyzed.

Microbiological methods have been developed for estimating a number of the amino acids which seem to be as accurate as those obtained by chemical methods. The equipment required is found in most laboratories. Assays can be made on extremely small samples of material. The methods are applicable both to isolated proteins and staple foods, and can be carried out in much shorter time than by chemical methods.

Protein Hydrolysates

Commercial products commonly referred to as protein hydrolysates are now available. They are prepared by hydrolyzing proteins with acids or by digestion with enzymes. They are, in fact, predigested proteins and consist chiefly of amino acids. These products have been found valuable for supplying amino acids for the use of patients who cannot take ordinary food in the normal way. Protein hydrolysates are used orally in a dry form or in solutions carefully prepared for parenteral administration.

Preparations for oral use are on the market under several trade names. They may be used directly or in cereals, sandwich spreads, milk, and other foods. Their use makes possible, when needed, a much greater intake of amino acids than can be supplied by the daily amount of protein food in the regular diet.

Parenteral injection of solutions of protein hydrolysates is of great value in cases of shock, extreme weakness, starvation, extensive losses of body nitrogen resulting from severe burns, and extensive loss of blood. There seems to be little advantage, however, in using protein hydrolysates for normally healthy persons, because the proteins in the diet are digested in the alimentary tract and yield the same amino acids as the hydrolysates supply.

Supplementary Relationships of Proteins

Several important foods contain proteins that are deficient in one or more of the nutritionally essential amino acids. When one of these foods constitutes the only source of protein in the diet, malnutrition inevitably results. It does not follow, however, that such foods may not have an important place in the diet as a source of protein, but they should not be relied upon as its only source.

When supplemented by certain other protein foods, even in relatively small proportions, they can satisfactorily constitute a large proportion of the daily protein requirement. The following are well known examples of some proteins of important foods that are deficient or lacking in one or more of the essential amino acids. Gliadin, one of the two chief proteins of wheat, is deficient in lysine. Zein of corn contains no tryptophane, and it is low in lysine. Phaseolin, of the common white navy bean, requires the addition of methionine or cystine in order to make it adequate to support satisfactory growth in young animals. Gelatine, a classic example of an incomplete protein, is deficient in valine, isoleucine, histidine, and other amino acids. Young animals fed deficient proteins as the only source of it will not grow unless the missing amino acids are supplied.

But most of the naturally occurring protein foods contain more than one kind of protein, each of which may have a different assortment of amino acids occurring in varying proportions. An amino acid deficiency in any one of the proteins may, therefore, be largely or entirely compensated by the other proteins present. Wheat, for instance, contains other proteins than gliadin, namely gluten and the proteins of the bran and germ. These proteins largely compensate for the amino acid deficiency of gliadin. Similarly, the low content of lysine and tryptophane in the zein of corn is corrected to a large extent by the other proteins present in the

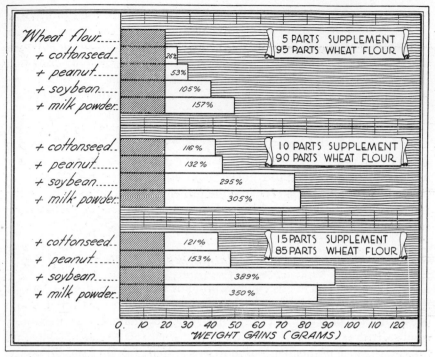

Small proportions of oil seed proteins, or milk, combined with patent wheat flour, greatly enhance the value of the flour. The unshaded sections of the bars give the weight gains of young rats in 6 weeks. The diets contained 9 percent protein.

seed. Conarachin in the peanut supplies methionine, a small amount of which is contained in arachin.

The proteins of soybean, peanut, and cottonseed flours are excellent supplements for correcting the amino acid deficiencies of patent wheat flour. Mixtures produced by adding as little as 5 parts of soybean, peanut, or cottonseed flours to 95 parts of wheat flour contain 16 to 19 percent more protein than the wheat flour alone, and have a definitely greater growth-promoting value of the protein.

When mixed with wheat flour in the proportions of 5 to 95 parts, soybean flour has a higher supplementary value than peanut or cottonseed flour, but is inferior to that of skim-milk powder. In a mixture of 10 parts of the supplement and 90 parts of wheat flour, soybean flour has practically the same supplementary value as skim-milk powder; animals grow four times faster on it than on wheat flour alone. A mixture consisting of 15 parts of soybean flour and 85 parts of wheat flour has been found to have a nutritional value exceeding that obtained with a mixture of skim-milk powder and wheat flour in the same proportions.

Available data leave little doubt that the relatively high lysine content of the oilseed proteins is the amino acid that is outstandingly effective in making up for its deficiency in wheat flour. The oilseeds also contain relatively larger proportions of valine and tryptophane than wheat flour.

When they are supplemented with small proportions of the oilseed proteins, the cereal grains could be utilized as an important source of nutritionally adequate protein at a relatively low cost.

Nutritive Value of Some Plant Proteins

When we saw that the animal proteins would be scarce, we set about getting more information on the nutritional value of plant proteins. Before the war, people in the United States got most of their protein from animal sources; in a land of plenty, with an abundance of meat, milk, and eggs, little thought had been given to the use of plant proteins.

There are several farm products that offer fine possibilities for supplying plant proteins for human use but that have been used chiefly as feed for farm animals. These include soybeans, peanuts, cottonseed, and wheat and corn germs, the potential production of which is very great. Heat-processed soybean flour and soybean grits are being produced for human consumption in large quantities. Peanut and cottonseed flours in limited amounts are also available. Most of the oil is first removed from the seeds by expression or by solvent extraction. The flours prepared from the residues contain from 45 to 50 percent of high-quality protein, a content exceeded by only very few other foods.

Soybeans have been used for centuries in the Orient as a source of protein in human diets. Until recently the small amount grown in the United States was used chiefly for oil. The byproduct, the press cake, has been highly regarded as feed for farm animals. But the war stimulated the growing of soybeans, and commercial methods were developed to produce soybean foods for human use. Large quantities of soybean flour and grits were shipped overseas for our armed forces, and for lend-lease supplies. Larger amounts were also consumed in the United States.

Dry, mature soybeans are one of the richest known sources of protein among naturally occurring foods, containing from 30 to 45 percent of protein, depending on variety, soil, and climatic conditions.

Three types of soybean flour are manufactured, low-fat, medium-fat, and full-fat. The low-fat flour is produced by solvent extraction, which removes practically all of the oil. It contains about 45 percent of protein. The medium-fat flour is made from the residue remaining after most of the oil has been removed by expression. It retains from 5 to 6 percent of oil and contains about 43 percent protein. The full-fat flour has all the oil of the seed and contains about 40 percent protein. All of the flours are subjected to heat processing.

It is characteristic of soybean protein that it requires heat treatment in the presence of water or steam in order to develop its maximum nutri-

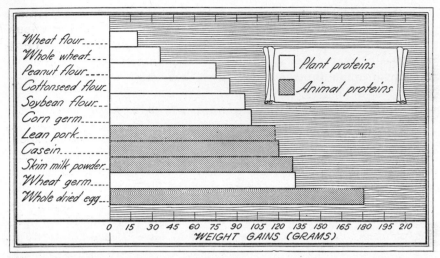

Here is shown the comparative nutritive value of plant and animal proteins. The data are based on 6-week tests on young man. All diets had 10 percent protein.

tional value. In the raw state, its protein has low value. Excessive heating, on the other hand, has an injurious effect. This may develop when the oil is removed by expeller processes. Discrepancies often observed in the protein value of oilseed products may be attributable to the effect of excessive or insufficient heat treatment.

As sources of nutritionally efficient protein, wheat germ and corn germ, particularly the former, stand foremost among plant foods. In a form suitable for human food they offer a relatively cheap source of high-quality protein potentially available in large quantities. The nutritive value of wheat-germ protein in some respects is nearly that of meat and milk.

The potential annual production of wheat germ in the United States is about 500 million pounds. The recent production has been between 30 million and 50 million pounds. Defatted wheat germ, containing 34 percent protein, prepared for human use and having excellent keeping qualities, is available in large quantities.

When fed at a 10-percent-protein level, wheat germ was found as efficient as skim-milk powder. But at higher levels the latter proved superior.

Defatted corn germ is also commercially prepared for human consumption. It contains about 20 percent protein. When fed at 10- and 15-percent-protein levels it gave values equal to, or greater than, that of peanut or soybean protein, but not so high as that of wheat germ.

Peanuts and soybeans, both legumes, have several characteristics in common. They have a high content of protein and oil, but contain insignificant quantities of starch. The protein content of peanut kernels ranges from 28 to 35 percent, but, unlike soybeans, peanuts do not require heat treatment to develop the maximum nutritional value of their proteins. Raw peanuts have essentially the same protein value as when heat processed.

Arachin and conarachin represent almost entirely the total protein content of the peanut. About 75 percent of it consists of arachin. This protein contains only a small amount of methionine, but conarachin has enough of this amino acid to compensate for its deficiency in arachin.

Some peanut flour can be bought in stores in limited amounts, but much more of it might be made and eaten. The flour contains more than 50 percent protein, comparable in nutritive value to that of soybean and cottonseed.

Cottonseed is another source of plant protein that merits particular attention. Cottonseed meal, the ground residue remaining after removal of most of the oil, has long been valued as a protein feed for farm animals. It contains all of the nutritionally essential amino acids and is particularly suitable for supplementing the proteins of cereal grains.

A partially defatted cottonseed flour produced for human consumption is available. Its high protein content, 55 percent, is exceeded by only a few other foods. Large quantities of the flour were shipped overseas during the war; in the United States it is used to a considerable extent in commercial bakery products. In digestibility, cottonseed protein compares favorably with animal products, and its growth-promoting value is about four and a half times that of wheat flour. But in order to be safe and suitable for use as food, cottonseed flour must be thoroughly processed.

THE AUTHOR

D. Breese Jones, as principal chemist in the Bureau of Human Nutrition and Home Economics, is in charge of the Bureau's investigations on proteins and amino acids. He has conducted research in the fields of proteins and nutrition for the Department since 1915 and, together with his associates, has published more than 200 articles. In 1938 he represented the Department at the Sixteenth International Physiological Congress in Zurich, Switzerland.

FOR FURTHER READING

Jones, D. B., and Widness, K.: *The Comparative Growth-Promoting Value of the Proteins of Wheat Germ, Corn Germ, and of Some Other Protein Foods of Plant and Animal Origin*, Journal of Nutrition, volume 31, pages 675–683, 1946.

Jones, D. B., and Divine, J. P.: *The Protein Nutritional Value of Soybean, Peanut, and Cottonseed Flours and Their Value as Supplements to Wheat Flour*, Journal of Nutrition, volume 28, pages 41–49, 1944.

Jones, D. B., and Horn, M. J.: *A Rapid Colorimetric Method for the Determination of Tryptophane in Proteins and Foods*, Journal of Biological Chemistry, volume 157, pages 153–160, 1945.

Sherman, Henry C.: *Principles of Nutrition and Nutritive Value of Food*, U. S. D. A. Miscellaneous Publication 546, 1944.

Known Nutrients in Milk

by C. A. CARY and A. M. HARTMAN

As CONSUMERS, we are interested in three practical problems in connection with a food. If, say, each of us consumes a quart of milk a day or 18 pounds of butter a year, as we did before the war, it is essential to know what nutrients and how much of each we actually obtain from these foods. It is essential also to know whether there are any precautions that we might take to preserve the nutrients in those foods or anything that can be done practically in their production to improve their nutritive value. And, thirdly, since there is certainly no reason to believe that we know all the nutrients in our foods and feeds or that we can live and thrive on a diet containing all the nutrients now known, it is essential to appraise the value of these foods as sources of still undiscovered or still unidentified nutrients that may play an important role in determining our welfare. Also, numerous observations indicate that it is hard to appraise fully the nutritive value of milk from information now available of the known nutrients reported to be present in it.

Milk is a rich source of protein; the nutritive value of milk proteins is unexcelled. S. K. Kon, of the National Institute for Research in Dairying, England, says: "The great value of the proteins of milk lies in their ability to enhance the biological value of the proteins of such staple vegetable foods as cereals and potatoes. Thus, for example, a combination of bread and cheese had, when tested on rats, the same biological value, 75.5, as cheese, though bread alone had a value of only 52.0; similarly a combination of milk and potato had a biological value of 86, almost as high as that of milk, 87, though potato alone had a value of only 71."

Similar results have been obtained with a mixture of corn and milk proteins, and results have been published that indicate a good utilization of the mixture of proteins in bread-and-milk. This is because milk proteins are rich in some of the essential amino acids that are relatively not so plentiful in many plant proteins.

Vitamin A Potency of Butter and Milk

Vitamin A itself is a product made only in animals, but animals can make it only from certain precursors, the carotenes, which are produced by plants. The green and leafy portions of plants are good sources of these precursors, as are also carrots and sweetpotatoes. We may eat some of these plant materials and make our own vitamin A, or we may eat animal products that contain ready-made vitamin A—milk, butter, cheese, egg yolk, fish oils, and others. In milk and milk products some still unchanged carotene and ready-made vitamin A occur together, about 85 to 95 percent of the natural yellow color of butter being due to the unchanged carotene, which is itself yellow and which we can use to make vitamin A. Each natural food or feed that we depend upon as a source of vitamin A varies greatly—sometimes severalfold—in its vitamin A value, or potency, depending in the case of plant foods or feeds on how they have been produced, harvested, or preserved, and in the case of animal products on how the animal was fed. Fortunately, animals, to a certain extent, have the capacity to accommodate themselves to variations in their intake of this vitamin or its precursor; they store it when it is plentiful in the diet, and use these reserves when the vitamin A value of the food is below current needs.

Because of the importance of vitamin A in nutrition, a knowledge of its potency—and the conditions that influence this potency—is exceedingly important in the case of any food that is widely depended upon as a source of this nutrient.

Before the war, the people of the United States consumed on an average about 18 pounds of butter per capita a year, and the domestic consumption of milk in all forms was about 1.05 quarts per person a day. In a period of food shortages, when one food might be substituted for another or when we might be asked to reduce consumption as far as possible without sacrifice of health, precise information regarding food values is imperative. The Committee on Food and Nutrition (now the Food and Nutrition Board) of the National Research Council recognized this condition in 1941. At their suggestion, and in cooperation with the Department and the Association of Land-Grant Colleges and Universities, 21 State agricultural experiment stations and one Federal laboratory undertook to determine the average vitamin A potency of the butter consumed in the United States, and the variation in that potency from month to month or from season to season during the year in different parts of the country.

Sixteen State experiment stations (Minnesota, Wisconsin, Ohio, Iowa, Nebraska, Kansas, North Carolina, Louisiana, Mississippi, Washington, Oregon, California, Idaho, Montana, Wyoming, and Arizona) did a thorough job of determining the vitamin A potency of the butter produced in their creameries. These States produce about 64 percent of the creamery butter produced in the United States.

This butter is representative of that produced in the North Central, South Atlantic and Gulf, and Rocky Mountain and Pacific Coast States, or of about 97 percent of the national output. Seven State stations (Wisconsin, Minnesota, Ohio, California, Montana, North Carolina, and Mississippi) have studied the effect on the vitamin A potency of various methods of commercial storage and handling of market butters and four States—Texas (independent of this survey), New York (Cornell), Pennsylvania, and Alabama—have determined the vitamin A potency of the butter sold on their retail markets, including both locally produced and nationally known brands.

The results of the survey (more than 4,000 samples of butter) may be summed up thus:

Except in Arizona and Montana, there was a distinct difference between the vitamin A potency of the creamery butter produced during the winter months and that produced during the summer. Of all the butter produced in the United States, close to 36 percent may be considered "winter" butter with an average vitamin A potency close to 11,000 I. U. per pound; and about 64 percent is summer butter, produced during summer months when cows are on pasture, and has an average vitamin A potency of about 18,000 I. U. a pound. The weighted annual average obtained by using the production in all States (average of 1942 and 1943 productions) in each area and the seasonal distribution of production in the participating States, was found to be 15,700 I. U. a pound, which is as close as it is now possible to approximate the average vitamin A potency of the total output of creamery butter in this country.

In the study of the effect of the storage and handling of butter on its vitamin A potency, samples were handled and stored under conditions identical with those used in practice. The results indicate that both carotene and vitamin A are very stable in butter under the conditions tested; that little if any loss of vitamin A potency occurs during the periods that commercial butter is ordinarily stored; and that, insofar as the effect of storage is concerned, one would expect the average vitamin A potency of the butter sold on the retail markets in this country not to be significantly different from the average of the creamery butter produced in the country as a whole. The results of the study of the vitamin A potency of market butters confirmed this conclusion.

On the basis of the above results, one can calculate the average vitamin

A potency of the milk produced in the United States. Winter milk—i. e., milk produced by cows on barn rations—would accordingly have an average vitamin A potency of 1,120 I. U. per quart; and summer milk—or milk produced by cows on pasture—an average potency of about 1,820 I. U. per quart. These calculations are based on milk with a fat content of 4 percent. It is estimated that about 60 percent of the milk consumed as milk or milk products by the people of the United States is summer milk. Thus the average vitamin A potency of milk, containing 4 percent of fat, consumed annually in this country is about 1,540 I. U. per quart; approximately one-third of the 5,000 units of vitamin A recommended by the National Research Council as the daily allowance for a normal adult is supplied by milk and milk products.

Vitamin D in Milk and Butter

A large number of studies have been made of the natural vitamin D content of milk. The factors affecting this content are reviewed by K. G. Weckel of the University of Wisconsin. In a study at the Michigan Agricultural Experiment Station, H. E. Bechtel and C. A. Hoppert found the vitamin D content of Guernsey milk to vary from 4.8 United States Pharmacopoeia units as a minimum during the winter months to 43.8 U. S. P. units a quart during summer months. Holstein milk was found to vary likewise from 3.1 to 27.7 U. S. P. units a quart. The vitamin D in the fat in the milk of both of these breeds varied from 0.11 to 0.9 U. S. P. units per gram. K. M. Henry and Dr. Kon obtained similar results for butterfat; and G. C. Wallis and T. M. Olson at the South Dakota State Agricultural Experiment Station obtained 8 or 9 U. S. P. units per quart for milk produced in November and April, but 32 U. S. P. units per quart for milk produced in July.

Wallis and Olson demonstrated that they could influence the vitamin D content of milk by variations in the vitamin D content of the diet. During stall feeding some of the vitamin D in milk is derived from the hays fed. The vitamin D content of milk has been increased by feeding cows materials rich in vitamin D, such as cod-liver oil, irradiated yeast, and irradiated ergosterol. But studies with irradiated yeast, which has often been fed to improve the vitamin D in milk, indicate that only 2 or 3 percent of the vitamin D fed is recovered in the milk. Increasing the vitamin D content of the feed is, therefore, not an efficient method of improving the vitamin D potency of milk.

Kon and his co-workers demonstrated that the vitamin D potency of milk from cows on winter rations may vary from 8.3 to 26.0 I. U. per kilogram and that from cows on pasture feed may vary from 5.3 to 17.0 I. U. per kilogram, depending in both cases upon whether the cows are kept indoors or are exposed to summer sunlight. They concluded that the vitamin D in summer milk is produced almost exclusively by the insolation of the cow; and efforts have been made to increase the vitamin D content of milk by irradiating the cow artificially with ultraviolet light. But this method also has not turned out to be effective for the purpose; and milk, as produced, is not an important source of vitamin D. Two methods are used commercially to increase the vitamin D content of market milks, namely the addition of vitamin D concentrates directly to the milk, or the direct irradiation of the milk itself with ultraviolet light. The former is now generally used; and most of the "vitamin D milk" on the market contains about 400 United States Pharmacopoeia units to the quart.

Vitamin C in Milk

As a result of the analysis of hundreds of samples of milk in various laboratories, the average vitamin C content of freshly drawn milk has been found to be close to 20 to 25 mg. per liter (approximately 1 quart).

Paul F. Sharp, K. S. Guthrie, and D. B. Hand of Cornell state: "Actually there is, in the milk obtained each year from the cows of the United States, approximately as much vitamin C as is present in our entire citrus crop . . . If the vitamin C which is present in fresh milk were preserved, then 1 quart of milk would be equivalent to the juice of one orange so far as the amount of vitamin C is concerned."

The vitamin C content of fresh milk does not vary materially with the season or the feed, and varies little—but possibly significantly in some cases—with the breed of the cow. But the vitamin C in milk is unstable, urban consumers probably receiving not more than one-half to one-third of that originally present.

Vitamin C as purchased in capsules or tablets is fairly stable, but in milk, in the presence of riboflavin and dissolved oxygen, it is rapidly changed by the action of daylight to a form which, although still active as a source of vitamin C, readily undergoes still further oxidation even in the dark. Thus bottled milk may lose fully half of its vitamin C potency as a result of exposure to sunlight for half an hour.

Dr. Kon, who with M. B. Watson discovered this effect of light on the vitamin C in milk, suggests: "There are two ways of preventing loss of vitamin C from this cause. Exposure to light may be avoided. Cartons, for example, give a good degree of protection. Brown glass bottles would be ideal . . . As oxygen is needed for the reaction its removal from milk abolishes the action of light."

Vitamin C is also destroyed more or less in various methods of pasteurization; but, according to Aubrey P. Stewart, Jr., and Paul F. Sharp, of the Research Laboratory of Golden State Co., Ltd., San Francisco, "The causes for losses of vitamin C are shown to be the result of copper contamination and presence of dissolved oxygen, during pasteurization and especially on holding after pasteurization."

The vitamin C in milk fresh from the udder—that is, that has not been exposed to light—is said not to undergo destruction when pasteurized by holding at 145° to 150° F. for 30 minutes.

Stewart and Sharp recently made a study of the vitamin C content of 364 samples of pasteurized milk (237 in quart cartons and 127 in quart glass bottles) from consumers' homes and retail stores in the metropolitan area around San Francisco and Oakland, Calif. Because much of the milk was delivered during the afternoons, the samples were placed in a refrigerator at 10° C. and analyzed the next morning following the date of delivery. The average total vitamin C content of the samples was 5.8 mg. per liter; 110 samples that were held for another day in a household type of electric refrigerator at approximately 10° and were re-analyzed, showed a loss of 30 percent as a result of this additional day's storage.

Stewart and Sharp also determined the vitamin C content of 12 major brands (25 samples) of evaporated milk purchased in the retail stores of San Francisco and Oakland. The samples contained an average of 2 mg. of vitamin C per liter of reconstituted evaporated milk. They also analyzed 2,890 samples of spray-process dried whole milk that were only a few days old. These contained an average of 12.5 mg. of vitamin C per 125 g. powdered whole milk—that is, in the amount of powder corresponding to 1 liter of whole milk; and samples of powdered whole milk that were stored at room temperature, air packed, retained 88.7, 85.5, and 79.7 percent of this vitamin C after 3, 6, and 12 months, respectively.

Apparently milk may or may not make a sizable contribution to human requirements for vitamin C, depending upon the conditions under which it is consumed and the way it has been handled or processed. When viewed in the light of the potency of the milk that the cow produces and the work that has been done on the control of factors affecting the loss of vitamin C in milk, one must agree with Sharp, Guthrie, and Hand when they said: "We can agree that the preservation of vitamin C in milk is important from the standpoint of the milk industry and of the nutrition of the nation."

Riboflavin in Milk

Although the vitamin riboflavin is synthesized by micro-organisms in the paunch of the cow, its concentration in milk can be altered somewhat by altering the quantity of it in the feed. The riboflavin content of milk also may vary with the breed of the cow, and has been reported to be influenced by other factors. Reports, therefore, of its concentration in milk show a wide variation, but all of the results agree in indicating that milk is an excellent source of the vitamin. Thus C. A. Elvehjem, in a review on the B vitamins, gives the average riboflavin content of milk as 2 mg. per liter; Sharp and Hand also give 2 mg. per liter, and state that winter milk may be 10 to 20 percent lower than that produced by cows on pasture. Arthur D. Holmes and associates at the Massachusetts station found that there were 1.43 mg. of riboflavin per liter of milk from cows on winter rations, and that there were no immediate increases in this amount when these cows were put to pasture.

Riboflavin is remarkably stable toward heat except in the presence of light. It is not destroyed in the homogenization, pasteurization, or boiling of milk. But, according to Sharp and Hand, "about one-fourth of the riboflavin in a bottle of milk is converted to lumiflavin," which is devoid of vitamin activity, "by exposure to bright sunlight for 1 hour." R. R. Williams and V. H. Cheldelin at the University of Texas demonstrated that as much as 26 percent of the riboflavin in milk may be destroyed by exposure to light for 5 minutes at 100° C.

Walter J. Peterson, F. M. Haig, and A. O. Shaw, at North Carolina State College, exposed fresh samples of milk in pint bottles at temperatures between 60° and 72° F. on sunny days at times between midmorning and midafternoon in direct sunlight on an open porch. The original riboflavin content of the samples varied from 0.83 to 2.60 (average 1.90) mg. per liter. The losses of riboflavin during periods of 30, 90, 120, and 210 minutes were, respectively, 28, 50, 66, and 72 percent. There was no loss of riboflavin in control samples of milk stored in the dark at room temperature for 24 hours, nor when stored for 7 days in a refrigerator; and, when samples that had been exposed to light were placed in the dark in a refrigerator, further loss was extremely small.

Olof E. Stamberg and D. R. Theophilus, at the Idaho Agricultural Experiment Station, made an extensive study of the losses of riboflavin in milk as a result of exposure to light and on methods of preventing this loss. They reported:

"The results of this study show that direct sunlight exposure of milk is very detrimental to the riboflavin content. It is a common practice to deliver milk bottles on doorsteps where they stand fully exposed for long periods. A shady place or lightproof box or cabinet should be provided unless protective types of containers are adopted.

"The results of this work show that as much as 40 percent of the riboflavin in milk was destroyed after 2 hours' exposure to direct sunlight in clear quart bottles even though the milk was quite cool. Good shade, brown glass bottles, or paper containers gave very good protection. One type of paper container was less efficient in this respect than three other types.

"After milk was exposed to sunlight and subsequently stored in the dark in a refrigerator, there was no further loss of riboflavin for the 20 hours investigated.

"Temperature is an important factor, and the photolysis of riboflavin at near freezing temperature was low as compared to near boiling temperature. The photolysis of riboflavin in raw milk was generally greater than in pasteurized milk and least in homogenized milk.

"Milk kept in a store showcase close to a window lost some riboflavin, but there was practically no loss in milk stored in a showcase where most of the light came from low intensity electric lights.

"As much as 11-12 percent of the riboflavin was lost due to daylight when milk was allowed to simmer for 30 minutes in covered glass pan or uncovered aluminum pan in a bright room, but there was practically no loss when a covered aluminum pan was used."

Thiamine and Other B Vitamins in Milk

The thiamine or vitamin B_1 concentration in milk does not appear to be affected by the diet of the cow probably because the vitamin is synthesized in sufficient amounts in the paunch of the cow to supply much of that required for the production of milk. The thiamine content of milk is relatively high early in lactation. Dr. Kon and his coworkers at Reading, for example, found that colostrum contained 0.60 to 1.00 mg. of thiamine per liter; that early milk contained about 0.6 mg., and that milk produced in mid- and late-lactation contained 0.3 to 0.4 mg. per liter. Kon has since given the average thiamine content of milk as 0.36 to 0.45 mg. per liter.

P. B. Pearson and A. L. Darnell of the Texas Agricultural Experiment Station found 0.56 to 0.58 mg. of thiamine per liter in milk produced during the first 9 days of lactation, and 0.38 mg. after the same cows had been in milk for 30 days. They arrive at an average of 0.38 mg. per liter for milks from 25 cows sampled separately after the first 30 days of lactation. Figures outside of these ranges have been obtained by various methods; it seems that an average of 0.4 mg. per liter is probably a fair estimate.

Thiamine is less stable toward heat than riboflavin and some of the other B vitamins, but the amount lost in the pasteurization of milk varies with the method used. Thus, Holmes and co-workers found 9.1 percent and Kon estimates that on an average about 10 percent of the thiamine in milk is destroyed when in pasteurization the milk is held for about 30 minutes at about 145° F.; Holmes found a negligible destruction (2.8 percent) when milk was pasteurized by heating at 161° to 181° F. for 22 seconds.

Nicotinic acid has been found to be synthesized in the paunch of the cow. Various research workers have reported values for the average nicotinic acid content of whole milk which range from 0.6 to 1.1 mg. per liter. Most of the values were obtained microbiologically; quite variable results have been reported by chemical methods—sometimes several times those given above.

A. E. Schaefer, J. M. McKibbin, and Dr. Elvehjem obtained much higher results for the niacin potency of milk, using niacin-deficient dogs. They concluded that a synthesis of niacin must take place either in the alimentary tract or the body tissues of dogs, and that "the effect of the milk must be related to specific precursors of nicotinic acid or to the protein content of the milk."

Subsequent papers have appeared that throw light on this problem, but a full understanding of the significance of these results apparently awaits further work.

Work has been done on the pantothenic acid, pyridoxin, biotin, inositol, choline, and folic acid content of milk. It is interesting to note their presence in this food.

Vitamins A and D occur in the fat of milk and, therefore, the value of skim milk and skim-milk products as sources of these nutrients would be negligible, but neither these vitamins nor riboflavin are destroyed in pasteurization, spray drying, roller drying, or in the making of condensed or evaporated milks. The effect of these processes upon the nutritive value of the protein in milk is generally negligible. Only with thiamine (vitamin B_1) and ascorbic acid are the losses considerable; and, as we have noted, the losses can be largely reduced in some instances by proper methods of processing. There is no evidence that the utilization of the calcium in milk is affected by any of the methods of processing we have mentioned.

THE AUTHORS

C. A. Cary joined the Bureau of Dairy Industry as a chemist in 1917, and engaged in research problems in biochemistry and nutrition. Since 1940 he has been head of the Division of Nutrition and Physiology in the Bureau.

A. M. Hartman, a chemist in the Bureau of Dairy Industry since 1924, is engaged in research problems in biochemistry and nutrition.

FOR FURTHER READING

Biennial Reviews on the Progress of Dairy Science, Section D. Nutritional Value of Milk and Milk Products, in the Journal of Dairy Research, Cambridge University Press (London). (Up to and including 1943 these reviews have been made by Dr. S. K. Kon, Head of Department of Physiology and Biochemistry, National Institute for Research in Dairying, University of Reading at Reading, England.)

ALSO, IN THIS BOOK

Unidentified Nutrients

by C. A. CARY and A. M. HARTMAN

R EMARKABLE progress has been made in identifying the nutrients in our foods and feeds, but results of work in various laboratories indicate that there are still other unidentified constituents in some foods and feeds that may play an important role in nutrition.

Altogether, the findings—with the rat, mouse, dog, monkey, and the human—constitute a body of evidence that should be regarded realistically in considering the question of whether we are well fed.

Here we shall present evidence obtained in the Bureau of Dairy Industry laboratory at Beltsville that we believe demonstrates that:

Milk and certain other foods and feeds contain an unidentified nutrient;

White flour, enriched white flour, whole-wheat flour, yeast, and certain other foods and feeds do not contain this nutrient;

When the young are deprived of this factor and then are fed a diet containing all known nutrients in adequate amounts or a diet containing these nutrients along with white flour, enriched white flour, whole-wheat flour, or yeast, their growth and development is by no means normal and under certain circumstances is impossible, unless they are supplied in some way with this unidentified factor.

The nonfat solids of milk are a good source of protein, calcium, and riboflavin, and contain other salts and known water-soluble vitamins of value in nutrition. These nutrients supplement the foods used as our principal sources of energy, such as bread, butter, oleomargarine, sugar, cereals, and so on. We believe, however, that these foods can be supplemented with all of these nutrients or with all known nutrients and not produce the effect—on growth, for example—that is produced by supplementation with milk itself or with dried skim milk. What we have said here about flours appears to be true of the grains in general; they are deficient in this unidentified nutrient. With livestock, this unidentified nutrient is supplied by roughages and leafy feeds.

In one experiment, we fed rats as much as they would eat of certain rations, as follows:

Group 1. A basal ration containing adequate amounts of all known nutrients;

Groups 2, 3, and 4. The same basal ration, containing 45.5 percent of white flour, enriched white flour, or whole-wheat flour, respectively, in place of carbohydrate;

Groups 5 and 6. The same enriched white flour and whole-wheat flour rations as fed to groups 3 and 4, except that the ration contained 10 percent of dried skim milk.

All of these rations contained amounts of all known nutrients that should be adequate for optimum growth. Nevertheless, the average growths of the rats in groups 1, 2, 3, and 4 were all about the same, and were not much more than half that of their sex-litter mates in groups 5 and 6, which received the dried skim milk. There is no question about the statistical significance of these results; we shall consider their interpretation and significance relative to the nutritive value of milk.

Some workers have reported that their rats do not eat a ration of enriched white flour bread as well as they do a bread made from this flour supplemented with milk solids. It is possible that our basal ration and the rations containing the white flour, enriched white flour, and whole-wheat flour were "unpalatable," and that the addition of the dried skim milk made these rations more "palatable." Unquestionably this was, in a sense, a fact; why then were these rations without the skim-milk powder in them unpalatable to our rats? Was this unpalatability due to some quality of these rations irrespective of the nutrients in them; or was it a response, which is familiar, of animals depleted in respect to some particular nutrient, to a ration deficient in that nutrient? If the latter is the explanation, might it not be possible to change the "palatability" of these rations to our rats, not by altering the rations themselves, but by correcting the nutritional deficiency in the test animals? That we tried to do.

In related experiments we fed 333 pairs of litter-mate male rats and 112 pairs of litter-mate female rats exactly the same basal ration as the one used with the rats previously mentioned. In these experiments one rat in each pair received in addition a few milligrams daily of a liver extract. Here, as before, the rats on the unsupplemented basal ration grew at a rate that was not much more than half of normal. By "normal growth" is meant the growth of our rats that received the basal ration plus an amount of the liver extract adequate for optimum growth. But the feeding of the liver extract, which was given separately from the basal ration, improved the palatability of this ration, increased consumption, and nearly doubled the growth. In fact, it was not even necessary to feed the liver extract to obtain the results; we obtained exactly the same results when the liver extract was injected under the skin or into the muscles of our rats. And the same results were also obtained when, instead of a few milligrams of liver extract, a few micrograms—a few millionths of a gram—of concentrated preparations of the growth-promoting material in these liver extracts were fed daily, separate from the basal ration.

The results show also that the administration of the liver extract separate from our basal ration brought about the same growth as the feeding of dried skim milk incorporated in this ration. It is obvious that the unpalatability of our basal ration can be just as effectively overcome in either of these ways, and that it is due to a nutrient deficiency in the basal ration and in our test animals.

But what nutrient was involved, and why were our test animals deficient?

We stated that the basal ration used in the experiments contained adequate amounts of all known nutrients for normal growth. The statement covers quite a bit of territory. We have found that our basal diet and the wheat-flour diets were deficient in some nutrient that can be supplied in a liver extract or in skim-milk powder. Before concluding that this nutrient actually is some still unidentified factor, let us consider what we mean by "all known nutrients," and how we have arrived at the conclusion that our basal rations is "adequate for normal growth" in respect to these nutrients.

There is nothing unique about the composition of what we have called "our basal ration." It is a ration often used in the biological assay of vitamin A, except that we added vitamin A to it. The minerals in the ration were supplied by a common mineral mixture that unquestionably is adequate; the B vitamins were supplied by 10 percent of yeast. No increase in the quantity or change in the kind of yeast improved the growth of our rats on this ration, and, as a result of many efforts to supplement the ration with various amounts of crystalline or pure vitamins, or to replace the yeast by mixtures of these vitamins, we concluded that our basal ration also supplied adequate amounts of all of the available fat-soluble and water-soluble vitamins—vitamins A, D, E, K, and C (ascorbic acid); choline, thiamine, riboflavin, pyridoxin, pantothenic acid, nicotinic acid, para-aminobenzoic acid, inositol, biotin, folic acid (or pteroylglutamic acid), also xanthopterin.

The protein in our basal ration (25 percent) was comprised of about 5 percent of yeast protein and 20 percent of casein, the principal protein in milk. Both proteins are ordinarily considered complete and the total amount adequate, but the casein we used had been heated for long periods with successive lots of alcohol as had been our custom in removing vitamin A from it. This method of removing the vitamin A was one that was formerly used in vitamin A assay work. Could our handling of this casein have injured its nutritive properties?

This question led to a study of the effect of using, in our basal ration, casein preparations made in various ways. One preparation that was being used in vitamin-assay work in another laboratory, and that had been quite extensively washed with acidulated water and then extracted with alcohol for 24 hours, gave results similar to our casein; one commercial "vitamin free" casein gave hardly significantly better growth than our casein; another commercial "vitamin free" casein, and other caseins prepared by milder treatments with alcohol, or with alcohol and ether, all gave decidedly better growth than our casein.

None of these caseins gave normal growth. But samples of "commercial" caseins that were tested gave almost normal growth, and a casein precipitated from skim milk by an 11-day dialysis against water and another centrifuged out of milk at 50,000 revolutions a minute and repeatedly washed and re-centrifuged, gave fully normal growth.

These results certainly mean either one of two things: That many researches are now being conducted with caseins in which the nutritive value has been impaired by various methods of treatment—in which case our casein would be one that had been the most impaired of any of those tested, or that many researches are being conducted today with caseins containing as an impurity more or less of some unidentified nutrient—in which case our casein would be one of those containing the least amount of this nutrient.

For three reasons, we believe that the latter alternative is correct:

1. Replacing our casein in our basal ration with an equal amount of heat-coagulated egg albumen (with or without a supplement of additional biotin), which would certainly be considered a complete protein and adequate in amount, gave the same growth as our casein.

2. Increasing the protein in our basal ration by increasing the percentage of our casein or of egg albumen, or by increasing the percentage of yeast, or increasing the percentage of protein by feeding soybean oil meal or linseed oil meal in place of carbohydrates, did not improve growth.

3. The work of Prof. W. C. Rose at the University of Illinois shows that the least of any amino acid necessary for the optimum growth of rats is about 20,000 micrograms daily; whereas one concentrated preparation of the growth-promoting nutrient in the liver extracts that we have used brought about optimum growth in daily doses of 20 micrograms, and another was active in daily doses as small as 2 micrograms.

It is evident, therefore, that our basal ration was not deficient in any "known" nutrient; but that this ration—and also our rations containing white flour, enriched white flour, and whole-wheat flour—lacked some still unidentified nutrient that was supplied by the liver extract and the dried skim milk. This unidentified factor is not in yeast; it would not be in white breads made from flours milled in any way or supplemented with all nutrients known to be deficient in white flour or supplemented with all known nutrients.

In our experiment we used flours. Is the unidentified nutrient so stable toward heat that if added to flour it would survive the baking of bread, or must we get this nutrient from products that do not require cooking? It occurs in dried skim milks that have been heated to various extents. Solutions of it, heated at various reactions for 3 hours under a steam pressure of 18 pounds, were still decidedly active, so it is quite stable.

The growths brought about by feeding various amounts of milk produced by cows fed in different ways, by feeding various samples of dried skim milks, and by feeding different kinds of cheese as supplements to our basal ration demonstrated that milk and these milk products are all good sources of the above unidentified factor.

We have not yet made an extensive survey of foods and feeds as sources of this unidentified factor. The results with the ones that we have tested:

Foods and feeds that do not contain the still unidentified factor:	Foods and feeds that do contain the unidentified factor:
White flour.	Milk.
Enriched white flour.	Skim milk (liquid or dried).
Whole-wheat flour.	Cheese (cottage, Swiss, Cheddar).
Yeast (bakers' or brewers').	Liver extracts.
Wheat bran.	Beef muscle.
Corn meal (yellow).	Pork muscle.
Soybean oil meal.	Egg yolk.
Linseed oil meal.	Lettuce.
Egg white (heat-coagulated).	Alfalfa and alfalfa hays.
Carrots.	Timothy hays.
Tomatoes.	Kentucky bluegrass.

The problem of supplementing rations deficient in this unidentified nutrient may therefore exist in the use of grains in general in either human or livestock feeding.

There has been much interest in the effect of the diet of a lactating mother upon the subsequent growth and development of her young.

We have found that our test animals at weaning are so deficient in a still unidentified nutrient that they are unable to grow normally on a diet containing adequate amounts of all known nutrients. How did this happen? The answer is that we fed their mothers, while the young were suckling, a diet much like our basal diet, which was deficient in the unidentified factor. Under this condition the young are almost invariably deficient in the unidentified factor by the time they are weaned, and at least 99 out of 100 of them fail to eat well and to grow well when placed on our basal ration. But this condition in these young can be alleviated so that the young will eat and grow decidedly better when placed at weaning on the same basal ration. This can be done simply by supplementing the ration of their mothers with liver extract or feeding the mothers an ordinary ration while the prospective test animals are suckling. We have conducted a number of experiments along this line, and the results indicate that the growth-capacity of the young can be influenced definitely through the milk of the mother fed on our basal ration.

We have spoken only of rate of growth. What happened eventually with these rats not fed our unidentified nutrient?

Some of the pairs of young in the above experiments were continued on experiment 33 weeks, that is, until they were 37 weeks of age. At this time, the rats receiving our basal ration without this nutrient had on an average ceased to grow and weighed about 100 grams less than their sex-litter mates that got this factor. How about the functional development of the young? The young females reached the same stage of development at 34 days of age, after being on the basal ration supplemented with this nutrient for 13 days, that their litter mates attained at 54 days, after being on the unsupplemented ration for 33 days. But do the animals on the unsupplemented ration eventually reproduce all right? It appears not. They have frequently failed to conceive or have conceived and failed to litter, or have borne small litters of young that have frequently failed to survive. The significance of these results on reproduction, which have only recently been obtained, is now under investigation.

The basal ration used in all the experiments referred to contained 10 percent of fat and a moderate amount of carbohydrate. What would happen if this fat were increased to 25 or 50 percent in place of carbohydrate—would our animals still need the unidentified factor? We tried it out, and found they would need it. Then we changed the kind of carbohydrate, and fed lactose, the sugar in milk.

The growth of rats fed our basal ration with 50 percent of dried skim milk in it was normal. This diet contained about 27 percent of lactose. But when practically this same proportion of lactose was fed in our basal ration separate from milk, the lactose depressed the growth of the rats to such an extent that it was only about 36 percent of normal. This was without our unidentified factor. With this factor in their diet, sex-litter mates grew normally, the average increment in growth due to adding this factor to the lactose-containing diet being 167 percent.

There has been considerable interest in the utilization by the rat of diets containing lactose, because it was hoped that such studies might throw light on the general function of this sugar in nutrition; but it may be that what we need to know first is how to construct a diet or prepare our test animals to conduct such experiments. Then possibly we can study the function and utilization of this sugar, which exists so universally in the milks of mammals; or we can select from the experiments of the past those which have—by chance or otherwise—met the conditions which would still make them of value.

The problems of supplying protein in the diet of humans and domestic animals, and of determining the effect of feeding high-protein diets, have received much attention. In all the experiments in which we increased the protein in the diets given rats by feeding soybean oil meal or linseed oil meal or increased amounts of yeast in place of carbohydrate, the growth of the rats has been decidedly depressed. Why? This depression of growth was not due to any quality of the rations which, irrespective of the nutrients in them, made them unpalatable. This was clear from the fact that the rate of growth of the rats fed soybean-oil and linseed-oil meal rations was increased twofold or more when they were fed a supplement of liver extract entirely separate from these rations and that the growth of rats fed the larger percentages of yeast was normal when they were fed this same supplement. In addition, the growth of young rats on the high-yeast diets without this factor was also not depressed by increasing the yeast when enough casein was removed from their ration to compensate for the protein in the yeast. This led us to question whether excessive amounts of protein are harmful in diets when this unidentified factor is deficient in them. There is now abundant evidence that they are harmful. A diet containing an excess of protein—even though it is a good protein—in a ration deficient in our unidentified factor, fed to rats depleted of this factor, actually depresses their growth, is definitely harmful, and may even be lethal. As stated earlier, our ordinary basal ration contained 25 percent of protein (20 percent casein from which the unidentified nutrient had been removed as described above and 5 percent yeast protein). When 20 percent of coagulated egg albumen replaced the 20 percent of casein in this ration, the rats grew at the same abnormally slow rate—not much more than half of normal.

When either of these proteins was increased to 40 percent in this ration, the rate of growth was reduced to only about 25 to 30 percent of normal; and when we increased the casein to 60 percent, the rats generally died within 2 weeks. These results were obtained when their diets did not contain the unidentified factor. When this was supplied, the growth of the sex-litter mates of the above rats when placed on the same 20-percent casein or 20-percent coagulated egg albumen diets almost doubled; the growth of those on the 40-percent casein and 40-percent coagulated egg-albumen diets almost quadrupled and tripled, respectively; and the sex-litter mates of the rats that died on the 60-percent casein ration survived and grew at rates about 85 percent of normal. After obtaining these results, we examined the kidneys of many of our rats that had been on the 20-percent casein diet. We observed no definite lesions, but the kidneys of all animals that had been on the diet without the unidentified factor for considerable periods of time were actually heavier than those of their much larger sex-litter mates receiving this factor. This would suggest that there was some metabolic condition that imposed extra work on the kidneys of the rats that did not receive the unidentified factor.

In appraising the practical significance of the results reported here, one must realize that we have dealt with animals that were purposely depleted of our unidentified factor; that, although our basal ration was adequate for normal growth and development in respect to all known nutrients, it was actually deficient; and that the results that we have noted apply to test animals under these conditions.

How about humans and livestock? Unquestionably the most urgent need today in the field of nutrition is a more complete knowledge of the list of constituents necessary for a complete diet. This need is emphasized by the fact that in the past each newly discovered nutrient has had a beneficial effect on our health and well being.

The experiments we have discussed disclose that we do not know all the nutrients in milk that contribute to its value in nutrition. We also do not know all the functions of the well known and recognized constituents in it.

For example: Casein is the main protein in milk. It is a peculiar protein in that it contains the element phosphorus in what has been called a "phosphopeptone" group. This same group occurs in a protein in another food, namely the vitellin of egg yolk, which like casein has evolved through the winnowing selection of ages in a food specifically adapted to the nutrition of the very young animal. For years there has been speculation regarding the function of these peculiar proteins. Recently, Ben H. Nicolet and Leo A. Shinn, of the Bureau of Dairy Industry laboratory at Beltsville, published several papers on the chemical composition and properties of these proteins, and developed an understanding of the chemical properties of this phosphopeptone group that may well form the basis for a study of its physiological function.

The war has emphasized both our ignorance and the necessity for more complete knowledge of the nutritive value of milk; fundamental work intended to broaden this knowledge is now in progress in many laboratories.

THE AUTHORS

C. A. Cary is head of the Division of Nutrition and Physiology in the Bureau of Dairy Industry.

A. M. Hartman is a chemist in the Bureau of Dairy Industry.

ALSO, IN THIS BOOK

Advances in Home Canning

by EDWARD W. TOEPFER and HOWARD REYNOLDS

AMERICAN housewives canned more than 4 billion cans and jars of food in 1943, and nearly 3½ billion quarts of food in 1944. The latter represented nearly one-half of the canned vegetables and two-thirds of the canned fruits that were available for civilian consumption that year. The market value of the canned foods exceeded a billion dollars a year. But much of it (45 million containers of the 4 billion put up in 1943) spoiled. The development of processes for home canning that will prevent such spoilage and give improved products is discussed here.

The process of preserving foods by canning was developed by Nicholas Appert, a French confectioner, less than 150 years ago. Neither Appert nor the scientists of his day knew why foods acquired the property of keeping after being heated in sealed containers. It was almost 50 years after Appert's discovery that Pasteur demonstrated that micro-organisms were the real cause of fermentation, putrefaction, and decay. With his discoveries, the ground work was prepared for developing canning processes on a scientific basis. It could then be shown that canned foods kept because heating destroyed spoilage micro-organisms present in the container and sealing prevented the entrance of others.

Appert used the boiling-water bath for heat treatments, which limited the heating temperature to 212° F. Often, however, the processes failed and the food spoiled. Eventually pressure canners were introduced to obtain the higher processing temperatures that seemed to be required for vegetables and meats. Processes or heat treatments were based on rule of thumb and experience. If foods spoiled, the process-time was increased until spoilage was eliminated or reduced. Such methods were used with reasonable satisfaction until about 1916. Between 1916 and 1922, a series of outbreaks of botulism that resulted in many fatalities in the United States focused attention upon shortcomings of the canning techniques in use. As a result, studies were undertaken to determine scientifically the times and temperatures required to destroy microorganisms causing spoilage of canned foods.

Cultures of *Clostridium botulinum,* the bacterium causing botulism, and other spoilage organisms were isolated and studied. It was found that many of these organisms would remain alive after heating for 5 to 6 hours or longer in boiling water. Bacteriologists also learned that bacteria subjected to lethal heat do not die instantly—both time and temperature are factors.

Since the object of the processing or heat treatment is to destroy all spoilage organisms within each container of food, information regarding the rate at which the temperature rises in the slowest heating part of the container was recognized as necessary. Studies of the penetration of heat, such as those reported by C. A. Magoon and C. W. Culpepper of the Department in 1921, were therefore undertaken. Foods were prepared and packed in cans or jars with thermometers or other temperature-measuring devices placed in the slowest heating spots. Data were obtained showing the temperature in the container at each instant during the process. Such heat-penetration data when combined with information on the time required to destroy spoilage bacteria at various temperatures provided the basis for computation of bacteriologically sound processes for canning.

W. D. Bigelow, G. S. Bohart, A. C. Richardson, and C. O. Ball in 1920 first solved the problem of applying the foregoing type of bacteriological and physical data to the calculation of thermal processes for canned foods. Later, Dr. Ball developed more flexible mathematical methods for thermal-process calculations. Further modifications and improvements were made by F. C. W. Olson and H. P. Stevens in 1939 and by O. T. Schultz and Mr. Olson in 1940.

Commercial processes for canning low-acid foods have been established largely by thermal-process calculations based on a reasonably adequate background of information, built up during years of research in laboratories of the can-manufacturing companies and the National Canners Association and in college and university laboratories aided by funds provided by the industry.

But the problems of home canning have not been solved so successfully. Much of the spoilage in 1943 was undoubtedly due to understerilization that resulted from the use of inadequate processes. Waterbath processes for low-acid foods continue to be recommended by some distributors of information on home canning and are still widely used. But research in bacteriology has shown that they are not adequate to destroy resistant spoilage organisms that may be present.

Water-bath processes are successful when resistant organisms are absent, but fail in their presence. This fact has often been demonstrated to home canners by outbreaks of gross spoilage after canning by methods that had been used successfully in previous years. It is on that basis that all canning technologists agree that only properly developed steam pressure processes are adequate to guarantee nonspoilage of low-acid foods.

Because research on processes for home canning has been limited, pressure processes recommended for use by home canners generally have been derived from commercial ones, often by arbitrarily increasing the processing time to provide additional factors of safety. Since there are many differences in home and commercial canning equipment and techniques, the arbitrary adaptation of commercial processes to home conditions is questionable. Foods that are home-canned in glass containers have long cooling periods, which add to the sterilizing values of processes; slower heating times add further to the thermal value of equal processing times. Improper evaluation of these factors frequently has resulted in the use of processes for home canning greatly in excess of those required.

Products home-canned in the steam-pressure canner frequently are overcooked and unattractive in comparison with the commercial products. To improve the processes for steam-pressure canning, more facts were needed on the effect of heating and cooling times on the sterilizing values of processes, on the rates of heat penetration from which sterilizing values for different processes are calculated, and on the bacteriological conditions likely to exist during home canning procedures.

On the basis of existing bacteriological information about the numbers and kinds of bacteria that might be encountered and their thermal behavior, it is possible to make a proper evaluation of the effect of home equipment and techniques from heat-penetration data.

Problems of wartime steam-pressure canners, jars, jar rings, and closures were added to the basic physical and bacteriological problems specifically related to home canning. In order to help meet urgent equipment problems, two studies were carried out by the Bureau of Human Nutrition and Home Economics.

Jar rings had contained 10 to 15 percent crude rubber, for which either new rubber compounds or reclaimed rubber would have to be substituted. The National Bureau of Standards cooperated in a study made to measure the physical and chemical properties of jar rings of different compositions and to correlate such data with the results of practical canning tests. Methods were developed to determine the sealing performance of jar rings under conditions of home canning. Within the limits of the tested irregularity of 0.02 inch in the sealing surfaces expected to be overcome by a ring in order to make a seal, the methods showed that rings made, of a suitable reclaimed rubber or 5 percent crude rubber, plus reclaimed rubber, maintained a good vacuum on freshly processed and on stored jars.

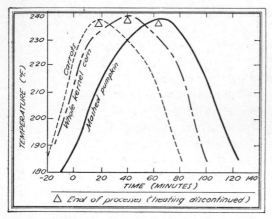

Studies have been made to determine the heat-penetration curves of typical fast, medium, and slow-heating vegetables in pint jars. The results are shown here.

The introduction of enamel on steel for aluminum in the construction of steam-pressure canners raised the question of the effect of different heating and cooling times on the sterilizing value of processes for vegetables in glass jars. Two enameled steel models and seven models of cast-molded, and sheet or pressed aluminum were included in the study. Each was designed to process 7 quart jars of food. The resulting data showed that, under standardized operating conditions, sterilizing values obtained by processing in canners of different materials, construction, design, and having the same container capacity (7 quart jars) are, for practical purposes, equivalent.

A few studies on home-canning procedures have been reported. W. B. Esselen, Jr., and R. G. Tischer of Massachusetts State College calculated processes for home canning from heat-penetration data. In two instances the processes were checked by inoculated packs. Their results indicated

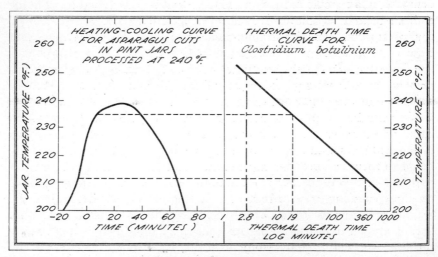

This chart gives the relationship between container temperature and the thermal death time of a known spoilage organism.

that home canning processes at 240° F., as now recommended, may be more severe than necessary. The increased sterilizing effect resulting from slow cooling in glass jars was recognized. The information presented in these and previous reports was, however, inadequate for making general recommendations with respect to processes for home canners.

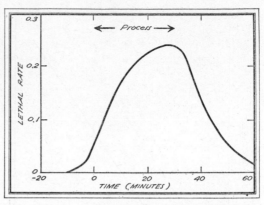

The lethality curve shown in this chart is for asparagus cuts in pint jars that were processed at 240° F.

Because of the lack of basic information, our Bureau undertook studies to obtain adequate data for the development of such processes. In making the investigations, the general methods developed for establishing commercial processes were used. They were modified as necessary to adapt them to the procedures and equipment commonly used in the home. Essentially three steps are involved in developing a process for each individual product. The first step is that of obtaining adequate information on rates of heat penetration. Second, the heat penetration data are used to calculate process times adequate to destroy *Clostridium botulinum* or other spoilage organisms of known heat resistance. Finally, calculated processes are checked by inoculated packs.

Heat-penetration data were obtained by packing the foods into containers carrying temperature-measuring devices. The foods were prepared and packed as they would be in the home. A thermocouple, a heat-sensitive instrument, was sealed into each container, with the temperature-measuring part placed at the slowest heating point. The containers were then placed in a home-type pressure canner equipped so that wire leads of the thermocouples could be passed through the lid for connection with a temperature recording device. The canner was closed and the containers of food processed in the usual manner; during the processing period the temperature of each container carrying a thermocouple was recorded continuously. At the end of the processing time the temperature recording continued until the containers were cool. Such heat penetration data were obtained from 12 or more of each of four types of containers (pint and quart glass jars, No. 2 and No. 2½ tin cans) for every product studied.

Rates of heat penetration vary widely with the size of the container, the kind of food, the size of the pieces of food, and the solidity of the pack. Dif-

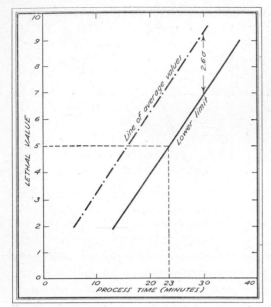

Here is shown the process time-lethal value for asparagus cuts in pint jars.

ferences in the rates of heating and cooling of sliced carrots, whole-kernel corn, and mashed pumpkin in pint jars are shown in the chart at the top of page 790.

The data on heat penetration were combined with those on the thermal-death times of known spoilage organisms in order to calculate adequate processes. The temperature at any instant during the heating and cooling of a food can be related to the thermal-death time required for the destruction of the spoilage organism. Thermal-death times so determined for a series of points along the heating-cooling curve are used to calculate corresponding lethal (death) rates. These rates are then plotted against heating and cooling times to give a lethality curve. When properly plotted, this curve shows the combined destructive effects of heating, holding, and cooling temperatures of the given process. This is known as the lethal value of the process. An adequate process is one which yields a lethal value equal to the thermal-death time of the spoilage organism at 250° F. This value for *Cl. botulinum* is 2.8 minutes.

These graphical-mathematical calculations are carried out with the data from each individual container used to follow rates of heat penetration for each kind of food. Such information is obtained for at least three processing times in order to have the data required for choosing a process that is adequate without being excessive. The next step is to plot the calculated lethal values to give a process-time, lethal-value curve from which the time required to yield a process with a desired lethal value can be read directly.

Heat-penetration data from a number of containers at each of the three process times were used for construction of the average time-lethal value curve. Because of the unavoidable variation in the factors that affect the rate of penetration of heat into canned foods during processing, the sterilizing values obtained from these containers of the same food given the same process, differed. The variation must be taken into consideration in calculating the processes. In a normal distribution, the data will vary about the average or mean value, half of the items falling above and half below the average. Thus, if only the average values were used to construct the time-lethal value curve to be used in determining required process time, the chances are that one jar in two would be underprocessed.

In order to fix a lower limit below which there is little chance that spoilage would occur among the processed jars, a line is drawn parallel to and at a distance of 2.6 times the standard error of estimate of the data below the line of average values. Assuming normal distribution of process values, the probability of an individual container having a process value below the lower line is only 0.005. Process times required in practice to yield the desired process values may be read from the lower curve, as illustrated by the solid line in the chart on page 792.

Finally, the accuracy of the calculated process must be checked by a trial canning of the food with a known contamination. This was done by the preparation of experimentally inoculated packs processed for varying times. For these checks, vegetables were prepared and packed in pint glass jars; home-canning procedures were adhered to as closely as possible. A minimum of 24 jars were each inoculated with 1 cubic centimeter of a suspension containing 10,000 spores of the test organism, putrefactive anaerobe #3679. This organism produces spores of somewhat greater resistance than does *Cl. botulinum,* and has been widely used for checking commercial processes. The inoculated jars, and at least 12 uninoculated or control jars, were then processed at 240° F. The procedure was repeated for at least three processing times with each product. The processing times used were chosen, on the basis of those calculated, to give 100 percent spoilage with the shortest process, decreasing to zero percent with the longest. The inoculated and control jars were incubated after processing and examined daily for signs of spoilage. After incubation for at least 3 months, remaining nonspoiled jars were examined for survival of the test organism.

After calculation of theoretical processes and completion of the inoculated pack checks, process recommendations were made by consideration of all the data. Processes for 12 vegetables considered adequate on the basis of these investigations are given. In general, the new processes are shorter than the old, the differences being greatest for packs in pint jars. Over-all reductions in process times averaged 38 percent for vegetables in pint jars, with 24, 10, and 12 percent reductions for quart jars, No. 2 tins, and No. 2½ tins, respectively.

This study has resulted in the establishment of processing times and temperatures for the home canning of low-acid foods that will destroy the most resistant spoilage organisms likely to be encountered. Such processes can be attained in reasonable periods of time only by the use of pressure canners or equipment permitting temperatures up to 240° F.

Recommended process times at 240° F. for vegetables in various containers

Vegetable	Glass jars		Tin cans	
	Pint	Quart	No. 2	No. 2½
	Min. at 240° F.	*Min. at 240° F.*	*Min. at 240° F.*	*Min. at 240° F.*
Asparagus, cuts....................	25	55	20	20
Snap beans.......................	20	25	25	30
Lima beans.......................	35	60	40	40
Beets, sliced......................	25	55	30	30
Carrots, sliced....................	20	25	20	25
Corn:				
Whole grain..................	55	85	60	60
Cream style..................	85	....	105	....
Okra, cut........................	25	40	25	35
Peas............................	40	40	30	30
Pumpkin:				
Cubed.....................	55	90	50	75
Mashed.....................	60	80	75	90
Spinach..........................	45	70	60	75
Summer squash...................	30	40	20	20
Sweetpotatoes:				90
Wet pack....................	55	90	75	95
Dry pack....................	65	95	80	

Further studies on the destruction or inhibition of growth of spoilage organisms in the different vegetable media and the numbers and kinds of such organisms likely to be encountered, may result in changes and possibly reductions in the severity of the processing conditions. Studies on the improvement in methods of preparing the food to standardize the packing conditions that affect the variability of the data may also yield information which would justify changes in the process times calculated from the heat-penetration data as presented in this report. Changes in preparation methods to increase the retention of nutrients and improve the palatability of canned products may bring about different conditions for which new heat-penetration data will be needed.

Reductions in process times at 240° F. from those previously recommended may be expected to improve palatability and nutritive value of home-canned vegetables. The ultimate goal of this work is to present procedures to home canners that will be safe, prevent loss due to spoilage, and yield products that are attractive and good to eat.

THE AUTHORS

Edward W. Toepfer is a technologist in the Food and Nutrition Division of the Bureau of Human Nutrition and Home Economics. He received his doctorate in chemistry from Columbia University in 1936.

Howard Reynolds is a bacteriologist in the same Division. He has been a research chemist with the Armour Packing Co., and for 6 years was assistant professor at the University of Arkansas. Dr. Reynolds is a graduate of Iowa State College.

Dried Foods in the Home

by ELSIE H. DAWSON

DRYING IS one of the oldest methods of preserving food. It is also one of the cheapest, easiest, and most widely used. Yet there is a great deal still to be learned about it. Especially is there a need for improving the quality of the products to meet present-day standards.

The factors that affect the quality of foods dried at home are pretreatment of the food before it is dehydrated, operation of the dehydrator, storage, and the preparation of the foods for the table. In the laboratories of the Bureau of Human Nutrition and Home Economics and cooperating institutions, we have given special attention to those points and, to meet an urgent wartime need, have developed some practical directions about them. Dehydration has three general steps: Preparation and pretreatment, dehydration, and storage. A fourth could be added: Reconstitution and cooking.

Vegetables and fruits are washed, peeled by hand or by mechanical device, and cut into small pieces for quick drying. With a few exceptions, among them onions, celery, peppers, and herbs, vegetables need partial cooking in boiling water or steam before drying. Cooking destroys the enzymes which, if left active in the dehydrated food, might cause the development of a disagreeable "hay" flavor, change the color, and lower the vitamin content. We chose vitamin C for study because it is the most easily destroyed by heat and oxidation. Vitamin C content is measured by dichlorophenolindophenol titration; color is determined by comparison with Munsell color standards; and flavor is evaluated by expert tasters.

In order to give the homemaker practical directions about precooking, most of our early work was set up on the basis of cooking until tender. We recognized, however, that overcooking is then likely to result when the dehydrated food is prepared for the table. On the other hand, if certain

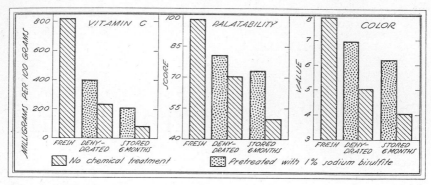

By pretreating light-colored fruits and vegetables that are to be dehydrated with 1 percent sodium bisulfate, the vitamin C content, palatability, and color of the dried product are greatly enhanced. The data in this chart are based on cauliflower.

foods are precooked insufficiently, they cannot be properly reconstituted after dehydration. Precooking in steam half the time required to cook tender is enough to inactivate the enzymes in precooked carrots and broccoli, which were selected as typical vegetables, and to keep the enzymes inactive in the stored, dehydrated vegetables. Their keeping quality is as good as those fully cooked before dehydration, and the food is softened sufficiently to insure complete reconstitution without overcooking. Leafy green vegetables must be precooked slightly more than half-time to wilt the leaves, but less than full-time to avoid matting on drier trays.

There are various methods of precooking vegetables. Precooking in steam or in a small amount of water saves time and fuel, retains flavor and food values better, and is preferred to precooking in much water.

Pretreatment of light-colored fruits and vegetables, such as apples and cauliflower, with 1-percent solutions of sodium sulfite or bisulfite improves the quality of the dehydrated product by preventing development of strong flavors and darkening of the color which occurs during dehydration and storage of untreated material. One can hardly taste the small quantity of sulfur dioxide present in the reconstituted samples. The retention of vitamin C, palatability, and color in dehydrated, stored cauliflower is greatly increased by dipping steamed cauliflower in the solution of sodium bisulfite for 15 seconds.

Chemical pretreatment of green vegetables like broccoli and snap beans helps to preserve the bright green color, crisp texture, and natural flavor during drying and storage. Dipping the steamed vegetable in one-fourth teaspoon of sodium bicarbonate per quart of water or one teaspoon of sodium sulfite per quart of water produces good results.

Food may be dried outdoors or indoors. Indoor drying is much faster and much more dependable because it is not affected by the weather. It also saves more vitamins. Artificial dehydration, as distinguished from natural drying in the sun, consists of passing hot air over the vegetable or

The yield of dehydrated food varies with the kind and quality of the fruit or vegetable used; the reduction in weight is tremendous, especially for foods with high water content. This table shows the average yield of dehydrated material

Product	Prepared fresh food	Dehydrated food	
	Yield from 100 pounds of fresh material as purchased	Yield from 100 pounds of prepared fresh material	Yield from 100 pounds of fresh material as purchased
	Pounds	*Pounds*	*Pounds*
Apples.........................	73	16	12
Beets..........................	78	11	9
Beet greens....................	59	13	8
Blackberries...................	100	15	15
Broccoli.......................	62	10	6
Carrots........................	83	13	11
Cauliflower....................	57	9	5
Celery.........................	31	5	1.6
Cherries.......................	86	18	16
Corn..........................	....	28	....
Green peppers..................	80	6	5
Kale...........................	31	13	4
Mushrooms.....................	99	10	9.9
Mustard greens.................	78	8	6
Peaches........................	87	13	11
Pears..........................	80	14	11
Peas...........................	33	25	8
Prune plums...................	96	16	15
Pumpkin.......................	76	6	4.5
Snap beans.....................	90	12	11
Squash.........................	57	11	6
Spinach........................	36	9	3
Sweetpotatoes..................	84	32	27
Swiss chard....................	100	9	9
Tomatoes......................	88	4	3.5
Turnip greens..................	54	9	5

fruit to remove moisture. The air must circulate freely around and over the food, and there must be sufficient heat to dry the food in the shortest possible time, but not enough to scorch it. The smaller the load on each tray the shorter the drying time. The most satisfactory results are obtained by using one-half to 1 pound per square foot of leafy green vegetables and 1 to 2 pounds per square foot of other vegetables and fruits. The smaller the pieces of food, the shorter the drying time.

Dehydration and Storage

Several designs of home equipment for the indoor dehydration of fruits and vegetables have been developed and adapted. We tested gas and electric ovens for dehydrating, as well as home-built units heated by kerosene heaters, coal and wood stoves, electric heating elements, and light

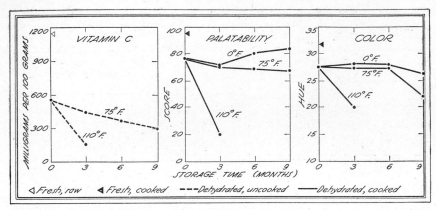

This chart shows the effect of dehydration and storage on the vitamin C content, palatability, and color of broccoli.

bulbs. In the electrically heated dehydrator, forced circulation of air was used. In all others the circulation of air was brought about by natural convection.

Dehydrated foods must be put into moisture-proof packages to prevent absorption of moisture—and consequent spoilage—during storage. Such containers as tin cans with tight-fitting covers, glass jars fitted with rubber rings, or sealed packages of moisture-proof materials may be used.

Most of the home-dried fruits can be stored at room temperature for several months without becoming inedible. Among the vegetables we tested, home-dehydrated sweetpotatoes, beets, broccoli, and green leaves are the most satisfactory. Their palatability remains high during 6 months of storage at room temperature. The loss of vitamin C parallels the losses of flavor and color. At temperatures above 100° F., most dehydrated foods will keep only a few weeks. The lower the storage temperature, the better are color, palatability, and vitamins retained.

Another way to retard the rate of deterioration is to reduce the moisture content as much as possible. In an experiment with home-dehydrated broccoli, we found that lowering the moisture content from 11 percent to 8 percent increased the storage life from 3 to 9 months at 75° F.

The Use of Home and Commercially Dehydrated Foods

Many foods that are dehydrated commercially because they require elaborate equipment are available to the homemaker.

Whole eggs, yolks, and whites in powder form are among them, and beef or pork as dry shreds or chunks, dehydrated vegetables and fruits in many forms—cubes, slices, flakes, powders, or nuggets—and these may even be compressed into blocks.

Powdered whole eggs of good quality can be used in cooking in much the same way as shell eggs are used except in sponge cakes, fluffy omelets, and similar products that depend on the whipping quality of eggs. For such products one should use a combination of dried egg white and dried egg yolk. When sucrose and lactose are added to the whole eggs before dehydration, even they can be used to make good sponge cake without the use of baking powder to lighten it. Allowance must be made for the sugar in the dry product when measuring the sugar for the recipe. Little time is needed for reconstitution; sugar-dried egg can be used immediately after the water is mixed with it. The presence of the sugar also improves the keeping quality of the dried egg. Untreated dried egg requires temperatures below 60° F. to keep well for longer than 6 months. The addition of sugar makes it possible to store dried egg at higher temperatures for longer periods..

Dehydrated meat for making stews, meat loaves, hamburgers, casserole dishes, and the like was developed during the war for shipping overseas without the danger of spoilage encountered in shipping fresh meat. Whether homemakers will continue using dehydrated meat will depend upon its initial quality and how well it retains high quality during distribution to the consumers. Dehydrated prefrozen raw meat more closely approaches fresh meat in quality than the cooked dehydrated meat; the former will remain edible for several months at room temperature when packed in vacuum-sealed cans. Refrigerator temperatures retard greatly the physical and chemical changes that are responsible for the changes in flavor and texture.

Dehydrated vegetables are easy to prepare because they are cleaned, trimmed, and cut—all ready to have water added and to be cooked, even without preliminary soaking in some cases. As they are semi-precooked before they are dried, they can be served in a short time. Differences in size of pieces, variety of vegetable used, and length of storage period are some of the factors that determine how much soaking and cooking are needed. It is important to cook dehydrated vegetables in a minimum amount of water if the product is to have maximum palatability and nutritive value.

Compression of dehydrated fruits and vegetables into blocks saves space, lowers the cost of packaging, and helps prevent deterioration by oxidation and fragmentation due to handling. Compression must not interfere with easy reconstitution of dehydrated foods, however. Compressed food blocks are especially useful where space is scarce, as in the small city apartment or on exploring and camping expeditions.

Dehydrated foods are a long way from being perfect, but they have served well in both local and national emergencies. If they are to be improved, we need to continue research work on the methods of preparing them for dehydration, on new and better dehydration procedures, on improved storage facilities to increase shelf life, and on quicker, easier methods of reconstitution. Only when one is certain of uniform quality will dehydrated foods take their place alongside canned and frozen foods in the homemaker's pantry when all types are equally available.

THE AUTHOR

Elsie H. Dawson, a food specialist in the Bureau of Human Nutrition and Home Economics, has done work in the field of dehydrated foods, including research on improvement in quality and use of dehydrated eggs, meat, milk, and many fruits and vegetables. She is a graduate of the University of California and taught food chemistry and experimental cookery there and at Syracuse University and Cornell University before joining the Bureau in 1941.

ACKNOWLEDGMENTS

Work on chemistry and nutritive value was done by Esther L. Batchelder, Kay Stein, and Joan Lorr; on dehydration equipment by Lenore E. Sater, Katherine Taube, and co-workers; on recipe development by Florence McDonough and staff, all of the Bureau of Human Nutrition and Home Economics.

FOR FURTHER READING

Agricultural Research Administration, Committee on Dehydration of Meat, *Meat Dehydration,* U. S. D. A. Circular 706, 1944.

Batchelder, E. L.: *Home Drying Methods and Their Effect on the Palatability, Cooking Quality and Nutritive Value of Foods,* American Journal of Public Health, volume 33, No. 8, pages 941–947, 1943.

Dawson, Elsie H., Shank, Dorothy E., Lynn, Jane M., and Wood, Elizabeth A.: *Effect of Storage on Flavor and Cooking Quality of Spray-Dried Whole Egg,* U. S. Egg and Poultry Magazine, volume 51, No. 4, pages 154–161, 1945.

Fenton, F., and Gifft, H.: *Palatability Studies of Commercially Dehydrated Vegetables: I. Effect of Several Methods of Storage on Palatability of Beets, Cabbage, and Rutabagas; II. Effect of Several Common Refreshing and Cooking Methods on Palatability and Water Adsorption of Beets, Cabbage, Rutabagas and Yellow Turnips,* Food Research, volume 8, No. 5, pages 364–376, 1943.

Magoon, C. A., and Associates: *Peacetime Food Compression,* Food Industries, volume 18, No. 3, pages 362–364, 472, 474, 476, 1946.

Stillman, J. T., Watts, B. M., and Morgan, A. F.: *Palatability Studies on Home Dehydrated Vegetables,* Journal of Home Economics, volume 36, No. 1, pages 28–34, 1944.

Tressler, D. K., Moyer, J. C., and Wheeler, K. A.: *Losses of Vitamins Which May Occur During the Storage of Dehydrated Vegetables,* American Journal of Public Health, volume 33, no. 8, pages 975–979, 1943.

Freezing Food at Home

by ESTHER L. BATCHELDER

IF HOME freezing of food is to give American families all they expect, there is need for better equipment and better directions for handling food. People want to know what to look for when they are deciding which type of freezer to buy. They want to know what are the most suitable kinds and varieties of foods to freeze; how to select, prepare, and freeze them; how long to store frozen foods; and how to thaw or cook them.

To get the facts needed, scientists in industry, colleges, and the Department have been making investigations on home freezing and preparing and serving frozen products. Methods of treating and packing foods before freezing are compared as to their effectiveness in conserving palatability and nutritive value throughout freezing and storage, and methods of thawing or cooking and serving frozen foods are similarly studied. Texture, flavor, and color are given chief attention as factors affecting palatability. Ascorbic acid (vitamin C) is used as the chief guide to changes in nutritive value because it is sensitive to heat and oxidation and is soluble in water. Success in retaining ascorbic acid is therefore a good sign that other nutrients are also saved. A beginning has been made in studying changes in another sensitive vitamin, thiamine, especially in foods low in ascorbic acid.

To stop the action of enzymes and thus slow down changes in the palatability and nutritive value of frozen foods during storage, vegetables or fruits are often scalded before freezing. Harmless chemicals are sometimes used instead of scalding, especially for fruits or vegetables usually eaten raw. It is possible to prevent some changes by cutting off contact with the air, for example, by adding sirup to fruit.

We learned in our tests that if raw peaches (September Elbertas) were covered with a sirup containing a fourth of a teaspoon of crystalline ascorbic acid to a cup, darkening was prevented without appreciably altering flavor and texture. The treatment also added considerable ascorbic acid to the fruit at an extra cost of slightly more than 1 cent a pint.

Unless peaches were completely covered by sirup to protect them from air, darkening occurred during frozen storage or after thawing. If dry sugar was used (1 cup of sugar to 4½ to 6 cups of fruit), it had to be dissolved completely in the juice from the fruit and the resulting sugar-juice sirup had to cover the fruit completely. Peaches also can be sliced, mixed with sugar and lemon juice, made into pies, and frozen. After 4 months, we found good retention of fresh flavor and no darkening of the peaches. Nectarines (Sure Crop and Garden State varieties) can be frozen satisfactorily after dipping in citric acid, 1 teaspoon per gallon.

Freezing applesauce is a good way to save early apples or others not suitable for winter storage. Baked apples also were frozen successfully.

Frozen blueberries retained their natural flavor well if packed in sirup or dry sugar and were successfully used in a variety of recipes. Most of these tests were done with seedlings; a few with Scammell and Jersey varieties. Cranberries retained their color and flavor well whether packed with or without sugar or sirup. The skins were tough, however, whether the berries were frozen raw or as cooked sauce.

Further work on fruit is under way to improve our methods for retaining natural texture, flavor, and appearance, as well as nutritive value.

Fruit purees were used as a base for home-made Velva Fruit. The freezing of purees is especially useful where there is fully ripe fruit which might otherwise go to waste.

Studies with asparagus, snap beans, broccoli, cauliflower, and peas indicate that satisfactory palatability and nutritive value can be maintained during freezing and storage when the vegetables are pretreated and frozen by practical home procedures. There was some loss of ascorbic acid as a result of scalding and freezing. There was also some loss of quality as indicated by the flavor and texture scores. Despite such losses, broccoli remained a rich source of ascorbic acid after freezing. It lost about one-third more during 9 months' storage. Cauliflower is also high in vitamin C and retained its value through several months of storage before dropping gradually to about one-half its freshly frozen value at the end of a year. Peas, snap beans, and asparagus are low in ascorbic acid. They suffered only small losses during scalding and freezing and retained their small supply well during frozen storage. Further research is under way to establish for these and other vegetables the treatments that will best save palatability and nutritive value.

We found that scalding with steam was better for broccoli, and water scalding for peas and cauliflower. With asparagus it did not make much difference whether steam or boiling water was used. According to preliminary work, the same was true for snap beans. Recent intensive studies on the Tendergreen variety indicate, however, that snap beans scalded in boiling water retain the appearance of fresh cooked beans, even after 12 months of frozen storage, and are less subject to development of off-flavor and toughness than are steam scalded beans.

The vitamin C values of frozen beans do not change greatly during frozen storage but in this respect, also, water scalding appears to give somewhat better results.

The scalding time that gives best results depends on enzyme activity of raw samples, scalding medium (steam or water), amount of food being scalded, size of pieces, altitude, and so on. Hence, in setting up directions for a homemaker to use, the research workers selected conditions that should insure a good product even though there is no chance in the kitchen to check enzyme activity or make other technical tests. Besides the scald best suited to conditions, factors that were found to help keep losses low were: Keeping the fresh vegetables cool; processing as soon after harvesting as possible; cutting and scalding only small amounts at a time; and keeping scalded, cooled vegetables in the refrigerator until they can be put in the home freezer or community locker.

Comparison of methods for cooling after scalding showed that cooling in iced water (60° F.) gave most satisfactory results from the standpoint of time, manipulation of equipment, and attention required. No difference in retention of ascorbic acid or palatability was found as a result of the different cooling methods tried.

Whole eggs or separated yolks require suitable mixing before freezing to prevent undesirable changes. Frozen eggs must not only taste good but must retain their cooking quality. For instance, they must coagulate smoothly in custard and scrambled egg and produce light and stable foams for sponge cake.

Most meat and poultry can be frozen raw without special pretreatment. The meat should be cut as desired for cooking later. Ground meat can be shaped into cakes of convenient size. The use of condiments, especially salt, may affect the length of time such meat can be stored. Boning saves freezer space on some cuts. Very bony pieces, like the backs and wings of chicken, can best be cooked and the pieces of meat removed from bones before freezing.

Frozen prepared foods relieve the homemaker who buys such products of much of the drudgery and time required for food preparation. For the woman who freezes her own food, the work of preparation is of course merely removed by days, weeks, or months from the time of serving. This has advantages. For instance, the farmer's wife can prepare in a slack season food to be served at harvesttime when the whole family is needed outside the kitchen, or when her own efforts should be directed toward preserving perishable fruits, vegetables, or meats for later use.

More research on factors that affect the quality of frozen prepared foods is under way. Results of preliminary studies on frozen baked goods indicate that rolls, biscuits, and cakes can be frozen and held successfully at least for short periods. Indications are that satisfactory storage time for baked goods may be relatively short, compared with that for meats, fruits, and vegetables. The freezing of baked products seems practical, however, as an economy measure for small families, as a means of postponing staling, or as a way of distributing the labor of cooking that otherwise might have to be done on a crowded and busy day.

The keeping quality is, of course, influenced by initial quality, as well as by techniques of handling and conditions of storage.

Fruit pies made and frozen during the summer can be baked and served in winter or spring when the supply of fresh fruits is more limited. Food and freezer space can be saved by preparing and freezing creamed chicken, for example, made from the bony pieces of birds at culling time.

Of the packaging materials available for wartime research, several were used during the course of the experiments. Heat-sealing Cellophane, which resists the passage of moisture or air, was found to give good results when used either inside or outside a stiff package. Where the protection of a stiff package was not feasible, as for large irregular cuts of meat or for pies, a wrapping of Cellophane was protected with stockinette. Angular package shapes were found to be better than round ones because they saved space when packed side by side in the freezer. A wider variety and adaptability of packaging materials for use in home freezing can be expected in the future. Two devices that can be made at home were developed to help the homemaker in packaging her food. One is a simple funnel for filling cartons. The other is a stand for use in heat-sealing food packages.

Home Freezers and Freezing Equipment

Operating characteristics of seven makes of home freezers were studied. More work needs to be done to establish the relationship between the results of engineering tests and the performance-in-use values that indicate a satisfactory piece of equipment. On the basis of the work done to date, however, it appears that in available chest-type cabinets, under normal operating conditions, temperatures in the upper fifth or tenth of the compartments are higher than that recommended for satisfactory storage of frozen food. A separate freezing compartment is desirable to reduce temperature variation in the stored frozen food while a new load is being frozen. Freezing compartments, however, should not be as large as those in many available freezers.

To find out how well home freezers could maintain low temperatures in the frozen food when the cooling system is not working (as when a storm cuts off electric current), five representative freezers were studied. With the current off, the time it took packages to reach the melting point of ice (32° F.) varied with the freezer and with the amount and position of frozen food in the cabinet. In one freezer, with the storage compartment filled, it was 44 hours before the first package reached 32° F. In another, similarly packed, it took 80 hours. The freezer that took 44 hours to reach 32° F., when full, took 33 hours when only one-fourth full. There is need for better insulation at certain points in the freezers in order to slow down the passage of heat from outside into the food compartment.

It is better to use dry ice (solid carbon dioxide) when the freezer is not working than to depend on blankets or other outside insulation to keep down the temperature of the frozen food. Freezing rates have been recorded under varied conditions. In a freezing compartment with a fan, the average time required for food to reach 0° F. was found to be 7 to 8 hours for small loads (6 to 12 pounds of food) and 15 to 20 hours for large loads (30 to 40 pounds of food). With a load of about 20 pounds of snap beans in pint cartons in a freezer without a fan, 24 hours elapsed before all the food reached 0° F. Double that load (about 40 pounds), in a freezer with a fan, reached 0° F. in only 15 hours. Little difference was found in the time needed to reach 0° F. in foods packaged in different kinds of cartons. A comparison of food in cartons with food frozen on open trays showed that green snap beans and asparagus in closed, sealed cartons needed 7 hours to reach 0° F. whereas those frozen on open trays required only 1 hour.

These figures help to set up instructions for homemakers as to when food may be ready to move from the freezing to the storage compartment. They cannot be used to indicate whether the rate of freezing affects palatability and nutritive value in the final product. No clearly defined results on this aspect of freezing rates are available at present.

Investigations were also started to determine the temperature limits allowable for long-term and short-term frozen storage. If higher temperatures and wide temperature fluctuations could be used, the cost of manufacturing and operating home freezers would be less. In cooperative work with Cornell University, it was found that with temperatures fluctuating between 0° F. and 20° F. foods tend to dry out unless properly packaged. It was also found that more ascorbic acid is lost as the temperature is raised. Thiamine in pork is not significantly affected by the temperature conditions or period of storage in the freezer. Rancidity, however, was greatly hastened when the pork was exposed to temperature above 0° F. The palatability of all products except meat was lower at 10° F. storage or following 0° F. to 20° F. fluctuations than at 0° F. All palatibility factors for pork were affected by length of storage but some were not affected by temperature.

If the temperature usually prevailing in the freezing compartment of a home refrigerator proves to be low enough for brief storage, frozen foods can be brought from community lockers or purchased and kept on hand for a few weeks by people who do not own home freezers. Studies are under way in cooperation with Iowa State College which will help to answer the question of allowable temperatures for short-term frozen storage. Results now available indicate considerable differences in frozen foods with respect to changes in palatability and vitamin C value. The temperatures used were 0, 5, 10, and 20° F.; the storage times were 2, 4, 6, and 8 weeks.

The concentration of the vitamins, thiamine and niacin, did not change in any of the foods studied—peaches, rhubarb, pineapple, soybeans, corn, peas, and snap beans.

Studies have recently been completed on frozen peas. Although thawed in different ways, the ascorbic acid value before cooking varied very little, from 54.5 to 51.6 milligrams per 100 grams. Frozen peas cooked in a small amount of water without previous thawing retained 85 percent of their uncooked value. A downward trend from this value was apparent for peas cooked as above but thawed 3 hours at room temperature, 9 hours in the refrigerator, or 33 hours in the refrigerator. The retentions were 81 percent, 76 percent, and 72 percent respectively. No differences in palatability were observed. From results on this one vegetable, it appears that, when possible, frozen vegetables should be cooked without preliminary thawing. On the other hand, if some unexpected event forces the holding of a thawed vegetable for an extra 24 hours in the refrigerator this will probably not affect palatability. It will result in some loss of vitamin C.

THE AUTHOR

Esther L. Batchelder is head of the Food and Nutrition Division of the Bureau of Human Nutrition and Home Economics. Besides general responsibility for the work of her Division, she has taken an active part in home dehydration and freezing research. Before joining the Bureau in 1942, Dr. Batchelder was director of Home Economics at Rhode Island State College. She has taught and done research in nutrition at the University of Arizona, the State College of Washington, and Columbia University.

ACKNOWLEDGMENTS

Many people have contributed to the results reported here. It is possible to mention by name only the project leaders, Lenore Sater and Enid Sater, Earl C. McCracken, Mary E. Kirkpatrick, and Sophie Marcuse, who, with the writer, have worked on various phases of the research at Beltsville. Acknowledgment is also due our cooperators, Louise Peet and Pearl Swanson of the Iowa State College and Experiment Station and Willis Gortner and Faith Fenton of Cornell University.

FOR FURTHER READING

Bureau of Animal Industry: *Freezing Meat and Poultry Products for Home Use,* U. S. D. A. Agricultural War Information Series 75, 1945.

Bureau of Human Nutrition and Home Economics: *Home Freezing of Fruits and Vegetables,* U. S. D. A. Agricultural Information Series 48, 1946.

Clothing That Works

by CLARICE L. SCOTT

AMERICAN women, like men, want and deserve their own work clothes. They are tired of having to wear the family's discards, or men's too big overalls for outdoor jobs. They are tired of fussy little house dresses made for looks alone. Instead, they want clothes planned and made for the different kinds of work they do—functional work clothes that are comfortable, safe, and practical, but handsome, too.

Women's need for work clothes long ago attracted the interest of the Bureau of Human Nutrition and Home Economics. Farm women often wrote to tell us their grievances. Some even took the pains to sketch styles of garments they had worked out themselves in an effort to get something satisfactory.

Our clothing unit investigated, and found that no manufacturers of ready-to-wear clothes had ever produced lines of women's work clothes. Farm women could not go to local stores and find special departments where they could buy their work clothes. Nor had manufacturers of patterns offered helps for women who could make their own. We found also that the clothing industry was just beginning to offer the time and incentive that designers need for studying and developing clothes for specific purposes. On the other hand, the buying public was reluctant to pay the additional money cost of good design, and did not appreciate the full worth of scientifically designed clothes, yet unwittingly was paying high for clothes—if not in initial costs, then in discomfort, fatigue, accidents, inconvenience, waste of time, and premature wearing out.

From that research we found that comfort and freedom of body activity are essential to working efficiency. If you can work in absolute comfort, forgetting all about the clothes you have on, you can concentrate on the job. But if attention and energy are divided because you are too warm, or too cold, or something about your clothes chafes or gets in the way, you waste both time and energy.

Actual wear can prove best when design, cut, fit, material and workmanship function together, making a garment responsive to body movements and the tempo of the job. We learned that some features of a design give and go back into place when activity is slow or normal, but for another kind of work that requires speed or extreme movement these features are not always adequate. We also found that closed protective garments, such as women wear for winter outdoor work, need more action features within them than do hot-weather outfits, which are comparatively open and cover only the body proper. The effect of climate and the temperature of workrooms must also be considered. For instance, if work causes one to perspire, fabrics cling, and free action is hindered unless design features are devised to prevent this restriction.

Since materials, like designs, affect body movement, their functional qualities need to be considered together. A hard, tightly woven, inelastic cloth contributes little or nothing to free movement, in contrast to one that is soft, elastic, and more loosely woven. Yet those hard fabrics are often desirable for their protection and durability. Then, design alone must provide free action.

A protect-all designed for farm women who prefer skirted work outfits illustrates this. The material, a closely woven shower- and wind-resistant cotton, was chosen for protection against cold and wet weather. It also resists soiling, a practical feature. To assure free action despite the lack of give in the cloth, the garment is loosely styled. It has reaching insets under arms and action pleats in back close to the sleeves. There, pleats and sleeves can function together to provide instantaneously ample shoulder and arm freedom. For further free action, the sleeves have shaped elbow room and surplice cuffs that fit automatically. The worker is not hampered by too full sleeves or buttoned cuffs that will not give.

Modern work clothes must be safe to work in. For women this takes extra planning, for their clothes are not standardized, as men's are. Styles and materials are varied, and generally have frills or extras that make them dangerous around machines. This we became particularly aware of during the war, when unsafe clothes caused many an accident and hampered production. In factories and homes we considered the hazards, and then devised ways of making clothes safe. But an outfit safe enough for one kind of work is not safe for another. Hazards differ. No rules can be set, but in general simple, streamlined styles that cannot catch and cause injury or hamper a worker's movements are found to be best.

Openings and fastenings, which so frequently cause trouble, can be planned so they are safe as well as convenient. For instance, front openings, which are easiest to manage, will not interfere with ordinary work if the fastenings are small, flat, and close enough to allow no gaps. Ties, belts, and sashes can be made to fit closely and fasten out of the way, at the back. And sleeves—why bother with any at all, unless they are needed for warmth or other protection? The looks of a dress, for instance, may be helped by wing extensions or similar devices that serve equally well. These are safer and give more freedom. If long or three-quarter sleeves are needed, they can be shaped for elbow room and made close fitting about the lower arm and wrist.

In work dresses, we found that it pays to watch the skirt length and width. If you must stoop, a long or full skirt drops down about your feet. It may easily catch on your shoe heels, or you may step on it and fall. You are safer in a skirt no longer than calf length, and just wide enough for your natural stride.

Every homemaker wants to save time and work. Often she looks to modern equipment or a new plan of work; too often she forgets that what she wears can save time and effort. Scientifically designed clothes can help her by assisting with the actual performance of a job, by being easy and quick to do up, and by being simple to put on and take off.

Pockets become functional and help in work when their size, shape, opening, and position are planned to suit you and the job. When placed below the waist they serve best if they are large enough so you can put your hand in and take out what you want without strain on pocket corners or the material. And they need to be placed where your hands slide into them naturally. Pockets awkwardly placed force you to stop and see how to get into them, a waste of time and a distraction.

Aprons can be designed to make kneeling jobs easier. One apron we made has a roomy buttoned-up pocket in which one can assemble all the little things needed in doing the work—seed packets, string, markers. On getting down to work you turn the pocket inside out and over the knees; knees and clothes are protected against dampness and soil. There's no discomfort from trying to work in a cramped position and no waste of time trying to hold dress skirts up out of the dirt. The apron saves laundering, too.

Functional work clothes do more than just make work easier. They are planned so that keeping them in order takes a minimum of time and energy. They have to be pleasing to look at. To make this possible, simplicity is the thing. We planned a hot-weather house dress in a straight style, held in at the waist with short sashes that tie in the back, well out of the way. So simple is the dress that it takes only 7 minutes to iron it. No time is wasted in maneuvering fussy little style details over the board to smooth them out. All construction is flat, smooth, and thin, easy to iron neatly and speedily.

A functional work garment is attractive. Otherwise it would not serve its purpose fully. Types and styles of garments are chosen for their suitability and good looks. And color, usually chosen for esthetic value, is found to have practical values as well. For example, a colorful print with a minimum of unbroken white ground will not show wrinkles, soil, and spots as readily as plain materials or a print with much white in it. Color has a psychological value as well. Most women find such colors as blue and green restful, cool, and clean-looking. They give a sense of well-being—and that contributes to self-confidence and the peace of mind so essential to good working conditions.

Durability is still another part of functionalism in clothing. Contrary to the opinion that durability depends on material alone, it depends on style and workmanship, too. Certain style features may function, but they may also be too weak to endure everyday wear and cleaning. Such factors have to be weighed as a design is developed, because only strong features and good workmanship can keep a garment functioning all its days.

Research in functional clothing is still in its infancy. We have more to learn about it—but that will come in further experimentation, and cooperation with housewives. It's worth the effort, the attempt to make work clothes mean more than mere coverings and dirt catchers. We have seen how men and women alike have been grateful for the functional clothes designed by the Quartermaster Corps to meet the various needs of men in the different services—comfort, freedom of action, health protection, safety, convenience, and saving of time.

Many of these new-type clothes take more cloth than the kinds we are used to. Production costs and retail prices may have to be higher, but functional clothes that are made for the job serve better and wear longer. In the end they cost less. When the public realizes this and demands scientifically designed work clothes, manufacturers will make them. Meanwhile, homemakers who sew need not wait. For them, cooperating commercial companies have made patterns for designs developed in the course of this research.

THE AUTHOR

Clarice L. Scott, a clothing specialist in the Bureau of Human Nutrition and Home Economics, designed the first functional work garments for women. These garments are credited with having started an entirely new development in the garment and pattern industries. Miss Scott is a graduate of Iowa State College.

FOR FURTHER READING

Scott, Clarice L.: *Work Clothes for Women,* U. S. D. A. Farmers' Bulletin 1905, 1942.

Scott, Clarice L., and Bruzgulis, Elizabeth: *Dresses and Aprons for Work in the Home,* U. S. D. A. Farmers' Bulletin 1963, 1944.

Smith, Margaret: *Making a Dress at Home,* U. S. D. A. Farmers' Bulletin 1954, 1944.

Smith, Margaret: *Pattern Alteration,* U. S. D. A. Farmers' Bulletin 1968, 1945.

Fabrics Without Mildew

by MARGARET S. FURRY

MILDEW ON cotton things is caused by micro-organisms, mainly fungi, that flourish wherever it is damp, dark, and warm. They discolor cloth, make it smell, sometimes cause it to rot. They particularly like canvas army tents in the Tropics, shower curtains, draperies in basement rooms, and porch awnings that are rolled up when wet. Losses from mildew used to be enormous—but no longer. Now we have mildew-resistant finishes that will markedly prolong the life of cotton fabrics.

The standards set for the finishes were high. They had to be comparatively easy to apply; they could not weaken the fabrics or cause excessive shrinkage; they had to be odorless and nontoxic to humans, and to be colorless or to dye the cloth a pleasing and usable shade. To be satisfactory for outdoor fabrics, mildew-resistant treatments had to withstand weathering and laundering and, preferably, resist attack by termites.

Research in the laboratories of the Bureau of Human Nutrition and Home Economics shows that it can be done. We applied more than 250 treatments to cotton fabric and subjected the treated material to chemical, physical, and biological tests.

The compounds we used were of several types: Chemicals, such as various acetylating mixtures and cuprammonium hydroxide, that change the form of the cellulose itself; resins condensed in the fibers of the material and those applied to the surface of the cloth; quaternary ammonium phosphates and halides; substituted phenolic compounds, such as o-phenylphenol, salicylanilide, tetrabromo-o-cresol, pentachlorophenol, and 2,2'-dihydroxy-5,5'-dichloro-diphenylmethane; mordants and dyes, especially extracts of natural dyes; organic salts of heavy metals, copper and zinc naphthenate, copper oleate, copper resinate, zinc dimethyl-dithiocarbamate, and various mercurial compounds; inorganic salts, used alone or combined with soap, morpholine, or 8-hydroxy-quinoline; common antiseptics like chlorothymol, phenyl salicylate, and various borates; and other organic and inorganic compounds recommended as having fungicidal properties.

The treatments were applied to cotton fabric by immersing strips of the material in a solution of the chemical at a specified concentration, temperature, and time. The strips were squeezed between rollers to remove the excess liquid, dried at room temperature, and rinsed twice. Then mildew resistance was determined by measuring the breaking strength of the treated strips after inoculation with mildew-producing organisms and incubation under controlled conditions favorable to their growth.

From the long list of finishes that proved satisfactory in resisting mildew, certain fabric treatments especially suitable for housefurnishing purposes were selected. They were applied to 7-ounce osnaburg cloth. The effectiveness of the protective treatments after exposure to weather and laundering was also determined, and some were tested for their ability to prevent termite damage.

Many methods for determining the mildew resistance of treated fabrics have been devised. They have been studied and compared by various industrial and governmental laboratories and by the Mildewproofing Subcommittee of the American Association of Textile Chemists and Colorists.

The soil-suspension method was used in this study. Samples of treated fabrics were first washed under a gentle flow of running water and then inoculated by immersing them in a suspension of soil. Thus they were subjected to many types of micro-organisms that attack cellulose. Next the test strips were placed in culture bottles and incubated under controlled temperatures and humidity for 14 days. At the end of the incubation period the samples were washed and dried and their breaking strength determined.

If cotton fabrics are to be used outside, micro-organisms are not the only influences responsible for their deterioration. Chemical tendering brought about by sunlight, air, and water also plays an important part. Unless the fabric is coated with some impervious material, no finishing treatment yet found completely reduces this atmospheric degradation. Many finishes give partial protection to fabric, however, although some mildew-resistant finishes hasten deterioration.

For this study, in order to determine the protection these mildew-resistant treatments give after weather exposure, samples of the treated fabrics were exposed to the weather for 6 weeks at Beltsville. They were tacked on racks, which faced the south and were inclined about 30° to the horizontal, so they were exposed to the sun all day. After 6 weeks, the fabrics were removed and cut into strips. Some were used for obtaining the breaking strength of the weathered material, the others were tested for their resistance to mildew.

. In determining the effectiveness of the finishing treatments after laundering, additional treated samples were washed in a 0.5 percent neutral soap solution at 38° C. The strips, five similarly-treated strips to a jar, were agitated in the soap solution for half an hour and rinsed in four changes of water. Then they were tested for mildew resistance by the soil-suspension method.

Although losses from termite attack are not so general as losses from micro-organisms, they can be very great and cause enormous waste.

Some of the treated fabrics reported here were also tested for their resistance to termite attack by a method recently developed in cooperation with the Bureau of Entomology and Plant Quarantine. Test samples of the treated fabrics were kept for 130 days on moist ground in a wooded area where a natural infestation of termites was known to exist. In preparation for the test, sticks and other debris on the surface of the ground were removed and an ordinary paper towel was placed on each cleared space and covered with a piece of 2 by 4 wood. The soil was carefully packed around the edges of the wood in order to conserve moisture. As soon as termite activity was noted beneath the paper, the fabric sample to be tested was inserted between the paper and the wood.

The resistance of the treatment to termite attack was measured by the extent to which it protected the fabric from damage. The following five degrees of infestation or damage to the strips were recognized: Heavy, 25 percent or more of the sample destroyed; medium, less than 25 percent of the sample destroyed, but more than three penetration holes; light, from one to three penetration holes; trace, no penetration holes, but light surface feeding; and none, sample undamaged.

Most of the finishes that were selected colored the fabric. Several finishes containing copper made the material blue: Copper sulfate with soap, copper naphthenate and oleate, and cuprammonium fluoride and hydroxide. The treatments using copper sulfate with 8-hydroxyquinoline colored the cloth greenish yellow. Similar treatments combining magnesium sulfate, stannous chloride, aluminum acetate and mercuric chloride with 8-hydroxyquinoline made the fabric light cream-colored, yellow, greenish yellow, and yellow orange, respectively. Lead acetate with potassium dichromate produced a yellow color. In general the natural dyes developed shades of yellow and brown. Quercitron and divi divi made the material mustard colored. The fabric dyed with osage orange was rust brown and that dyed with quebracho and cutch, chocolate brown. Fustic and logwood made the fabric greenish yellow and steel gray, respectively. The three other finishes did not color the material.

None of the treatments weakened the fabric. Some appreciably strengthened it. All except three of these treatments gave excellent protection against mildew and rotting. However, additional cuprammonium fluoride in the fabric makes this treatment equally as effective as the others. Cadmium chloride with soap was not effective although in previous studies it made cotton resistant to *Chaetomium globosum*.

In general, exposure to weather greatly lowered the breaking strength of the treated material. However, 14 of the 23 weathered treated fabrics retained most of their original strength and were somewhat stronger than the untreated weathered control. When tested for their resistance to mildew, the results showed that 11 of the 14 treatments still gave excellent protection. They are: Copper naphthenate, copper naphthenate with copper oleate, copper oleate, cuprammonium fluoride, cuprammonium hydroxide, copper sulfate with 8-hydoxyquinoline, salicylanilide, and two treatments each of osage orange and quercitron extract applied with copper sulfate and potassium dichromate.

On laundering the treated fabrics and subsequently determining their resistance to mildew, the results indicated that 8 of the 11 treatments listed above, and also mercuric chloride with 8-hydroxyquinoline, were still effective. Cuprammonium fluoride, cuprammonium hydroxide, and salicylanilide gave no protection after laundering.

In regard to resistance against termite attack, all of the finishing treatments that contained copper and mercury in their formulation—including the natural dyes—gave good to excellent protection to the fabric. All other treatments, under the conditions of this test and in the concentrations used, were ineffective in preventing termite damage.

Protective treatments for cloth must be nontoxic. If the finishes are to be used for sheets, towels, or wearing apparel, certainly tests should be made to determine whether or not the treated fabric will cause dermatitis. Another point worthy of considerable developmental work: Treatments should be practical and simple enough that they can be applied in the home without excessive cost or special equipment. Also, the behavior of treated materials on prolonged use or storage at various temperatures and humidities should be known.

THE AUTHOR

Margaret S. Furry is a textile chemist in the Bureau of Human Nutrition and Home Economics. Besides her publications on mildew prevention Miss Furry is the author of one of the Department's most popular bulletins, *Stain Removal from Fabrics: Home Methods,* as well as various technical bulletins on starches and sizes used in finishing cotton fabrics, and circulars giving methods for home dyeing with both commercial and natural dyes.

FOR FURTHER READING

Furry, Margaret S., Robinson, Helen M., and Humfeld, Harry: *Mildew-Resistant Treatments on Fabrics,* Industrial and Engineering Chemistry, Industrial Edition, volume 33, pages 538–545, 1941.

Marsh, Paul B., Greathouse, G. A., Butler, Mary L., and Bollenbacher, Katharine: *Testing Fabrics for Resistance to Mildew and Rot,* U. S. D. A. Technical Bulletin 892, 1945.

Some New Farm Machines

by R. B. GRAY

THE ACUTE labor shortage and high crop-production goals during the war emphasized the need for labor-saving machines. But before the war and after there has been a steady effort to make farming even more efficient—although, as the wartime production of American farmers proved, agriculture in the United States had reached a high point of efficiency.

A limited output of standard machines was possible during the war. Some new types even appeared in small numbers. Others were scheduled for production at the close of hostilities, but the scarcity of materials and labor held up their manufacture. Now we are on the threshold of a new era of mechanization: Many machines are now in the experimental stage; others are so recent that we do not have full information describing them and their performance; others are on draftsmen's boards, but more than a dream, because farmers, agricultural engineers, and implement manufacturers have determined that there is a need for them.

The new equipment is of the kind to excite men's imagination: A cultivator that uses a flame to kill weeds, for example; a potato harvester that digs, gathers, grades, sacks, weighs, and delivers the potatoes to a waiting truck, with an estimated saving of $50 a day or more over the old way of handling the crop; an experimental planter, developed by Department engineers for southern planters of corn and peanuts, that opens the beds, plants the seed, and places fertilizer at one time; the cotton picker that extracts the lint cotton from the open bolls; sugarcane harvesting machines that cut the cane and load it—at a speed of 7 or 8 miles an hour, and an estimated saving of one-half to two-thirds of the hand-harvest labor.

A striking feature of these and many other developments is the growing interest of farmers in the South in mechanization. Another feature is that designers of implements are determined to furnish machines that will reduce the small farmer's drudgery at a price he can pay.

Great strides have been made in improving the design and uses of tractors, the main source of mechanical power on the farm. Emphasis now is on small units for the Southeast and on garden tractors. For the crawler tractor an adaptation from war service is the rubber-tread track (next page, at the top), to replace the conventional steel type. A tractor so equipped can do about 14 miles an hour on highways with less vibration. An hydraulic lift now incorporated in most wheel tractors permits fingertip control in lifting plows, harrows, mowers, and such from the ground, lowering them to a wanted position, or (middle, next page) raising the tractor to change tires. A tractor, shown (lower left) with a direct-connected vegetable planter, is between the conventional one-plow tractor and the garden tractor in size, and is rated at 10 horsepower on the belt. It will pull a 10- or 12-inch single-furrow plow or handle the type of attachments and drawn equipment commonly used with larger row-crop tractors. A speed range up to 6 miles an hour makes it possible to plow 3 acres a day with a 12-inch plow. On large farms it can supplement larger tractors. A new 1½-horsepower garden tractor (lower right) has a speed change based on the shifting of a driven disk with which the driving rolls engage. As the going gets tougher the disk is automatically moved for slower travel without altering, theoretically, the power output. Attachments available are a 7-inch plow, small disk harrow, mower, and cultivator. A maximum speed of 4 miles per hour and a plowing speed of 1 mile per hour is claimed for it. Other new tractors of this class have appeared.

THE AUTHOR

R. B. Gray is an agricultural engineer in charge of the Division of Farm Power and Machinery of the Bureau of Plant Industry, Soils, and Agricultural Engineering. After graduation from Iowa State College, he entered commercial tractor experimental work and spent most of the following 10 years in such investigations in Europe and South Africa. During the First World War he was loaned to the British Government to conduct educational demonstrations and schools on the use of tractors in connection with the food production program. Later, at the request of the British Government, he organized similar programs in France and Italy. From 1920 to 1924 Mr. Gray was head of the Agricultural Engineering Department at the University of Idaho.

TILLAGE MACHINERY.—Several new machines plow, disk, and harrow a seedbed in one operation. One, at right, uses a steel cutter spiral revolving in the soil transversely to the direction of travel and powered by the power take-off. As the machine moves forward soil and surface trash are thrown up against the leveling hood; the broken trash is distributed through the top inches of soil, and the soil is more or less pulverized. We do not know definitely what effect such seedbed preparation has on soil structure and crop growth. For breaking up hardpan formed after years of ordinary plowing at the same depth, a double-decker moldboard plow (below) is being offered. The lower bottom breaks the hardpan without bringing it to the surface, is adjustable vertically, and may be set 2 to 4 inches below the upper bottom, according to the soil. The shares on both the upper and lower bottom are of 10-inch size, but the lower one is set outward and backward and offset away from the upper base by 4 inches, thereby making a full 14-inch cut. It is said that very little additional pull is required for this plow than with the conventional 14-inch tractor plow and that its use increases yields of certain crops.

PLANTING MACHINERY.—Special attention has been given the development of quick methods of attaching and detaching planter equipment. A four-row tractor-mounted corn planter with fertilizer attachment is available; it can be attached or removed quickly. The fertilizer is placed in bands a few inches to the side of the seed and at the depth of the seed. Available also are two- or four-row corn planters with rope-controlled power lifts for pulling behind tractors. Covering wheels are independent of transport wheels and are lifted automatically with the planting shoes and marker when the power-lift rope is pulled. A differential is provided for the transport wheels. It is said that 60 acres a day can be planted with the four-row machine. Airplanes are frequently used to plant large acreages, for example rice, range grasses, and mustard. Rice fields to be air-planted usually are flooded first and seeded at about 50 acres an hour.

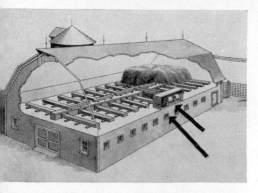

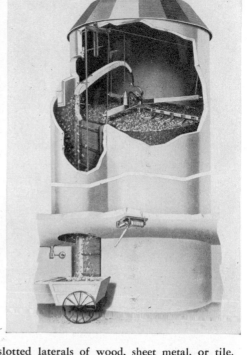

A two-row corn harvester cuts the stalks, passing them butts first into the machine. The ears are picked, husked, discharged into a wagon; stalks are shredded and most of the corn borers inside them are killed.

To preserve leafiness and carotene in curing hay mow-drying is becoming popular. Usually built in the mow, the system is essentially an electric-motor-driven blower and a system of ducts (top, left). The blower forces cold air through a main duct of wood and then through slotted laterals of wood, sheet metal, or tile. Sometimes a slatted floor replaces the laterals. Hay in mows should be dried to a moisture content below 20 percent in 8 days for best results. Before the hay is dried it is cut in the field, wilted to 40–50 percent, then put in the mow about 8 feet deep atop the laterals.

A new silo unloader (above) has scrapers that revolve as a unit, booms to hold it in the center, a 2-horsepower electric motor, suction fan, and a discharge pipe.

A unit for stacking hay, loading manure, piling logs, gathering grain shocks, etc., is shown to the right. Its hydraulic system permits control from the tractor seat.

WEEDS.—A new one-man flame weeder (above) appears to perform well on crops like cotton and corn and on certain weeds. A hot air-blast flame burns weed leaves as the machine is drawn along the rows. Two burners flame one row. A 3-mile speed prevents undue heating of plants. The four-row size can cultivate up to 50 acres a day.

HARVESTING.—Many innovations have appeared in harvesting machinery. Several are shown on next page. A self-propelled one-man combine, 7 to 14 feet wide, has a front cutter bar so that fields can be opened, finished, and weed patches bypassed. Propelling and supporting unit is usually an adaptation of a rubber-tired tractor (top picture). The combine harvests all threshable crops in one operation. As the machine proceeds in the field the cut grain is conveyed from both sides of the swath to the center of the platform, then up to the cylinder and threshed. For harvesting rice, tires on drive wheels have large lugs—sometimes crawler tracks. For combining grain gathered into windrows, a pick-up device replaces the cutter bar (second picture from top).

HAYING.—A new way to harvest hay is the pick-up baler (third photo from top). Hay is cut by a mower, dried a few hours to moisture content of about 20 percent, windrowed, then baled with this type of machine. A pick-up device lifts the hay to a conveyor and thence to the baling chamber where a knife slices it just before compressing. Bales are up to 42 inches long and 85 pounds. Capacity ranges to 6 tons an hour.

Another new method of haying is the pick-up chopper (lower picture). Generally operated by the power take-off from a tractor, it chops field-cured hay from windrow or standing green hay for silage. By use of a suitable attachment it also chops row crops like corn and sorghum. In field-harvesting grass silage, the unit is provided with a cutter bar and a special reel for picking up mowed material and to aid in getting the material to the chopping box where the grass is chopped and conveyed into a wagon. It is then taken to the silo, dumped into a screw conveyor leading to a blower which blows the material through pipes into a silo as with the regular stationary silage cutter.

POTATO DIGGERS.—Of several new potato harvesters, one is said to dig, pick, and sack potatoes in any kind of soil. Two men run it. A power take-off of a tractor or auxiliary engine furnishes power (upper picture). For another type a rate of 400 bushels an hour is claimed.

COTTON PICKERS.—The first patent for a machine to pick cotton was granted in 1850; ever since, cotton farmers have been intensely interested in mechanical harvesting and inventors patented more than 1,800 devices, most of them of doubtful practicality. Wartime labor shortages, however, added incentive to making and using the pickers. Different views of one model are shown at left and below. Its mechanism includes rotating barbed spindles that pick cotton from each side of the plant, rubber doffers to remove the cotton from the spindles, vacuum conveyor system, and grates for removing dirt. Its speed is about 2 miles an hour. Its maker says it averages a 500-pound bale in 75 minutes—40 or 50 times faster than average hand pickers. The use of a preharvest defoliant is of material aid to picking.

OTHER LABOR SAVERS.—Special attachments increase the utility of tractors. A manure loader (top picture) scoops manure from pile or shed onto a spreader. One man can load 20 tons an hour, five times faster than loading by hand. A post-hole digger (above, left) makes fast work of a slow job. One man can operate it. Of several new kinds of saws, the one shown above fells trees, cuts logs, and clears brush. Machines are now available to harvest much of the sugarcane crop like the one shown below operating in a field near Houma, La.

Several types of sugar-beet harvesters are now available (top picture). An attachment on a two-bottom plow (above) places fertilizer in a single band on the bottom of each plow furrow. A simple machine (at right) can turn out 300 pounds of shelled seed peanuts an hour, the amount a man can shell by hand in 300 hours, and do it better. Airplanes dust and spray crops (below), transport farm produce, seed fields, and protect forests.

NEW USES
FOR
FARM PRODUCTS

Specifications for new farm products and new ways of using them have resulted from research carried on by the Department, mainly at its four regional research laboratories, and under the direction of the Bureau of Agricultural and Industrial Chemistry. A quick glimpse of some of the accomplishments of recent years is given in these pages. Special equipment is required to test the merits of a new product or process, as indicated in the picture above that shows a section of the pilot plant at Peoria, Ill., where new ways of making alcohol from grain are tried out on a semicommercial scale. The 200-gallon vat fermenter (right), also at the Peoria laboratory, is used to produce penicillin in submerged culture.

As a result of research to make starch from wheat, two processes have been developed for producing wheat starch that is convertible into sirup, sugar, or industrial alcohol. One step of the so-called batter process is demonstrated above, left, by a pilot-plant aide at the Peoria laboratory. At right, above, Walter M. Scott, Director of the Southern Regional Laboratory at New Orleans, examines some attractive new fabrics made from a low-grade cotton not before used for such purposes. Chemical Engineer Samuel Aronovsky grinds peanut shells (below) into a material known as Noreseal. It is being tested for use in bottle closures.

Research at the regional laboratory at Philadelphia has made possible the commercial manufacture of rutin, a preparation prescribed for strengthening capillary walls. The green buckwheat plant is an economical source of the drug, a fact that was disclosed by James F. Couch of the Department's laboratory staff after a 2-year search. In the above photo Dr. Couch (left) and J. Naghski examine a sample of rutin powder. Some of the equipment used in extracting the medicinal rutin from green buckwheat on a pilot-plant scale is shown below.

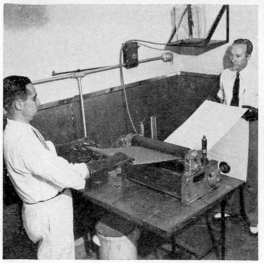
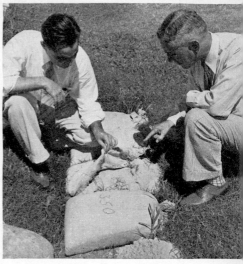

At the New Orleans laboratory W. B. Strickland (above, left) and W. N. Berard apply a rot-proof treatment to cotton fabric from which sandbags are made. The effectiveness of the treatment is shown at right, above. The treated bag (in foreground) resisted rot damage, while the untreated one, under identical conditions, almost completely disintegrated. Another ac-complishment of the New Orleans laboratory is a semielastic bandage fabric shown at left, below. Made by a modified mercerization process, this new all-cotton material will bend and stretch with the flexing of a joint and will expand with the swelling of an injury. Medical authorities say this fabric has many advantages over the ordinary bandage.

The scope of farm products from which new things can be made is virtually limitless. At the regional laboratory at Albany, Calif., R. A. O'Connell (above) prepares to test the merits of an experimental fiber of which poultry feathers are the main ingredient. A domestic source of tannin may result from research at the Philadelphia laboratory where Western hemlock bark, canaigre, and scrub oak bark are being used in experiments. Below, Technologist W. D. May takes from a vacuum drum drier test batch of scrub oak bark tanning extract.

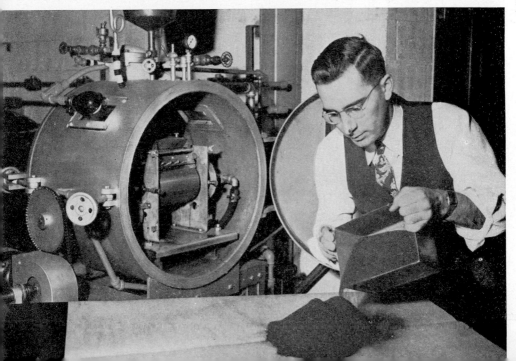

An improved process for manufacturing pectin from apple pomace (above, left) has been developed at the Albany, Calif., laboratory. Apple essence, another byproduct of apples, is being tested at the Philadelphia laboratory. In the photo at right, above, apple essence is being added to jelly to give it a flavor obtainable in no other way. Below, a laboratory aide measures out the right amount of apple essence to give candy a characteristic apple flavor. For a general article regarding various developments in farm byproducts, see page 689.

From whey, a byproduct of milk, the laboratory at Philadelphia has produced a rubber-like material known as lactoprene. Being resistant to oil, oxidation, sunlight, and heat, it seems to have possibilities for many special uses. In the picture at left, above, a laboratory worker adds the initiator or catalyst to the lactoprene emulsion. At right, above, a tensile strength test is given to a strip of the vulcanized product and, below, a chunk of the lactoprene compound is being refined on a roll mill before it is vulcanized. (For further details see page 694.)

A wool-like fiber has been developed from casein, another byproduct of milk. Above, Earle O. Whittier of the Bureau of Dairy Industry examines a tray of moist casein that has been partially dried in a special oven. The fiber takes wool dyes and thus can be blended with wool in making fabrics. Among the many uses found for soybeans, oil paint is significant. In the picture below, its qualities for marking traffic lines are being given a practical test.

Simplifying Farm Work

by E. C. YOUNG and L. S. HARDIN

CAREFUL thought and study can reveal ways to do almost every farm job easier, faster, and more effectively. The job may be dairy chores, or cutting potatoes, raising tobacco, making hay, feeding hogs, picking tomatoes; the time spent in doing it can be reduced and a better job can be done.

Efficient farm production involves management decisions of at least two major types. One is concerned primarily with what to do—what crops and livestock to produce, what to feed the animals, what fertilizer and crop varieties to use, and what sanitary precautions to take against diseases. Such decisions are important. But much more is involved in getting efficient production than determining just what should be done.

Once the "what" is decided, the second type of decision, "how-to-do-it," must be made. The simplification of farm work is concerned primarily with the how—the work methods used in performing the countless tasks of the farm worker. It is the systematic application of ingenuity and common sense to searching out, developing, and using the easiest, most effective, and economical way to do a job.

As production scientists develop new technical improvements in what to do, a knowledge of how to use the innovations may be essential to their acceptance. Studies of how hog producers in the Corn Belt do their work, for example, show that most farmers know what should be done to produce hogs free of disease and parasites. But many farmers fail to raise hogs on clean rotation pasture because it is hard to get water to the hogs. When an easy way to water the hogs is not readily available, the whole hog sanitation program may break down.

In the past 20 years the average labor requirements for crops like corn, wheat, oats, and soybeans have dropped 20 to 40 percent. Recent studies of small groups of farms in Illinois show that an acre of corn can be produced with only about 7 hours of labor, and an acre of soybeans can be produced with about 4 hours of work; 20 years ago labor requirements were more than double those figures. While for the most part mechanical methods have replaced the man labor, there has been a net reduction in farm costs.

The average labor requirements for livestock work show no such decreases, however. It still takes farmers around 140 to 150 hours a year to care for a milk cow, 5 to 7 hours to raise a market hog, and around 2 hours a year to care for a hen. Requirements were essentially the same 20 years ago. The figures are especially significant when we recognize that chore work with livestock enterprises takes up one-third to one-half of the average farmer's yearly labor requirements.

The figures, however, are averages. Studies on individual farms by research workers in 12 State experiment stations show that farmers can do something about improving their work methods, that farmers are doing jobs easier and better while increasing production and reducing costs. How they are doing it is but a sample of how other alert farmers can and will improve their methods.

Work methods used by five efficient hog farmers in Indiana were studied for a year. There is still room for improvement, of course, but the farmers produced 225-pound market hogs in an average of 1.7 hours of work per head, compared to the Indiana average of 5 to 7 hours. The farmers produced 100 market hogs (raising spring and fall litters) in a total of about 7 weeks (500 hours) less work than average.

To do this they worked out and used a definite system of hog management and housing. Cropping systems were arranged for adequate clean rotation pasture. Pigs, sows, and fattening hogs had a definite place each season of the year. Preparatory jobs—cleaning, arranging houses, storing feed—were completed at odd times before needed. An easy method of providing adequate water was worked out. Depending upon the particular farm's arrangement and needs, pressure water systems, field wells, or large-capacity water hauling systems were used. Feed was stored, prepared, and handled economically. Self-feeders, convenient field storage, self-feeding cribs, and feeding floors were used to minimize handling of grain. Adequate, economical equipment was provided. Plenty of farrowing houses, adequate fencing, supplemental farrowing heat (often homemade hovers), and a generous supply of small equipment aided in getting jobs done well with a minimum of time, cost, and hard work.

Some dairymen care for their herds in far less than the average 140 to 150 hours a cow a year. In northern Indiana a group of farmers with herds of 13 to 20 cows did the work in 92 hours per cow. A group of their neighbors with the same numbers of cows and similar equipment but poorer work methods spent an average of 153 hours per cow. Production rates and feeding efficiency were similar for the two groups of farms but the men with the larger labor requirements had higher costs.

In Vermont a dairy farmer, who had 22 cows and was already above average in efficiency, decided to improve his methods. In 4 months, with the aid of a research worker from the University of Vermont, he reduced his daily chore time by 2 hours, 5 minutes and reduced daily walking by 2 miles. His annual saving of 760 hours and 730 miles of walking was accomplished by practicing correct machine milking on a 4-minute time interval, rearranging the interior of the barn to permit circular travel, removing obstructive posts and sills and changing doors, putting loads on wheels, using feed, silage, and manure carts, locating hay chutes near mangers, throwing silage directly from silo to cart, and providing a convenient, readily accessible work center for equipment and supplies. He spent less than $50 and now does his work much more easily even though he has increased the size of his herd.

A Minnesota dairyman keeping 13 cows and 14 other cattle accomplished similar savings. He reduced his daily winter dairy chores from 3 hours, 39 minutes, to 2 hours and 45 minutes—a 27-percent saving. In doing this he is saving 37 percent of the walking, or 138 miles a year. His changes in work methods were similar to those of the Vermont farmer. Milking, feeding, and watering methods were changed, chore routes rearranged, and small equipment, including carts and drinking cups, were added. These and other studies provide some standards for comparison. They suggest, for example, that if machine milking is not completed in around 4 minutes per cow, methods need improvement.

In a preliminary study of methods used with Indiana farm poultry flocks, one poultryman did his daily chores in 1½ minutes for each 100 hens; another spent more than an hour for that number of hens.

Preliminary studies of this kind indicate that poultry-chore time on some farms can be reduced by as much as one-half through proper planning, convenient feed storage, using deep litter and roosting racks, and making each trip count. A study in New York revealed that some poultrymen take care of 1,000 hens in 2 hours a day, but others care for the same number in 21 minutes.

Study of haying jobs on 72 Vermont farms shows that how a man works is more important than what he works with. This is illustrated by the fact that on one farm the total time required to move hay from windrow to mow was 62 man-minutes of work per ton. Another farm required 313 man-minutes. The 10 farmers handling hay the fastest required 62 to 85 minutes a ton—and these 10 farmers used all types and combinations of equipment. True, method and equipment can eliminate some work as with the chopper or by using a barn mower—a tilting platform used to distribute hay in the mow. But every operator can find easier ways to use his existing equipment and can benefit by planning the harvesting job through, giving attention to the tracks and doors of the storage barn, and maintaining machinery in the best possible working order. It is important to know how to get the most out of existing tools. For poor operators, little is to be gained by purchasing complicated machinery. For each of the haying jobs some farmers using out-of-date equipment are able to beat the average operating time of operators using much more modern haying devices.

In studies of tobacco production and harvesting, improved methods that save from one-fourth to two-thirds of the labor previously required have been developed and tested for several important tasks. Tobacco jobs are largely repetitive, equipment is relatively simple, and labor requirements per acre with usual methods are great. In tobacco work, specific recommendations as to how the work should be done can have general application. The Kentucky studies of burley tobacco production have developed improved methods which result in per acre savings of about 10 hours in pulling plants; 11 hours in machine setting; 19 to 20 hours in priming; 20 to 40 percent in cutting and spearing; and 15 percent in housing and stripping. None of the improved methods involves costly equipment.

Significant improvements in methods of harvesting vegetable crops— celery, potatoes, tomatoes, green beans—have been made by studying and improving commonly used practices. For example, in Colorado an improved method of cutting seed potatoes was developed that enables the average farm worker to cut 25 percent more seed potatoes in a day and do it easier than by any other disinfected knife or mechanical disk previously in use. Pathological tests have been completed that show that the new method is entirely satisfactory from a disease-control standpoint. The use of the method extends to any farmer a satisfactory method of controlling ring rot with an investment of only $10 to $20 in equipment. The method involves use of a stationary, vertical, double-edged knife attached to a specially designed gravity-feed cutting table.

In a Florida study of celery production, harvesting, and packing, improved methods resulting in an over-all saving up to about 40 percent in labor requirements were developed.

Another food processing study involving tomato-canning factory operations is also nearing completion. These two studies show that variations in efficiency and cost among processing and marketing organizations are about as great as among farms.

Where hand work, rather than mechanical methods of harvest, must still be used, increases in a worker's accomplishment of 5 to 40 percent have been achieved. Because conditions for doing field work are more uniform from farm to farm than with livestock, rather specific suggestions can be made. They are simple, make good common sense, and for the most part summarize what good, efficient workers do.

Arrange the job so that both hands can work. Equal, simultaneous use of both hands usually increases output by about 40 percent over use of one hand alone.

Keep both hands fairly close together for greater hand-eye coordination. Some jobs may be made easier by using the hands rhythmically.

Fill hands full before moving them to the container. As much as 70 percent of picking time is spent in moving fruit or vegetables from the plant to picking container.

Keep picking container—wagon, basket, bag, or bucket—as close to the fruits or plants as possible to reduce hand and foot travel.

Use a picking container adapted to the job. For apple picking a lightweight picking bucket of full-box capacity attached to the worker with comfortable harness, speeds up the job and makes it easier. A detachable handle for the hamper makes tomato picking easier. And the use of a potato picking belt (which supports a bag dragged between the worker's legs) has been found to increase the quantity of potatoes picked by as much as 30 percent.

Approach any hand-harvest job in an orderly fashion. Determine whether one or two rows should be picked at a time. Work over a plant (cotton or tomato, for example) or fruit tree systematically to avoid re-working the same area several times.

Follow through and simplify the removal of the harvested crop from the field. Have adequate field roads. Arrange the picking path to have a full container when road or assembly area is reached.

Give inexperienced workers clear, complete instructions on how the job is to be done.

To summarize the results of the studies: It may be said that farmers seldom take time to save time. Yet the commercial farmer's time is becoming increasingly valuable as managerial requirements become more exacting. A man working with a hoe wastes no one's time but his own if he works inefficiently. But if inefficient methods tie up and delay the work of $5,000 worth of farm machinery, the time lost has a high dollar value. And with growing plants and animals timeliness often means the difference between success and failure, profit and loss. Anything that breaks the production sequence on a modern commerical farm creates losses at a rapid rate. That is why time invested in study and improvement of work methods may be among the most profitable hours put in by the farm manager.

In the improvement of any job, as in the examples cited, one or more of the following types of improvements may be made:

Physical work can be simplified through the use of easier body motions, fuller use of both hands, arrangement for less walking, stooping, lifting, and carrying, increased comfort and safety for workers, reduced hours, provision of rest periods, adjustments in crew size, integration of responsibilities of crew members, and better integration of man and machine work.

Equipment and lay-out can be changed by altering the kind or design of a machine tool or device to displace man labor or meet more economically the job requirements; relocating equipment, supplies, or facilities for better accessibility and greater convenience; rearranging building and fence locations and building interiors to decrease travel and permit improved work routines.

Production processes and practices may be changed by rescheduling certain jobs into less busy seasons, increasing the timeliness of crop and livestock operations, or otherwise altering production processes and practices for greater effectiveness.

This involves a study of practices, such as fall versus spring plowing, drilling versus checking corn, around-the-field versus back-and-forth planting, self-feeding versus hand feeding, hand stripping versus machine stripping of cows, and producing hogs on the one- or two-litter system.

Farm people need not wait for research workers to bring them suggestions for improved work methods. They can continue to develop many improvements themselves. Farmers should think about any job they do in terms of chances for improvement. Just what should be accomplished? Why do it? Is there a good reason for doing each part of the job just as planned? How many hours of work, how much machinery expense, walking, carrying, or shoveling will this method require? Do neighbors do it easier or cheaper and at the same time do an equally good or better job?

Chances are that serious answers to questions like these will reveal that some easier, better ways are already known. Some of the things we do serve no useful purpose. They may be holdovers from old methods of other jobs. Past experience, tradition, and the way Dad did it are all helpful guides if they do not prevent our keeping up-to-date on improved methods and equipment.

Because no two farms are exactly alike, no master plan or schedule of work will fit every farm. Each farmer must work out for himself the easiest, least expensive way of getting his jobs done properly and on time. Studies such as those reported above help; the pamphlets listed at the end of this article might also be useful. To improve methods on your own:

Figure out just what you now do and how you now do it. Note your accomplishment, time, and cost.

Compare your methods and accomplishments with others. Make a point of observing how neighbors do their field and chore work, how they arrange their barns and care for their livestock. You probably have been too busy doing your own work to see how others do theirs. Go visiting.

Question the details of your work method for chances to eliminate and rearrange, reduce man or machine travel, and avoid practices that cause delay and waste time. Strive for greater comfort for the worker. Relocate tools and supplies for convenience.

Apply the results of your analysis. Give yourself time to become reasonably familiar with the changed procedure so that the new method has a fair trial. Then go ahead to improve another job.

THE AUTHORS

E. C. Young is dean of the Graduate School and professor of agricultural economics at Purdue University. Dr. Young has made significant research and teaching contributions in farm management, agricultural prices, and agricultural finance during his 25 years of work in this field. Research in farm work simplification was initiated and carried forward under his supervision and guidance as Director of the National Farm Work Simplification Project.

L. S. Hardin is assistant professor of agricultural economics at Purdue University. Dr. Hardin's principal area of work is research and teaching in farm management and work simplification.

ACKNOWLEDGMENT

Twelve agricultural experiment stations cooperated in the 2-year experimental Farm Work Simplification Research Project, 1943–45. This research was made possible by a grant from the General Education Board. Cooperating States are Colorado, Florida, Illinois, Indiana, Kentucky, Minnesota, New York, New Jersey, Nebraska, Oregon, Vermont, and Washington. Many of these, and other States in addition, are continuing or developing work-simplification research projects.

FOR FURTHER READING

Bierly, I. R.: *Steps Take Time in Watering Hens,* Cornell University Extension Leaflet, 1945.

Byers, G. B., Nesius, E. J., and Young, Earl: *Easier Ways to do Farm Work,* series of University of Kentucky Extension leaflets on tobacco, numbers 75, 76, 79, 84, 86, 90, 92, 1944, 1945.

Carter, R. M.: *Labor Saving Through Farm Job Analysis,* Vermont Experiment Station Bulletin 503, 1943.

Carter, R. M.: *Hay Harvesting,* Vermont Experiment Station Bulletin 531, 1946.

Eugene, S. A.: *Saving Seconds,* Minnesota Farm Business Notes, No. 269, May 1945.

Hardin, L. S.: *Study Your Own Farm Work Methods,* Purdue Agricultural Experiment Station Circular 307, 1947.

Mundel, M. E., and Fraser, R. R.: *An Easy Way to Peel Canning Tomatoes,* Purdue University Extension Leaflet 258, 1944.

Oberholtzer, J. W., and Hardin, L. S.: *Simplifying the Work and Management of Hog Production,* Purdue University Extension Bulletin 506, 1945.

Paschal, J. L.: *Easier and Faster Ways of Cutting Seed Potatoes,* Colorado Experiment Station Bulletin, 1946.

Young, E. C.: *A Study of Farm Lay-out in Indiana,* Purdue Agricultural Experiment Station Bulletin 423, 1937.

Machines for Sweetpotatoes

by O. A. BROWN

Machines for tilling and harvesting sweetpotatoes can be used to just as good advantage as those used for other crops if a well-organized procedure is followed. Friable soil, ridges of equal width and uniform spacing, a good stand of plants in the ridge centers, and rows that can be followed with a tractor are prerequisites for mechanical cultivation.

Equipment used for building sweetpotato ridges should be, if possible, useful in other tillage operations. Single ridges can be built quickly and easily with 12-inch disks on the cultivator of a one-row tractor. Two disks, which can be adjusted independently, placed on each side of the cultivator will build suitable ridges. The disks should be adjusted to build a broad bed at least 8 inches high. It is common practice to build the rows on 42-inch centers.

For making ridges for two-row cultivation, a tractor that can build two rows at a time is needed. A middlebuster mounted on the center line of the tractor and two 14-inch triple-gang disks to build up the outer sides of the beds make a good combination for the purpose.

Ridges should be built 2 or 3 weeks before transplanting time so that the soil will become firm and weed seeds on the surface will germinate. Heavy rains may beat down the ridges and wash loose soil into the middles, but it is necessary to recondition the ridges at transplanting time and they may be rebuilt to the desired shape just before transplanting.

Texas-type sweeps have been found satisfactory for the reconditioning operation. Two 26-inch sweeps may be used for one row and one full and two half sweeps for two rows. Adjustment of the sweeps is important, for they fix the shapes of the ridges for cultivating. Sides of the ridges have the correct slope and the sweeps are adjusted correctly when the loose soil moves up the blades and is deposited on the tops of the beds. If all the soil flows across the blades, the sweeps are running too deep or are too flat or are too close together.

The height of the beds may be gaged by a plank mounted on the rear cultivator frame of a one-row tractor or on the drawbar of a two-row tractor. The plank, measuring 8 by 2 by 24 inches, should be mounted so that its 2 by 24-inch edge is in contact with the ridge directly over its center and parallel to the axle of the tractor. It should be set to board off the bed at the proper height for transplanting. The operations of shaping the ridges, boarding them off, and putting down fertilizer may be done at one time.

A simple transplanter—consisting of a water tank (a 55-gallon drum), a water distributor with a valve for regulating the water flow, a furrow opener, and two slides for packing the plants—may be mounted on a tractor. The furrow opener should be mounted as nearly under the center line of the rear axle of the tractor as possible. Such mounting will make it easy to follow the center of the ridges in fields where the rows are curved.

The equal distribution of plants will facilitate cultivation, and a uniform stand will shade the soil and help to prevent weed growth on the tops of the beds. Weed competition is an important factor in cultivation, and any delay in planting gives the weeds an advantage. Plants should be given the best possible start; early planting and plenty of water, with the soil well-packed around the plant roots, are important in proper tillage.

The mechanical cultivation of sweetpotatoes has two objectives: Removing weeds from the rows and keeping the ridges uniformly shaped. The first cultivating can be done with 26-inch Texas-type sweeps. Adjustment of the sweeps is important, as a very small difference in angle will make the difference between good and poor cultivation. The sweeps should be run shallow, so that the soil will be pulverized and move along the blades to the tops of the beds and be deposited near the small plants. The speed of the tractor is also important.

As soon as the plants begin to put them out, the runners should be directed along the tops of the beds and not permitted to run into the middles. Spring-tooth cultivators mounted on the tractor may be used effectively for removing small weeds from the tops of the ridges and for pulling the sweetpotato vines so that the first runners are parallel with the rows. The tractor should always be driven in the same direction along the rows and at a speed to prevent breaking the vines. As the vines grow, more space should be left between the spring teeth. This method of cultivation should be continued until the tops of the beds are completely covered with vines. The sweeps should be used to cultivate the middles and to shape the sides of the ridges.

Frequent shallow cultivation is most effective. Very young weeds can be killed much easier than older ones and do not clog the cultivating equipment. It is good practice to cultivate sweetpotatoes as soon after a rain as the soil can be worked and as often between rains as is needed. Weeds should not be permitted to get a start.

Sweetpotato vines for feed are available for the cost of harvesting and processing. It is an advantage to have the vines out of the way of the digging operation. The engineering problem of designing and building a machine that will meet requirements of the average sweetpotato grower for removing sweetpotato vines for feed is being solved. In 1944 we began developing a machine for collecting sweetpotato vines for feed. A tractor-operated machine was designed and built, and had its first field trials in the summer of 1945. In a field with uniform ridges and clear of weeds we found that vines can be harvested at the rate of one-half acre an hour; in heavy vine 10 to 20 tons can be harvested in 1 day with a light tractor.

The vine-harvesting machine has two parts: A mechanism for freeing the vines from the soil and adjacent rows, and a drum and elevator for picking them up and loading them. Two 8-inch moon coulters with two 32-inch Texas-type half sweeps free the vines from one row so that they may be lifted. A cast-iron wheel 15 inches in diameter, with a 5-inch tread, rolls just behind the sweeps and presses the vines against the top of the ridge.

The pick-up drum and elevating mechanism is attached to the drawbar of the tractor. A 12-inch drum with four sets of disappearing fingers picks up the vines from the ridges and delivers them to the elevator, which carries them high enough to be loaded onto a trailer.

Sweetpotatoes may be plowed out with a turning plow, a middlebuster, or a potato digger. In preliminary tests, the broad-based bottom plow (16-inch) has shown the least damage to the sweetpotatoes. The Irish-potato digger, however, has the advantage of bringing all the roots to the surface. Less time is then required to pick them up.

Removing the vines from the rows makes digging operations easier with any method but it is especially beneficial when the potato digger is used. The throat does not clog, and there are no vines to hold the roots while they are being bruised by the moving chain or to hairpin around the blade at the ends of the rows. If the moisture condition is right, the sweetpotatoes will ride up the digger chain cushioned by a layer of soil and will fall onto a pulverized bed. More experimenting is being done with digging and handling methods to determine the injury caused by each method. Our data are not conclusive, but there are factors that are in favor of the potato digger for handling a large crop.

THE AUTHOR

O. A. Brown, an agricultural engineer in the Bureau of Plant Industry, Soils, and Agricultural Engineering, has specialized in the improvement of the castor-bean, peanut, and tung nut hulling machines, and the peanut digging machine. Dr. Brown holds degrees from West Virginia University and Iowa State College.

New Fertilizer Machines

by GLENN A. CUMINGS

FERTILIZERS do the most good when the right amount of the right kind is applied in exactly the right place. It must be applied at a constant rate and evenly, so that all plants get equal amounts of food. The right place is a definite position with respect to the seed or plant. To do this, many new machines have been developed for one crop or condition after another in recent years. More than 100 American manufacturers now make several hundred items of equipment for distributing fertilizer. Improvements and changes in details of design are frequent as new needs and ideas develop, plant-food materials are produced in different forms, farm practices change, and research men and engineers are called on to find answers to new problems.

Placing the fertilizer in a band at one side or both sides of the row is an effective and reliable method that can be used under a wide range of conditions for a large number of crops. The best location of the band in most cases is 2 to 3 inches to the side of the seed or transplant, and 3 to 5 inches below the surface of the soil. The desirable position of the fertilizer at the side of the row differs somewhat for the various crops, amounts of fertilizer, and other conditions.

Even in the case of unusually heavy applications, where major portions of the fertilizer can be deeply applied in several different ways before planting, it is well to put a reasonable amount of the plant food at the side of the row to stimulate the growth of the very young seedling. A possible exception is in highly specialized crops grown in closely spaced rows, when it may be best to incorporate thoroughly adequate amounts of fertilizer all over the tilled area.

The first machines for side placement of the fertilizer, produced by a few manufacturers 10 years ago, consisted mainly of certain types of corn, cotton, and potato planters, and tractor attachments for cotton. The runner-frame type of corn planter was equipped to place the fertilizer along each side of the row, slightly above seed level, either in continuous bands or short bands at each hill. The other machines placed the fertilizer in a continuous band at one side or both sides of the row. The newer improved equipment for the purpose includes planting and fertilizer distributing attachments for general-purpose and garden tractors, various types of cotton planters, machines solely for applying fertilizer, transplanters, vegetable crop drills, and beet and bean drills.

Equipment regularly mounted on general-purpose tractors of various sizes is available for placing the fertilizer in a band at the side of the row. Two arrangements are employed. One provides for a single placement of the fertilizer by having the seed and fertilizer furrow openers mounted closely together in a fixed relative position.

The other makes use of the cultivator frame as a part of the fertilizer attachment, thus permitting the shifting of the furrow opener to different positions and also the use of different kinds of furrowing shovels or tools. The equipment can be used for various crops, including corn, cotton, and beans, through use of interchangeable seed plates.

Cultivators of both horse-drawn and tractor-mounted types with fertilizer attachments and walking-type, single-row distributors are ordinarily used for side dressing fertilizer to crops at different stages of growth. Side dressing during cultivation combines the two operations and permits placing the plant food below the surface of the soil. In some areas special tractor attachments have been devised for custom work.

Sometimes on irrigated land it is desirable to side dress fertilizer as deep as 6 inches. Tools for the purpose have been developed to deposit the fertilizer in narrow bands with little disturbance of the soil.

The potato planter is one of the types of machines on which the fertilizer side-placement feature was first used. Two single disks are most commonly employed to open a furrow at each side of the row for the fertilizer. Such equipment is available on one-row, horse-drawn planters and two- and four-row tractor-operated planters. Provision also is made for using one disk of regular size and another larger disk, by means of which one band of fertilizer is placed about 2 inches deeper than the other. Or, the fertilizer can either be divided equally between the two bands or a larger amount can be deposited in the deeper band.

Changes with respect to placement have also been made on a number of the single-row, walking-type machines extensively used over a large part of the Cotton Belt. Separate distributing machines have been equipped to deposit the customary amounts of fertilizer in two bands about 6 inches apart. Combination planting and fertilizer-distributing machines have been designed to apply relatively small amounts of fertilizer in a band at the side of the row. In some instances, two or more of these small walking-type machines have been mounted on tractors.

A newly developed machine applies the usual amounts of fertilizer in the desired position at each side of the row. The planting unit is free to swing to either side as required in following curved rows. The planting unit can also be detached to permit the use of the distributor separately.

A number of conventional machines and some special ones other than those mentioned are now equipped to place the fertilizer at the side of the row. For example, the latest designs of four-row and six-row beet and bean drills permit the placement of the fertilizer about an inch to one side and an inch below the level of the seed. Vegetable crop drills of various sizes also have the fertilizer side-placement feature. Special multiple-row distributors for applying fertilizer in two bands as a separate operation before setting plants have been assembled.

Several methods of placing fertilizer deeply in the soil—intended mainly for heavy applications—have been included in field experiments and used on a number of farms. A part of the fertilizer, however, is usually placed at the side of the row near the seed for immediate benefit to the young seedling.

In one of the deep-placement methods, the fertilizer is deposited in a single narrow band on the bottom of each plow furrow usually at depths 6 to 8 inches below the soil surface. New equipment for this purpose consists of a fertilizer attachment for a wheel-type two-bottom plow. The power required to drive the hopper mechanism is obtained from a separate ground wheel. When the plow bottoms are raised, the wheel is also lifted from the ground and the discharge of fertilizer is stopped.

A modification of the plow-furrow method consists of either broadcasting or drilling the fertilizer on the surface and then plowing the land. In turning the furrow slice, part of the fertilizer reaches the bottom of the preceding furrow and the remainder is held between the furrow slices.

In another method recently introduced, the fertilizer is deeply placed after the land has been plowed. The fertilizer is placed in narrow bands at plow depth or somewhat deeper, usually during the preparation of the seedbed. The machines used for this purpose are deep-tillage cultivators on which suitable fertilizer attachments are mounted. Other adaptable equipment consists of a universal tool bar extending across the tractor on which furrowing tools can be mounted in desired positions.

The deep-tillage cultivators known as chisels, tractor cultivators, and utility cultivators are used for loosening the soil to a depth of 15 inches and deeper under some conditions. The use of these cultivators for applying fertilizer, besides tillage, permits the use of fertilizer hoppers of unusually large capacity and, furthermore, the application of fertilizer deeply in the spring on spring- or fall-plowed land.

The placement of all or most of the fertilizer at plow depth or deeper has advantages under certain conditions, but under other conditions is not superior to previously approved methods. Further experience is required to define the conditions under which it is most effective.

For example, under conditions on the Eastern Shore of Virginia, the recommended side placement of fertilizer produced higher yields of potatoes than placement of all or a major part of it in a band on the bottom of each plow furrow. In Pennsylvania and New York, however, plowing under one-half of the fertilizer with the remainder side-placed gave higher potato yields than placing all of it at each side of the row.

In soil where a dense layer is gradually formed immediately below the plowing depth, it is necessary to break up the layer to permit water and plant roots to penetrate it.

Placing and Handling Lime

Types of new machines for breaking the hardpan and loosening the subsoil include subsoilers, deep-tillage cultivators, and special plows. Attachments have been developed for applying lime and fertilizer as required at depths below the ordinary plow furrow. One attachment is mounted on a wheel-type plow and has a hopper with two compartments, one for lime and the other for fertilizer. A special shoe is attached back of the plow bottom and extends 4 to 5 inches below the bottom of the plow furrow during the plowing operation. A part of the lime and fertilizer enters the special furrow opened in the subsoil.

Another attachment developed for deep, subsoil application of lime and fertilizer is mounted on a subsoiling machine.

Lime is often distributed over the fields by means of spreading attachments on large trucks in which the material is hauled in bulk from the railroad car or stock pile directly to the field. The method practically eliminates hand labor, relieves the farmer of an unpleasant job, and expedites the handling of the material. To some extent the method is also used in applying fertilizer. The trucks are most commonly equipped with two rotating horizontal plates at the rear for spreading the material and a conveyor in the bottom of the truck bed; the conveyor feeds the material to the scattering plates at the desired rates. Other equipment includes various types of hoppers with spreaders mounted on the truck or trailed behind it. In the latter case, hand labor is usually required for transferring the material from the truck bed to the hopper of the spreading equipment. The most recent developments include improvements in the conveying mechanism and spreader plates for more positive operation and more uniform spreading of the material.

The application of soluble fertilizers with irrigation water has been practiced in some areas for several years. Special mixing equipment provides for introducing the desired amount of fertilizer steadily into the stream of irrigation water.

The application of fertilizer in liquid form with field machines is a recent practice that is not yet extensively used. Equipment for the purpose is essentially a container with some means of regulating the flow of liquid through tubes to furrows in the soil or directly to the soil surface. When the liquid is allowed to flow by gravity from the container to the soil, the flow is regulated either by an adjustable clamp on a rubber delivery tube or by the size of the fixed discharge openings. Gravitational or natural flow decreases as the level of liquid in the container is lowered. To overcome this objection the tank or container has been sealed in such a way that the liquid pressure remains constant as the tank is emptied. The principle is similar to that of common waterers for chickens and livestock. Positive regulation of flow according to the rate of travel of the machine is obtained by means of various types of pumps.

Anhydrous ammonia, and other materials like it, are applied as a liquid under pressure; they change to gas or vapor under ordinary air pressure. The material is stored in heavy steel cylinders. For field-tillage machines, special equipment has been devised so that the compressed gas or liquid is released at a point near the bottom of the furrow. Provision for immediately closing the furrow is essential to prevent the escape of the gas.

THE AUTHOR

Glenn A. Cumings is an agricultural engineer in the Bureau of Plant Industry, Soils, and Agricultural Engineering. After graduation from Iowa State College, he did engineering research in the Colorado Agricultural Experiment Station from 1919 to 1927, and since then has been a project leader on fertilizer placement and fertilizer distributing machinery research in the Department. Mr. Cumings is the author and coauthor of numerous bulletins, articles, and other reports on fertilizer-application methods; chairman of the Committee on Fertilizer Application in the American Society of Agricultural Engineers; Past General Chairman of the National Joint Committee on Fertilizer Application and present Chairman of two subcommittees.

FOR FURTHER READING

Cumings, G. A.: *Fertilizer-Placement Machinery for Southern Crops,* Commercial Fertilizer Yearbook, 1941.

National Joint Committee on Fertilizer Application: *Methods of Applying Fertilizer,* Recommendations of the Joint Committee, Unnumbered Circular, April 1938.

ALSO, IN THIS BOOK

Cotton Ginning

by CHARLES A. BENNETT

THE PROCESSES that are broadly termed ginning in the cotton industry have undergone many changes and advances in the years since 1935, in keeping pace with farm production. The number of active gins has declined from approximately 13,000 in 1935 to 8,632 in 1945, but the ginning volume of each gin has increased and features have been added that sharply distinguish the modernized gins from the old.

Although mechanization in cotton production was in sight in 1935, it had become a reality by 1947. It has forced improvements and advances upon the ginning industry without which the cotton producer could not now continue. Among the improvements are all-metal buildings and machinery, standardized interchangeable parts, and machine production on dimensioned jigs under closer tolerances of finish and fit; these have replaced wooden construction and rough castings. Cotton driers, gin stands of greater capacity, better pneumatic apparatus, and greater accessibility are pronounced improvements.

Cotton drying processes, fostered and developed by the Department since 1929, have spread to more than a third of all of the active cotton gins—the third that handles at least 65 percent of all the cotton. Research in drying cotton has been extended to the application of a series of drying stages in succeeding machines, and the art of cleaning seed cotton has been furthered by many new designs.

Bulk extracting of heavier foreign materials from the harvested cottons gave way to the highly specialized development of unit extracting and feeding processes over each cotton gin stand; the result has been a resurgent improvement of the large master extractors to a position of primary importance in the mechanized production of cotton. Outstanding examples are the several types of cleaning and extracting machines that have angular bar grids, revolving knuckle-tooth disk grids, reciprocating cleaner cylinders in staggered vertical decension, and other ingenious devices for removing foreign matter gathered by machine harvesting. Two other research studies have been started: One seeks to find a way to restore necessary moisture to very dry fiber during ginning, and the other to clean even better the ginned fiber as it passes from gin-stands to the bale press.

The vigorous adoption of single-variety cotton planting by farsighted communities has effected a further advance in ginning processes for protecting purity of ginned cotton seed, cleaners and graders for the seed, and better methods for testing germination and prospective betterments in yield and fiber quality. The trend toward single-variety cotton communities has been sound and healthy, and should lead to visual bale identification in coverings and tags to assure consumers that they are receiving a specialized variety of cotton fiber from dependable producers.

The desirability of having definite supplies of quality cotton of preferred variety induces the spinner and processor of fibers to obtain such cottons direct from the producer. Here the greatest opportunity may exist for standard-density cotton gin presses, which are foreseen in the findings by the research engineers and technologists that cotton bales of standard density (22 to 25 pounds per cubic foot needed for domestic shipment at favorable rates) as compared to low density, bulky, gin bales (11 to 15 pounds per cubic foot) can be readily produced at the larger volume cotton gins in a mechanically practicable and economically feasible manner.

The size of the 500-pound square bale of standard density from a cotton gin press is approximately 22 inches wide, 30 inches high, and 56 inches long. It has eight ties, preferably held by heavy-duty steel rod buckles; and the cotton gin machinery ahead of the press needs no change from its present forms and dimensions.

The gin standard density presses now in use are of both down and up packing type, but new designs utilize either two or three rams, although three 9½ inch rams have heretofore appeared to be somewhat preferable.

These presses do not kill the natural resilience of the cotton fibers, and the bales consequently open quickly at the spinning mills during the first blending processes that are otherwise delayed by the extreme crushing encountered when low-density bales undergo commercial compression between the gins and mills. The gin standard-density bales are pleasing in appearance, well protected, compact, and economical in floor space in the opening and picking processes at the mills.

Bale fires have not been experienced in any instance within standard-density gin bales, although fires during ginning processes have occurred at the gins where these presses have been installed.

A standard-density gin bale also effectively lends itself to high-density recompression, because it fits between the side doors of the high-density presses; the layering of the bale contents is therefore not disturbed by the high-density pressing.

It is estimated that the ginning volume of 5,000 or more bales a year at large cotton gins would enable the operators to produce standard-density gin bales for 7 cents each more than it costs to produce low-density or flat bales, and that in small volume gins of 1,000 bales capacity a season the increased cost would reach 27 cents a bale.

There are certain limitations, of course, in most industrial methods, and the immediate possibilities for beneficial use of standard-density gin presses appear to reside in the availability of single-variety cottons direct to the mills from large individual or cooperative producers. On 1,000-bale volume basis, the single stage compression of standard-density gin bales may save 43 cents per bale for the industry, while a 5,000-bale volume production at the gin could save up to 63 cents a bale.

It is realized that established methods of marketing must give way rather slowly to innovations and advances. The standard-density gin bale cannot quickly replace the need for commercial compression services in many regions where small volumes and irregular lots of cottons must be concentrated, sorted, and reassembled for trade disposal. But with mechanical sampling of bales during ginning now proved to be dependable, and with mechanized production of single-variety cottons revolutionizing the cotton industry in the United States, it is reasonable to conclude that standard-density gin bales will increasingly come into production by producer-to-consumer marketing.

THE AUTHOR

Charles A. Bennett, as an agricultural engineer in the Bureau of Plant Industry, Soils, and Agricultural Engineering, has been in charge of the Bureau's Cotton Ginning Laboratory at Stoneville, Miss., since it was established in 1930. After graduation from the University of Nebraska, he worked successively as a draftsman in Omaha, a member of a firm of consulting engineers, a supervising draftsman with the machinery division of the United States Navy Yard at Puget Sound during the First World War, and a registered engineer at Portland, Oreg., and Alhambra, Calif. From 1926 to 1930 he engaged in cotton drying research with the Department at Tullulah, La.

FOR FURTHER READING

Bennett, Charles A.: *Handling Mechanically Harvested Cotton at the Gin,* The Cotton and Cotton Oil Press, volume 46, No. 13, pages 5–8, June 30, 1945.

Bennett, Charles A., and Gerdes Francis L.: *The Vertical Drier for Seed Cotton,* U. S. D. A. Miscellaneous Publication 239, 1941.

Bennett, Charles A., Harmond, J. E., and Shaw Charles S.: *Standard-Density Cotton-Gin Presses,* U. S. D. A. Circular 733, 1945.

Air War Against Pests

by H. H. STAGE and FRANK IRONS

THE AIRPLANE holds a bright new hope in the farmers' uphill struggle with insects. Since 1922, when Department engineers and entomologists developed a practical method for dusting cottonfields with calcium arsenate to protect the crop against the boll weevil, commercial airplane dusting has become routine, particularly in cultivated fields that spread over a wide area unbroken by trees or shrubs. Later, and in a more limited manner, the airplane has been used regularly and effectively to control malaria-carrying mosquitoes and pests that destroy shade trees and timber in forests where spraying from the ground is difficult and expensive.

Working with State and commercial aircraft dusting companies and growers and, during the war, with the Army, Navy, and Coast Guard, the Department has found practical ways to spray plants and trees from the air and with the use of DDT to combat adult mosquitoes and other insects. Before these tests had been run no practical means for destroying adult mosquitoes over large areas was known. By using a quart or two of a 5-percent DDT solution per acre we can reduce the adult mosquito population by nearly 100 percent in wooded areas in a few hours.

Equipment for spraying can be installed easily in an airplane or a helicopter. In some designs the forward speed of the plane drives a small propeller attached to a pump, which provides the pressure needed to force the insecticidal solution from its holding tank through a special nozzle, or a series of nozzles, in the form of tiny droplets or a mist.

Several types of distribution apparatus were improved and simplified for military needs during the war. Many of these lend themselves readily to agricultural use. The forerunner of these more recently developed mechanisms for distributing baits and dusts for insect control was de-

835

scribed by a co-worker, Chester N. Husman, of the Orlando, Fla., laboratory—a hopper having a capacity of 29 cubic feet for installation in a biplane that is powered by a 285-horsepower engine with cruising speed
of 90 miles an hour and can carry a pay load of 984 pounds.

In 1945 large aircraft, C–47's and B–25's, were used by the military
as a means for dispersing insecticides mainly against mosquitoes and
flies. The B–25 equipment consists of spray tanks of about 550 gallons
capacity produced by connecting the standard fixed bomb-bay tank with
the standard droppable bomb-bay tank. A sump valve connects the tanks
with the dispenser and serves to regulate the flow. The end of the straight
discharge-pipe dispenser is cut off at a 45° angle with its opening to the
rear. The C–47 equipment consists of a standard A–26 droppable bomb-
bay fuel tank of 625-gallon capacity. A manually operated control valve
connects this tank with the straight discharge-pipe dispenser.

Investigations showed that the best conditions for running spray missions with the B–25 and C–47 equipment were as follows: Altitude of
release of spray, 150 feet above ground or treetops; indicated air speed
for B–25, 200 miles per hour; for C–47, 170 miles per hour; droplet size,
50 to 150 microns; wind velocity, 3 to 10 miles per hour; line of flight,
crosswind or within 22.5° thereof; and a distance between lines of flight
about 300 feet. In using the lighter types of aircraft, the pilot found it
necessary to fly within a few feet of the crop being treated.

Early in 1943 tests were made in cooperation with the Tennessee Valley Authority. The first tests, in which a 20-percent DDT dust was
used against disease-bearing mosquitoes, proved unsatisfactory because
the hopper failed to feed the dust into the venturi and because there was
an insufficient breaking-up of the dust particles by the air currents in the
venturi. During September of that year in the vicinity of Stuttgart and
Walnut Ridge, Ark., the entomologists used a 5-percent DDT dust successfully against *Anopheles quadrimaculatus* Say larvae in rice fields.
Both Waco and Huff Deland planes were used. Somewhat later tests were
made on military reservations near Orlando, Fla., with Cub and Stearman trainer planes equipped with a special portable hopper designed
by Husman. In open areas a 90- to 100-percent control of *Anopheles*
mosquito larvae was obtained. In tree-covered areas, however, the Cub
plane was not powerful enough to create sufficient downdraft to force
the dust to the water that contained the larvae.

A semiportable hopper for the J3–65 Piper Cub was designed for
mounting in the rear-seat compartment without interfering with the pilot
or controls. The hopper, venturi tube, and power unit are mounted by
clamping metal clamps to fuselage members and wing struts. There are
no structural changes or alterations in any part of the aircraft nor are
there holes bored in any of the structural members. The hopper has a
dust-sealed cover, and the cabin is provided with adjustable ventilators

to protect the pilot from dust while in flight. The hopper is so installed that as the weight of its contents changes, the center of gravity is still within the approved range. The venturi is held in place by bolting brackets which are mounted on the sides of the venturi to the brackets which are clamped to the lower longerons. The venturi is constructed of 24-gage galvanized iron or 0.065 aluminum.

Spraying Concentrated DDT From an Airplane

The use of concentrated DDT sprays dispersed from an airplane has proved very satisfactory when used over marshes for controlling mosquitoes, and over heavily forested areas for controlling tree-defoliating insects. One such spray is a simple one made by dissolving 5 pounds of technical DDT in 100 pounds of kerosene. This formula, used at the rate of 1 to 2 quarts an acre, has kept adult mosquitoes under control.

A portable spray unit for use on the L–4 (Army Cub), J3–65, and NE–1 Navy Cub planes was developed by Husman and O. M. Longcoy in October 1943. Since that time it has been used in many parts of the world as an effective and satisfactory device for dispersing DDT sprays. The unit, with a capacity of 25 gallons, was simple in design, with a venturi beneath the fuselage of the airplane. A half-inch gear pump, powered by a two-bladed, wind-driven propeller, forced the spray material through the nozzles. Six splatter-plate nozzles were attached to the spray boom near the outer and lower edge of the venturi. Each nozzle was provided with a No. 60 wire gage opening.

The gear pump operated at a pressure of about 50 pounds at an air speed of 70 miles per hour; delivery rate was about 2¾ gallons a minute.

A spray unit for the PT–17 Stearman airplane was a modification of the one designed for the L–4 series plane. The tank, however, had a capacity of 60 gallons and the venturi was considerably larger, also. A 4-bladed, 18-inch, wind-driven wooden propeller was mounted on the pump shaft to build up pressure in the lines. The spray boom, situated near the lower trailing edge of the venturi, consisted of 12 nozzles provided with No. 60 wire gage orifices with an operating pressure of 120 pounds; the delivery rate of the spray solution was 7¼ gallons per minute. The effective swath width was about 80 feet. The droplet size of the spray ranged from 3 microns to more than 200 microns.

Although the original portable spray units produced satisfactory results, there were a number of objections to them. It was desirable to decrease the weight and air resistance and to provide for more uniform distribution of the spray.

The first unit, constructed by Husman while on duty in the Pacific with the Navy, uses the same tank, pump, and wind-driven propeller. The venturi, however, is replaced by two breaker-bar spray booms, one mounted under each of the wing struts. The booms are clamped to the wing struts just outside the slip stream. Each boom is 4 feet long and has 24 orifices the size of No. 71 wire. The space between the booms is 8 feet, 6 inches on an L–4 airplane. The spray booms are constructed of ⅜-inch (i. d.) aircraft tubing, the 24 orifices being drilled horizontally along the tube. A duralumin spray-breaker bar, ⅝ by ¼ inch, with a 5° convex face, is mounted on the tubing with a space of ½ inch between the tubing and the bar. Since the spray is forced out over a total length of 8 feet, it becomes dispersed through air turbulence caused by the plane. When 5⅗ gallons of solution are applied per minute, the dosage per acre is 2.32 quarts when the plane is flown at 60 miles per hour. At 70 miles per hour the dosage is 1.99 quarts an acre.

The breaker-bar sprayer has several advantages over the original spray unit and is the type now recommended. It is lighter than the original sprayer, and the absence of the venturi reduces air resistance. A wider swath, smaller droplets, and a more uniform distribution of the spray within the swath is also obtained. The droplet size ranges from 10 to 460 microns. Another advantage of this equipment is that the delivery rate and size of the droplets can be readily changed by having available several sets of tubing with different sizes and numbers of orifices.

To treat agricultural crops, uniform swath coverage and close control of dosage are prime essentials to insure effective and economical control. Also, the dosage must remain within limits of the plant tolerance to the spray. In 1945 a J3–65 Piper Cub was fitted with a spray unit at Toledo, Ohio, for insecticide applications for corn borer control. The unit was made portable so it could be easily installed or removed. This unit consisted of a liquid tank, ¾-inch gear pump with wind-driven propeller, pressure regulating relief valve, and nozzle booms. The booms, one on each side, were 11 feet long. They were supported by brackets from the wing struts which held them parallel to a line from the bottom of the fuselage and the wing tips. Each boom carried 11 conventional hollow-cone spray nozzles. The delivery rate was approximately 2 gallons per acre. A uniform swath 40 to 50 feet wide was obtained.

Spraying insecticides from aircraft is not the complete answer to the control of insects. In many instances ground methods of control remain more feasible. The field of application is broadening, however; today the airplane is regularly used to dust and spray forest and shade trees, fresh- and salt-water swamps, orchards, and many other crops.

THE AUTHORS

H. H. Stage is assistant leader, Division of Insects Affecting Man and Animals, Bureau of Entomology and Plant Quarantine.

Frank Irons, of the Bureau of Plant Industry, Soils, and Agricultural Engineering, is in charge of work at Toledo, Ohio, on machines for pest and plant-disease control.

Blowers for Insecticides

by W. L. POPHAM

FOR A LONG time there has been need for improved methods for spraying fruit trees, vegetable crops, wood lots, and ornamentals to control certain insects and plant diseases. Maybe what the public wants is a new high-velocity blower that atomizes and evenly distributes small quantities of highly toxic insecticides and fungicides. Department entomologists are now experimenting with equipment that will spray an acre of vegetable crops with 1 to 3 gallons, a fruit tree with 4 to 6 ounces, and the largest street trees with a fourth to a half pint of liquid insecticide.

The idea of using high-velocity air to distribute insecticides stems from work in 1921 and 1922, when technicians visualized the possibility of using aircraft for crop dusting and began experiments to determine its practicality. Their immediate objective was to perfect devices for releasing an even flow of dust into the slip stream of an airplane flying low over the crops, relying upon the propeller blast, the forward speed of the plane, and the turbulent air created by the wings to distribute the insecticide evenly.

Success in crop dusting with aircraft and ground blowers led to interest in the possibility of using high-velocity air for applying liquid insecticides. Many standard insecticides and fungicides are more effective when applied as sprays, and an adhesive or other conditioner may be readily added to a spray, so that the effective period is extended. As in the case of lead arsenate for the control of codling moth, it is frequently impossible to secure and retain with dusts the type of coverage necessary to insure protection. On the other hand, the common way of applying dilute sprays to orchards, field crops, street trees, and forest cover requires a lot of water and heavy equipment that is costly to operate.

The problems encountered in attempting to control the white-fringed beetle, a destructive insect of foreign origin that has become established in limited areas of the Gulf Coast States, prompted a pooling of the efforts of entomologists, chemists, and engineers assigned to the project to find a method of applying insecticide concentrates in liquid form. On this project the shortcomings of conventional methods of applying insecticides became particularly obvious.

Dusts, both calcium arsenate and cryolite, were reasonably effective in reducing the numbers of white-fringed beetles if they could be kept on the vegetation, but, unfortunately, rains day after day during the season when treatments were applied did much to neutralize the effort. Dilute sprays required heavy equipment that could not be taken off hard-surfaced roads when fields and pastures were wet. It was costly to operate and awkward to handle in small fields and in suburban areas, where treatment often was necessary. The situation demanded light-weight equipment that would distribute arsenicals or cryolite as concentrated sprays to which could be added adhesives that would withstand Gulf coast weather in June, July, and August.

Although many devices, involving several different principles, were tried and found inadequate for the purpose, a unit conceived in 1940 that involved the use of high-velocity air and low pressure on the liquid feed line began to take shape. By 1943 the unit was ready for field testing; in 1944 it became standard equipment on the white-fringed beetle control project. This tractor-mounted equipment is a combination duster-sprayer. The basic principle is high-velocity air delivered through a 3½-inch flexible hose, which atomizes and projects in an even pattern either dusts or liquids, or both. The dust hopper is mounted directly back of the seat and above the fan housing, and the powdered insecticides are released through the fan. The spray tanks are mounted on either side of the engine and the liquid insecticides are injected into the air stream at the mouth of the hose, using any one of several types of nozzles, depending upon the nature or consistency of the materials used. Adding a spray that may contain an adhesive, or other conditioner if desired, to insecticidal dusts as they leave the mouth of the hose makes it possible to reduce drift substantially, and, in effect, to stick the dust to the foliage as it is applied.

When the fan is driven at 4,000 revolutions per minute, the air is forced through the hose at about 160 miles an hour. By starting a breakup of the liquid with 30 to 50 pounds pressure on the nozzle that injects the liquid into the air stream, atomization is completed by the fast-moving air, and the size of particles is reduced to a range of 150 to 300 microns in diameter. Thus it becomes possible to treat an acre of field crops, pastures, or even forests with as little as 1 to 3 gallons of liquid.

During the 1945 season, units of this type were used to dispense both

DDT and cryolite for white-fringed beetle control, almost entirely replacing other types of sprayers and dusters previously used on the project. Both chemicals were applied as dust and as sprays to vegetation along roadsides and railroad rights-of-way and to field crops and uncultivated pasture lands. The rate of application with DDT was 8 pounds of 10 percent dust or 1 pound of technical DDT in 2 gallons of solution per acre. Cryolite was applied in concentrations of 4 to 6 pounds in a gallon of water with an emulsifier and adhesive added.

At normal working speeds for a tractor, these units gave an effective distribution of insecticide over a swath 30 to 50 feet wide, depending upon the density of the vegetation receiving treatment, terrain, and the directional adjustment of the hose. One man with a tractor treated approximately 8 to 10 acres an hour, using 1 to 3 gallons of concentrated spray to the acre; with dilute sprays the same area required much heavier equipment, 3 to 5 men for satisfactory operation, and the application of 300 to 500 gallons of liquid.

The tractor equipment established beyond a doubt that high-velocity air could be used to atomize and distribute liquid insecticides. But as developmental work progressed, it became evident that a blower that would deliver a larger volume of air with some increase in velocity would extend the swath of effective treatment, give better atomization of liquids, and better penetration of dense vegetation. This led to an investigation of fans or blowers of various designs that might better meet requirements and resulted in securing the interest and collaboration of engineers trained and experienced in air dynamics, who cooperated with the Bureau of Entomology and Plant Quarantine in developing an axial-flow-type blower for the purpose. The unit was designed to provide maximum volume, velocity, and pressure in relation to size, weight, and power.

The specific objective of the original design was a simple, relatively inexpensive device that would project finely atomized liquids in an even pattern for at least 100 feet from the nozzle, which would be adequate for treating street trees, ornamental plantings, wood lots, and any types of field crops. The pilot model was given exhaustive tests in connection with experimental work for the control of forest and shade tree insects in 1945, using DDT in various formulations. At a speed of 3,800 to 4,000 revolutions per minute it gave good coverage for a distance of 125 feet from the nozzles. The air stream containing the insecticide feathered out to a pattern about 18 to 20 feet wide at a distance of 100 feet from the nozzle. At this fan speed the spray particles ranged in size from about 50 to 150 microns. Some were smaller and some larger, but the bulk of them fell within this range.

When operated under a wide variety of conditions in the field, no difficulty was encountered in reaching the tops of the largest trees. When spraying along roadsides, coverage adequate for control of many of the forest insects that cause defoliation in the New England area was obtained for a distance of 200 to 300 feet from the nozzle. As in the case of the tractor equipment, this experimental unit may be used either as a duster or sprayer, or the dust may be conditioned with moisture as it leaves the nozzle. Power is furnished by a 22- to 25-horsepower gasoline motor and the total weight of the unit with the insecticide tank full is somewhat less than 1,000 pounds.

Both manufacturers of spray equipment and chemical companies engaged in the formulation of insecticides are showing great interest in the possibilities that exist for applying many of our more commonly used insecticides as liquid concentrates or conditioned dusts. Manufacturers made available to entomologists and chemists in 1945 several types of portable blowers for experimental work. These were used to treat mosquito and fly breeding grounds, street trees, wood lots, recreational areas, orchards, and row crops with good results.

Only a limited number of insecticides have been applied experimentally with blower equipment of this general character. These include DDT in various formulations, nicotine in concentrations up to 1 quart of alkaloid in 1 gallon of solution, benzene hexachloride, and cryolite in concentrations of 4 to 6 pounds in a gallon of water with an emulsifier and an adhesive added. During 1946 experimental work was continued and expanded to include other insecticides and additional crops. Soon entomologists, chemists, and engineers expect to be much closer to an answer to the question: To what extent will finely atomized insecticide concentrates and conditioned dusts replace dilute sprays and conventional dusting procedures?

THE AUTHOR

W. L. Popham since 1941 has been an assistant chief of the Bureau of Entomology and Plant Quarantine. A native of Montana and a graduate of Montana State College, Mr. Popham joined the Department in 1924, as State leader for Montana in black stem rust control; in 1930 he became a field supervisor for 13 North Central States, and in 1934, in Washington, he was placed in charge of barberry eradication work.

FOR FURTHER READING

Palm, C. E.: *New Equipment for Insecticide Application,* Agricultural Chemicals, volume 1, No. 3, pages 14–18, 62–65, 1946.

Popham, W. L.: *Airplane Spraying of Insecticides,* Agricultural Chemicals, volume 1 (Part I), No. 2, pages 16–19, 63, 64; Part II, No. 3, pages 19–20, 1946.

Sheals, R. A.: *New Developments in Gypsy Moth Control,* Agricultural Chemicals, volume 1, No. 5, pages 22–25, 1946.

Machine-Made Forests

by PAUL O. RUDOLF

PLANTING a forest takes a good deal of work. On a few acres, hand labor may make up nine-tenths of the cost. Even on the large public forest projects in the Lake States, where some machinery is used, a third or a half of the cost usually goes into hand labor. Add to that the fact that the season for planting trees is short, and you have the reasons why farmers and foresters are greatly interested in any machines that can do part or most of the planting operation.

Much of the preparation of the ground for planting can be done mechanically. In some places trees are planted without previous preparation of the ground. If there is much growth of sod, weeds, brush, or other trees, however, competition usually is too severe for the young seedlings. In the Lake States and some other regions, competition for the first few years is reduced by skinning off patches of vegetation 1 to 2 feet in diameter (called scalping) or by plowing furrows about 6 feet apart. The latter method has proved cheaper and better and has been used on a million-odd acres in Minnesota, Wisconsin, and Michigan.

Fairly light, horse-drawn sulky plows were used to prepare most of the planting sites in the Lake States before 1930; walking plows were also used to some extent. Then a little heavier type of plow, usually drawn by a 15–20 horsepower wheel tractor, came into use. After the opener areas had been planted, plows had to be developed for use in heavier growth of brush and weed trees. Several heavy, middle-buster plows, usually drawn by 35 horsepower crawler-type tractors, proved quite satisfactory. These plows threw the furrow slice in both directions and opened a furrow at least 18 inches wide. The lighter plows threw the furrow slice in one direction and opened a furrow about 12 inches wide. Furrowing has the advantage of reducing competition by other plants for moisture and soil nutrients, but, by removing the topsoil, furrowing makes it necessary to place the tree roots in a poorer layer of soil.

Disking gives promise of being an effective and useful method of preparing planting sites in the Lake States. Where it has been used on brushy sites, thorough disking has reduced competition effectively and has had the added advantage of working the more fertile topsoil into the surface layer in which the roots are planted. In about 200 acres of disked plantations on the Chippewa National Forest in Minnesota, 4-year-old red pine transplants 2 years after planting had better survival and height growth than on a comparable area of furrowed plantation.

The best apparatus for disking brushy areas so far developed has been the Athens-type disk plow drawn by a 40 horsepower tractor. The area must be cross-disked; that is, the disk should be pulled over the ground twice, the second time in a direction at right angles to the first trip. It is even better if a third trip in a diagonal direction can be made, although this may make the cost too high. Experience on the Chippewa National Forest indicates that with a skillful operator cross-disking can be done at a cost less than 10 percent above furrowing.

Several machines that prepare the ground and plant in one operation have been developed and used to some extent in the United States. Although they differ in detail, most of the machines contain these features: A coulter to cut the sod and small roots, a plow to turn a furrow, a trencher to open a slit, packing wheels to close the slit, and a container for the planting stock. One or two planters ride the machine and insert the tree roots in the slit just ahead of the packing wheels. Most of the machines are tractor drawn. In the Northeast, two machines, differing chiefly in size, were developed several years ago and have been used fairly extensively. During the later years of shelterbelt planting in the Plains Region by the Prairie States Forestry Project and the Soil Conservation Service, most planting was done by machines, which, however, were adapted only for planting in ground completely prepared as for farm planting. The Naber tree-planting machine was developed by the Forest Service for planting in the Nebraska sand hills. None of these machines, however, has found acceptance in the Lake States.

Tree-planting machines have been developed by State agencies in Wisconsin, Michigan, and Minnesota with which a crew (tractor driver and one to two planters) can set out 1,200 to 2,000 trees an hour. The Michigan and Minnesota machines are still in the trial stage. The machines developed in Wisconsin, have been used quite extensively since their development in 1943.

Under the leadership of Extension Forester Fred B. Trenk, two types of tree-planting machines were built. One is designed for use by farmers on old fields, principally on sandy soils, and the other is designed for use on cut-over sandy areas where some stumps and brush may occur.

The farm-type tree-planting machine designed by the Wisconsin Agricultural Experiment Station is built around the modern, single-bottom, heavy-duty tractor plow. The standard plow bottom is replaced with a middle-breaker plow, under which is attached a box shoe about 4 inches wide, 8 inches deep, and 3 feet long. On the front of the shoe is a chisel snout that serves the double purpose of holding the shoe in the ground and elevating the soil out of the planting trench instead of merely prying apart a slit in the soil. A rear assembly with press wheels provides a seat for the operator as he places the trees (carried in one or two boxes just ahead of the planter) in the trench shoe. The press wheels pack the soil around the tree roots after a pair of plates flow loose soil into the trench. Trees up to 4 years of age may be planted easily in the 4- by 8-inch trench, but in general 3-year-old stock has been proved most satisfactory except for jack pine, which handles best as 2-year-old stock.

The second model, designed by the Wisconsin Conservation Department, is generally similar to the farm model, but is built around a middle-breaker fire plow. Because of its extremely heavy construction, it will operate in land too stony or stumpy for the lighter farm machine. The ordinary farm tractor will operate the lighter machine, while a moderately heavy crawler type tractor is needed to operate the heavier machine.

The tree-planting machine parts, which cost from $60 to $75 in 1943–45, may be made detachable from each of these two designs, so the plows can be used during the rest of the year for regular farm work.

A three-man crew consists of a tractor driver, a planter, and a stockman. The latter takes care of the stock, loosens and separates the trees for easy planting, and hands them to the planter. The crew can plant up to 16,000 trees in an 8-hour day with either machine. However, the daily production usually runs from 6,500 to 11,000 trees.

The economy of planting with the machines may be illustrated by records obtained in 1944 and 1945 from operations in which four machines, two of each type, planted a million trees on 800 acres in 850 hours of operation. Not counting the cost of the planting stock, which would add up to $5 a thousand trees planted, the work was done at a cost of about $3.30 a thousand, or $4.65 an acre—only a little more than half the cost with conventional methods of ground preparation and hand planting. Naturally, with higher wages and costs of equipment and materials, the costs of planting will go above those figures.

A tree-planting machine called the Michigan State College reforestator, which combines some of the features of the Wisconsin and Plains Shelterbelt machines, has been developed by T. D. Stevens and L. E. Bell at Michigan State College. Mounted on a standard farm implement "uni-carrier" with power lifts, as is the Shelterbelt tree-planting machine, it is otherwise quite similar to the Wisconsin machine. It differs principally in that the plow can be raised up for use on prepared ground and that through the use of the uni-carrier it is easy to adjust the plows to varying depths and, by lowering one wheel and raising the other, to do contour planting on slopes up to 30 percent. Although the standard trencher on this machine makes an opening 4 inches wide and 8 inches deep (as does the Wisconsin machine), it is removable and may be replaced with a trencher that will make a larger opening to accommodate larger planting stock.

The reforestator can be pulled by an ordinary farm tractor, although wheel-type tractors are not satisfactory on loose sands or steep slopes. Because truck wheels are substituted for the standard uni-carrier wheels, the machine is easily transported as a trailing unit behind a tractor or automobile. Reports are that a two-man crew can set out 10,000 trees in an 8-hour day with the reforestator.

The Forestry Division of the Minnesota Conservation Department, under the supervision of Raymond Clement, has developed a machine for planting trees on open sand plains. The machine differs from the Wisconsin and Michigan machines in that it was not developed particularly for farm use, no plow is used, and two planters ride the machine. The ground is broken by the trenching shoe. Fairly extensive trials in 1945 indicated that a 3-man crew, 2 planters and a tractor driver, could plant an average of 1,500 trees an hour.

Of course, planting machines also have some disadvantages: Areas with much rock, stumps, brush, or other cover, or heavy soil cannot be planted; roots over 8 inches long may be looped or improperly placed; and only areas that are comparatively level can be planted. Nevertheless, these tree-planting machines are promising and merit widespread trial to explore their full possibilities. Individual farmers probably could not afford to own a tree-planting machine, but groups or organizations could own machines to be used by their members. In Wisconsin, machines owned by public agencies are rented to farmers.

THE AUTHOR

Paul O. Rudolf is a silviculturist at the Lake States Forest Experiment Station, maintained by the Department in cooperation with the University of Minnesota. For the past 15 years Mr. Rudolf has been doing research in forest planting in the Lake States.

FOR FURTHER READING

Stevens, T. D., and Bell, L. E.: *Michigan State College Reforestator,* Michigan Agricultural Experiment Station Quarterly Bulletin, volume 28, pages 1–4, 1945.

Toumey, J. W., and Korstian, C. F.: *Seeding and Planting in the Practice of Forestry,* Third Edition, pages 483–485, 1942.

Trenk, Fred B.: *Tree Planting Machine to Speed Reforestation,* Wisconsin Conservation Bulletin, volume 9, pages 3–6, 1944.

Equipment for Oil Crops

by I. F. REED

THE DEVELOPING war situation in 1939–40 indicated that the United States should get in position to produce many of the vegetable oils normally imported, as supplies might be cut off. The program that was started to prepare for such an emergency called for the production of substitute oils to replace coconut oil, olive oil, and others that could not be produced readily in this country.

The need for equipment to handle many of the jobs encountered in producing and harvesting the oil crops soon became evident. Many of the operations were being done by hand methods because of the surplus of labor in the area where they formerly were produced. Under war conditions it was impossible to obtain labor to do the jobs except at prohibitive costs. Efforts of the staff of the Tillage Machinery Laboratory at Auburn, Ala., were directed toward the development of equipment to aid in producing castor beans, peanuts, and tung nuts, which yield oils important in their applications in medicines, foods, paints, and so forth.

The acres in peanuts increased from about 2 million before the war to more than 3 million in 1945 despite the shortage of farm labor and machinery. The increase was made possible by making the use of all available equipment that would reduce man hours required to produce and harvest the crop. Seedbed preparation, planting, and cultivating could be handled effectively with the available equipment. The bottleneck was in harvesting.

Before 1940 most of the peanuts grown in the Southeast were loosened with a plow arrangement and lifted out of the ground, shaken, piled, and stacked by hand; harvesting and picking in that way took about 32 man-hours per acre. Farmers began using tractor-mounted bean harvesters or peanut blades on the cultivators to plow two rows of peanuts loose

847

at a time, after which they were lifted out of the ground and windrowed with heavy-duty side-delivery rakes. In that way the man-hours required for the two operations were reduced from 13 to 1.25. Repair costs were high, vines in the windrows were tangled, and too many peanuts were knocked off the vines, but the rake helped get the job done, and no doubt made possible the increased production despite the reduced manpower on farms.

A tractor-mounted peanut shaker is one of the machines developed especially for harvesting peanuts. With it one man lifts, shakes, and windrows two rows of peanuts that have been loosened by blades on the tractor cultivator frame. The windrow is loose and can be stacked as easily as hand-piled peanuts or, if left, dries out rapidly so that in favorable weather the peanuts can be picked from the windrow in 5 to 8 days. A combine equipped for picking peanuts from the windrow or a picker arranged to do it will do this job in 3 man-hours per acre. As the stacking operation is eliminated, the man-hours required for harvesting an acre of peanuts can be reduced from 32.0 to 3.75.

Several of the USDA-type peanut shakers have been built and have proved effective. Manufacturers are developing other types of shakers.

Peanuts may be planted with or without shelling, but most farmers prefer to plant shelled seed. It is much easier to handle, requires less time and moisture for germination, and usually produces a more uniform stand. Getting seed shelled by hand is tedious and costly and most shelling plants split or otherwise damage a relatively high proportion of the nuts. In either case, the farmer often gets back only 50 to 55 pounds of shelled seed per 100 pounds of unshelled stock, whereas his peanuts may grade 65 to 70 percent sound kernels. This led to the development of a sheller for seed peanuts.

The USDA sheller, as it is called, for seed peanuts is only a little larger than the well-known one-hole hand-operated corn sheller and requires about 1½ horsepower for its operation. It will turn out in 1 hour 300 pounds of shelled nuts, the amount a man can shell by hand in 30 days of 10 hours each. The sheller is simple in its construction, operation, and adjustments. Tests show that seed shelled in this machine and disinfected as recommended to control disease organisms will germinate about as well as hand-shelled seed, even if stored as long as 9 weeks before planting.

Since this country was not in a position to grow enough castor beans to meet its needs, a program to increase the seed supply was started in 1941; in 1942 about 10,000 acres were grown in the lower Mississippi Valley and Texas. A 700,000-acre production program was planned for 1943. However, Mexico and other countries furnishing us castor beans and castor oil joined the Allies. We were assured of a source of supply, so the production program was abandoned.

As countries furnishing castor beans before the war used hand methods for harvesting and hulling, no effective equipment was available. Harvesting was complicated by lack of uniformity in ripening of the seed. Often ripe beans, green beans, and blooms could be found on the same plant, and the early spikes would drop their seed before the later ones were ripe. Some castor beans were harvested experimentally with a modified grain combine, but the method was not considered satisfactory. Observations indicated that plant breeders could in time produce plants adapted to mechanical harvesting.

Although the small acreage of castor-beans grown in this country could be harvested by hand methods, success of even the seed-increase program required development of an effective huller. A huller, developed in 1942 and improved in 1943 and 1944 by the Department at the Tillage Machinery Laboratory, consists of a simple rubber-covered cylinder operating a definite distance from a rubber-covered concave. The beans are fed between these units at a fixed rate and the rubbing, rolling action loosens the hulls. The beans are then cleaned by use of a suction arrangement for removing the loosened hulls and other light material and screens for removing small heavy material. Efforts spent in developing this machine were not wasted, as 20 hullers manufactured and shipped to Mexico and 6 to South America were used in producing castor beans for this country's needs.

In another huller, developed at the University of Tennessee, the hulls are loosened by passing the beans between stationary and rotating rubber-faced plates spaced a definite distance apart. All separation of hulls and dirt from the hulled beans is by means of air. Five hullers of each type described were built and used for hulling the 1942 crop.

The production of tung nuts has increased slowly in the United States since 1932. The production for 1945 was estimated at about 9,000,000 pounds which, however, is less than 10 percent of normal consumption, based on imports from 1935 to 1939.

More than 80 percent of the tung oil used in American industries is utilized by paint and varnish manufacturers, who prefer American oil, because it is generally superior to that produced in China. Tung oil is used also in the linoleum industry, in the manufacture of certain insulating materials, in the electrical industry, as an ingredient in some automobile brake linings, and in other products.

Tung fruit fall from the trees as they ripen over a period of 6 weeks or 2 months. The common practice is to allow them to lie on the ground until dry enough to store without heating, and then to gather by hand and store them in ventilated bins or sheds until dry enough for milling. Much labor is required in both gathering and handling. Equipment is needed to reduce the labor in these operations and the amount of storage space required for handling the crop. The problems thus fall into two phases—gathering and hulling, handling and storage. Attempts have been made to develop gathering equipment. Several projects look promising, however, and tung growers are changing tillage methods in their orchards so as to have the ground surface relatively smooth at harvesttime to enable them to use gathering equipment that might be developed.

The only tung nut hullers heretofore available on the market are adaptations of heavy-duty plate-type grinders. They are not effective when the hulls are relatively wet, which means that the fruit must be stored 4 to 8 weeks before hulling.

The USDA portable tung nut huller perfected in 1945 consists essentially of a perforated basket surrounding a rotor that causes the tung fruit to be broken up and the hulls removed from the nuts. The nuts and hulls fall onto a shaker screen and are carried under a suction nozzle. The action of these units removes all the debris. It will handle wet fruit as gathered in the orchard so that only the nuts have to be stored and these require less than half the space for whole fruit. Since the hull normally contains more moisture than the nuts, it is possible to gather and handle wetter fruit than under the normal arrangement.

The huller is especially effective if used with a drier as the nuts from wet fruit can be readily dried for milling. With the machine, the hulls are removed and scattered in the orchard; that saves handling, hauling, and storage space and leaves them where their fertilizer value may be utilized. Moist fruit can be hulled and the nuts dried rapidly for milling, thus making it possible to start oil mills earlier in the fall. Fruit containing too much moisture to store safely can be hulled, so that gathering crews can start sooner after rains.

Stationary tung nut hullers using the hulling principle developed in the portable unit are being installed at tung oil mills and have proved to be very satisfactory.

THE AUTHOR

I. F. Reed is a senior agricultural engineer in the Bureau of Plant Industry, Soils, and Agricultural Engineering.

ACKNOWLEDGMENTS

O. A. Brown, R. E. Jezek, E. C. Hansen, and J. W. Miller assisted in developing the equipment described.

FOR FURTHER READING

Brown, O. A., and Reed, I. F.: *A Sheller for Seed Peanuts,* Agricultural Engineering, volume 25, pages 424, 426, 1944.

Reed, I. F., and Brown, O. A.: *Developments in Peanut Harvesting Equipment,* Agricultural Engineering, volume 25, pages 125–126, 128, 1944.

Reed, I. F., and Jezek, R. E.: *A Portable Tung Nut Decorticator,* Agricultural Engineering, volume 26, pages 413–414, 420, 1945.

New Sugar-Beet Machinery

by S. W. McBIRNEY

THE SUGAR-BEET crop is one of our last field crops to be mechanized. Sugar beets have been grown commercially sixty-odd years in the United States and the acreage had increased to nearly a million at the beginning of the war. Yet at that time blocking and thinning the crop in the spring, and the harvest operations of topping and loading in the fall were still largely done by hand.

Thinning, topping, and loading are the three jobs in which mechanization can save the most, because when they are done by hand they make up 60 to 75 percent of the total manual labor, which amounts to 75 to 120 man-hours an acre.

Engineers got encouraging results from their early investigations of equipment and methods for mechanical blocking and thinning in the 1930's, but the early trials showed that the then common practice of planting about 20 pounds of seed an acre in 20-inch rows, largely with fluted feed drills, produced thick and irregular stands of seedlings that were not well suited to mechanized thinning.

The first major step leading to mechanization of the spring hand work was the development of single-seed planting, by agricultural engineers in the California and Colorado agricultural experiment stations and the Department. The new way to plant produced much more uniform seed distribution, so that the rates of seeding could be decreased and the seedling stands could be thinned more rapidly. Single-seed planting of smaller sized screened seed, furthermore, produced stands that were even better because they contained more single plants. The reason is that sugar-beet seed actually are seed balls that vary from about one-eighth to one-quarter inch in diameter and contain from one to five or even more true seeds or germs per ball; the smaller balls contain fewer germs.

Single-seed planting proved so promising that one manufacturer of beet planters began building special equipment in 1939 to adapt his plate-type planters for the new method of planting. Commercial adoption of the planting began, and others began to build suitable equipment.

The second major step in improved planting was the development of segmented or sheared seed—that is, seed with fewer germs per segment. That work began in 1941 at the California Agricultural Experiment Station at Davis. The machine developed at Davis has an enclosed, coarse-grit grinding wheel and a stationary hardened steel shear bar set to give a desired clearance between it and the wheel. Beet seed is fed down onto the grinding wheel from a hopper. The revolving wheel carries the seed by the shear bar and, because of the restricted clearance, part of the seed ball is broken away and the size of the seed unit is reduced. The seed is then cleaned and graded to a suitable size and quality.

Usually the recovery of segmented seed is from 40 to 50 percent of the original weight, but the number of seed units recovered is usually not much less than that of the original seed. The degree of singleness obtained by the segmenting process varies with adjustments. Whole seed averaging two sprouts per viable ball is commonly reduced to seed averaging 50 to 60 percent of viable segments as singles; some average 70 to 80 percent.

Th development of segmented seed fitted in ideally with single-seed planting, as seed segments have to be planted singly to get the maximum benefit from the segmenting. Old-style planting does not benefit from segmented seed. Furthermore, the benefits of single-seed planting increase as the percentage of singleness of the seed unit increases. The development of both the seed processing and the planting equipment has been continued throughout the war years and commercial acceptance has been rapid. In 1941 segmented seed planted with a suitable planter was used on only an acre or so. The large savings possible in thinning labor were so apparent and the need for labor saving was so great that several thousand acres were planted in 1942. By 1945 more than 80 percent of our commercial sugar-beet acreage in the United States was planted with segmented seed.

The best present practice is to use single-seed planting of good segmented seed in well prepared seed beds at seeding rates of around 4 to 5 pounds an acre, often even less. Such planting is now saving beet growers thousands of man-hours of tedious hand work. Even where the beets are thinned by hand, as in the past, the thinning labor can be reduced about a fourth. Thinners prefer this planting and will often pass up old-style plantings with whole seed for the newer type. Furthermore, this planting is much better suited to mechanized thinning and where long-handled hoe or machine thinning is used, the manual labor can be reduced to a fourth or less.

A great deal of investigation has been done on mechanical harvesting.

Many experimental machines have been devised and much work has been done on them. For many years the problems seemed insurmountable. One by one, the difficulties are being overcome. Four different types of harvesters were made in 1946, and several others were being developed.

The first harvester to be manufactured on a rather large scale is a single row, two-unit machine adapted, at first, only to more friable soils. It tops the beets in the ground, windrows the tops, digs the beets, and kicks them back onto a conveyor, which windrows them. The windrowed beets are later loaded into beet trucks with a separate loader. The topping is done well and the tops are left in excellent condition, either for immediate loading and ensiling or for field curing for stock feed. The harvester was originally built by a Colorado beet grower in much its present form in 1940 and 1941. It looked so promising that it was taken over by a manufacturer who continued developing it. Since 1943, 200 or 300 machines have been built each year; with them, nearly all of the machine harvesting of beets outside of California was done up to 1946 and many thousand tons have been harvested. Further work is being done on it with the aim of adapting it to a wider range of conditions.

A second, completely different type of harvester has been developed in California primarily to meet conditions there. It is a large, spiked-wheel machine built in one-row and two-row models; a large tractor is needed to pull it. A lighter draft, single-row model has been designed that may be suited to other areas. With this harvester, untopped beets are loosened in the row and then picked up by the spikes on the 6-foot wheel. Topping chisels remove the beets from the spiked wheel at the top and a sickle cuts off any leaf streamers on the beets. Beets are cleaned from dirt on a roll-type screen and are elevated directly to a truck. Beet tops and adhering soil are scraped from the wheel and onto the ground.

Topping done by the machine is slightly poorer than ordinary hand topping, but sugar factories have found it acceptable. It does not leave beet tops in particularly good shape, but a better method of top handling is under development. The machines, particularly the two-row models, have large capacity, and seem to be a reasonably satisfactory answer to California's harvest problem. More than 30 percent of California's 1945 beet crop and nearly 60 percent of its 1946 crop were harvested by these machines, some two-row machines harvesting more than 500 acres each season. The grower's cost per ton harvested for one company in 1945 on 10,000 acres was $1.28, compared to $2.13 a ton for hand harvest.

A third harvester, in commercial production for the first time in 1946, is of still another type. It utilizes hand sorting of topped beets from clods where necessary on heavier soils and has shown this method to be practical and economical. Operations in 1945 by farmers using these machines where hand sorting was necessary showed that the hand labor required for harvest could be cut to a third of that normally required. The cost of harvest could be reduced one-third to one-half by use of the harvester. Where hand sorting was not needed on friable soils, the labor and cost of harvest could be still further reduced. This machine tops beets in the ground, then digs, cleans, and elevates them to the sorting table, if needed, or drops them directly into a trailer-hopper if no clods are present. The beets are transferred from the trailer by a built-in elevator to beet trucks. The topping is done well, but the tops are dropped back directly onto the ground in only fair shape. A suitable method of top handling is being developed, however. The beets are clean and the machine can be used on dry, cloddy soil where other machines have failed. It is a single-row harvester having a capacity of about 2½ acres a day.

The fourth harvester, in commercial production for the first time in 1946, is a single-row machine that plows the untopped beets loose and lifts them by the tops. They are elevated into the machine where they are topped and then delivered directly into a truck driven alongside. The tops are dropped back onto the ground one row at a time. A top windrower is under development. The machine eliminates the problem of clods by lifting the beets by the leaves, but it is necessary to have good leaf growth on the beets. So far these harvesters have gone into the Michigan-Ohio territory where, in 1946, they took out about 7 percent of the crop.

Thus, mechanical harvesting is coming into its own. Before 1943 the commercial acreage harvested by machine was negligible; in 1944 it was 7 percent. Approximately 12 percent of our beet acreage in 1945 was machine harvested. In 1945, about 400 harvesters were manufactured; in 1946, the estimated number was 1,200.

THE AUTHOR

S. W. McBirney is an agricultural engineer in the Bureau of Plant Industry Soils, and Agricultural Engineering. He is in charge of the sugar-beet machinery research project of the Bureau and has been working on the mechanization of the labor peaks of the sugar-beet crop for several years. His outstanding work has been on the mechanization of the spring work, particularly on the development of single-seed planting and low seeding rates. He is a graduate of Iowa State College and began his work with the Department in 1927.

FOR FURTHER READING

Beresford, Hobart: *March of Mechanization of Sugar-Beet Production in Idaho,* Idaho Agricultural Experiment Station Circular 111, July 1946.

Hansen, C. M., Smith, L. E., and Bell, R. W.: *Sugar-Beet Harvester Trials in Michigan in 1945,* Michigan Agricultural Experiment Station Quarterly Bulletin, volume 28, No. 4, pages 338–343, May 1946.

McBirney, S. W.: *Sugar-Beet Blocking by Machinery,* U. S. D. A. Farmers' Bulletin 1933, 1943.

Mervine, E. M., and Barmington, R. D.: *Mechanical Thinning of Sugar Beets,* Colorado Agricultural Experiment Station Bulletin 476, 1943.

Sugarcane Culture

by GEORGE ARCENEAUX

ALONG WITH the introduction of new sugarcane varieties, improved methods of cultivation have been developed, primarily in the time of planting and in mechanization of cultivation and weed control.

Planting sugarcane in the South has been done traditionally in late fall and early spring. Within the past two decades the average planting date has been sharply advanced. Now almost all of the planting in Louisiana is done before the old crop is harvested. Preharvest planting is also practiced in Florida and is being adopted in the sirup-producing States. This change has been due partly to the introduction of hardier varieties adapted to Temperate Zone conditions and partly to a clearer understanding of factors that affect the satisfactory overwintering of plants.

Poor stands and stunted spring growth frequently resulted from planting in September. During the initial growth, sugarcane shoots withdraw sugar from the seed piece and at a certain stage of growth reduce food reserves to critically low levels. Satisfactory overwintering of young cane plants and prompt resumption of growth in the spring depend upon large supplies of sugar in the seed pieces.

Old varieties planted in early September often gave poor stands because the young plants were killed by freezing at a stage when sugar reserves were low. But when planting is done in early August, sugar supplies in the seed piece are usually restored before winter. Food is also stored in the protected tissues of the new plant. These large reserves of food enable the young plants to make rapid growth in the spring, with increased yields of cane and a higher sugar content at harvest.

There are now available hardier new varieties that can be planted during late August and early September. By selecting the right varieties, the farmer can begin planting in early August and continue until early winter. The need for spring planting has been practically eliminated.

Mechanization, well under way before the war, was greatly stimulated by shortages of labor. Mule-drawn plows and cultivators had been largely replaced by tractor-drawn row plows and cultivators of various types. Weeding by means of hoes and other hand implements has been largely replaced by improved shaving devices, mechanical hoes, and flame cultivators.

Shaving ridge surfaces to remove winter weeds and dead growth of cane is commonly done by means of a circular blade revolving in a horizontal plane at the proper height. Recently, friction-type shavers have been extensively replaced by cutting disks that revolve at a high speed and are powered by the tractor. This improvement has greatly reduced damage to sugarcane plants.

Tractor-drawn cultivators equipped with two middle units, each made up of two shovels and a double moldboard, are now commonly used for the first cultivation. Distribution of fertilizer may be combined with this operation by using two distributors attached to the tractor. With this equipment one man can cultivate and fertilize 35 acres a day.

Subsequent cultivation is most efficiently done by means of three-row, disk-type, tractor-drawn cultivators. Improved units can be operated by two men and will ordinarily cover 80 or more acres a day.

Flaming for control of weeds is widely practiced in Louisiana. It is based on the principle that shoots of sugarcane will be less injured by a moving flame of moderate intensity than will the weeds. It is possible, under some conditions at least, to control weeds among growing cane with relatively little injury to the crop. Thus young, succulent weeds among well-developed cane shoots can be readily killed by flaming, whereas hand-hoeing would be laborious and costly. Heat treatment is commonly applied by means of a three-row unit, using fuel oil. The cane row is double-flamed—a burner on one side of the row slightly preceding a similar one on the other side.

Recently tests with 2,4–D (2,4–dichlorophenoxyacetic acid), 1 part per 1,000, generally proved superior to flaming for control of susceptible weeds. Sugarcane plants are not injured by the concentration required for control of alligatorweed (*Alternanthera philoxeroides*) and other susceptible weeds. Appropriate dosages of this selective weed killer satisfactorily suppressed heavy infestations of susceptible weeds in advanced stages of growth. Under such conditions, chemical control gave larger yields of cane and sugar than either flaming or hand weeding, and resulted in a greatly reduced residual infestation of the weed.

Considerable attention has been given more economical methods of controlling weeds along ditchbanks and other waste areas that are sources of weed infestation. For years the extensive ditches, needed for

The Cold Storage of Apples

by W. V. HUKILL and EDWIN SMITH

THE METHODS of storing apples have improved a great deal in recent years. The progress does not depend so much on new discoveries or revolutionary changes as on closer attention to practical ways of providing the best conditions for keeping the fruit good.

For best results in storage, apples must be harvested when mature but not fully ripe and stored under conditions that will arrest the rate of ripening and the growth of rot-producing fungi, avoid shrivelling, and not result in low-temperature disorders. With a few exceptions, these conditions embody a storage temperature of 30° F., or slightly above the freezing point of apples, and a relative humidity of 85 percent. A few varieties grown in certain regions are susceptible to low-temperature disorders and have to be stored at temperatures of 36° or 38° F. This has resulted in the development and use of controlled-atmosphere storage. McIntosh apples can be stored at 40° in a controlled atmosphere of 5 percent carbon dioxide and 2 percent oxygen for longer periods than they can be stored in air at 32°. Varieties, however, have specific atmospheric requirements as to this type of storage.

Complex chemical changes in the tissue of apples continue during ripening until the fruit becomes overripe and unpalatable, with subsequent collapse. The changes are retarded as the temperature is lowered; thus the storage life of the fruit is lengthened. Research has shown that at 30° F. about a fourth more time is needed for apples to ripen than at 32°. Apples standing in an orchard at 70° may ripen as much in 3 days as they would during a month's storage at 30°. When held in a cold storage room that has a temperature of 36° at one end and 30° at the other, apples, although alike when stored, will become overripe in the one place but remain in excellent condition in the other.

The degree to which the requirements can be filled depends upon the management of all the processes through which apples must go on their way from the tree to the table, equipment that is available for each process, and the operation of equipment or the execution of each process. Progress in cold storage of apples begins with management of the movement of the fruit through the various processes of growing, harvesting, packaging, storing, transporting, and distributing.

No apples should be assigned for late storage unless they are of good quality. Those to be stored should be moved to the storage promptly. The length of storage period should be limited by the variety and quality of the fruit. Apples should be moved from storage while they still have enough life to withstand normal handling and exposure during transportation to market and distribution. Good storage can be wasted on apples poorly chosen for storage or poorly handled before and after storage, just as good apples can be lost by poor storage. This principle is being applied more and more, and much of the current progress in apple storage is due to improvement in this kind of management.

The improvement of buildings and equipment can be traced from the early fruit cellar through the ventilated storage cooled by night air, to refrigerated storages that have come into common use in the past 20 years or so. Methods of applying refrigeration to apples have likewise been changing. In recent years the cooling is mostly accomplished by moving cooled air through the storage rooms rather than by having cooling coils spaced about the rooms. Perhaps the most common way to cool the circulating air in modern plants is to pass it through a spray of chilled brine.

The first objective in a refrigerated storage is to cool the fruit promptly and maintain a temperature at or near the optimum. If cooling is to be done quickly there will be a large demand upon the refrigerating machinery at harvesttime. A large volume of air must be circulated to distribute the refrigeration to all the stored fruit. Even after the apples are cooled, there is always some variation in temperature from time to time in a storage room, and the fruit in some parts of the room is necessarily warmer than that in other parts. Best storage conditions are those that will keep the variation in temperature to a minimum.

In order to effect prompt cooling and uniform low temperatures, three requirements must be met. The first is ample refrigerating capacity; in the Pacific Northwest this would be about 6 tons of refrigeration for each 1,000 field boxes of apples brought to the storage daily. The second is ample volume of air circulation; 1,000 cubic feet of air a minute for each ton of refrigeration is considered a minimum. The third requirement is provision for the air to move effectively among all the packages; this depends upon the arrangement of air ducts, freedom from obstruction to air movement through the room, and arrangement of the stacks of boxes to permit access of air.

The first and second requirements—ample refrigeration and air circulation—can be provided by machinery. A plant loaded beyond its capacity cannot cool the apples promptly.

The third requirement, good air distribution, is more than a matter of plant capacity; it calls for careful attention to detail in design and operation. A large number of methods of air distribution are in use. The simplest is to discharge the cold air through nozzles at one point in the storage room and pick up the return air nearby. This is likely to result in a relatively wide range of temperatures in different parts of the room. Perhaps the most elaborate method is to discharge cold air from a large number of openings in ducts spaced through the room, and to pick up the return in an equal number of return ducts. In that method, the air velocities through the room may be slow. The most effective placement of ducts for providing uniform air distribution is a single discharge duct along one wall of the room and a single return duct along the opposite side. For good operation, the air is delivered to and returned from the room at the ceiling or near it.

Whatever the arrangement of the ducts, it is necessary to have a clear space at the ceiling throughout the room. Girders that extend across the path of air flow or packages stacked too close to the ceiling prevent free movement of air. Failure to leave an open space between stacks of packages results in poor circulation.

Even with plenty of refrigerating capacity and air volume, and with the best possible air distribution, absolute uniformity of temperature cannot be had. The air leaving the room will be warmer than that entering. For that reason, the fruit nearest the delivery openings is exposed to the coldest air. In the most modern plants, the variation in temperature of the fruit at different points is held to a minimum by automatically reversing periodically the direction of air movement. By doing so, none of the fruit is continuously exposed to the coldest air, and none to the warmest. When warm apples are brought into a storage room, it is desirable that they be cooled as quickly as possible. Reversing the air direction periodically permits using air as cold as 22° to 25° F. to get rapid cooling without danger of freezing.

For economy, several inches of insulation are used on all outside walls, the roof and the floor. In the Pacific Northwest, as much as 24 inches of dry mill shavings are often used for insulating the roof of storage houses. Mineral materials are best for ground-floor insulation; they should be protected from ground water by a waterproof membrane. Wall and ceiling insulation is protected by a vapor-proof lining between it and the outside air. No amount of insulation will totally prevent heat from coming through a wall or floor. Packages of fruit sitting directly on a ground floor receive heat from the ground, and they are kept too warm.

Persistent attention to details of operation is essential even in the best apple storage. In a well-operated plant, packages are spaced so that air may move freely among the stacks and between the fruit and the walls. A clear space is left for air to circulate over the packages and under the ceiling at all points. Outside doors are not left open unnecessarily. Temperatures and conditions of fruit are observed regularly.

A number of apple storages are now equipped for effective reversed-air circulation. In constructing most of these plants, careful attention was given refrigerating capacity, blower capacity, and all details that affect the distribution of air. Fruit temperatures in this type of storage both during the cooling period and after storage temperatures are reached, have shown that it represents a distinct step toward meeting all the requirements for highest apple quality. The modern apple storage can furnish consumers with crisp, juicy apples throughout the season with a program of management that segregates apples most suitable for late storage from those that should be consumed early. It gives special attention to getting storage apples into storage promptly, prevents overloading the storage facilities, and handles the fruit in all stages in conformity with its requirements.

THE AUTHORS

W. V. Hukill is an agricultural engineer in the Bureau of Plant Industry, Soils, and Agricultural Engineering. He has been with the Department since 1924, studying farm buildings, particularly crop storages, and engineering problems in the transportation and storage of fruits and vegetables.

Edwin Smith is a horticulturist in the Bureau of Plant Industry, Soils, and Agricultural Engineering. He is in charge of handling, transportation, and storage investigations of fruits and vegetables at Wenatchee, Wash., field station.

FOR FURTHER READING

Britton, J. E., Fisher, D. V., and Palmer, R. C.: *Apple Harvesting and Storage in British Columbia,* Canada Department of Agriculture Farmers' Bulletin 105, 1941.

Fisher, D. F.: *Handling Apples From Tree to Table,* U. S. D. A. Circular 659, 1942.

Gerhardt, Fisk, and Ezell, D. B.: *Physiological Investigations on Fall and Winter Pears in the Pacific Northwest,* U. S. D. A. Technical Bulletin 759, 1941.

Hukill, W. V., and Smith, Edwin: *Cold Storage for Apples and Pears,* U. S. D. A. Circular 740, 1946.

Marshall, Roy E.: *Construction and Management of Farm Storages—With Special Reference to Apples,* Michigan State College Circular Bulletin 143, 1945.

Rose, D. H., Wright, R. C., and Whiteman, T. M.: *The Commercial Storage of Fruits, Vegetables, and Florists' Stocks,* U. S. D. A. Circular 278, 1941.

Shell-Cooled Potato Storage

by ALFRED D. EDGAR

RESEARCH into problems of storing potatoes used to have the rather simple aims of keeping potatoes above freezing and below sprouting temperatures so that they would meet local requirements for seed and eating. Now the marketing of potatoes and, therefore, the objectives of research in their storage have become more complicated.

A larger proportion of the seed potatoes for central and southern areas is grown in the North, and northern-grown seed potatoes may have to be stored under one of three sets of conditions: At a relatively cold temperature for 7 or 8 months, when intended for seed to be used locally; at moderate temperatures for 6 or 7 months, for planting in the Central States; or at a relatively high temperature, to get them through the dormant period quickly, for early planting in the South.

The storage of table-stock potatoes also has become more complex. Potatoes for early consumption can be kept in warm-temperature storage with minimum air circulation, and it is now known that a higher vitamin content is retained by this treatment. Low temperatures, however, are required for long-period storage. It is obvious, therefore, that the temperatures at which potatoes are stored will depend largely on the specific use to which they are to be put and the time at which they are to be marketed. Potatoes for dehydration and those used in the manufacture of potato chips require special storage conditions.

There is a growing tendency also for areas of different climates and different harvesting dates to grow and store potatoes for overlapping markets. For example, potatoes harvested early in the North may be kept in low-temperature storage for planting in the South, while those harvested farther South later must be stored at a higher temperature to get them through the dormant period in time for southern planting.

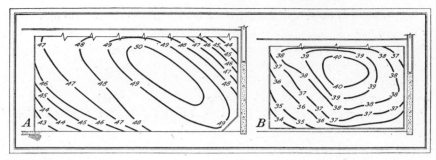

Here are cross-sections of two potato storage bins illustrating different methods of
cooling. The areas of similar temperatures within the bins on January 1 are shown.
Bin *A* is 8x23x11 feet deep, and has an earth floor and gravity air circulation, regulated at 38° F. minimum in tight double-bin partitions and outside wall. Bin *B* is
8x15x10 feet deep, and has tight single partitions with gravity air circulation, regulated to 32° minimum in tight double floor and outside wall.

For many years, potato storage construction, particularly for the
humid part of the country with average temperatures of 25° to 30° F.
during January and February, featured bins having double slatted floors
and bin partitions, so the air could circulate through the mass of potatoes. Such through-the-bin circulation, however, reduces the vitamin
content and increases the shrinkage of stored potatoes.

Shell cooling of potato bins to reduce shrinkage and preserve better
table quality has proved effective in the potato storage investigations
of the Department in cooperation with several experiment stations in the
late-crop potato States. The shell-cooling process consists of circulating
air under and around the bins with tight walls and floors, rather than
through the mass of potatoes. It is most satisfactory in large storages
where power-operated blowers and thermostatic controls are used.

In the fall, outside air is drawn into the building and circulated to
remove field heat from the potatoes. A differential thermostat can be
set to start the blower whenever the outside temperature is lower than
that of the potatoes. As the temperature drops, a second thermostat protects the potatoes from freezing by breaking the circuit. During the
winter further cooling of the potatoes is not necessary, but air circulation
is still required to maintain uniform temperatures and reduce condensation of moisture. Blower dampers are therefore arranged to recirculate
air within the storage house around, under, and over the bins. In smaller
houses that have a capacity of fewer than 10,000 bushels, gravity air
circulation is usually satisfactory.

Potatoes kept in storages built and operated according to recommendations of agricultural engineering research show shrinkage losses from
1 percent to 10 percent less than other types of houses. At least 10 million bushels annually of late-crop potatoes are now stored in buildings
of improved design, and the annual saving in shrinkage alone approxi-

mates $120,000. Heavy losses from freezing and decay are prevented, and the potatoes for table use have higher nutritive value.

Additional savings are effected by shell circulation because the storage houses last longer, being less subject to damage by moisture. The new designs in these houses eliminate the condensation of moisture on the structural parts without allowing the potatoes to dry out.

Another problem that has come up in connection with the storage of potatoes in the past few years is the need for centralized washing and grading in storages. Twenty years ago most of the crop was sold ungraded and none of it was washed. When grading first became common, it was done by portable graders, which were moved right into the bins. Until recently, therefore, the principal handling problem was to design storages so that potatoes could be put into the bins with the least injury. Now, however, many storages use stationary washing and grading equipment and large stationary brushers. Some means must be worked out for moving potatoes from bins to graders, and various methods are being compared. Forty-bushel portable bins can be handled with industrial lift-trucks; potatoes in sacks or small boxes can be stacked on pallets and moved with industrial or hand-operated lift-trucks; or conveyors designed to avoid bruising the tubers can be used both from truck to storage and from storage to graders.

THE AUTHOR

Alfred D. Edgar, an agricultural engineer in the Bureau of Plant Industry, Soils, and Agricultural Engineering and a graduate of Kansas State College, started specializing in potato storage research in his present position in 1931, when he was put in charge of the potato storage research project that the Department has maintained continuously in various States, so that findings in one area can be tried in another, and new developments in the later locations taken to the earlier locations for refinement. He was one of eight Department specialists sent by Congress to Alaska in 1946 to determine agricultural problems upon which research is most needed.

ACKNOWLEDGMENT

Cooperation of the many Federal and State experiment station workers, especially R. C. Wright of the Department and those listed as coauthors in the bulletins below, has helped bring the work to the present point.

FOR FURTHER READING

Edgar, Alfred D., Jefferson, C. H., and Wheeler, E. J.: *Potato Storages for Michigan,* Michigan Agricultural Experiment Station Special Bulletin 320, 1942.

Edgar, Alfred D., and Long, Thomas E.: *Ventilating Red River Valley Potato Storage Structures,* North Dakota Agricultural Experiment Station Circular 72, 1944.

Ramsey, G. B., Lutz, J. M., Werner, H. O., and Edgar, A. D.: *Experiments on Shipping Washed Early Potatoes,* Nebraska Experiment Station Bulletin 364, 1944.

Pests in Stored Products

by R. T. COTTON

UNTIL RECENTLY the only really effective insecticides available for controlling insect pests of grains and food products stored in bulk or packages were those that could be used in the vapor stage as fumigants. Contact sprays did little good. Insects harbored in the woodwork of farm and elevator grain bins, warehouses, storerooms, flour mills, ships, and railway cars are not readily controlled by fumigation, and constitute a source of infestation whose importance to our food industries can scarcely be overestimated. Newly harvested grain placed in wooden bins, boxcars, warehouses, and such quickly becomes infested with insects that emerge from the cracks in walls and floors.

Now the so-called residual spray has assumed an important role in the control of these pests. The residual spray, when applied to the surface of walls, floors, partitions, et cetera, leaves a protective film of a toxic chemical that causes the death of insects that touch it.

Several chemicals with residual properties have been developed, many of them highly effective against the insect pests of stored grain and milled cereals. The best known is DDT, which can be had in many different forms and concentrations, and can be used in either a water or an oil-base spray. Two analogs of DDT, which possess quite similar characteristics, are di(paramethoxyphenyl) trichloroethane and dichlorodiphenyl-dichloroethane. Other residual chemicals are a chlorinated campene with the empirical formula $C_{10}H_{10}Cl_8$, and a chlorinated hydrocarbon, with the empirical formula $C_{10}H_6Cl_8$.

A 5-percent concentration of any one of the first four compounds or a 2-percent concentration of the last in a deodorized kerosene are highly effective against even the most resistant type of stored-product insect. They should be applied at the rate of not more than 1 gallon per 1,000 square feet of surface area. These residual poisons are relatively slow in action. The addition of a "knock-down" agent, such as pyrethrum or one of the thiocyanates, improves the efficiency of their performance.

Because all the residual insect toxicants are poisonous to warm-blooded animals, they must not be used to spray grain or milled cereal products intended for human food or animal feed. Precautions must also be taken to avoid spraying food containers and to prevent foodstuffs from coming into direct contact with sprayed surfaces.

DDT may also be useful for incorporation into wrappers for preventing the entry of insects into bagged and packaged foodstuffs. The adaptation of DDT to this use is still in the experimental stage, but it shows promise of being invaluable for the purpose of protecting many types of susceptible foodstuffs from invasion by insects after manufacture and packaging.

As a dust, DDT has been found highly efficient in protecting bagged and packaged seed from insect attack and provides one of the cheapest and best methods of long-time protection known. Effective when mixed with seed at the rate of only 15 parts per million, it is best used in combination with a carrier dust. The carrier, by increasing the volume, insures a better distribution over the seed. Dust composed of 3 percent of DDT in magnesium oxide or pyrophyllite has been found satisfactory, although any commercially available dust containing 3 percent DDT can be used.

DDT dust of this concentration should be applied at the rate of a half ounce to a bushel of seed. Seed-treating machines can be used efficiently to coat the seeds with a uniform layer of the protective dust. The treatment does not affect germination in any way. DDT is a chemically active dust that kills insects by contact, so it is effective regardless of the moisture content of the seed.

Certain chemically inactive dusts have also been found useful for protecting seed. Their effectiveness is thought to be due to their abrasive action that breaks the waterproof, fatty covering of insects, so that the insects die as a result of the evaporation of excessive amounts of body moisture. Because of their mode of action, the effectiveness of inert dusts decreases as the moisture content of the seed rises above 12 percent.

Of numerous chemically inert dusts that we have tested, we found magnesium oxide especially good for protecting seed from insects. It is a nonpoisonous dust used medicinally in cases of stomach acidity. Many types of magnesium oxide are available on the market, and extensive laboratory tests have shown that those having a particle size of 1 micron or less afford excellent protection when mixed, at the rate of 1 ounce to the bushel, with seed containing not more than 12 percent moisture. In general, the finer the dust the more effective it is. Besides its killing effect, magnesium oxide has a repellent property, and seeds treated with it are rarely invaded by insects; besides, it is inexpensive and gives a clean and attractive appearance to seed.

The gamma isomer of benzene hexachloride is reported to be highly effective in extremely small quantities against some types of stored-product insects and may prove to be a useful insecticide in combating them. Supplies now available commercially have a bad smell that will have to be eliminated before it will be suitable for use in protecting foodstuffs. The fact that it is poisonous to warm-blooded animals will also have to be considered carefully in connection with its possible use in foodstuffs. As an insecticide benzene hexachloride has the merit of acting not only as a stomach poison but as a contact agent and as a fumigant.

Fumigants

Many new compounds are proving to be useful for fumigating mills, warehouses, and granaries to kill insects. Methyl bromide has outstanding value for treating bulk commodities in vaults, boxcars, and warehouses. Because it is sorbed to a lesser extent than other fumigants in common use, it easily penetrates bulk commodities and can be successfully used at relatively low concentrations. In airtight enclosures, dosages of 1 to $1\frac{1}{2}$ pounds per 1,000 cubic feet of space are generally satisfactory at temperatures of 60° F. or above. At temperatures below 60° F. the dosage should be increased a half pound per 1,000 cubic feet of space for every 5° drop in temperature.

In recent work on the fumigation of wheat in tightly calked steel bins, it was found that some fumigants are retained by the wheat for unusually long periods; their insecticidal action, therefore, lasts much longer than one would ordinarily expect. Because of this phenomenon, we can use successfully fumigants that once were considered too low in toxicity to be of practical value. Carbon tetrachloride, long used in admixture with flammable chemicals to reduce the fire hazard and with more toxic compounds to increase volume and aid in uniformity of distribution, is being used alone with excellent results at dosages of 3 gallons per 1,000 bushels. At the end of exposure lasting a week, consistently high kills of all stages of grain-infesting insects are obtained.

A mixture of three parts of ethylene dichloride and one part of carbon tetrachloride when applied to wheat in steel bins at the rate of 4 gallons to 1,000 bushels may be retained in killing concentration for as long as 4 months. Applied to wheat bins in Kansas in late August or early September, it protects the grain from insects that migrate to the bins during the rest of the summer and fall.

For fumigating wheat or corn in steel bins, methyl bromide in combination with various chemicals or combinations of chemicals is highly effective. A dosage of 2 gallons per 1,000 bushels of wheat or corn of the following mixtures gives a consistently good kill: Methyl bromide,

PESTS IN STORED PRODUCTS

10 percent by volume mixed with carbon tetrachloride or ethylene dichloride or methylene chloride or propylene dichloride; or a 3-to-1 mixture of ethylene dichloride and carbon tetrachloride; or a 3-to-1 mixture of propylene dichloride and carbon tetrachloride.

Other fumigants effective for treating grain in steel bins are B-methylallyl chloride and 1,1-dichloro-1-nitroethane. Two pounds of B-methylallyl chloride in sufficient carbon tetrachloride to make 1 gallon can be used at the rate of 2 gallons per 1,000 bushels for wheat or corn, and 1 pound of 1,1-dichloro-1-nitroethane in sufficient carbon tetrachloride to make 1 gallon can be used at the rate of 1 gallon per 1,000 bushels of corn or 1½ gallons per 1,000 bushels of wheat.

Ethylene dibromide, suggested as a possible grain fumigant by I. E. Neifert and associates in the Department, has recently become available in commercial quantities. A mixture of one part by volume of ethylene dibromide to nine parts of carbon tetrachloride gives a satisfactory kill of insects in stored wheat at dosages of 2 gallons of the mixture per 1,000 bushels in steel bins, and at 4 gallons per 1,000 bushels in wooden farm bins. Because a considerable part of the ethylene dibromide is sorbed by the wheat near the surface of the bin, the mixture is admirably suited for the treatment of wooden bins in which it is hard to kill the insects in the surface grain.

Of a number of nitriles (organic cyanides) tested as possible grain fumigants, 2-chloroacrylonitrile and 2-chloroacetonitrile compare favorably in toxicity with acrylonitrile and trichloroacetonitrile. In admixture with carbon tetrachloride at the rate of one part by volume of the nitrile to nine parts of carbon tetrachloride, both compounds were found to be highly toxic to insects in wheat stored in tight steel bins, when used at the rate of 1 gallon per 1,000 bushels. A mixture composed of 5 percent by volume of 2-chloroacrylonitrile, 5 percent 2,2,3-trichlorobutyronitrile, and 90 percent carbon tetrachloride, used at the rate of 1 gallon per 1,000 bushels of wheat, proved to be superior in performance to the other combinations I have mentioned. The compounds 2-chloroacrylonitrile and 2-chloroacetonitrile should be handled carefully to avoid spilling the liquid on clothing or skin or exposing the perspiring body to the vapors, because severe skin irritation may result from such exposure.

For the spot fumigation of milling units in flour mills, mixtures of equal parts by volume of acrylonitrile and carbon tetrachloride and 15 parts by volume of ethylene dibromide in 85 parts of carbon tetrachloride have been found effective. In flour mills insect infestation is more or less concentrated in the milling machinery wherever milling stock accumulates and is relatively undisturbed. The application of a fumigant to the milling units every 3 or 4 weeks will hold the insect population in a flour mill to a low level at all times.

Individual-package fumigation with ethyl or methyl formate has been practiced in the dried-fruit industry for many years. More recently isopropyl formate has come into use for the purpose, and the method has been adapted for the treatment of other food products. In treating packages of pea soup stock, 1 cubic centimeter of isopropyl formate is injected into stout paper bags holding 5 pounds of the soup stock. The bag is then heat-sealed in two transparent viscose bags. This method of fumigation should increase in popularity for treatment of high-priced commodities.

THE AUTHOR

R. T. Cotton, an entomologist in the Bureau of Entomology and Plant Quarantine, has been in charge of field research on the control of the insect pests of stored grain and milled cereal products since 1934. He has specialized on fumigation and other methods of controlling the insect pests of stored foodstuffs. Dr. Cotton holds degrees from Cornell University and George Washington University. In 1940 he was given a Modern Pioneer award in recognition of achievement in science and invention. In 1946 he was awarded a Certificate of Appreciation by the Quartermaster Subsistence Research and Development Laboratory for meritorious service in research and development phases of the Army's food program.

ACKNOWLEDGMENTS

H. H. Walkden, of the Bureau of Entomology and Plant Quarantine, and R. B. Schwitzgebel, formerly of the Bureau, made numerous observations on grain fumigation discussed in this article.

FOR FURTHER READING

Cotton, R. T.: *Protection of Stored and Dried Processed Foods and Seed Supplies from Insect Attack,* Journal of Economic Entomology, volume 37, No. 3, pages 380–384, 1944.

Cotton, R. T., and Frankenfeld, J. C.: *Dust Treatment for Protecting Stored Seed,* Seed World, volume 58, No. 9, pages 22–24, 1945.

Cotton, R. T., Walkden, H. H., and Schwitzgebel, R. B.: *The Role of Sorption in the Fumigation of Stored Grain and Milled Cereal Products,* Kansas Entomological Society Journal, volume 17, No. 3, pages 98–103, 1944.

Glass, E. H.: *Recirculation in Atmospheric Fumigation with Nitriles,* Journal of Economic Entomology, volume 37, No. 3, pages 388–391, 1944.

Neifert, I. E., Cook, F. C., Roark, R. C. and others: *Fumigation Against Grain Weevils with Various Volatile Organic Compounds,* U. S. D. A. Department Bulletin 1313, 1925.

Richardson, C. H., and Walkden, H. H.: *B-methylallyl Chloride as a Fumigant for Insects Infesting Stored Corn,* Journal of Economic Entomology, volume 38, No. 4, pages 471–477, 1945.

Slade, R. E.: *The Gamma-isomer of Hexachlorocyclohexane (Gammexane),* Chemistry and Industry, volume 40, pages 314–319, 1945.

ALSO, IN THIS BOOK

Prefabrication on the Farm

by JOHN A. SCHOLTEN

IN RECENT YEARS prefabricated brooder and poultry houses, hog houses, granaries, corn cribs, and other farm buildings have been manufactured and used in increasing numbers. Those manufactured at centrally located plants are usually of the panel type, which can be readily transported and assembled on the site. Those made at local shops are frequently built in the conventional manner, mounted on skids, and delivered to the site intact and ready for use. Because these small prefabricated buildings can be erected in a short time with little or no labor at the building site, they meet the demands for rapid expansion and fulfill a useful purpose by furnishing housing or storage facilities when regular structures are lacking or inadequate. An appealing feature of these smaller structures has been that they can be obtained in successive units without a large outlay of cash at any one time, and because they are small and portable they can be adapted to a changing farm program. Another factor that has contributed to their expanded use is the increasing difficulty of obtaining the needed skilled and semiskilled labor on the farm.

These small prefabricated units have, however, frequently been built to fill immediate needs without adequate consideration of their permanence or future usefulness. Their portable features, whether or not the building is ever moved after it is once erected, have led some farmers to overlook the need for adequate foundations and suitable anchorage. The framework is sometimes too flimsy to withstand the wear and tear of continuous service in structures that are hastily manufactured and inadequate in design. Furthermore, the material used for coverage has frequently been selected without consideration of the service condition to which it will be exposed and as a result has not proved suitable for the purpose. Certain wallboards, for example, manufactured for use as

879

sheathing or as a plaster base have been used for subflooring, for roof boards, and in other ways not recommended by the manufacturers. That has been due partly to the wartime necessity of using anything that could be obtained, but it has also been due to a failure to consider the suitability of various materials for specific parts.

Factors that must be considered in evaluating a prefabricated farm structure are structural stability, permanence, and functional utility. These are important in any structure but must be reevaluated for prefabricated structures, which incorporate newer sheet materials and unusual structural and design features. Besides resisting the loads ordinarily imposed in use, such as pressures exerted by grains or external loads from the wind, such structures must be strong enough to meet the unusual racking strains imposed in transit and at the same time must be as light as possible to facilitate movement. In order to accomplish this the designer must have a knowledge of the properties of the materials, the mechanics of construction, and the techniques required to put the materials together so that the most satisfactory results can be obtained.

The new trend in prefabrication of farm structures is as much the result of the development of improved materials intended primarily for conventional construction, particularly the various sheet materials such as plywood and the fiberboards, as it is of jig-assembly and other factory methods. Possibly the most spectacular development along this line has been the improvement in plywood and its increased use in farm structures. The development of synthetic-resin adhesives, particularly the phenols, has made possible glue bonds that are waterproof and do not come apart in service even when exposed to severe moisture conditions.

Engineers have been working on a plywood or wood impregnated with highly moisture-resistant synthetic resins to reduce grain raising and checking and to provide a sheet which does not require paint or other protective coating. Another development in the experimental stage is plywood faced with sheets of impregnated cloth or paper. Exposure tests have shown satisfactory results with plywood surfaced with a three-sheet impregnated paper cover.

The new synthetic resins have also accelerated the development of "sandwich" structures of various kinds. Active experimentation is going on with cores of light material such as insulating board, balsa wood, and cellulose acetate plastics faced with hard, durable surface materials like metals, fabric, or paper laminates, and plywood. The resulting combination of light weight, high insulating value, and strength is reportedly suitable for use as the complete wall. Some sandwich panels would be capable of carrying the loads on the structures; others would have to be inserted into load-carrying frames of timber or other material.

Many of the new wall materials, except the sandwich panels, are now in production. In general, the costs of these materials run higher than traditional clapboard and their application to farm structures still requires considerable development.

In housing, considerable progress has also been made in prefabrication. Estimates of the number of prefabricated houses built during the war vary from 100,000 to 125,000; 133 manufacturers were listed by the National Housing Agency as builders of such houses. Most of these houses were erected in urban centers, but the principles incorporated in their construction can readily be adapted to farm homes.

Prefabricators of houses follow generally pioneer work by the Forest Products Laboratory and aircraft designers in building floor and wall panels employing the stressed-skin principle. In these panels the covering sheets, generally plywood, are firmly glued to a skeleton of structural ribs to form a strong rigid panel. The ribs and covering act together to withstand stresses imposed by weights and loads encountered in service. The interior of the panels can be filled with insulating material. Windows and doors are generally built in at the factory. Such construction eliminates to a large extent the need for a structural framework. It also makes possible quick assembly of all the component parts of a house. The coverings of the stressed-skin panel form both the exterior and interior surfaces of the wall.

Apart from the fully prefabricated units, more and more of the material used in farm buildings will be precut and at least partly assembled into units before delivery. Barn and house rafters and other members can be notched and cut to length at shops where power equipment is available instead of on the building site where slower hand methods are required.

One system of partial prefabrication that has been used extensively in many new barns and other farm structures involves the use of glued laminated members. Such members in the form of laminated beams, arches, or other structural units are used in conjunction with standard construction. In a building these members form continuous framing members running from foundation to roof ridge. They are made by gluing together laminations or boards, usually not more than an inch thick. In gluing, the laminations are bent to the required curvature, which is retained in the member when the glue sets. The curvature of the rafters provides a pleasing appearance and their continuity facilitates erection by eliminating some of the joints and supporting members required in structures erected with straight members.

Laminated rafters for farm use may be glued with casein glue. Resorcinol and phenol glues can be used where moisture conditions are severe. Joints properly made with casein glue will last as long as the rafters if the wood remains dry. If the wood becomes wet or damp, however, even for relatively short periods, the glue will gradually deteriorate and the joints will weaken. The kinds of wood used in laminated rafters are generally the same as in solid rafters. Some kinds used for rafters are more easily glued than others, but all can be satisfactorily glued.

Improved casein glues containing preservatives have recently been developed. The chief advantage of a casein glue containing a preservative lies in its ability to resist deterioration caused by molds and other microorganisms when exposed to damp conditions. Intermediate-temperature-setting phenol and resorcinol resin glues have higher water resistance than casein glues and will give greater permanence under prolonged exposure to severe moisture conditions. It should be pointed out, however, that conditions unfavorable to casein glue joints in barn rafters, if maintained for long periods, are also harmful to untreated wood either in solid members or in laminations, regardless of the type of glue employed.

Casein glue resists moisture, but should not be used in wood members that stay damp or wet for a long time. Where such conditions are likely to occur, the use of a phenol or resorcinol glue is required to assure durable glue joints. The important fact to remember is that conditions that cause the moisture content of the wood to remain high for long periods favor decay of untreated wood as well as deterioration of casein glue, just as contact with the ground prohibits the successful use, in a permanent structure, of most woods without thorough preservative treatment.

In the Northern States safeguards should be made in the modern dairy or stock barn against moisture sweating within or on the wall or roof structure in cold weather. Studies at our laboratory on various types of wall sections have shown that, apart from ventilation, the most positive and least expensive method of preventing condensation of moisture within the walls is to provide vapor-resistant barriers at or near the inner face of exterior walls, or at or on the under face of stable ceilings. Among the materials that have been tested and found to be highly resistant to the passage of water vapor and hence suitable for these purposes are: Asphalt-impregnated and glossy surface-coated sheathing paper, weighing 35 to 50 pounds per roll of 500 square feet; the better grades of laminated sheathing paper made of two or more sheets of heavy paper cemented together with asphalt; and double-faced reflective insulation mounted on paper.

THE AUTHOR

John A. Scholten, as a staff member of the Forest Products Laboratory, has devoted the past 16 years to research to establish engineering design requirements for wood buildings, aircraft, and other structures. In 1943 he went to Costa Rica as a structural consultant to the Engineer Corps of the Army, and in 1946 he was an adviser to the Supreme Commander of the Allied Powers in Japan.

Fungi in Forest Products

by CARL HARTLEY

ONE WAY in which wood can be made to give better service to the user is to increase its durability. As a matter of fact, wood is already more lasting than is needed for many uses—it remains unharmed in air that is moist enough to cause serious corrosion of steel, and most of the timber that comes out of buildings that have been in service for centuries is practically as good as when it went in. Nevertheless it is true that decay fungi destroy considerable quantities of wood in some situations, and the uncertainty they cause is sometimes more serious than the actual total damage. The labor cost of replacements is high. Because an increasing part of our lumber supply is from young stands with a large proportion of sapwood, losses from decay will increase unless more precaution is taken to prevent them.

One way to get reliable service at low cost is to select wood intelligently. During the war, species were put to exacting uses, particularly in production of training planes and gliders, where maximum strength with minimum weight were prime considerations. In yellow birch, sweetgum, and yellow poplar for plywood, and in the poplar that also went into aircraft frames when spruce was scarce, material of the best texture and grain was in great demand.

Discolorations not previously studied led to the rejection of much of the wood that otherwise would have been accepted, because of the suspicion that the discolorations indicated weakening by incipient decay. Microscopical and cultural studies were conducted on them; we learned that, for those species and also for beech, only the brownish tints indicated infection with decay fungi. Most of the conspicuously discolored wood, sometimes pink, purple, green, or even nearly black, was found to contain no decay organisms. Thousands of strength tests showed that most such discolorations indicated no highly important decrease in strength.

Studies were also made on Sitka spruce, western hemlock, noble fir, and mahogany. Hundreds of sets of specimens demonstrating the acceptable and objectionable discolorations were prepared for use by Government inspectors and men in the wood-working industries. With their help, it was possible to use safely much valuable material that was badly needed and would otherwise have been rejected. We estimated that the information on yellow poplar made possible a 20-percent increase in the aircraft grades accepted, at a time when the production of poplar veneer was far below the requirements.

The black streaks in wood that extend in both directions from nails are familiar to everyone who has worked with wood. Most of the darkening of wood at nail holes comes from the chemical interaction of the iron with the tannic acid of the wood; small quantities of iron tannate, a common component of black ink, are formed. Such darkening is generally harmless except where appearances are important. It is frequently observed, however, that decay by fungi is more common at nail holes, and decay at those places may be important because it weakens the joint. This localization of decay is probably due mostly to water that condenses on the nail or penetrates the wood by following the nail, but it may be that the iron in the nail sometimes has an additional effect.

In a study of the darkening and molding of mahogany-faced aircraft plywood near nails used during the gluing process, it was found that iron inactivated the toxic extractives on which the wood depends for its resistance to fungi, thus allowing the fungi to develop. A similar but less pronounced effect was found with white oak heartwood. In redwood and in nondurable woods, the iron had no consistent effect on decay by the test fungi used. Since the wood and the extracts tested were heat-sterilized after the iron was added, further tests in which there is no heating are needed before final conclusions can be drawn.

Another precaution that would avoid some failures of wood in service is to use only seasoned lumber for building. Since the beginning of the war, too much of the lumber intended for buildings has been shipped green, and some of it is still shipped without seasoning. Green lumber is physically less desirable and, besides, may contain the first stages of decay, developed during transit or storage. Decay is not always easy to recognize, but lumber that is reasonably free from sapstain or blue stain is usually free from decay, since the stain fungi develop under the same conditions that permit decay fungi to start. For uses in which great strength is required, wood that is heavily blue-stained should be avoided. In the substructure of a basementless building on a moist site, or in a wall assembly in which vapor barriers will hinder drying, lumber that has not been dried may further cause the spread of decay.

Even when mills consider it necessary to ship green lumber, it has been possible to reduce materially the danger that serious infection will develop in it before it has a chance to dry out. The chemical dips that were previously used before open piling have been shown to delay the establishment of heavy stain infections or of decay fungi in bulk-piled green lumber for weeks or months, and sometimes as long as a year. The concentrations found in wartime experiments to be most effective are somewhat stronger than those used on open-piled lumber, but it was found that lower concentrations, which are less likely to irritate the skin of men who handle the lumber, can be made effective by adding rather large quantities of borax to the solutions.

Much deterioration in service can be avoided by using decay-resistant wood in the places where it is needed. It has long been known that heartwood from certain species of trees, as, for example, black locust, osage orange, bald cypress, redwood, and some of the cedars, is highly resistant to decay, and that a number of other species furnish moderately durable wood. Laboratory studies on shipbuilding timbers have confirmed previous opinions as to the general superiority of white oak to the red and black oaks. They also indicated that among the white oaks, chestnut oak is more resistant than true white oak. Studies completed recently in cooperation with the Soil Conservation Service show that there are large differences between different strains of black locust. The shipmast and flowerfield varieties, both in field experience and in accelerated laboratory tests, were decidedly more resistant to decay than ordinary locust.

It has also been found that there are large differences between trees of different ages and between parts of the same tree. In the white oaks, locust, western red cedar, and Douglas fir, and in most other resistant species on which tests have been made, higher resistance or a larger amount of the extractives on which resistance depends has been found in wood of older trees, and in the outer rather than inner heartwood. The central part of the heart at the base sometimes has very little decay resistance. These findings open the way for selecting more resistant wood when it is needed for situations that especially favor decay, such as tank staves, boat ribs, and wood that is placed in contact with the soil.

One of the advances toward making wood more useful has been the increase in the amount of wood treated with fire-retardant chemicals. These usually contain ammonium salts, which in weak solutions many fungi can use as a source of nitrogen, an element of which there is little in untreated wood. It was therefore feared that treated wood would be more susceptible to decay than untreated wood. Laboratory tests made with pure cultures of three common decay fungi on pine sapwood, however, showed that while the treatments did favor some of the mold fungi, they actually hindered or prevented decay in wood not subject to leaching. In contact with soil, deterioration of treated wood was no more rapid than of untreated.

Fiberboard containers are sometimes subjected to moist conditions. The weakening of the board due to the moisture is frequently aggravated by the attack of micro-organisms. The paper layers of which fiberboards are built up are bonded with glue. When urea-formaldehyde resin is used in the glue, it is extended with several parts of starch. This mixture is susceptible to attack by fungi, which sometimes cause the fiberboard to delaminate; the fiber itself is also affected by fungi. Tests showed that this could be much delayed by the use of 2 percent sodium pentachlorophenate in the fiber, or "furnish." Loss in tensile strength in moist exposure was reduced to less than one-third of that in untreated board, and a higher concentration should give still better results.

Preliminary tests indicated that the contents of moist packages might be protected against mildew by volatile fungicides incorporated in the packing material. Of 40 different chemicals tested, the familiar paradichlorobenzene used for moth control appeared most promising; it prevented mold both on wood and on other materials exposed with it.

Plywood and Modified Woods

Protein glues used in bonding plywood were found to be destroyed by either molds or bacteria; the latter were able to attack the glue in submerged specimens in which delamination had been previously attributed to direct effect of moisture, but require much more moisture than do the molds. This points to the possibility of better protection by adding preservatives that are bactericides as well as fungicides.

The synthetic resins coming into use for gluing generally resist fungi and bacteria, when not extended with other materials, although most of them give little or no evidence of any lasting toxicity to fungi. Hot-pressed phenol- and resorcinol-formaldehyde and melamine resin glues applied in liquid form have hindered effectively in laboratory tests the passage of decay fungi from one wood ply to the next.

Cold-pressed urea resins were less effective, and cold-pressed resorcinol resins still less so. When a hot-press phenolic resin was used in the sheet form in which it is often applied, fungi spread through the glue lines with little hindrance, though two sheets used together proved very effective. The number of representatives tested in each type of glue was small, and additional tests may alter these findings. Phenolic resin used as a varnish had value in preventing the surface molding of wood, if enough coats were applied to give a continuous cover. Resin glue lines materially delayed the decay of the wood under experimental conditions in special types of plywood in which the veneers used were only $\frac{1}{50}$ inch thick, but not in specimens made of $\frac{1}{16}$-inch veneers.

Woods that have been modified by impregnation with resins or otherwise are of interest for use as face plywood and for other purposes. Both compressed wood and pulp impregnated with phenol-formaldehyde resin (compreg and papreg) have shown a high degree of resistance to decay fungi in laboratory tests. Acetylated wood has also been highly resistant in preliminary trials of Forest Service material.

Paint and Surface Application of Fungicides

A somewhat controversial question was the effect of paint on the decay hazard. A coating may influence decay by acting as a barrier to the entrance of fungi, by hindering the entrance of the water the fungi need, or by hindering its evaporation. These last two effects tend to balance each other, and paint can not ordinarily be regarded as an important preventive of decay. Painting wood that is still green should increase the chance of decay; that should also be true for paint on the inside of ship planking, or on any surface through which water would normally be escaping rather than entering. On the other hand, unpainted wood that is exposed to intermittent wetting by rain may become moist enough for decay during periods of wet weather, when painted wood with the same exposure might not reach the moisture content of 25–30 percent, which the decay fungi require. The effect of cracks and unpainted ends exposed in joints complicates the situation and makes it difficult to predict for a particular structure or weather cycle what effect paint may have. There has been similar doubt as to the usefulness of brush or dip treatments with fungicides, despite the strong claims of some dealers.

In laboratory tests with southern pine sapwood, brief dip treatments in oil solutions of pentachlorophenol were quite effective in preventing the entrance of the important decay fungus, *Poria xantha,* despite heavy inoculation with it. The treatment was particularly effective in protecting exposed ends. This agrees with expectation since penetration of solutions through end grain is much deeper than through side surfaces. The futility of drawing general conclusions from tests made under only one set of conditions was shown by the results obtained when some of this same treated wood was buried in soil in two widely separated localities. In both places, the pentachlorophenol gave little protection, while copper compounds that had been decidedly inferior in the inoculation test proved much better than the pentachlorophenol in the soil. In general, for nondurable wood in contact with soil no mere surface treatment is adequate, and thorough impregnation is needed.

Experiments were conducted in warm moist surroundings in southern Mississippi in which pieces of 2 × 4-inch pine sapwood were joined in pairs, the end of a diagonal piece being fastened against the side of a vertical one. Part of these assemblies were given 30-minute soak treatment with the oil-soluble preservatives, copper naphthenate, pentachlorophenol, and phenyl mercury oleate. All of the treated and part of the untreated were then painted. The preservatives were allowed to reach all faces of the pieces, but assembling was done before painting, so the end of the diagonal piece that was in the joint was not painted. All were exposed outdoors on racks for $3\frac{1}{2}$ or 4 years; at the end of that time decay had made marked progress in most of the untreated assemblies. There was still very little decay in those with the preservative.

Painted assemblies without preservatives, in which the painting had been done very carefully so as to seal the joint, were in nearly as good condition as those with the preservative. A rather high proportion of the painted assemblies in which the joint was not sealed, and which were thus more like the ordinary paint job, showed decay, but it was mainly limited to the wood near the joint, with total damage slightly less than in the unpainted, a result that needs confirmation by further experiments.

Many additional tests are needed before positive statements can be made as to how much brush or dip treatments with preservatives decrease the decay hazard, and in what situations the increase in safety justifies the cost of the treatment. Pending further evidence it would seem advisable to give such treatments to lumber used in porches and outside steps, for houses in moist climates. For houses built over moist soil, such treatments might well be used on sills and outer ends of joists, unless preservative-impregnated wood is readily available. The lower siding boards might also profitably be treated, at least to the extent of dipping their ends. Treatment to be most effective should be on unpainted wood, but paint applied afterward and properly maintained should prolong the effectiveness of the preservative.

An experiment was set up in southern Mississippi with modifications of construction such as might be applied in rails of porches, stairs, and fences. A rail that passes over the top of a post without a break should lower the absorption of rain water by the post; in the experiment, such assemblies actually remained nearly free from decay after 3 years. Where the end of the rail met the end of another rail on top of the post or where the end of a rail was fastened against the side of the post, decay has started in most of the assemblies that have so far been opened. Builders have gone far in the development of metal flashing and overlapping joints to keep water out of the roofs and walls of frame buildings, but there is still room for improvement in this respect in some details of buildings, and still more in fences, platforms, bridges, tank supports, and similar outdoor structures.

Houses Without Basements

In the defense housing projects started since 1940, the chief concern as to decay hazard was the fact that the houses and barracks were mostly built close to the ground and without basements. The error of putting decay-susceptible wood members in direct contact with the ground or imbedding them in moist concrete was less frequent than in the emergency construction of the First World War. The principal concern was for the lack of ventilation under many of the houses set on moist sites. Particularly in the winter in the colder parts of the country, moisture condenses on the inner faces of the sills of some of the houses, and in a smaller number on the joists near the outside foundation, or throughout the substructure if the building above is unheated. Occupants of the houses usually are unwilling to keep ventilators open during the colder parts of the year.

Evidence was obtained indicating that vapor from soil was an important source of this condensation moisture, and a simple method was devised for shutting it off. Asphalt roll roofing was laid on the soil under buildings that were too moist. There was a surprising decline in the moisture content of the wood; no more moisture condensation has been observed during the 3½ years since the cover was put on, although nearby houses that had the same moisture content before the beginning of the test continued to show high moisture and in some cases condensation. Many houses, even on moist sites and with mineral-board skirting completely closed around the base during the winter, do not reach the moisture danger point. The houses that do become moist enough for decay can apparently be safeguarded sufficiently by the use of roofing of the grade weighing 55 pounds per 108 square feet and costing at retail about 3 cents a square foot. Ordinary asphalt-impregnated roofers' felt, the 15-pound grade costing about a fourth as much as the asphalt roofing, also appeared to be a sufficient vapor barrier in the places where it has been tested, but it will deteriorate when lying on moist soil, so its use under buildings should be limited to those that will be needed for only a very few years. Tests have been extended to buildings with ordinary types of foundations in addition to the houses with mineral-board skirting but conclusions are not yet final.

THE AUTHOR

Carl Hartley is a pathologist in the Division of Forest Pathology, Bureau of Plant Industry, Soils, and Agricultural Engineering. Except for 3 years of general plant-disease investigations for the Instituut voor Plantenziekten, Netherlands East Indies, Dr. Hartley has been continuously with the Department since 1909. His principal contributions have been on diseases of forest nursery stock and deterioration of forest products.

Advances in Rodent Control

by E. R. KALMBACH

BEFORE THE WAR our three most useful rodent poisons were imported. Red squill came from the Mediterranean Sea area. Strychnine came from India and French Indochina. Thallium sulfate came from Germany, France, and Belgium. Hostilities cut off almost all those sources at the time that the armed forces were planning and executing the Pacific campaigns that sent our troops into areas where many strange rat-borne diseases existed. Other factors added to the urgency: Rodents destroy crops, and there was great need of food; in many theaters of war we had concentrations of men and supplies, which were prey to attack by rats and mice; there were contacts with species and populations of rats not previously encountered by great numbers of human beings.

The shortage of effective rat poisons was extremely serious. A start had been made in the search for substitute materials. Two independent groups had intensified their efforts and each had made progress. Curt P. Richter, of Johns Hopkins University, had discovered the toxicity to laboratory rats of ANTU, or alphanapthylthiourea. The Fish and Wildlife Service, of the Department of the Interior, at its Wildlife Research Laboratory in Denver, studied a number of promising compounds. When the emergency appeared to be acute, the value of the research programs was recognized by the Office of Scientific Research and Development, and funds were provided to put them into high gear. The accomplishments that resulted were distinctly a product of war, but they are now available to enhance the peacetime welfare and economy.

ANTU soon was produced in quantity adequate for widespread testing, and, at Dr. Richter's request, the Fish and Wildlife Service entered into cooperation with his group to determine the value of the new poison for the control of both rats and field rodents. Although ANTU killed

Norway rats readily, black and Alexandrine rats were less susceptible, and house mice and most field rodents were relatively unaffected by it. It was found to be dangerous to dogs, cats, hogs, and chickens, but almost nontoxic to monkeys. These findings indicated that ANTU should be useful in areas where the Norway rat predominated, that it should be used with a degree of caution where pets are present, but that it appeared to resemble red squill in the matter of safety to human beings.

The search for new poisons led to the demonstration of compound 1080, or sodium fluoroacetate, as a rodenticide. In this discovery the Patuxent Wildlife Research Refuge in Maryland accumulated and tested many potential rodenticides, among which was 1080. The Denver Wildlife Research Laboratory confirmed the findings and demonstrated the utility and hazards of the material under field conditions.

Compound 1080 differs from ANTU in that it is toxic to all forms of life on which it has been tested. It has been found to be an effective poison for the control of all types of rats, mice, ground squirrels, and prairie dogs. It is highly soluble in cold water, and consequently one of the best methods of using it against rats and mice in buildings is to expose it as water solutions at frequent intervals along the rodent runways.

The indiscriminate toxicity of compound 1080 is its one serious disadvantage. So susceptible are dogs, cats, and hogs to it that they may be killed by eating sick or dead rats that have been poisoned by it. This secondary hazard is in addition to the danger to animals that might pick up baits or drink the poisoned water. There is no known antidote for 1080, so it is essential that this new poison be used with utmost caution. It is recommended by the Fish and Wildlife Service that compound 1080 be used only by experienced persons who are trained to handle poisons and who will treat it with the respect that it deserves.

Compound 1080 was first employed in the control of field rodents in October 1944, when it was used with signal success against California ground squirrels. Its performance in the control of these and other field rodents has rarely been equalled, and, if baits prepared with it are protected by color, it appears to be a reasonably safe poison from the standpoint of bird mortality.

There are, however, certain objections to compound 1080 in field use. Its toxicity is high for the mammals tested, especially for certain carnivores. Domestic dogs and cats, coyotes, bobcats, foxes, and badgers, that are likely to feed on surface-killed rodents, are greatly endangered. A 20-pound coyote or dog can be killed by a dose of compound 1080 that would not kill an 8-ounce rat. It is for that reason that the Fish and Wildlife Service has emphatically recommended that this rodenticide not be released to the public for unskilled use until adequate safeguards have been evolved that will protect both human life and beneficial creatures.

Both ANTU and 1080 are being produced in the United States from raw materials that are readily available. No future disruption of world trade can now cause a serious shortage of effective rodenticides in this country. But since ANTU and 1080 may still not be the ideal rodent killers, research is continuing to develop even more satisfactory ones and to learn better and safer ways to use them.

While in no sense a new discovery during the war, another poison, zinc phosphide, was used rather extensively in place of the rodenticides that had become scarce. Previously developed as a control agent for meadow and pine mice, zinc phosphide was found to give excellent control of house rats and mice, and even of ground squirrels and prairie dogs. Because of its black color and marked odor and taste, it is not readily eaten by game and other seed-eating birds. The secondary poisoning hazard to carrion-feeding birds and mammals also is low. Zinc phosphide, however, is toxic to all forms of life, and the preparation of baits containing it and their exposure in the field should be entrusted only to personnel trained in rodent control.

The use of zinc phosphide to control range rodents takes more skill than is commonly used in such programs. Prebaiting, a practice of exposing unpoisoned grain at rodent burrows several days before the exposure of the poisoned grain, is necessary. This poison is unstable and loses its toxicity with exposure. There also are seasons when it cannot be used effectively. Thus, although zinc phosphide proved to be a valuable emergency tool, it will eventually be replaced in general rodent control by other poisons as they become available.

The Story of Red Squill

Red squill (*Urginea maritima*), a liliaceous plant, the bulbs of which are harvested as a wild crop in the Mediterranean region, long has been used as a lethal agent in rat control. The distastefulness of red squill to human beings and to most domestic animals and its inherent strong emetic action to animals other than rats combine to make it the most specific raticide. It can be used with comparative safety by the general public to combat rats.

With the outbreak of war in Europe, the supply of red squill from the Mediterranean sources became a matter of immediate concern, and in 1939 drug dealers imported 889,664 pounds of bulbs and dried bulb slices. This was in marked contrast with a total import of 121,027 pounds in 1938 and reflects the effort put forth to increase inventories of this item. To procure all the red squill possible, little regard was given to the quality of the material obtained; as a result, there was on hand in this country a large supply of red squill having a potency so low that it was of little value in rat control.

To cope with the situation, the Wildlife Research Laboratory at

Denver developed a method of fortifying this poorer quality squill. The method consists essentially of preparing concentrated extracts of the rat-killing principles present in small quantities in the weaker squills and impregnating with them a predetermined amount of similar unextracted material in such a proportion that the final product is adequately toxic. Standardized powders of this type became generally known as fortified red squill powder. Since there is no chemical method known for determining the potency of red squill, all toxicity determinations were carried out by feeding known quantities to captive rats.

After fortified red squill powder had been produced in some quantity in a small pilot plant erected and operated at the Denver laboratory, a larger plant for processing this material was constructed under the laboratory's supervision for the Louisiana Health Department at New Orleans. This unit turned out a considerable quantity of fortified red squill, which was used to combat the rats causing typhus in that city and surrounding territory.

Along with research designed to increase the effectiveness of squill preparations sold to the public, studies were undertaken to propagate red squill in the Western Hemisphere. Southern California and Baja California, Mexico, where the climate resembles that of North Africa, were found to be suitable areas for growing the plant. Highly toxic bulbs have been produced on an experimental basis in these localities. Later the Bureau of Plant Industry, Soils, and Agricultural Engineering of the Department took over the propagative aspects of this program, in charge of D. M. Crooks. The Fish and Wildlife Service collaborates in determining the toxicity of the bulbs produced.

Development of Deterrents Against Mammals

Beginning even before the war, increasing importance was placed on the use of deterrents as a means of reducing damage by rodents. The early work emphasized the reduction of damage by field mammals through repellent sprays and paints. The animals concerned included principally deer, rabbits, mice, and tree squirrels—creatures that damage seed and seedlings in reforestation projects, shelterbelt plantings, farm wood lots, and orchards. Hundreds of compounds were studied. In cooperation with the Forest Service, Soil Conservation Service, State game and fish departments, and other organizations, tests were conducted in Montana, Louisiana, Texas, the Lake States, the Great Plains shelterbelt area, New York, and the New England States.

A rabbit repellent paint known as "96a" was then developed. It consists of copper carbonate, copper sulfate, and dry lime-sulfur as the active ingredients and a synthetic resin and asphalt emulsion dissolved in ethylene dichloride as the adhesive. When applied to the bark of dormant trees, "96a" is effective in preventing damage by rabbits. It is now being manufactured by the Fish and Wildlife Service at its Supply Depot at Pocatello, Idaho, where it is available to the public.

As the war progressed, the study of repellents for rats, mice, pocket gophers, and other animals that damage stored foods, communication lines, and other vital war goods was stressed. A search was made for suitable repellent materials, which, when applied to such army subsistence packs as 10–1 ration and K-ration, would minimize damage done by rodents, both in this country and overseas. The work was carried out in cooperation with the Quartermaster Corps Subsistence Research Laboratory, and seventy-odd materials were evaluated.

Microcrystalline waxes, used by the Army to waterproof packaged food, were found particularly effective in preventing rodent damage. Only where adverse storage conditions prevailed did rats gnaw through this protective barrier, and then only after protracted exposure of the wax-dipped boxes to almost constant dripping of water. Under dry or moderately dry storage conditions, such boxes were completely undamaged regardless of the contents. Other substances found to be of particular value in minimizing rodent damage when applied to food packages were water glass (37-percent sodium silicate) and prepared tung oil.

Ammonium sulfate (approximately 20 percent) was found useful in such insulating materials as cotton, ground paper, and sawdust, in preventing nesting of mice and rats.

A commercial insulating material consisting of porous glass brick was also found to be impervious to rat damage. When the material was placed so as to obstruct the movements of wild rats, the animals either abandoned that route or gnawed into adjoining sections of the wall. Commercial installations of this product in refrigeration rooms have further demonstrated its value as a rodent-proofing material. Contributions were also made to the problem of protecting overhead and underground telephone cables from tree squirrels and pocket gophers, and synthetic tires and tubes from porcupines, rats, and mice.

Despite the progress made, there is much yet to be done in the field of animal deterrents. What appears to be of value under one set of conditions often fails under another. The cumulative effect of several animals, also, may enable them to break through a protective barrier, whereas one animal alone could not do so. The ultimate answers will have to be obtained under the exacting conditions presented by a host of varied field conditions. The outlook is not overly promising, but it does present a challenge to painstaking and persevering research.

An outstanding attribute of red squill as a raticide is its emetic property, which serves as a protection against the fatal poisoning of domestic animals. Rats, being unable to vomit, are, on the other hand, subjected to its toxic action. In periods when effective squill is not obtainable or under conditions where squill has not given effective rat control, other poisons have had to be used. These do not as a rule possess marked emetic properties, and accidental poisoning of dogs and cats often follows their use.

As early as 1937 the Biological Survey undertook a study of modifying poisoned baits exposed for rats so as to make them relatively harmless to other animals. Various emetics, including copper sulfate, zinc sulfate, and tartar emetic (antimony-potassium tartrate) were used in food baits containing thallium sulfate or zinc phosphide as the toxic principles. Although certain combinations gave a reasonable degree of protection to dogs when the concentration of the emetic principle was adequate, difficulties were encountered with the acceptance by field mice of such baits. The subject later was dropped when it was learned that dogs were not likely to be poisoned in field-mouse control.

In 1942, however, the study was resumed in view of the need of protecting domestic pets in cities where intensive rat control was being conducted through the use of such poisons as thallium sulfate, zinc phosphide, and barium carbonate. As a result of this work, the following conclusions were reached. The primary toxic action of one to five lethal doses of zinc phosphide, thallium sulfate, and barium carbonate can be appreciably reduced or nullified in dogs and cats that might feed on rat baits by including tartar emetic in the following proportions: Zinc phosphide, 8 parts; tartar emetic, 3 parts; thallium sulfate, 7 parts; tartar emetic, 4 parts; barium carbonate, 140 parts; tartar emetic, 3 parts. There is no assurance, however, from these experiments that similar benefits would accrue to human beings who accidentally ingest such materials.

Use of Color in Protecting Seed-Eating Birds

To make poisoned grain baits exposed for the control of field rodents less dangerous to seed-eating birds, including valuable game species, use is now being made of the rather simple physiological fact that birds perceive and react to color, while rodents, being almost if not completely color blind, do not. After the announcement of the first experiments in 1943, field tests have confirmed the utility of the practice, and it is used in the preparation of all grain baits by the Fish and Wildlife Service in which the highly toxic compound 1080 is employed.

The aversion of birds to feeding on unnaturally colored food items is a fact known for many years and one that was employed in preventing birds from feeding on newly sown grain. The procedure originated in Europe, where a brilliant blue pigment was used as a protective material. In the United States red lead has been used to a limited extent for the same purpose. Using the principle to safeguard birds that might otherwise feed on poisoned grain exposed for rodents is, however, a development that was timed with the war effort. Although much remains to be done, sufficient progress has now been made to warrant the assertion that the addition of color to poisoned baits has definitely increased their safety to birds and permitted their use under conditions where formerly they were hazardous.

On the basis of work so far completed, the most effective deterring colors for birds are those near the center of the humanly visible spectrum, the yellow and green bands. There are reasons for believing, however, that future work will disclose variations in this concept that may even involve color differences attributable to particular species.

In regard to rodents, which do not have an aversion to color, several problems are still to be solved. These involve not so much the visual acceptance of colored baits as the preparation of baits with dyes that do not have an odor or taste objectionable to rodents. At present, baits readily acceptable to rodents are being prepared with yellow dyes, which are considered to be less effective in deterring birds than green dyes. Eventually we hope to develop a dye that is perfect in keeping birds away but at the same time is thoroughly acceptable to rodents.

THE AUTHOR

E. R. Kalmbach, a senior biologist in the Fish and Wildlife Service, United States Department of the Interior, is in charge of the Wildlife Research Laboratory at Denver. Before joining the Biological Survey in 1910 he was engaged in museum work in Michigan.

FOR FURTHER READING

Garlough, F. E., and Spencer, Donald A.: *Control of Destructive Mice,* U. S. Department of the Interior, Fish and Wildlife Service, Conservation Bulletin 36, 1944.

Garlough, F. E., Welch, J. F., and Spencer, H. J.: *Rabbits in Relation to Crops,* U. S. Department of the Interior, Fish and Wildlife Service, Conservation Bulletin 11, 1942.

Kalmbach, E. R.: *Birds, Rodents, and Colored Lethal Baits.* Transactions, Eighth North American Wildlife Conference, American Wildlife Institute, pages 408–416, 1943.

Kalmback, E. R., and Welch, J. F.: *Colored Rodent Bait and Their Value in Safeguarding Birds,* Journal of Wildlife Management, volume 10, pages 353–360, October 1946.

Silver, James, and Garlough, F. E.: *Rat Control,* U. S. Department of the Interior, Fish and Wildlife Service, Conservation Bulletin 8, 1941.

Spencer, H. J.: *Emetic Agent in Toxic Rat Bait, a Safeguard for Dogs and Cats,* U. S. Department of the Interior, Fish and Wildlife Service, Wildlife Leaflet 264, 1944 (processed).

Regrassing the Range

by C. KENNETH PEARSE

A NEW CHAPTER is being written in the history of the West. It concerns the restoration of 80,000,000 acres of range land to proper productivity. It begins with the first realization, about 50 years ago, by the more far-sighted stockmen that their mountain meadows and grassy parks, their best grazing grounds and source of livelihood, were producing less and less forage with each year of use. They thought of restoring the ranges by artificial reseeding, and called in technicians, who, quite naturally, sought to use the common pasture species and the methods of cultivated agriculture. Their efforts were confined mainly to the meadows and mountain parks that seemed to offer the best chance for success with such methods.

Successful plantings were made in some especially favored places, but costs were always too high to justify the returns. Conditions worsened. By 1935 it was estimated that of the 728,000,000 acres of western range lands, 87 percent were producing much less forage than they should; 589,000,000 acres were seriously eroding because of reduced plant cover. On some of the land that retains a remnant of the better kinds of grass and some good topsoil, improved grazing management is enough to restore proper forage and watershed conditions. In other places, the elimination of noxious or low-value plants such as mesquite and sage-brush that compete for available moisture will permit the recovery of weakened good forage plants. But on about 80,000,000 acres, the better forage plants have been largely eliminated. On them, reseeding is the only hope of restoration in our lifetime. That is being done. So far, some four million acres have been reseeded by modern methods.

Stockmen of a generation ago would stare in wonder if they could see the result. Mountain meadows, which their sheep and cattle had grazed and trampled to dust beds, are again densely sodded with tall meadow oatgrass, smooth brome, and other introduced forage plants. Acre after acre of vigorous crested wheatgrass, originally introduced from Siberia, covers dry foothill ranges that a few years ago supported little more than big sagebrush. Crested wheatgrass is reclaiming the abandoned fields of deserted dry farms, unwisely plowed in a land whose rainfall is too low for sustained crop production. Successful reseeding is spreading to other western types and conditions rapidly, as researchers find other satisfactory species and methods.

The success of plantings on the 4,000,000 acres and hopes for success on the 76,000,000 acres still to be planted rest on a new research attack.

The first problem for research men was to classify the many sites to evaluate the possibilities of reseeding and the likeliest methods and species for each, in order to answer the questions the stockmen and range administrators wanted answered—what, when, and how to plant on a great variety of depleted types of range. There were extensive foothill and valley ranges where big sagebrush or cheatgrass had replaced the valuable perennial grasses, the potentially productive aspen and mountain brush types, timber and brush burns, abandoned lands that were once cultivated, and many semidesert brush and grass ranges. Growing conditions on these types vary widely: Rainfall ranges from less than 8 inches to more than 40 inches; soils vary from sands to clays, deep and fertile in some places but shallow and rocky in others. The existing plant cover varies from little or none on fresh burned-over areas or recently abandoned fields to dense stands of low-value annuals or brush, which rob the soil of its available moisture.

After classifying the sites, the technicians concentrated on the types of range that were most in need and where success seemed most probable. The researchers knew that they could not apply ordinary farming methods and the common pasture plants to range lands. Instead, they searched among native forage plants and those growing under similar conditions in foreign countries for aggressive, drought-resistant species. They studied their growing habits, soil and moisture requirements, and other ecological and physiological needs to find out where they might be adapted, and what must be done to give the seedlings a chance to become established. They sought to devise planting methods and equipment that would provide these conditions economically on rough and rocky range lands, and, where necessary, reduce the stand of undesirable competing vegetation.

The first principle of reseeding—select only the better sites in each type—was recognized when studies brought out the importance of climate, soils, plant and animal life, and other site factors. The success of a properly made planting can now be fairly well foretold. In general, the higher the precipitation and the better its distribution throughout the growing season the better is the chance for success. Where the top few inches of soil are likely to remain moist during the first few weeks of the growing season, good establishment is likely. Dark colored, deep, light-textured soils, well covered with plant litter, favor the establishment of seedlings and produce highest forage yields.

Vegetation is a good indication of the suitability of a site for reseeding. Reseeding is seldom justified on ranges with enough good forage remnants to provide recovery under better management alone. On the other hand, if the existing vegetation is sparse, and plants are stunted and produce poor seed crops, the site may be too poor for successful seeding. A dense stand of vigorous, low-value vegetation on ranges that formerly produced good forage also usually indicates a good reseeding site. Dense stands of existing vegetation that would use the available soil moisture and prevent the reseeded species from getting established must often be reduced before reseeding.

Adaptability of Species

Planting only species and mixtures that are adapted to the soil and climate and that will persist under reasonable grazing use is another important principle. To find adapted species for each of the many conditions needing reseeding, more than 400 grasses, other herbs, and shrubs have been tested. These are first tried in range nurseries established in each of the range types under study. Nurseries are selected to provide average or slightly better than average growing conditions for the type. They are fenced against livestock and, where necessary, rodents and insects are controlled, and weedy vegetation is reduced by plowing and cultivation. Species that appear suitable are carefully planted by hand in small row plots. Repeat plantings, using several seasons and depths of plantings and sources of seed, are made of species that fail in the first trial. Some 80 to 100 of the 400 species, varieties, and strains tested have been found suited to the local soil and climatic conditions covered by these nurseries.

In the next step, the successful species from the nursery rows are planted in test plots on the range in the same vicinity. Methods resemble as nearly as possible those that would be used in large-scale plantings in the type. No attempt is made to reduce competition or provide favorable conditions beyond what would be obtained in actual reseeding practice.

The range-plot tests usually indicate 8 or 10 species that appear adapted to each type. These are planted in large pilot plantings under actual field operating conditions as a final test of suitability. The pilot plantings are also used to determine the cost of reseeding and the value returned by reseeding, to provide information on satisfactory grazing management of reseeded areas, and to demonstrate reseeding to ranchers and other potential users of research findings.

Species that have passed such series of tests and can be recommended for planting under specific conditions are listed in many Federal and State bulletins. For the northern great plains and the valley and foothill ranges of Idaho, Utah, and Nevada, crested wheatgrass is widely used. It is also useful on similar ranges in Washington, Oregon, northern California, Wyoming, and Colorado. Other species recommended for the same situations include western wheatgrass and, in some limited areas, bulbous bluegrass. Slender wheatgrass, smooth brome, tall meadow oatgrass, timothy, and orchard grass have proved their adaptability and are being used on higher ranges with more favorable precipitation. Others have passed the range tests, but have not yet been widely used, principally because of lack of seed. These include Siberian and blue wildrye, tall, intermediate, stiffhair and bearded wheatgrass, big bluegrass, Indian ricegrass, meadow brome, and many others. For annual-type ranges in California, Harding grass, African veldt grass, and Burnett grass are ready for further trials, at least in pilot plantings. On southwestern semidesert and plains ranges, several lovegrasses, gramas, and chamisa can be recommended.

Another principle of reseeding—plant mixtures wherever possible—has been developed from studies of the adaptability of species. Mixtures of several species are most likely to include at least one species that is adapted to the many local soil and moisture conditions of the area. They provide fuller stands, more forage, and a longer grazing season.

Methods of Planting

How much to plant? How deep to plant? What season to plant? How to prepare the land for planting? What machines to use? These questions are as important as the question, what to plant, and the answers vary as much from one condition to another.

The establishment of just enough plants to produce the maximum forage that the climate and soil can support depends on using the correct rate of seeding. For each range and each species this depends on the size, purity, and the germination of the seed and the efficiency of the method of planting. Correct seeding rates are being determined in small plot plantings for many conditions. Aggressive, moderately small-seeded species, such as crested wheatgrass, should be planted at from 3 to 6 pounds to the acre. Eight to 10 pounds are required for smooth brome, western wheatgrass, and other large-seeded species. Lower rates of planting will result in delay and possibly excessive growth of weeds before a full stand is developed. Heavier seeding increases cost, may cause excessive competition for the small amount of moisture available, and may result in low yields of forage.

With only a few exceptions, the seed must be covered. The surface of western range soils usually dries out so quickly that seedlings cannot survive unless the seed is planted deep enough to assure reliable moisture in the root zone. Under range conditions, grasses must be planted deeper than on good cultivated land which has more moisture, but the small seeds of perennial grasses cannot push through if planted 1½ to 2 inches deep, as are most cereal grains. Covering with ½ to 1 inch of soil—¼ to ½ inch for small seeded species—usually gives best results. If planted deeper, except in sandy soils, seed and work will be wasted. Drilling with a disk grain drill is one of the best methods of seeding. The drill may be set to cut a furrow 2 or more inches deep to conserve moisture and protect the seedlings from drying winds, but the seed should not be covered more than ½ to 1 inch in the drill furrow. If seed must be broadcast, it should be covered by a disk or harrow unless it is a species, such as bulbous bluegrass, which does not require covering.

Under only a few conditions has broadcast seeding without soil covering been successful. On recent timber or brush burns, ashes may provide suitable covering. But the ashes must be at least 2 inches deep and not settled or washed by heavy rains before broadcasting. Also, some excellent stands have been obtained at low cost by broadcasting adapted species on deteriorated aspen ranges at the time of leaf fall. The falling leaves cover the seed and favor establishment.

Drilling directly into stands of such annual plants as Russian thistle, which makes most of its growth after the planted seedlings have become established, is one of the cheapest and best methods of reseeding. The Russian thistle acts as a nurse crop. But one must reduce or eliminate dense stands of big sagebrush, cheatgrass, tarweed, and other undesirable plants that compete directly with reseeded species for moisture. It is hard to get rid of such plants, but many can be reduced practically and economically. Shallow plowing with a wheatland or heavy one-way disk plow will kill 90 percent of the sagebrush and provide good conditions for drilling. Broadcasting can be used immediately after fall plowing. Where the soil is too rocky for wheatland plows, improved rail drags or heavy pipe harrows can be used to obtain 80 to 90 percent sagebrush kills. Prescribed burning is an excellent method for clearing big sagebrush, but it must be attempted only where the fire can be fully controlled and where erosion will not occur before the reseeded stand is established. For planting in dense cheatgrass and tarweed, methods that give assured success have not yet been perfected.

Planting should be done when the soil of the root zone will remain reasonably moist and temperatures will favor germination and growth for as long a period as possible, or until the seedlings are established. Where the spring growing period may be cut short by early summer drought, fall planting is best. Seed planted in late fall will germinate and make considerable growth before spring planting can begin. In regions where favorable fall rains will keep the upper few inches of soil moist until freezing weather, early fall planting is even better than late fall. Plantings made just before an early fall rain frequently grow as much before winter as do late fall plantings during the entire spring growing period. Thus a whole year may be saved in the establishment of the stand. In regions with good rains throughout the warm season, as in the mountains and in many parts of the Southwest, spring or summer planting is often best. Legumes and some other species should be planted in the spring in regions with thin snow cover and severe cold to avoid frost heaving and winter killing.

The final principle of range reseeding—apply wise-grazing management after seeding—is necessary to assure rapid development of the young plants and maintenance of the stand.

Grazing of newly seeded areas will kill many seedlings by trampling them into the ground or pulling them up before their root systems are strongly developed. New seedings should generally be protected from grazing until the first seed crop is produced. This may take only 1 year under good conditions, or 2 or 3 years if weather and site are unfavorable. Thereafter, improper grazing will damage a reseeded range as surely as it deteriorated the original forage cover. Degree of utilization, season of grazing, distribution of use over the range, and handling of livestock should be based on the best available information. Where guides have not been developed for proper management of reseeded ranges, standards developed for comparable native ranges give a valuable basis for grazing. Stockmen should see that livestock are removed when they have taken only a half to three-fourths of the available leafage and that considerable stubble remains to protect the soil and maintain the plants. If plants begin to lose vigor, or if low-value species invade the stand, prompt adjustment in management should be made.

Costs and Benefits

The basic principles and detailed specifications developed by the new research attack make it possible to establish productive forage stands with reasonable assurance of success on many deteriorated western range lands. But the final test—the real value of range reseeding—rests in the answer to the question, Does it pay?

Reseeding costs vary greatly from one range type to another because of such differences as the accessibility of the area, the amount and kinds of seed used, the planting and preplanting treatment required, and the cost of fencing or otherwise controlling grazing of the reseeded stand. On previously cultivated land that has not been invaded by cheatgrass or sagebrush, hundreds of thousands of acres have been successfully drilled to crested wheatgrass, with no other treatment, for less than $2 an acre. On extremely depleted range, where drilling is not hindered by rough topography, rocky soil, or vegetation, the same method can be used at comparable costs. Where sagebrush or other competing vegetation must be reduced before planting, total costs amount to from $3 to $5 an acre for large plantings of several hundred acres or more. Costs are higher on smaller areas because heavy machinery cannot be efficiently used, and all fixed overhead charges, including planning, supervision, getting materials and machinery on the job, fencing, and the like, are proportionately greater. Most large areas seeded in the past few years cost less than one-half of the $8 to $10 an acre required before the results of the new research attack were available.

The annual value of increased forage production gained by reseeding selected areas amounts to as much as 50 cents an acre. The increased returns from grazing are generally greatest on ranges that supported only a fraction of their potential stands before seeding. The grazing capacity of ranges that have lost their good forage plants but retained good soil is commonly increased between one and two animal-unit months per acre by reseeding. Ranges that are only moderately depleted, or those whose potential forage production is limited by poor soil or low rainfall, have less scope for improvement. On many of the sites where reseeding is, or should be, considered, annual grazing capacity can probably be increased about one animal-unit month an acre. Smaller increases, but nevertheless worth-while, and not less than one-half animal-unit months an acre a year, can be expected on less favorable sites.

An animal-unit month of grazing is worth what you can get for it. The value varies with the type of range, its location, and the demand for forage. Most stockmen would agree, however, that good reseeded range is normally worth 35 cents an animal-unit month. Under present conditions 50 to 60 cents is commonly paid.

Under such relationships between costs and returns, careful reseeding of selected range areas is profitable. An investment of 2 to 5 dollars will yield between 17 and 35 cents annually from increased forage alone. Under proper management, such a return will continue indefinitely.

The increased grazing values received from successful range reseeding do not stop with the forage produced on the reseeded area alone. Often the reseeded range can be used during periods when forage would otherwise be extremely scarce. It thus rounds out the forage supply, fills a critical gap in the yearlong maintenance of livestock, and makes possible more efficient operation, higher calf and lamb crops, and greater livestock production. In many parts of the West, where spring forage is especially limited, crested wheatgrass range, which can be grazed 2 to 3 weeks before native range is ready, reduces the need for expensive feeding of hay or concentrates, helps to overcome too early and too heavy use of the native range, and insures ample milk for suckling calves and lambs.

In addition to improving grazing conditions, reseeding has a value for the protection it provides to the soil. The cost of erosion in the West, in terms of flooded valley lands, washed out railroads, highways, and other improvements, silted irrigation developments and municipal water supply systems, and devastated range and croplands, totals millions of dollars annually. Maintaining a dense stand of vegetation on range and watershed lands is one of the most effective means of controlling abnormal floods, excessive erosion, and dust storms. Reseeding, which provides a practical means for establishing a vegetative cover on denuded lands, has thus become an important tool in watershed improvement and management. Frequently floods can be controlled by treating the sore spots or critical areas that make up only a small portion of the entire watershed.

Stockmen, long faced with the unhappy necessity of reducing their herds to keep up with an ever dwindling forage supply, are finding a more pleasant and healthier outlook—the production of adequate forage through reseeding. Better and more intensive management of range lands, to make each acre contribute its full share of forage and play its part in soil protection, through the application of research findings, is the new objective. The prospect of fully productive ranges, abundant forage, and efficient and stable livestock production is the new outlook.

THE AUTHOR

C. Kenneth Pearse has been assistant chief of the Division of Range Research of the Forest Service since August 1943. For the preceding 5 years he was in charge of range reseeding studies of the Intermountain Forest and Range Experiment Station, Ogden, Utah, where many of the fundamental principles of reseeding arid and semi-arid western range lands were developed. He directed studies of the classification of sites for range reseeding, the testing of species for adaptation to the varied growing conditions, and the development of methods and machinery for effective and economical planting.

FOR FURTHER READING

Bridges, J. O.: *Reseeding Trials on Arid Range Land,* New Mexico College of Agriculture and Mechanic Arts, Agricultural Experiment Station Bulletin 278, 1941.

Flory, Evan L., and Marshall, Charles G.: *Regrassing for Soil Protection in the Southwest,* U. S. D. A. Farmers' Bulletin 1913, 1942.

Franzke, C. J., and Hume, A. N.: *Regrassing Areas in South Dakota,* South Dakota State College Agricultural Experiment Station Bulletin 361, 1942.

Pickford, G. D., and Jackman, E. R.: *Reseeding Eastern Oregon Summer Ranges,* Oregon State College, Agricultural Experiment Station Circular 159, 1944.

Plummer, A. Perry, Hurd, Richard M.; and Pearse, C. Kenneth: *How to Reseed Utah Range Lands,* Intermountain Forest and Range Experiment Station, Research Paper No. 1, 1943.

Savage, D. A.: *Grass Culture and Range Improvement in the Central and Southern Great Plains,* U. S. D. A. Circular 491, 1939.

Short, L. R.: *Reseeding to Increase the Yield of Montana Range Lands,* U. S. D. A. Farmers' Bulletin 1924, 1943.

Stewart, George, Walker R. H., and Price, Raymond: *Reseeding Range Lands of the Intermountain Region,* U. S. D. A. Farmers' Bulletin 1823, 1939.

Planning Farm Returns

by NEIL W. JOHNSON and C. P. BARNES

MORE AND MORE farmers are putting the farm on a business basis by using budgeting methods to help plan changes in their farming systems. In doing this they can be helped by knowing about the yields generally experienced by farmers who have used land like their own for different crops and under different methods.

A good farmer knows that before he makes a major shift in crop or livestock production he had better do some figuring to find out how his income is likely to be affected.

Before he buys a new farm he will work out as best he can how much he can make from it. He knows that a fair price to pay for the farm depends on how much income it will return over the years. Perhaps he will calculate what his returns might be if he kept dairy cows and sold cream, and then compare them with what the returns would likely be if he fed hogs and beef cattle. He might also work out his probable income if he raised grain and sold it instead of feeding it. At any rate, he can do a better job of figuring how much the farm will produce if he knows what soil types are on his farm and what the yield experience of many farmers who use these types has been on the average.

How is this figuring done? Is it just a matter of making a few long-range guesses? Not if we want to know what we are really getting into when we buy a new farm or make a major change in the way we farm an old one. It means getting down on paper some definite figures on acres of crops and numbers of livestock; on expected production and expected receipts; on quantities and cost of labor, fertilizer, feed, seed, gasoline, and equipment; on taxes, insurance, and other expenses; and finally, on the probable income from the whole farm operation. It is possible to bring all these considerations together on a single work sheet

1. Work sheet for farm planning

Item	Acres or head	Production: Unit	Production: Per acre or head	Production: Total	Amount kept for: Feed	Amount kept for: Seed	Amount kept for: Household	Cash income: Amount sold	Cash income: Price	Cash income: Value	Farm expenses: Cash operating expense	Farm expenses: Value
Crops:											*Crop expense*	
Cotton											Seed	$30
Lint	16	Lb.	208	3,328				3,328	$0.16	$532	Fertilizer and lime	16
Seed	16	Lb.		5,568	3,556	461		1,551	.015	23	Other supplies	186
Corn	10	Bu.	25	250	249	1					Seasonal labor	1
Oats	7	Bu.	35	245	224	21					*Livestock expense*	
Cane	3	Lb.	6,000	18,000	18,000						Purchased feeds	86
Rotation pasture	8										Other supplies	20
											Veterinary	
Livestock and livestock products:											Service fees	
Work stock	2										Seasonal labor	
Dairy cows	4						237	711	.36	256	*General expenses*	
Butterfat	½	Lb.	250	1,000	¹52			280	.04	11		
Cull cow		Lb.	560	280				300	.08	24	Monthly labor	68
Veal		Lb.		300							Machinery repair	68
Hogs (sows)	3										Building and fence repair	60
Pork		Lb.		600			450	150	.09	14	Gas and oil	60
Poultry	150										Automobile, tractor, truck	20
Eggs		Doz.	8⅓	1,250		²45	182	1,023	.27	276	Property insurance	
Meat		Lb.		600			250	350	.216	76	Cash rent	276
											Current interest	76
											Farm taxes	21
											Irrigation drainage charges	
Other farm income:												
Total cash income (a)										(a) 1,212		
Total cash operating expense (b)												(b) 575
Net cash income (a − b)												637

¹ Calves allowed to suck cows to equivalent of 52 pounds butterfat.   ² Used for hatching.

2. Five plans for operating a Georgia farm with probable income from each under different prices and costs

Item	1942 plan	Alternative plans for 1942			
		I	II	III	IV
Crops:	Acres	Acres	Acres	Acres	Acres
Cotton, upland..............	11.0	11.0	11.0	8.0	....
Tobacco.....................	1.7	1.7	1.7	1.7	1.7
Peanuts grazed................	2.0	....	....	....	....
Peanuts for digging...........	7.0	7.0	13.0	16.0	24.0
Corn interplanted.............	27.0	˙20.0	17.0	17.0	17.0
Oats and vetch grazed.........	....	11.0	8.0	8.0	8.0
Oats for hay.................	1.0	....	....	....	....
Millet......................	....	2.0	2.0	2.0	2.0
Watermelons..................	1.0	1.0	1.0	1.0	1.0
Garden and patches...........	1.3	1.3	1.3	1.3	1.3
Idle cropland................	3.0	....	....	....	....
Total cropland..............	55.0	55.0	55.0	55.0	55.0
Livestock:	Number	Number	Number	Number	Number
Mules.......................	2	2	2	2	2
Cows........................	3	5	5	5	6
Brood sows..................	3	3	3	3	3
Chickens....................	30	0	30	30	30
Family's cash farm income with 1942 prices and costs.................	Dollars 1,479	Dollars 2,091	Dollars [1] 2,208	Dollars [1] 2,174	Dollars [1] 2,136

[1] Peanuts at $130 per ton.

as shown in the first table. Putting them all down like this helps one think through the production process without overlooking important items.

Suppose we want to compare the prospective returns from this particular plan of operating the farm with other plans. We can make a similar budget for each one and see how the returns compare. The second table shows how this was done for a certain Georgia farm. One should notice how the possible alternatives varied—from cotton to no cotton, from a small peanut enterprise to one that is three times larger, from three cows to six, et cetera. The alternatives seem able to produce more income than the regular plan being followed.

This was true with prices and costs as they were in 1942. But we shall not always have these costs and prices—those items vary from year to year. The budget process permits us to compare returns under different prices and costs. We can find how we would get along with cotton at 10 cents and at 25 cents a pound. Thus we can get an idea of what the income might be over the long pull, in periods of depression as well as in prosperity. We can then appraise the ability of the farm to weather the lean years as well as to prosper in the fat ones. For instance, on this

3. Estimated average yields per acre of important crops on some soils of Tama County, Iowa, under different systems of soil management. From unpublished manuscript of the Soil Survey Report for Tama County, Iowa, by A. R. Aandahl, and others. Data for many of the soils are omitted to save space.

Soil (type or phase)	System	Crop rotation[1]	Lime[2]	Fertilizer[3] (Lbs.)	Manure[4] (Tons)	Engineering aids[5]	Corn (Bu.)	Soybeans (Bu.)	Oats (Bu.)	Clover and timothy (Tons)	Alfalfa[6] (Tons)	Pasture[7] (Cow-acre days)
Bremer silt loam	A	CCO	None	None	None	Tile-drained if necessary	55	24	40	(8)	....	150
	B	CCOM	None	None	4	..do..	65	26	45	1.4	....	190
	C	CCOM	Yes	None	8	..do..	75	28	50	2.0	[10]3.8	....
Bremer silty clay loam	A	CCO	None	None	None	..do..	40	18	30	(8)	....	140
	B	CCOM	None	None	4	..do..	50	20	35	.8	....	170
	C	CCOM	Yes	None	8	..do..	60	22	40	1.2	[10]2.0	....
Buckner sandy loam	A	CCO	None	None	None	None..	10	4	15	.2	....	20
	B	CCOM	None	None	4	..do..	15	8	20	.4	....	40
	C	COMM	Yes	None	8	..do..	30	14	35	.6	.8	....
Carrington loam	A	CCO	None	None	None	..do..	30	10	27	(8)	....	100
	B	CCOM	None	None	4	..do..	45	14	40	1.2	....	170
	C	CCOMM	Yes	200	8	Contour cultivation	60	22	52	2.0	3.4	....
Carrington loam, eroded gently rolling phase	A	CCO	None	None	None	None..	25	4	17	(8)	....	70
	B	CCOM	None	None	4	..do..	35	8	27	1.0	....	140
	C	COMM	Yes	200	8	Contour strip cropping	50	16	40	1.7	3.0	....
Carrington silt loam	A	CCO	None	None	None	None..	35	12	30	(8)	....	105
	B	CCOM	None	None	4	..do..	45	16	40	1.4	....	180
	C	CCOMM	Yes	200	8	Contour cultivation	60	24	52	2.0	3.6	....
Carrington silt loam, eroded gently rolling phase	A	CCO	None	None	None	None..	25	6	20	(8)	....	80
	B	CCOM	None	None	4	..do..	35	10	30	1.2	....	150
	C	COMM	Yes	200	8	Contour strip cropping	55	18	45	1.8	3.2	....
Carrington silt loam, eroded rolling phase	A	CCO	None	None	None	None..	20	2	15	(8)	....	60
	B	CCOM	None	None	4	..do..	30	6	25	.8	....	110
	C	COMMM	Yes	200	8	Contour strip cropping	50	12	40	[9]1.6	2.8	....

The footnotes are on the next page.

Georgia farm the net cash income of $1,479 when figured with 1942 prices and costs, was only $665 under 1940 conditions, and only $370 at the prices and costs that prevailed in 1932.

To estimate the returns from any farm it is, of course, necessary to know how much the farm will produce. A new feature of the most recent county soil reports issued by the Department and the State colleges gives average crop-yield estimates for different soil types and different systems of soil management. These will help us if we know what soils are on the farm. Take, for example, a farmer in Alabama who has grown cotton mainly and is thinking of improving part of his land by putting it in pasture, growing some feed crops, and getting some beef animals. Naturally he wants to know how much this will increase his income. He can use a work sheet like the one shown in the first table, and set down all his estimated costs and returns. But to do that he will need to decide what land he will use to grow his feed and forage, what feed or grazing crops he will grow, with what rotations and practices, and how much they will produce each year.

If he has not grown these crops before, he cannot rely on his own experience to tell him these things. If his figures are to be anything but guesses, he must rely on the experience of other farmers. But he can

---

[1] The crops included in the rotations are indicated by the following letters: C, O, and M. The letter C means corn with one exception. When the average acre-yield of soybeans is estimated, one crop of soybeans is substituted for one crop of corn in the rotation, except for continuous corn when it is considered that soybeans are raised every third year. The letter O indicates oats. Meadow, M, is meant to include a mixture of timothy with red, white, and/or alsike clover except when the yield of alfalfa is estimated or when there are 3 or more years of meadow in the rotation. Meadow is meant to be alfalfa for these 2 exceptions.

[2] When lime is included in the system of soil management, it means one application during the rotation in amounts sufficient to neutralize the soil acidity. It is applied prior to the planting of the legumes.

[3] Fertilizer application is superphosphate (20 percent P_2O_5) applied on oats.

[4] Manure applications are made once during rotation on first or second corn crop.

[5] Grassed waterways are included with contour cultivation and contour strip cropping.

[6] Because alfalfa is very sensitive to acid conditions, no estimate of yield is given except under system C, which includes lime.

[7] Only 2 systems of management are defined for purposes of estimating the productivity of the soils for pasture. Pasture management system A is as follows: (1) No application of lime or fertilizer is made; (2) the vegetation consists principally of grasses although no effort is made to improve the species or to add legumes; (3) weeds are not eradicated; (4) the pastures are not overgrazed.

Pasture management system B is as follows: (1) Enough lime is applied every 6 to 10 years to maintain neutrality of the soil; (2) a good stand of grasses and legumes is maintained; (3) phosphate fertilizer (125 pounds 20 percent P_2O_5) is applied at the time of seeding the legumes and every 6 years thereafter; (4) weeds are eradicated; (5) the pastures are not overgrazed.

[8] As defined, the system of soil management does not include this crop in the rotation.

[9] The rotation is COMM for estimating the average acre-yield of clover and timothy.

[10] The rotation is COMMM for estimating the average acre-yield of alfalfa.

depend on others' experience only if their soils and practices were similar to those he will use.

Yield estimates for some of our important soil types have been made in connection with the Nation-wide soil survey program. More will be made and published in the county soil survey reports as soil maps are made of additional counties.

The third table illustrates the considerations that are necessary if we really get down to brass tacks in estimating yields. Soils can be used or abused. They can be cropped continuously or they can be handled under careful systems of rotation. Fertilizer, lime, or manure can be applied at regular intervals where needed to get better yields. Wet land can be drained and dry land can be treated in ways to control soil moisture better and to discourage erosion. Eventually we come to know how best to handle each type of soil and the probable effect on crop yields of each common system of management. It is this kind of information that is provided in table 3 and in the newer soil survey reports. It enables us to benefit from the experience of many farmers who have used the particular soil types. The yield estimates are more likely to represent what can be expected on the average than the yields experienced by any one farmer or any small group of farmers in a given locality.

With a map of the farm showing the soil types and phases, and with the estimated yields of different crops and pasture under stated cropping systems and practices for each soil, the cropping program can be planned so that each of the different bodies of soil can be used in the way that will contribute most toward profits and stability in farming. Different field arrangements can be laid out on the map and alternative cropping systems can be considered, until the most satisfactory plan is worked out.

The county agricultural agent will know whether detailed soils maps and accompanying data on yields to be expected under different systems of management, are available for his county. If information of this kind is still lacking, he may be able to assist in making satisfactory approximations for an individual farm.

The process of thinking through all the steps and items in the farm's operation—fitting new methods in crop and livestock production to the land, labor, and capital resources that are available, and then making actual estimates of costs and returns in the light of thorough consideration of market and price prospects—can go a long way toward improving farm profits and adding satisfaction and permanency to farm life.

THE AUTHORS

Neil W. Johnson is assistant head of the Division of Farm Management and Costs, Bureau of Agricultural Economics.

C. P. Barnes is chief analyst in the Division of Soil Survey, Bureau of Plant Industry, Soils, and Agricultural Engineering.

sible more sanitary conditions than when the food is handled in bulk. Packaging of staple products has become standard procedure, but packaging of highly perishable fresh fruits, vegetables, and meat is still in the experimental stage. The development of suitable transparent films has made the prepackaging of perishable food practical, because through them the buyer can see the food she is purchasing.

The housewife is accustomed to go to modern markets and select the packaged products from the shelves, but when she comes to the produce and meat departments she, or a clerk, has to select and weigh the products she wants. The satisfaction of the housewife varies with the number of other purchasers who have previously handled and selected from the produce displayed in the racks. Produce sold in this way is usually accompanied by a high proportion of waste for the retail store. When the fresh fruit and vegetables are wrapped in transparent films, most of the reasons for the objections are removed. When making her purchases, the housewife is able to obtain a more uniform quality and a more sanitary commodity than previously. Most prepackaged produce and meat have been trimmed and partly prepared for immediate cooking. This partial preparation keeps refuse out of the kitchen and saves housewives' time in preparation.

Fresh fruit and vegetables may be packaged at almost every stage of distribution. Any stage of distribution at which the operation is performed has certain advantages and disadvantages varying from one commodity to another. Packaging in the production area makes possible the preservation of the greatest amount of the food value of the products. It also makes possible the elimination of a great deal of waste that would otherwise be transported and sent through the channels of trade. Growers want to do the packaging in the producing area because they see possibilities in identifying their goods all the way to the table.

Packaging at the terminal has the advantages of a continuous operation throughout the entire year. The terminal operator can also more easily achieve the desired goal of having all of his produce packaged in consumer-sized units. Packaging at the terminal also makes possible a later check on the quality of the produce.

Much remains to be learned as to proper stage for packaging, the kind of materials to use, handling methods to be employed, and the proper way of refrigerating. The quality of packaged goods is of the greatest importance, because when the housewife buys them she expects to find all the contents of uniform quality. When bulk merchandise is displayed, a bad apple may be left in the basket and only good apples purchased. When these apples are sold in a closed package, the housewife pays for all the apples in the package regardless of whether they are all good or not. If, after making several purchases, she finds too many bad apples in the package, she will discontinue buying them.

Because consumer packaging makes possible the branding of the packages, more care is likely to be given produce in its handling after the brand is put on a consumer package. This in itself will tend to improve greatly the marketing of perishables, because each handler now has little personal interest in the commodity after he has sold it to the next person in the marketing chain. Branded, packaged perishables will encourage the entrance into the field of wholesaling of more service wholesalers whose function is more one of seeing that the produce is sold in the best accepted methods rather than the present wholesaler's function, which is simply to supply retailers.

Prepackaged fresh meat has many of the advantages of prepackaged frozen meat. It is possible that cost of selling fresh meat prepackaged will be less than selling prepackaged frozen meat. Many of the difficulties encountered in selling prepackaged frozen meat will also have to be overcome by retailers who sell prepackaged fresh meat; prepackaged fresh meat has the disadvantage of turning dark when exposed to the light and is more perishable than frozen or uncut fresh meat.

The net cost of handling perishables packaged in consumer-sized units, compared to handling them in bulk, must be calculated all the way from the grower to the net quantity available to the housewife for cooking. With savings in transportation, waste, and retail store labor, the additional costs of cleaning and for packaging material will be largely offset by the saving. We also believe that the housewife will receive a greatly superior product if the prepackaged produce is properly handled from the grower through the marketing chain to the retail store. The net cost of prepackaging should be computed in terms of cost per nutritive unit rather than cost per pound of produce, that is, a pound of pre-packaged snap beans when properly handled may be twice as nutritive as a pound of ordinary bulk beans.

New Developments in Transportation and Dehydration

The war has made possible the movement in volume of air freight, many new refrigerator cars of different design, and improved trucks.

The improvements in transportation are in the form of speed and better refrigeration. As refrigeration is improved, the need for greater speed is lessened; the reverse is also true. The speed of some truck deliveries and of most air-freight deliveries sometimes makes artificial refrigeration unnecessary. When produce is properly refrigerated, the rate of deterioration is greatly retarded, and properly refrigerated produce may retain its original quality as well for 2 weeks as unrefrigerated produce does for only a day.

Planeloads of highly perishable flowers, fruits, and vegetables have been moving from production areas to eastern consumption centers on a daily basis since 1946. This movement has been made possible because of the availability of the large number of surplus war cargo planes and the thousands of trained pilots and mechanics. Rates based on 70 cents a ton-mile have been reduced to rates based on 12 cents to 15 cents a ton-mile. At the higher figure there was little movement of perishables; now entire crops of some of the more highly perishable commodities are being moved. Air-freight rates for the next few years probably will be too high to move the bulk of the fruits and vegetables, but it is likely that most of the flowers and a large proportion of the most highly perishable fruits and vegetables will be carried by air.

Air transportation has made it possible to move many commodities—field-grown flowers from the South and tropical fruits, for example—that formerly could not be shipped more than 200 or 300 miles from their production centers. Processors will be able more nearly to reach a goal of making produce "pot ready" in the production area when air transport is used than when any other existing method of transportation is used. Lima beans and peas may be shelled and packaged, sweet corn may be husked and packaged, spinach may be washed, selected, packaged, and delivered more successfully by the use of air transportation than by railway or truck. Air transportation of perishables is still in the experimental stage and its adoption by merchandisers will depend largely upon new developments in packaging and merchandising. The indirect benefit of air transportation to producers in the long run may be more beneficial than its direct effect; that is, air transportation may serve as a pace setter for surface carriers.

During the war a large number of refrigerator cars wore out and many of those that remained needed major repairs. The accumulated need for new cars made it more feasible than before the war for the car manufacturers and railroads to adopt new designs for refrigerator cars. New techniques that have already been proved have been incorporated into most of the new designs and, before a substantial number are built, additional improvements will no doubt be incorporated. These improvements make it possible to hold lower and more uniform temperatures at less cost than the units in the old cars. Truck owners are rapidly installing new and improved mechanical units that have certain advantages over the use of ice. Truck schedules and rail schedules are being speeded up in order to give better service to the shipper.

Dehydrated foods, because of their high nutritive value per pound of product, were in much demand during the war by Army officers. A considerable amount of research was done to improve the texture and flavor of the dried foods, but despite the improvements, most of them were poor substitutes for the fresh product. Dehydration is simply the preservation of food by the removal of most of the water in the product either by exposure to the sun, in which case the process is called drying, or by exposure to hot air or treatment in a mechanically heated drum, which is known as dehydration. Care must be taken in dehydrating produce to preserve as many of the vitamins as possible, prevent the processed product from acquiring any off-flavors, and to get a product that can be reconstituted satisfactorily. Generally speaking, some dehydrated products are inferior to fresh, frozen, or canned products in nutritive value and taste. Even though they are equal to fresh in taste and wholesomeness, their appearance prevents rapid acceptance by housewives. Dehydrated foods on the whole are less costly to process, store, transport, and retail per pound of edible product than are frozen or canned foods.

A limited market for special uses does exist for some of the dehydrated products, and for a few other uses the dehydrated product is superior to the fresh. For example, many housewives prefer dehydrated onion flakes to fresh onions. Dried fruit, such as prunes and peaches, have been generally accepted by consumers. Dried eggs, a relatively new product, are finding acceptance in prepared cake and ice cream mixes and on the breakfast table as scrambled eggs during the period of seasonal high prices of fresh eggs. Dried milk is also being used in prepared mixes as well as for cooking in place of whole milk.

New developments in marketing will affect differently producers, consumers, and marketing agencies. Seasonal supplies and prices of many fruits and vegetables will be more stable. Not many years ago the housewife was limited in her purchases of fresh fruits and vegetables to those grown within a radius of 10 to 50 miles of her residence. Now she can purchase lettuce every day of the year because lettuce is grown on the west coast the entire year. What has happened to lettuce has also happened to many other fruits and vegetables. As transportation and other marketing techniques improve, the story of lettuce will be repeated more and more often. Formerly, producers of strawberries received relatively low prices because the strawberries had to be sold quickly when they were ripe for immediate consumption or for preserving. Now, with facilities for freezing and good transportation, the producers are not forced to sell all their berries in the local market; rather, the berries that they cannot sell locally are sold in distant markets or are frozen to be sold in seasons when fresh berries are not available.

On the whole, local producers have more to lose than gain because of improved marketing methods. Agricultural commodities will be produced in areas of lowest costs, that is, where natural conditions of climate and soil make it cheapest to grow them. Formerly the consumer depended entirely on local production; now he can get his supplies from other areas if those supplies are cheaper or better. Thus the consumer gains from having a wider choice of good quality merchandise at widely competitive prices.

The gradual shifting of stores to a more completely self-service basis will favor the processors whose merchandise can win recognition among consumers and the trade. Retailers emphasize efficient service, sanitary methods, and the importance of preserving food values. Costs of giving the same marketing services will be reduced as a result of many of these developments, but the services may be increased to the extent that marketing costs as a whole may be much higher—that is, if the processors do part of the housewife's work, she will have to pay for it in higher costs.

Farmers will be variously affected, depending on their geographic location and competitive position. Greater emphasis will be put upon efficiency in production, and those growers so situated that they can produce high-quality products at relatively low cost per unit have everything to gain from improvements in marketing. The growers who stand to lose the most are the ones whose products sold because housewives had no other choice. Those producers will be forced to look to greater efficiency and higher quality in order to maintain their competitive position.

Marketing agencies will be affected most of all. Established enterprises that try to rest on laurels won under different conditions will be among the first to lose their business to enterprises that have had the imagination to adopt the new methods. Periods of rapid technological change offer opportunities for enterprises smart enough to take advantage of the changes.

No attempt has been made to discuss the established pattern of marketing cotton, grain, livestock and livestock products, poultry and eggs, and fruits and vegetables. Department research workers are concerned with increasing the producers' returns and giving the consumers an improved product at lower cost. This may be accomplished by improving the established marketing pattern as well as by establishing new ones.

THE AUTHOR

R. W. Hoecker, a principal agricultural economist in the Bureau of Agricultural Economics, was reared on a Missouri livestock and grain farm and educated at Iowa State College and Cornell University. Before joining the Department, Dr. Hoecker was assistant loan agent and farm manager for a life insurance company and assistant professor of marketing in Kansas State College. He is in charge of the marketing and transportation research on fruits, vegetables, dairy products, and poultry.

ALSO, IN THIS BOOK

Farm Science and Citizens

by SHERMAN E. JOHNSON

SINCE CREATION, men have joined to conquer nature or separated to fight for her fruits. Science has furnished them increasingly effective tools to make nature more productive and increasingly effective weapons for seizing a larger share of the goods produced.

When men, as allies, use science to get the most from each acre, each worker, each machine, each animal, they make it possible for the earth or a part of it to support more people—and so to postpone indefinitely the day when the pressure of a population increasing faster than life-supporting resources would impel men to fight one another. For example, 140 million Americans now live in relative peacefulness in an area where a fraction of a million Indians once fought for hunting grounds.

Scientific progress enables some people to live better, and more people to live. But history affords evidence that technological improvements, which bring profits to the producers who can adopt them, and which benefit mankind in general, also bring misery and distress to the individuals who cannot adjust themselves to the new conditions. Such individuals are likely to resist and may be strong enough to delay technological progress: Lancashire spinners and weavers, ruined by the invention of power spindles and looms, for instance, tried to destroy them before they gave up to become workers in the English textile mills.

The farmer has an indirect interest in the effects upon the consumer of higher farm production from each acre and each hour of labor because the market outlet for his product affects his income. But he is interested directly in the effects of technology upon him as a producer.

These points raise two questions for us to consider: What effect has science had on farm production and the well-being of farm people? What effect is it likely to have?

920

Recurrent seasons of planting and harvest characterize technological progress in agriculture, as they characterize farming itself. The score of years between the wars was a time of tilling and planting. Progress was swift in the development of mechanical equipment, in discovering the use of lime, fertilizer, cover crops, and conservation, in improving plants, animals, and feeds, and in controlling insects and diseases. But low income and drought made it difficult for this new technology to bear fruit.

Luckily, good weather returned at the beginning of the Second World War, just when the needs of our Allies and then of our own armies combined with rising farm incomes to impel farmers toward the highest production we have ever had. Fed by the combination of knowledge, good weather, fairly adequate tools, and hard work, farm production shot up like weeds in midsummer; the war abundantly harvested the 20-year period of technological preparation and growth.

Machines

I mean to limit this discussion to improvements in farm technology, but as we seek out the reasons for the wartime increase in agricultural production we will have to remember that some improvements in marketing and industry outside agriculture may also significantly affect farmers and farm workers. Air transportation, for example, or quick-freezing and other improved processes may greatly enlarge the market for some farm products. Decentralization of industry into rural areas may provide nearby markets for products that are new to many farmers. On the unfavorable side, improvements that cause labor displacement, when substitute employment is not available, shrink the market outlet for farm products. In examining the record of improvements, we have to consider separately the developments in farm mechanization, the use of land, and the growing of crops and animals. When that is done, we shall trace the effects of these developments on the total volume of production, costs, prices, and returns for farm products, and, finally, on farmers and farm workers. We have to remember in all this that what affects farmers affects all of us.

The steel plow and other new tillage machines, the mower, the reaper, the thresher, and in time the self-binder, were the key machines in this development. The human labor used to produce 100 bushels of wheat dropped from 320 hours in 1830 to 108 hours in 1900; by 1940 a new series of improvements had reduced the labor used to 47 hours.

The new machines made it easier to settle the fertile Midwest and later the far Western States. They helped provide the exports of farm goods that paid part of the interest and principal on the foreign debts incurred to build our railroads and factories.

The number of tractors rose steadily from 1910 to 1945, interrupted only by the drought and depression of the early 1930's. On the other hand, the number of horses and mules declined steadily, beginning in 1919. The introduction of the general-purpose tractor in the 1920's and the shift to rubber tires in the 1930's made tractors versatile enough to furnish power for most farm operations. With these improvements came almost equally significant changes in the equipment for use with tractors. Indeed, most of our tractor-powered machines today have been especially designed for use with tractors.

The improvements and higher farm incomes hastened the shift to mechanized farming. In 1945 there were 2,425,000 tractors on farms— an increase of 57 percent from 1940. In the same period, the number of grain combines increased 74 percent, corn pickers 53 percent, and milking machines 117 percent—despite wartime limitations on the manufacture of farm machinery—although the limitations on manufacturing new machinery during the war were relatively less restrictive on the labor-saving types of machines I have mentioned. If more new machinery had been available, mechanization would have been farther along at the end of the war, especially in the South.

If, as seems likely, food needs remain fairly high and farm income moderately high in the transition from war to peace, farmers will continue to buy a great deal of machinery for several years. They probably will own about 3,000,000 tractors by 1950.

Some segments of American agriculture are still relatively untouched by mechanization, notably cotton and tobacco in the Southeastern States. But mechanization of cotton production in the South is not far off. The use of tractor power is likely to be followed by machine cultivation and harvesting of cotton. In the next few years perhaps some progress will be made in adapting machinery to tobacco production.

Machines will continue to replace horses and mules until most of this substitution has been accomplished. The introduction of the small one-plow tractor will speed up the shift. Machines will be further adapted for use with mechanical power, and each phase of farming and farm living will become more mechanized.

Land and Crops

The total acreage of cropland (including failure and fallow land) increased considerably before and during the First World War. The total cropland acreage was a little lower in the 1920's than in 1919, but it rose slowly from 1927 to 1931, with the breaking of sod lands in the Great Plains and the West. To some extent the abandonment of farms in the East offset the increase in the West. From 1932 to 1939 the acreage generally went down. It remained low until 1943, when it approached the peak of 1928–32, where it remained the rest of the war.

Changes in the use of cropland, in the amount of lime and fertilizer applied, and other practices have affected the volume of crop production much more than shifts in the total acreage. The acreage of intertilled crops expanded somewhat in the war years, with a counterbalancing decline in close-growing crops; but the acreage in hay and rotation pasture was fairly well maintained, despite the drive for cash crops. Summer fallow in the Great Plains was reduced considerably from the peak reached in 1939, and land that was previously idle was put back into crops or pasture all over the United States.

Farmers seeded more green-manure and winter cover crops during the war. The acreage of winter cover crops in the South was about four times larger in 1944 than in prewar years. The use of strip cropping and of contour farming also grew steadily, but the rate of construction of new terraces slowed down a little.

Farmers used gradually increasing quantities of lime and commercial fertilizers in the late 1930's as a result of economic recovery and the stimulation of conservation programs, and they used more and more of them during the war. In 1945, the use of plant nutrients in commercial fertilizer was nearly twice the prewar average. The quantity of lime used in 1945 was four and one-half times the prewar level; many farmers used lime and commercial fertilizer for the first time. If the prices of farm products drop, farmers would buy less fertilizer for cash crops, but it does not seem at all likely that sales would drop back to prewar levels. And the Nation as a whole is vitally interested in the use of lime and fertilizer to help establish stable, soil-maintaining systems of farming.

The crop changes that have contributed the most to higher production have been the improved strains and varieties that have increased the yields per acre of our most important crops. Hybrid seed corn is an outstanding example; in 1933 only about 143 thousand acres were planted with hybrid seed corn; in 1945, about 60 million.

Farmers harvested nearly 40 percent more corn in 1944 than they did between 1935 and 1939. A significant point: The acreage harvested was only 5 percent greater, but yields per acre were 32 percent higher. A part of the increase was due to better growing weather, and a smaller part to the use of more fertilizer and better farming. But most important was the greater use of hybrid seed. If we assume an average increase in yield of 20 percent over the old open-pollinated corn, we can figure that hybrid seed added 400 million bushels to the 1944 corn crop. Nearly 16 million more acres would have been required to grow that much corn if ordinary seed had been used. Three-billion-bushel corn crops are now the rule rather than the exception in this country. The 1946 crop was 3.3 billion bushels.

Outstanding changes have also taken place in the oil crops. Soybeans were grown on a paltry half a million acres in 1914; more than 14.2

million acres of soybeans were grown in 1945. The acreage of peanuts also was greatly expanded in 1940–1944, and the crop contributed significantly to the food supply. The growing of flaxseed was greatly expanded in the early war years, but dropped back a little in 1944 and 1945.

A change that developed gradually over the interwar and the war years was the shift in hay acreage from grasses to the higher-yielding legumes, which also have a higher protein content and so help to balance the livestock ration. From 1940 to 1944 nearly 39 percent more digestible protein was available for each roughage-consuming unit of livestock than in the 5 years from 1920 to 1924. The change in the supply of hay has profoundly influenced the protein balance of the available feed supply and, thereby, the production of livestock.

Significant changes also have occurred in growing dry beans and peas, potatoes, and other vegetable crops. Recent increases in the production of fruits are accounted for largely by the expanded acreage and higher yields of citrus fruits, which constituted almost half of the total tonnage of the fruit crop in 1945.

The most important changes in growing cotton have come in higher yields to the acre. The average yields since 1937 are all much greater than in earlier years; the average between 1941 and 1945 was 260 pounds an acre, compared to 174 pounds in 1928 to 1932—a jump of nearly 50 percent. That remarkable rise we can attribute largely to the use of more fertilizer, a shift to higher yielding areas with reduction in acreage, better land selection within each area and on individual farms, improved varieties, and the use of legumes and cover crops.

We can expect even higher yields from improved varieties of crops that have greater resistance to drought and disease. Lincoln soybeans and Clinton oats in the Corn Belt, hybrid corn suited to the South, Ladino clover for the Northeast and Lake States, and many another improvement adapted to other regions seem destined to do their part in enhancing the yield of each acre; so, also, drainage and irrigation in some places. With these changes, plus the use of more lime and fertilizer, legume rotations, cover crops, and other conservation practices, it will be quite possible to continue for some time the gradual upward trend of recent years.

Livestock

Three major forces have changed livestock production since 1919: The shift from animal power to mechanical power, the changes in the total feed supply, and higher production per animal.

The constantly shrinking number of horses and mules has released land that could grow direct food crops or feed for producing livestock and livestock products for human use. Land thus released between 1920 and 1945 was enough to feed 16 million head of cattle. The saving in grain alone from the smaller number of work animals amounted to about 13 million tons in 1944. If that much grain had all been used for hogs, it could have fed 26 million hogs to market weight.

Year-to-year changes in the total supply of feed have caused fluctuations in livestock production. The severe drought in 1934 and 1936 reduced the production of feed about 30 percent and 25 percent, respectively, below the level of 1928 to 1932. But feed production during 1942 to 1944 averaged about 20 percent above that of 1928 to 1932, and made it possible to raise about 25 percent more livestock per year than in 1935–39.

Farmers can increase production per unit of livestock by using better breeding animals and balanced rations, reducing losses from death, feeding more heavily, and observing other improved practices. The combination of these has lifted the recent production per unit of breeding livestock to a point 25 percent higher than the level of 1919. We have not measured adequately the efficiency of feeding, but significant gains apparently have been made in all classes of livestock. An example: Corn Belt records indicate that the amount of feed used per 100 pounds of pork was cut by as much as 10 to 15 percent from the 1920's to the 1930's.

Further substitution of mechanical power for horses and mules will release more hay, grain, and pasture for use by other livestock. Therefore, the production of livestock and livestock products for human use will tend to go up. In the South the new developments in pasturage and forage and the changes in systems of farming that might accompany the introduction of tractors will reinforce the tendency. Farmers will grow more hay, grain, and pasture than in former years because they can handle those crops with mechanical equipment.

Total Output of Farm Products

The production-increasing effects of the scientific advances that were made in the early part of the interwar period were obscured by the drought and depression of the 1930's. But the wartime need for farm products provided an opportunity for the fuller use of the improvements that were developed in the two previous decades.

Farm output has risen more sharply than gross farm production because of the shift from work animals to tractor power. In 1945 it was 28 percent above the average of the five prewar years. Special studies indicate that only about a fourth of this increase was due to better weather. Probably less than 15 percent resulted from expansion of cropland acreage. The rest—about 60 percent—is largely accounted for by fuller use of the improvements in crops, livestock, and machinery that I have mentioned.

Larger production per acre of cropland is the most important part of the increase in farm output. By comparison with production per acre, the cropland acreage has been relatively stable since 1919. Production per acre was reduced severely by the droughts of 1934 and 1936. The upward wartime climb stands out in sharp contrast. The increases above the 1935–39 average reflect partly better-than-average weather, but more especially the combination of greater use of lime and fertilizer, legume rotations, winter cover crops, terracing, strip cropping, contour farming, crop variety improvements, and some shifting to crops that yield a larger product to the acre.

A larger volume of crop production provides more hay, pasture, and feed grains; and this makes it possible to produce more livestock. These changes also reflect the larger feed supplies of recent years and the release of feed by the shift from work animals to tractors. Increases in total livestock production have resulted both from keeping more breeding animals and from producing more per animal in the breeding herd.

Improvements in soils, plants, animals, mechanization, pest control, and conservation of moisture—the entire growth of science in agriculture—have enlarged the output of crops and livestock in recent years. It is not likely that this trend will be reversed in the years ahead, unless temporarily in periods of bad weather. Once farm output is expanded it tends to remain high—almost regardless of changes in economic conditions. Farm output is responsive to price increases and other production incentives on the upward side, but it is quite unresponsive to unfavorable conditions on the downward side.

A special study conducted by the Department in cooperation with the land-grant colleges in 1944 indicated that under conditions of relative prosperity it would be profitable for farmers to increase their output of farm products in the years ahead. The changes in farming that were suggested as profitable under relatively favorable conditions would result in further increases in production per acre and per animal and in a total farm output about 43 percent above the 1935–39 average after the transition to peacetime conditions had been completed. That would be 12 percent above the 1945 level. This is not a forecast of what will come to pass even in prosperous times. There is always a lag in adopting practices that would pay, but it would not be unreasonable to assume that continued prosperity for as long as a decade would bring total farm output up to that level.

If relatively unfavorable economic conditions should prevail, production would not be likely to go below the wartime levels, unless growing conditions are below average. Investments once made for capital improvements in farming constitute fixed resources that will be used regardless, almost, of changes in the price of the product. The tractors and other farm machinery will be available for use even in depression, and unemployment in nonfarm occupations usually results in pressure of workers on the land. On the other hand, less commercial fertilizer might be purchased in a period of low prices for farm products, but the effect of such a change on the level of production might be offset by more workers on farms and the pressure to provide some income for the farm family even in a depression. A shrinkage of the producing plant in agriculture is not likely to occur except when fewer workers are employed on farms. Only in prosperous times, when other employment opportunities are available, can workers no longer needed in farming find work elsewhere.

Costs, Prices, and Returns to Farmers

Improvements that bring a higher total farm output need to be analyzed in terms of their effects on farm costs, farm prices, and net incomes to farmers.

Individual farmers make the most profitable use of their resources by producing abundantly, especially just after a shift from animal power to tractor power, because the change enables the farm family to cultivate more acres or to produce more per acre on the farms they now operate. After they have shifted to tractor power, many farmers tend to buy or rent additional land. But if more land is not available, they tend to increase the output per acre by shifting, for example, from oats to soybeans, or from beef cattle to dairy cattle, and perhaps by increasing the poultry flock.

As farmers increase the output per farm, the average cost per unit of output—whether bushel, gallon, barrel, hundredweight—usually goes down because they make fuller use of their machinery and labor. That means more product for each man and each dollar invested in machinery. Therefore, improvements that increase production per farm result in lower unit costs and larger net incomes to farmers unless the total volume of the product that goes to market is increased sufficiently to lower the price received. When farm families increase output by operating larger farms, the total output is not so likely to increase because the extra land was formerly operated by some other family. But when more produce is grown per acre it usually means a net increase in output, and if a large number of farmers produce more potatoes per acre, for example, there will be more bushels of potatoes going to market.

The farmers who first adopt cost-reducing techniques retain all the gain from those improvements until or unless production increases enough to lower the price of the product. If the price is reduced, at least a part of the gain is shifted from producers to other groups. But even if the entire gain were shifted to processors, distributors, and consumers, farmers might still benefit indirectly because more purchasing power would be available for other things—including other farm products. And the farmers who have adopted improved practices would have lower costs and larger output per farm to more than offset the loss from lower prices. So, they are likely to retain part of the gain even with lower prices.

It is the farmers who cannot take advantage of cost-reducing techniques that will have lower incomes if the price goes down as a result of larger output. The workers who are displaced by a labor-saving improvement also will be disadvantaged unless they can find other and more attractive employment.

Although technological improvements usually result in gains to those who can take advantage of them, and in benefits to society as a whole, especially over a period of years, they frequently bring distress to those who cannot readily adjust themselves to the new conditions. The price of progress can be reduced by helping those who are disadvantaged by the change to adapt themselves to the new situation.

But farmers of the United States cannot afford to stop the march of technology. They must keep in step with progress in other industries and with agriculture in other countries; it is necessary for them to adapt their operations to take advantage of the new methods, or to shift to other types of farming. And those who cannot find profitable work in agriculture will need to seek employment off the farm.

Attention needs to be centered, therefore, on the most effective adjustments to the major strides in technology; and especially on ways of aiding those who cannot readily adapt themselves to the new conditions. Price reductions from the increased output that results from technological advances alone are not likely to be great enough to offset all the advantage of lower costs and increased volume to the farmers who are in a position to make full use of the particular improvements. Therefore, one important means of helping farmers to meet the effects of technology is to devise educational and other programs that result in rapid and more general adoption of cost-reducing practices. A dollar saved in cash production expenses is just as important an addition to the farmer's net income as the dollar that comes from sales of the product.

Even those farmers who cannot take advantage of important improvements will not be injured by technological advances unless they result in larger marketings and lower prices. For example, the introduction of the corn picker will not reduce incomes of farmers who continue to pick corn by hand unless it results in more corn going to market at lower prices. But the range in incomes between those who cannot take advantage of the new technique and those who are in a position to do so will be widened. Farmers who cannot adopt cost-reducing improvements, therefore, may need assistance in shifting into other types of farming, or perhaps into other lines of work.

Farm workers who are displaced by technological developments may be greatly disadvantaged by the change unless other nearby employment is readily available. For example, if there should be rapid adoption of the cotton picker, and no expansion of other employment in adjacent areas, the displaced workers would have to migrate to other areas in search of work. And their eventual adjustment to the new situation would depend on the availability of satisfactory jobs for relatively untrained workers.

If a labor-displacing improvement results in unemployment to a large group of farm workers, the cost of finding other work for those who are displaced must be included in the calculation of net social gain from the improvement. Efforts may need to be directed toward finding new and profitable employment for those who are displaced.

If market outlets for farm products could be increased at the same time that farmers were expanding their production and reducing their costs farmers would not need to fear the tendency of production increasing improvements to result in lower prices. In fact, they would then tend to get the full benefit from both the larger volume of output and the lower cost per unit. And fewer farm workers would be displaced.

Future market outlets for farm products are dependent upon the growth of population, and upon the levels of economic activity and employment that are maintained in this country and abroad; also upon the measures that are taken to meet human needs for food and fiber when consumer incomes are inadequate. Those needs are just as real in depression as in prosperity. It is true that the capacity of the human stomach is limited, but those limits have not been reached by a large number of people even in this country, especially from the standpoint of diets of minimum nutritional adequacy. The foods richest in nutrients are, in general, the ones that require the most land and labor per pound or per bushel. Therefore, if people could buy better food, farmers would have a much greater market for their products.

Farms, Farmers, and Farm Workers

The population of the United States is still increasing, even though the rate of increase is slower than in former years. There were 20 million more people in this country on January 1, 1946, than on January 1, 1929, and about 10 million more than in 1939. By 1950 the population is likely to be 15 million more than in 1939. If per capita purchasing power is maintained, the larger population will constitute a significant addition to the domestic market for farm products.

In many parts of the world the levels of food consumption are insufficient even in quantity, to say nothing of quality. If methods could be worked out to exchange goods and services with other nations in a way that would give farmers an opportunity to provide part of the food needed to supplement the diets in some countries that do not have enough food, the market for farm products could be greatly expanded.

One of the most important effects of technological advances is the resulting increase in output per farm worker. Labor-saving machines and the improvements in crop and livestock production that increase production per acre and per animal make it possible for each worker to produce more farm products. That, in turn, means that fewer workers are needed to produce a given product. In fact, total production can increase at the same time that the number of farm workers is reduced. For example, in 1945, when gross farm production was 123 percent of the 1935–39 level, there were only 90 percent as many workers employed on farms. As a result of fewer workers and greatly increased production, the production per worker averaged 137 percent of 1935–39.

If recent trends should continue for a decade from 1945, the level of gross farm production in 1955 would be about 136 percent of 1935–39. There would be only 85 percent as many workers on farms as in those years, and production per worker would be 160 percent of the levels of 1935 to 1939. The figures are straight projections from the changes that took place in the immediate prewar and war years, but they are reinforced by the results of the cooperative study on peacetime adjustments in farming which indicate that similar changes would be profitable under prosperity conditions after the transition from war to peace had been completed.

Production per worker in the South has been relatively low compared with that in other regions over a period of years. We can expect much larger increases in production of each worker in the South than in other regions. Such increases would be possible with accelerated mechanization, which would also result in a larger acreage of cropland per worker.

In 1939, the acres of cropland and value of land, buildings, and livestock per worker in the South Atlantic and East South Central States were less than one-half of the national average and the value of equipment per worker was about one-third of the average for the country as a whole. In other words, in 1939 the average farm worker in those States had less than half as much land, buildings, and livestock and only about a third as much machinery to help him in his farm production job as the average for all farm workers in the United States. For production per worker to be increased materially, it is necessary for each worker to have sufficient land, equipment, and livestock to make his work effective; and production on the farm needs to be planned in such a way that productive employment can be furnished over most of the year.

It is evident that if farmers in all sections of the country are to take full advantage of technological advances more land and capital need to be associated with each farm worker. A man working without tools produces very little except in an environment where it is possible to harvest the goods supplied directly by nature. It is also difficult to achieve a high production per man on land that yields, say, only 15 bushels of corn to the acre unless one man can farm a large acreage or can greatly increase the yield by use of fertilizer, legume crops, etc. This means a larger investment per man. In some areas a larger investment per man will also mean a higher total investment of capital. On the other hand, fewer full-time workers will be needed for each 100 acres of land. If these changes were made they would mean that in most areas each farm family on a full-time farm would operate more land, use more machinery, and, in livestock areas, would handle more livestock.

Although such shifts would result in fewer and larger full-time commercial farms, there might also be an opposite trend toward more part-time farms and rural homes. If there should be a tendency toward decentralization of industry, and if service enterprises were established to meet the needs of farmers on mechanized farms, considerable nearby nonfarm work would be available for workers who are not needed in agriculture. This work would then be so located that many workers could combine part-time farming and rural living with nonfarm work. Such a development would enable more people to take advantage of the benefits of rural life even though their livelihood would come largely from nonfarm sources.

The net result of changes in the direction of fewer full-time commercial farms and more part-time farms might be little or no reduction in the total number of farm units. But there would be fewer small farms that had no off-farm employment or outside source of income. Operators of small full-time farms usually have the greatest difficulty in adopting new techniques. Many improvements are not adapted for the smaller units. Sometimes, however, it is possible to develop specialty lines for small farms that can compete successfully with larger family farm units.

The changes that have taken place and are coming make farming a complex business, even on family-operated farms. Young men who look forward to farming as an occupation will need to learn the skills associated with mechanized farming and how to conduct a complex business enterprise. Those who are well adapted for managing a business of this kind are likely to find opportunities in agriculture as good as in any other occupation. But farm youths who do not have adequate training, or who do not have the type of ability that is needed for successful farm management are likely to find themselves at a disadvantage. If they are to remain in farming they will need to seek out specialty lines, such as poultry or small fruits, that can compete most effectively with the larger family farms. Many of them will find their best alternatives in nonfarm employment; and some will be able to combine this with part-time farming.

Although advances in technology tend to push agriculture in the direction of fewer and larger full-time commercial farms, there is no evidence to indicate that the competitive position of the efficiently operated family farm is weakened by this change. Recent developments in mechanization have resulted in adapting mechanical power and machinery to family farms. But because the size of the family farm will be larger and more machinery will be needed, the total investment per farm will be high. These changes will make it more difficult for a young man to get started as a farm operator. And the management job becomes more involved. More training will be needed for successful farming. On the more favorable side, tractor and electric power equipment will eliminate most of the drudgery of both farm and home work on the efficient farm.

In Summary

The effects of technology on farm people may be both good and bad. Those who can take advantage of the new techniques are likely to increase their net incomes a great deal. On the other hand, those who cannot adapt their operations to the new conditions may find themselves at a relative disadvantage. And workers who are displaced may suffer hardships unless other employment is readily available. Those growing pains of technological progress can be softened. Special educational and other programs can be provided for those who are disadvantaged by technological changes. Progress in farm technology can result in net social gain, but this is a potentiality and not an inevitable consequence. Farm people will need to learn how to live with the new techniques, and to use them to their advantage. To attempt to stop, or even to slow down, the tide of progress would be too costly to farmers over a period of years.

If farming, as well as other sectors of our economy, is rapidly adjusted to the technical improvements that become available it will be possible to produce more with less effort. More time will be available for other things including education, recreation, and increased leisure. And the real incomes per farm and per family will be larger.

THE AUTHOR

Sherman E. Johnson is assistant chief of the Bureau of Agricultural Economics. He was head of that Bureau's Division of Farm Management and Costs for 8 years. Before coming to the Department of Agriculture he was head of the department of agricultural economics at South Dakota State College. He has also been a staff member of land-grant colleges in Montana, Louisiana, and his home State of Minnesota.

What Next?

BY W. V. LAMBERT, Administrator, Agricultural Research
Administration

THE GREAT strides that have been made in agricultural
research in a few years are truly impressive. The pages of this book
bear witness to the fruit of our labors. I look back over this period with
pride in our accomplishments, but I look forward with serious concern,
born of the knowledge that we must keep everlastingly on the job if
we are to meet the challenges of the future.

We know that livestock diseases and parasites still take a terrific toll
from farmers every year. Poultry diseases reduce farm income by 40 to
50 million dollars a year, and poultry parasites cost four times as much.
Much remains to be done to eradicate Bang's disease and other widespread diseases of cattle. In some cases further progress in eradication
of livestock diseases awaits new discoveries by those engaged in research.

Every cattleman has observed that certain animals gain faster than
others grazing side by side. We know that this difference in ability to
gain is due in part at least to heredity, and that the more efficient
animals may pass on this trait to their offspring. In general, we know that
the same is true for other classes of livestock, but except for dairy cattle
we have only begun to work out practical methods that farmers can use
to build up the productivity of their herds.

We must not be misled by the brilliant work that gave us DDT. The
use of that wonderful insecticide creates many new problems—questions
on toxicity to livestock, to man, and to the soil. Research must answer
these questions. Meanwhile, the search for still other insecticides must
go on, so that insects not controlled by DDT may be subdued.

Neither must we become complacent about our successes in breeding
crop plants that resist diseases. When disease-resistant varieties of crops
are developed, the disease organisms may undergo changes that ulti-

933

mately enable them to attack the new variety. If we are to keep ahead of the diseases we must constantly develop new varieties.

Our soils are being depleted constantly by losses from erosion and by the crops that are being removed from them. Ways and means must be found for checking such losses and for developing fertilizer and farm-management practices that will permit farmers to keep up production.

As we make progress in more efficient production, we must make even greater strides in more efficient utilization and distribution of farm products. We must find wider use for those products that we now harvest and find ways to convert into byproducts much that is now left in the fields to rot. Current research looking to the use of cereal straws and corncobs as a source of motor fuel is just one example of the kind of research that will pay dividends in the future.

In taking stock of progress in agricultural research, we should not forget that much of the effort that normally would have gone into the accumulation of basic scientific facts was diverted to other, more urgent problems during the war. The result is that our storehouse of facts has been reduced. Basic knowledge must be available before it can be applied to the solution of practical farm problems. That is the reason for stressing basic research in the immediate future.

As we look ahead, we may be led to ask ourselves if the research developments of the past are less wonderful than they have been portrayed. I do not believe they are. But we must remember that agricultural research is not a static thing. Many of the problems of farm production are so intimately bound together that when one factor is changed, the whole system may be changed. Limiting factors under one system of farming may be eliminated, but new limiting factors may develop as the result of a new discovery. In a dynamic, rapidly changing world, all elements, man-made and natural, must be considered.

The broad scope of research developments during the war show the enormous complexity and magnitude of the tasks assigned to agricultural research. The multiplicity of conditions under which plants and animals are grown, changes in economic conditions, the wear and tear on the soil from continued cropping, and the biological changes continually occurring in plants and animals and their parasites make this a never-ending task.

The faith American farmers have placed in research by their continued support has been justified. Their representatives in Congress have reaffirmed this faith in the passage of the Research and Marketing Act of 1946, which promises greater support than ever before for agricultural research. With a better understanding of the interrelationships of the many sciences that enter into the production and utilization of farm products, I believe we are on the threshold of new discoveries that will in their own way take their places beside the notable ones of the past.

Index